MyLab Statistics

*Support You **Need**, When You **Need** It*

MyLab Statistics has helped millions of students succeed in their math courses. Take advantage of the resources it provides.

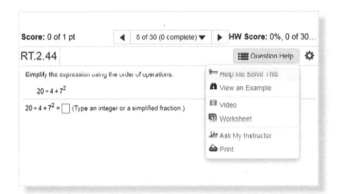

Interactive Exercises

MyLab Statistics's interactive exercises mirror those in the textbook but are programmed to allow you unlimited practice, leading to mastery. Most exercises include **learning aids**, such as "Help Me Solve This," "View an Example," and "Video," and they offer helpful feedback when you enter incorrect answers.

Instructional Videos

Instructional videos cover key examples from the text and can conveniently be played on any mobile device. These videos are especially helpful if you miss a class or just need further explanation.

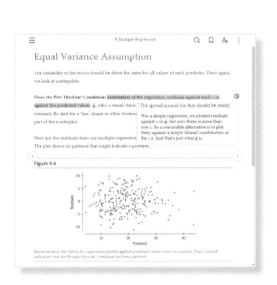

Interactive eText

The **Pearson eText** gives you access to your textbook anytime, anywhere. In addition to note taking, highlighting, and bookmarking, the Pearson eText app offers access even when offline.

pearson.com/mylab/statistics

A Guide to Learning From the Art in This Text

For **inference about a population proportion p** we use blue for the normal sampling distribution of the sample proportion $\hat{p}$.

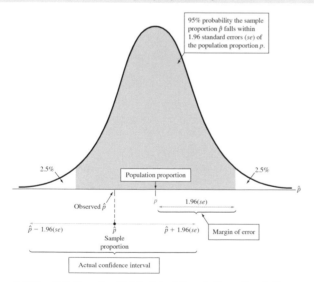

95% probability the sample proportion $\hat{p}$ falls within 1.96 standard errors (se) of the population proportion p.

2.5%   Population proportion   2.5%

$\hat{p}$

Observed $\hat{p}$

p $1.96(se)$

$\hat{p} - 1.96(se)$ $\hat{p}$ $\hat{p} + 1.96(se)$ Margin of error

Sample proportion

Actual confidence interval

▲ **Figure 8.3 Sampling Distribution of Sample Proportion $\hat{p}$.** For large random samples, the sampling distribution is approximately normal and centered at the population proportion p. Then, with 95% probability, $\hat{p}$ falls within $1.96(se)$ of p. As a consequence, $\hat{p} \pm 1.96(se)$ is a 95% confidence interval for p. **Question** Why is the confidence interval $\hat{p} \pm 1.96(se)$ instead of $p \pm 1.96(se)$?

For **inference about a population mean μ,** we use green for the symmetric t distribution when finding percentiles or P-values.

Sampling distribution of t test statistic when H_0 is true

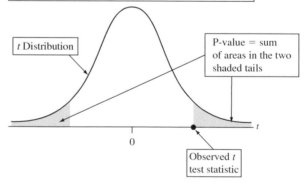

t Distribution

P-value = sum of areas in the two shaded tails

0

t

Observed t test statistic

▲ **Figure 9.7 The t Distribution of the t Test Statistic.** The t distribution looks like the standard normal but has more variability, i.e., fatter tails. The precise shape depends on the df. There is stronger evidence against H_0 when the t test statistic falls farther out in a tail. The P-value for a two-sided H_a is a two-tail probability as indicated in the figure. **Question** Why is it that t-scores farther out in the tails provide stronger evidence against H_0?

**Read and think about the questions that appear in selected figures.
The answers are given at the beginning of each Chapter Review section.**

Statistics

The Art and Science of Learning from Data

Fifth Edition

Alan Agresti

University of Florida

Christine Franklin

University of Georgia

Bernhard Klingenberg

Williams College and New College of Florida

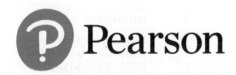 Pearson

Please contact https://support.pearson.com/getsupport/s/ with any queries on this content

Cover Image by Peter Kotoff/Shutterstock

Library of Congress Cataloging-in-Publication Data

Names: Agresti, Alan, author. | Franklin, Christine A., author. |
  Klingenberg, Bernhard, author.
Title: The art and science of learning from data / Alan Agresti, University
  of Florida, Christine Franklin, University of Georgia, Bernhard
  Klingenberg, Williams College.
Description: Fifth edition. | Boston: Pearson, [2021] | Includes index.
Identifiers: LCCN 2019059746 | ISBN 9780136468769 (paperback)
Subjects: LCSH: Statistics—Textbooks.
Classification: LCC QA276.12 .A35 2020 | DDC 519.5—dc23
LC record available at https://lccn.loc.gov/2019059746

1 2020

Access Code Card
ISBN-10:   0-13-655989-1
ISBN-13: 978-0-13-655989-4

Rental Edition
ISBN-10:   0-13-646876-4
ISBN-13: 978-0-13-646876-9

Instructor's Review Copy:
ISBN-10:   0-13-660882-5
ISBN-13: 978-0-13-660882-0

Dedication

To my wife, Jacki, for her extraordinary support, including making numerous suggestions and putting up with the evenings and weekends I was working on this book.

ALAN AGRESTI

To Corey and Cody, who have shown me the joys of motherhood, and to my husband, Dale, for being a dear friend and a dedicated father to our boys. You have always been my biggest supporters.

CHRIS FRANKLIN

To my wife, Sophia, and our children, Franziska, Florentina, Maximilian, and Mattheus, who are a bunch of fun to be with, and to Jean-Luc Picard for inspiring me.

BERNHARD KLINGENBERG

Contents

Part One   Gathering and Exploring Data

Part Two   Probability, Probability Distributions, and Sampling Distributions

Part Three   Inferential Statistics

Part Four   Extended Statistical Methods and Models for Analyzing Categorical and Quantitative Variables

An Introduction to the Web Apps

The website ArtofStat.com links to several web-based apps that run in any browser. These apps allow students to carry out statistical analyses using real data and engage with statistical concepts interactively. The apps can be used to obtain graphs and summary statistics for exploratory data analysis, fit linear regression models and create residual plots, or visualize statistical distributions such as the normal distribution. The apps are especially valuable for teaching and understand sampling distributions through simulations. They can further guide students through all steps of inference based on one or two sample categorical or quantitative data. Finally, these apps can carry out computer intensive inferential methods such as the bootstrap or the permutation approach. As the following overview shows, each app is tailored to a specific task.

- The **Explore Categorical Data** and **Explore Quantitative Data** apps provide basic summary statistics and graphs (bar graphs, pie charts, histograms, box plots, dot plots), both for data from a single sample or for comparing two samples. Graphs can be downloaded.

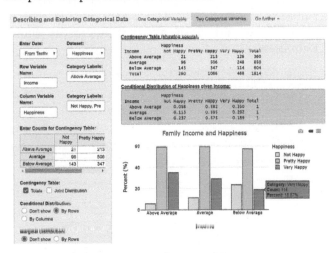

Screenshot from the *Explore Categorical Data* app

- The **Times Series** app plots a simple time series and can add a smooth or linear trend.
- The **Random Numbers** app generates random numbers (with or without replacement) and simulates flipping (potentially biased) coins.
- The **Mean vs. Median** app allows users to add or delete points by clicking in a graph and observing the effect of outliers or skew on these two statistics.
- The **Scatterplots & Correlation** and the **Explore Linear Regression** apps allow users to add or delete points from a scatterplot and observe how the correlation coefficient or the regression line are affected. The **Guess the Correlation** app lets users guess the correlation for

randomly generated data sets. The **Fit Linear Regression** app provides summary statistics, an interactive scatterplot, a smooth trend line, the regression line, predictions, and a residual analysis. Options include confidence and prediction intervals. Users can upload their own data. The **Multivariate Relationships** app explores graphically and statistically how the relationship between two quantitative variables is affected when adjusting for a third variable.

Screenshot from the *Linear Regression* app

- The **Binomial, Normal, t, Chi-Squared**, and **F Distribution** apps provide an interactive graph of the distribution and how it changes for different parameter values. Each app easily finds percentile values and lower, upper, or interval probabilities, clearly marking them on the graph of the distribution.

Screenshot from the *Normal Distribution* app

- The three **Sampling Distribution** apps generate sampling distributions of the sample proportion or the sample mean (for both continuous and discrete populations). Sliders for the sample size or population parameters help with discovering and exploring the Central Limit Theorem interactively. In addition to the uniform, skewed, bell-shaped, or bimodal population distributions, several real population data sets (such as the distances traveled by all taxis rides in NYC on Dec. 31) are preloaded.

Screenshot from the *Sampling Distribution for the Sample Mean* app

- The **Inference for a Proportion** and the **Inference for a Mean** apps carry out statistical inference. They provide graphs and summary statistics from the observed data to check assumptions, and they compute margin of errors, confidence intervals, test statistics, and P-values, displaying them graphically.

Screenshot from the *Inference for a Population Mean* app

- The **Explore Coverage** app uses simulation to demonstrate the concept of the confidence coefficient, both for confidence intervals for the proportion and for the mean. Different sliders for true population parameters, the sample size, or the confidence coefficient show their effect on the coverage and width of confidence intervals. The **Errors and Power** app visually explores and provides Type I and Type II errors and power under various settings.

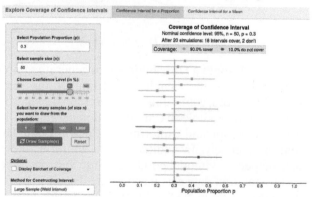

Screenshot from the *Explore Coverage* app

- The **Bootstrap for One Sample** app illustrates the idea behind the bootstrap and provides bootstrap percentile confidence intervals for the mean, median, or standard deviation.

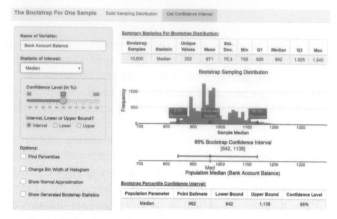

Screenshot from the *Bootstrap for One Sample* app

- The **Compare Two Proportions** and **Compare Two Means** apps provide inference based on data from two independent or dependent samples. They show graphs and summary statistics for data preloaded from the textbook or entered by the user and compute confidence intervals or P-values for the difference between two proportions or means. All results are illustrated graphically. Users can provide their own data in a variety of ways, including as summary statistics.

Screenshot from the *Compare Two Means* app

- The **Bootstrap for Two Samples** app illustrates how the bootstrap distribution is built via resampling and provides bootstrap percentile confidence intervals for the difference in means or medians. The **Scatterplots & Correlation** app provides resampling inference for the correlation coefficient. The **Permutation Test** app illustrates and carries out the permutation test comparing two groups with a quantitative response.

Screenshot from the *Bootstrap for Two Samples* app

- The **Chi-Squared Test** app provides the chi-squared test for independence. Results are illustrated using graphs, and users can enter data as contingency tables. The corresponding permutation test is available in the **Permutation Test for Independence (Categ. Data)** app and for 2×2 tables in the **Fisher's Exact Test** app.

Screenshot from the *Chi-Squared Test* app

- The **ANOVA (One-Way)** app compares several means and provides simultaneous confidence intervals for multiple comparisons. The **Wilcoxon Test** and the **Kruskal-Wallis Test** apps for nonparametric statistics provide the analogs to the two-sample t test and ANOVA, both for independent and dependent samples.

Screenshot from the *ANOVA (One-Way)* app

- The **Multiple Linear Regression** app fits linear models with several explanatory variables, and the **Logistic Regression** app fits a simple logistic regression model, complete with graphical output.

Preface

Each of us is impacted daily by information and decisions based on data, in our jobs or free time and on topics ranging from health and medicine, the environment and climate to business, financial or political considerations. In 2020, never was data and statistical fluency more important than with understanding the information associated with the COVID-19 pandemic and the measures taken globally to protect against this virus. Fueled by the digital revolution, data is now readily available for gaining insights not only into epidemiology but a variety of other fields. Many believe that data are the new oil; it is valuable, but only if it can be refined and used in context. This book strives to be an essential part of this refinement process.

We have each taught introductory statistics for many years, to different audiences, and we have witnessed and welcomed the evolution from the traditional formula-driven mathematical statistics course to a concept-driven approach. One of our goals in writing this book was to help make the conceptual approach more interesting and readily accessible to students. In this new edition, we take it a step further. We believe that statistical ideas and concepts come alive and are memorable when students have a chance to interact with them. In addition, those ideas stay relevant when students have a chance to use them on real data. That's why we now provide many screenshots, activities and exercises that use our online web apps to learn statistics and carry out nearly all the statistical analysis in this book. This removes the technological barrier and allows students to replicate our analysis and then apply it on their own data. At the end of the course, we want students to look back and realize that they learned practical concepts for reasoning with data that will serve them not only for their future careers, but in many aspects of their lives.

We also want students to come to appreciate that in practice, assumptions are not perfectly satisfied, models are not exactly correct, distributions are not exactly normal, and different factors should be considered in conducting a statistical analysis. The title of our book reflects the experience of statisticians and data scientists, who soon realize that statistics is an art as well as a science.

What's New in This Edition

Our goal in writing the fifth edition was to improve the student and instructor experience and provide a more accessible introduction to statistical thinking and practice. We have:

- Integrated the online apps from ArtofStat.com into every chapter through multiple screenshots and activities, inviting the user to replicate results using data from our many examples. These apps can be used live in lectures (and together with students) to visualize concepts or carry out analysis. Or, they can be recorded for asynchronous online instructions. Students can download (or screenshot) results for inclusion in assignments or projects. At the end of each chapter, a new section on statistical software describes the functionality of each app used in the chapter.
- Streamlined Chapter 1, which continues to emphasize the importance of the statistical investigative process. New in Chapter 1 is an introduction on the opportunities and challenges with Big Data and Data Science, including a discussion of ethical considerations.

- Written a new (but optional) section on linear transformations in Chapter 2.
- Emphasized in Section 3.1 the two descriptive statistics that students are most likely to encounter in the news media: differences and ratios of proportions.
- Expanded the discussion on multivariate thinking in Section 3.3.
- Explicitly stated and discussed the definition of the standard deviation of a discrete random variable in Section 6.1.
- Included the simulation of drawing random samples from *real* population distributions to illustrate the concept of a sampling distribution in Section 7.2.
- Significantly expanded the coverage of resampling methods, with a thorough discussion of the bootstrap for one- and two-sample problems and for the correlation coefficient. (New Sections 7.3, 8.3, and 10.3.)
- Continued emphasis on using interval estimation for inference and less reliance on significance testing and incorporated the 2016 American Statistical Association's statement on P-values.
- Provided commented R code in a new section on statistical software at the end of each chapter which replicates output obtained in featured examples.
- Updated or created many new examples and exercises using the most recent data available.

Our Approach

In 2005 (and updated in 2016), the American Statistical Association (ASA) endorsed guidelines and recommendations for the introductory statistics course as described in the report, "Guidelines for Assessment and Instruction in Statistics Education (GAISE) for the College Introductory Course" (www.amstat.org/education/gaise). The report states that the overreaching goal of all introductory statistics courses is to produce statistically educated students, which means that students should develop statistical literacy and the ability to think statistically. The report gives six key recommendations for the college introductory course:

1. Teach statistical thinking.
   - Teach statistics as an investigative process of problem solving and decision making.
   - Give students experience with multivariable thinking.
2. Focus on conceptual understanding.
3. Integrate real data with a context and purpose.
4. Foster active learning.
5. Use technology to explore concepts and analyze data.
6. Use assessments to improve and evaluate student learning.

We wholeheartedly support these recommendations and our textbook takes every opportunity to implement these guidelines.

Ask and Answer Interesting Questions

In presenting concepts and methods, we encourage students to think about the data and the appropriate analyses by posing questions. Our approach, learning by framing questions, is carried out in various ways, including (1) presenting a structured approach to examples that separates the question and the analysis from the scenario presented, (2) letting the student replicate the analysis with a specific app and not worrying about calculations, (3) providing homework exercises that encourage students to think and write, and (4) asking questions in the figure captions that are answered in the Chapter Review.

Present Concepts Clearly

Students have told us that this book is more "readable" and interesting than other introductory statistics texts because of the wide variety of intriguing real data examples and exercises. We have simplified our prose wherever possible, without sacrificing any of the accuracy that instructors expect in a textbook.

A serious source of confusion for students is the multitude of inference methods that derive from the many combinations of confidence intervals and tests, means and proportions, large sample and small sample, variance known and unknown, two-sided and one-sided inference, independent and dependent samples, and so on. We emphasize the most important cases for practical application of inference: large sample, variance unknown, two-sided inference, and independent samples. The many other cases are also covered (except for known variances), but more briefly, with the exercises focusing mainly on the way inference is commonly conducted in practice. We present the traditional probability distribution–based inference but now also include inference using simulation through bootstrapping and permutation tests.

Connect Statistics to the Real World

We believe it's important for students to be comfortable with analyzing a balance of both quantitative and categorical data so students can work with the data they most often see in the world around them. Every day in the media, we see and hear percentages and rates used to summarize results of opinion polls, outcomes of medical studies, and economic reports. As a result, we have increased the attention paid to the analysis of proportions. For example, we use contingency tables early in the text to illustrate the concept of association between two categorical variables and to show the potential influence of a lurking variable.

Organization of the Book

The statistical investigative process has the following components: (1) asking a statistical question; (2) obtaining appropriate data; (3) analyzing the data; and (4) interpreting the data and making conclusions to answer the statistical questions. With this in mind, the book is organized into four parts.

Part 1 focuses on gathering, exploring and describing data and interpreting the statistics they produce. This equates to components 1, 2, and 3, when the data is analyzed descriptively (both for one variable and the association between two variables).

Part 2 covers probability, probability distributions, and sampling distributions. This equates to component 3, when the student learns the underlying probability necessary to make the step from analyzing the data descriptively to analyzing the data inferentially (for example, understanding sampling distributions to develop the concept of a margin of error and a P-value).

Part 3 covers inferential statistics. This equates to components 3 and 4 of the statistical investigative process. The students learn how to form confidence intervals and conduct significance tests and then make appropriate conclusions answering the statistical question of interest.

Part 4 introduces statistical modeling. This part cycles through all 4 components. The chapters are written in such a way that instructors can teach out of order. For example, after Chapter 1, an instructor could easily teach Chapter 4, Chapter 2, and Chapter 3. Alternatively, an instructor may teach Chapters 5, 6, and 7 after Chapters 1 and 4.

Features of the Fifth Edition

Promoting Student Learning

To motivate students to think about the material, ask appropriate questions, and develop good problem-solving skills, we have created special features that distinguish this text.

Chapter End Summaries

Each chapter ends with a high-level summary of the material studied, a review of new notation, learning objectives, and a section on the use of the apps or the software program R.

Student Support

To draw students to important material we highlight key definitions, and provide summaries in blue boxes throughout the book. In addition, we have four types of margin notes:

- **In Words:** This feature explains, in plain language, the definitions and symbolic notation found in the body of the text (which, for technical accuracy, must be more formal).
- **Caution:** These margin boxes alert students to areas to which they need to pay special attention, particularly where they are prone to make mistakes or incorrect assumptions.
- **Recall:** As the student progresses through the book, concepts are presented that depend on information learned in previous chapters. The Recall margin boxes direct the reader back to a previous presentation in the text to review and reinforce concepts and methods already covered.
- **Did You Know:** These margin boxes provide information that helps with the contextual understanding of the statistical question under consideration or provides additional information.

Graphical Approach

Because many students are visual learners, we have taken extra care to make our **figures** informative. We've annotated many of the figures with labels that clearly identify the noteworthy aspects of the illustration. Further, many figure captions include a question (answered in the Chapter Review) designed to challenge the student to interpret and think about the information being communicated by the graphic. The graphics also feature a pedagogical use of color to help students recognize patterns and distinguish between statistics and parameters. The use of color is explained in the very front of the book for easy reference.

Hands-On Activities and Simulations

Each chapter contains activities that allow students to become familiar with a number of statistical methodologies and tools. The instructor can elect to carry out the activities in class, outside of class, or a combination of both. These hands-on activities and simulations encourage students to learn by doing.

Statistics: In Practice

We realize that there is a difference between proper academic statistics and what is actually done in practice. Data analysis in practice is an art as well as a science. Although statistical theory has foundations based on precise assumptions and

In Words

To find the **95% confidence interval,** you take the sample proportion and add and subtract 1.96 standard errors.

Recall

From Section 8.2, for using a confidence interval to estimate a proportion p, the **standard error** of a sample **proportion** $\hat{p}$ is

$$\sqrt{\frac{\hat{p}(1-\hat{p})}{n}}. \blacktriangleleft$$

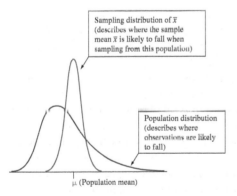

Sampling distribution of $\bar{x}$ (describes where the sample mean $\bar{x}$ is likely to fall when sampling from this population)

Population distribution (describes where observations are likely to fall)

μ (Population mean)

conditions, in practice the real world is not so simple. **In Practice** boxes and text references alert students to the way statisticians actually analyze data in practice. These comments are based on our extensive consulting experience and research and by observing what well-trained statisticians do in practice.

Examples and Exercises

Innovative Example Format

Recognizing that the worked examples are the major vehicle for engaging and teaching students, we have developed a unique structure to help students learn by relying on five components:

- **Picture the Scenario** presents background information so students can visualize the situation. This step places the data to be investigated in context and often provides a link to previous examples.

- **Questions to Explore** reference the information from the scenario and pose questions to help students focus on what is to be learned from the example and what types of questions are useful to ask about the data.

- **Think It Through** is the heart of each example. Here, the questions posed are investigated and answered using appropriate statistical methods. Each solution is clearly matched to the question so students can easily find the response to each Question to Explore.

- **Insight** clarifies the central ideas investigated in the example and places them in a broader context that often states the conclusions in less technical terms. Many of the Insights also provide connections between seemingly disparate topics in the text by referring to concepts learned previously and/or foreshadowing techniques and ideas to come.

- **Try Exercise:** Each example concludes by directing students to an end-of-section exercise that allows immediate practice of the concept or technique within the example.

Concept tags are included with each example so that students can easily identify the concept covered in the example.

 App integration allows instructors to focus on the data and the results instead of on the computations. Many of our Examples show screenshots and their output is easily reproduced, live in class or later by students on their own.

Relevant and Engaging Exercises

The text contains a strong emphasis on real data in both the examples and exercises. We have updated the exercise sets in the fifth edition to ensure that students have ample opportunity (with more than 100 exercises in almost every chapter) to practice techniques and apply the concepts. We show how statistics addresses a wide array of applications, including opinion polls, market research, the environment, and health and human behavior. Because we believe that most students benefit more from focusing on the underlying concepts and interpretations of data analyses than from the actual calculations, many exercises can be carried out using one of our web apps.

We have exercises in two places:

- **At the end of each section.** These exercises provide immediate reinforcement and are drawn from concepts within the section.
- **At the end of each chapter.** This more comprehensive set of exercises draws from all concepts across all sections within the chapter. There, you will also find multiple-choice and True/False-type exercises and those covering more advanced material.

Each exercise has a descriptive label. Exercises for which an app can be used are indicated with the icon. Exercises that use data from the General Social

Survey are indicated by a GSS icon. Larger data sets used in examples and exercises are referenced in the text, listed in the back endpapers, and made available for **download** on the book's website ArtofStat.com.

Technology Integration

Web Apps

Screenshots of web apps are shown throughout the text. An overview of the apps is available on pages vii–ix. At the end of each chapter, in the Statistical Software section, the functionality of each app used in the chapter is described in detail. A list of apps by chapter appears on the second to last last page of this book.

R

We now provide R code in the end of chapter section on statistical software. Every R function used is explained and illustrated with output. In addition, annotated R scripts can be found on ArtofStat.com under "R Code." While only base R functions are used in the book, the scripts available online use functions from the tidyverse.

Data Sets

We use a wealth of real data sets throughout the textbook. These data sets are available for download at ArtofStat.com. The same data set is often used in several chapters, helping reinforce the four components of the statistical investigative process and allowing the students to see the big picture of statistical reasoning. Many data sets are also preloaded and accessible from within the apps.

StatCrunch®

StatCrunch® is powerful web-based statistical software that allows users to perform complex analyses, share data sets, and generate compelling reports of their data. The vibrant online community offers more than 40,000 data sets for instructors to use and students to analyze.

- **Collect.** Users can upload their own data to StatCrunch or search a large library of publicly shared data sets, spanning almost any topic of interest. Also, an online survey tool allows users to collect data quickly through web-based surveys.
- **Crunch.** A full range of numerical and graphical methods allows users to analyze and gain insights from any data set. Interactive graphics help users understand statistical concepts and are available for export to enrich reports with visual representations of data.
- **Communicate.** Reporting options help users create a wide variety of visually appealing representations of their data.

Full access to StatCrunch is available with MyLab Statistics, and StatCrunch is available by itself to qualified adopters. For more information, visit www.statcrunch.com or contact your Pearson representative.

An Invitation Rather Than a Conclusion

We hope that students using this textbook will gain a lasting appreciation for the vital role that statistics plays in presenting and analyzing data and informing decisions. Our major goals for this textbook are that students learn how to:

- Recognize that we are surrounded by data and the importance of becoming statistically literate to interpret these data and make informed decisions based on data.
- Become critical readers of studies summarized in mass media and of research papers that quote statistical results.

- Produce data that can provide answers to properly posed questions.
- Appreciate how probability helps us understand randomness in our lives and grasp the crucial concept of a sampling distribution and how it relates to inference methods.
- Choose appropriate descriptive and inferential methods for examining and analyzing data and drawing conclusions.
- Communicate the conclusions of statistical analyses clearly and effectively.
- Understand the limitations of most research, either because it was based on an observational study rather than a randomized experiment or survey or because a certain lurking variable was not measured that could have explained the observed associations.

We are excited about sharing the insights that we have learned from our experience as teachers and from our students through this book. Many students still enter statistics classes on the first day with dread because of its reputation as a dry, sometimes difficult, course. It is our goal to inspire a classroom environment that is filled with creativity, openness, realistic applications, and learning that students find inviting and rewarding. We hope that this textbook will help the instructor and the students experience a rewarding introductory course in statistics.

Resources for
Success

Instructor Resources

Additional resources can be downloaded from **www.pearson.com**.

Online Resources Students and instructors have a full library of resources, including apps developed for in-text activities, data sets and instructor-to-instructor videos. Available through MyLab Statistics and at www.pearsonhighered.com/mathstatsresources.

Updated! Instructor to Instructor Videos provide an opportunity for adjuncts, part-timers, TAs, or other instructors who are new to teaching from this text or have limited class prep time to learn about the book's approach and coverage from the authors. The videos focus on those topics that have proven to be most challenging to students and offer suggestions, pointers, and ideas about how to present these topics and concepts effectively based on many years of teaching introductory statistics. The videos also provide insights on how to help students use the textbook in the most effective way to realize success in the course. The videos are available for download from Pearson's online catalog at www.pearson.com and through MyLab Statistics.

Instructor's Solutions Manual, by James Lapp, contains fully worked solutions to every textbook exercise. Available for download from Pearson's online catalog at www.pearson.com and through MyLab Statistics.

PowerPoint Lecture Slides are fully editable and printable slides that follow the textbook. These slides can be used during lectures or posted to a website in an online course. Fully accessible versions are also available. The PowerPoint Lecture Slides are available from Pearson's online catalog at www.pearson.com and through MyLab Statistics.

TestGen® (www.pearson.com/testgen) enables instructors to build, edit, print, and administer tests using a computerized bank of questions developed to cover all the objectives of the text. TestGen is algorithmically based, allowing instructors to create multiple but equivalent versions of the same question or test with the click of a button. Instructors can also modify test bank questions or add new questions. The software and test bank are available for download from Pearson's online catalog at www.pearson.com and through MyLab Statistics.

The Online Test Bank is a test bank derived from TestGen®. It includes multiple choice and short answer questions for each section of the text, along with the answer keys. Available for download from Pearson's online catalog at www.pearson.com and through MyLab Statistics.

Student Resources

Additional resources to help student success.

Online Resources Students and instructors have a full library of resources, including apps developed for in-text activities and data sets (Available through MyLab Statistics and at www.pearsonhighered.com/mathstatsresources).

Student's Solutions Manual, by James Lapp, contains fully worked solutions to odd-numbered exercises. ISBN-10: 0-13-655962-X; ISBN-13: 978-0-13-655962-7

Study Cards for Statistics Software This series of study cards, available for Excel®, MINITAB®, JMP®, SPSS®, R®, StatCrunch®, and the TI family of graphing calculators provides students with easy, step-by-step guides to the most common statistics software. These study cards are available through MyLab Statistics.

Acknowledgments

We appreciate all of the thoughtful contributions and additions to the fourth edition by Michael Posner Villanova University. We are indebted to the following individuals, who provided valuable feedback for the fifth edition:

John Bennett, *Halifax Community College, NC*; Yishi Wang, *University of North Carolina Wilmington, NC*; Scott Crawford, *University of Wyoming, WY*; Amanda Ellis, *University of Kentucky, KY*; Lisa Kay, *Eastern Kentucky University, KY*; Inyang Inyang, *Northern Virginia Community College, VA*; Jason Molitierno, *Sacred Heart University, CT*; Daniel Turek, *Williams College, MA*.

We are also indebted to the many reviewers, class testers, and students who gave us invaluable feedback and advice on how to improve the quality of the book.

ARIZONA Russel Carlson, University of Arizona; Peter Flanagan-Hyde, Phoenix Country Day School ▪ **CALIFORINIA** James Curl, Modesto Junior College; Christine Drake, University of California at Davis; Mahtash Esfandiari, UCLA; Brian Karl Finch, San Diego State University; Dawn Holmes, University of California Santa Barbara; Rob Gould, UCLA; Rebecca Head, Bakersfield College; Susan Herring, Sonoma State University; Colleen Kelly, San Diego State University; Marke Mavis, Butte Community College; Elaine McDonald, Sonoma State University; Corey Manchester, San Diego State University; Amy McElroy, San Diego State University; Helen Noble, San Diego State University; Calvin Schmall, Solano Community College; Scott Nickleach, Sonoma State University; Ann Kalinoskii, San Jose University ▪ **COLORADO** David Most, Colorado State University ▪ **CONNECTICUT** Paul Bugl, University of Hartford; Anne Doyle, University of Connecticut; Pete Johnson, Eastern Connecticut State University; Dan Miller, Central Connecticut State University; Kathleen McLaughlin, University of Connecticut; Nalini Ravishanker, University of Connecticut; John Vangar, Fairfield University; Stephen Sawin, Fairfield University ▪ **DISTRICT OF COLUMBIA** Hans Engler, Georgetown University; Mary W. Gray, American University; Monica Jackson, American University ▪ **FLORIDA** Nazanin Azarnia, Santa Fe Community College; Brett Holbrook; James Lang, Valencia Community College; Karen Kinard, Tallahassee Community College; Megan Mocko, University of Florida; Maria Ripol, University of Florida; James Smart, Tallahassee Community College; Latricia Williams, St. Petersburg Junior College, Clearwater; Doug Zahn, Florida State University ▪ **GEORGIA** Carrie Chmielarski, University of Georgia; Ouida Dillon, Oconee County High School; Kim Gilbert, University of Georgia; Katherine Hawks, Meadowcreek High School; Todd Hendricks, Georgia Perimeter College; Charles LeMarsh, Lakeside High School; Steve Messig, Oconee County High School; Broderick Oluyede, Georgia Southern University; Chandler Pike, University of Georgia; Kim Robinson, Clayton State University; Jill Smith, University of Georgia; John Seppala, Valdosta State University; Joseph Walker, Georgia State University; Evelyn Bailey, Oxford College of Emory University; Michael Roty, Mercer University ▪ **HAWAII** Erica Bernstein, University of Hawaii at Hilo ▪ **IOWA** John Cryer, University of Iowa; Kathy Rogotzke, North Iowa Community College; R. P. Russo, University of Iowa; William Duckworth, Iowa State University ▪ **ILLINOIS** Linda Brant Collins, University of Chicago; Dagmar Budikova, Illinois State University; Ellen Fireman, University of Illinois; Jinadasa Gamage, Illinois State University; Richard Maher, Loyola University Chicago; Cathy Poliak, Northern Illinois University; Daniel Rowe, Heartland Community College ▪ **KANSAS** James Higgins, Kansas State University; Michael Mosier, Washburn University; Katherine C. Earles, Wichita State University ▪ **KENTUCKY** Lisa Kay, Eastern Kentucky University ▪ **MASSACHUSETTS**

Richard Cleary, Bentley University; Katherine Halvorsen, Smith College; Xiaoli Meng, Harvard University; Daniel Weiner, Boston University ■ **MICHIGAN** Kirk Anderson, Grand Valley State University; Phyllis Curtiss, Grand Valley State University; Roy Erickson, Michigan State University; Jann-Huei Jinn, Grand Valley State University; Sango Otieno, Grand Valley State University; Alla Sikorskii, Michigan State University; Mark Stevenson, Oakland Community College; Todd Swanson, Hope College; Nathan Tintle, Hope College; Phyllis Curtiss, Grand Valley State; Ping-Shou Zhong, Michigan State University ■ **MINNESOTA** Bob Dobrow, Carleton College; German J. Pliego, University of St.Thomas; Peihua Qui, University of Minnesota; Engin A. Sungur, University of Minnesota–Morris ■ **MISSOURI** Lynda Hollingsworth, Northwest Missouri State University; Robert Paige, Missouri University of Science and Technology; Larry Ries, University of Missouri–Columbia; Suzanne Tourville, Columbia College ■ **MONTANA** Jeff Banfield, Montana State University ■ **NEW JERSEY** Harold Sackrowitz, Rutgers, The State University of New Jersey; Linda Tappan, Montclair State University ■ **NEW MEXICO** David Daniel, New Mexico State University ■ **NEW YORK** Brooke Fridley, Mohawk Valley Community College; Martin Lindquist, Columbia University; Debby Lurie, St. John's University; David Mathiason, Rochester Institute of Technology; Steve Stehman, SUNY ESF; Tian Zheng, Columbia University; Bernadette Lanciaux, Rochester Institute of Technology ■ **NEVADA** Alison Davis, University of Nevada–Reno ■ **NORTH CAROLINA** Pamela Arroway, North Carolina State University; E. Jacquelin Dietz, North Carolina State University; Alan Gelfand, Duke University; Gary Kader, Appalachian State University; Scott Richter, UNC Greensboro; Roger Woodard, North Carolina State University ■ **NEBRASKA** Linda Young, University of Nebraska ■ **OHIO** Jim Albert, Bowling Green State University; John Holcomb, Cleveland State University; Jackie Miller, The Ohio State University; Stephan Pelikan, University of Cincinnati; Teri Rysz, University of Cincinnati; Deborah Rumsey, The Ohio State University; Kevin Robinson, University of Akron; Dottie Walton, Cuyahoga Community College - Eastern Campus ■ **OREGON** Michael Marciniak, Portland Community College; Henry Mesa, Portland Community College, Rock Creek; Qi-Man Shao, University of Oregon; Daming Xu, University of Oregon ■ **PENNSYLVANIA** Winston Crawley, Shippensburg University; Douglas Frank, Indiana University of Pennsylvania; Steven Gendler, Clarion University; Bonnie A. Green, East Stroudsburg University; Paul Lupinacci, Villanova University; Deborah Lurie, Saint Joseph's University; Linda Myers, Harrisburg Area Community College; Tom Short, Villanova University; Kay Somers, Moravian College; Sister Marcella Louise Wallowicz, Holy Family University ■ **SOUTH CAROLINA** Beverly Diamond, College of Charleston; Martin Jones, College of Charleston; Murray Siegel, The South Carolina Governor's School for Science and Mathematics; Ellen Breazel, Clemson University ■ **SOUTH DAKOTA** Richard Gayle, Black Hills State University; Daluss Siewert, Black Hills State University; Stanley Smith, Black Hills State University ■ **TENNESSEE** Bonnie Daves, Christian Academy of Knoxville; T. Henry Jablonski, Jr., East Tennessee State University; Robert Price, East Tennessee State University; Ginger Rowell, Middle Tennessee State University; Edith Seier, East Tennessee State University; Matthew Jones, Austin Peay State University ■ **TEXAS** Larry Ammann, University of Texas, Dallas; Tom Bratcher, Baylor University; Jianguo Liu, University of North Texas; Mary Parker, Austin Community College; Robert Paige, Texas Tech University; Walter M. Potter, Southwestern University; Therese Shelton, Southwestern University; James Surles, Texas Tech University; Diane Resnick, University of Houston-Downtown; Rob Eby, Blinn College—Bryan Campus ■ **UTAH** Patti Collings, Brigham Young University; Carolyn Cuff, Westminster College; Lajos Horvath, University of Utah; P. Lynne Nielsen, Brigham Young University ■ **VIRGINIA** David Bauer, Virginia Commonwealth University; Ching-Yuan Chiang, James Madison University; Jonathan Duggins, Virginia Tech; Steven

Garren, James Madison University; Hasan Hamdan, James Madison University; Debra Hydorn, Mary Washington College; Nusrat Jahan, James Madison University; D'Arcy Mays, Virginia Commonwealth University; Stephanie Pickle, Virginia Polytechnic Institute and State University ■ **WASHINGTON** Rich Alldredge, Washington State University; Brian T. Gill, Seattle Pacific University; June Morita, University of Washington; Linda Dawson, Washington State University, Tacoma ■ **WISCONSIN** Brooke Fridley, University of Wisconsin–LaCrosse; Loretta Robb Thielman, University of Wisconsin–Stoutt ■ **WYOMING** Burke Grandjean, University of Wyoming ■ **CANADA** Mike Kowalski, University of Alberta; David Loewen, University of Manitoba

The detailed assessment of the text fell to our accuracy checkers, Nathan Kidwell and Joan Sanuik.

Thank you to James Lapp, who took on the task of revising the solutions manuals to reflect the many changes to the fifth edition.

We would like to thank the Pearson team who has given countless hours in developing this text; without their guidance and assistance, the text would not have come to completion. We thank Amanda Brands, Suzanna Bainbridge, Rachel Reeve, Karen Montgomery, Bob Carroll, Jean Choe, Alicia Wilson, Demetrius Hall, and Joe Vetere. We also thank Kim Fletcher, Senior Project Manager at Integra-Chicago, for keeping this book on track throughout production.

Alan Agresti would like to thank those who have helped us in some way, often by suggesting data sets or examples. These include Anna Gottard, Wolfgang Jank, René Lee-Pack, Jacalyn Levine, Megan Lewis, Megan Mocko, Dan Nettleton, Yongyi Min, and Euijung Ryu. Many thanks also to Tom Piazza for his help with the General Social Survey. Finally, Alan Agresti would like to thank his wife, Jacki Levine, for her extraordinary support throughout the writing of this book. Besides putting up with the evenings and weekends he was working on this book, she offered numerous helpful suggestions for examples and for improving the writing.

Chris Franklin gives a special thank-you to her husband and sons, Dale, Corey, and Cody Green. They have patiently sacrificed spending many hours with their spouse and mom as she has worked on this book through five editions. A special thank-you also to her parents, Grady and Helen Franklin, and her two brothers, Grady and Mark, who have always been there for their daughter and sister. Chris also appreciates the encouragement and support of her colleagues and her many students who used the book, offering practical suggestions for improvement. Finally, Chris thanks her coauthors, Alan and Bernhard, for the amazing journey of writing a textbook together.

Bernhard Klingenberg wants to thank his statistics teachers in Graz, Austria; Sheffield, UK; and Gainesville, Florida, who showed him all the fascinating aspects of statistics throughout his education. Thanks also to the Department of Mathematics & Statistics at Williams College and the Graduate Program in Data Science at New College of Florida for being such great places to work. Finally, thanks to Chris Franklin and Alan Agresti for a wonderful and inspiring collaboration.

ALAN AGRESTI, *GAINESVILLE, FLORIDA*

CHRISTINE FRANKLIN, *ATHENS, GEORGIA*

BERNHARD KLINGENBERG, *WILLIAMSTOWN, MASSACHUSETTS*

About the Authors

Alan Agresti is Distinguished Professor Emeritus in the Department of Statistics at the University of Florida. He taught statistics there for 38 years, including the development of three courses in statistical methods for social science students and three courses in categorical data analysis. He is author of more than 100 refereed articles and six texts, including *Statistical Methods for the Social Sciences* (Pearson, 5th edition, 2018) and *An Introduction to Categorical Data Analysis* (Wiley, 3rd edition, 2019). He is a Fellow of the American Statistical Association and recipient of an Honorary Doctor of Science from De Montfort University in the UK. He has held visiting positions at Harvard University, Boston University, the London School of Economics, and Imperial College and has taught courses or short courses for universities and companies in about 30 countries worldwide. He has also received teaching awards from the University of Florida and an excellence in writing award from John Wiley & Sons.

Christine Franklin is the K-12 Statistics Ambassador for the American Statistical Association and elected ASA Fellow. She is retired from the University of Georgia as the Lothar Tresp Honoratus Honors Professor and Senior Lecturer Emerita in Statistics. She is the co-author of two textbooks and has published more than 60 journal articles and book chapters. Chris was the lead writer for American Statistical Association Pre-K-12 Guidelines for the Assessment and Instruction in Statistics Education (GAISE) Framework document, co-chair of the updated Pre-K-12 GAISE II, and chair of the ASA Statistical Education of Teachers (SET) report. She is a past Chief Reader for Advance Placement Statistics, a Fulbright scholar to New Zealand (2015), recipient of the United States Conference on Teaching Statistics (USCOTS) Lifetime Achievement Award and the ASA Founders Award, and an elected member of the International Statistical Institute (ISI). Chris loves being with her family, running, hiking, scoring baseball games, and reading mysteries.

Bernhard Klingenberg is Professor of Statistics in the Department of Mathematics & Statistics at Williams College, where he has been teaching introductory and advanced statistics classes since 2004, and in the Graduate Data Science Program at New College of Florida, where he teaches statistics and data visualization for data scientists. Bernhard is passionate about making statistical software accessible to everyone and in addition to co-authoring this book is actively developing the web apps featured in this edition. A native of Austria, Bernhard frequently returns there to hold visiting positions at universities and gives short courses on categorical data analysis in Europe and the United States. He has published several peer-reviewed articles in statistical journals and consults regularly with academia and industry. Bernhard enjoys photography (some of his pictures appear in this book), scuba diving, hiking state parks, and spending time with his wife and four children.

Gathering and Exploring Data

Statistics: The Art and Science of Learning From Data

Example 1

How Statistics Helps Us Learn About the World

Picture the Scenario

In this book, you will explore a wide variety of everyday scenarios. For example, you will evaluate media reports about opinion surveys, medical research studies, the state of the economy, and environmental issues. You'll face financial decisions, such as choosing between an investment with a sure return and one that could make you more money but could possibly cost you your entire investment. You'll learn how to analyze the available information to answer necessary questions in such scenarios. One purpose of this book is to show you why an understanding of statistics is essential for making good decisions in an uncertain world.

Questions to Explore

This book will show you how to collect appropriate information and how to apply statistical methods so you can better evaluate that information and answer the questions posed. Here are some examples of questions we'll investigate in coming chapters:

- How can you evaluate evidence about global warming?
- Are cell phones dangerous to your health?
- What's the chance your tax return will be audited?
- How likely are you to win the lottery?
- Is there bias against women in appointing managers?
- What "hot streaks" should you expect in basketball?
- How successful is the flu vaccine in preventing the flu?
- How can you predict the selling price of a house?

Thinking Ahead

Each chapter uses questions like these to introduce a topic and then introduces tools for making sense of the available information. We'll see that **statistics** is the art and science of designing studies and analyzing the information that those studies produce.

In the business world, managers use statistics to analyze results of marketing studies about new products, to help predict sales, and to measure employee performance. In public policy discussions, statistics is used to support or discredit proposed measures, such as gun control or limits on carbon emissions. Medical studies use statistics to evaluate whether new ways to treat a disease are better than existing ones. In fact, most professional occupations today rely heavily on statistical methods. In a competitive job market, understanding how to reason statistically provides an important advantage. New jobs, such as data scientist, are created to process the amount of information generated in a digital and connected world and have statistical thinking as one of their core components.

But it's important to understand statistics even if you will never use it in your job. Understanding statistics can help you make better choices. Why? Because every day you are bombarded with statistical information from news reports, advertisements, political campaigns, surveys, or even the health app on your smartphone. How do you know how to process and evaluate all the information? An understanding of the statistical reasoning—and, in some cases, statistical misconceptions—underlying these pronouncements will help. For instance, this book will enable you to evaluate claims about medical research studies more effectively so that you know when you should be skeptical. For example, does taking an aspirin daily truly lessen the chance of having a heart attack?

We realize that you are probably not reading this book in the hope of becoming a statistician. (That's too bad, because there's a severe shortage of statisticians and data scientists—more jobs than trained people. And with the ever-increasing ways in which statistics is being applied, it's an exciting time to work in these fields.) You may even suffer from math phobia. Please be assured that to learn the main concepts of statistics, logical thinking and perseverance are more important than high-powered math skills. Don't be frustrated if learning comes slowly and you need to read about a topic a few times before it starts to make sense. Just as you would not expect to sit through a single foreign language class session and be able to speak that language fluently, the same is true with the language of statistics. It takes time and practice. But we promise that your hard work will be rewarded. Once you have completed even part of this book, you will understand much better how to make sense of statistical information and, hence, the world around you.

1.1 Using Data to Answer Statistical Questions

Does a low-carbohydrate diet result in significant weight loss? Are people more likely to stop at a Starbucks if they've seen a recent Starbucks TV commercial? Information gathering is at the heart of investigating answers to such questions. The information we gather with experiments and surveys is collectively called **data**.

For instance, consider an experiment designed to evaluate the effectiveness of a low-carbohydrate diet. The data might consist of the following measurements for the people participating in the study: weight at the beginning of the study, weight at the end of the study, number of calories of food eaten per day, carbohydrate intake per day, body mass index (BMI) at the start of the study, and gender. A marketing survey about the effectiveness of a TV ad for Starbucks could collect data on the percentage of people who went to a Starbucks since the ad aired and analyze how it compares for those who saw the ad and those who did not see it.

Today, massive amounts of data are collected automatically, for instance, through smartphone apps. These often personal data are used to answer statistical questions about consumer behavior, such as who is more likely to buy which product or which type of applicant is least likely to pay back a consumer loan.

Defining Statistics

You already have a sense of what the word *statistics* means. You hear statistics quoted about sports events (number of points scored by each player on a basketball team), statistics about the economy (median income, unemployment rate), and statistics about opinions, beliefs, and behaviors (percentage of students who indulge in binge drinking). In this sense, a statistic is merely a number calculated from data. But statistics as a field is a way of thinking about data and quantifying uncertainty, not a maze of numbers and messy formulas.

Statistics

Statistics is the art and science of collecting, presenting, and analyzing data to answer an investigative question. Its ultimate goal is translating data into knowledge and an understanding of the world around us. In short, *statistics is the art and science of learning from data*.

The statistical investigative process involves four components: (1) formulate a statistical question, (2) collect data, (3) analyze data, and (4) interpret and communicate results. The following scenarios ask questions that we'll learn how to answer using such a process.

Scenario 1: Predicting an Election Using an Exit Poll   In elections, television networks often declare the winner well before all the votes have been counted. They do this using exit polling, interviewing voters after they leave the voting booth. Using an exit poll, a network can often predict the winner after learning how several thousand people voted, out of possibly millions of voters.

The 2010 California gubernatorial race pitted Democratic candidate Jerry Brown against Republican candidate Meg Whitman. A TV exit poll used to project the outcome reported that 53.1% of a sample of 3,889 voters said they had voted for Jerry Brown. Was this sufficient evidence to project Brown as the winner, even though information was available from such a small portion of the more than 9.5 million voters in California? We'll learn how to answer that question in this book.

Scenario 2: Making Conclusions in Medical Research Studies   Statistical reasoning is at the foundation of the analyses conducted in most medical research studies. Let's consider three examples of how statistics can be relevant.

Heart disease is the most common cause of death in industrialized nations. In the United States and Canada, nearly 30% of deaths yearly are due to heart disease, mainly heart attacks. Does regular aspirin intake reduce deaths from heart attacks? Harvard Medical School conducted a landmark study to investigate. The people participating in the study regularly took either an aspirin or a placebo (a pill with no active ingredient). Of those who took aspirin, 0.9% had heart attacks during the study. Of those who took the placebo, 1.7% had heart attacks, nearly twice as many.

Can you conclude that it's beneficial for people to take aspirin regularly? Or, could the observed difference be explained by how it was decided which people would receive aspirin and which would receive the placebo? For instance, might those who took aspirin have had better results merely because they were healthier, on average, than those who took the placebo? Or, did those taking aspirin have a better diet or exercise more regularly, on average?

For years there has been controversy about whether regular intake of large doses of vitamin C is beneficial. Some studies have suggested that it is. But some scientists have criticized those studies' designs, claiming that the subsequent statistical analysis was meaningless. How do we know when we can trust the statistical results in a medical study that is reported in the media?

Suppose you wanted to investigate whether, as some have suggested, heavy use of cell phones makes you more likely to get brain cancer. You could pick half the students from your school and tell them to use a cell phone each day for the next 50 years and tell the other half never to use a cell phone. Fifty years from now you could see whether more users than nonusers of cell phones got brain cancer. Obviously it would be impractical and unethical to carry out such a study. And who wants to wait 50 years to get the answer? Years ago, a British statistician figured out how to study whether a particular type of behavior has an effect on cancer, using already available data. He did this to answer a then controversial question: Does smoking cause lung cancer? How did he do this?

This book will show you how to answer questions like these. You'll learn when you can trust the results from studies reported in the media and when you should be skeptical.

Scenario 3: Using a Survey to Investigate People's Beliefs   How similar are your opinions and lifestyle to those of others? It's easy to find out. Every other year, the National Opinion Research Center at the University of Chicago conducts the General Social Survey (GSS). This survey of a few thousand adult Americans provides data about the opinions and behaviors of the American public. You can use it to investigate how adult Americans answer a wide diversity of questions, such as, "Do you believe in life after death?" "Would you be willing to pay higher prices in order to protect the environment?" "How much TV do you watch per day?" and "How many sexual partners have you had in the past year?" Similar surveys occur in other countries, such as the Eurobarometer survey within the European Union. We'll use data from such surveys to illustrate the proper application of statistical methods.

Reasons for Using Statistical Methods

The scenarios just presented illustrate the three main components for answering a statistical investigative question:

- **Design:**   Stating the goal and/or statistical question of interest and planning how to obtain data that will address them
- **Description:**   Summarizing and analyzing the data that are obtained
- **Inference:**   Making decisions and predictions based on the data for answering the statistical question

Design refers to planning how to obtain data that will efficiently shed light on the statistical question of interest. How could you conduct an experiment to determine reliably whether regular large doses of vitamin C are beneficial? In marketing, how do you select the people to survey so you'll get data that provide good predictions about future sales? Are there already available (public) data that you can use for your analysis, and what is the quality of the data?

Description refers to exploring and summarizing patterns in the data. Files of raw data are often huge. For example, over time the GSS has collected data about hundreds of characteristics on many thousands of people. Such raw data are not easy to assess—we simply get bogged down in numbers. It is more informative to use a few numbers or a graph to summarize the data, such as an average amount of TV watched or a graph displaying how the number of hours of TV watched per day relates to the number of hours per week exercising.

Inference refers to making decisions or predictions based on the data. Usually the decision or prediction applies to a larger group of people, not merely those in the study. For instance, in the exit poll described in Scenario 1, of 3,889 voters sampled, 53.1% said they voted for Jerry Brown. Using these data, we can predict (infer) that a majority of the 9.5 million voters voted for him. Stating the percentages for the sample of 3,889 voters is *description*, whereas predicting the outcome for all 9.5 million voters is *inference*.

In Words

The verb **infer** means to arrive at a decision or prediction by reasoning from known evidence. **Statistical inference** does this using data as evidence.

Statistical description and inference are complementary ways of analyzing data. Statistical description provides useful summaries and helps you find patterns in the data; inference helps you make predictions and decide whether observed patterns are meaningful. You can use both to investigate questions that are important to society. For instance, "Has there been global warming over the past decade?" "Is having the death penalty available for punishment associated with a reduction in violent crime?" "Does student performance in school depend on the amount of money spent per student, the size of the classes, or the teachers' salaries?"

Long before we analyze data, we need to give careful thought to posing the questions to be answered by that analysis. The nature of these questions has an impact on all stages—design, description, and inference. For example, in an exit poll, do we just want to predict which candidate won, or do we want to investigate *why* by analyzing how voters' opinions about certain issues related to how they voted? We'll learn how questions such as these and the ones posed in the previous paragraph can be phrased in terms of statistical summaries (such as percentages and means) so that we can use data to investigate their answers.

Finally, a topic that we have not mentioned yet but that is fundamental for statistical reasoning is **probability**, which is a framework for quantifying how likely various possible outcomes are. We'll study probability because it will help us answer questions such as, "If Brown were actually going to lose the election (that is, if he were supported by less than half of all voters), what's the chance that an exit poll of 3,889 voters would show support by 53.1% of the voters?" If the chance were extremely small, we'd feel comfortable making the inference that his reelection was supported by the majority of all 9.5 million voters.

▶ Activity 1

Using Data Available Online to Answer Statistical Questions

Did you ever wonder about how much time people spend watching TV? We could use the survey question "On the average day, about how many hours do you personally watch television?" from the General Social Survey (GSS) to investigate this statistical question. Data from the GSS are accessible online via http://sda.berkeley.edu. Click on Archive (the second box in the top row) and then scroll down and click on the link labeled "General Social Survey (GSS) Cumulative Datafile 1972–2018." You can also access this site directly and more easily via the link provided on the book's website www.ArtofStat.com. (You may want to bookmark this link, as many activities in this book use data from the GSS.)

As shown in the screenshot,

- Enter TVHOURS in the field labeled Row. TVHOURS is the name the GSS uses for identifying the responses to the TV question.
- Enter YEAR(2018) in the Selection Filter field. This will select only the data for the 2018 GSS, not data from earlier (or later) iterations of the GSS, when this question was also included.
- Change the Weight to No Weight. This will specify that we see the actual frequency for each of the possible responses to the survey question and not some numbers adjusting for the way the survey was taken.

| Tables | Means | Correl. matrix | Comp. correl. | Regression |
| Logit/Probit | List values | | | |

SDA Frequencies/Crosstabulation Program
Help: General / Recoding Variables

Row: TVHOURS (Required)

Column:

Control: ⑦

Selection Filter(s): YEAR(2018) ⑦

Weight: ⑦ No Weight

▸ Output Options

▸ Chart Options

▸ Decimal Options

Run the Table   Clear Fields

Press the Run the Table button on the bottom, and a new browser window will open that shows the frequencies (e.g., 145 and 349) and, in bold, the percentages (e.g., 9.3 and 22.4) of people who made each of the possible responses. (See the screenshot on the next page, which displays the top and bottom of the table.)

A **statistical analysis question** we can ask is, "What is the most common response?" From the bottom of the table we see that a total of 1,555 persons answered the question, of which 376 or, as shown, 24.2% (= 100 × (376/1,555)) watched two

Frequency Distribution	
Cells contain: -Column percent -N of cases	Distribution
0	9.3 145
1	22.4 349
2	24.2 376
3	15.4 240
4	10.9 169
5	6.4 100
20	.3 4
24	.3 4
COL TOTAL	100.0 1,555

hours of TV. This is the most common response. What is the second most common response? What percent of respondents watched zero hours of TV?

Another survey question asked by the GSS is, "Taken all together, would you say that you are very happy, pretty happy, or not too happy?" The GSS name for this question is HAPPY. Return to the initial table but now enter HAPPY instead of TVHOURS as the row variable. Keep YEAR(2018) for the selection filter (if you leave this field blank, you get the cumulative data for all years for which this question was included in the GSS) and No Weight for the Weight box. Press Run the Table to replicate the screenshot shown below, which tells us that 29.9% (= $100 \times (701/2,344)$) of the 2,344 respondents to this question in 2018 said that they are very happy.

Frequency Distribution		
Cells contain: -Column percent -N of cases		Distribution
HAPPY	1: VERY HAPPY	29.9 701
	2: PRETTY HAPPY	55.8 1,307
	3: NOT TOO HAPPY	14.3 336
	COL TOTAL	100.0 2,344

You can use the GSS to investigate statistical questions such as what kinds of people are more likely to be very happy. Those who have high incomes (GSS variable INCOME16) or are in good health (GSS variable HEALTH)? Are those who watch less TV more likely to be happy? We'll explore how to investigate and answer these statistical questions using the statistical problem solving process throughout this book.

Try Exercises 1.3 and 1.5 ◀

1.1 Practicing the Basics

1.1 **Aspirin and heart attacks** The Harvard Medical School study mentioned in Scenario 2 included about 22,000 male physicians. Whether a given individual would be assigned to take aspirin or the placebo was determined by flipping a coin. As a result, about 11,000 physicians were assigned to take aspirin and about 11,000 to take the placebo. The researchers summarized the results of the experiment by using percentages. Of the physicians taking aspirin, 0.9% had a heart attack, compared to 1.7% of those taking the placebo. Based on the observed results, the study authors concluded that taking aspirin reduces the risk of having a heart attack. Specify the aspects of this study that pertain to (a) design (including the statistical question of interest), (b) description, and (c) inference.

1.2 **Poverty and Race** The Current Population Survey (CPS) is a survey conducted by the U.S. Census Bureau for the Bureau of Labor Statistics. It provides a comprehensive body of data on the labor force, unemployment, wealth, poverty, and so on. The data can be found online at www.census.gov/cps/. The data for 2018 included about 75,000 households and showed that 15.5% of households identifying as White, 28.3% of households identifying as Black, and 10.5% of households identifying as Asian had an annual household income below the poverty line. Based on these results, a report concludes that the percentage of all such Black households with annual incomes below the poverty line is between 27.5% and 29.1%. Specify the aspects of this study that pertain to (a) design (including the statistical question of interest), (b) description, and (c) inference.

1.3 **GSS and heaven** Go to the General Social Survey website, http://sda.berkeley.edu, press Archive, scroll down a bit and then select the "General Social Survey (GSS) Cumulative Datafile 1972–2018", or whichever appears as the top (most recent) one. Alternatively, go there directly via the link provided on the book's website, www.ArtofStat.com (see Activity 1). Enter the variable HEAVEN as the row variable; leave all other fields blank, but be certain to select No Weight for the Weight field. HEAVEN refers to the GSS question, "Do you believe in heaven?"

a. Overall, how many people gave a valid response to the question whether they believe in heaven?

b. What percent of respondents said yes, definitely; yes, probably; no, probably not; and no, definitely not? (You can compute these percentages from the numbers given in each category and the total shown in the last row of the frequency table, or just read them off from the percentages given in bold.)

c. The questions in parts a and b refer to the cumulative data over all the years the GSS included this question (which was in 1991, 1998, 2008, and 2018). To get the percentages for each year separately, enter HEAVEN in the row variable and YEAR in the column variable. Press Run the Table (keeping Weight as No Weight). What is the proportion of respondents that answered yes, definitely in 2018? How does it compare to the proportion 10 years earlier?

1.4 GSS and heaven and hell Refer to the previous exercise, but now type HELL into the row variable box to obtain data on the question, "Do you believe in hell?" Keep all other fields blank and select No Weight.

a. What percent of respondents said yes, definitely; yes, probably; no, probably not; and no, definitely not for the belief in hell question?

b. To get data for this question for each year separately, type YEAR into the column variable field. Find the percentage of respondents who said yes, definitely to the hell question in 2018. How does this compare to the proportion of respondents in 2018 who believe in heaven?

1.5 GSS and work hours Go to the General Social Survey website, http://sda.berkeley.edu, press Archive, scroll down a bit and then select the "General Social Survey (GSS) Cumulative Datafile 1972–2018", or whichever appears as the top (most recent) one. Alternatively, go there directly via the link provided on the book's website, www.ArtofStat.com (see Activity 1). Enter the variable USUALHRS as the row variable, type YEAR(2016) in the selection filter, and choose No Weight for the Weight field. USUALHRS refers to the question, "How many hours per week do you usually work?"

a. Overall, how many people responded to this question?

b. What was the most common response, and what percentage of people selected it?

1.2 Sample Versus Population

We've seen that statistics consists of methods for **designing** investigative studies, **describing** (summarizing) data obtained for those studies, and making **inferences** (decisions and predictions) based on those data to answer a statistical question of interest.

We Observe Samples but Are Interested in Populations

The entities that we measure in a study are called the **subjects**. Usually subjects are people, such as the individuals interviewed in a General Social Survey (GSS). But they need not be. For instance, subjects could be schools, countries, or days. We might measure characteristics such as the following:

- For each school: the per-student expenditure, the average class size, the average score of students on an achievement test
- For each country: the percentage of residents living in poverty, the birth rate, the percentage unemployed, the percentage who are computer literate
- For each day in an Internet café: the amount spent on coffee, the amount spent on food, the amount spent on Internet access

The **population** is the set of all the subjects of interest. In practice, we usually have data for only *some* of the subjects who belong to that population. These subjects are called a **sample**.

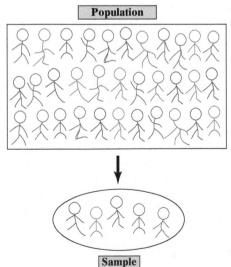

Population and Sample

The **population** is the total set of subjects in which we are interested. A **sample** is the subset of the population for whom we have (or plan to have) data, often randomly selected.

In the 2018 GSS, the sample consisted of the 2,348 people who participated in this survey. The population was the set of all adult Americans at that time—about 240 million people.

Sample and Population ◀

Did You Know?

Examples in this book use the five parts shown in this example: **Picture the Scenario** introduces the context. **Question to Explore** states the question addressed. **Think It Through** shows the reasoning used to answer that question. **Insight** gives follow-up comments related to the example.

(TRY) **Try Exercises** direct you to a similar "Practicing the Basics" exercise at the end of the section. Also, each example title is preceded by a label highlighting the example's **concept**. In this example, the concept label is "Sample and population." ◀

In Practice

Sometimes the population is well-defined, but sometimes it is a hypothetical set of subjects that is not enumerated. For example, in a clinical trial to examine the impact of a new drug on lowering cholesterol, the population would be all people with high cholesterol who might have signed up for such a trial. This set of people is not specifically listed. And sometimes, the population is not even a population in the conventional sense, but refers to a theoretical statistical model for our data.

Example 2

An Exit Poll

Picture the Scenario

Scenario 1 in the previous section discussed an exit poll. The purpose was to predict the outcome of the 2010 gubernatorial election in California. The exit poll sampled 3,889 of the 9.5 million people who voted.

Question to Explore

For this exit poll, what was the population and what was the sample?

Think It Through

The population was the total set of subjects of interest, namely, the 9.5 million people who voted in this election. The sample was the 3,889 voters who were interviewed in the exit poll. These are the people from whom the poll obtained data about their votes.

Insight

The ultimate goal of most studies is to learn about the *population*. For example, the sponsors of this exit poll wanted to make an inference (prediction) about *all* voters, not just the 3,889 voters sampled by the poll.

▶ *Try Exercises 1.9 and 1.10*

Occasionally data are available from an entire population. For instance, every 10 years the U.S. Census Bureau gathers data from the entire U.S. population (or nearly all). But the census is an exception. Usually, it is too costly and time-consuming to obtain data from an entire population. It is more practical to get data for a sample. The GSS and polling organizations such as the Gallup poll or the Pew Research Center usually select samples of about 1,000 to 2,500 Americans to learn about opinions and beliefs of the population of *all* Americans. The same is true for surveys in other parts of the world, such as the Eurobarometer in Europe.

Similarly, a manufacturing company may not be able to inspect the entire production of the day (the population), which could consist of thousands of items. It has to rely on taking a small sample of the entire production to learn about potential quality issues with the production process.

Descriptive Statistics and Inferential Statistics

Using the distinction between samples and populations, we can now tell you more about the use of **description** and **inference** in statistical analyses.

Description in Statistical Analyses

Descriptive statistics refers to methods for summarizing the collected data (where the data constitute either a sample or a population). The summaries usually consist of graphs and numbers such as averages and percentages.

A descriptive statistical analysis usually combines graphical and numerical summaries. For instance, Figure 1.1 shows a bar graph that summarizes (as percentages) the responses of 743 U.S. teenagers to the question of whether they lose focus in class due to checking their cell phone. The main purpose of descriptive statistics is to reduce the data to simple summaries without distorting or losing much information. Graphs and numbers such as percentages and averages are easier to comprehend than the entire set of data. It's much easier to get a sense of the data by looking at Figure 1.1 than by reading through the surveys filled out

▲ Figure 1.1 Result of a survey of 743 teenagers (ages 13–17) about their handling of screen time and distraction. (*Source:* Pew Research Center, http://www.pewinternet .org/2018/08/22/how-teens-and-parents-navigate-screen-time-and-device-distractions/ © 2020 Pew Research Center)

by the 743 teenagers. From this graph, it's readily apparent that about 40% never lose focus and only 8% lose focus often.

Descriptive statistics are also useful when data are available for the entire population, such as in a census. By contrast, inferential statistics are used when data are available for a sample only, but we want to make a decision or prediction about the entire population.

Inference in Statistical Analyses

Inferential statistics refers to methods of making decisions or predictions about a population, based on data obtained from a sample of that population.

In most surveys, we have data for a sample, not for the entire population. We use descriptive statistics to summarize the sample data and inferential statistics to make predictions about the population.

Example 3

Descriptive and Inferential Statistics ◀

Banning Plastic Bags

Picture the Scenario

Suppose we'd like to investigate what people think about banning single-use plastic bags from grocery stores. California was the first state to issue a law banning plastic bags, and similar measures were under consideration for the state of New York at the beginning of 2019. Let's consider as our population all eligible voters in the state of New York, a population of more than 14 million people.

Because it is impossible to discuss the issue with all these people, we can study results from a January 2019 poll of 929 New York State voters conducted by Quinnipiac University.[1] In that poll, 48% of the sampled subjects said they would support a state law that bans stores from providing plastic bags. The reported margin of error for how close this number falls to the population percentage is 4.1%. We'll see (later in the book) that this means we can predict with high confidence (about 95% certainty) that the percentage of all New York voters supporting the ban of plastic bags falls within 4.1% of the survey's value of 48%, that is, between 43.9% and 52.1%.

---

[1]Quinnipiac University. (2019). *New York State voters split on plastic bag ban, Quinnipiac University poll finds* [press release]. Retrieved from https://poll.qu.edu/new-york-state/ release-detail?ReleaseID=2595

Question to Explore

In this analysis, what is the descriptive statistical analysis and what is the inferential statistical analysis?

Think It Through

The results for the sample of 929 New York voters are summarized by the percentage, 48%, who support banning plastic bags. This is a descriptive statistical analysis. We're interested, however, not just in those 929 people but in the population of the entire state of New York. The prediction that the percentage of all New York voters who support banning plastic bags falls between 43.9% and 52.1% is an inferential statistical analysis. In summary, we describe the sample and we make inferences about the population.

Insight

The press release about this study mentioned that New York State voters are split on a plastic bag ban. This is because the interval from 43.9% to 52.1% includes values on both sides of 50%, showing that supporters may be in the minority or in the majority. If such a percentage and margin of error were observed in an election poll, New York State would be called "too close to call."

In April 2019, New York State lawmakers agreed to impose a statewide ban, which went into effect in March 2020.

▶ *Try Exercises 1.11, part a, and 1.12, parts a–c*

An important aspect of statistical inference involves reporting the likely *precision* of a prediction. How close is the *sample* value of 48% likely to be to the true (unknown) percentage of the *population* in support of banning plastic bags? We'll see (in Chapters 4 and 7) why a well-designed sample of 929 people yields a sample percentage value that is very likely to fall within about 3–4% (the so-called *margin of error*) of the population value. In fact, we'll see that inferential statistical analyses can predict characteristics of entire populations quite well by selecting samples that are small relative to the population size. Surprisingly, the absolute size of the sample matters much more than the size relative to the population total. For example, the population of the United States is about 35 times larger than the population of Austria (312 million versus 9 million), but a random sample of 1,000 people from the U.S. population and a random sample of 1,000 people from the Austrian population would achieve similar levels of accuracy. That's why most polls take samples of only about a thousand people, regardless of the size of the population. In this book, we'll see why this works.

Sample Statistics and Population Parameters

In Example 3, the percentage of the sample supporting the ban of plastic bags is an example of a **sample statistic**. It is crucial to distinguish between sample statistics and the corresponding values for the population. The term **parameter** is used for a numerical summary of the population.

Recall

A **population** is the total group of individuals about whom you want to make conclusions. A **sample** is a subset of the population for whom you actually have data. ◀

Parameter and Statistic

A **parameter** is a numerical summary of the population. A **statistic** is a numerical summary of a sample taken from the population.

For example, the percentage of the population of all voters in New York State supporting a ban on plastic bags is a parameter. We hope to learn about parameters so that we can better understand the population, but the true parameter values are almost always unknown. Thus, we use sample statistics to estimate the parameter values.

Example 4

Gallup Poll

Picture the Scenario

On April 20, 2010, one of the worst environmental disasters took place in the Gulf of Mexico: the Deepwater Horizon oil spill. In response to the spill, many activists called for an end to deepwater drilling off the U.S. coast. Meanwhile, approximately nine months after the Gulf of Mexico disaster, political turbulence gripped the Middle East, causing the price of gasoline in the United States to approach an all-time high.

In March 2011, Gallup's annual environmental survey showed that 60% of Americans favored offshore drilling as a means to reduce U.S. dependence on foreign oil.[2] The poll was based on interviews conducted with a random sample of 1,021 adults, aged 18 and older, living in the continental United States, selected using random digit dialing.

Question to Explore

In this study, identify the sample statistic and the population parameter of interest.

Think It Through

The 60% refers to the percentage of the 1,021 adults in the survey who favored offshore drilling. It is the sample statistic. The population parameter of interest is the percentage of the entire U.S. adult population favoring offshore drilling in March 2011.

Insight

This and previous examples have focused on percentages as examples of sample statistics and population parameters because they are so ubiquitous. But there are many other statistics we compute from samples to estimate a corresponding parameter in the population. For instance, the U.S. government uses data from surveys to estimate population parameters such as the median household income or the average student debt. The corresponding sample statistics used to predict these parameters are the median income or the average student debt computed from all the people included in the survey.

► **Try Exercise 1.7**

[2]Saad, Lydia., U.S. Satisfaction Still Running at Improved Level. Gallup, Inc, 2018 © 2020 Gallup, Inc.

Randomness

Random is often thought to mean chaotic or haphazard, but randomness is an extremely powerful tool for obtaining good samples and conducting experiments. A sample tends to be a good reflection of a population when each subject in the population has the same chance of being included in that sample. That's the basis of **random sampling**, which is designed to make the sample representative of the population. A simple example of random sampling is when a teacher puts each student's name on slips of paper, places them in a hat, shuffles them, and then draws names from the hat without looking.

- Random sampling allows us to make powerful inferences about populations.
- Randomness is also crucial to performing experiments well.

If, as in Scenario 2 on page 4, we want to compare aspirin to a placebo in terms of the percentage of people who later have a heart attack, it's best to randomly select those in the sample who use aspirin and those who use the placebo. This approach tends to keep the groups balanced on other factors that could affect the results. For example, suppose we allowed people to choose whether to use aspirin (instead of randomizing whether the person receives aspirin or the placebo). Then, the people who decided to use aspirin might have tended to be healthier than those who didn't, which could produce misleading results.

Variability

An essential goal of Statistics is to study and describe variability: How observations vary from person to person **within** a sample, and how statistics computed from samples vary from one sample to the next, i.e., **between** samples.

Within Sample Variability: People are different from each other, so, not surprisingly, the measurements we make on them *vary* from person to person. For the GSS question about TV watching in Activity 1 on page 6, different people included in the sample reported different amounts of TV watching. In the exit poll sample of Example 2, not all people voted the same way. If subjects did not vary, we'd need to sample only one of them. We learn more about this variability by sampling more people. If we want to predict the outcome of an election, we're better off sampling 100 voters than one voter, and our prediction will be even more reliable if we sample 1,000 voters.

Between Sample Variability: Just as observations on people vary, so do results computed from samples. Suppose you take a random sample of 1,000 voters to predict the outcome of an election the next week. Suppose the Gallup organization also takes a random sample of 1,000 voters. Your sample will have different people than Gallup's. Consequently, the predictions will differ between these two samples. Perhaps your poll of 1,000 voters has 480 voting for the Republican candidate, so you predict that 48% of all voters are going to vote for that person. Perhaps Gallup's poll of 1,000 voters has 460 voting for the Republican candidate, so they predict that 46% of all voters are going to vote for that person.

A very interesting and useful, yet surprising, fact with random sampling is that the amount of variability in the results from one sample to another is actually quite predictable. (Activity 2 at the end of this section will show this.) For instance, the two predictions from your and the Gallup poll are likely to fall within just three percentage points of the actual population percentage voting Republican. This gives us some idea about the variability (and, hence, precision) of our predictions.

If, however, the polls cannot be regarded a random sample from the population, perhaps because Republicans are more likely than Democrats to refuse to participate, then we would need to account for this, resulting in a loss of precision in our predictions. Issues such as the difficulty of obtaining a truly random sample or people not responding can dramatically limit the accuracy of polls in predicting the actual population percentage. We will discuss such issues in Chapter 4.

Margin of Error

With statistical inference, we try to estimate the value of an unknown population parameter, using information the data provide. Such an estimate should always be accompanied by a statement about its precision so that we can assess how useful it is in predicting the unknown parameter. For instance, the Gallup poll from Example 4 reported that 60% of Americans favored offshore drilling. How close is such a sample estimate to the true, unknown population percentage? To address this, many studies publish the margin of error associated with their estimates, in statements such as "The margin of error in this study is plus or minus 3 percentage points." The margin of error is a measure of the expected variability in the results from one random sample to the next random sample. As we have discussed (and will illustrate in Activity 2), there is variability between samples. A second sample of the same size about offshore drilling could yield a proportion of 58%, whereas a third might yield 61%. A margin of error of plus or minus 3 percentage points summarizes this variability numerically and indicates that it is very likely that the population percentage

In Practice

In February 2019, Gallup's survey on the job the U.S. president is doing found a 44% approval rating among U.S. adults. As Gallup writes: "For results based on the total sample of national adults, the margin of sampling error is ±3 percentage points at the 95% confidence level."

is no more than 3% lower or 3% higher than the reported sample percentage. When Gallup reports that 60% favor offshore drilling and they mention a margin of error of plus or minus 3%, it's very likely that in the entire population, the percentage that favor offshore drilling is between about 57% and 63% (that is, within 3 percentage points of 60%). "Very likely" typically means that about 95 times out of 100, such statements are correct. We refer to such a range of plausible numbers as a 95% confidence interval. Chapter 8 will show details about the margin of error and how to calculate it. For now, we'll use an interactive app to get a feel for and visualize the variability in the results we get from one sample to the next and the corresponding margin of error.

> ### Margin of Error
>
> The margin of error measures how close we expect an estimate to fall to the true population parameter.

▶ Activity 2

Using Simulation to Understand Randomness and Variability

To get a feel for randomness and variability, let's simulate taking a poll for an upcoming student body president election using the *Sampling Distribution for the Sample Proportion* web app available from the book's website, www.ArtofStat .com. When accessing this app, a graph will appear with two bars over the numbers 0 (representing a "failure") and 1 (representing a "success"). In our context, this graph refers to a student population where each student can vote for one out of only two candidates, say William and Diana. For the purpose of this exercise, let's denote a vote for William a "failure" and a vote for Diana a "success". (In the app, we checked the box for Provide Labels for 0 and 1 to make this explicit on the graph.)

Let's explore what could happen with randomly selecting a sample from a student population that is split between these two candidates, i.e., where each candidate has exactly 50% support. We'll use a small poll of only 10 students first. Because of the 50% support for each of the two candidates, we can represent the outcome (prefer William, prefer Diana) of this poll by flipping a fair coin 10 times. Let the number of heads represent the number who preferred Diana. In your 10 flips of a coin, what proportion preferred Diana?

Now, instead of flipping a coin, let's work with the app. To reflect that 50% in the population prefer Diana, set the population proportion (p) to 0.5 with the top slider. This updates the bar graph to now show a 50% chance for each of the two candidates. To select a sample of size 10, move the slider for the sample size to 10. Next, click on the blue Draw Sample(s) button and you will see two more graphs appearing. The first will show exactly how many failures (votes for William) and successes (votes for Diana) occurred in the sample of size 10 that you just generated. When we did this, we got three successes and seven failures. This simulates polling 10 students from a population where 50% prefer Diana and the other 50% prefer William and obtaining three students who prefer Diana and seven students who prefer William. (You might get different numbers.) The result from this one

sample corresponds to a sample proportion of $3/10 = 0.30$ voting for Diana.

Now generate another sample of size 10 and find the sample proportion by clicking the Draw Sample(s) button a second time. What did you get? We got a sample proportion of 0.5. Repeat taking samples of size 10 at least 25 times by repeatedly clicking the button. The "Data Distribution" bar graph in the middle shows the results of the most recent sample generated. Observe how in this graph the sample proportion for each sample (indicated by the blue triangle) "jumps around" the population proportion of 0.50 (indicated by the orange half-circle). Are they always close? How often did you get a sample proportion different from 0.5? The bottom graph keeps track of all the sample proportions generated and how often they occur. Note how much the different sample proportions vary from the population proportion of 0.5. In our 25 simulations, as shown in Figure 1.2, they were as low as 0.2 and as large as 0.7.

Now repeat this process for a larger poll, taking a sample of 100 students instead of just 10 (press Reset and set the sample size to 100 in the app). What proportion in the sample of size 100 you generated preferred Diana? (We got 0.53.) Repeat taking samples of size 100 at least 25 times (press Draw Sample(s) repeatedly). Are the sample proportions preferring Diana closer to 0.50 compared to the situation with a sample size of 10? How close? We predict that almost all of your simulated sample proportions now fall between 0.40 and 0.60, or within 0.1 of $p = 0.5$. In other words, the margin of error is approximately equal to ± 0.1. Are we correct?

This activity visualizes the margin of error, a measure of how close the sample proportion is expected to fall to the population proportion, p. The activity also illustrates that sample proportions tend to be closer to the population proportion when the sample size is larger. This implies that the margin of error decreases as the sample size increases. In Chapter 8, we'll develop a formula for the margin of error that will show this explicitly. For now, investigate results using different values for the population proportion (or sample size), such as $p = 0.6$, indicating 60% support for Diana. Now, when simulating polls with a sample size of 100, are you ever getting a poll for which the sample proportion is less than 0.5? (Such a poll would wrongly indicate that the support for Diana is less than 50%.) What do you estimate as the margin of error when $p = 0.6$ and the sample size is 100?

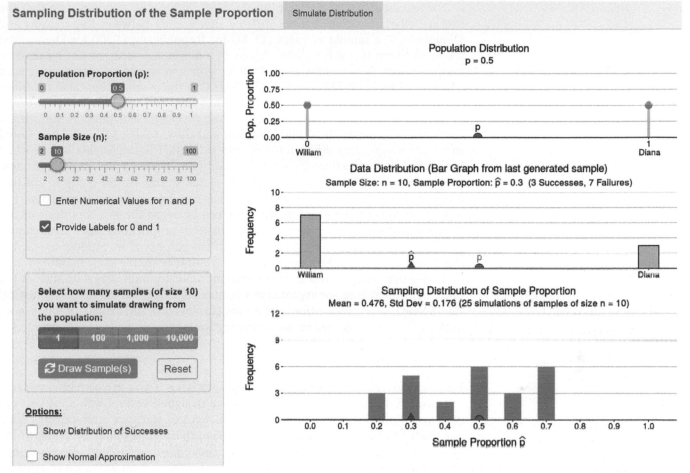

▲ Figure 1.2 Simulate Taking Polls to See How Sample Proportions Vary. Screenshot from the *Sampling Distribution for the Sample Proportion* app. Using the top slider, we set the population proportion *p* equal to 0.5. The top graph then shows that a proportion of 0.5 (or 50%) of the students in the entire student population prefer Diana as the next student body president and the other half prefer William. Pressing the blue Draw Sample(s) button once simulates taking one sample of size 10, set via the slider labeled "Sample Size (n)", from this population. The graph in the middle shows the outcome of this simulation (here: 3 students preferred Diana, 7 preferred William) and marks the sample proportion voting for Diana (0.3) with a blue triangle labeled $\hat{p}$. Repeatedly clicking Draw Sample(s) will generate a new sample of 10 students with each click, illustrating how the sample proportion varies from one sample to another. (Watch the blue triangle in the middle plot jump around.) The bottom plot keeps track of the frequencies of all the sample proportions generated throughout the simulations. Play around with this app, selecting different values for *p* and the sample size, and observe how much the sample proportion varies. Other features of this app will be explained in Chapter 7.

Try Exercises 1.16, part c and d, 1.37 and 1.41 ◄

Statistical Significance

In many applications, we want to **compare two population parameters**, such as the proportion of elderly patients suffering a heart attack between those taking a daily dose of aspirin and those just taking a placebo. Or, we may want to compare voters who identify with one of two political parties, for instance Democrats and Republicans, in terms of their amount of charitable contributions. In both cases, we can investigate if the population parameter in one group differs from the population parameter in the other group, and by how much. For instance, we can ask the **statistical questions**, "Is the average amount given by Republicans different from the average amount given by Democrats? If yes, by how much?"

If the information from the two samples provides strong evidence that there is a difference, we say that the two groups **differ significantly** with respect to the two population parameters. For statisticians, the word *significantly* implies that the observed difference computed between the two samples is larger than what would be expected from ordinary random sample-to-sample variability. Sample-to-sample variability refers to variability that occurs naturally, just by chance.

For instance, based on data from the GSS in 2014, we can conclude that the average charitable contributions *differed significantly* between Republicans and Democrats. The sample averages ($3,900 for Republicans, $1,300 for Democrats) are so different that it is unlikely that such a difference occurred just by random sample-to-sample variability alone. In other words, we would not expect to see such a large difference of $3,900 − $1,300 = $2,600 in the average charitable contributions if voters identifying with these two parties gave the same amounts, on average.

On the other hand, the difference in the proportion of patients suffering a heart attack between those taking aspirin and those taking a placebo was found to be *not significantly different* for elderly patients. This conclusion was reached based on data from a five-year study in elderly (≥ 70 years) subjects.[3] The sample proportion of 5.0% that suffered a heart attack in the aspirin group is not that different from the 5.4% that suffered a heart attack in the placebo group. The difference of 0.4 percentage points observed between the *two samples* was not large enough to conclude that the *two population* proportions differ significantly. In other words, the observed difference of 0.4 can occur by random variability alone, and even when the proportion of heart attacks are the same in both groups.

Two-group comparisons and statistical methods for analyzing data such as the ones mentioned here are explored in Chapter 10. There, we will discuss statistical significance, how it may differ from practical relevance, and explain that it is more useful to estimate the size of the difference together with a margin of error.

Web Apps

Just like riding a bike, it's easier to learn statistics if you are actively involved, learning by doing. For this reason, we have designed several web apps that engage you with the ideas, concepts, and practices of statistics interactively. We'll use them throughout this book. You can find these apps online by going to the book's website, www.ArtofStat.com, and clicking on Web Apps. Because they run in any browser (no installation necessary), we call them web apps or apps for short. Activity 2 already showcased one of these apps to explore the concept of a margin of error for estimating a population proportion. Other apps explore a variety of statistical concepts that we will encounter later. The apps can also be used to carry out statistical analyses on data you provide or with data from this book, which are often implemented with the app. This allows you to easily reproduce almost all statistical output we show in the book on your own.

Another advantage of these apps is that each one is tailored to a specific statistical task, which makes learning more straightforward as you expand your statistical knowledge. Asking the right statistical question will lead to a specific app that can carry out the appropriate statistical analysis, from producing the right graphs to running the correct inference. As you will see, we have an app for almost every statistical analysis we cover in this book. This makes reproducing our output from examples and exercises easy and provides a great way to study and learn.

The Basic Ideas of Statistics

This section introduced you to some of the big ideas and concepts of statistical thinking and the specific vocabulary statisticians use, such as descriptive and inferential statistics, sample and population, statistic and parameter, random sample, margin of error and statistical significance. Here is a summary of how all these ideas will be developed further in this book and applied to analyze data to answer statistical questions:

Chapter 2: Exploring Data with Graphs and Numerical Summaries How can you present simple summaries of data? You replace lots of numbers with

In Practice

We provide web apps published at www.ArtofStat.com for carrying out almost all statistical analyses we present in this book, as well as interactively exploring various statistical concepts. You can use these apps for completing exercises, but also with your own data to run descriptive and inferential statistics.

Did You Know?

Exercises marked with an **APP** icon can be completed using an app from www.ArtofStat.com. ◄

---

[3]McNeil, J. J. et al. (2018, October 18). Effect of aspirin on cardiovascular events and bleeding in the healthy elderly, *New England Journal of Medicine, 379*, 1509–1518. Accessible via https://www.nejm.org/doi/full/10.1056/NEJMoa1805819?query=recirc_curatedRelated_article

simple graphs (such as the bar graph in Figure 1.1) and numerical summaries (statistics such as means or proportions).

Chapter 3: Relationships Between Two Variables   How does annual income 10 years after graduation correlate with college tuition? You can find out by studying the relationship between those characteristics.

Chapter 4: Gathering Data   How can you design an experiment or conduct a survey to get data that will help you answer questions? You'll see why results may be misleading if you don't use randomization.

Chapter 5: Probability in Our Daily Lives   How can you determine the chance of some outcome, such as winning a lottery? Probability, the basic tool for evaluating chances, is also a key foundation for inference.

Chapter 6: Probability Distributions   You've probably heard of the normal distribution, a bell-shaped curve, that describes people's heights or IQs or test scores. What is the normal distribution, and how can we use it to find probabilities?

Chapter 7: Sampling Distributions   Why is the normal distribution so important? You'll see why, and you'll learn its key role in statistical inference.

Chapter 8: Statistical Inference: Confidence Intervals   How can an exit poll of 3,889 voters possibly predict the results for millions of voters? You'll find out by applying the probability concepts of Chapters 5, 6, and 7 to find the margin of error and make statistical inferences about population parameters.

Chapter 9: Statistical Inference: Significance Tests About Hypotheses   How can a medical study make a decision about whether a new drug is better than a placebo? You'll see how you can control the chance that a statistical inference makes a correct decision about what works best.

Chapters 10–15: Applying Descriptive and Inferential Statistics and Statistical Modeling to Many Kinds of Data   After Chapters 2 to 9 introduce you to the key concepts of statistics, the rest of the book shows you how to apply them in a variety of situations. For instance, Chapter 10 shows how to compare two groups of students, one using cell phones and another one just listening to the radio in a simulated driving experiment, to make inference about the reaction time when seeing a red light. In Chapters 12 and 13 you will learn how to formulate statistical models and use them to make predictions, such as predicting the selling price of a house or the probability that a consumer accepts a credit card offer.

1.2   Practicing the Basics

1.6   Description and inference

   a. Distinguish between *description* and *inference* as reasons for using statistics. Illustrate the distinction, using an example.

   b. You have data for a population, such as obtained in a census. Explain why descriptive statistics are helpful but inferential statistics are not needed.

1.7   Censorship   The General Social Survey in 2012 asked
TRY   whether we should allow antireligious books in the library. Of the 3,077 people who responded, 23% said they should be removed. Identify (a) the sample, (b) the population, (c) the sample statistic reported, and (d) the population parameter of interest.

1.8   Concerned about global warming?   The Institute for Public Opinion Research at Florida International University has conducted the FIU/Florida Poll of about 1,200 Floridians annually since 1988 to track opinions on a wide variety of issues. In 2006 the poll asked, "How concerned are you about the problem of global warming?" The possible responses were very concerned, somewhat concerned, not very concerned, and haven't heard about it. The poll reported percentages (44, 30, 21, 6) in these categories.

   a. Identify the sample and the population.

   b. Are the percentages quoted statistics or parameters? Why?

1.9   Graduate school information   Suppose a liberal arts
TRY   student is interested in exploring graduate school in the northeast. The student identifies a program of interest and finds the name of a few students from that program to interview. In this context, identify what is meant by the (a) subject, (b) sample, and (c) population.

1.10 Is globalization good? The Voice of the People poll asks a random sample of citizens from different countries around the world their opinion about global issues. Included in the list of questions is whether they feel that globalization helps their country. The reported results were combined by regions. In the most recent poll, 74% of Africans felt globalization helps their country, whereas 38% of North Americans believed it helps their country. (a) Identify the samples and the populations. (b) Are these percentages sample statistics or population parameters? Explain your answer.

1.11 Graduating seniors' salaries The job placement center at your school surveys *all* graduating seniors at the school. Their report about the survey provides numerical summaries such as the average starting salary and the percentage of students earning more than $30,000 a year.

a. Are these statistical analyses descriptive or inferential? Explain.

b. Are these numerical summaries better characterized as statistics or as parameters?

1.12 At what age did women marry? A historian wants to estimate the average age at marriage of women in New England in the early 19th century. Within her state archives she finds marriage records for the years 1800–1820, which she treats as a sample of all marriage records from the early 19th century. The average age of the women in the records is 24.1 years. Using the appropriate statistical method, she estimates that the average age of brides in early 19th-century New England was between 23.5 and 24.7.

a. Which part of this example gives a descriptive summary of the data?

b. Which part of this example draws an inference about a population?

c. To what population does the inference in part b refer?

d. The average age of the sample was 24.1 years. Is 24.1 a statistic or a parameter?

1.13 Age pyramids as descriptive statistics The figure shown is a graph published by Statistics Sweden. It compares Swedish society in 1750 and in 2010 on the numbers of men and women of various ages, using age pyramids. Explain how this indicates that

a. In 1750, few Swedish people were old.

b. In 2010, Sweden had many more people than in 1750.

c. In 2010, of those who were very old, more were female than male.

d. In 2010, the largest five-year group included people born during the era of first manned space flight.

1.14 Margin of Error in labor statistics The Current Population Survey (www.census.gov/cps) is used by the U.S. Bureau of Labor Statistics to provide U.S. population estimates of the median family income or the percent unemployed. How close is a sample estimate from this survey to the true, unknown population parameter?

a. Based on 2018 data from this survey, the median family income was estimated as $74,900, with a margin of error of plus or minus $680. Is it plausible that the median income of all families in the United States is $75,000? Explain.

b. The survey estimated the unemployment rate at 4.1%, with a margin of error of plus or minus 0.1%. Is it plausible that the actual unemployment rate in the entire United States is less than 3.5%? Explain.

1.15 National service Consider the population of all students at your school. A certain proportion support mandatory national service (MNS) following high school. Your friend randomly samples 20 students from the school and uses the sample proportion who support MNS to predict the population proportion at the school. You take your own, separate random sample of 20 students and find the sample proportion that supports MNS. For the two studies,

a. Are the populations the same?

b. How likely is it that the samples are the same? Explain.

c. How likely is it that the sample proportions are the same? Explain.

1.16 Samples vary less with more data We'll see that the amount by which statistics vary from sample to sample always depends on the sample size. This important fact can be illustrated by thinking about what would happen in repeated flips of a fair coin.

a. Which case would you find more surprising—flipping the coin five times and observing all heads or flipping the coin 500 times and observing all heads?

b. Imagine flipping the coin 500 times, recording the proportion of heads observed, and repeating this experiment many times to get an idea of how much the proportion tends to vary from one sequence to another. Different sequences of 500 flips tend to result in proportions of heads observed which are less variable than the proportion of heads observed in sequences of only five flips each. Using part a, explain why you would expect this to be true.

c. We can simulate flipping the coin five times with the *Sampling Distribution for the Sample Proportion* web app mentioned in Activity 2. Access the app from the book's website, www.ArtofStat.com, and set the population proportion to 0.5 (so that we are simulating flipping a fair coin) and the sample size n to 5 (so that we are simulating flipping a coin five times). Then press Draw Sample(s) once. What proportion of heads (=successes) did you observe in these five flips? Press the Generate Sample(s) button 24 more times. What is the smallest and what is the largest sample proportion you observed? Which sample proportion occurred the most often in these 25 simulations?

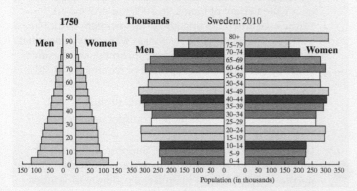

Age pyramids, 1750 and 2010

Graphs of number of men and women of various ages, in 1750 and in 2010. (*Source:* Statistics Sweden.)

d. Press *Reset* and set the sample size n to 500 instead of 5, to simulate flipping the coin 500 times. Then press Draw Sample(s) once. What proportion of heads (=successes) did you observe in these five flips? Press the Generate Sample(s) button 24 more times. What is the smallest and what is the largest sample proportion you observed? (*Hint:* Check Show Summary Statistics to see the smallest and largest value generated.)

1.17   Comparing polls   The following table shows the result of the 2012 presidential election along with the vote predicted by several organizations in the days before the election. The sample sizes were typically a bit above 1,000 people, and the reported margin of error was around plus or minus 3 percentage points. (The percentages for each poll do not sum to 100 because of voters who indicated they were undecided or preferred another candidate.)

Predicted Vote		
Poll	Obama	Romney
Rasmussen	48	49
CNN	49	49
Gallup	48	49
Pew Research	50	47
Rand	54	43
Fox	46	46
Actual Vote	50.6	47.8

Source: NCPP, http://ncpp.org

a. The CNN poll predicted that 49% were going to vote for Obama, with a margin of error of plus or minus 3 percentage points. Explain what that means.

b. Do most of the predictions fall within 3% (the margin of error) of the actual vote percentages? Considering the relative sizes of the sample, the population, and the undecided factor, would you say that these polls had good accuracy?

c. Access the *Sampling Distribution for the Sample Proportion* web app at www.ArtofStat.com (see Activity 2) and set the population proportion to 51% (the actual percentage of votes for Obama, rounded to two significant digits) and the sample size to 1,100 (a typical sample size for the polls shown here). Press the Generate Sample(s) button 10 times to simulate taking a poll of 1,100 voters 10 times. The bottom graph now marks 10 potential results obtained from exit polls of 1,100 voters under this scenario. You can see the smallest and largest value of these 10 proportions by checking the "Summary Statistics for Samp. Dist." box under Options. What are the smallest and largest proportions you obtained in your simulation of 10 exit polls?

1.18   Ebola outbreaks   Ebola virus disease outbreaks have a case fatality rate of 90% (meaning 90% of people who get it die). In a hospital that is treating 20 patients with Ebola, 14 died. Is this result surprising? To reason an answer, use the *Sampling Distribution for the Sample Proportion* web app as described in Activity 2 to conduct at least 25 simulations of taking samples of size 20 from a population with a proportion of "success" (here: dying from Ebola) of 0.90. Note the sample proportions. Do you observe any sample proportions equal to or less than 14/20, or 0.70? (Click on

Show Distribution of Number of Successes to get a graph that shows the potential number of successes and not the proportion of successes for this simulation.)

1.19   Statistical Significance   A study performed by Florida International University investigated how musical instruction in an after-school program affected overall competence, confidence, caring, character, and connection (known as the "Five Cs"). The study compared a group of students who received music instruction to another group who didn't. One of the findings was that those receiving music instruction showed, on average, a *significant increase* in their character. Character was measured by scoring answers to questions such as "I finish whatever I begin," with scores ranging from 1 ("not at all like me") to 5 ("very much like me"). For each part, select (i) or (ii).

a. For the two groups to be called significantly different, the difference in the average character scores computed from the participants in the study had to be (i) much smaller or (ii) much larger than one would expect under regular sample-to-sample variability.

b. What does a *significant increase* imply in this context? That the difference in the average score to questions such as "I finish whatever I begin" between the group receiving music instruction and the group that didn't was (i) much larger than would be expected if music instruction didn't have an effect or (ii) nearly identical in the two groups.

c. Suppose the two groups did *not differ significantly* in terms of the average confidence score. This indicates that the difference in the average confidence score of participants (i) can be explained by regular sample-to-sample variability or (ii) cannot be explained by regular sample-to-sample variability.

1.20   Smoking cessation   A study published in 2010 in *The New England Journal of Medicine* investigated the effect of financial incentives on smoking cessation. As part of the study, 878 employees of a company, all of whom were smokers, were randomly assigned to one of two treatment groups. One group (442 employees) was to receive information about smoking cessation programs; the other (436 employees) was to receive that same information as well as a financial incentive to quit smoking. The outcome of interest of the study was smoking cessation status six months after the initial cessation was reported. After implementation of the program, 14.7% of individuals in the financial incentive group reported cessation six months after the initial report, compared to 5.0% of the information-only group. Assume that the observed difference in cessation rates between the groups (14.7% − 5.0% = 9.7%) is statistically significant. What does it mean to be statistically significant? (choose the best option from a–d)

a. The financial option was offered to 9.7% more smokers in the study than the nonsmokers who were employees of the company.

b. 9.7% was calculated using statistical techniques.

c. The observed difference of 9.7% is so large that it is unlikely to have occurred by chance alone.

d. We know that if the financial incentive were given to all smokers, 9.7% would quit smoking.

1.3 Organizing Data, Statistical Software, and the New Field of Data Science

Today's researchers (and students) are lucky: Unlike those in the previous generation, they don't have to do complex statistical calculations by hand. Powerful user-friendly computing software and calculators are now readily available for statistical analyses. For instance, the web apps published on the book's website, www .ArtofStat.com, can carry out almost all of the analyses presented in this book. This makes it possible to do calculations that would be extremely tedious or even impossible by hand, and it frees time for interpreting and communicating the results.

Using (and Misusing) Statistical Software and Calculators

> **In Practice**
> Almost everyone can use statistical software to produce output, but you need a basic understanding of statistics to draw the correct interpretations and conclusions.

Web apps or statistical software packages such as StatCrunch (www.statcrunch .com), MINITAB, JMP (from SAS), STATA, or SPSS, are popular computer programs for carrying out statistical analysis in practice. The free software R (www.r-project.org), together with its integrated development environment, R-Studio (www.rstudio.com), is a very popular program among statisticians and data scientists, but it requires some computer programming experience. (We show R code relevant to each chapter in the end of chapter material.) The TI-family of calculators are portable tools for generating simple statistics and graphs. Microsoft Excel can conduct some statistical methods, sorting and analyzing data with its spreadsheet program, but its capabilities are limited. Although statistical software is essential in carrying out a statistical analysis, the emphasis in this book is on how to interpret the output, not on the details of using such software.

Given the current software capabilities, why do you still have to learn about statistical methods? Can't computers do all this analysis for you? The problem is that a computer will perform the statistical analysis you request whether or not it is valid for the given situation. Just knowing how to use software does not guarantee a proper analysis. You'll need a good background in statistics to understand which statistical method to use, which options to choose with that method, and how to interpret and make valid conclusions from the computer output. This book provides you with this background.

Data Files

Today's researchers (and students) are also lucky when it comes to data. Without data, of course, we couldn't do any statistical analysis. Data is now electronically available almost instantly from many different disciplines and a variety of sources. We will show some examples at the end of this section.

When statisticians speak of data, they typically refer to the type of data that is organized in a spreadsheet. That's why most of the statistical software packages mentioned above start with a blank spreadsheet to input or import data. Figure 1.3 shows an example of such a spreadsheet created with Excel, where various information on student characteristics have been entered:

- Gender (f = female, m = male, nb = nonbinary)
- Racial–ethnic group (b = Black, h = Hispanic, w = White, o = other)
- Age (in years)
- Average number of hours per week watching or streaming TV
- Whether a vegetarian (yes, no)
- Political party (Dem = Democrat, Rep = Republican, Ind = independent)
- Opinion on Affirmative Action (y = in favor, n = oppose)

Such data files created with a spreadsheet program can be saved in the .csv (which stands for "comma separated values") format, which every statistical

A column refers to data on a particular characteristic

A row refers to data for a particular student

	A	B	C	D	E	F	G	H
1	Student	Gender	Ethnicity	Age	TV_hours	Vegetarian	PolParty	AffirmAction
2	1	m	h	32	3	n	Dem	n
3	2	f	h	23	15	y	Rep	y
4	3	f	w	27	0	y	Rep	n
5	4	nb	w	35	5	n	Dem	y
6	5	nb	b	23	6	n	Dem	n
7	6	m	w	39	4	y	Ind	y
8	7	m	h	24	5	n	Rep	n
9	8	f	w	31	5	n	Ind	y
10	9	m	w	34	7	n	Dem	y

▲ **Figure 1.3** A spreadsheet to organize data. Saved as a .csv file, it can be imported into many statistical software packages.

software program can import. Regardless of which program you use to create the data file, there are certain conventions you should follow:

- Each row contains measurements for a particular subject (for instance, person).
- Each column contains measurements for a particular characteristic.

Some characteristics have numerical data, such as the values for hours of TV watching. Some characteristics have data that consist of categories or labels, such as the categories (yes, no) for vegetarians or the labels (Dem, Rep, Ind) for political affiliation.

Figure 1.3 resembles a larger data file from a questionnaire administered to a sample of students at the University of Florida. That data file, which includes other characteristics as well, is called "FL student survey" and is available for download from the book's website, www.ArtofStat.com, together with many other data files. To construct a similar data file for your class, try the exercise "Getting to know the class" in the Student Activities at the end of the chapter.

Data Files ◀

← → C ⌂ 🔒 https://analytics.google.com/analytics/web/?utm

All accounts > ArtofStat Home
📊 **All Web Site Data ▾**   🔍 Try searching "Week

🏠 Home

▸ ⚏ Customization

REPORTS

▸ 🕐 Realtime

▾ 👤 Audience

Users
10,102

New Users
8,023

Example 5

Google Analytics

Picture the Scenario

Many websites track user traffic using a tool called Google Analytics (a small amount of code that loads with the site) which records various characteristics on who is accessing the site. Suppose you built a website and decide to record some data on people who visit that site, using information that Google Analytics provides: (i) the country where the visitor's IP address is registered, (ii) the type of browser a visitor is using, (iii) whether the visitor accesses the site through a desktop, tablet, or smartphone, (iv) the amount of minutes the visitor stayed on your site, and (v) the age and (vi) gender of your visitors.

For a particular day in March, you tracked 85 visitors to your site. The first visitor was from the United States, used Safari as the browser on a mobile device, spent six minutes on your site before moving on, and was a 28-year-old female. The second visitor came from Brazil, used Chrome as a browser running on a desktop, spent two minutes on your site, and was a 38-year-old female. The third visitor was from the United States, used Chrome as a browser on a mobile device, spent eight minutes on your site, and was a 16-year-old with nonbinary gender information.

Question to Explore

a. How do you create a data file for the first three visitors to your site?

b. How many rows and columns will your data file have once you are finished entering the six characteristics tracked on each visitor to your site?

Think It Through

a. Each row in your data file will correspond to a visitor and each column will correspond to one of the six characteristics of tracking information that you collected. So, the first three rows (below a row that includes the column names) in your data file are:

Visitor	Country	Browser	Device	Minutes	Age	Gender
1	US	Safari	mobile	6	28	female
2	Brazil	Chrome	desktop	2	38	female
3	US	Chrome	mobile	8	16	nonbinary

b. With 85 visitors to the site, your data file will have 85 rows, not counting the first row that holds the column names. And because you tracked six characteristics on each visitor, it will have six columns, not counting the first column that holds the visitor number.

Insight

From the entire data file you could now find summary statistics such as the proportion of visitors who access it on a mobile device. Once the data file is available in an electronic format, you can open it in a statistical software package for further analysis.

Each of the six characteristics measured in this study is called a **variable**. The variables measured make up the columns of the data set. We will learn more about variables in Chapter 2.

▶ *Try Exercise 1.22*

In Words

Variables refer to the characteristics being measured, such as the type of browser or the number of minutes visiting the site.

Messy Data

The two examples of data files you saw in Figure 1.3 and in Example 5 were "clean": Every column had well defined values and there was **no missing information,** i.e., empty cells. Raw data are typically a lot messier than what you will see in this book. For instance, when you asked your fellow students for information on gender, some may have entered "m," "f," and "nb" and others may have entered "male," "female," and "nonbinary." Some may leave out the hyphen in "non-binary," others may write "man" and "woman," and still others don't identify with any of the options and left the cell blank. Perhaps some students filled in the survey twice. Similarly, the column for married in Figure 1.3 shows values of 0 for not married and 1 for married, but this may already be processed information from the original responses.

In practice, considerable effort initially has to be dedicated to **importing, cleaning, and preprocessing the raw data** into a format that is useful for statistical analysis. Along the way, decisions have to be made, such as how to code observations and how many categories to use, how to identify duplicates, and what to do with missing values. Missing values are especially tricky. A single missing value may lead to the entire row being discarded in the statistical analysis, which throws away information. What's more, sometimes the fact that the observation is missing is informative in itself. To check if and how decisions made during preprocessing may have affected the statistical analysis, the entire analysis is repeated under some alternative scenarios.

In Practice

Data importing, cleaning, and preprocessing often are the most time-consuming steps of the entire statistical analysis. However, they are an essential part of the statistical investigative process.

Databases

Most studies design experiments or surveys to collect data to answer the questions of interest. Often, though, it is adequate to take advantage of existing archived collections of data files, called **databases**. Many Internet databases are available. By browsing various websites, you can obtain information about many topics.

The GSS discussed in Activity 1 is one such database that is accessible via the Internet by following the link on the book's website, www.ArtofStat.com. This site also contains several data files that you'll use in examples and exercises. Here are some other databases that can be fun and informative to browse:

- Google provides a starting place for finding databases: datasetsearch.research .google.com. (This is currently in the beta version and the url may change.) Type in the topic you want to research, and you may find relevant databases published by governments or academic and private institutions. Google also maintains a list of over 100 databases at www.google.com/publicdata.

- The World Bank (data.worldbank.org) publishes a vast amount of economic and other indicators, including climate statistics such as CO_2 emissions, for hundreds of countries.

- Are you interested in results of Gallup polls about people's beliefs? See news.gallup.com.

- For public opinion surveys that involve some 20,000 interviews in 18 Latin American countries, check out www.latinobarometro.org.

- Are you interested in pro baseball, basketball, or football? Click the statistics links at www.mlb.com, www.nba.com, or www.nfl.com.

- The U.S. government hosts www.data.gov, which has data on topics ranging from agriculture to public safety. The equivalent site in the European Union, with thousands of data sets, can be accessed at data.europa.eu.

- For a huge variety of data about all sorts of topics, check out www.kaggle .com/datasets, which provides over 14,000 different data sets, many of them provided by private companies. Users of that site also often contribute some statistical analysis involving these data.

> **In Practice** Always Check Sources
>
> Not all databases or reported data summaries give reliable information. Before you give credence to such data, verify that the data are from a trustworthy source and that the source provides information about the way the data were gathered.

For example, many news organizations and search websites ask you to participate in a "topic of the day" poll on their home page. Their summaries of how people responded are not reliable indications of how the entire population feels. They are biased because it is unlikely that the people who respond are representative of the population. We'll explain why in Chapter 4.

Data Science

The data sets used in examples so far are the size of a few hundred to a few thousand subjects. But as more and more of our daily life happens online and is connected, and with the ever-increasing capabilities of storing vast amounts of data, we now encounter data sets reporting thousands of characteristics on millions of subjects. Instead of laboriously entering data by hand, these types of data are available in digital form (i.e., electronically) almost instantaneously and can be automatically accessed and processed from almost anywhere. In addition, the **digital revolution** provides many new types of data, such as data on text (e.g., millions of tweets or Facebook posts, analyzed to learn about sentiments), sounds (e.g., millions of Spotify songs, analyzed to measure characteristics such as "acousticness," "danceability," or "speechiness"), or images (such as the millions of images from eight telescopes that were processed to provide the first picture of a dark hole in 2019). Such data are called **unstructured data** and often don't fit into a rectangular data file such as the one shown in Figure 1.3.

Because of their size and complexity, such data (both structured and unstructured) are referred to as **Big Data**. The new and still-evolving field of **data science** uses ideas, concepts, and tools from both statistics and computer science, coupled with domain knowledge, to analyze such large data sets.

Data scientists try to leverage the amount of their data to extract knowledge in the form of finding patterns, making predictions or classifying observations into groups. Various terms such as **data mining**, **machine learning** or often just **artificial intelligence** are used for such processes. You might have heard these buzzwords in reference to developing self-driving vehicles, smart speakers, credit-card fraud detection or personalized advertising. Extracting knowledge is accomplished via algorithms that can handle the volume and complexity of the data. One of the most common goals of such algorithms is to predict consumer behavior based on the information available from a large customer database.

Example 6

Data Science ◀

The Netflix Prize

Picture the Scenario

In October 2006, the movie streaming company Netflix (which back then mailed out red envelopes containing DVDs that subscribers ordered online) announced a million-dollar prize for improving the accuracy of its own in-house movie recommendation system. They released a data set of movie ratings from 470,000 of their subscribers, each providing 200 movie ratings on average. Overall, this so-called **training data set** contained more than 100 million ratings on 18,000 different movies. The goal of the competition was to use the training data to build an algorithm that predicts ratings subscribers would give to movies they haven't watched yet. From Netflix's business perspective, it will recommend to a subscriber those movies that have a high predicted rating. If the recommendations are largely accurate, the subscriber has a positive experience and is likely to keep watching (and subscribing to) Netflix.

Over 40,000 teams from 186 different countries took part in the competition by building a prediction algorithm based on the training data. In order to win the grand prize of $1,000,000, a team's algorithm had to improve on the accuracy of Netflix's own algorithm by more than 10%. This was judged by testing each team's algorithm on a second data set, called the **test data**, for which Netflix withheld information on how subscribers in that data set rated certain movies. Each team's algorithm had to make predictions for the ratings that were withheld based on the other available information on the subscribers in the test data. All Netflix had to do was to compare these predictions to the actual ratings and assess the overall accuracy.

Question to Explore

How are teams able to build such prediction algorithms from the training data?

Think It Through

Several approaches using tools from data science contributed to building a successful prediction algorithm. As the winners of the competition wrote after being awarded the grand price three years into the contest: "Our original team consisted of two statisticians and a computer scientist, and the diversity of expertise and perspective across these two disciplines was an important factor in our success." One approach looks for similarities between movies. Someone rating *Saving Private Ryan* favorably is generally more likely to rate other war movies, or other movies directed by Steven Spielberg or other movies starring Tom Hanks more favorably. Then, when trying to predict the ratings for a movie like *The Thin Red Line*, another war movie released the same year and also featuring big-name male actors (Sean Penn, Nick Nolte), what the algorithm learned about a user's rating of *Saving Private Ryan* and similar movies for which ratings are available can be exploited for the prediction of the rating of *The Thin Red Line*.

A second approach tries to incorporate information on what type of movies a subscriber rated (i.e., did a user only rate romantic comedies?), and a third approach tries to incorporate information on how ratings change over time (and also tries to adjust for the fact that ratings may have been submitted by different members of a family sharing a Netflix account). One key insight of the teams that did the best in the competition was that **averaging the predictions of many different but relatively simple models** led to a better overall prediction than any single model was able to provide. This is quite a departure from typical statistical modeling approaches, where usually one model is selected and inference is based on it.

Insight

The winning team and the runner-up (which achieved the same overall accuracy but submitted their predictions 20 minutes later) all used various tools and methods from data science to build their prediction algorithms. Some of the more basic methods for prediction, such as linear or logistic regression models (which were the tools used by Netflix's in-house prediction algorithm), will be discussed in this book in Chapters 3, 12, and 13, but other more advanced methods (such as classification algorithms) are not covered in an introductory statistics course.

▶ *Try Exercise 1.27*

The results of data science applications are permeating our daily lives. They lead to more accurate diagnoses of skin cancers (by training algorithms on thousands of medical images of patients with and without skin cancer), prevent fraudulent activities in our credit card accounts (by modeling our shopping habits and locations, sounding an alarm if a transaction doesn't seem to fit the usual patterns) or assists aid organizations in more efficiently dealing with crisis situations, such as natural disasters or refugee crises (by using GPS and social media data from the cell phones of those in need).

Fueled by the digital revolution in the 21st century, data, personal and non-personal, are now one of the most important assets for many private and public organizations, including governments. Data science, using methods from statistics and computer science, paired with domain knowledge, helps inform decision-making processes in such organizations by building algorithms that explore rich and complex data sets.

Examples of Data Science Projects

Figure 1.4 is a screenshot (taken in March 2019) from the website Kaggle (www .kaggle.com), which is a popular platform that hosts data science projects and competitions (and provides a ton of accessible data supplied by companies). The projects are varied, ranging from predicting stock price movements or transactions on credit cards to predicting earthquakes, gender pronouns, or the outcome of a women's basketball tournament. Common to all these projects is that they supply a wealth of data:

- **Predicting Stock Price Movements:** The project for predicting stock price movements provides classical financial market data, such as opening and closing prices or trading volumes of stocks, and tries to link movements in stock prices to nontraditional data such as the positive, negative, or neutral sentiment of news media articles.

- **Customer Transaction Prediction:** In this project, a large bank tries to identify which customers will make a specific transaction in the future, based on characteristics they know about their customers. They supply a training data set that includes, for each of 200,000 bank customers, a profile of 200 characteristics and whether the customer initiated a transaction. The goal is to predict whether 200,000 other customers contained in a test data set will or will not make a transaction based on their profiles.

- **Earthquake Prediction:** In this project (sponsored by Los Alamos National Laboratory, which, among others, is tasked with securing the U.S. nuclear stockpile), the goal is to predict the time between the sensing of seismic (acoustic) signals and the actual occurrence of the next earthquake, based on a wealth of data collected on realistic experiments carried out in a laboratory setting.

- **Gender Pronouns:** For this project the goal is to identify the target of a pronoun within a text passage, based on a data set with over 12,000 text passages. For instance, who is the target of the pronoun "her" in the following text passage from Wikipedia: "Upon her retirement as its London Advisor, the Felton Bequest commissioned from John Brack a portrait of Ursula Hoff, which it then donated to the National Gallery of Victoria"? The correct answer that an algorithm should spit out is "Ursula Hoff." To make it a bit easier, in this competition you are presented with three choices for the target: "John Brack," "Ursula Hoff," or "Neither"; and the data science algorithm should assign a percentage to each choice reflecting the likelihood of it being the target of the pronoun. The overall goal is to make algorithms that process and analyze text less gender biased.

- **Basketball tournament:** The goal for this project is to predict the winning probabilities for every possible matchup of teams taking part in the 2019 NCAA women's basketball tournament. The data provided are based on thousands of games played in the years before the tournaments and data on each basketball team.

Typical steps in such data science project are:

- Gather large amounts of data electronically
- Clean the data for further processing
- Split the data into training and testing data
- Train an algorithm on the training data
- Evaluate results of the algorithm on the testing data
- Implement and use the refined algorithm to find patterns or make predictions as new data comes in

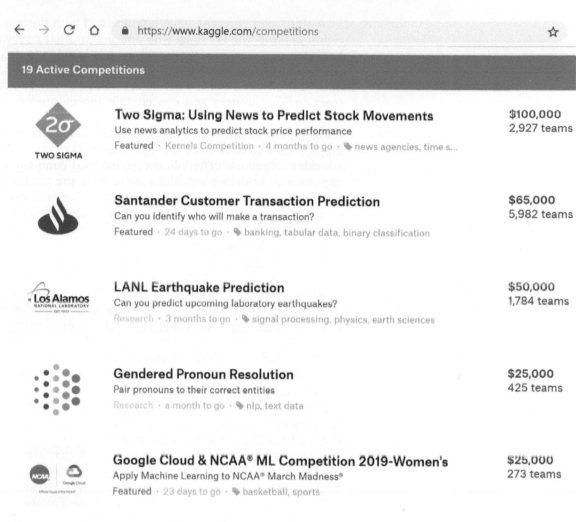

▲ **Figure 1.4** Screenshot (taken in March 2019) from the website www.kaggle.com/competition, which hosts data science competitions on a variety of projects.* **Question:** What type of projects are posted when you access this website now?

Ethics and Biases in Data Analysis

As decisions using statistical and data science tools affect many aspects of our personal lives, ethical considerations must be taken into account. We will mention appropriate ways to gather data and avoid biases in Chapter 4. Here, we mention three issues particularly relevant when dealing with data on a large scale: first, the issue of **data privacy**. Big Data often consist of personal information that users have supplied while signing up for Internet, banking, or social media services and are enhanced with information on browsing history, online shopping habits, or geolocation data from mobile devices. How much of these data can be shared (or sold) and processed further? (See Exercise 4.35 for a large scale Facebook study which manipulated the news feed of more than 680,000 users to learn about emotional responses.) Currently, in the United States once you opt in (which often means pressing "I agree" to the terms and conditions of a smartphone app) there are few restrictions on the use of the data that has been collected. (The European Union, on the other hand, has stricter laws governing the use of private data, including the right to have your data deleted.)

Second, the issue of **data security**. If the data are supposed to be private (such as credit card or social security numbers), they have to be protected and encrypted so that others can't gain access. This is an ongoing struggle, and high-profile cases where millions of passwords and credit card numbers are stolen are in the news too often.

---

*Used with permission by Kaggle, Inc., which was not involved in the production of, and does not endorse, this product.

A third, and different, issue is concerned with the way data are used in **decision making**, for example, who and under what conditions someone gets a bank loan, an insurance policy, or even a job. Increasingly, such vital (to the economy, but also our personal lives) decisions are made not by humans but automatically by algorithms trained on large databases. These databases come from various sources and can contain inaccurate or outdated information. They can also carry biases. For example, if a large company trains and optimizes their resume-screening algorithm based on the characteristics of the employees who have risen through their ranks (i.e., what the company would consider a "successful" application), but that company engaged in gender or racial biases in their promotions in the past, the prediction algorithm is going to mirror such behavior. If relatively few of the "successful" employees are female or Black, then being female or Black (and related characteristics) will not be associated with success and, hence, will be downweighted in the algorithm relative to other factors.

The prediction models build with statistical and data science tools are only as good as the data that feed them. And even though such training data may be enormous, "bigger" data may not imply better data. If inherent biases exists in such databases, unintended consequences can arise, resulting in decisions based on such algorithms that may discriminate against certain parts of the population.

For example, the United States (which accounts for 4% of the world population) contributed over 45% of the data for ImageNet, a huge database of more than 14 million labelled images. Meanwhile, China and India combined contribute just 3% of images, despite accounting for over 36% of the world population. As a result of this skewed data distribution, image classification algorithms that use the ImageNet database as training data would often correctly label an image of a traditional U.S. bride with words like "bride" and "wedding" but label an image of an Indian bride with words like "costume."[4]

A more serious problem arises when potentially biased data science algorithms are used for important life decisions. For instance, it is illegal to use age, gender, ethnicity, or race in evaluating the creditworthiness of a loan applicant. But these days, creditors use predictive modeling to evaluate how risky applicants are. These models are built on historical data which take every available proxy for such demographics into account, such as zip codes or information on school districts. What the models typically find is that historically, applicants from certain zip codes (or school districts) are more risky, i.e., tend to default on their loans more often. These zip codes typically have a larger population of Blacks or other minorities. If a new applicant's zip code or school district matches (or looks similar in certain characteristics) to the ones a creditor has identified as dangerous, the predictive algorithm will tend to assign a higher risk to the application, leading to higher interest rates or outright denial of the loan. What's worse, because such loans now carry higher interest, they tend to default more often, creating a feedback loop. Such algorithms have then demonstrated that they can correctly predict someone's risk, further spreading their use.

One big issue and criticism with many of the data science or machine learning algorithms is that they often act like **black boxes**. They are fed with large and increasingly personal data and spit out a prediction or sort people into groups, such as those getting a loan and those who can't. But how exactly these algorithms arrived at their conclusions and on what basis is often not clear. Because of their widespread use, their opaqueness, and their effect on people's personal lives, especially minorities or the poor, author Cathy O'Neil has called

---

[4] Feng, A., & Wu, S. (2019, May 1). The myth of the impartial machine. *Parametric Press, 1*. Retrieved from https://parametric.press/issue-01/the-myth-of-the-impartial-machine/

them "weapons of math destruction."[5] What is needed, she and others argue, is some oversight and a pledge for good and ethical data science, not unlike the Hippocratic Oath taking by physicians to uphold ethical standards. A recent report on introducing the field of data science at the undergraduate level[6] details such an oath, which, in part, reads: "I will remember that my data are not just numbers without meaning or context, but represent real people and situations, and that my work may lead to unintended societal consequences, such as inequality, poverty, and disparities due to algorithmic bias. My responsibility must consider potential consequences of my extraction of meaning from data and ensure my analyses help make better decisions."

---

[5]O'Neil, C. (2016). *Weapons of math destruction: How big data increases inequality and threatens democracy*. New York, NY: Crown Publishers.

[6]National Academies of Sciences, Engineering, and Medicine. (2018). *Data science for undergraduates: Opportunities and options*. Washington, D.C.: The National Academies Press. https://doi.org/10.17226/25104

1.3 Practicing the Basics

1.21 Data file for friends   Construct (by hand or with your favorite spreadsheet program) a data file of the form of Figure 1.3 for two characteristics with a sample of four of your friends. One characteristic should take numerical values, and the other should take values that are categories.

1.22 Shopping sales data file   Construct a data file about the purchasing behavior of four customers, described below, who visit a shopping mall. Enter the purchase amounts each spent on clothes, sporting goods, books, and food. Customer 1 spent $49 on clothes and $16 on food; customer 2 spent $150 on sporting goods, $43 on books, and $25 on food; customer 3 didn't purchase anything; and customer 4 spent $87 on clothes, $15 on sporting goods, and $12 on food.

1.23 Cleaning data and missing values   An airline consulting firm sends interviewers to an international airport to interview travelers. Among the questions the interviewers ask are the time it took to check in, how much they had to pay extra for their luggage, and whether they were going to use an Airbnb while traveling. Here are the responses for three travelers as compiled by the interviewers: Traveler 1: 30 minutes, $25, No; Traveler 2: 1.5 hours, €50, Airbnb; Traveler 3: Didn't check in yet, not available yet, Yes. Create a clean version of these data that can be used for further statistical analysis. (*Hints:* Use an exchange rate of 1€ = $1.2. Use NA for any missing observations.)

1.24 Wealth and health   Suppose you wish to explore the relationship between the economic wealth of a country (as measured by per capita GDP) and the average life expectancy of its citizens. Using the internet, search for data on per capita GDP and average life expectancy for at least 10 countries. Use the data you collected to create a data file. (*Hint:* The World Bank database at https://data.worldbank.org lets you search for both "per capita GDP" and "life expectancy" and displays results for various countries.)

1.25 Create a data file with software   Your instructor will show you how to create or import data files by using the software for your course. Use it to create or import the data file you constructed in Exercise 1.21, 1.22, or 1.24.

1.26 Downloading a data file   You may need to learn how to open a data file from the book's website or download one from the Web for use with the software for your course.
  a. Practice this by opening the data file "FL student survey" from the book's website, www.ArtofStat.com (click on Datasets).
  b. Practice this by first downloading and then opening one of the data files published by the Federal Emergency Management Agency at www.fema.gov/data-feeds.

1.27 Train and Test Data   You want to create a computer algorithm for a hospital that predicts whether a digital medical image of a tissue sample shows whether a tumor is absent or present. Two data sets are provided. One data set contains the medical images of patients together with the label of "no tumor" or "tumor" based on the biopsy result performed on these patients. A second data set contains medical images for which only the hospital knows the tumor status. Which of these two data sets plays the role of the training data and which the role of the test data?

1.28 Cambridge Analytica   In 2018, the consulting firm Cambridge Analytica was said to have illegally obtained data on millions of Facebook users. With the help of data science tools, they used these data to construct targeted ads that tried to influence the outcome of the Brexit vote (Britain leaving the European Union) and the U.S. presidential election, both in 2016. Research this story and write a short paragraph on your findings.

1.29 Ethics in Data Analysis   Refer to the suggestion of a Hippocratic Oath for data analysts, in particular the passage "[...] my work may lead to unintended societal consequences, such as inequality, poverty, and disparities due to algorithmic bias" mentioned at the end of Section 1.3. Using any one of the examples given for the use of data science in Section 1.3, briefly explain how an algorithm may be biased.

Chapter Review

CHAPTER SUMMARY

- Statistics consists of methods for conducting research studies and for analyzing and interpreting the data produced by those studies. **Statistics is the art and science of learning from data**.

- The first part of the statistical process for answering a statistical question involves **design**—planning an investigative study to obtain relevant data for answering the statistical question. The design often involves taking a **sample** from a **population** where the population contains *all* the **subjects** (usually, people) of interest. Summary measures of samples are called **statistics**; summary measures of populations are called **parameters**. After we've collected the data, there are two types of statistical analyses:

  Descriptive statistics summarize the sample data with numbers and graphs.

  Inferential statistics make decisions and predictions about the entire population, based on the information in the sample data.

- Using **random sampling** to obtain the sample gives each subject in the population the same chance of being included in the sample. This is desirable because then the sample tends to be a good reflection of the population. Randomization is also important for good experimental design, for example, randomly assigning who gets the medicine and who gets the placebo in a medical study.

- The measurements we make of a characteristic **vary** from individual to individual. Likewise, results of descriptive and inferential statistics **vary**, depending on the sample chosen. We'll see that the study of **variability** is a key part of statistics.

- **Online apps** can **simulate** what would happen if we took thousands of samples and visualized the results. They provide a way of learning about the impact of randomness and variability from sample to sample.

- The **margin of error** is a measure of variability of a statistic from one random sample to the next. It is used to express the precision of an estimate or prediction.

- Results of a study are considered **statistically significant** if they would rarely be observed with only ordinary random variation.

- Exploratory and inferential statistics are carried out using **statistical software**. The data for such software are provided in a **data file**, organized such that each row holds the characteristics (which make up the columns) for a given subject. A good background in statistics is needed to correctly choose the appropriate statistical procedure and interpret the output from such software.

- The **digital revolution** (internet of things) means that more and more data are collected on many aspects of our daily lives, resulting in massive and complex datasets called **Big Data**. The field of **Data Science** uses tools and algorithms to extract knowledge from such data and uses it for prediction or classification.

- The use of personal data necessitates **ethical standards** that ensure **data privacy** and **security** but also the correct and responsible use of data in developing algorithms that do not discriminate against certain groups.

LEARNING OBJECTIVES

1. Define statistics.

2. Understand that the statistical investigative process involves four components: formulating a statistical question; planning a study and collecting data; analyzing the data; and interpreting and communicating the results.

3. Define population and sample and the different terminology used for their numerical summaries: sample statistic and population parameter.

4. Explain the difference between descriptive and inferential statistics.

5. Explain random sampling and what it is designed to do.

6. Begin to understand the concept of margin of error as a measure of sample to sample variability expressing how close a sample statistic is expected to be to a population parameter.

7. Recognize the importance of efficiently organizing data and dealing with 'messy data' before the statistical analysis phase.

8. Recognize the contributions and challenges in the field of 'data science' and the prevalence of 'big data'.

9. Understand the role simulation plays in learning statistical concepts and in practicing statistics. Begin using web apps from www.ArtofStat.com to carry out simulations.

STATISTICAL SOFTWARE

Art of Stat Web Apps

■ **Data Entry** Many of the apps have a spreadsheet-like interface to allow for data entry and some allow for uploading a data file in .csv format. (The .csv file extension stands for "comma separated values," and you can save your data file in Excel in that format by choosing "Save As" and then selecting "csv.") Many apps come preloaded with data files used in this book. For instance, to create the bar chart shown in Figure 1.1, access the *Explore Categorical Data* app and select "Losing Focus" from the "Choose Dataset" dropdown menu. You can also provide your own data by selecting "Frequency Table" under "Enter Data" and entering category descriptions together with their frequencies, or you can copy and paste values (e.g., from a spreadsheet) into a box when selecting "Individual Observations" under "Enter Data."

■ **Random Numbers** The *Random Numbers* app allows the generation of random numbers that are helpful for selecting random samples when the population can be numbered. (See, for instance, Exercise 1.49.)

R

We set apart the R code in a different font, and preface it with a ">" symbol. This is the symbol that appears on the R console after which you type in the command. Don't type in the > symbol itself. After you are done typing in the code for a particular command, press *Return* (i.e., the Enter key). More information on R, including scripts that go along with many of the examples in each chapter is available on the book's website www.ArtofStat.com.

■ **Data Entry:** To create a single list of observations of, say, numbers of hours watching TV, use the `c()` command, as in > `tvhours <- c(3, 1, 0, 0, 2, 1, 3)` for entering seven observations. The `c` stands for concatenate. To see the result of your entry, type > `tvhours` and press *Return*. For reading in descriptions instead of numbers, such as seven observations on happiness, use > `happiness <- c('very', 'not', 'very', 'pretty', 'very', 'not', 'pretty')`. You can use single quotes (as in 'very') or double quotes (as in "very") to enclose each description.

For reading in more complex data, it is best to create a data file as discussed in Section 1.3 with a spreadsheet program (i.e., Excel or Google Sheets) and save it in .csv format. Then, in R, use the `read.csv()` function to read in the data file. To automatically open a dialogue that lets you select the file, use > `mydata <- read.csv(file.choose())`. Then, to see the result, type > `mydata` and press *Return*. Here is how your screen should look like when entering the above commands:

```
> tvhours <- c(3, 1, 0, 0, 2, 1, 3)
> tvhours
[1] 3 1 0 0 2 1 3
> happiness <- c('very', 'not', 'very', 'pretty',
  'very', 'not', 'pretty')
> happiness
[1] "very"   "not"    "very"   "pretty"
[5] "very"   "not"    "pretty"
> mydata <- read.csv(file.choose())
> mydata
  Student Gender Ethnicity Age TV_hours
1       1      m         h  32        3
2       2      f         h  23       15
3       3      f         w  27        0
```

■ **Random Samples:** The R command `sample()` generates random numbers. For instance, > `sample(30, 5)` provides five numbers randomly selected from the numbers 1 through 30.

CHAPTER EXERCISES

Practicing the Basics

1.30 **UW student survey** In a University of Wisconsin (UW) study about alcohol abuse among students, 100 of the 40,858 members of the student body in Madison were sampled and asked to complete a questionnaire. One question asked was, "On how many days in the past week did you consume at least one alcoholic drink?" (*Source:* Alcoholism Studies, University of Wisconsin © 2020 Board of Regents - University of Wisconsin System)

   a. Identify the population and the sample.

   b. For the 40,858 students at UW, one characteristic of interest was the percentage who would respond "zero" to this question. For the 100 students sampled, suppose 29% gave this response. Does this mean that 29% of the entire population of UW students would make this response? Explain.

   c. Is the numerical summary of 29% a sample statistic or a population parameter?

1.31 **Euthanasia** The General Social Survey asked, in 2012, whether you would commit suicide if you had an incurable disease. Of the 3,112 people who had an opinion about this, 1,862, or 59.8%, indicated that they would commit suicide.

   a. Describe the population of interest.

   b. Explain how the sample data are summarized using descriptive statistics.

   c. For what population parameter might we want to make an inference?

1.32 **Sleep disorders among college students** An article in the *Journal of American College Health* reports that, in a survey of 1,845 college students from a large, southeastern public university, 27% were at risk for at least one sleep disorder, with a margin of error of 2%. Explain how this margin of error provides an *inferential* statistical analysis.

1.33 **Breaking down Brown versus Whitman** Example 2 of this chapter discusses an exit poll taken during the 2010 California gubernatorial election. The administrators of the poll also collected demographic data, which allows for further breakdown of the 3,889 voters from whom information was collected. Of the 1,633 voters registered as Democrats, 91% voted for Brown, with a margin of error of 1.4%. Of the 1,206 voters registered as Republicans, 10% voted for Brown, with a margin of error of 1.7%. And of the 1,050 Independent voters, 42% voted for Brown, with a margin of error of 3.0%.

a. Do these results summarize sample data or population data?

b. Identify a descriptive aspect of the results.

c. Identify an inferential aspect of the results.

1.34 **Online learning** Your university is interested in determining the proportion of students who would be interested in completing summer courses online, compared to on campus. A survey is taken of 100 students who intend to take summer courses.

a. Identify the sample and the population.

b. For the study, explain the purpose of using (i) descriptive statistics and (ii) inferential statistics.

1.35 **Website tracking** Example 5 mentioned data collected on visitors to a website for one day in March. Identify the (a) sample and potential population of interest for this study and (b) descriptive and inferential aspects of this study.

1.36 **Support of labor unions** The Gallup organization has asked opinions about support of labor unions since its first poll in 1936, when 72% of the American population approved of them. In its 2018 poll, it found that support of labor unions was at 62%. The 2018 poll was based on a random sample of 1,024 adults aged 18 and older and had a margin of error of plus or minus 4%.

a. What is a range of likely values for the proportion of Americans who supported labor unions in 2018?

b. The statistics from Gallup mentioned in the exercise are an example of (i) descriptive statistics or (ii) inferential statistics?

c. The question in part a of this exercise is an example of (i) descriptive statistics or (ii) inferential statistics?

Concepts and Investigations

1.37 **How sample proportions vary from one sample to the next** Refer to Activity 2 in Section 1.2 and the *Sampling Distribution for the Sample Proportion* web app.

a. Repeat the activity, using a population proportion p of 0.60: Generate at least 25 samples of size $n = 10$ each. Observe how the sample proportions of successes vary around 0.60. Write down the smallest and largest sample proportion you obtained in your 25 simulations. (Check the box Show Summary Statistics, which will show you the smallest and largest sample proportion simulated.)

b. Repeat part a, but now use a sample size of $n = 100$. (Hit the reset button to clear the simulation results from part a.) What are now the smallest and largest values of the sample proportions in your simulations?

c. From your simulations in parts a and b, which sample size ($n = 10$ or $n = 100$) do you think will lead to a smaller margin of error?

d. Repeat part b, but with a larger sample size yet, of $n = 1,000$. (In the app, click on Enter Numerical Values for n and p.) With a sample of size $n = 1,000$, the margin of error in estimating a population proportion of 0.6 is plus or minus 3 percentage points. Are any of your simulated sample proportions more than 3 percentage points (i.e., more than 0.03) away from 0.6, i.e., less than 0.57 or larger than 0.63?

1.38 **How sample means vary from one sample to the next** Activity 2 explored the sample-to-sample variability of sample proportions. In this exercise, we will explore how the sample mean, the average of all observations in a sample, varies from sample to sample. Open the *Sampling Distribution for the Sample Mean (Discrete Population)* web app from the book's website, www.ArtofStat.com. From the first drop-down menu, select Fair Die. This shows the distribution of the outcome of rolling a fair die with numbers 1 through 6, each with probability 1/6. (We will learn more about such distributions in Chapter 5.) We can think of a sample as consisting of several observations of this die.

a. Set the value for the sample size equal to 2. This means we make two observations of this die, each of which is a number between 1 and 6. The average of the two observations can be 1 (if each die shows a 1), 1.5, 2, ... , 5.5, and 6. Press the Draw Sample(s) button 25 times and observe how the sample average varies between these numbers. What is the smallest and largest average you simulated, and which average(s) appeared the most often? (*Hint:* Click the Show Summary Statistic check box to see the smallest and largest average simulated.)

b. Now, press the Reset button and move the slider for n to 20, for a sample of 20 observations of rolls of this die. Press Draw Sample(s) 25 times and observe how the sample average varies, but that now the variability is much more restricted compared to the scenario in part a. What is now the smallest and largest average you simulated?

1.39 **Statistics in the news** Pick up a recent issue of a national newspaper, such as *The New York Times* or *USA Today,* or consult a news website, such as www.msnbc.com or www.cnn.com. Identify an article that used statistical methods. Did it use descriptive statistics, inferential statistics, or both? Explain.

1.40 **What is statistics?** On a final exam that one of us recently gave, students were asked, "How would you define 'statistics' to someone who has never taken a statistics course?" One student wrote, "You want to know the answer to some question. There's no answer in the back of a book. You collect some data relevant to the question. Statistics is the body of procedures that helps you analyze the data to figure out the answer and how sure you can be about it." Pick a question that interests you and explain how you might be able to use statistics to investigate the answer.

1.41 **Surprising suicide data?** In Exercise 1.31, of 3,112 people who responded, 59.8% or 1,862 people, said they would commit suicide if they had an incurable disease. Suppose that 50% of the entire population shares this view about suicide. If the sample of 3,112 people were a random sample, would this sample proportion of 0.598 be surprising? Investigate, using the *Sampling Distribution for the Sample Proportion* web app described in Activity 2, setting the population proportion to 0.5, the samples size to 3,112 (click on Enter Numerical Values for n and p) and simulating thousands of potential sample proportions that could be observed with these settings. (*Hint:* Check Show Summary Statistics to see the smallest and largest sample proportion generated.)

1.42   Create a data file   Using the statistical software that your instructor has assigned for the course, find out how to enter a data file. Create a data file by using the data in Figure 1.3.

Multiple Choice or True/False

1.43   Use of inferential statistics?   Inferential statistics are used

   a. to describe whether a sample has more females or males.

   b. to reduce a data file to easily understood summaries.

   c. to make predictions about populations by using sample data.

   d. when we can't use statistical software to analyze data.

   e. to predict the sample data we will get when we know the population.

1.44   NYC vs. Upstate significantly different?   Example 3 mentioned a poll about a potential New York State law on banning plastic bags from grocery stores. When dividing the 929 voters included in the poll by region, the results show that among voters from New York City, 46% supported the ban, while 52% of voters from upstate New York supported the ban. Based on these results, the study authors conclude that a statistically significant difference exists between the proportion of voters in favor of banning plastic bags in upstate New York and New York City. This means that

   a. in a future referendum about the state law, 6% more voters will support the ban in upstate New York compared to New York City.

   b. Differences such as the observed 6 percentage point difference between voters from New York City and upstate New York are likely to occur when the proportion of supporters is the same in both regions.

   c. Differences such as the observed 6 percentage point difference between voters from New York City and upstate New York are unlikely to occur when the proportion of supporters is the same in both regions.

   d. The margin of error in this study was plus or minus 6 percentage points.

1.45   True or false?   In a particular study, you could use descriptive statistics, or you could use inferential statistics, but you would rarely need to use both.

1.46   True or false?   The smaller the margin of error, the less precise the prediction of the population parameter.

Student Activities

1.47   Margin of error   Refer to the *Sampling Distribution for the Sample Proportion* app used in Activity 2.

   a. For a population proportion of 0.50, simulate one random sample of size 1,000. (In the app, click on

Enter Numerical Values for n and p.) What is the sample proportion of successes? Repeat this for a total of 10 times, keeping track of the 10 sample proportions you generate (the middle graph in the app shows the sample proportion in the subtitle).

   b. The margin of error with a sample of size 1,000 is approximately 3 percentage points. Using each of the 10 sample proportions from part a as the midpoint, construct 10 intervals by adding or subtracting this margin of error. Remember that the margin of error tells you how close to the population proportion the sample proportion is likely to fall. How many of the 10 intervals you constructed actually contain the population proportion of 0.50?

   c. Collect the 10 intervals from each member of the class. (If there are 20 students, 200 intervals will be collected.) What percentage of these intervals captured the actual population proportion, 0.50?

1.48   Choosing a random sample   We mentioned in Section 1.2 that a simple example of random sampling is when a teacher puts each student's name on slips of paper, places them in a hat, shuffles them, and then draws names from the hat without looking. We can simulate such a process with the *Random Numbers* app available from the book's website, www.ArtofStat.com. Access that app and leave the minimum at 1, but choose your class size as the maximum. Number the members of the class consecutively, starting with 1. Choose as the number of samples to draw a number that is relatively small compared to the class size; e.g., when the class size is 30, select 5 as the sample size. Finally, check No for "Sampling with Replacement?" in the app.

   a. Press the Generate button once. The numbers displayed indicate a random sample of the corresponding members of the class. Which numbers did you obtain?

   b. Keep on pressing Generate multiple times to see how eventually all members have about the same chance of being included in the sample, indicated by the frequencies in the bar chart below. After pressing 20 times, how often was the number 2 selected? (To get the bars in the chart to have about equal height, you may have to press Generate many hundreds of times.)

1.49   Gallup polls   Go to the website news.gallup.com for the Gallup poll. Each member of the class clicks on one of the multiple reports listed there and finds a quote that mentions a descriptive statistic. Randomly sample some members of the class (e.g., using the *Random Numbers* web app mentioned in exercise 1.48) to read their quote aloud.

1.50   Getting to know the class   Your instructor will help the class create a data file consisting of your responses to a questionnaire like the one that follows. Using a spreadsheet program or the statistical software the instructor has chosen for your course, create a data file containing this information. What are some statistical questions you might ask about these data?

GETTING TO KNOW THE CLASS

Please answer the following questions. Do not put your name on this sheet. Skip any question that you feel uncomfortable answering. These data are being collected to learn more about you and your classmates and to form a database for the class to analyze.

1. What is your height (recorded in inches)? ____

2. What is your gender (M = Male, F = Female, NB = Non-binary)? ____

3. How much did you spend on your last haircut? ____

4. Do you have a paying job during the school year at which you work, on average, at least 10 hours a week (y = yes, n = no)? ____

5. Aside from class time, how many hours a week, on average, do you expect to spend studying and completing assignments for this course? ____

6. Do you vape (y = yes, n = no)? ____

7. How many people have you dated in the past 30 days? ____

8. What was (is) your high school GPA (based on a 4.0 scale)? ____

9. What is your current college GPA? ____

10. What is the distance (in miles) between your current residence and this class? ____

11. How many minutes each day, on average, do you spend on social media sites such as Facebook, Instagram, Twitter, etc.? ____

12. How many minutes each day, on average, do you watch or stream TV? ____

13. How many hours each week, on average, do you participate in sports or have other physical exercise? ____

14. How many times a week, on average, do you read a daily newspaper? ____

15. Do you consider yourself a vegetarian (y = yes, n = no)? ____

16. How would you rate yourself politically (1 = very liberal, 2 = liberal, 3 = slightly liberal, 4 = moderate, 5 = slightly conservative, 6 = conservative, 7 = very conservative)? ____

17. What is your political affiliation (D = Democrat, R = Republican, I = Independent)? ____

We learned in Chapter 1 that every statistical analysis starts with describing the available data. This chapter presents ways of visualizing and summarizing data with appropriate graphs and numbers (i.e., statistics). Both will help us accurately describe key features of the data.

Exploring Data With Graphs and Numerical Summaries

Example 1

Statistics Informs About Threats to Our Environment

Picture the Scenario

Air pollution concerns many people, and the consumption of energy from fossil fuels affects air pollution. Most technologically advanced nations, such as the United States, use vast quantities of a diminishing supply of nonrenewable fossil fuels. Countries fast becoming technologically advanced, such as China and India, are greatly increasing their energy use. The result is increased emissions of carbon dioxide and other pollutants into the atmosphere. Emissions of carbon dioxide may also contribute to global warming. Scientists use descriptive statistics to explore energy use, to learn whether air pollution has an effect on climate, to compare different countries in how they contribute to the worldwide problems of air pollution and climate change, and to measure the impact of global warming on the environment.

Questions to Explore

- How can we investigate which countries emit the highest amounts of carbon dioxide or use the most nonrenewable energy?
- Is climate change occurring, and how serious is it?

Thinking Ahead

Chapter 1 distinguished between the ideas of **descriptive statistics** (summarizing data) and **inferential statistics** (making a prediction or decision about a population using sample data). In this chapter, we discuss both graphical and numerical summaries that are the key elements of descriptive statistics. And, we will use these summaries to investigate questions like the ones asked above. Several exercises (2.13, 2.34, 2.76, 2.83) and Examples 11 and 17 explore data on CO_2 emission and energy consumption for the United States and other nations. Example 9 uses descriptive statistics to analyze data about temperature change over time.

Before we begin our journey into the art and science of analyzing data by using descriptive statistics, we need to learn a few new terms. We'll then study ways of using graphs to describe data, followed by ways of summarizing the data numerically.

2.1 Different Types of Data

Life would be uninteresting if everyone looked the same, ate the same food, and had the same thoughts. Fortunately, **variability** is everywhere, and statistical methods provide ways to measure and understand it. For some characteristics in a study, we often see variation among the subjects. For example, there's variability among your classmates in height, major, GPA, favorite sport, and religious affiliation. Other characteristics may vary both by subject and across time. For instance, the amount of time spent studying in a day can vary both by student and by day.

Variables

Variables are the characteristics observed in a study. In the previous paragraph, height and favorite sport are two variables we might want to study.

> ### Variable
> A **variable** is any characteristic observed in a study.

In Practice

Variables are typically listed in the columns of a data set, with the rows referring to different observations on a variable.

The term *variable* highlights that data values *vary*. For example, to investigate whether global warming has occurred where you live, you could gather data on the high temperature each day over the past century at the nearest weather station. The variable you measure is the high temperature. Examples of other variables for each day are the low temperature, the cloud cover, whether it rained that day, and the number of centimeters of precipitation.

Variables Can Be Quantitative (Numerical) or Categorical (in Categories)

The data values that we observe for a variable are called **observations**. Each observation can be a **number**, such as the number of centimeters of precipitation in a day. Or each observation belongs to a **category**, such as "yes" or "no" for whether it rained.

In Words

Consider your classmates. From person to person, there is variability in age, GPA, major, and whether they are dating someone. These are **variables**. Age and GPA are **quantitative**—their values are numerical. Major and dating status are **categorical** because observations fall into distinct categories, such as "psychology," "business," or "history" for major and "yes" or "no" for dating status.

> ### Categorical and Quantitative Variables
> A variable is called **categorical** if each observation belongs to one of a set of distinct categories.
>
> A variable is called **quantitative** if observations on it take numerical values that represent different magnitudes of the variable.

The daily high temperature and the amount of precipitation are quantitative variables. Other examples of quantitative variables are age, number of siblings, annual income, and number of years of education completed. The cloud cover (with categories cloudy, partly cloudy, sunny) or whether it rained on a given day (with categories yes and no) are categorical variables. For human subjects, examples of categorical variables include race (with categories such as White, Black or African American, American Indian or Alaska Native, Asian, or Native Hawaiian or Other Pacific Islander as classified by the U.S. Census Bureau), religious affiliation (with categories such as Catholic, Jewish, Muslim, Protestant, Other, None), type of residence (house, condominium, apartment, dormitory, other), and belief in life after death (yes, no).

In the definition of a quantitative variable, why do we say that numerical values must *represent different magnitudes*? Quantitative variables measure "how much" of something (that is, *quantity* or *magnitude*). With quantitative variables, we can find arithmetic summaries such as averages. However, some numerical variables, such as area codes or bank account numbers, are not considered quantitative variables because they do not vary in quantity. For example, a bank might be interested in the average amount of loans made to its customers, but an "average" bank account number for its loan accounts does not make sense.

Graphs and numerical summaries describe the main features of a variable:

- For **quantitative** variables, key features to describe are the **center** and the **variability** (sometimes referred to as **spread**) of the data. For instance, what's a typical annual amount of precipitation? Is there much variation from year to year?
- For **categorical** variables, a key feature to describe is the relative number of observations in the various categories. For example, what percentage of days were sunny in a given year?

Quantitative Variables Are Discrete or Continuous

For a quantitative variable, each value it can take is a number, and we classify quantitative variables as either **discrete** or **continuous**.

> ### Discrete and Continuous Variables
>
> A quantitative variable is **discrete** if its possible values form a set of separate numbers, such as 0, 1, 2, 3, ... A quantitative variable is **continuous** if its possible values form an interval.

Examples of discrete variables are the number of pets in a household, the number of children in a family, and the number of foreign languages in which a person is fluent. Any variable phrased as "the number of..." is discrete. The possible values are separate numbers such as {0, 1, 2, 3, 4,...}. The outcome of the variable is a count. *Any variable with a finite number of possible values is discrete.*

Examples of continuous variables are height, weight, age, and the amount of time it takes to complete an assignment. The collection of all the possible values of a continuous variable does not consist of a set of separate numbers but, rather, an infinite region of values. The amount of time needed to complete an assignment, for example, could take the value 2.496631... hours. *Continuous variables have an infinite continuum of possible values.*

Categorical Variables Are Nominal or Ordinal

Similar to quantitative variables, we can distinguish two types of categorical variables as either nominal or ordinal.

> ### Nominal and Ordinal Variables
>
> A categorical variable is **nominal** if its categories do not have an inherent ordering. A categorical variable is **ordinal** if its categories can be ordered.

Examples of nominal categorical variables are gender (with categories such as female, male, nonbinary, or other) or religious affiliation. The categories of such variables do not follow any ordering; no one category is better than any other

Caution

A variable using numbers as labels for its categories is still a categorical variable and not quantitative. ◄

In Words

A **discrete** variable is usually a count ("the number of..."). A **continuous** variable has a continuum of infinitely many possible values (such as time, distance, or physical measurements such as weight and height).

In Practice Data Analysis Depends on Type of Variable

Why do we care whether a variable is *quantitative* or *categorical*, or whether a quantitative variable is *discrete* or *continuous*? We'll see that the method used to analyze a variable will depend on its type.

Classification of Variables

category in any sense. Examples of ordinal categorical variables are letter grades (in the U.S. system, an A is better than a B, and the least favorable outcome is an F), stages of cancer (e.g., stages I through IV, with stage I the least severe and stage IV the most severe), or opinion on some topic expressed on a Likert scale, with categories Strongly Disagree, Disagree, Neutral, Agree, and Strongly Agree. Typically, a Likert scale ranges over five or sometimes seven categories and is common on opinion surveys. In the statistical analysis, often the categories are assigned numbers, such as 1 to 5, and one speaks of a 5-point Likert scale. The ordinal variable is then actually treated as a discrete quantitative variable. The same is also true for letter grades when computing the grade point average, where numbers are assigned to the letter grades and an average of those numbers is computed. Treating an ordinal variable as a discrete quantitative variable by assigning numbers to categories only makes sense if the numbers roughly represent the distances between the categories.

Distribution of a Variable

The first step in analyzing data collected on a variable is to look at the observed values by using graphs and numerical summaries. The goal is to describe key features of the **distribution** of a variable.

Distribution

The **distribution** of a variable describes how the observations fall (are distributed) across the range of possible values.

For a categorical variable, the possible values are the different categories, and each observation falls in one of the categories. The distribution for a categorical variable then simply shows all possible categories and the number (or proportion) of observations falling into each category. For a quantitative variable, the entire range of possible values is split up into separate intervals, and the number (or proportion) of observations falling in each interval is given.

The distribution can be displayed by a graph (see next section) or a table. Features to look for in the distribution of a categorical variable are the category with the largest frequency, called the **modal category**, and more generally how frequently each category was observed. Features to look for in the distribution of a quantitative variable are its **shape** (do observations cluster in certain intervals and/or are they spread thin in others?), **center** (where does a typical observation fall?), and **variability** (how tightly are the observations clustering around a center?). We will learn more about these features and how to visualize them in the next section.

In Practice

When describing the distribution of a quantitative variable, comment on (i) shape, (ii) center and, (iii) variability.

Frequency Table

A frequency table displays the distribution of a variable numerically.

Frequency Table

A **frequency table** is a listing of possible values for a variable, together with the number of observations for each value.

For a categorical variable, a frequency table lists the categories and the number of times each category was observed. A frequency table can also display the proportions or percentages of the number of observations falling in each category.

Proportion and Percentage (Relative Frequencies)

The **proportion** of observations falling in a certain category is the number of observations in that category divided by the total number of observations. The **percentage** is the proportion multiplied by 100. Proportions and percentages are also called **relative frequencies** and serve as a way to summarize the distribution of a categorical variable numerically.

Distribution of a Variable ◄

Example 2

Shark Attacks

Picture the Scenario

The International Shark Attack File (ISAF) collects data on unprovoked shark attacks worldwide. When a shark attack is reported, the region where it took place is recorded. For the 10-year span from 2004 to 2013, a total of 689 unprovoked shark attacks have been reported, with most of them, 203, occurring in Florida. The **frequency table** in Table 2.1 shows the count for Florida and counts for other regions of the world (other U.S. states and some other countries that report shark attacks). For each region, the table lists the number (or **frequency**) of reported shark attacks in that region. The proportion is found by dividing the frequency by the total count of 689. The percentage equals the proportion multiplied by 100.

Questions to Explore

a. What is the variable that was observed? Is it categorical or quantitative?
b. How many observations were there? Show how to find the proportion and percentage for Florida.
c. Identify the modal category for this variable.
d. Describe the distribution of shark attacks.

Think It Through

a. For each observation (a reported shark attack), the **region** was recorded where the attack occurred. Each time a shark attack was reported, this created a new data point for the variable. **Region of attack is the variable**. It is categorical, with the categories being the regions shown in the first column of Table 2.1.

b. There were a total of 689 observations (shark attack reports) for this variable, with 203 reported in Florida, giving a proportion of 203/689 = 0.295. This tells us that roughly three out of every 10 reported shark attacks occurred in Florida. The percentage is 100(0.295) = 29.5%.

c. For the regions listed, the greatest number of attacks occurred in Florida, with three-tenths of all reported attacks. Florida is the modal category because it shows the greatest frequency of attacks.

d. The relative frequencies displayed in Table 2.1 are numerical summaries of the variable region. They describe how shark attacks are distributed across the various regions: Most of the attacks (29%) reported in the International Shark Attack File occurred in Florida, followed by Australia (18%), Hawaii (7%), and South Africa (6%). The remaining 40% of attacks are distributed across several other U.S. states and international regions, with no single region having more than 5% of all attacks.

Table 2.1 Frequency of Shark Attacks in Various Regions for 2004–2013*

Region	Frequency	Proportion	Percentage
Florida	203	0.295	29.5
Hawaii	51	0.074	7.4
South Carolina	34	0.049	4.9
California	33	0.048	4.8
North Carolina	23	0.033	3.3
Australia	125	0.181	18.1
South Africa	43	0.062	6.2
Réunion Island	17	0.025	2.5
Brazil	16	0.023	2.3
Bahamas	6	0.009	0.9
Other	138	0.200	20.0
Total	**689**	**1.000**	**100.0**

*Source: Data from www.flmnh.ufl.edu/fish/sharks/statistics/statsw.htm, University of Florida. Visit this site for the most current data.

Insight

Don't mistake the frequencies or counts as values for the variable. They are merely a summary of how many times the observation (a reported shark attack) occurred in each category (the various regions). The variable summarized here is the region in which the attack took place. For tables that summarize frequencies, *the total proportion is 1.0, and the total percentage is 100%*, such as Table 2.1 shows in the last row. In practice, the separate numerical summaries may sum to a slightly different number (such as 99.9% or 100.1%) because of rounding.

(APP) You can reproduce Table 2.1 with the *Explore Categorical Data* app, which has the international shark attack data preloaded.

▶ *Try Exercises 2.10 and 2.11*

Frequency Table: Waiting Time Between Two Consecutive Eruptions of the Old Faithful Geyser

Minutes	Frequency	Percentage
< 50	21	7.7
50–60	56	20.6
60–70	26	9.6
70–80	77	28.3
80–90	80	29.4
> 90	12	4.4
Total	**272**	**100.0**

Table 2.1 showed the distribution (as a frequency table) for a categorical variable. To show the **distribution** for a **discrete quantitative variable**, we would similarly list the distinct values and the frequency of each one occurring. (The table in the margin next to Example 6 on page 49 shows such a frequency table.) For a **continuous quantitative variable** (or when the number of possible outcomes is very large for a discrete variable), we divide the numeric scale on which the variable is measured into a set of nonoverlapping intervals and count the number of observations falling in each interval. The frequency table then shows these intervals together with the corresponding count. For example, in Section 2.5, we show the distribution of the waiting time (measured in minutes) between eruptions of the Old Faithful geyser in Yellowstone National Park. A frequency table for this variable is shown in the margin and uses six nonoverlapping intervals.

2.1 Practicing the Basics

2.1 Categorical/quantitative difference
  a. Explain the difference between categorical and quantitative variables.
  b. Give an example of each.

2.2 U.S. married-couple households According to a recent Current Population Survey of U.S. married-couple households, 13% are traditional (with children and with only the husband in the labor force), 31% are dual-income with children, 25% are dual-income with no children, and 31% are other (such as older married couples whose children no longer reside in the household). Is the variable "household type" categorical or quantitative? Explain.

2.3 Identify the variable type Identify each of the following variables as categorical or quantitative.
  a. Number of pets in family
  b. County of residence
  c. Choice of auto to buy (domestic or import)
  d. Distance (in kilometers) of commute to work

2.4 Categorical or quantitative? Identify each of the following variables as either categorical or quantitative.
  a. Choice of diet (vegan, vegetarian, neither)
  b. Time spent shopping online per week
  c. Ownership of a tablet (yes, no)
  d. Number of siblings

2.5 Discrete/continuous
  a. Explain the difference between a discrete variable and a continuous variable.
  b. Give an example of each type.

2.6 Discrete or continuous? Identify each of the following variables as continuous or discrete.
  a. The length of time to run a marathon
  b. The number of people in line at a box office to purchase theater tickets
  c. The weight of a dog
  d. The number of people you have dated in the past month

2.7 Discrete or continuous 2 Repeat the previous exercise for the following:
  a. The total playing time of a CD
  b. The number of courses for which a student has received credit
  c. The amount of money in your pocket (*Hint:* You could regard a number such as $12.75 as 1,275 in terms of "the number of cents.")
  d. The distance between where you live and your statistics classroom, when you measure it precisely with values such as 0.5 miles, 2.4 miles, 5.38 miles

2.8 Nominal/ordinal
  a. Explain the difference between a nominal and ordinal categorical variable.
  b. Give an example of each type.

2.9 Nominal or ordinal? Identify each of the following variables as nominal, ordinal, or neither.
  a. Gender (with categories female, male, nonbinary, other)
  b. Favorite color
  c. Pain as measured on the 11-point pain scale, with a score of 0 meaning no pain, a score between 1 and 3 describing mild pain, a score between 4 and 6 describing moderate pain, and a score between 7 and 10 describing severe pain.
  d. Effectiveness of teacher (not effective, slightly effective, moderately effective, very effective, extremely effective)

2.10 Number of children In the 2018 General Social Survey (GSS), 2,344 respondents answered the question, "How many children have you ever had?" The results were

	Number of Children									
	0	1	2	3	4	5	6	7	8+	Total
Count	663	349	623	383	166	74	47	23	16	2,344

  a. Is the variable, number of children, categorical or quantitative?
  b. Is the variable, number of children, discrete or continuous?
  c. Add proportions and percentages to this frequency table. (You can use the *Explore Categorical Data* app for this.)
  d. Describe the distribution of the variable "Number of Children" by finding the modal category and mentioning some of the other category frequencies.

2.11 Fatal shark attacks Few of the shark attacks listed in Table 2.1 are fatal. Overall, 63 fatal shark attacks were recorded in the ISAF for the 10-year period from 2004 to 2013, with 2 reported in Florida, 2 in Hawaii, 4 in California, 15 in Australia, 13 in South Africa, 6 in Réunion Island, 4 in Brazil, and 6 in the Bahamas. The rest occurred in other regions.
  a. Construct the frequency table for the regions of the reported fatal shark attacks.
  b. Identify the modal category.
  c. Describe the distribution of fatal shark attacks across the regions.

2.12 Smartphone use in class A survey of 743 teenagers (ages 13–17) about losing focus when checking their cellphones during class revealed that 291 never lost focus, 214 rarely lost focus, 178 sometimes lost focus, and 60 often lost focus. Construct the frequency table for the different categories of losing focus and describe the distribution by finding the modal category and mentioning other category frequencies. (You can use the *Explore Categorical Data* app to obtain the frequency table.)

2.2 Graphical Summaries of Data

Looking at a graph often gives you more of a feel for a variable and its distribution than looking at the raw data or a frequency table. In this section, we'll learn about graphs for categorical variables and then graphs for quantitative variables. We'll find out what we should look for in a graph to help us understand the distribution better.

Graphs for Categorical Variables

The two primary graphical displays for summarizing a categorical variable are the **pie chart** and the **bar graph**.

- A **pie chart** is a circle having a slice of the pie for each category. The size of a slice corresponds to the percentage of observations in the category.
- A **bar graph** displays a vertical bar for each category. The height of the bar shows the percentage of observations in the category. Typically, the vertical bars for each category are apart, not side by side.

Pie Charts and Bar Graphs ◄

Example 3

Shark Attacks in the United States

Picture the Scenario

For the United States alone, a total of 387 unprovoked shark attacks were reported between 2004 and 2013. Table 2.2 shows the breakdown by state; states such as Oregon, Alabama, or Georgia, with only a few reported attacks, are summarized in the Other category.

Questions to Explore

a. Display the distribution of shark attacks across U.S. states in a pie chart and a bar graph.
b. What percentage of attacks occurred in Florida and the Carolinas?
c. Describe the distribution of shark attacks across U.S. states.

Think It Through

a. The state where the attack occurred is a categorical variable. Each reported attack for the United States falls in one of the categories listed in Table 2.2. Figure 2.1 shows the pie chart based on the frequencies listed in Table 2.2. States with more frequent attacks have larger slices of the pie. The percentages are included in the labels for each slice of the pie. Figure 2.2 shows the bar graph. The states with larger percentages have higher bars. The scale for the percentages is shown on the vertical axis. The width is the same for each bar.

b. Of all U.S. attacks, 67% (52% + 9% + 6%) occurred in Florida and the Carolinas.

c. As the bar graph (or pie chart) shows, 52% of all shark attacks reported for the United States occurred in Florida. Florida is the modal category. Far fewer attacks were reported for Hawaii (13%), South Carolina (9%), California (9%), North Carolina (6%), and Texas (4%). The remaining 7% of attacks occurred in other U.S. states.

Table 2.2 Unprovoked Shark Attacks in the U.S. Between 2004 and 2013*

U.S. State	Frequency	Proportion	Percentage
Florida	203	0.525	52.5
Hawaii	51	0.132	13.2
South Carolina	34	0.088	8.8
California	33	0.085	8.5
North Carolina	23	0.059	5.9
Texas	16	0.041	4.1
Other	27	0.070	7.0
Total	**387**	**1.000**	**100.0**

*Source: http://www.flmnh.ufl.edu/fish/sharks/statistics/statsus.htm University of Florida

Pie Chart of Shark Attacks by U.S. State

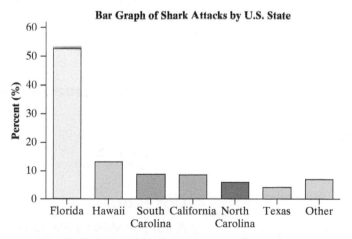

▲ **Figure 2.1** Pie Chart of Shark Attacks Across U.S. States. The label for each slice of the pie gives the category and the percentage of attacks in a state. The slice that represents the percentage of attacks reported in Hawaii is 13% of the total area of the pie. **Question** Why is it beneficial to label the pie wedges with the percent? (*Hint:* Is it always clear which of two slices is larger and what percent a slice represents?)

Bar Graph of Shark Attacks by U.S. State

▲ **Figure 2.2** Bar Graph of Shark Attacks Across U.S. States. Except for the Other category, which is shown last, the bars are ordered from largest to smallest based on the frequency of shark attacks. **Question** What is the advantage of ordering the bars this way, rather than alphabetically?

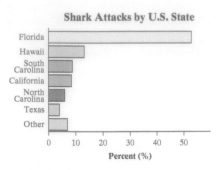

Shark Attacks by U.S. State

Horizontal Bar Graph

Insight

The pie chart and bar graph are both simple to construct using software. The pie chart works well in displaying how different categories are part of the whole, but a bar graph is generally easier to read and more flexible. With a pie chart, when two slices are about the same size, it's often unclear which value is larger. This distinction is clearer when comparing heights of bars in a bar graph. We'll see that the bar graph can easily summarize how results compare for different groups (for instance, if we wanted to compare fatal and nonfatal attacks in the United States). Also, the bar graph is a better visual display when there are many categories. The bar graph can also be plotted horizontally, as shown in the margin. A horizontal bar graph is appropriate if there are many categories to compare, such as all 50 of the United States.

To construct vertical or horizontal bar graphs or a pie chart with your own data, or to reproduce the bar graphs and the pie chart shown here, use the *Explore Categorical Data* app, which has the U.S. shark attack data preloaded.

▶ **Try Exercise 2.13**

The bar graph in Figure 2.2 displays the categories in decreasing order of the category percentages except for the Other category. This order makes it easy to separate the categories with high percentages visually. In some applications, it is more natural to display them according to their alphabetical order or some other criterion. For instance, if the categories have a natural order, such as summarizing the percentages of grades (A, B, C, D, F) for students in a course, we'd use that order in listing the categories on the graph.

Pareto Charts

Market Share of Operating Systems for Smartphones Shipped in 2013

Source: idc.com, IDC (International Data Corporation)

A bar graph with categories ordered by their frequency is called a **Pareto chart**, named after Italian economist Vilfredo Pareto (1848–1923), who advocated its use. The Pareto chart is often used in business applications to identify the most common outcomes, such as identifying products with the highest sales or identifying the most common types of complaints that a customer service center receives. The chart helps to portray the **Pareto principle**, which states that a small subset of categories often contains most of the observations. For example, the Pareto chart in the margin shows that of all the smartphones shipped in 2013 (about 1 billion), the two most common operating systems for these smartphones captured almost all (94%) of the market, with the remaining ones only contributing a tiny fraction.

Graphs for Quantitative Variables

Now let's explore how to summarize *quantitative* variables graphically and visualize their distribution. We'll look at three types of displays—the dot plot, stem-and-leaf plot, and histogram—and illustrate the graphs by analyzing data for a common daily food (cereal).

Dot Plots

A **dot plot** shows a dot for each observation, placed just above the value on the number line for that observation. To construct a dot plot,

■ Draw a horizontal line. Label it with the name of the variable and mark regular values of the variable on it.

■ For each observation, place a dot above its value on the number line.

Example 4

Health Value of Cereals

Picture the Scenario

Let's investigate the amount of sugar and salt (sodium) in breakfast cereals. Table 2.3 lists 20 popular cereals and the amounts of sodium and sugar contained in a single serving. The sodium and sugar amounts are both quantitative variables. The variables are continuous because they measure amounts that can take any positive real number value. In this table, the amounts are rounded to the nearest number of grams for sugar and milligrams for sodium.

Questions to Explore

a. Construct a dot plot for the sodium values of the 20 breakfast cereals. (We'll consider sugar amounts in the exercises.)

b. What does the dot plot tell us about the distribution of sodium values?

Table 2.3 Sodium and Sugar Amounts in 20 Breakfast Cereals

The amounts refer to one National Labeling and Education Act (NLEA) serving. A third variable, Type, classifies the cereal as being popular for adults (Type A) or children (Type C).

Cereal	Sodium (mg)	Sugar (g)	Type
Frosted Mini Wheats	0	11	A
Raisin Bran	340	18	A
All-Bran	70	5	A
Apple Jacks	140	14	C
Cap'n Crunch	200	12	C
Cheerios	180	1	C
Cinnamon Toast Crunch	210	10	C
Crackling Oat Bran	150	16	A
Fiber One	100	0	A
Frosted Flakes	130	12	C
Froot Loops	140	14	C
Honey Bunches of Oats	180	7	A
Honey Nut Cheerios	190	9	C
Life	160	6	C
Rice Krispies	290	3	C
Honey Smacks	50	15	A
Special K	220	4	A
Wheaties	180	4	A
Corn Flakes	200	3	A
Honeycomb	210	11	C

Source: www.weightchart.com (click Nutrition).

Caution

Continuous data is often recorded to the nearest whole number. Although the data may now appear as discrete, the data are still analyzed and interpreted as continuous data. ◀

Did You Know?

Nutritionists recommend that daily consumption should not exceed 2,400 milligrams (mg) for sodium and 50 grams for sugar (on a 2,000-calorie-a-day diet). ◀

Think It Through

a. Figure 2.3 shows a dot plot. Each cereal sodium value is represented with a dot above the number line. For instance, the labeled dot above 0 represents the sodium value of 0 mg for Frosted Mini Wheats.

▲ **Figure 2.3** Dot Plot for Sodium Content of 20 Breakfast Cereals. The sodium value for each cereal is represented with a dot above the number line. **Question** What does it mean when more than one dot appears above a value?

b. The dot plot gives us an overview of all the data. We see clearly that the sodium values fall between 0 and 340 mg, with most cereals falling between 125 mg and 225 mg.

Insight

The dot plot displays the individual observations. The number of dots above a value on the number line represents the frequency of occurrence of that value. From a dot plot, we can reconstruct (at least approximately) all the data in the sample.

APP

To construct a dot plot with your own data or to reproduce the one above, use the *Explore Quantitative Data* app, which has the cereal data preloaded.

▶ **Try Exercises 2.18 and 2.20, part b**

Stem-and-Leaf Plots

Another type of graph, called a **stem-and-leaf plot**, is similar to the dot plot in that it displays individual observations.

Stems	Leaves
7	69
8	00125699
9	12446

Observation = 92, in a sample of 15 test scores

- Each observation is represented by a **stem** and a **leaf**. Usually the stem consists of all the digits except for the final one, which is the leaf.
- Sort the data in order from smallest to largest. Place the stems in a column, starting with the smallest. Place a vertical line to their right. On the right side of the vertical line, indicate each leaf (final digit) that has a particular stem. List the leaves in increasing order.

Example 5

Stem-and-Leaf Plot ◀

Health Value of Cereals

Picture the Scenario

Let's reexamine the sodium values for the 20 breakfast cereals, shown in Table 2.3.

Questions to Explore

a. Construct a stem-and-leaf plot of the 20 sodium values.
b. How does the stem-and-leaf plot compare to the dot plot?

Think It Through

a. In the stem-and-leaf plot, we'll let the final digit of a sodium value form the leaf and the other digits form the stem. For instance, the sodium value for Honey Smacks is 50. The stem is 5, and the leaf is 0. Each stem is placed to the left of a vertical bar. Each leaf is placed to the right of the bar. Figure 2.4 shows the plot. Notice that a leaf has only one digit, but a stem can have one or more digits.

Cereal	Sodium
Frosted Mini Wheats	0
Raisin Bran	340
All-Bran	70
Apple Jacks	140
Cap'n Crunch	200
Cheerios	180
Cinnamon Toast Crunch	210
Crackling Oat Bran	150
Fiber One	100
Frosted Flakes	130
Froot Loops	140
Honey Bunches of Oats	180
Honey Nut Cheerios	190
Life	160
Rice Krispies	290
Honey Smacks	50
Special K	220
Wheaties	180
Corn Flakes	200
Honeycomb	210

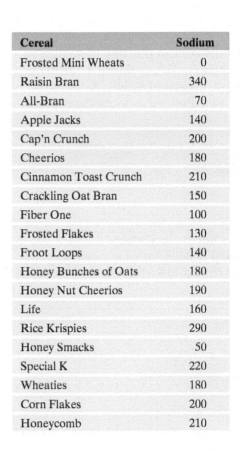

```
Stems | Leaves
  0   | 0
  1   |
  2   |        This data point is the Honey
  3   |        Smacks sodium value, 50.
  4   |        The stem is 5 and the leaf is 0.
  5   | 0
  6   |
  7   | 0
  8   |
  9   |
 10   | 0
 11   |
 12   |
 13   | 0
 14   | 00
 15   | 0        These two leaf values are for
 16   | 0        Cap'n Crunch and Corn Flakes.
 17   |          Each has 200 mg of sodium per
 18   | 000      serving. The stem is 20 and
 19   | 0        each leaf is 0.
 20   | 00
 21   | 00
 22   | 0
 23   |
 24   |
 25   |
 26   |
 27   |
 28   |
 29   | 0
 30   |
 31   |
 32   |
 33   |
 34   | 0
```

▲ **Figure 2.4 Stem-and-Leaf Plot for Cereal Sodium Values.** The final digit of a sodium value forms the leaf, and the other digits form the stem. **Question** Why do some stems not have a leaf?

The Honey Smacks observation of 50 is labeled on the graph. Two observations have a stem of 20 and a leaf of 0. These are the sodium values of 200 for Cap'n Crunch and Corn Flakes.

b. The stem-and-leaf plot looks like the dot plot turned on its side, with the leaves taking the place of the dots. Often, with a stem-and-leaf plot, it is easier to read the actual observation value. In summary, we generally get the same information from a stem-and-leaf plot as from a dot plot.

Insight

A stem is shown for each possible value between the minimum and maximum even if no observation occurs for that stem. A stem has no leaf if there is no observation at that value. These are the values at which the dot plot has no dots.

   To construct a stem-and-leaf plot with your own data, or to reproduce some of the stem-and-leaf plots shown here, use the *Explore Quantitative Data* app, which has the cereal data preloaded.

▶ *Try Exercise 2.19, parts a and b*

Truncated Data	
Frosted Mini Wheats	0
Raisin Bran	34
All-Bran	7
Apple Jacks	14
Cap'n Crunch	20
Cheerios	18
Cinnamon Toast Crunch	21
Crackling Oat Bran	15
Fiber One	10
Frosted Flakes	13
Froot Loops	14
Honey Bunches of Oats	18
Honey Nut Cheerios	19
Life	16
Rice Krispies	29
Honey Smacks	5
Special K	22
Wheaties	18
Corn Flakes	20
Honeycomb	21

To make a stem-and-leaf plot more compact, we can **truncate** these data values: Cut off the final digit (it's not necessary to round it), as shown in the margin, and plot the data as 0, 34, 7, 14, 20, and so on, instead of 0, 340, 70, 140, 200,.... Arranging the leaves in increasing order on each line, we then get the stem-and-leaf plot

```
0 | 057
1 | 0344568889
2 | 001129
3 | 4
```

This is a bit *too* compact because it does not portray where the data fall as clearly as Figure 2.4 or the dot plot. We could instead list each stem twice, putting leaves from 0 to 4 on the first stem and from 5 to 9 on the second stem. We then get

```
0 | 0
0 | 57
1 | 0344
1 | 568889
2 | 00112
2 | 9
3 | 4
```

Like the dot plot, this gives us the sense that most sodium values are relatively high, with a couple of cereals being considerably lower than the others.

Histograms

With a dot plot or a stem-and-leaf plot, it's easy to reconstruct the original data set because the plot shows the individual observations. This becomes unwieldy for large data sets. In that case, a histogram is a more versatile way to graph the data and picture the distribution. It uses bars to display and summarize frequencies of different outcomes.

Histogram

A **histogram** is a graph that uses bars to portray the frequencies or the relative frequencies of the possible outcomes for a quantitative variable.

	Histogram for a Discrete Variable ◀

Example 6

TV Watching

Picture the Scenario

The 2012 General Social Survey asked, "On an average day, about how many hours do you personally watch television?" Figure 2.5 shows the histogram of the 1,298 responses, constructed from the data shown in the margin.

Frequency Table for Histogram in Figure 2.5

Hours	Count	Hours	Count
0	90	13	2
1	255	14	4
2	325	15	3
3	238	16	1
4	171	17	0
5	61	18	1
6	58	19	0
7	19	20	2
8	31	21	0
9	3	22	1
10	17	23	0
11	0	24	5
12	11		

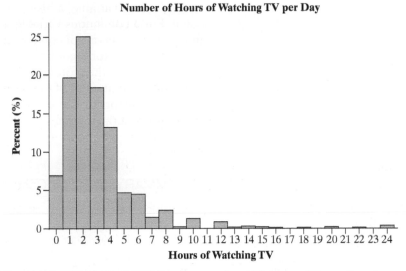

▲ **Figure 2.5** Histogram of GSS Responses about Number of Hours Spent Watching TV on an Average Day. *Source:* Data from CSM, UC Berkeley.

Questions to Explore

a. What was the most common outcome?

b. What does the histogram reveal about the distribution of TV watching?

c. What percentage of people reported watching TV no more than 2 hours per day?

Think It Through

a. The most common outcome is the value with the highest bar. This is 2 hours of TV watching. We call the most common value of a quantitative variable the **mode**. The distribution of TV watching has a mode at 2 hours.

b. We see that most people watch between 1 and 4 hours of TV per day. Very few watch more than 8 hours.

c. To find the percentage for "no more than 2 hours per day," we need to look at the percentages for 0, 1, and 2 hours per day. They seem to be about 7, 20, and 25. Adding these percentages together tells us that about 52% of the respondents reported watching no more than 2 hours of TV per day. (This is corroborated using the table in the margin, where $(90 + 255 + 325)/1{,}298 = 0.516$.)

Insight

In theory, TV watching is a continuous variable. However, the possible responses subjects were able to make here were $0, 1, 2, \ldots, 24$, so it was measured as a discrete variable. Figure 2.5 is an example of a histogram of a discrete variable. Note that since the variable is treated as discrete, the histogram in

Number of Hours of Watching TV per Day

Figure 2.5 could have been constructed with the bars apart instead of beside each other as shown in the margin.

While it is easy to calculate the mode, we usually use a different statistic to describe a typical value for a quantitative variable. Here, we would use the median, which also equals 2; see Section 2.3.

▶ *Try Exercise 2.27, parts a and b*

For a discrete variable, a histogram usually has a separate bar for each possible value. For a continuous variable, we need to divide the range of possible values into smaller intervals of equal width, just as we have discussed when forming the frequency table for a continuous response. We can also do this when a discrete variable, such as the score on an exam, has a large number of possible values. We then count the number of observations falling in each interval. The height of the bars in the histogram represent the frequency (or relative frequency) of observations falling in the intervals.

Caution

The term *histogram* is used for a graph with bars representing frequencies of a quantitative variable. The term *bar graph* is used for a graph with bars representing frequencies of categories of a categorical variable. In a bar graph, you can switch the position of bars without affecting the interpretability of the graph. In a histogram, you cannot switch positions of bars. ◀

SUMMARY: Steps for Constructing a Histogram

- Divide the range of the data into intervals of equal width. For a discrete variable with few values, use the actual possible values.
- Count the number of observations (the frequency) in each interval, forming a frequency table.
- On the horizontal axis, label the values or the endpoints of the intervals. Draw a bar over each value or interval with height equal to its frequency (or percentage), values of which are marked on the vertical axis.

Example 7

Histogram for a Continuous Variable ◀

Health Value of Cereals

Picture the Scenario

Let's reexamine the sodium values of the 20 breakfast cereals. Those values are shown again in the margin of the next page.

Questions to Explore

a. Construct a frequency table.
b. Construct a corresponding histogram to visualize the distribution.
c. What information does the histogram not show that you can get from a dot plot or a stem-and-leaf plot?

Think It Through

a. To construct a frequency table, we divide the range of possible sodium values into separate intervals and count the number of cereals in each. The sodium values range from 0 to 340. We created Table 2.4 using nine intervals, each with a width of 40. The intervals are: 0–40, 40–80, 80–120,..., 280–320, and 320–360. For each interval, we count how many observations fall in that interval. For instance, the interval 40–80 contains two observations: The sodium value of 50 mg from Honey Smacks and the sodium value of 70 mg from All-Bran. If a sodium value falls

Cereal	Sodium
Frosted Mini Wheats	0
Raisin Bran	340
All-Bran	70
Apple Jacks	140
Cap'n Crunch	200
Cheerios	180
Cinnamon Toast Crunch	210
Crackling Oat Bran	150
Fiber One	100
Frosted Flakes	130
Froot Loops	140
Honey Bunches of Oats	180
Honey Nut Cheerios	190
Life	160
Rice Krispies	290
Honey Smacks	50
Special K	220
Wheaties	180
Corn Flakes	200
Honeycomb	210

Table 2.4 Frequency Table for Sodium in 20 Breakfast Cereals

The table summarizes the sodium values using nine intervals and lists the number of observations in each as well as the corresponding proportions and percentages.

Interval	Frequency	Proportion	Percentage
0 to 40	1	0.05	5%
40 to 80	2	0.10	10%
80 to 120	1	0.05	5%
120 to 160	4	0.20	20%
160 to 200	5	0.25	25%
200 to 240	5	0.25	25%
240 to 280	0	0.00	0%
280 to 320	1	0.05	5%
320 to 360	1	0.05	5%

right on the boundary of an interval, such as the value 200 mg for Corn Flakes, we counted it in the larger of the two adjacent intervals 160–200 and 200–240. So, the Corn Flakes value contributed to the count of 5 shown for the interval 200–240. Likewise, Life's value of 160 mg is counted in the interval 160–200 and not in the interval 120–160.

h. Figure 2.6 shows the histogram for this frequency table. A bar is drawn over each interval of values, with the height of each bar equal to its corresponding frequency.

c. The histogram does not show the actual numerical values. For instance, we know that one observation falls below 40, but we do not know its actual value. In summary, with a histogram, we may lose the actual numerical values of individual observations, unlike with a dot plot or a stem-and-leaf plot.

Insight

The bars in the histogram in Figure 2.6 display the frequencies in each interval (or bin), and the vertical axis shows the counts. If we had used relative frequencies (proportions or percentages) on the vertical axis instead, the

▲ **Figure 2.6** Histogram of Breakfast Cereal Sodium Values. The rectangular bar over an interval has height equal to the number of observations in the interval.

Histogram of sodium values using relative frequencies

APP

Histogram with too few intervals

Histogram with too many intervals

In Practice Technology Can Construct Graphical Displays

Graphical displays are easily constructed using statistical software such as our web apps. They choose the intervals for you when they construct histograms. In practice, you won't have to draw graphs yourself. But it is important to understand *how* they are drawn and *how to interpret* them.

---

appearance of the histogram would be identical (see margin). Only the label on the vertical axis would change. Each of these histograms shows that most cereals have a sodium value between 120 mg and 240 mg, with few having smaller or larger amounts.

You can supply your own data or reproduce the histograms in Figures 2.5 and 2.6 with the *Explore Quantitative Data* app, which has the data from these examples preloaded. The app features a slider that controls the width of the bins. In practice, the initial bin width and lower bound of the first bin are selected automatically and are often not nice, round numbers. Then, the labeling on the x-axis might look a bit different than the ones shown in Figures 2.5 or 2.6.

▶ *Try Exercise 2.19, part c*

How do you select the intervals? If you use too few intervals, the graph is usually too crude (see margin). It may consist mainly of a couple of wide bars. If you use too many intervals, the graph may be irregular, with many very short bars and/or gaps between bars (see margin). You can then lose information about the shape of the distribution. Usually about 8 to 12 intervals are adequate, with perhaps additional intervals when the sample size is quite large. There is no one right way to select the intervals. Software can select them for you, find the counts and percentages, and construct the histogram, but it is always a good idea to override the default and look at a few options.

The *Explore Quantitative Data* app provides a slider that allows you to interactively change the length (and, hence, the number) of the intervals used in a histogram. Use this feature to explore how selecting different numbers of intervals affects the appearance. You can do this with the histogram for the sodium data, which are implemented with the app.

Choosing a Graph Type

We've now studied three graphs for quantitative variables—the dot plot, stem-and-leaf plot, and histogram. How do we decide which to use? We suggest **always plotting the histogram** to get an idea about the distribution. If the number of observations is small (e.g., less than 50), supplement the histogram with a stem-and-leaf plot or a dot plot to show the numerical values of the observations.

The Shape of a Distribution

A histogram (or a stem-and-leaf or dot plot) visualizes the distribution of a quantitative variable. Here are important questions to ask when describing this distribution:

- Does the distribution have a single mound or peak? If so, the distribution is called **unimodal**, and the value that occurs most often is called the **mode**. A distribution with *two* distinct mounds is called **bimodal**. The graphs on the following page illustrate both a unimodal and a bimodal distribution. A bimodal distribution can result, for example, when a population is polarized on a controversial issue. Suppose each subject is presented with 10 scenarios in which a person found guilty of murder may be given the death penalty. If we count the number of those scenarios in which subjects feel the death penalty would be just, many responses would be close to 0 (for subjects who oppose the death penalty generally) and many would be close to 10 (for subjects who think it's always or usually warranted for murder).

Unimodal

Bimodal

This observation deviates from the rest.

A bimodal distribution can also result when the observations come from two different groups. For instance, a histogram of the height of students in your school might show two peaks, one for females and one for males (see plot in the margin).

- What is the **shape** of the distribution? The shape of a unimodal distribution is often described as **symmetric** or **skewed**. A distribution is *symmetric* if the side of the distribution below a central value is a mirror image of the side above that central value. The distribution is *skewed* if one side of the distribution stretches out longer than the other side.

- Do the data cluster together, or is there a **gap** such that one or more observations noticeably deviate from the rest, as in the histogram in the margin? We'll discuss such "outlier" observations later in the chapter.

In picturing features such as symmetry and skew, it's common to use smooth curves as in Figure 2.7 to summarize the shape of a histogram. You can think of this as what can happen when you choose more and more intervals (making each interval narrower) and collect more data, so the histogram gets smoother. The parts of the curve for the lowest values and for the highest values are called the **tails** of the distribution.

Symmetric   Skewed to the left   Skewed to the right

▲ **Figure 2.7** Curves for Distributions Illustrating Symmetry and Skew. **Question** What does the longer tail indicate about the direction of skew?

Skewed Distribution

To **skew** means to stretch in one direction.

A distribution is **skewed to the left** if the left tail is longer than the right tail.

A distribution is **skewed to the right** if the right tail is longer than the left tail.

A left-skewed distribution stretches to the left, a right-skewed to the right.

Identifying Skew

Let's consider some variables and think about what shape their distributions would have. How about IQ? Values cluster around 100 and tail off in a similar fashion in both directions. The appearance of the distribution on one side of 100 is roughly a mirror image of the other side, with tails of similar length. The distribution is approximately symmetric (see the green shaded graph in the margin).

How about life span for humans? Most people in advanced societies live to be at least about 70 years old, but some die at a very young age, so the distribution of life span would probably be skewed to the left (see the tan shaded graph below).

What shape would we expect for the distribution of annual incomes of adults? There would probably be a long right tail, with some people having incomes much higher than the overwhelming majority of people. This suggests that the distribution would be skewed to the right (see the purple shaded graph below).

In Practice

Sometimes, especially with small data sets, the shape of the distribution might not be so obvious.

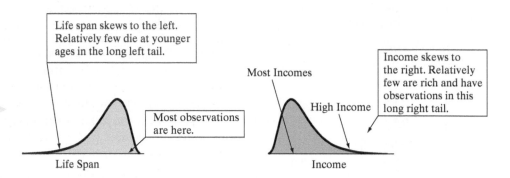

Example 8

Shape of a Distribution ◄

TV Watching

Picture the Scenario

In Example 6, we constructed a histogram of the number of hours of TV watching reported in the GSS. It is shown again in the margin.

Question to Explore

How would you describe the shape of the distribution?

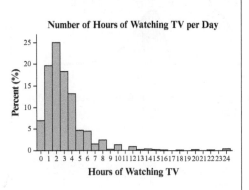

Think It Through

The distribution for the number of hours watching TV is unimodal, with most values around 2 hours. The distribution is right skewed because of the long tail extending to the right.

Insight

In surveys, the observation that a subject reports is not necessarily the precise value. Often they either round or don't remember exactly and just guess. In this distribution, the percentage is quite a bit higher for 8 hours than for 7 or 9. Perhaps subjects reporting high values tend to pick even numbers.

▶ *Try Exercises 2.24 and 2.27, part c*

Time Plots: Displaying Data over Time

For some variables, observations are recorded over time. Examples include the daily closing price of a stock and the population of a country measured every decade in a census. A data set collected over time is called a **time series**.

We can display time-series data graphically using a **time plot**. This charts each observation, on the vertical scale, against the time it was measured, on the horizontal scale. A common pattern to look for is a **trend** over time, indicating a tendency of the data to either rise or fall. To see a trend more clearly, it is beneficial to connect the data points in their time sequence.

Example 9

Time Plot ◀

Warming Trend in New York City

Picture the Scenario

In a given year, the annual average temperature is the average of the daily average temperatures for that year. Let's analyze data on annual average temperatures (in degrees Fahrenheit) in Central Park, New York City, from 1869 to 2018. This is a continuous, quantitative variable. The data are in the Central Park Yearly Temps data file on the book's website, and preloaded in the *Time Series* app.[1]

Question to Explore

What do we learn from a time plot of these annual average temperatures? Is there a trend toward warming in New York City?

Think It Through

Figure 2.8 shows a time plot, constructed using the *Time Series* app from our website, www.ArtofStat.com, connecting the observations from each year.

▲ **Figure 2.8** Screenshot from the *Time Series* app, plotting a time series of average annual temperatures in Central Park, New York City, from 1869 to 2018. A smoothing curve is superimposed. **Question** Are the annual average temperatures tending to increase, decrease, or stay the same over time?

[1]*Source:* www.weather.gov

The observations fluctuate considerably, by about three to four degrees over several years, but the figure does suggest an increasing trend in the annual average temperatures in New York City.

Insight

The short-term fluctuations in a time plot can mask an overall trend. It's possible to get a clearer picture by smoothing the data. Although the specifics of smoothing (which, in its most basic form, is like a running average) are beyond the scope of this book, the app has an option to superimpose a smooth trend. This is the smooth curve you see passing through the data points in Figure 2.8. It shows an increase from about 51.5 degrees in 1869 to about 56.2 degrees in 2018.

The data reported in Figure 2.8 refer to one location in the United States. In a study of climate change, it would be important to explore other locations around the world to see whether similar trends are evident.

You can supply your own data for a time plot or reproduce the one in Figure 2.8 with the *Time Series* app.

▶ **Try Exercises 2.30 and 2.31**

▶ On the Shoulders of...Florence Nightingale

Graphical Displays Showing Deaths From Disease Versus Military Combat

Florence Nightingale

During the Crimean War in 1854, the British nurse Florence Nightingale (1820–1910) gathered data on the number of soldiers who died from various causes. She prepared graphical displays such as time plots and pie charts for policy makers. The graphs showed that more soldiers were dying from contagious diseases than from war-related wounds. The plots were revolutionary for her time. They helped promote her national cause of improving hospital conditions.

After implementing sanitary methods, Nightingale showed with time plots that the relative frequency of soldiers' deaths from contagious disease decreased sharply and no longer exceeded that of deaths from wounds.

Throughout the rest of her life, Nightingale promoted the use of data for making informed decisions about public health policy. For example, she used statistical arguments to campaign for improved medical conditions in the United States during the Civil War in the 1860s (Franklin, 2002).

2.2   Practicing the Basics

2.13   **Generating electricity**   In 2012 in the United States, most electricity was generated from coal (37%), natural gas (30%), or nuclear power plants (19%). Hydropower accounted for 7% of the total electricity produced; other renewable sources, such as wind or solar power, accounted for 5%. Other nonrenewable sources (such as petroleum) made up the remaining 2%. (*Source:* http://www.eia.gov/electricity/annual/html/epa_01_01.html)

  a. Display this information in a bar graph.

  b. Which is easier to sketch relatively accurately, a pie chart or a bar chart?

  c. What is the advantage of using a graph to summarize the results instead of merely stating the percentages for each source?

  d. What is the modal category?

2.14   **What do alligators eat?**   The following bar chart is from a study[2] investigating the factors that influence alligators' choice of food. For 219 alligators captured in four Florida lakes, researchers classified the primary food choice (in volume) found in the alligator's stomach in one of the categories—fish, invertebrate (snails, insects, crayfish), reptile (turtles, baby alligators), bird, or other (amphibian, mammal, plants). (Data available on the book's website.)

---

[2]Data courtesy of Clint Moore.

a. Is primary food choice categorical or quantitative?

b. Which is the modal category for primary food choice?

c. About what percentage of alligators had fish as the primary food choice?

d. This type of bar chart, with categories listed in order of frequency, has a special name. What is it?

Primary Food Choice of Alligators

2.15 Weather stations   The pie chart shown (constructed using Excel) portrays the regional distribution of weather stations in the United States.

a. Do the slices of the pie portray (i) variables or (ii) categories of a variable?

b. Identify what the two numbers mean that are shown for each slice of the pie.

c. Without inspecting the numbers, would it be easier to identify the modal category by using this graph or the corresponding bar graph? Why?

Regional Distribution of Weather Stations

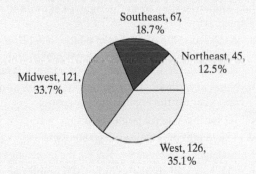

2.16 Most popular national park   Which national parks are the most visited? The following table shows results for the top eight most visited parks in 2018, according to the National Geographic website.

a. Is "national park visited" a categorical or a quantitative variable?

b. In creating a bar graph of these data, would it be most sensible to list the parks alphabetically or in the form of a Pareto chart? Explain.

c. Does either a dot plot or stem-and-leaf plot make sense for these data? Explain.

APP d. Use the *Explore Categorical Data* app (enter data as a frequency table) or other software to construct a bar graph for these data.

Most Visited National Parks, 2018	
Park	**Number of Visitors (millions)**
Great Smoky Mountains	11.4
Grand Canyon	6.4
Rocky Mountain	4.6
Zion	4.3
Yellowstone	4.1
Yosemite	4.0
Acadia	3.5
Grand Teton	3.5

Source: https://www.nationalgeographic.com/travel/national-parks/most-visited-parks-photos/, © 1996–2020 National Geographic Society

2.17 Pareto chart for fatal shark attacks   The frequencies stated in Exercise 2.11 refer to fatal shark attacks for different regions. Using software such as the *Explore Categorical Data* app or sketching, construct a bar graph, ordering the regions (i) alphabetically and (ii) as in a Pareto chart. Which graph do you prefer? Why?

2.18 Sugar dot plot   For the breakfast cereal data given in Table 2.3, a dot plot for the sugar values (in grams) is shown (screenshot taken from the *Explore Quantitative Dat* app):

a. Identify the minimum and maximum sugar values.

b. Which sugar outcomes occur most frequently? What are these values called?

APP c. Reproduce the dot plot using the *Explore Quantitative Data* app. Moving the slider for "binwidth" in the app groups neighboring observations together and plots their dots on top of each other.

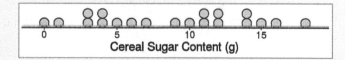

Cereal Sugar Content (g)

2.19 Spring break hotel prices   For a trip to Miami, Florida, over spring break, the data below (obtained from www.travelocity.com) show the price per night (in U.S. dollars) for a random sample of hotel rooms.

239	237	245	310	218	175	330	196	178
245	255	190	330	124	162	190	386	145

a. Construct a stem-and-leaf plot by hand. Truncate the data to the first two digits for purposes of constructing the plot. For example, 239 becomes 23.

b. Reconstruct the stem-and-leaf plot in part a by using split stems; that is, two stems of 1, two stems of 2, and so on. Compare the two stem-and-leaf plots. Explain how one may be more informative than the other.

c. Sketch a histogram by hand, using 6 intervals of length 50, starting at 100 and ending at 400. What does the plot tell about the distribution of hotel prices? (Mention where most prices tend to fall and comment about the shape of the distribution.)

2.20 Graphing exam scores A teacher shows her class the scores on the midterm exam in the following stem-and-leaf plot:

TRY
APP

6	588
7	01136779
8	1223334677789
9	011234458

a. Identify the number of students and their minimum and maximum scores.

b. Sketch (or use the *Explore Quantitative Data* app) how the data could be displayed in a dot plot.

c. Sketch (or use the *Explore Quantitative Data* app) how the data could be displayed in a histogram.

2.21 Fertility rates The fertility rate for a nation is the average number of children per adult woman. The following table shows results for western European nations, the United States, Canada, and Mexico, as reported by the World Bank in 2019.

a. Construct a stem-and-leaf plot by hand using stems 1 and 2 and the decimal parts of the numbers for the leaves. What is a disadvantage of this plot?

b. Construct a stem-and-leaf plot by hand using split stems. (Take the first stem for 1 to have leaves 2 to 3, the second 4 to 5, the third 6 to 7, and the fourth 8 to 9, and the stem 2 to have leaves 0 to 1 and 2 to 3.

c. Construct a histogram by using the intervals 1.2–1.4, 1.4–1.6, 1.6–1.8, 1.8–2.0, 2.0–2.2.

APP d. Obtain a stem-and-leaf plot and histogram by entering the data in the *Explore Quantitative Data* app

Country	Fertility	Country	Fertility
Austria	1.5	Netherlands	1.7
Belgium	1.7	Norway	1.7
Denmark	1.8	Spain	1.3
Finland	1.6	Sweden	1.6
France	1.9	Switzerland	1.5
Germany	1.6	United Kingdom	1.8
Greece	1.4	United States	1.8
Ireland	1.8	Canada	1.5
Italy	1.3	Mexico	2.2

2.22 Histogram of fertility rates Exercise 2.21 presented the fertility rates of just a few countries. Below is a histogram of the fertility rates from 200 countries, as given in the file Fertility on the book's website.

a. How many bins were formed?

b. Mexico, with a fertility rate of 2.2, would fall in which bin?

c. What's wrong with this interpretation of the histogram: About 60% of countries have a fertility rate between 1.5 and 2.

2.23 Histogram for sugar For the breakfast cereal data, the figure below shows a histogram for the sugar values in grams.

a. Identify the intervals of sugar values used for the plot.

b. Describe the shape of the distribution. What do you think might account for this unusual shape? (*Hint:* How else are the cereals classified in Table 2.3?)

c. What information can you get from the dot plot (Exercise 2.18) or a stem-and-leaf plot of these data that you cannot get from this plot?

d. This histogram shows frequencies. If you were to construct a histogram by using the *percentages* for each interval, how (if at all) would the shape of this histogram change?

2.24 Shape of the histogram For each of the following variables, indicate whether you would expect its histogram to be symmetric, skewed to the right, or skewed to the left. Explain why.

TRY

a. Assessed value of houses in a large city (*Hint:* Would the relatively few homes with extremely high assessed value result in a long right tail or a long left tail?)

b. Number of times checking account overdrawn in the past year for the faculty in your school

c. IQ for the general population

d. The height of female college students

2.25 More shapes of histograms Repeat the preceding exercise for

a. The scores of students (out of 100 points) on a very easy exam in which most score perfectly or nearly so, but a few score very poorly

b. The weekly church contribution for all members of a congregation, in which the three wealthiest members contribute generously each week

c. Time needed to complete a difficult exam (maximum time is 1 hour)

d. Number of music CDs (compact discs) owned, for each student in your school.

2.26 Gestational period The Animals data set from the book's website contains data on the length of the gestational period (in days) of 21 animals. (*Source*: Wildlife Conservation Society)

APP

a. Using software (such as the *Explore Quantitative Data* app, where you can copy and paste the data from the spreadsheet), obtain a histogram of the gestational period.

b. Do you see any observation that is unusual? Which animal is it?

c. Is the distribution right-skewed or left-skewed?

d. Try to override the default setting and plot a histogram with only very few (e.g., 3 or 4) intervals and one with many (e.g., 30) intervals. (In the app, you can do this with the slider for binwidth.) Would you prefer either one to the histogram created in part a? Why or why not?

2.27 How often do students read the newspaper? One of TRY the questions on the class survey from Chapter 1 asked: "Estimate the number of times a week, on average, that you read a daily newspaper."

a. Is this variable continuous or discrete? Explain.

b. The histogram shown gives results of this variable when this survey was administered to a class of 36 University of Georgia students. Report the (i) minimum response, (ii) maximum response, (iii) number of students who did not read the newspaper at all, and (iv) mode.

c. Describe the shape of the distribution.

d. Find the proportion (or percent) of students that read a newspaper at least 6 times per week, on average.

2.28 Blossom widths A data set (available on the book's website) analyzed by the famous statistician R. A. Fisher consisted of measurements of different varieties of iris blossoms. The following plots show histograms of the widths of petals for two such species, Iris setosa and Iris versicolor.

a. Describe the shape of the distribution of *setosa* petal widths.

b. Describe the shape of the distribution of *versicolor* petal widths.

c. Of the 50 *versicolor* blossoms in the data set, approximately what percentage has a petal width less than 3.2 inches?

d. Is it possible to determine accurately the percentage of *versicolor* blossoms with a width of more than 3 inches? Why or why not?

2.29 Central Park temperatures The first graph shows a histogram of the Central Park, New York, annual average temperatures from 1869 to 2018.

a. Describe the shape of the distribution.

b. What information can the time plot show that a histogram cannot provide?

c. What information does the histogram show that a time plot does not provide?

2.30 Is whooping cough close to being eradicated? In the TRY first half of the 20th century, whooping cough was a frequently occurring bacterial infection that often resulted in death, especially among young children. A vaccination for whooping cough was developed in the 1940s. How effective has the vaccination been in eradicating whooping cough? One measure to consider is the **incidence rate** (number of infected individuals per 100,000 population) in the United States. The table shows incidence rates from 1925 to 1970.

Incidence Rates for Whooping Cough, 1925–1970	
Year	**Rate per 100,000**
1925	131.2
1930	135.6
1935	141.9
1940	139.6

Incidence Rates for Whooping Cough, 1925–1970	
Year	Rate per 100,000
1945	101.0
1950	80.1
1955	38.2
1960	8.3
1965	3.5
1970	2.1

Source: Data from Historical Statistics of the United States, Colonial Times to 1970, U.S. Department of Commerce, p. 77.

a. Sketch a time plot. What type of trend do you observe? Based on the trend from 1945 to 1970, was the whooping cough vaccination proving effective in reducing the incidence of whooping cough?

b. The following figure is a time plot of the incidence rate from 1980 to 2012, based on numbers reported by the Center for Disease Control and Prevention.[3] Describe the time series. Is the United States close to eradicating whooping cough? What do you think contributes to the recent trend? (Data available on the book's website in the pertussis.csv file.)

[3]*Source:* www.cdc.gov/pertussis, U.S. Department of Health & Human Services

c. Would a histogram of the incidence rates since 1935 address the question about the success of the vaccination for whooping cough? Why or why not?

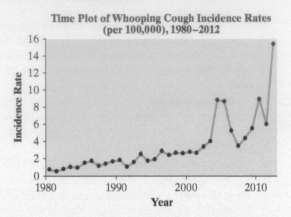

Time Plot of Whooping Cough Incidence Rates (per 100,000), 1980–2012

2.31 Fertility rate over time Access the USFertility data file on the book's website or access it using the *Time Series* app. This data set gives, for the years 1960 to 2017, the fertility rate (average number of children per adult woman) in the United States. Construct a time plot to investigate possible trends over time and comment briefly.

TRY
APP

2.3 Measuring the Center of Quantitative Data

Section 2.2 introduced **graphs for displaying the distribution** of categorical and quantitative variables. For a categorical variable, a bar graph shows the proportion of observations in each category and the modal category. For a quantitative variable, a histogram shows the important feature of the **shape** of the distribution. It's always a good idea to look first at a variable with the appropriate graph to get a feel for the data. You can then consider computing **numerical summaries (statistics)** for the data to describe several other important features of a distribution. For instance, when describing a quantitative variable, we would like to know "What is a typical value for the observations?" and "Do the observations take similar values, or do they vary quite a bit?" Statistics that answer the first question describe the **center** of the distribution. Statistics that answer the second question describe the **variability (or spread)** of the distribution. We'll study how the shape of the distribution influences our choice of which statistics are appropriate to describe center and variability.

Recall

A statistic is a numerical summary of a sample (i.e., the data observed for a variable). A parameter is a numerical summary of the population. ◄

Describing the Center: The Mean and the Median

The best-known and most frequently used measure of the center of a distribution of a quantitative variable is the **mean**. It is found by averaging the observations.

In Words

The **mean** refers to averaging, that is, adding up the data points and dividing by how many there are. The **median** is the point that splits the data in two, half the data below it and half above it (much like the median on a highway splits a road into two equal parts).

Mean

The **mean** is the sum of the observations divided by the number of observations. It is interpreted as the balance point of the distribution.

Another popular measure is the **median**. Half the observations are smaller than it, and half are larger.

Median

The **median** is the middle value of the observations when the observations are ordered from the smallest to the largest (or from the largest to the smallest).

Mean and Median ◄

Example 10

Center of the Cereal Sodium Data

Picture the Scenario

In Examples 4, 5, and 7 in Section 2.2, we investigated the sodium level in 20 breakfast cereals and saw various ways to graph the data. Let's return to those data and learn how to describe their center. The observations (in mg) are

0	340	70	140	200	180	210	150	100	130
140	180	190	160	290	50	220	180	200	210

Questions to Explore

a. Find the mean.
b. Find the median.

Think It Through

a. We find the mean by adding all the observations and then dividing this sum by the number of observations, which is 20:

$$\text{Mean} = (0 + 340 + 70 + \ldots + 210)/20 = 3{,}340/20 = 167.$$

b. To find the median, we arrange the data from the smallest to the largest observation.

0	50	70	100	130	140	140	150	160	180
180	180	190	200	200	210	210	220	290	340

For the 20 observations, the smaller 10 (on the first line) range from 0 to 180, and the larger 10 (on the second line) range from 180 to 340. The median is 180, which is the average of the two middle values, the tenth and eleventh observations, (180 + 180)/2.

Insight

The mean and median take different values. Why? The median measures the center by dividing the data into two equal parts, regardless of the actual numerical values above that point or below that point. The mean takes into account the actual numerical values of all the observations.

 You can replicate the above results or find the mean and median for your own data with the *Explore Quantitative Data* app.

► *Try Exercise 2.34*

In this example, what if the smaller 10 observations go from 0 to 180, and the larger 10 go from 190 to 340? Then, the median would be the average of the two middle observations, which is (180 + 190)/2 = 185. What do we do when we have an odd number of observations, such as 21 observations instead of 20? Then, there is a unique number that is in the middle of the sorted data: the 11th largest observation. Ten observations are smaller than it and 10 observations are larger than it. In this case, the median is simply this middle number and there is no need to take an average of two middle numbers.

> ### SUMMARY: How to Determine the Median
>
> - Put the n observations in order of their size.
> - When the number of observations n is odd, the median is the middle observation in the ordered sample.
> - When the number of observations n is even, two observations from the ordered sample fall in the middle, and the median is their average.

A Closer Look at the Mean and the Median

Notation for the mean is used both in formulas and as a shorthand in text.

In Words

The formula

$$\bar{x} = \frac{\Sigma x}{n}$$

is short for "sum the values on the variable x and divide by the sample size."

> ### Notation for a Variable and Its Mean
>
> Variables are symbolized by letters near the end of the alphabet, most commonly x and y. The sample size is denoted by n. For a sample of n observations on a variable x, the mean is denoted by $\bar{x}$ (pronounced "x bar"). Using the mathematical symbol Σ for "sum," the mean has the formula
>
> $$\bar{x} = \frac{\Sigma x}{n}.$$

For instance, the cereal data set has $n = 20$ observations. As we saw in Example 10,

$$\bar{x} = (\Sigma x)/n = (0 + 340 + 70 + \ldots + 210)/20 = 3{,}340/20 = 167.$$

Here are some basic **properties of the mean:**

Did You Know?

The mean is also interpreted as the "fair share" value; for example, when considering these 20 cereals, the mean of 167 mg can be interpreted as the amount of sodium each cereal serving contains if all 20 cereals have the same amount. ◄

- The mean is the *balance point* of the data: If we were to place identical weights on a line representing where the observations occur, then the line would balance by placing a fulcrum at the mean.

The Fulcrum Shows the Mean of the Cereal Sodium Data

$\bar{x} = 167$

- Usually, the mean is not equal to any value that was observed in the sample. (For n odd, the median is always equal to an observed value.)
- For a skewed distribution, the mean is pulled in the direction of the longer tail, relative to the median. The next example illustrates this idea.
- The mean can be highly influenced by an **outlier**, which is an unusually small or unusually large observation.

> ### Outlier
>
> An **outlier** is an observation that falls well above or well below the overall bulk of the data.

Outliers typically call for further investigation to see, for example, whether they resulted from an error in data entry or from some surprising or unusual occurence.

Example 11

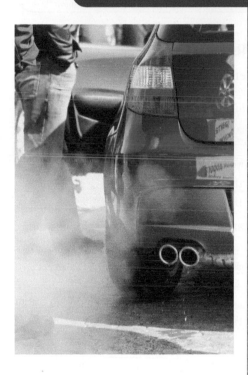

> Mean, Median, and Outliers ◄

CO_2 Pollution

Picture the Scenario

The Pew Center on Global Climate Change[4] reports that global warming is largely a result of human activity that produces carbon dioxide (CO_2) emissions and other greenhouse gases. The CO_2 emissions from fossil fuel combustion are the result of electricity, heating, industrial processes, and gas consumption in automobiles. The International Energy Agency[5] reported the per capita CO_2 emissions by country (that is, the total CO_2 emissions for the country divided by the population size of that country) for 2011. For the nine largest countries in population size (which make up more than half the world's population), the values were, in metric tons per person:

China 5.9	Indonesia 1.8	Nigeria 0.3
India 1.4	Brazil 2.1	Bangladesh 0.4
United States 16.9	Pakistan 0.8	Russian Federation 11.6

Questions to Explore

a. For these nine values, the mean is 4.6. What is the median?

b. Is any observation a potential outlier? Discuss its impact on how the mean compares to the median.

c. Using this data set, explain the effect an outlier can have on the mean.

Think It Through

a. The CO_2 values have $n = 9$ observations. The ordered values are

$$0.3, \ 0.4, \ 0.8, \ 1.4, \ 1.8, \ 2.1, \ 5.9, \ 11.6, \ 16.9$$

Because n is odd, the median is the middle value, which is 1.8.

Per Capita CO_2 Emissions (in metric tons)

b. Let's consider a dot plot, as shown. The relatively high value of 16.9 falls well above the rest of the data. It is an outlier. This value, as well as the value at 11.6, causes the mean, which is 4.6, to fall well above the median, which is 1.8.

c. The size of the outlier affects the calculation of the mean but not the median. If the observation of 16.9 for the United States had been the same as for China (5.9), the nine observations would have had a mean of 3.4 instead of 4.6. The median would still have been 1.8. In summary, a single outlier can have a large impact on the value of the mean.

Did You Know?

A metric ton is 1,000 kilograms, which is about 2,200 pounds. ◄

---

[4]*Source:* www.pewclimate.org/global-warming-basics/facts_and_figures/.
[5]*Source:* www.iea.org/.

Insight

The mean may not be representative of where the bulk of the observations fall. This is fairly common with small samples when one observation is much larger or much smaller than the others. It's not surprising that the United States is an outlier because the other nations are not nearly as economically advanced. Later in the chapter (Example 17), we'll compare carbon dioxide emissions for the United States with those of European nations.

▶ **Try Exercise 2.35**

Comparing the Mean and Median

The shape of a distribution influences whether the mean is larger or smaller than the median. For instance, an extremely large value out in the right-hand tail pulls the mean to the right. The mean then usually falls above the median, as we observed with the CO_2 data in Example 11.

Generally, if the shape is

- perfectly symmetric, the mean equals the median.
- skewed to the left, the mean is smaller than the median.
- skewed to the right, the mean is larger than the median.

As Figure 2.9 illustrates, the mean is drawn in the direction of the longer tail.

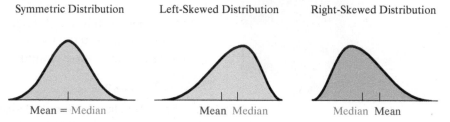

Symmetric Distribution   Left-Skewed Distribution   Right-Skewed Distribution

Mean = Median   Mean Median   Median Mean

▲ **Figure 2.9** Relationship Between the Mean and Median. **Question** For skewed distributions, what causes the mean and median to differ?

When a distribution is close to symmetric, the tails will be of similar length, and therefore the median and mean are similar. For skewed distributions, the mean lies toward the direction of skew (the longer tail) relative to the median, as Figure 2.9 shows. This is because extreme observations in a tail affect the balance point for the distribution, which is the mean. The more highly skewed the distribution, the more the mean and median tend to differ.

Example 11 illustrated this property. The dot plot of CO_2 emissions shown there is skewed to the right. As expected, the mean of 4.6 falls in the direction of the skew, above the median of 1.8. Another example is given by mean household income in the United States. The 2018 Current Population Survey (www.census .gov/cps) reports (for 2017) a mean household income of $86,220 and a median household income of $61,372. This suggests that the distribution of household incomes in the United States is skewed to the right.

Why is the median not affected by an outlier? How far an outlier falls from the middle of the distribution does not influence the median. The median is determined solely by having an equal number of observations above it and below it.

For the CO_2 data, for instance, if the value 16.9 for the United States were changed to 90, the median would still equal 1.8. However, the calculation of the mean uses *all* the numerical values. So, unlike the median, it depends on how far observations fall from the middle. Because the mean is the balance point, an extreme value on the right side pulls the mean toward the right tail. Because the median is not affected, it is said to be **resistant** to the effect of extreme observations.

> Resistant
>
> A numerical summary of the observations is called **resistant** if extreme observations have little, if any, influence on its value.

> ### The Median Is Resistant to Outliers
>
> **1.** Change 16.9 to 90 for United States.
>
> $$0.3, 0.4, 0.8, 1.4, 1.8, 2.1, 5.9, 11.6, 90$$
> $$\text{median} = 1.8 \text{ (as before)}$$
>
> **2.** Find the mean using the value of 90.
>
> $$0.3, 0.4, 0.8, 1.4, 1.8, 2.1, 5.9, 11.6, 90$$
> $$\text{mean} = 12.7 \text{ (before: 4.6)}$$

The median is resistant. The mean is not.

From these properties, you might think that it's always better to use the median rather than the mean. That's not true. When describing a discrete variable with only a few different values, the mean is often more useful to summarize the observations. For instance, for a survey question about the number of times a person has been married, the mean provides a better summary, especially when comparing different groups. Also, the mean has other useful properties that we'll learn about and take advantage of in later chapters.

In practice, it is a good idea to report *both* the mean and the median when describing the center of a distribution. For the CO_2 emission data in Example 11, the median is the more relevant statistic because of the skew resulting from the extremely large value for the United States. However, knowing the mean for all the observations and then for the observations excluding the United States (in which case, the mean is 3.0) provides additional information.

> **In Practice** Effect of Shape on Choice of Mean or Median
>
> - If a distribution is highly skewed, the median is usually preferred over the mean because it better represents what is typical.
> - If the distribution is close to symmetric or only mildly skewed, the mean is usually preferred because it uses the numerical values of all the observations.

The Mode

We've seen that the **mode** is the value that occurs most frequently. It describes a typical observation in terms of the most common outcome. The concept of the mode is most often used to describe the category of a categorical variable that has the highest frequency (the modal category). With quantitative variables, the mode is most useful with discrete variables taking a small number of possible values. For instance, for the TV-watching data of Example 6, the mode is 2 hours of daily watching. For continuous observations, it is usually not meaningful to look for a mode because there can be multiple modes or no mode at all. For the CO_2 data, for example, there is no mode. All values just occurred once.

Caution

The mode need not be near the center of the distribution. It may be the largest or the smallest value. Thus, it is somewhat inaccurate to call the mode a measure of center, but often it is useful to report the most common outcome. ◀

▶ **Activity 1**

Explore the Relationship Between the Mean and Median

The *Mean versus Median* app accessible via the book's website allows you to add and delete data points from a sample. When you access the app, select Skewed from the drop-down menu for the initial distribution. A dot plot with 30 observations from a skewed distribution is shown.

■ Observe the relative location of the mean and median as you change the skewness from "Right" to "Symmetric" to "Left."

■ Click in the gray area to add points or click on a point to delete it, each time observing how the mean and median

changes. Try this for different initial distributions or create your own plot by choosing the Create Your Own option from the drop-down menu.

■ Under a skewed initial distribution and 100 points (i.e., a large sample size), does deleting one or two outliers have much of an effect on the mean or median?

■ You can also supply your own data points. Select this option from the drop-down menu. By default, the per capita CO_2 emissions for the nine countries mentioned in Example 11 are shown. Investigate what happens when you change the largest observation from 16.9 to 90. (In the textbox showing the numerical values, replace 16.9 with 90.) Does the median change much from its original value of 1.8? What about the mean?

Try Exercise 2.41 ◀

2.3   Practicing the Basics

2.32   Median versus mean   For each of the following variables, would you use the median or mean for describing the center of the distribution? Why? (Think about the likely shape of the distribution.)

   a. Salary of employees of a university

   b. Time spent on a difficult exam

   c. Scores on a standardized test

2.33   More median versus mean   For each of the following variables, would you use the median or mean for describing the center of the distribution? Why? (Think about the likely shape of the distribution.)

   a. Charges on a credit card

   b. Weight of male students in your class this semester

   c. Life expectancy of females in developed nations

2.34   More on CO_2 emissions   The Energy Information [TRY] Agency reported the CO_2 emissions (measured in gigatons, Gt) from fossil fuel combustion for the top 10 emitting countries in 2011. These are China (8 Gt), the United States (5.3 Gt), India (1.8 Gt), Russia (1.7 Gt), Japan (1.2 Gt), Germany (0.8 Gt), Korea (0.6 Gt), Canada (0.5 Gt), Iran (0.4 Gt), and Saudi Arabia (0.4 Gt).

   a. Find the mean and median CO_2 emission.

   b. The totals reported here do not take into account a nation's population size. Explain why it may be more sensible to analyze *per capita* values, as was done in Example 11.

2.35   Resistance to an outlier   Consider the following three [TRY] sets of observations:

   Set 1: 8, 9, 10, 11, 12

   Set 2: 8, 9, 10, 11, 100

   Set 3: 8, 9, 10, 11, 1000

   a. Find the median for each data set.

   b. Find the mean for each data set.

   c. What do these data sets illustrate about the resistance of the median and mean?

2.36   Income and health insurance   According to the U.S. Census Bureau, *Current Population Reports 2013*, the mean and median income for households with health insurance was $86,431 and $66,000, respectively. For households without health insurance, the mean and median income was $53,373 and $39,000, respectively. Does this suggest that the distribution of income for households with health insurance is symmetric, skewed to the right, or skewed to the left? What about for households without health insurance? Explain.

2.37   Labor dispute   The workers and the management of a company are having a labor dispute. Explain why the workers might use the median income of all the employees to justify a raise but management might use the mean income to argue that a raise is not needed.

2.38   Cereal sodium   The dot plot shows the cereal sodium values from Example 4. What aspect of the distribution causes the mean to be less than the median?

Dot Plot of Sodium Values for 20 Breakfast Cereals

mean = 167 median = 180

2.39   Center of plots   The figure shows dot plots for three sample data sets.

    a. For which, if any, data sets would you expect the mean and the median to be the same? Explain why.

    b. For which, if any, data sets would you expect the mean and the median to differ? Which would be larger, the mean or the median? Why?

2.40   Public transportation—center   The owner of a company in downtown Atlanta is concerned about the large use of gasoline by her employees due to urban sprawl, traffic congestion, and the use of energy-inefficient vehicles such as SUVs. She'd like to promote the use of public transportation. She decides to investigate how many miles her employees travel on public transportation during a typical day. The values for her 10 employees (recorded to the closest mile) are

$$0\quad 0\quad 4\quad 0\quad 0\quad 0\quad 10\quad 0\quad 6\quad 0$$

    a. Find and interpret the mean, median, and mode.

    b. She has just hired an additional employee. He lives in a different city and travels 90 miles a day on public transport. Recompute the mean and median. Describe the effect of this outlier.

2.41   Public transportation—outlier   Refer to the previous exercise.

APP

    a. Use the *Mean versus Median* app (see Activity 1) to investigate what effect adding the outlier of 90 to the data set has on the mean and median. (In the app, select Supply Numerical Values and type the data plus the value 90 into the textbox.)

    b. Now add 10 more data values that are near the mean of 2 for the original 10 observations. Does the outlier of 90 still have such a strong effect on the mean?

2.42   Baseball salaries   The players on the New York Yankees baseball team in 2014 had a mean salary of $7,387,498 and a median salary of $5,500,000.[6] What do you think causes these two values to be so different (data in NYYsalary file on the book's website)?

2.43   More baseball salaries   Find information on Major League Baseball players' salaries for a (or your favorite) team online, such as at www.spotrac.com/mlb/. Copy the salary figures for the players into a software program (such as the *Explore Quantitative Data* app) and create a histogram. Describe the shape of the distribution for salary and comment on its center by quoting appropriate statistics.

APP

2.44   Fertility statistics   The fertility rates (mean number of children per adult woman) from Exercise 2.21 are shown again in the table.

    a. Find the median of the fertility rates. Interpret.

    b. Find the mean of the fertility rates. Interpret.

    c. For each woman, the number of children is a whole number, such as 2 or 3. Explain why it makes sense to measure a *mean* number of children per adult woman (which is not a whole number) to compare fertility levels, such as the fertility levels of 1.5 in Canada and 2.2 in Mexico.

Country	Fertility	Country	Fertility
Austria	1.5	Netherlands	1.7
Belgium	1.7	Norway	1.7
Denmark	1.8	Spain	1.3
Finland	1.6	Sweden	1.6
France	1.9	Switzerland	1.5
Germany	1.6	United Kingdom	1.8
Greece	1.4	United States	1.8
Ireland	1.8	Canada	1.5
Italy	1.3	Mexico	2.2

2.45   Sex partners   A recent General Social Survey asked female respondents, "How many sex partners have you had in the last 12 months?" Of the 365 respondents, 102 said 0 partners, 233 said 1 partner, 18 said 2 partners, 9 said 3 partners, 2 said 4 partners, and 1 said 5 partners. (*Source*: Data from CSM, UC Berkeley.)

    a. Display the data in a table. Explain why the median is 1.

    b. Show that the mean is 0.85.

    c. Suppose the 102 women who answered 0 instead had answered 5 partners. Show that the median would still be 1. (The mean would increase to 2.2. The mean uses the numerical values of the observations, not just their ordering.)

2.46   Marriage statistics for 20- to 24-year-olds   The following table shows the number of times 20- to 24-year-old U.S. residents have been married, based on a Census Bureau report from 2004. The frequencies are actually *thousands* of people. For instance, 8,418,000 men never married, but this does not affect calculations about the mean or median.

Number of Times Married, for Subjects of Age 20–24		
	Frequency	
Number Times Married	**Women**	**Men**
0	7,350	8,418
1	2,587	1,594
2	80	10
Total	**10,017**	**10,022**

    a. Find the median and mean for each gender. (*Hint:* You can do this using the *Explore Quantitative Data* app, where you select Your Own under Enter Data and then choose Frequency Table to enter the values from the table. Do this separately for women and men. You can also get the mean by multiplying each score by the frequency it occurred, summing up these values, and then dividing by the total number of observations.)

b. On average, have women or men been married more often? Which statistic do you prefer to answer this question? (The mean, as opposed to the median, uses the numerical values of all the observations, not just the ordering. For discrete data with only a few values such as the number of times married, it can be more informative.)

2.47 Accidents One variable in a study measures how many serious motor vehicle accidents a subject has had in the past year. Explain why the mean would likely be more useful than the median for summarizing the responses of the 60 subjects.

2.4 Measuring the Variability of Quantitative Data

A measure of the center is not enough to describe a distribution for a quantitative variable adequately. It tells us nothing about the variability of the data. With the cereal sodium data, if we report the mean of 167 mg to describe the center, would the value of 210 mg for Honeycomb be considered quite high, or are most of the data even farther from the mean? To answer this question, we need numerical summaries of the variability of the distribution.

Measuring Variability: The Range

To see why a measure of the center is not enough, let's consider Figure 2.10. This figure compares hypothetical income distributions of music teachers in public schools in Denmark and in the United States. Both distributions are symmetric and have a mean of about $40,000. However, the annual incomes in Denmark (converted to U.S. dollars) go from $35,000 to $45,000, whereas those in the United States go from $20,000 to $60,000. Incomes are more similar in Denmark and vary more in the United States. A simple way to describe this is with the **range**.

▲ **Figure 2.10** Income Distributions for Music Teachers in Denmark and in the United States. The distributions have the same mean, but the one for the United States shows more variability around the mean. **Question** How would the range for Denmark change if one teacher earned $100,000?

Range

The **range** is the difference between the largest and the smallest observations.

In Denmark the range is $45,000 − $35,000 = $10,000. In the United States the range is $60,000 − $20,000 = $40,000. The range is a larger value when the data vary more in the distribution.

The range is simple to compute and easy to understand, but it uses only the extreme values and ignores the other values. Therefore, it's affected severely by outliers. For example, if one teacher in Denmark made $100,000, the range would change from $45,000 − $35,000 = $10,000 to $100,000 − $35,000 = $65,000.

The range is not a resistant statistic. It shares the worst property of the mean, not being resistant, and the worst property of the median, ignoring the numerical values of nearly all the data.

Measuring Variability: The Standard Deviation

Although it is good practice to mention the smallest and largest value when describing the distribution of a variable, we usually don't use the range to measure variability. A much better numerical summary of variability uses *all* the data, describing a typical distance of how far the data falls from the mean. It does this by summarizing **deviations** from the mean.

■ The **deviation** of an observation x from the mean $\bar{x}$ is $(x - \bar{x})$, the difference between the observation and the sample mean.

For the cereal sodium values, the mean is $\bar{x} = 167$. The observation of 210 for Honeycomb has a deviation of $210 - 167 = 43$. The observation of 50 for Honey Smacks has a deviation of $50 - 167 = -117$. Figure 2.11 shows these deviations.

▲ **Figure 2.11** Dot Plot for Cereal Sodium Data, Showing Deviations for Two Observations. **Question** When is a deviation positive and when is it negative?

■ Each observation has a deviation from the mean.
■ A deviation $x - \bar{x}$ is *positive* when the observation falls *above* the mean. A deviation is *negative* when the observation falls *below* the mean.
■ The interpretation of the mean as the balance point implies that the positive deviations counterbalance the negative deviations. Because of this, *the sum (and therefore the mean) of the deviations always equals zero*, regardless of the actual data values. Hence, summary measures of variability from the mean use either the **squared deviations** or their absolute values.
■ The **average** of the squared deviations is called the **variance**. Because the variance uses the *square* of the units of measurement for the original data, its square root is easier to interpret. This is called the **standard deviation**
■ The symbol $\Sigma(x - \bar{x})^2$ is called a **sum of squares**. It represents finding the deviation for each observation, squaring each deviation, and then adding them.

> ### The Standard Deviation s
>
> The **standard deviation** s of n observations is
>
> $$s = \sqrt{\frac{\Sigma(x - \bar{x})^2}{n - 1}} = \sqrt{\frac{\text{sum of squared deviations}}{\text{sample size} - 1}}.$$
>
> This is the square root of the **variance s²**, which is an average of the squares of the deviations from their mean,
>
> $$s^2 = \frac{\Sigma(x - \bar{x})^2}{n - 1}.$$

Our apps (i.e., the *Explore Quantitative Data* app) or a calculator can compute the standard deviation *s* easily. Its interpretation is quite simple: *Roughly, the standard deviation s represents a typical distance or a type of average distance of an observation from the mean.* The most basic property of the standard deviation is this:

- The larger the standard deviation *s*, the greater the variability of the data.

A small technical point: You may wonder why the denominators of the variance and the standard deviation use $n - 1$ instead of n. We said that the variance was an *average* of the *n* squared deviations, so should we not divide by *n*? Basically it is because the deviations provide only $n - 1$ pieces of information about variability: That is, $n - 1$ of the deviations determine the last one, because the deviations sum to 0. For example, suppose we have $n = 2$ observations and the first observation has deviation $(x - \bar{x}) = 5$. Then the second observation must have deviation $(x - \bar{x}) = -5$ because the deviations must add to 0. With $n = 2$, there's only $n - 1 = 1$ nonredundant piece of information about variability. And with $n = 1$, the standard deviation is undefined because with only one observation, it's impossible to get a sense of how much the data vary.

Standard Deviation ◄

Example 12

Women's and Men's Ideal Number of Children

Picture the Scenario

Students in a class were asked on a questionnaire at the beginning of the course, "How many children do you think is ideal for a family?" The observations, classified by student's gender, were

Men: 0, 0, 0, 2, 4, 4, 4

Women: 0, 2, 2, 2, 2, 2, 4

Question to Explore

Both men and women have a mean of 2 and a range of 4. Do the distributions of data have the same amount of variability around the mean? If not, which distribution has more variability?

Think It Through

Let's check dot plots for the data.

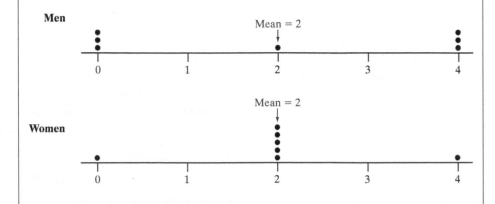

The typical deviation from the mean for the male observations appears to be about 2. The observations for females mostly fall right at the mean, so their typical deviation is smaller.

Let's calculate the standard deviation for men. Their observations are 0, 0, 0, 2, 4, 4, 4. The deviations and squared deviations about their mean of 2 are

Value	Deviation	Squared Deviation
0	$(0 - 2) = -2$	4
0	$(0 - 2) = -2$	4
0	$(0 - 2) = -2$	4
2	$(2 - 2) = 0$	0
4	$(4 - 2) = 2$	4
4	$(4 - 2) = 2$	4
4	$(4 - 2) = 2$	4

The sum of squared deviations equals

$$\Sigma(x - \bar{x})^2 = 4 + 4 + 4 + 0 + 4 + 4 + 4 = 24.$$

The standard deviation of these $n = 7$ observations equals

$$s_M = \sqrt{\frac{\Sigma(x - \bar{x})^2}{n - 1}} = \sqrt{\frac{24}{6}} = \sqrt{4} = 2.0.$$

This indicates that for men a typical distance of an observation from the mean is 2.0. By contrast, you can check that the standard deviation for women is $s_F = 1.2$. The observations for males tended to be farther from the mean than those for females, as indicated by $s_M = 2.0 > s_F = 1.2$. In summary, the men's observations varied more around the mean.

Insight

The standard deviation is more informative than the range. For these data, the standard deviation detects that the women were more consistent than the men in their viewpoints about the ideal number of children. The range does not detect the difference because it equals 4 for each gender.

▶ **Try Exercise 2.48**

In Practice Rounding

Statistical software and calculators can find the standard deviation s for you. Try calculating s for a couple of small data sets to help you understand what it represents. After that, rely on software or a calculator. To ensure accurate results, don't round off while doing a calculation. (For example, use a calculator's memory to store intermediate results.) When presenting the solution, however, round off to two or three significant digits. In calculating s for women, you get $s_F = \sqrt{1.3333\ldots} = 1.1547005\ldots$. Present the value $s_F = 1.2$ or $s_F = 1.15$ to make it easier for a reader to comprehend.

Example 13

Standard Deviation ◀

Exam Scores

Picture the Scenario

The first exam in your statistics course is graded on a scale of 0 to 100. Suppose that the mean score in your class is 80.

Question to Explore

Which value is most plausible for the standard deviation s: 0, 0.5, 10, or 50?

Think It Through

The standard deviation s is a *typical distance* of an observation from the mean. A value of $s = 0$ seems unlikely. For that to happen, every deviation would have to be 0. This implies that every student must have scored 80, the mean. A value of $s = 0.5$ is implausibly small because 0.5 would not be a typical distance above or below the mean score of 80. Similarly, a value of $s = 50$ is implausibly large because 50 would also not be a typical distance of a student's score from the mean of 80. (For instance, it is impossible to score 130.) We would instead expect to see a value of s such as 10. With $s = 10$, a typical distance is 10, as occurs with the scores of 70 and 90.

Insight

In summary, we've learned that s is a typical distance of observations from the mean, larger values of s represent greater variability, and $s = 0$ means that all observations take the same value.

▶ *Try Exercises 2.51 and 2.52*

Caution

The size of the standard deviation also depends on the units of measurement. For instance, a value of $s = 1,000$ measured on the millimeter scale corresponds to $s = 1$ on the meter scale. ◀

SUMMARY: Properties of the Standard Deviation, s

- The more the individual observations deviate from the overall mean, the larger the value of s.
- $s = 0$ only when all observations take the same value. For instance, if the reported ideal number of children for seven people is 2, 2, 2, 2, 2, 2, 2, then the mean equals 2, each of the seven deviations equals 0, and $s = 0$. This is the smallest possible variability for a sample.
- s can be influenced by outliers. It uses the mean, which we know can be influenced by outliers. Also, outliers have large deviations, so they tend to have *extremely* large squared deviations. We'll see (for example, in Exercise 2.48 and the beginning of Section 2.6) that these can inflate the value of s and make it sensitive to outliers.

Bell Shaped Distribution

Interpreting the Magnitude of s: The Empirical Rule

Suppose that a distribution is unimodal and approximately symmetric with a **bell shape**, as in the margin figure. The value of s then has a more precise interpretation. Using the mean and standard deviation alone, we can form intervals that contain certain percentages (approximately) of the data.

In Words

- $\bar{x} - s$ denotes the value 1 standard deviation below the mean.
- $\bar{x} + s$ denotes the value 1 standard deviation above the mean.
- $\bar{x} \pm s$ denotes the values that are 1 standard deviation from the mean in either direction.

Empirical Rule

If a distribution of data is bell shaped, then approximately

- 68% of the observations fall within 1 standard deviation of the mean, that is, between the values of $\bar{x} - s$ and $\bar{x} + s$ (denoted $\bar{x} \pm s$).
- 95% of the observations fall within 2 standard deviations of the mean ($\bar{x} \pm 2s$).
- All or nearly all observations fall within 3 standard deviations of the mean ($\bar{x} \pm 3s$).

Figure 2.12 is a graphical portrayal of the empirical rule.

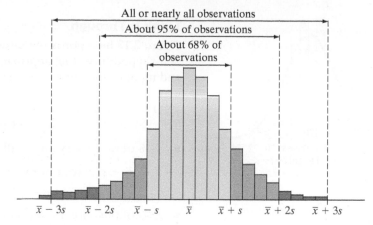

▲ Figure 2.12 The Empirical Rule. For bell-shaped distributions, this tells us approximately how much of the data fall within 1, 2, and 3 standard deviations of the mean. **Question** About what percentage would fall *more than* 2 standard deviations from the mean?

Did You Know?

The **empirical rule** has this name because many distributions of data observed in practice (*empirically*) are approximately bell shaped. ◄

Empirical Rule ◄

Example 14

Female Student Heights

Picture the Scenario

Many human physical characteristics have bell-shaped distributions. Let's explore height. Figure 2.13 shows a histogram of the heights from responses to a survey of 261 female students at the University of Georgia. (The data are in the Heights data file on the book's website or in the *Explore Quantitative Data* app. Note that the height of 92 inches was omitted from the analysis.) Table 2.5 presents some descriptive statistics as presented by the app.

▲ Figure 2.13 Histogram of Female Student Height Data. This summarizes heights, in inches, of 261 female college students. **Question** How would you describe the shape, center, and variability of the distribution?

Question to Explore

Can we use the empirical rule to describe the variability from the mean of these data? If so, how?

Table 2.5 Output of Explore Quantitative Data App for Descriptive Statistics of Student Height Data

Sample Size	Mean	Std. Dev.	Min.	Q1	Median	Q3	Max.	IQR
261	65.3	2.95	56	63.8	65	67	77	3.25

Caution

The empirical rule (which applies only to bell-shaped distributions) is not a general interpretation for what the standard deviation measures. The general interpretation is that the standard deviation measures the typical distance of observations from mean (for any kind of distribution). ◄

Caution

The empirical rule may approximate the actual percentages falling within 1, 2, and 3 standard deviations of the mean poorly if the data are highly skewed or highly discrete (the variable taking relatively few values). See Exercise 2.58. ◄

Think It Through

Figure 2.13 has approximately a bell shape. The figure in the margin shows a bell-shaped curve that approximates the histogram. From Table 2.5, the mean and median are close, about 65 inches, which reflects an approximately symmetric distribution. The empirical rule is applicable.

From Table 2.5, the mean is 65.3 inches and the standard deviation (labeled Std. Dev.) is 3.0 inches (rounded). By the empirical rule, approximately

- 68% of the observations fall between

$$\bar{x} - s = 65.3 - 3.0 = 62.3 \text{ and } \bar{x} + s = 65.3 + 3.0 = 68.3,$$

  that is, within the interval (62.3, 68.3), about 62 to 68 inches.

- 95% of the observations fall within

  $\bar{x} \pm 2s$, which is $65.3 \pm 2(3.0)$, or (59.3, 71.3), about 59 to 71 inches.

- Almost all observations fall within $\bar{x} \pm 3s$, or (56.3, 74.3).

Of the 261 observations, by actually counting, we find that

- 187 observations, 72%, fall within (62.3, 68.3).
- 248 observations, 95%, fall within (59.3, 71.3).
- 258 observations, 99%, fall within (56.3, 74.3).

In summary, the percentages predicted by the empirical rule are near the actual ones.

Insight

Because the distribution is close to bell shaped, we can predict simple summaries effectively using only two numbers—the mean and the standard deviation. We can do the same if we look at the data for the 117 male students included in the survey, who had a mean of 70.9 and standard deviation of 2.9.

▶ **Try Exercise 2.53**

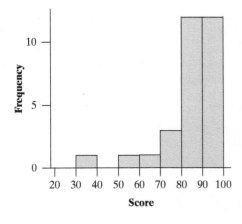

With a bell-shaped distribution for a large data set, the observations usually extend about 3 standard deviations below the mean and about 3 standard deviations above the mean.

When the distribution is highly skewed, the most extreme observation in one direction may not be nearly that far from the mean. For instance, on a recent exam, the scores ranged between 30 and 100, with median = 88, $\bar{x}$ = 84, and s = 16. The maximum score of 100 was only 1 standard deviation above the mean (that is, $100 = \bar{x} + s = 84 + 16$). By contrast, the minimum score of 30 was more than 3 standard deviations below the mean. This happened because the distribution of scores was highly skewed to the left. (See the margin figure.)

Remember that the empirical rule is only for bell-shaped distributions. In Chapter 6, we'll see why the empirical rule works. For a special family of smooth, bell-shaped curves (called the **normal distribution**), we'll see how to find the percentage of the distribution in *any* particular region by knowing only the mean and the standard deviation.

Sample Statistics and Population Parameters

Of the numerical summaries introduced so far, the mean $\bar{x}$ and the standard deviation s are the most commonly used in practice. We'll use them frequently in the rest of this book. The formulas that define $\bar{x}$ and s refer to *sample* data. They are *sample statistics*.

We will distinguish between sample statistics and the corresponding *parameter* values for the population. The population mean is the average of all observations in the population. The population standard deviation describes the variability of the population observations about the population mean. Both of these population parameters are usually unknown. Inferential statistical methods help us make decisions and predictions about the population parameters based on the sample statistics.

In later chapters, to help distinguish between sample statistics and population parameters, we'll use different notation for the parameter values. Often, Greek letters are used to denote the parameters. For instance, we'll use μ (the Greek letter, mu) to denote the population mean and σ (the Greek letter, sigma) to denote the population standard deviation.

Recall

From Section 1.2, a **population** is the total group about whom you want to make conclusions. A **sample** is a subset of the population for whom you actually have data. A **parameter** is a numerical summary of the population, and a **statistic** is a numerical summary of a sample. ◄

2.4   Practicing the Basics

2.48   Sick leave   A company decides to investigate the amount of sick leave taken by its employees. A sample of eight employees yields the following numbers of days of sick leave taken in the past year:

          0 0 4 0 0 0 6 0

a. Find and interpret the range.

b. Find and interpret the standard deviation *s*.

c. Suppose the 6 was incorrectly recorded and is supposed to be 60. Redo parts a and b with the corrected data and describe the effect of this outlier.

2.49   Life expectancy   The *Human Development Report 2013*, published by the United Nations, showed life expectancies by country. For Western Europe, some values reported were

Austria 81, Belgium 80, Denmark 80, Finland 81, France 83, Germany 81, Greece 81, Ireland 81, Italy 83, Netherlands 81, Norway 81, Portugal 80, Spain 82, Sweden 82, Switzerland 83. For Africa, some values reported were

Botswana 47, Dem. Rep. Congo 50, Angola 51, Zambia 57, Zimbabwe 58, Malawi 55, Nigeria 52, Rwanda 63, Uganda 59, Kenya 61, Mali 55, South Africa 56, Madagascar 64, Senegal 63, Sudan 62, Ghana 61.

a. Which group (Western Europe or Africa) of life expectancies do you think has the larger standard deviation? Why?

b. Find the standard deviation for each group, for instance by typing the values for each group into the *Explore Quantitative Data* app. Compare them to illustrate that *s* is larger for the group that shows more variability from the mean.

2.50   Life expectancy including Russia   For Russia, the United Nations reported a life expectancy of 70. Suppose we add this observation to the data set for Western Europe in the previous exercise. Would you expect the standard deviation to be larger, or smaller, than the value for the Western European countries alone? Why?

2.51   Shape of home prices?   According to the National Association of Home Builders, the median selling price of new homes in the United States in

February 2014 was $261,400. Which of the following is the most plausible value for the standard deviation: −$15,000, $1,000, $60,000, or $1,000,000? Why? Explain what's unrealistic about each of the other values.

2.52   Exam standard deviation   For an exam given to a class, the students' scores ranged from 35 to 98, with a mean of 74. Which of the following is the most realistic value for the standard deviation: −10, 0, 3, 12, 63? Clearly explain what's unrealistic about each of the other values.

2.53   Heights   From the survey of college students from Georgia in Example 14, the males had $\bar{x} = 71$ and $s = 3$, and the females had $\bar{x} = 65$ and $s = 3$.

a. Use the empirical rule to describe the distribution of heights for males.

b. The standard deviation for the overall distribution (combining females and males) was 4. Why would you expect it to be larger than the standard deviations for the separate male and female height distributions? Would you expect the overall distribution still to be unimodal? Would the empirical rule apply?

2.54   Histograms and standard deviation   The figure shows histograms for three samples, each with sample size $n = 100$.

a. Which sample has the (1) largest and (ii) smallest standard deviation?

b. To which sample(s) is the empirical rule relevant? Why?

Histograms and relative sizes of standard deviations

2.55 Female strength The High School Female Athletes data file on the book's website has data for 57 female high school athletes on the maximum number of pounds they were able to bench press. The data are roughly bell shaped, with $\bar{x} = 79.9$ and $s = 13.3$. Use the empirical rule to describe the distribution.

2.56 Female body weight The College Athletes data file on the book's website has data for 64 female college athletes. The data on weight (in pounds) are roughly bell shaped, with $\bar{x} = 133$ and $s = 17$.
a. Give an interval within which about 95% of the weights fall.
b. Identify the weight of an athlete who is 3 standard deviations above the mean in this sample. Would this be a rather unusual observation? Why?

2.57 Shape of cigarette taxes A recent summary for the distribution of cigarette taxes (in cents) among the 50 states and Washington, D.C., in the United States reported $\bar{x} = 73$ and $s = 48$. Based on these values, do you think that this distribution is bell shaped? If so, why? If not, why not, and what shape would you expect?

2.58 Empirical rule and skewed, highly discrete distribution The table below shows data on the number of times 20- to 24-year-old men have been married. (*Source:* Bureau of the Census report 2004, U.S. Department of Commerce.)

No. Times	Count	Percentage
0	8,418	84.0
1	1,594	15.9
2	10	0.1
Total	**10,022**	**100.0**

a. Verify that the mean number of times men have been married is 0.16 and that the standard deviation is 0.37.
b. Find the actual percentages of observations within 1, 2, and 3 standard deviations of the mean. How do these compare to the percentages predicted by the empirical rule?
c. How do you explain the results in part b?

2.59 How much TV? The 2018 General Social Survey asked, "On the average day, about how many hours do you personally watch television?" Of 1,555 responses, the mode was 2, the median was 2, the mean was 2.9, and the standard deviation was 2.8. Based on these statistics, what would you surmise about the shape of the distribution? Why? (*Source:* Data from CSM, UC Berkeley.)

2.60 How many friends? A recent General Social Survey asked respondents how many close friends they had. For a sample of 1,467 people, the mean was 7.4 and the standard deviation was 11.0. The distribution had a median of 5 and a mode of 4. (*Source:* Data from CSM, UC Berkeley.)
a. Based on these statistics, what would you surmise about the shape of the distribution? Why?
b. Does the empirical rule apply to these data? Why or why not?

2.61 Judging skew using $\bar{x}$ and s If the largest observation is less than 1 standard deviation above the mean, then the distribution tends to be skewed to the left. If the smallest observation is less than 1 standard deviation below the mean, then the distribution tends to be skewed to the right. A professor examined the results of the first exam given in her statistics class. The scores were

$$35 \quad 59 \quad 70 \quad 73 \quad 75 \quad 81 \quad 84 \quad 86$$

The mean and standard deviation are 70.4 and 16.7. Using these, determine whether the distribution is either left or right skewed. Construct a dot plot to check.

2.62 Youth unemployment in the EU The Youth Unemployment data file on the book's website and preloaded with the *Explore Quantitative Data* app contains 2013 unemployment rates in the 28 EU countries for people between 15 and 24 years of age. (The data are also shown in Exercise 2.65). Using the app or other software,
a. Construct an appropriate graph to visualize the distribution of the unemployment rate.
b. Find the mean, median, and standard deviation.
c. Write a short paragraph summarizing the distribution of the youth unemployment rate, interpreting some of the above statistics in context.

2.63 Create data with a given standard deviation Use the *Mean versus Median* app on the book's website to investigate how the standard deviation changes as the data change. Select Create Your Own for the initial distribution to start with a blank graph. Under Options, you can request to show the standard deviation of the points you create by clicking in the graph.
a. Create three observations (by clicking in the graph) that have a mean of about 50 and a standard deviation of about 20. (Clicking on an existing point deletes it.)
b. Create three observations (click Refresh to clear the previous points) that have a mean of about 50 and a standard deviation of about 40.
c. Placing four values between 0 and 100, what is the largest standard deviation you can get? What are the values that have that standard deviation?

2.5 Using Measures of Position to Describe Variability

The mean and median describe the center of a distribution. The range and the standard deviation describe the variability of the distribution. We'll now learn about some other ways of describing a distribution using measures of **position**.

One type of measure of position tells us the point where a certain percentage of the data fall above or fall below that point. The median is an example. It specifies a location such that half the data fall below it and half fall above it. The range uses two other measures of position, the maximum value and the minimum value. Another type of measure of position, called a *z-score*, tells us *how far* an observation falls from a particular point, such as the number of standard deviations an observation falls from the mean.

Measures of Position: The Quartiles and Other Percentiles

The median is a special case of a more general set of measures of position called **percentiles**.

*p*th Percentile

90th Percentile

> ### Percentile
>
> The **pth percentile** is a value such that *p* percent of the observations fall at or below that value.

Suppose you're informed that your score of 1,200 (out of 1,600) on the SAT college entrance exam falls at the 90th percentile. Set $p = 90$ in the definition above. Then, 90% of those who took the exam scored 1,200 or below. Only 10% of the scores were higher than yours.

Substituting $p = 50$ in this definition gives the 50th percentile. For it, 50% of the observations fall at or below it and 50% above it. But this is simply the median. *The 50th percentile is usually referred to as the median.*

Three useful percentiles are the **quartiles**. The **first quartile** has $p = 25$, so it is the 25th percentile. Twenty-five percent of the data fall below it, 75% above it. The **second quartile** has $p = 50$, so it is the 50th percentile, which is the median. The **third quartile** has $p = 75$, so it is the 75th percentile. The highest 25% of the data fall above it. *The quartiles split the distribution into four parts, each containing one quarter (25%) of the observations.* See Figure 2.14.

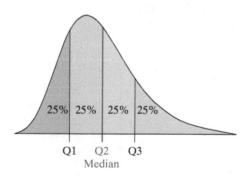

▲ **Figure 2.14 The Quartiles Split the Distribution into Four Parts.** Twenty-five percent is below the first quartile (Q1), 25% is between the first quartile and the second quartile (the median, Q2), 25% is between the second quartile and the third quartile (Q3), and 25% is above the third quartile. **Question** Why is the second quartile also the median?

The quartiles are denoted by Q1 for the first quartile, Q2 for the second quartile, and Q3 for the third quartile. Notice that one quarter of the observations fall below Q1, two quarters (one half) fall below Q2 (the median), and three quarters fall below Q3. We usually rely on software to compute the quartiles, especially for larger data sets, but the following summary shows how to find them.

> **SUMMARY: Finding Quartiles**
> - Arrange the data in order.
> - Consider the median. This is the **second quartile, Q2**.
> - Consider the lower half of the observations (excluding the median itself if n is odd). The median of these observations is the **first quartile, Q1**.
> - Consider the upper half of the observations (excluding the median itself if n is odd). Their median is the **third quartile, Q3**.

Example 15

The Quartiles ◄

Cereal Sodium Data

Picture the Scenario

Let's again consider the sodium values for the 20 breakfast cereals.

Questions to Explore

a. What are the quartiles for the 20 cereal sodium values?

b. Interpret the quartiles in the context of the cereal data.

Think It Through

a. From Table 2.3 the sodium values, arranged in ascending order, are

$$Q1 = 135$$

0	50	70	100	**130 140**	140	150	160	**180**
180	180	190	200	**200 210**	210	220	290	340

$$Q3 = 205$$

- The median of the 20 values is the average of the 10th and 11th observations, 180 and 180, which is **Q2 = 180 mg**.
- The first quartile Q1 is the median of the 10 smallest observations (in the top row), which is the average of 130 and 140, **Q1 = 135 mg**.
- The third quartile Q3 is the median of the 10 largest observations (in the bottom row), which is the average of 200 and 210, **Q3 = 205 mg**.

b. The quartiles tell you how the data split into four parts. The sodium values range from 0 mg to 135 mg for the first quarter, 135 mg to 180 mg for the second quarter, 180 mg to 205 mg for the third quarter, and 205 mg to 340 mg for the fourth quarter. So the smallest 25% of sodium values observed in our data are between 0 mg and 135 mg, and the largest 25% are between 205 mg and 340 mg. By dividing the distribution into four quarters, we see that some quarters of the distribution are more spread out than others.

Insight

The quartiles also give information about shape. The distance of 45 from the first quartile to the median exceeds the distance of 25 from the median to the third quartile. This commonly happens when the distribution is skewed to the left, as shown in the margin figure. Although each quarter of a distribution may span different lengths (indicating different amounts of variability within the quarters of the distribution), each quarter contains the same number (25%) of observations.

The *Explore Quantitative Data* app displays the quartiles (Q1, Median, and Q3) under Descriptive Statistics, as shown in Table 2.5.

APP

► *Try Exercise 2.64*

135   180 205
Q1   Q2 Q3

45   25

Measuring Variability: The Interquartile Range

The quartiles are also used to define a measure of variability that is more resistant than the range and the standard deviation. This measure summarizes the range for the *middle half* of the data. The middle 50% of the observations fall between the first quartile and the third quartile—25% from Q1 to Q2 and 25% from Q2 to Q3. The distance from Q1 to Q3 is called the **interquartile range**, denoted by **IQR**.

In Words

If the **interquartile range** of U.S. music teacher salaries equals $16,000, this tells us that the middle 50% of the distribution stretches over a distance of $16,000.

Interquartile Range (IQR)

The **interquartile range** is the distance between the third and first quartiles,

$$\text{IQR} = \text{Q3} - \text{Q1}$$

For instance, for the breakfast cereal sodium data, we just saw in Example 15 that

- Minimum value $= 0$
- First quartile Q1 $= 135$
- Median $= 180$
- Third quartile Q3 $= 205$
- Maximum value $= 340$

The range is $340 - 0 = 340$. The interquartile range is $Q3 - Q1 = 205 - 135 = 70$. The middle 50% of sodium values stretches over a range of 70 mg.

As with the range and standard deviation s, the more variability in the observations, the larger the IQR tends to be. But unlike those measures, the IQR is not affected by any observations below the first quartile or above the third quartile. In other words, it is not affected by outliers. In contrast, the range depends solely on the minimum and the maximum values, the most extreme values, so the range changes as either extreme value changes. For example, if the highest sodium value were 1,000 instead of 340, the range would change dramatically from 340 to 1,000, but the IQR would not change at all. So, it's often better to use the IQR instead of the range or standard deviation to compare the variability for distributions that are very highly skewed or that have severe outliers.

Detecting Potential Outliers

Examining the data for unusual observations, such as outliers, is important in any statistical analysis. Is there a formula for flagging an observation as potentially being an outlier? One way uses the interquartile range.

The 1.5 × IQR Criterion for Identifying Potential Outliers

An observation is a potential outlier if it falls a distance of more than 1.5 × IQR below the first quartile or a distance of more than 1.5 × IQR above the third quartile.

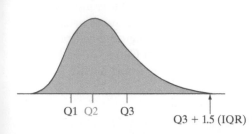

Q1 Q2   Q3   Q3 + 1.5 (IQR)

From Example 15, the breakfast cereal sodium data has Q1 = 135 and Q3 = 205. So, IQR = Q3 − Q1 = 205 − 135 = 70. For those data

- $1.5 \times IQR = 1.5 \times 70 = 105$.
- $Q1 - 1.5 \times IQR = 135 - 105 = 30$ (lower boundary, potential outliers below),

and

- $Q3 + 1.5 \times IQR = 205 + 105 = 310$ (upper boundary, potential outliers above).

By the $1.5 \times IQR$ criterion, observations below 30 or above 310 are potential outliers. The only observations below 30 or above 310 are the sodium values of 0 mg for Frosted Mini Wheats and 340 mg for Raisin Bran. These are the only potential outliers.

Why do we identify an observation as a *potential* outlier rather than calling it a *definite* outlier? When a distribution has a long tail, some observations may be more than $1.5 \times IQR$ below the first quartile or above the third quartile even if they are not outliers, in the sense that they are not separated far from the bulk of the data. For instance, for a distribution with a long right tail, the largest observation may not be that far away from the remaining observations, and there isn't enough of a gap to call it an outlier.

The Box Plot: Graphing a Five-Number Summary of Positions

The quartiles and the maximum and minimum values are five numbers often used as a set to summarize positions that help describe center and variability of a distribution.

> **The Five-Number Summary of Positions**
>
> The five-number summary of a data set consists of the minimum value, first quartile Q1, median, third quartile Q3, and the maximum value.

←—IQR—→

Min   Q1 Median Q3   Max

The **five-number summary** is the basis of a graphical display called the **box plot**. The **box** of a box plot indicates the central 50% of the distribution, from the first quartile to the third quartile (see the margin figure). A line inside the box marks the median. The lines extending from each side of the box are called **whiskers**. These extend to show the stretch of the rest of the data, except for potential outliers, which are shown separately.

> **SUMMARY: Constructing a Box Plot**
>
> - A **box** goes from the lower quartile Q1 to the upper quartile Q3.
> - A line is drawn inside the box at the median.
> - A line goes from the lower end of the box to the smallest observation that is not a potential outlier. A separate line goes from the upper end of the box to the largest observation that is not a potential outlier. These lines are called **whiskers**. The potential outliers (more than 1.5 IQR below the first quartile or above the third quartile) are shown separately with special symbols (such as a dot or a star).

Sodium (mg)

Box Plot   ◄

Example 16

Cereal Sodium Data

Picture the Scenario

Example 7 constructed a histogram for the cereal sodium values. That figure is shown again in the margin. Figure 2.15 shows a box plot for the sodium values. Labels are also given for the five-number summary of positions.

▲ **Figure 2.15** Box Plot and Five-Number Summary for 20 Breakfast Cereal Sodium Values. The central box contains the middle 50% of the data. The line in the box marks the median. Whiskers extend from the box to the smallest and largest observations that are not identified as potential outliers. Potential outliers are marked separately. The box plot can also be drawn vertically (see margin). **Question** Why is the left whisker drawn down only to 50 rather than to 0?

Questions to Explore

a. Which, if any, values are considered outliers?
b. Explain how the box plot in Figure 2.15 was constructed and how to interpret it.

Think It Through

a. We can identify outliers using the 1.5 * IQR criterion. We know that Q1 − 135 mg and Q3 − 205 mg. Thus IQR − 205 − 135 = 70 mg, and the lower and upper boundaries are 135 − 1.5 * 70 − 30 mg and 205 + 1.5 * 70 = 310 mg, respectively. The sodium value of 0 mg for Frosted Mini Wheats is less than 30 mg, and the value of 340 mg for Raisin Bran is greater than 310 mg, so each of these values is considered an outlier.

b. The five-number summary of sodium values shown on the box plot is minimum = 0, Q1 = 135, median = 180, Q3 = 205, and maximum = 340. The middle 50% of the distribution of sodium values range from Q1 = 135 mg to Q3 = 205 mg, which are the two outer lines of the box. The median of 180 mg is indicated by the center line through the box. As we saw in part a, the 1.5 * IQR criterion flags the sodium values of 0 mg for Frosted Mini Wheats and 340 mg for Raisin Bran as outliers. These values are represented on the box plot as asterisks. The whisker extending from Q1 is drawn down to 50, which is the smallest observation that is not below the lower boundary of 30. The whisker extending from Q3 is drawn up to 290, which is the largest observation that is not above the upper boundary of 310.

Insight

Most software identifies observations that are more than 1.5 IQR from the quartiles by a symbol, such as * or a dot, as in the *Explore Quantitative Data* app, which shows a histogram together with a box plot.

Vertically Drawn Box Plot of Sodium Data

► Screenshot of *Explore Quantitative Data* app, showing histogram and box plot for the cereal sodium data. The two outliers, one on either end, are shown as dots in the box plot. For the histogram, you can use a slider to change the width of the bins. The app has options for changing the title or the color of the plots. Download either plot by pressing the camera symbol that appears as you hover over a plot.

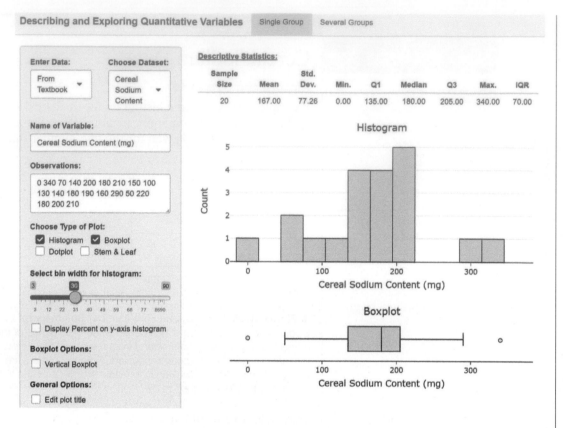

Why show potential outliers separately? One reason is to identify them for further study. Was the observation incorrectly recorded? Was that subject fundamentally different from the others in some way? Often it makes sense to repeat a statistical analysis without an outlier, to make sure the results are not overly sensitive to a single observation. For the cereal data, the sodium value of 0 (for Frosted Mini Wheats) was not incorrectly recorded. It is merely an unusually small value, relative to sodium levels for the other cereals. The sodium value of 340 for Raisin Bran was merely an unusually high value.

► **Try Exercises 2.73 and 2.75**

Another reason for keeping outliers separate in a box plot is that they do not provide much information about the shape of the distribution, especially for large data sets.

The Box Plot Compared with the Histogram

A box plot does not portray certain features of a distribution, such as distinct mounds and possible gaps, as clearly as a histogram. For example, the histogram and box plot in the margin refer to the same data, the waiting time between eruptions of the Old Faithful geyser in Yellowstone National Park. The histogram suggests that the distribution is bimodal (two distinct mounds), but we could not learn this from the box plot. This comparison shows that more than one type of graph may be needed to summarize a data set well.

A box plot does indicate skew from the relative lengths of the whiskers and the two parts of the box. The side with the larger part of the box and the longer whisker usually has skew in that direction. However, the box plot will not show us whether there is a large gap in the distribution contributing to the skew. But, as we've seen, **box plots are useful for identifying potential outliers.** We'll see next that they're also very useful for graphical comparisons of distributions.

Side-by-Side Box Plots Help to Compare Groups

In Example 14, we looked at female college student heights from the Heights data file on the book's website. To compare heights for females and males, we could look at side-by-side box plots, as shown in Figure 2.16.

The side-by-side comparison immediately shows that generally males are taller than females. The median (the center line in a box) is approximately 71 inches for the males and 65 inches for the females. Although the centers differ, the variability of the middle 50% of the distribution is similar, as indicated by the width of the boxes (which is the IQR) being similar. Both samples have heights that are unusually short or tall, flagged as potential outliers. The upper 75% of the male heights are higher than the lower 75% of female heights. That is, 75% of the female heights fall below their third quartile, about 67 inches, whereas 75% of the male heights fall above their first quartile, about 69 inches. Although the histograms for the two genders more clearly show the shape (see margin figure), it is easier to describe key differences and similarities (such as the difference in center and the similarity in variability) between the distributions from the side-by-side box plots.

In Practice

The histogram works best for larger data sets. For smaller data sets (those easily constructed by hand), the dot plot is a useful graph of the actual data to construct along with the box plot.

Histogram of Height for Female and Male Students

▶ **Figure 2.16** Box Plots of Male and Female College Student Heights. This is a screenshot from the *Explore Quantitative Data* app. The box plots use the same scale for height. **Question** Do the quartiles given under Descriptive Statistics match those shown in the box plot for each group?

Describing and Exploring Quantitative Variables   Single Group   Several Groups

Enter Data:
From Textbook

Choose Dataset:
Student Heights

Variable Name:
Height (inches)

Group Name:
Gender

Group Labels:
Female, Male

Female:
56 57 58
60 60 60
60 60 60

Male:
62 65 65
65 65 66
66 66.5

Choose Type of Plot:
⦿ Boxplot ◯ Histogram ◯ Dotplot

Descriptive Statistics:

Gender	n	Mean	Std. Dev.	Min.	Q1	Median	Q3	Max.	IQR
Female	261	65.28	2.95	56.00	63.75	65.00	67.00	77.00	3.25
Male	117	70.93	2.86	62.00	69.38	71.00	73.00	78.00	3.62

Side-by-Side Boxplots

The z-Score Also Identifies Position and Potential Outliers

The empirical rule tells us that for a bell-shaped distribution, it is unusual for an observation to fall more than 3 standard deviations from the mean. An alternative criterion for identifying potential outliers uses the standard deviation.

Recall

For bell-shaped distributions, according to the empirical rule, the interval $\bar{x} \pm 3s$ contains (almost) all observations. ◄

■ An observation in a bell-shaped distribution is regarded as a potential outlier if it falls more than 3 standard deviations from the mean.

How do we know the number of standard deviations that an observation falls from the mean? When $\bar{x} = 84$ and $s = 16$, a value of 100 is 1 standard deviation above the mean because $(100 - 84) = 16$. Alternatively, $(100 - 84)/16 = 1$.

Taking the difference between an observation and the mean and dividing by the standard deviation tells us the number of standard deviations that the observation falls from the mean. This number is called the **z-score**.

z-Score for an Observation

The **z-score** for an observation is the number of standard deviations that it falls from the mean of all observations. A positive z-score indicates the observation is above the mean. A negative z-score indicates the observation is below the mean. The z-score for an observation is calculated as

$$z = \frac{\text{observation} - \text{mean}}{\text{standard deviation}} = \frac{x - \bar{x}}{s}.$$

The z-score allows us to tell quickly how surprising or extreme an observation is. The z-score converts an observation (regardless of the observation's unit of measurement) to a common scale of measurement, which allows comparisons.

Example 17

z-Scores ◄

Pollution Outliers

Picture the Scenario

Let's consider air pollution data for the European Union (EU). The Energy-EU data file[7] on the book's website or in the *Explore Quantitative Data* app contains data on per capita carbon-dioxide (CO_2) emissions, in metric tons, for the 28 nations in the EU. The mean was 7.9 and the standard deviation was 3.6. Figure 2.17 shows a box plot of the data; the histogram is shown in the margin. The maximum of 21.4, representing Luxembourg, is highlighted as a potential outlier.

CO₂ Emission per Capita (metric tons)

▲ **Figure 2.17** Box Plot of Carbon Dioxide Emissions for European Union Nations. Question Can you use this plot to approximate the five-number summary?

---

[7]*Source:* www.iea.org, International Energy Agency

Questions to Explore

a. How many standard deviations from the mean was the CO_2 value of 21.4 for Luxembourg?

b. The CO_2 value for the United States was 16.9. According to the 3 standard deviation criterion, is the United States an outlier on carbon dioxide emissions relative to the EU?

Think It Through

a. Since $\bar{x} = 7.9$ and $s = 3.6$, the z-score for the observation of 21.4 is

$$z = \frac{\text{observation} - \text{mean}}{\text{standard deviation}} = \frac{21.4 - 7.9}{3.6} = \frac{13.5}{3.6} = 3.75$$

The carbon dioxide emission (per capita) for Luxembourg is 3.75 standard deviations above the mean. By the 3 standard deviation criterion, this is a potential outlier. Because it's well removed from the rest of the data, we'd regard it as an actual outlier. However, Luxembourg has only about 500,000 people, so in terms of the *amount* of pollution, it is not a major polluter in the EU.

b. The z-score for the CO_2 value of the United States is $z = (16.9 - 7.9)/3.6 = 2.5$. This value does not flag the United States as an outlier relative to EU nations in terms of per capita emission. (If we considered total emission, the situation would be different.)

Insight

The z-scores of 3.75 and 2.5 are positive. This indicates that the observations are *above* the mean, because an observation above the mean has a positive z-score. In fact, these large positive z-scores tell us that Luxembourg and the United States have very high per capita CO_2 emissions compared to the other nations. The z-score is negative when the observation is *below* the mean. For instance, France has a CO_2 value of 5.6, which is below the mean of 7.9 and has a z-score of -0.64.

▶ *Try Exercises 2.76 and 2.77*

2.5   Practicing the Basics

2.64   Vacation days   National Geographic Traveler magazine recently presented data on the annual number of vacation days averaged by residents of eight countries. They reported 42 days for Italy, 37 for France, 35 for Germany, 34 for Brazil, 28 for Britain, 26 for Canada, 25 for Japan, and 13 for the United States.

a. Report the median.

b. By finding the median of the four values below the median, report the first quartile.

c. Find the third quartile.

d. Interpret the values found in parts a–c in the context of these data.

2.65   Youth unemployment   For the 28 EU nations, the following table shows the unemployment rate among 15- to 24-year-olds in 2013, also available as a file on the book's website or in the *Explore Quantitative Data* app. (*Source:* World Bank.) If you are computing the statistics below by hand, it may be easier to arrange the data in increasing order and write them in four rows of seven values each.

a. Find and interpret the second quartile (=median).

b. Find and interpret the first quartile (Q1).

c. Find and interpret the third quartile (Q3).

d. Will the 10th percentile be around the value of 6 or 16? Explain.

Belgium 8.4	Germany 5.3	Spain 26.4
Bulgaria 13.0	Estonia 8.6	France 10.3
Czech Republic 7.0	Ireland 13.1	Croatia 17.2
Denmark 7.0	Greece 27.3	Italy 12.2
Cyprus 15.9	Netherlands 6.7	Slovakia 14.2

Latvia 11.9	Austria 4.9	Finland 8.2
Lithuania 11.8	Poland 10.3	Sweden 8.0
Luxembourg 5.8	Portugal 16.5	United Kingdom 7.5
Hungary 10.2	Romania 7.3	
Malta 6.5	Slovenia 10.1	

2.66 Female strength   The High School Female Athletes data file on the book's website has data for 57 high school female athletes on the maximum number of pounds they were able to bench press, which is a measure of strength. For these data, $\bar{x} = 79.9, Q1 = 70$, median $= 80, Q3 = 90$.

a. Interpret the quartiles.

b. Would you guess that the distribution is skewed or roughly symmetric? Why?

2.67 Female body weight   The College Athletes data file on the book's website has data for 64 college female athletes. The data on weight (in pounds) has $\bar{x} = 133$, $Q1 = 119$, median $= 131.5, Q3 = 144$.

a. Interpret the quartiles.

b. Would you guess that the distribution is skewed or roughly symmetric? Why?

2.68 Ways to measure variability   The standard deviation, the range, and the interquartile range (IQR) summarize the variability of the data.

a. Why is the standard deviation s usually preferred over the range?

b. Why is the IQR sometimes preferred to s?

c. What is an advantage of s over the IQR?

2.69 Variability of cigarette taxes   Here's the five-number summary for the distribution of cigarette taxes (in cents) among the 50 states and Washington, D.C., in the United States.

Minimum $= 2.5, Q1 = 36$, Median $= 60$,
Q3 $= 100$, Maximum $= 205$

a. About what proportion of the states have cigarette taxes (i) greater than 36 cents and (ii) greater than $1?

b. Between which two values are the middle 50% of the observations found?

c. Find the interquartile range. Interpret it.

d. Based on the summary, do you think that this distribution was bell shaped? If so, why? If not, why not, and what shape would you expect?

2.70 Sick leave   Exercise 2.48 showed data for a company that investigated the annual number of days of sick leave taken by its employees. The data are

0   0   4   0   0   0   6   0

a. The standard deviation is 2.4. Find and interpret the range.

b. The quartiles are $Q1 = 0$, median $= 0, Q3 = 2$. Find the interquartile range.

c. Suppose the 6 was incorrectly recorded and is supposed to be 60. The standard deviation is then 21.1 but the quartiles do not change. Redo parts a and b with the correct data and describe the effect of this outlier. Which measure of variability, the range, IQR, or standard deviation is least affected by the outlier? Why?

2.71 Infant mortality Africa   The Human Development Report 2006, published by the United Nations, showed infant mortality rates (number of infant deaths per 1,000 live births) by country. For Africa, some of the values reported were:

South Africa 54, Sudan 63, Ghana 68, Madagascar 76, Senegal 78, Zimbabwe 79, Uganda 80, Congo 81, Botswana 84, Kenya 96, Nigeria 101, Malawi 110, Mali 121, Angola 154.

a. Find the first quartile (Q1) and the third quartile (Q3).

b. Find the interquartile range (IQR). Interpret it.

2.72 Infant mortality Europe   For Western Europe, the infant mortality rates reported by the Human Development Report 2006 were:

Sweden 3, Finland 3, Spain 3, Belgium 4, Denmark 4, France 4, Germany 4, Greece 4, Italy 4, Norway 4, Portugal 4, Netherlands 5, Switzerland 5, UK 5.

Show that Q1 = Q2 = Q3 = 4. (The quartiles, like the median, are less useful when the data are highly discrete.)

2.73 Computer use   During a recent semester at the University of Florida, students having accounts on a mainframe computer had storage space use (in kilobytes) described by the five-number summary, minimum $= 4, Q1 = 256$, median $= 530, Q3 = 1,105$, and maximum $= 320,000$.

a. Would you expect this distribution to be symmetric, skewed to the right, or skewed to the left? Explain.

b. Use the $1.5 \times$ IQR criterion to determine whether any potential outliers are present.

2.74 Central Park temperature distribution revisited   Exercise 2.29 showed a histogram for the distribution of Central Park annual average temperatures. The box plot for these data is shown here.

Annual Average Temperature

a. If this distribution is skewed, would you expect it to be skewed to the right or to the left? Explain.

b. Approximate each component of the five-number summary and interpret.

2.75 Box plot for exam   The scores on an exam have mean $= 88$, standard deviation $= 10$, minimum $= 65$, Q1 $= 77$, median $= 85$, Q3 $= 91$, maximum $= 100$. Sketch a box plot, labeling which of these values are used in the plot.

2.76 Energy statistics   The Energy Information Administration records per capita consumption of energy by country. The following box plot shows 2011 per capita energy consumption (in millions of BTUs) for 36 OECD countries, with a mean of 195 and a standard deviation of 120. (The data are available in the file Energy_Consumption_OECD on the book's website and in the *Explore Quantitative Data* app.) Iceland had the largest per capita consumption at 665 million BTU.

a. Use the box plot to give approximate values for the five-number summary of energy consumption. (You can reconstruct the box plot with the app.)

b. Italy had a per capita consumption of 139 million BTU. How many standard deviations from the mean was its consumption?

c. The United States was not included in the data, but its per capita consumption was 334 million BTU. Relative to the distribution for the included OECD nations, the United States is how many standard deviations from the mean?

50 150 250 350 450 550 650
Per Capita Energy Consumption
(in millions BTU)

2.77 European Union youth unemployment rates   The 2013 unemployment rates of countries in the European Union shown in Exercise 2.65 and available in the *Explore Quantitative Data* app range from 4.9 to 27.3, with Q1 = 7.2, median = 10.1, Q3 = 13.1, a mean of 11.1, and a standard deviation of 5.6.

a. In a box plot, what would be the values at the outer edges of the box, and what would be the values to which the whiskers extend? (To check your answers, use the *Explore Quantitative Data* app.)

b. Which two countries will show up as outliers in the box plot? Why?

c. Greece had the highest unemployment rate of 27.3. Is it an outlier according to the 3 standard deviation criterion? Explain.

d. What unemployment value for a country would have a z-score equal to 0?

2.78 Air pollution   Example 17 discussed EU carbon dioxide emissions, which had a mean of 7.9 and standard deviation of 3.6.

a. Finland's observation was 11.5. Find its z-score and interpret.

b. Sweden's observation was 5.6. Find its z-score, and interpret.

c. The UK's observation was 7.9. Find the z-score and interpret.

2.79 Female heights   For the 261 female heights shown in the box plot in Figure 2.16, the mean was 65.3 inches and the standard deviation was 3.0 inches. The shortest person in this sample had a height of 56 inches.

a. Find the z-score for the height of 56 inches.

b. What does the negative sign for the z-score represent?

c. Is this observation a potential outlier according to the 3 standard deviation distance criterion? Explain.

2.80 Hamburger sales   The manager of a fast-food restaurant records each day for a year the amount of money received from sales of food that day. Using software, he finds a bell-shaped histogram with a mean of $1,165 and a standard deviation of $220. Today the sales equaled $2,000. Is this an unusually good day? Answer by providing statistical justification.

2.81 Big Data: Airbnb prices in New York City   The data file NYCAirbnb on the book's website and available in the *Explore Quantitative Data* app lists the daily prices of 28,489 rooms for rent on the website Airbnb.com for New York City. Use the app (or other software) to look at the summary statistics, histogram, and box plot and write a paragraph describing the distribution. (You can download the histogram or box plot from the app as .png files by pressing the camera symbol in the upper right-hand corner when you hover over the plot.)

2.82 Airbnb prices by type of room   Refer to the previous exercise. When broken down by type of rental room (shared room, private room, entire apartment), the box plots for each type of room are shown below. (You can reconstruct this side-by-side box plot by switching to the Several Groups tab in the *Explore Quantitative Data* app, where you can hover over the box plots to see the 5-number summaries.)

a. The median price for which type of room is the largest?

b. The variability in the prices is the largest for which type of room?

c. Is the distribution for the price of rooms for the rental type "shared room" left- or right-skewed or symmetric?

d. Write a short paragraph comparing the distribution of price across the three rental types. Go to the *Explore Quantitative Data* app if you need specific values, such as medians, for your descriptions.

2.83 CO_2 comparison   The vertical side-by-side box plots on the next page compare per capita carbon dioxide emissions in 2011 for many Central and South American and European nations. (Data available on the book's website or in the *Explore Quantitative Data* app, where you can reconstruct the side-by-side box plot and hover over the boxes to read off the summary statistics. *Source:* www.eia.gov, U.S. Energy Information Administration)

a. Give the approximate value of carbon dioxide emissions for the outliers shown. (There are actually two outliers.)

b. What shape would you predict for the distribution in Central and South America? Why?

c. Summarize how the carbon dioxide emissions compare between the two regions.

2.6 Linear Transformations and Standardizing

When working with real data, it is often necessary to change units of measurements, such as going from inches to centimeters or Fahrenheit to Celsius or converting between different currencies. We call such conversions linear transformations. How are the distribution of a variable and the statistics that describe it affected by linear transformations?

Linear Transformations

The z-score that we defined at the end of the last section is an example of what is called a linear transformation of observations. Linear transformations take the original observations and transform them by adding, subtracting, multiplying or dividing by constant numbers. To obtain the z-score for each observation in a sample, we first subtract the sample mean $\bar{x}$ (a constant number) from each observation and then divide the result by the standard deviation s (another constant number). So, in effect, we applied two linear transformations, first a subtraction and then a division. In contrast, nonlinear transformations use more complicated operations, such as taking the square root or the logarithm of observations. In practice, you can think of linear transformations as **scaling** (multiplying or dividing) and/or **shifting** (adding or subtracting) the observations.

Why do we need to consider linear transformations? We have already seen their use as z-scores, but beyond that they are ubiquitous when dealing with real data. Any change of units, such as converting from feet to meters, pounds to kilograms, minutes to seconds, U.S. dollars to Japanese yen, or Fahrenheit to Celsius, is a linear transformation. And such transformations happen all the time, when combining data from different sources, when sharing or publishing data, or when complying with pre-defined standards of measurements.

As an example, to convert an observation x measured in Fahrenheit to Celsius, you apply the following linear transformation: Subtract 32 from x and then multiply the result by $5/9$, or, as a formula, $(x - 32)*(5/9)$. Note that this is not a z-score: we did not subtract the overall mean and then divide by the standard deviation, but it is a linear transformation: we subtracted the constant 32 and then multiplied by the constant $5/9$. Equivalently, we can write this as $-(160/9) + (5/9)x$, which leads us to the general definition of a linear transformation:

Recall

The z-score for an observation x

is given by $z = \dfrac{x - \bar{x}}{s}$. ◀

Linear Transformations

A linear transformation takes the value x of the original measurement and transforms it into the new value y according to the formula $y = c + dx$, where c and d are given constants.

For instance, to transform observations measured in Fahrenheit to Celsius, set $c = -(160/9)$ and $d = 5/9$; i.e., when the original observation $x = 71$ degrees measured in Fahrenheit, then the transformed observation $y = -(160/9) + (5/9)(71) = 21.7$ degrees Celsius. For converting a variable x that measures the final eBay auction price of used iPhones in USD to Japanese yen, using the currency conversion of 1 USD = 108 yen from June 2019, set $c = 0$ and $d = 108$. For instance, if a particular auction goes for $x = 100$ USD, then the corresponding transformed observation $y = 108(100) = 10,800$ yen.

Histogram of original (in USD) and transformed (in yen) observations

Price in USD

Price in Yen

Recall

To describe the distribution of a variable, comment on shape, center and variability. ◄

Effect of Linear Transformations on the Distribution

How do linear transformations affect the distribution of a variable? First, the shape of the distribution of the transformed variable is the same as the shape of the distribution of the original variable. (This is not true for nonlinear transformations.) For instance, if the distribution of final eBay auction prices for used iPhones in USD was left-skewed, the distribution of the linearly transformed (to yen) observations is also left-skewed. A histogram of the original and the transformed auction prices show the same left skew, see the margin figures. Similarly, if the distribution of the original variable is symmetric, then the distribution of the linearly transformed variable is also symmetric.

What about measures for center (i.e., mean or median) and variability (e.g., standard deviation or IQR)? One can simply find all these statistics by applying the formulas from Section 2.3 and 2.4 to the transformed observations. In practice, just enter the transformed values into software to find the new summary statistics such as the mean and standard deviation.[8] However, we can actually predict what is going to happen. For instance, if you know that the mean of the final eBay auction prices is $\bar{x} = 90$ USD, then the mean of the transformed (to yen) auction prices is going to be $\bar{y} = 108(90) = 9,720$ yen. Why? Because you simply apply the same currency transformation that you applied to each observation to the mean. (Remember, we used a currency conversion of 1 USD = 108 yen.)

If the standard deviation of the original observations is $s_x = 20$ USD, can you guess what the standard deviation of the transformed (to yen) observations is? We will present the formula in the summary box at the end, but remember that we can interpret the standard deviation as a typical **distance** from the mean. If that typical distance is 20 when measured in USD, it is going to be $108(20) = 2,160$ when measured in yen. So, the standard deviation of the transformed variables is $s_y = 108(20) = 2,160$ yen. In summary, we have the following relationships between statistics for the original and transformed observations:

Summary: Linear Transformation

A linear transformation converts observations from one set of units to another through the formula $y = c + dx$, where x are the original observations, y are the transformed observations, and c and d are given constants.

■ The shape of the distribution does not change under linear transformations.
■ The mean $\bar{y}$ of the transformed observations can be computed from the mean $\bar{x}$ of the original observations through $\bar{y} = c + d\bar{x}$. The same is true for the median (or any other percentiles): Median of $y = c + d$ (Median of x).

---

[8]The *Explore Quantitative Data* app allows you to apply any linear transformation to a set of original observations. Check the Apply Linear Transformation checkbox under the General Options heading. The app computes all the new summary statistics for the transformed variable.

■ The standard deviation s_y of the transformed observations can be computed from the standard deviation s_x of the original observations through $s_y = |d|s_x$, where $|d|$ is the absolute value of d. In particular, the amount c by which observations are shifted does not affect the standard deviation. The same logic and formula holds true for the IQR: $IQR_y = |d|IQR_x$.

Same distance

The last bullet point says that the amount c by which we shift (by adding or subtracting c) the original observations does not affect the standard deviation or the IQR. This is because the standard deviation is an average **distance** measure between the observations and their mean. By adding c to all observations, the mean also increases by c, but the distance between the transformed observations and their mean stays the same (see figure in the margin). Similarly, the IQR is the distance between Q3 and Q1, and while each of these quartiles increases by c when c is added to all observations, the difference between them remains the same.

Example 18

Linear Transformations ◄

Fees and Markups

Picture the Scenario

An electronics retailer receives a shipment of various models of brand new phones from a smartphone manufacturer. The average price the retailer pays the manufacturer per smartphone equals $\bar{x} = \$800$, with a standard deviation of $s_x = \$100$.

Questions to Explore

a. To recuperate fixed costs for operating its business, suppose the retailer decides to add a $10 fee to the manufacturer's price. If x denotes the manufacturer's price and y denotes the price the retailer wants to sell the phone for, what is the mean retail price of all smartphones in the shipment? What is their standard deviation? (*Hint:* First, find the constants c and d for this linear transformation.)

b. Instead of adding a constant $10 fee to the manufacturer's price, suppose the retailer decides to add 10% to the manufacturer's price of each smartphone. What are the constants c and d for this linear transformation and what are the mean and standard deviation of the retail prices now?

c. In reality, the retailer first applies a 10% markup and then adds an additional $10 fee to the manufacturer's price for determining the retail price. What are the constants c and d for such a linear transformation and what are the mean and standard deviation of the retail prices?

Think It Through

a. If we had the data on the manufacturer's prices for all smartphones included in the shipment, we could add $10 to each, enter the new values into software and find the mean and standard deviation that way. However, all we know is the mean manufacturer's price of $\bar{x} = \$800$ and the standard deviation of $s_x = \$100$. But we know that $10 has been added to the original manufacturer's price, so we know that $y = 10 + x$ for each observation. This is a linear transformation of the form $y = c + dx$, with $c = 10$ and $d = 1$. When the price of each phone is increased by $10, the average price also goes up by $10, so the mean retail price is $\bar{y} = \$800 + \$10 = \$810$. What about the standard deviation? Originally, the typical distance between a smartphone's price and the overall mean of $800 was $100. This distance doesn't change when we add $10 to both the observation and the mean, so the typical distance stays the same. That's why the standard deviation s_y of the retail prices is the same as the standard deviation s_x of the original (manufacturer's) prices, i.e., $s_y = s_x = \$100$. You also get this result when plugging into the formula in the third bullet point in the Summary box: $s_y = |d|s_x = |1|s_x = s_x = \$100$. Summing up, when adding $10 to the manufacturer price to determine the retail price for each smartphone, the mean retail price is $810 and the standard deviation of the retail prices is $100.

b. Again, if we had the data on the manufacturer's prices for all smartphones included in the shipment, we could simply add 10% to each, enter the new values into software and find the mean and standard deviation that way. What does it mean to add 10%? It means that we take the manufacturer's price and add to it 0.1 times the manufacturer's price (i.e., add one-tenth of the manufacturer's price). Equivalently, we **multiply** the manufacturer's price by 1.1 to obtain the retail price. This is a linear transformation of the form $y = c + dx$, where $c = 0$ and $d = 1.1$, i.e., $y = 1.1x$. The mean manufacturer's price of $\bar{x} = \$800$ then also increases by 10%, or one-tenth of $800, which is $80, and we obtain the mean retail price of $\bar{y} = 1.1(\$800) = \$880$. Now, because we scaled the units of the original observations by a factor of 1.1, the standard deviations (the typical distances) are no longer the same (see the figure in the margin). The standard deviation of the retail prices is larger by a factor of 1.1, i.e., $s_y = |d|s_x = 1.1s_x = 1.1(100) = \$110$. In summary, when increasing the manufacturer's price by 10% to determine the retail price for each smartphone, the mean retail price is $880 and the standard deviation of the retail prices is $110.

c. For this third scenario, the linear transformation is of the form $y = c + dx$, with $c = 10$ and $d = 1.1$, i.e., $y = 10 + 1.1x$. This represents both a scaling (by a factor of 1.1) and a shift (by $10) of the original observations. The mean retail price of the smartphones is given by $\bar{y} = a + b\bar{x} = 10 + 1.1(\$800) = \$890$. The standard deviation is not affected by adding the constant amount of $10, but it is affected by the scaling factor of 1.1, so $s_y = |d|s_x = 1.1s_x = 1.1(100) = \$110$. In summary, when increasing the manufacturer's price by 10% and then adding another $10 to determine the retail price for each smartphone, the mean retail price is $890 and the standard deviation of the retail prices is $110.

Insight

Figure 2.18 shows smooth curves representing the distribution of the original (light green) and transformed (dark green) data. The distribution of the transformed data (the retail prices) has the same shape (bell shaped) as the distribution of the original data. However, the distribution for the retail prices is first stretched (by a factor of 1.1) and then shifted to the right (by $10) compared to the one for the original data.

Not same distance

▲ **Figure 2.18** Smooth Curves Representing Distributions of Original (Manufacturer) and Linearly Transformed (Retailer) Prices. The linear transformation is given by: Retailer Price = 10 + 1.1 (Manufacturer Price). The triangles indicate the mean for the original and transformed prices, respectively. **Question** If the *median* manufacturer's price is $790, what is the median retail price?

▶ *Try Exercise 2.85*

Standardizing Variables

Now that we understand linear transformations and how they affect the mean and standard deviation, we can briefly turn back to z-scores. Remember, to obtain the z-score for a particular observation x, we first subtract the overall mean $\bar{x}$ from it and then divide by the standard deviation s.[9] When we do this for each observation of a variable, we transform the original variable into z-scores.

Here are two important facts about z-scores:

■ z-scores have mean 0
■ z-scores have standard deviation 1

We call a variable with such properties (mean=0, standard deviation=1) a **standardized variable** and the process of transforming a variable to z-scores as **standardizing** a variable. (To show the above two properties of z-scores, refer to Exercise 2.156.)

Standardizing is a powerful concept and we will see it applied in a variety of situations, as early as when deriving the correlation in Chapter 3. Standardizing is also important when your data set contains variables measured on different scales and you want to use these variables to build statistical models or algorithms, such as the ones we mentioned in the Data Science section of Chapter 1. A first step in such an analysis is often to standardize each variable so that the units are comparable and one doesn't dominate any other. (Imagine how unreliable statistical methods would be if their results depended on the units of measurements.) In its most basic form, standardization helps in comparing two variables measured on different scales.

Example 19

Standardizing ◀

Women's Heptathlon

Picture the Scenario

The women's heptathlon (which consists of 100 meters hurdles, high jump, shot put, 200 meters, long jump, javelin throw, and 800 meters) is one of the toughest Olympic events for athletes. How can performances in each of these seven

---

[9]In terms of the linear transformation formula $c + dx$, this can be written as $z = -(\bar{x}/s) + (1/s)\,x$, i.e., the shift constant $c = -(\bar{x}/s)$ and the scale constant $d = 1/s$.

Table 2.6 Performance of six athletes in the 200 meters and javelin events in the 2017 Summer Olympics.

	200 Meters		Javelin		Combined
Athlete	seconds	z-score	meters	z-score	z-score
Claudia Rath	24.48	0.76	39.39	0.09	−0.67
Jessica Ennis-Hill	23.49	−1.00	46.06	1.64	2.64
Katarina Johnson-Thompson	23.26	−1.41	36.36	−0.61	0.80
Katerina Cachova	24.32	0.48	37.77	−0.28	−0.76
Kendell Williams	24.09	0.07	40.93	0.45	0.38
Uhunoma Osazuwa	24.67	1.10	33.42	−1.29	−2.39
Mean	**24.05**	**0.00**	**38.99**	**0.00**	
Standard Deviation	**0.56**	**1.00**	**4.32**	**1.00**	

events be compared and combined when they are measured on different scales? Table 2.6 shows the results of just two heptathlon disciplines, the 200 meters and the javelin events, and for just six of the 31 athletes who competed in the 2017 Summer Olympics.

Questions to Explore

How can we compare athletes across these two disciplines? Who did the best overall?

Think It Through

We clearly can't directly compare or combine the measurements for each discipline. For the 200 meters, the observations are measured in seconds; for the javelin event, in meters. For the 200 meters, the best performance is the one that is the smallest; for the javelin event, the best performance is the one with the largest thrown distance. We can standardize each variable to make them comparable. Table 2.6 also shows the z-scores for the 200-meter event and the z-scores for the javelin event. For the z-scores for the 200-meter event, we took the observation of each athlete, subtracted 24.05 (the mean for the 200-meter times) and then divided by 0.56 (the standard deviation of the 200-meter times). Similarly, to get the z-scores for the javelin event, we subtracted 38.99 from each individual athlete's distance and then divided by 4.32. Notice how the mean and standard deviation are 0 and 1, respectively, for each column of z-scores.

Katarina Johnson-Thompson did the best in the 200-meter event. Her performance is 1.41 standard deviations below the mean finishing time. Jessica Ennis-Hill did the best in the javelin event. Her distance is 1.64 above the mean distance of the 6 athletes. But we already knew who did the best before computing z-scores, by simply looking at the original observations. What we didn't know is how good the performances were in relative terms. By standardizing each of the two variables, they are now on equal footing, and we can combine them to come up with an overall ranking. For instance, we can take the negative of the 200-meter z-score (so that larger means better) and add to it the javelin z-score. The last column in Table 2.6 shows these combined z-scores. Jessica Ennis-Hill had the largest combined z-score and we can consider her combined performance the best. She was 1.00 standard deviations below the mean in the 200-meter event and 1.64 standard deviations above the mean in the javelin event, for a combined z-score of 2.64.

Insight

At the Olympics, a more complicated (and nonlinear) scoring system is used that awards proportionally more points the more outstanding the performance is. This system also ensures that results are comparable from one Olympic game to the next, which is not the case when using z-scores, which express performances only relative to the other athletes participating in the same games.

▶ **Try Exercise 2.89**

2.6 Practicing the Basics

2.84 Purchasing apps   A survey of a group of teenagers found that the average amount of money they spent on purchasing smartphone apps equals $0.85 each month, with a standard deviation of $0.32.

   a. If you convert the observations to cents, what would be their mean and standard deviation?

   b. When reporting these statistics to a European audience, you want to report the mean and standard deviation in euros. Using the exchange rate USD 1 = EUR 0.9, what are the mean and standard deviation of these observations in euros?

2.85 Boosting scores after difficult exam   Scores on a difficult statistics exam have a mean of 60 and a standard deviation of 10.

   TRY

   a. The teacher considers boosting the scores by adding 10 points to all exams. What is the mean and what is the standard deviation of the scores after the 10 points are added to each student's score?

   b. Suppose instead the teacher considers increasing each student's score by 10%. What is the mean and what is the standard deviation of the adjusted scores now?

   c. The teacher decides to boost each student's score by first increasing each score by 5% and then adding a constant of 10 points. Find the mean and standard deviation of the boosted scores.

   d. If the distribution of the original scores was left-skewed, what is the shape of the distribution of the boosted scores?

   e. If the teacher wanted to just bring the average score from 60 up to 80 points, without changing the standard deviation, how should the teacher adjust each student's score?

2.86 Central Park temps in Celsius   The average annual temperatures in Central Park over the period from 1869 to 2018 had a mean of 54 degrees Fahrenheit, with a standard deviation of 1.7 degrees Fahrenheit. If the average annual temperatures are converted to degrees Celsius, using the linear transformation $C = -(160/9)+(5/9)F$, what are the mean and the standard deviation of the Celsius values?

2.87 Dealer markup for cars   The lot of a car dealership contains cars with an average invoice price (that's the price the dealer paid the manufacturer) of $45,000, with a standard

deviation of $10,000. The median invoice price was $40,000. To protect its profits, the dealership decides to set the sales price 20% higher than the invoice price for each of its cars.

   a. What is the mean of the sales prices for the cars on the lot?

   b. What is the median of the sales prices for the cars on the lot?

   c. What is the standard deviation of the sales prices for the cars on the lot?

2.88 Taxes and fees at CarMax   Prices for a sample of used Audi A4s available on the website www.carmax.com have a mean of $23,800 and standard deviation of $4,380.

   a. Prices quoted on www.carmax.com are without sales tax. To account for this, a sales tax of 6% is applied to the prices of all cars in the sample. How are the mean and standard deviation of the prices affected?

   b. In addition to the sales tax, CarMax adds a $199 processing fee when a vehicle is sold through its webpage. How are the mean and standard deviation of the prices affected when both the sales tax and this fee are taken into account?

2.89 Rotten Tomatoes reviews   The website Rotten Tomatoes publishes both an aggregate professional critic's score and an audience score (computed from users of their website) for movies. For six movies released in 2015, the following scores were reported:

   TRY

   APP

Film	Critics Score	Users Scores
The Imitation Game	90	92
Ant-Man	80	90
Mission: Impossible–Rogue Nation	92	90
Inside Out	98	90
Avengers: Age of Ultron	74	86
Selma	99	86
Mean	**88.8**	**89.0**
Standard Deviation	**10.0**	**2.4**

Based on both critics and user's score, which movie among those six would you rank as the most highly rated? Explain. (You can find z-scores for each column by entering the scores in the *Explore Quantitative Data* app and checking the box for Linear Transformation.)

2.7 Recognizing and Avoiding Misuses of Graphical Summaries

In this chapter, we've learned how to describe data. We've learned that the nature of the data affects how we can effectively describe them. For example, if a distribution is very highly skewed or has extreme outliers, just reporting the mean without also quoting the median can be misleading. To finish this chapter, let's look at how we also need to be on the lookout for misleading graphical summaries.

Beware of Poor Graphs

With modern computer-graphic capabilities, websites, advertisers, newspapers and other periodicals use graphs in an increasing variety of ways to portray information. The graphs are not always well designed, however, and you should look at some of them skeptically.

Example 20

Misleading Graphical Summaries ◄

Recruiting STEM Majors

Picture the Scenario

Look at Figure 2.19. According to the title and the two-sentence caption, the graph is intended to display how total enrollment has risen at a U.S. university from 2004 to 2012, while the number of STEM (science, technology, engineering, and mathematics) students has "dipped just about every year." A graphic designer used a software program to construct a graph for use in a local newspaper. The Sunday headline story was about the decline of STEM majors. The graph is a time plot showing the enrollment between 2004 and 2012, using outlined human figures to portray total enrollment and blue human figures to portray STEM enrollment.

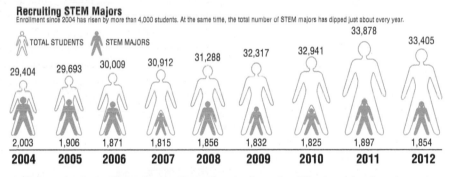

Recruiting STEM Majors
Enrollment since 2004 has risen by more than 4,000 students. At the same time, the total number of STEM majors has dipped just about every year.

2004	2005	2006	2007	2008	2009	2010	2011	2012
29,404	29,693	30,009	30,912	31,288	32,317	32,941	33,878	33,405
2,003	1,906	1,871	1,815	1,856	1,832	1,825	1,897	1,854

▲ **Figure 2.19** An Example of a Poor Graph. **Question** What's misleading about the way the data are presented?

Questions to Explore

a. Do the heights of the human figures accurately represent the counts? Are the areas of the figures in accurate proportions to each other? Answer by first comparing the two observations for 2004 and then by comparing those for 2004 to those for 2012.

b. Is an axis shown and labeled as a reference line for the enrollments displayed?

c. What other design problems do you see?

Think It Through

a. In the year 2004, the number of STEM majors (2,003) is about 7% of the total of 29,404. However, the height of the number of STEM majors figure is about two-thirds the height of the total enrollment figure. The graphs also mislead by using different widths for the figures. Compare, for instance, the figures for total enrollment in 2004 and 2012. The total enrollments are not nearly as different as the areas taken up by the figures make them appear.

b. Figure 2.19 does not provide a vertical axis, much less a labeling of that axis. It is not clear whether the counts are supposed to be represented by the heights or by the areas of the human figures.

c. It is better to put the figures next to each other rather than to overlay the two sets of figures as was done here. The use of solid blue figures and outlined figures can easily distort your perception of the graph. Although it might not have been deliberate, the design obscures the data.

Insight

The intent of Figure 2.19 was to provide an intriguing visual display that quickly tells the story of the newspaper article. However, deviating from standard graphs gave a misleading representation of the data.

▶ **Try Exercise 2.93**

SUMMARY: Guidelines for Constructing Effective Graphs

- Label both axes and provide a heading to make clear what the graph is intended to portray. (Figure 2.19 does not even provide a vertical axis.)
- To help our eyes visually compare relative sizes accurately, the vertical axis should usually start at 0.
- Be cautious in using figures, such as people, in place of the usual bars or points. It can make a graph more attractive, but it is easy to get the relative percentages that the figures represent incorrect.
- It can be difficult to portray more than one group on a single graph when the variable values differ greatly. (In Figure 2.19, one frequency is very small compared to the other.) Consider instead using separate graphs or plotting relative sizes such as ratios or percentages.

Improving Graphical Summaries ◀

Example 21

Recruiting STEM Majors

Picture the Scenario

Let's look at Figure 2.19 again—because it's such a good example of how things can go wrong. Suppose the newspaper asks you to repair the graph, providing an accurate representation of the data.

Questions to Explore

a. Show a better way to graphically portray the same information about the enrollment counts in Figure 2.19.

b. Describe two alternative ways to portray the data that more clearly show the number of STEM majors relative to the size of the student body over time.

Think It Through

a. Because the caption of Figure 2.19 indicates that counts are the desired data display, we can construct a time plot showing total and STEM major enrollments on the same scale. Figure 2.20 shows this revised graph. This time plot clearly labels the horizontal and vertical axes. There is the natural reference starting point of 0 for the vertical axis, allowing for better relative comparison of the two groups. We can see that the STEM major enrollment is a small part of the total enrollment. Between 2004 and 2012, there's been some tendency upward in the total enrollment, with relatively little change in the STEM major enrollment.

b. Figure 2.20 is better than Figure 2.19 but is not ideal. Any trend that may be there for STEM majors is not clear because their counts are small compared to the total enrollment counts. Given that both the total and the STEM major counts vary from year to year, it's more meaningful to look at the STEM major *percentage* of the student body and plot that over time. See Exercise 2.89, which shows that this percentage went down from 2004 to 2012.

Even if we plot the counts, as in Figure 2.20, it may be better to show a separate plot on its own scale for the STEM major counts. Or, in a single graph, rather than comparing the STEM major counts to the *total* enrollment (which contains the STEM majors group), it may be more meaningful to compare them to the *rest* of the enrollment, that is, the total enrollment minus the number of STEM majors.

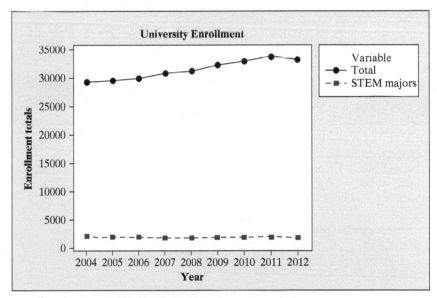

▲ **Figure 2.20** A Better Graph for the Data in Figure 2.19. **Question** What trends do you see in the enrollments from 2004 to 2012?

Insight

In constructing graphs, strive for clarity and simplicity. Data visualization is becoming more important than ever, in particular with the explosion of the size and complexity of data we now must visualize. Several books and blog posts have been written in recent years to help users tell the story of their data visually. Search the Internet for "Data Visualization," and you will get lots of inspiration, ranging from simple graphs such as bar graphs to interactive scatterplots and Infographics.

▶ **Try Exercise 2.92**

When you plan to summarize data by graphical and numerical descriptive statistics, think about questions such as the following: What story are you attempting to convey with the data? Which graphical display and numerical summaries will most clearly and accurately convey this story?

On the Shoulders of...John Tukey

John Tukey

"The best thing about being a statistician is that you get to play in everyone's backyard."
—John Tukey (1915–2000)

In the 1960s, John Tukey of Princeton University was concerned that statisticians were putting too much emphasis on complex data analyses and ignoring simpler ways to examine and learn from the data. Tukey developed new descriptive methods, under the title of **exploratory data analysis (EDA)**. These methods make few assumptions about the structure of the data and emphasize data display and ways of searching for patterns and deviations from those patterns. Two graphical tools that Tukey invented were the stem-and-leaf plot and the box plot.

Initially, few statisticians promoted EDA. However, in recent years, some EDA methods have become common tools for data analysis. Part of this acceptance has been inspired by the availability of computer software and calculators that can implement some of Tukey's methods more easily.

Tukey's work illustrates that statistics is an evolving discipline. Almost all of the statistical methods used today were developed in the past century, and new methods continue to be created, largely because of increasing computer power.

2.7 Practicing the Basics

2.90 Great pay (on the average)   The six part-time employees of Linda's Tanning Salon near campus had annual incomes last year of $8,900, $9,200, $9,200, $9,300, $9,500, $9,800. Linda herself made $250,000.

a. For the seven annual incomes at Linda's salon, report the mean and median.

b. Why is it misleading for Linda to boast to her friends that the average salary at her business is more than $40,000?

2.91 Market share for food sales   The pie chart shown was displayed in an article in *The Scotsman* newspaper (January 15, 2005) to show the market share of different supermarkets in Scotland.

a. Pie charts can be tricky to draw correctly. Identify two problems with this chart.

b. From looking at the graph without inspecting the percentages, would it be easier to identify the mode using this graph or using a bar graph? Why?

Market Share of Scottish Supermarket Chain

Source: Copyright The Scotsman Publications, Ltd.

2.92 Enrollment trends Examples 19 and 20 presented graphs showing the total student enrollment at a U.S. university between 2004 and 2012 and the data for STEM major enrollment during that same time period. The data are repeated here.

Enrollment at the U.S. University

Year	Total Students	STEM Majors
2004	29,404	2,003
2005	29,693	1,906
2006	30,009	1,871
2007	30,912	1,815
2008	31,288	1,856
2009	32,317	1,832
2010	32,941	1,825
2011	33,878	1,897
2012	33,405	1,854

a. Construct a graph for only STEM major enrollments over this period. Describe the trend in these enrollment counts. To construct the graph, you can use the *Time Series* app where you simply enter one column for the years and another for the total students.

b. Find the percentage of enrolled students each year who are STEM majors and construct a time plot of the percentages.

c. Summarize what the graphs constructed in parts a and b tell you that you could not learn from Figures 2.19 and 2.20 in Examples 19 and 20.

2.93 Terrorism and war in Iraq In 2004, a college newspaper reported results of a survey of students taken on campus. One question asked was, "Do you think going to war with Iraq has made Americans safer from terrorism, or not?" The figure shows the way the magazine reported results.

a. Explain what's wrong with the way this bar chart was constructed.

b. Explain why you would not see this error made with a pie chart.

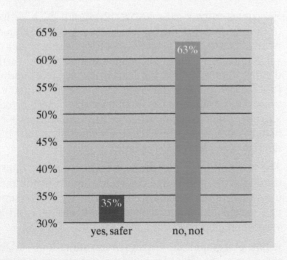

2.94 BBC license fee Explain what is wrong with the time plot shown of the annual license fee paid by British subjects for watching BBC programs. *(Source: Evening Standard, November 29, 2006.)*

2.95 Federal government spending Explain what is wrong with the following pie chart, which depicts the federal government breakdown by category for 2010.

Federal Spending for 2010

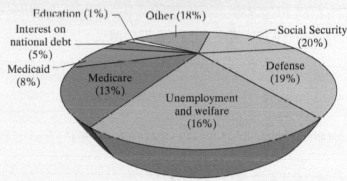

Source: www.gpoaccess.gov/usbudget/fy10, U.S. Government Publishing Office

2.96 Bad graph Search some publications and find an example of a graph that violates at least one of the principles for constructing good graphs. Summarize what's wrong with the graph and explain how it could be improved.

2.97 Bush-era tax cuts The following graph (created based on how it was displayed by a major TV network) shows how the top tax rate would change from 35% to 39.6% when the Bush-era tax cuts expired in 2013. Judging from the height of the bars, it appears that on Jan. 1, 2013, the tax rate will be almost five times higher than before, when in fact it will go up only by 4.6 percentage points from 35%. How could this misleading graph be improved to better reflect the situation?

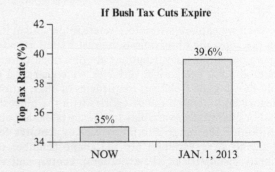

2.98 Median income The following graph shows the median income from 1980 to 2015 for Whites and Blacks in the U.S., who are in the 45-55 age group and have a high school education or less. (*Source:* A. Case and A. Deaton, "Mortality and Morbidity in the 21st Century," Brookings Papers on Economic Activity, 2017.)

a. At first glance, the median income of whites and blacks appears similar over the years. Explain.

b. The article wanted to stress that "black household incomes rose and fell in line with white household incomes over the years." To portray this, the graph uses two different scales on the left and right y-axis in the same plot. (The labels for the curves alert you to this fact.)

However, the difference in scales is easy to overlook. Describe an alternative way to display these data.

Chapter Review

SUMMARY OF NOTATION

Mean $\bar{x} = \dfrac{\Sigma x}{n}$ where x denotes the variable, n is the sample size, and Σ indicates to sum

Standard deviation $s = \sqrt{\dfrac{\Sigma(x - \bar{x})^2}{n - 1}}$, Variance $= s^2$

$z\text{-score} = \dfrac{\text{observed value} - \text{mean}}{\text{standard deviation}} = \dfrac{x - \bar{x}}{s}$

Linear Transformation $y = c + dx$ where x is the original variable, y the transformed variable, and c and d are shifting and scaling constants

CHAPTER SUMMARY

This chapter introduced **descriptive statistics**—graphical and numerical ways of **describing** data. The characteristics of interest that we measure are called **variables**, because values on them vary from subject to subject.

- A **categorical variable** has observations that fall into one of a set of categories. If those categories follow no particular order, the variable is called **nominal**; if the categories can be ordered, it is called **ordinal**.

- A **quantitative variable** takes numerical values that represent different magnitudes of the variable.

- A quantitative variable is **discrete** if it has separate possible values, such as the integers 0, 1, 2,... for a variable expressed as "the number of..." It is **continuous** if its possible values form an interval.

When we explore a variable, we are interested in its **distribution** (i.e., how the observations are distributed across the range of possible values). Distributions are described through graphs and tables. For categorical variables, we construct a **frequency table** showing the (relative) frequencies of observations in each category and mention the categories with the highest frequencies. For quantitative variables, frequency tables are obtained by partitioning the range into intervals. Key features to describe for quantitative variables are the **shape** (number of distinct mounds, symmetry or skew, outliers), **center**, and **variability**. No description of a variable is complete without showing a

graphical representation of its distribution through an appropriate **graph**.

Overview of Graphical Methods

- For categorical variables, data are displayed using **pie charts** and **bar graphs**. Bar graphs provide more flexibility and make it easier to compare categories having similar percentages.

- For quantitative variables, a **histogram** is a graph of a frequency table. It displays bars that specify frequencies or relative frequencies (percentages) for possible values or intervals of possible values. The **stem-and-leaf plot** (a vertical line dividing the final digit, the leaf, from the stem) and **dot plot** (dots above the number line) show the individual observations. They are useful for small data sets. These three graphs all show shape, such as whether the distribution is approximately bell shaped, skewed to the right (longer tail pointing to the right), or skewed to the left.

- The **box plot** has a box drawn between the first quartile and third quartile, with a line drawn in the box at the median. It has whiskers that extend to the minimum and maximum values, except for potential **outliers**. An **outlier** is an extreme value falling far below or above the bulk of the data.

- A **time plot** graphically displays observations for a variable measured over time. This plot can visually show **trends** over time.

Overview of Measures of the Center and of Position

Measures of the center attempt to describe a typical or representative observation.

- The **mean** is the sum of the observations divided by the number of observations. It is the balance point of the data.

- The **median** divides the ordered data set into two parts of equal numbers of observations, half below and half above that point. The median is the 50th percentile (second quartile). It is a more representative summary than the mean when the data are highly skewed and is resistant against outliers.

- The lower quarter of the observations fall below the **first quartile (Q1)**, and the upper quarter fall above the **third quartile (Q3)**. These are the 25th percentile and 75th percentile. These quartiles and the median split the data into four equal parts.

Overview of Measures of Variability

Measures of variability describe the variability of the observations.

- The **range** is the difference between the largest and smallest observations.

- The **deviation** of an observation x from the mean is $x - \bar{x}$. The **variance** is an average of the squared deviations. Its square root, the **standard deviation**, is more useful, describing a typical distance from the mean.

- The **empirical rule** states that for a bell-shaped distribution:

About 68% of the data fall within 1 standard deviation of the mean, $\bar{x} \pm s$.

About 95% of the data fall within 2 standard deviations, $\bar{x} \pm 2s$.

Nearly all the data fall within 3 standard deviations, $\bar{x} \pm 3s$.

- The **interquartile range (IQR)** is the difference between the third and first quartiles, which span the middle 50% of the data in a distribution. It is more **resistant** than the range and standard deviation, being unaffected by extreme observations.

- An observation is a potential **outlier** if it falls (a) more than $1.5 \times$ IQR below Q1 or more than $1.5 \times$ IQR above Q3, or (b) more than 3 standard deviations from the mean. The **z-score** is the number of standard deviations that an observation falls from the mean.

Linear Transformations

Linear transformations convert observations from one set of units (e.g., Fahrenheit) to another set of units (e.g., Celsius) through shifting (adding or subtracting a constant value) and/or scaling (multiplying or dividing by a constant value).

- Shifting and scaling does not affect the shape of the distribution.

- Measures of center (mean, median) and position (quartiles) undergo the same transformation as the individual observations.

- Measures of variability (standard deviation, IQR) are only affected by scaling, but not by shifting.

To **standardize** a variable means to transform it to z-scores, which have mean 0 and standard deviation 1.

LEARNING OBJECTIVES

1. Distinguish whether a variable is categorical or quantitative and, if quantitative, whether discrete or continuous.

2. Construct and describe pie charts and bar graphs for categorical data. Describe how many observations occur in a category and the modal category.

3. Construct and describe a histogram, stem-and-leaf plot, dot plot, or box plot for quantitative data. Describe the shape (symmetric or skewed), center (using mean or median), and variability (using range, standard deviation, or interquartile range) for the distribution of quantitative data.

4. Calculate and understand how to use measures of position in describing a distribution for quantitative data, including the minimum, first quartile (Q1), median, third quartile (Q3), and maximum.

5. Distinguish between a resistant and nonresistant numerical summary.

6. Construct a time plot and interpret trends over time.

7. Describe and understand how to use the empirical rule.

8. Calculate and understand what a z-score measures and how to apply the z-score (as a measure of relative standing and as a way to identify outliers).

9. Understand how to use the 1.5*IQR criterion to identify potential outliers.

10. Understand how linear transformations affect the shape, center, and variability of a distribution and the statistics that measure these features.

11. Recognize when a graph is misleading.

ANSWERS TO THE CHAPTER FIGURE QUESTIONS

Figure 2.1 It is not always clear exactly what portion or percentage of a circle the slice represents, especially when a pie has many slices. Also, some slices may be representing close to the same percentage of the circle; thus, it is not clear which is larger or smaller.

Figure 2.2 Ordering the bars from largest to smallest immediately shows the (few) categories that are the most frequent. It also shows how rapidly the heights of the bars decrease.

Figure 2.3 The number of dots above a value on the number line represents the frequency of occurrence of that value.

Figure 2.4 There's no leaf if there's no observation having that stem.

Figure 2.7 The direction of the longer tail indicates the direction of the skew.

Figure 2.8 The annual average temperatures are tending to increase over time.

Figure 2.9   The mean is pulled in the direction of the longer tail since extreme observations affect the balance point of the distribution. The median is not affected by the size of the observation.

Figure 2.10   The range would change from $10,000 to $65,000.

Figure 2.11   A deviation is positive when the observation falls above the mean and negative when the observation falls below the mean.

Figure 2.12   Since about 95% of the data fall within 2 standard deviations of the mean, about 100% − 95% = 5% fall more than 2 standard deviations from the mean.

Figure 2.13   The shape is approximately bell shaped. The center appears to be around 66 inches. The heights range from 56 to 77 inches.

Figure 2.14   The second quartile has two quarters (25% and 25%) of the data below it. Therefore, Q2 is the median since 50% of the data falls below the median.

Figure 2.15   The left whisker is drawn only to 50 because the next lowest sodium value, which is 0, is identified as a potential outlier.

Figure 2.16   The quartiles for females are (rounded) Q1 = 64, Q2 = 65, and Q3 = 67 and are shown in their correct position on the box plot for females. The quartiles for males are Q1 = 69, Q2 = 71, and Q3 = 73 and also are shown in their correct position on the box plot for the males.

Figure 2.17   Yes. The left whisker extends to the minimum (about 3.5), the left side of the box is at Q1 (about 5.5), the line inside the box is at the median (about 7), the right side of the box is at Q3 (about 9), and the outlier identified with a star is at the maximum (about 21).

Figure 2.18   The median retail price is 10 + 1.1(790) = $879.

Figure 2.19   Neither the height nor the area of the human figures accurately represents the frequencies reported.

Figure 2.20   The total enrollment increases until 2011. The STEM enrollment seems to be constant, but it would be better to plot STEM enrollments separately on a smaller scale.

STATISTICAL SOFTWARE

Art of Stat Web Apps

- **Explore Categorical Data**   This app describes the distribution of categorical variables by constructing frequency tables (proportions, percentages) and corresponding bar graphs (with various options, such as horizontal bars or Pareto charts) or pie/donut charts. Data sets from this chapter are preloaded, but you can also enter your own frequency table or raw data, e.g., by copying and pasting values from a spreadsheet. You can customize the title, subtitle, or caption of a bar chart as well as the color of the bars. You can download the bar chart as a .png file (for instance, to include it in homework) by clicking the little camera symbol in the upper right corner.

- **Explore Quantitative Data**   This app describes the distribution of quantitative data by finding all relevant summary statistics and providing histograms, box plots, dot plots and stem-and-leaf plots. Data sets used in this chapter are preloaded, but you can supply your own data by either entering (or copying and pasting from a spreadsheet) numerical observations or, for discrete data with only a few categories, enter a frequency table. A slider allows you to change the bin width of the histogram. Hovering over the histogram shows the interval and the count within that interval. Both horizontal and vertical box plots are supported, and hovering over a box plot shows the 5-number summary. Titles and subtitles for each plot are customizable, as is the color for the histogram or box plot. Download either plot as a .png file by clicking on the camera symbol that appears in the upper right corner.

- **Time Series**   This app allows you to plot basic time series data and overlay a smooth or linear trend.

R

Check out the sample R scripts posted on www.ArtofStat.com (go to the tab titled "R Code"), which replicate the entire analysis from Examples 2 through 10. Here is just a short summary.

- **Frequency Tables and Bar and Pie Charts:**   To create a frequency table when data are already available in summarized form, use the `data.frame` command to create two columns, as in:

```
> favcol <- c('red', 'blue', 'green')
```

```
> frequency <- c(25, 17, 14)
> mytab <- data.frame(favcol, frequency)
```

Then, get percentages for each category through

```
> mytab$percent <- 100*mytab$frequency/
  sum(mytab$frequency)
> mytab
  favcol frequency  percent
1    red        25 44.64286
2   blue        17 30.35714
3  green        14 25.00000
```

You can obtain a pie chart with

```
> pie(mytab$frequency, labels=mytab$favcol)
```

and a bar graph with

```
> barplot(mytab$frequency, names.arg=
mytab$ favcol)
```

If you prefer to plot percentages, use `mytab$percent` instead. If you have the individual observations, as in

```
> favcol <- c('blue', 'red', 'red', 'blue',
'green', 'red', 'blue', 'red', 'red', 'green')
```

you can get a frequency table like this

```
> mytab <- as.data.frame(table(favcol))
> colnames(mytab) <- c('favcol', 'frequency')
> mytab$percent <- 100*mytab$frequency/
sum(mytab$frequency)
```

and continue with plots as before.

- **Summary Statistics, Histograms, and Box Plots:**   If `> tvhours = c(3, 1, 0, 0, 2, 1, 3)` then `> summary(tvhours)` gives the 5-number summary and the mean. `mean, median, sd, IQR` are individual R commands used as in `> mean(tvhours)`. `> hist(tvhours)` and `> boxplot(tvhours)` give the corresponding plots.

CHAPTER EXERCISES

Practicing the Basics

2.99 Categorical or quantitative? Identify each of the following variables as categorical or quantitative.

a. Number of children in family

b. Amount of time in football game before first points scored

c. College major (English, history, chemistry,...)

d. Type of music (rock, jazz, classical, folk, other)

2.100 Continuous or discrete? Which of the following variables are continuous, when the measurements are as precise as possible?

a. Age of mother

b. Number of children in a family

c. Cooking time for preparing dinner

d. Latitude and longitude of a city

e. Population size of a city

2.101 Young noncitizens in the United States The table shows the number of 18- to 24-year-old noncitizens living in the United States between 2010 and 2012.

Noncitizens aged 18 to 24 in the United States	
Region of Birth	**Number (in Thousands)**
Africa	115
Asia	590
Europe	148
Latin America & Caribbean	1,666
Other	49
Total	**2,568**

Source: www.census.gov, U.S. Department of Commerce

a. Is Region of Birth quantitative or categorical? Show how to summarize results by adding a column of percentages to the table.

b. Which of the following is a sensible numerical summary for these data: Mode (or modal category), mean, median? Explain, and report whichever is/are sensible.

c. How would you order the Region of Birth categories for a Pareto chart? What's its advantage over the ordinary bar graph?

2.102 Cool in China A recent survey[10] asked 1,200 university students in China to pick the personality trait that most defines a person as "cool." The possible responses allowed, and the percentage making each, were individualistic and innovative (47%), stylish (13.5%), dynamic and capable (9.5%), easygoing and relaxed (7.5%), other (22.5%).

a. Identify the variable being measured.

b. Classify the variable as categorical or quantitative.

c. Which of the following methods could you use to describe these data: (i) bar chart, (ii) dot plot, (iii) box plot, (iv) median, (v) mean, (vi) mode (or modal category), (vii) IQR, (viii) standard deviation?

2.103 Chad voting problems The 2000 U.S. presidential election had various problems in Florida. One was overvotes—people mistakenly voting for more than one presidential candidate. (There were multiple minor-party candidates.) There were 110,000 overvote ballots, with Al Gore marked on 84,197 and George W. Bush on 37,731. These ballots were disqualified. Was overvoting related to the design of the ballot? The figure shows MINITAB dot plots of the overvote percentages for 65 Florida counties organized by the type of voting machine—optical scanning, Votomatic (voters manually punch out chads), and Datavote (voter presses a lever that punches out the chad mechanically)—and the number of columns on the ballot (1 or 2).

a. The overvote was highest (11.6%) in Gadsden County. Identify the number of columns and the method of registering the vote for that county.

b. Of the six ballot type and method combinations, which two seemed to perform best in terms of having relatively low percentages of overvotes?

c. How might these data be summarized further by a bar graph with six bars?

Overvote Percentages by Number of Columns on Ballot and Method of Voting

Source: A. Agresti and B. Presnell, *Statistical Science*, vol. 17, pp. 1–5, 2002.

2.104 Losing Focus A Pew Research survey of a random sample of teenagers asked how often they lose focus in class because of checking their cellphones. Of the 743 teenagers interviewed, 291 said they never lose focus, 214 said they rarely lose focus, 178 responded that they sometimes lose focus, and 60 admitted that they often lost focus.

a. Is losing focus a nominal or ordinal categorical variable?

b. When constructing a bar graph, you can order the four answer categories (i) alphabetically, (ii) from never losing focus to often losing focus, or (iii) as in a Pareto chart, according to the frequency of each category? Which do you prefer? Why?

---

[10]*Source:* Public relations firm Hill & Knowlton, as reported by *TIME* magazine.

APP **c.** Using the *Explore Categorical Data* app or some other software or by sketching, construct the bar graph for these data.

2.105 Longevity The Animals data set on the book's website has data on the average longevity (measured in years) for 21 animals. (If you use the *Explore Quantitative Data* app for this exercise, you can type or copy and paste the values for longevity from the data set into the app by selecting Your Own under Enter Data.)

APP

a. Construct a stem-and-leaf plot of longevity.

b. Construct a histogram of longevity.

c. Summarize what you see in the histogram or stem-and-leaf plot. (Most animals live to be how old? Is the distribution skewed?)

2.106 Newspaper reading Exercise 2.27 gave results for the number of times a week a person reads a daily newspaper for a sample of 36 students at the University of Georgia. The frequency table is shown below. (If you use the *Explore Quantitative Data* app for this exercise, you can enter the frequency table by first selecting Your Own under Enter Data and then selecting Frequency Table. Provide a variable name and then enter the table below.)

APP

a. Construct a dot plot of the data.

b. Construct a stem-and-leaf plot of the data. Identify the stems and the leaves.

c. The mean is 3.94. Find the median.

d. Is the distribution skewed to the left, skewed to the right, or symmetric? Explain.

No. Times	Frequency
0	2
1	4
2	4
3	8
4	4
5	5
6	2
7	4
8	2
9	1

2.107 Match the histogram Match each lettered histogram with one of the following descriptions: Skewed to the left, bimodal, symmetric, skewed to the right.

a   b

c   d

2.108 Sandwiches and protein Listed in the table below are the prices of six-inch Subway sandwiches at a particular franchise and the number of grams of protein contained in each sandwich.

APP

Sandwich	Cost ($)	Protein (g)
Black Forest Ham	3.89	19
Chicken & Bacon Ranch Melt	4.99	36
Cold Cut Combo	3.89	16
Italian B.M.T.®	4.39	19
Meatball Marinara	3.99	20
Oven Roasted Chicken	4.39	23
Roast Beef	5.09	25
Rotisserie-Style Chicken	4.89	29
Spicy Italian	3.99	18
Steak & Cheese (with American)	4.89	23
Subway Club®	4.89	24
Sweet Onion Chicken Teriyaki	4.89	25
Tuna	4.39	19
Turkey Breast	4.49	18
Veggie Delite®	3.89	9

a. Construct a stem-and-leaf plot of the protein amounts in the various sandwiches. (If you use the *Explore Quantitative Data* app, select Your Own under Enter Data, and enter the protein values in the provided box.)

b. What is the advantage of using the stem-and-leaf plot over a histogram?

c. Summarize your findings from these graphs.

2.109 Sandwiches and cost Refer to the previous exercise. Construct a stem-and-leaf plot for the cost of the sandwiches and describe the distribution.

APP

2.110 What shape do you expect? For the following variables, indicate whether you would expect its histogram to be bell shaped, skewed to the right, or skewed to the left. Explain why.

a. Number of times arrested in past year

b. Time needed to complete difficult exam (maximum time is 1 hour)

c. Assessed value of house

d. Age at death

2.111 Sketch plots For each of the following, sketch roughly what you expect a histogram to look like and explain whether the mean or the median would be greater.

a. The selling price of new homes in a city.

b. The number of children ever born per woman age 40 or over.

c. The score on an easy exam (mean = 88, standard deviation = 10, maximum = 100, minimum = 50)

d. Number of months in which subject drove a car last year

2.112 Wine Harvest in Burgundy Access the WineHarvest data set on the book's website or through the *Time Series* web app.[11] This data set holds, for each year and starting as early as 1354 (!), the number of days past August 31 that the wine harvest began for vineyards in the Burgundy region of France. A negative value implies that the harvest occurred before August 31. Construct a time plot to investigate possible trends over time and briefly comment. Data sets like this are used by climate researchers.

2.113 Median versus mean sales price of new homes The U.S. Census Bureau reported a median sales price of new houses sold in April 2019 of $342,200. Would you expect the mean sales price to have been higher or lower? Explain.

2.114 Household net worth A study reported that in 2007 the mean and median net worth of American families were $556,300 and $120,300, respectively.

a. Is the distribution of net worth for these families likely to be symmetric, skewed to the right, or skewed to the left? Explain.

b. During the Great Recession of 2008, many Americans lost wealth due to the large decline in values of assets such as homes and retirement savings. In 2009, mean and median net worth were reported as $434,782 and $91,304. Why do you think the difference in decline from 2007 to 2009 was larger for the mean than the median?

2.115 Golfers' gains During a recent Professional Golfers Association (PGA) season, 90 golfers earned at least $1 million in tournament prize money. Of those, 5 earned at least $4 million, 11 earned between $3 million and $4 million, 21 earned between $2 million and $3 million, and 53 earned between $1 million and $2 million.

a. Would the data for all 90 golfers be symmetric, skewed to the left, or skewed to the right?

b. Two measures of central tendency of the golfers' winnings were $2,090,012 and $1,646,853. Which do you think is the mean and which is the median?

2.116 Hiking In a guidebook about interesting hikes to take in national parks, each hike is classified as easy, medium, or hard and by the length of the hike (in miles). Which classification is quantitative and which is categorical? Distinguish further between nominal/ordinal and discrete/continuous.

2.117 Lengths of hikes Refer to the previous exercise.

a. Give an example of five hike lengths such that the mean and median are equal.

b. Give an example of five hike lengths such that the mode is 2, the median is 3, and the mean is larger than the median.

2.118 Central Park monthly temperatures The graph below (obtained from the second tab of the *Explore Quantitative Data* app) uses dot plots to compare the distributions of Central Park temperatures from 1869 to 2018 for the months of January and July.

a. Describe the shape of each of the two distributions.

b. Estimate the balance point for each of the two distributions and compare.

c. Compare the variability of the two distributions. Estimate from the dot plots how the range and standard deviation for the January temperature distribution compare to the July temperature distribution. Are you surprised by your results for these two months?

2.119 What does s equal?

a. For an exam given to a class, the students' scores ranged from 35 to 98, with a mean of 74. Which of the following is the most realistic value for the standard deviation: −10, 1, 12, 60? Clearly explain what is unrealistic about the other values.

b. The sample mean for a data set equals 80. Which of the following is an impossible value for the standard deviation? 200, 0, −20? Why?

2.120 Female heights According to a recent report from the U.S. National Center for Health Statistics, females between 25 and 34 years of age have a bell-shaped distribution for height, with a mean of 65 inches and a standard deviation of 3.5 inches.

a. Give an interval within which about 95% of the heights fall.

b. What is the height for a female who is 3 standard deviations below the mean? Would this be a rather unusual height? Why?

2.121 Energy and water consumption In parts a and b, what shape do you expect for the distributions of electricity use and water use in a recent month in Gainesville, Florida? Why? (Data supplied by N. T. Kamhoot, Gainesville Regional Utilities.)

---

[11] *Source:* Daux, Garcia de Cortazar-Atauri, Yiou et al., An open-database of Grape Harvest dates for climate research: data description and quality assessment. Climate of the Past, vol. 8, pp. 1403–1418, 2012

a. Residential electricity used had mean = 780 and standard deviation = 506 kilowatt hours (Kwh). The minimum usage was 3 Kwh and the maximum was 9,390 Kwh.

b. Water consumption had mean = 7,100 and standard deviation = 6,200 (gallons).

2.122 Hurricane damage The histogram shows the distribution of the damage (in billion dollars) of the 30 most costly hurricanes hitting the U.S. mainland between 1900 and 2010. (Numbers are inflation adjusted and in 2010 dollars). The data are available in the Hurricane file on the book's website and in the *Explore Quantitative Data* app.

a. Describe the shape of the distribution.

b. Would you use the mean or median to describe the center? Why?

c. Verify with technology that the mean is 13.6, Q1 = 5.7, median = 7.9, and Q3 = 11.8. (Note that different software uses slightly different definitions for the quartiles.)

d. Write a short paragraph describing the distribution of hurricane damage.

2.123 More hurricane damage Refer to the previous exercise about hurricane damage and the histogram shown there.

a. For this data, 93% of damages (i.e., all but the two most expensive) fall within 1 standard deviation of the mean. Why is this so different from the 68% the empirical rule suggests?

b. How would removing the costliest hurricane (Katrina in 2005, shown on the far right in the histogram) from the data set affect the (i) mean, (ii) median, (iii) standard deviation, (iv) IQR, and (v) 10th percentile?

2.124 Student heights The Heights data file on the book's website or in the *Explore Quantitative Data* app when selecting the Several Groups tab has heights for female and male students (in inches). For males, the mean is 70.9 and the standard deviation is 2.9. For females, the mean is 65.3 and the standard deviation is 3.0.

a. Describe the male heights by using the empirical rule.

b. Compare the center and variability of the height distributions for females and males.

c. The lowest observation for males was 62. How many standard deviations below the mean is it?

2.125 Cigarette tax How do cigarette taxes per pack vary from one state to the next? The data set of 2003 cigarette taxes for all 50 states and Washington, D.C., is in the Cigarette Tax data file on the book's website. (If you use the *Explore Quantitative Data* app, open the file and copy and paste the values into the app by selecting Your Own under Enter Data.)

a. Use the app or other software to construct a histogram. Write a short description of the distribution, noting shape and possible outliers.

b. Find the mean and median for the cigarette taxes. Which is larger, and why would you have expected that from the histogram?

c. Find the standard deviation and interpret it.

2.126 Cereal sugar values Revisit the sugar data for breakfast cereals that are given in Example 4.

a. Interpret the box plot in the figure (constructed via the *Explore Quantitative Data* app) by giving approximate values for the five-number summary.

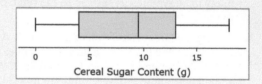

b. What does the box of the box plot suggest about possible skew?

c. The mean is 8.75 and the standard deviation is 5.32. Find the z-score associated with the minimum sugar value of 0. Interpret.

2.127 NASDAQ stock prices The data values below represent the closing prices of the 20 most actively traded stocks on the NASDAQ Stock Exchange (rounded to the nearest dollar) for a particular trading day. (If you use the *Explore Quantitative Data* app, you can enter these values in the box after selecting Your Own under Enter Data.)

| 3 | 60 | 40 | 87 | 26 | 9 | 37 | 23 | 26 | 9 |
| 4 | 78 | 4 | 7 | 26 | 7 | 52 | 8 | 52 | 13 |

a. Sketch a dot plot or construct a stem-and-leaf plot.

b. Find the median, the first quartile, and the third quartile.

c. Sketch a box plot. What feature of the distribution displayed in the plot in part a is not obvious in the box plot? (*Hint:* Are there any gaps in the data?)

2.128 Temperatures in Central Park Access the Central Park temps data file on the book's website. (If you are using the *Explore Quantitative Data* app, click on the Several Groups tab and copy and paste the March values into one box and the November values into the second box, selecting Your Own under Enter Data and setting the number of groups equal to 2. The app provides side-by-side histograms and box plots.)

a. Using software, construct a histogram of average March temperatures and interpret, noting shape, center, and variability.

b. Construct a histogram of average November temperatures and interpret, noting shape, center, and variability.

c. Using the two histograms, make comparative statements regarding the March and November temperatures.

d. Make a side-by-side box plot of March and November temperatures. How is the side-by-side box plot more useful than the histograms for comparing the two months?

2.129 Teachers' salaries According to the Statistical Abstract of the United States, 2012, average salary (in dollars) of primary and secondary school classroom teachers in 2009 in the United States varied among states with a five-number summary of: minimum = 35,070, Q1 = 45,840, median = 48,630, Q3 = 55,820, maximum = 69,118. (Data available in the teacher_salary file.)

a. Find and interpret the range and interquartile range.

b. Sketch a box plot, marking the five-number summary on it.

c. Predict the direction of skew for this distribution. Explain.

d. If the distribution, although skewed, is approximately bell shaped, which of the following would be the most realistic value for the standard deviation: (i) 100, (ii) 1,000, (iii) 7,000, or (iv) 25,000? Explain your reasoning.

2.130 Health insurance In 2009, the five-number summary statistics for the distribution of statewide percentage of people without health insurance had a minimum of 4.4% (Massachusetts), Q1 = 12.35%, median = 14.8%, Q3 = 17.3%, and maximum of 26.1% (Texas). (Statistical Abstract of the United States, data available on the book's website as health_coverage.)

a. Do you think the distribution is symmetric, skewed right, or skewed left? Why?

b. Which is most plausible for the standard deviation: −16, 0, 4, 20, or 25? Why? Explain what is unrealistic about the other values.

2.131 What box plot do you expect? For each of the following variables, sketch a box plot that would be plausible.

a. Exam score (min = 0, max = 100, mean = 87, standard deviation = 10)

b. IQ (mean = 100 and standard deviation = 16)

c. Weekly religious contribution (median = $10 and mean = $17)

2.132 High school graduation rates The distribution of high school graduation rates in the United States in 2009 had a minimum value of 79.9 (Texas), first quartile of 84.0, median of 87.4, third quartile of 89.8, and maximum value

of 91.8 (Wyoming). (Statistical Abstract of the United States, data available on the book's website.)

a. Report the range and the interquartile range.

b. Would a box plot show any potential outliers? Explain.

c. The mean graduation rate is 86.9, and the standard deviation is 3.4. For these data, does any state have a z-score that is larger than 3 in absolute value? Explain.

2.133 SAT scores The U.S. statewide average total SAT scores math + reading + writing for 2010 are summarized in the box plot. These SAT scores are out of a possible 2,400. (Data available on the book's website.)

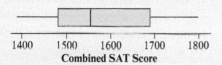

Combined SAT Score

a. Explain how the box plot gives you information about the distribution shape.

b. Using the box plot, give the approximate value for each component of the five-number summary. Interpret each.

c. A histogram for these data is also shown. What feature of the distribution would be missed by using only the box plot?

Combined SAT Score

2.134 Blood pressure A World Health Organization study (the MONICA project) of health in various countries reported that in Canada, systolic blood pressure readings have a mean of 121 and a standard deviation of 16. A reading above 140 is considered to be high blood pressure.

a. What is the z-score for a blood pressure reading of 140? How is this z-score interpreted?

b. The systolic blood pressure values have a bell-shaped distribution. Report an interval within which about 95% of the systolic blood pressure values fall.

2.135 No cereal sodium The cereal sodium values have a mean of 167 and a standard deviation of 77.3. Find the z-score for the cereal that has a sodium value of 0. Interpret.

2.136 Who was Roger Maris? Roger Maris, who spent most of his professional baseball career with the New York Yankees, held the record for the most home runs in one season (61) from 1961 until 1998, when the record was broken by Mark McGwire. Maris played in the major leagues from 1957 to 1968. The number of home runs he hit in each year that he played is summarized in MINITAB output as shown.

```
Variable  N        Mean      Median   StDev
RMHR      12       22.92     19.50    15.98
Variable  Minimum  Maximum   Q1       Q3
RMHR      5.00     61.00     10.00    31.75
```

a. Use the 3 standard deviation criterion to determine whether any potential outliers are present.

b. The criterion in part a requires the distribution to be approximately bell shaped. Is there any evidence here to contradict this? Explain.

c. A sports writer commented that Roger Maris hit *only* 13 home runs in 1966. Was this unusual for Maris? Comment, using statistical justification.

Concepts and Investigations

2.137 Inconvenient Truth The data journalism website fivethirtyeight.com, which often uses statistical analysis on topics in politics, economics, science, life, and sports, published the following graph on ratings of the 2017 movie "An Inconvenient Sequel: Truth to Power," a documentary by Al Gore about climate change.[12] Of the 2,645 IMDb users who rated the film as of August 2017, about 38% gave the film a 1 out of 10 while about 34% gave the film a 10 out of 10.

a. Is this a unimodal or bimodal distribution?

b. What do you think may have contributed to the particular shape of this distribution?

c. What would you predict to be the shape of the distribution of ratings for a popular movie such as "Avengers: Endgame"? Symmetric, left- or right-skewed, or bimodal? Explain.

2.138 How much spent on haircuts? Is there a difference in how much males and females spend on haircuts? Access the Georgia Student Survey data file on the book's website or use your class data to explore this question, using appropriate graphical and numerical methods. Write a brief report describing your analyses and conclusions. You can use the *Explore Quantitative Data* app to copy and paste the values from the data file into the app. Click on the Several Groups tab and select Own Data under Enter Data. Then, copy

and paste the values into the boxes and obtain summary statistics and plots such as side-by-side box plots.

2.139 Controlling asthma A study of 13 children suffering from asthma (*Clinical and Experimental Allergy,* vol. 20, pp. 429–432, 1990) compared single inhaled doses of formoterol (F) and salbutamol (S). Each child was evaluated using both medications. The outcome measured was the child's peak expiratory flow (PEF) eight hours following treament. Describe the distribution of PEF under each treatment and compare them. You can use the *Explore Quantitative Data* app to enter the data below. Go to the Several Groups tab, select Own Data under Enter Data and then type in the data below. This will show summary statistics and plots like side-by-side box plots or dot plots to compare the distributions graphically.

Child	F	S
1	310	270
2	385	370
3	400	310
4	310	260
5	410	380
6	370	300
7	410	390
8	320	290
9	330	365
10	250	210
11	380	350
12	340	260
13	220	90

a. Construct plots to compare formoterol and salbutamol. Write a short summary comparing the two distributions of the peak expiratory flow.

b. Consider the distribution of differences between the PEF levels of the two medications. Find the 13 differences and construct and interpret a plot of the differences. If on the average there is no difference between the PEF level for the two brands, where would you expect the differences to be centered?

2.140 Youth unemployment by gender The side-by-side box plots below show the unemployment rate among 15- to 24-year-olds in 28 European nations for each gender. The two outliers shown for each box plot refer to the same countries, Greece and Spain. Write a short paragraph comparing the distribution for the males to the one for the females. (Data in youth_unemployment available on the book's website.)

2.141 **You give examples** Give an example of a variable that you'd expect to have a distribution that is

a. Approximately symmetric

b. Skewed to the right

c. Skewed to the left

d. Bimodal

e. Skewed to the right, with a mode and median of 0 but a positive mean

2.142 **Political conservatism and liberalism** Where do Americans tend to fall on the conservative–liberal political spectrum? The General Social Survey asks, "I'm going to show you a seven-point scale on which the political views that people might hold are arranged from extremely liberal, point 1, to extremely conservative, point 7. Where would you place yourself on this scale?" The table shows the seven-point scale and the distribution of 2,247 respondents for a survey conducted in 2018.

Score	Category	Frequency
1	Extremely liberal	122
2	Liberal	278
3	Slightly liberal	256
4	Moderate	855
5	Slightly conservative	283
6	Conservative	354
7	Extremely conservative	99

(*Source:* Data from CSM, UC Berkeley.)

a. What type of variable results from the question the GSS is asking? And what type of variable is implied when using the scores 1 through 7 to represent the initial categories?

APP b. Find the mean score. (*Hint:* You can do this using the *Explore Quantitative Data* app, where you select Your Own under Enter Data and then choose Frequency Table to enter the table below. You can also get the mean by multiplying each score by the frequency it occurred, summing up these values and then dividing by the total number of observations.)

c. Identify the mode (or modal category).

d. In which category does the median fall? Why?

2.143 **Mode but not median and mean** The previous exercise showed how to find the mean and median when a categorical variable has ordered categories.

a. A categorical variable that does *not* have ordered categories (such as choice of religious affiliation or choice of major in college) is called what?

b. Why does it not make sense to assign scores to such a variable?

c. For such a variable, the mode (or modal category) applies, but not the mean or median. Explain why.

Multiple Choice or True/False

2.144 **GRE scores** In a study of graduate students who took the Graduate Record Exam (GRE), the Educational Testing Service reported that for the quantitative exam, U.S. citizens had a mean of 529 and a standard deviation of 127, whereas non-U.S. citizens had a mean of 649 and a standard deviation of 129. Which of the following is true?

a. Both groups had about the same amount of variability in their scores, but non-U.S. citizens performed better, on the average, than U.S. citizens.

b. If the distribution of scores was approximately bell shaped, then almost no U.S. citizens scored below 400.

c. If the scores range between 200 and 800, then probably the scores for non-U.S. citizens were symmetric and bell shaped.

d. A non-U.S. citizen who scored 3 standard deviations below the mean had a score of 200.

2.145 **Fact about s** Which statement about the standard deviation s is false?

a. s can never be negative.

b. s can never be zero.

c. For bell-shaped distributions, about 95% of the data fall within $\bar{x} \pm 2s$.

d. s is a nonresistant (sensitive to outliers) measure of variability, as is the range.

2.146 **Relative GPA** The mean GPA for all students at a community college in the fall semester was 2.77. A student with a GPA of 2.0 wants to know her relative standing in relation to the mean GPA. A numerical summary that would be useful for this purpose is the

a. standard deviation

b. median

c. interquartile range

d. number of students at the community college

2.147 **Facts about z-scores** A set of observations has mean 80 and standard deviation 10. When converting these observations to z-scores, the z-scores will have

a. mean 80 and standard deviation 10

b. mean 80 and standard deviation 1

c. mean 1 and standard deviation 1

d. mean 0 and standard deviation 1

2.148 **Histograms and box plots** Which two features of a distribution are apparent from a histogram but not from a box plot:

a. Left-skew

b. Right-skew

c. Number of mounds

d. Extreme Outliers

e. Gaps

2.149 True or false: Statistics for location

a. The mean, median, and mode can never all be the same.

b. The mean is always one of the data points.

c. When n is odd, the median is one of the data points.

d. The median is the same as the second quartile and the 50th percentile.

2.150 Bad statistic A teacher summarizes grades on an exam by Min = 26, Q1 = 67, Q2 = 80, Q3 = 87, Max = 100, Mean = 76, Mode = 100, Standard deviation = 76, IQR = 20. She incorrectly recorded one of these. Which one was it?

a. Q1

b. Median

c. Q3

d. Mean

e. Standard deviation

f. IQR

2.151 True or false: Soccer According to a story in the Guardian newspaper (football.guardian.co.uk), in the United Kingdom the mean wage for a Premiership player in 2006 was £676,000. True or false: If the income distribution is skewed to the right, then the median salary was even larger than £676,000.

Advanced Exercises

2.152 Male heights According to a recent report from the U.S. National Center for Health Statistics, for males aged 25–34 years, 2% of their heights are 64 inches or less, 8% are 66 inches or less, 27% are 68 inches or less, 39% are 69 inches or less, 54% are 70 inches or less, 68% are 71 inches or less, 80% are 72 inches or less, 93% are 74 inches or less, and 98% are 76 inches or less. These are called **cumulative percentages**.

a. Which category has the median height? Explain why.

b. Nearly all the heights fall between 60 and 80 inches, with fewer than 1% falling outside that range. If the heights are approximately bell-shaped, give a rough approximation for the standard deviation of the heights. Explain your reasoning.

2.153 Range and standard deviation approximation Use the empirical rule to explain why the standard deviation of a bell-shaped distribution for a large data set is often roughly related to the range by evaluating Range $\approx 6s$. (For small data sets, one may not get any extremely large or small observations, and the range may be smaller, for instance about 4 standard deviations.)

2.154 Range the least resistant We've seen that measures such as the mean, the range, and the standard deviation can be highly influenced by outliers. Explain why the range is worst in this sense. (*Hint:* As the sample size increases,

explain how a single extreme outlier has less effect on the mean and standard deviation but can still have a large effect on the range.)

2.155 Using MAD to measure variability The standard deviation is the most popular measure of variability from the mean. It uses squared deviations because the ordinary deviations sum to zero. An alternative measure is the **mean absolute deviation**, $\Sigma|x - \bar{x}|/n$.

a. Explain why larger values of this measure indicate greater variability of the observations.

b. Would the MAD be more, or less, resistant than the standard deviation? Explain.

2.156 Proof that z-scores have mean 0, standard deviation 1 Using the results given in the summary box in the chapter on linear transformations (Section 2.6), show that

a. the mean for the z-scores is 0. (*Hint:* Show that the sum of the deviations $x - \bar{x}$ is zero.)

b. the standard deviation of the z-scores is 1. (*Hint:* Write z-scores as a linear transformation of the form $z = c + dx$, find c and d and then apply the formulas in the summary box.)

Student Activities

2.157 Open the *Explore Quantitative Data* app, pick one of the preloaded data sets, and use the provided slider for the binwidth of the histogram to change it. Mention if your interpretation of the shape of a distribution changes as you change the binwidth.

2.158 Access the *Mean versus Median* app, select Create Your Own for the initial distribution, and click in the gray area to create points (data) that follow

a. a roughly symmetric distribution over the range from 0 to 100.

b. a right-skewed distribution over the range from 0 to 100.

c. a left-skewed distribution over the range from 0 to 100.

2.159 The average student Refer to the data file you created in the end of Chapter 1 class survey (Exercise 1.50). For variables chosen by your instructor, describe the "average student" in your class. Prepare a one-page summary report. In class, students will compare their analyses of what makes up an average student. In fact, the "average student" is a misnomer. For example, rather than saying "The average student spends $12 per haircut and studies for 2 hours per day," it is better to say that "On average, students spend $12 per haircut and study 2 hours per day."

2.160 **GSS** Access the General Social Survey at sda.berkeley
.edu. (See Activity 1 in Chapter 1.)

  a. Find the frequency table and histogram for Example
  6 on TV watching from the 2018 survey. (*Hint:* Enter
  TVHOURS as the row variable, YEAR(2018) as
  the selection filter, select No Weights as the weight

option, choose bar chart for Type of Chart, and click
Run the Table.)

  b. Repeat part a but now with the row variable
  POLVIEWS, which measures a respondent's political
  view ranging from very liberal to very conservative.
  See Exercise 2.142.

BIBLIOGRAPHY

Franklin, Christine A. (2002). "The Other Life of Florence
Nightingale," *Mathematics Teaching in the Middle School*
7(6): 337–339.

Tukey, J. W. (1977). *Exploratory Data Analysis*. Reading,
MA: Addison-Wesley.

In Chapter 2, we distinguished between two major types of variables (categorical and quantitative) and explored ways of describing their distribution by using graphs and numerical summaries. However, we rarely look at a single variable in isolation and would miss important connections if we did. Many interesting questions revolve around the relationship between two variables and how they interact. This chapter presents methods of exploring and describing the nature of such relationships.

Exploring Relationships Between Two Variables

Example 1

Smoking and Your Health

Picture the Scenario

Although numerous studies have concluded that cigarette smoking is harmful to your health in many ways, one study found conflicting evidence. As part of the study, 1,314 women in the United Kingdom were asked whether they smoked.[1] Twenty years later, a follow-up survey observed whether each woman was deceased or still alive. The researchers studied the possible link between whether a woman smoked and whether she survived the 20-year study period. During that period, 24% of the smokers died and 31% of the non-smokers died. The higher death rate for the nonsmokers is surprising.

Questions to Explore

■ How can we describe the relationship between smoking and survival with numbers (descriptive statistics)?

■ Is smoking actually beneficial to your health, considering that a smaller percentage of smokers died?

■ If we observe a link between smoking status and survival status, is there something that could explain how this happened?

Thinking Ahead

In this study, we can identify two categorical variables. One is smoking status—whether a woman was a smoker (yes or no). The other is survival status—whether a woman survived the 20-year study period (yes or no). In practice, research investigations almost always analyze more than one variable. Exploring the relationship between two variables is often the primary focus.

This chapter presents descriptive statistics for examining data on two variables. We'll analyze what these data suggest about the link between smoking and survival and learn that a third variable can influence the results. In this case, we'll see that the age of the woman is important. We'll revisit this example in Example 17 and analyze the data while taking age into account as well.

---

[1]Described by D. R. Appleton et al., *American Statistician*, vol. 50, pp. 340–341 (1996).

Example 1 has two categorical variables, but we'll also learn how to examine links between pairs of quantitative variables. For instance, we might want to answer questions such as, "What's the relationship between the daily amount of gasoline use by automobiles and the amount of air pollution?" or "Do high schools with higher per-student funding tend to have higher mean SAT scores for their students?"

Response Variables and Explanatory Variables

When we analyze data on two variables, our first step is to distinguish between the **response variable** and the **explanatory variable**.

In Words

The data analysis examines how the outcome on the **response** variable *depends on* or is *explained by* the value of the **explanatory** variable.

Response Variable and Explanatory Variable

The **response variable** is the outcome variable on which comparisons are made for different values of the **explanatory variable**.

When the **explanatory variable** is categorical, it defines the groups to be compared with respect to the response variable. When the explanatory variable is quantitative, we examine how different values of the explanatory variable relate to changes in the response variable.

In Example 1, survival status (whether a woman is alive after 20 years) is the response variable. Smoking status (whether the woman was a smoker) is the explanatory variable. We are interested in how survival (the response) compares across the two groups (smokers/nonsmokers) defined by the explanatory variable. In a study of air pollution in several countries, the carbon dioxide (CO_2) level in a country's atmosphere might be a response variable, and the explanatory variable could be the country's amount of gasoline use for automobiles. We would then investigate how more or less gasoline usage relates to changes in CO_2 levels. In a study of achievement for a sample of college students, college GPA might be a response variable, and the explanatory variable could be the number of hours a week spent studying. In each of these studies, there is a natural explanatory/response relationship between these quantitative variables.

Some studies regard *either* or *both* variables as response variables. For example, this might be the case if we were analyzing data on smoking status and on alcohol status (whether the subject has at least one alcoholic drink per week) or data on the relationship between height and weight. There is no clear distinction as to which variable would be explanatory for the other.

The main purpose of a data analysis with two variables is to investigate whether there is an **association** and to describe the nature of that association.

In Words

When there's an **association**, the likelihood of particular values for one variable depends on the values of the other variable. It is more likely that students with a high school GPA near 4 will have a college GPA above 3.5 than students whose high school GPA is near 3. So high school GPA and college GPA have an association.

Association Between Two Variables

An **association** exists between two variables if particular values for one variable are more likely to occur with certain values of the other variable.

In Example 1, surviving the study period was more likely for smokers than for nonsmokers. So, there is an association between survival status and smoking status. For higher levels of gasoline use, does the CO_2 level in the atmosphere tend to be higher? If so, then there is an association between gasoline use and CO_2 level.

This chapter presents methods for studying whether associations exist and for describing how strong they are. We explore associations between categorical variables in Section 3.1 and between quantitative variables in Sections 3.2 and 3.3.

3.1 The Association Between Two Categorical Variables

How would you respond to the question, "Taken all together, would you say that you are very happy, pretty happy, or not too happy?" We could summarize the percentage of people who have each of the three possible outcomes for this categorical variable using a table, a bar graph, or a pie chart. However, we'd probably want to know how the percentages depend on the values for other variables, such as a person's marital status (married, unmarried). Is the percentage who report being very happy higher for married people than for unmarried people?

We'll now look at ways to summarize the association between two categorical variables, such as happiness and marital status. You can practice these concepts with data from the General Social Survey in Exercises 3.3, 3.11, and 3.64.

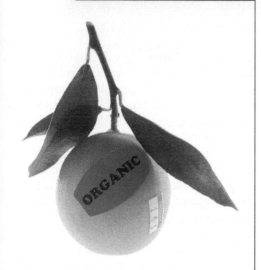

Categorical Explanatory and Response Variables ◄

Example 2

Pesticides in Organic Foods

Picture the Scenario

One appeal of eating organic foods is the belief that they are pesticide-free and thus healthier. However, little cropland acreage is organic (less than 2% in the United States), and consumers pay a premium for organic food.

How can we investigate how the percentage of foods carrying pesticide residues compares for organic and conventionally grown foods? The Consumers Union led a study based on data from the U.S. Department of Agriculture (USDA), which collected food samples from a representative sample of retail outlets across the United States.[2] The presence or absence of pesticide residues on these food samples and whether the food was grown conventionally or organically are categorical variables. As in the case of a single categorical variable (frequency table), we are going to display counts for the categories in a table. But because we now have two variables, we list the categories of one variable in the rows and the categories of the other variable in the columns of the table. Table 3.1 illustrates this with the data for this study. The body of this table shows the counts for the four possible combinations of the categories of the two variables.

Table 3.1 Frequencies for Food Type and Pesticide Status

The row totals and the column totals are the frequencies for the categories of each variable. The counts inside the table give information about the association.

Food Type	Pesticide Residues		Total
	Present	Not Present	
Organic	29	98	127
Conventional	19,485	7,086	26,571
Total	19,514	7,184	26,698

Questions to Explore

a. What is the response variable, and what is the explanatory variable?

b. Only 127 organic food types were sampled compared to 26,571 conventional ones. Despite this huge imbalance, can we still make a fair comparison?

---

[2]*Source: Food Additives and Contaminants* 2002, vol. 19. no. 5, 427–446.

c. How does the proportion of foods showing pesticide residues compare for the two food types?

d. What proportion of all sampled food types contained pesticide residues?

Think It Through

a. Pesticide residues, namely whether pesticide residues are present or absent, is the outcome of interest. The food type, organic or conventionally grown, is the variable that defines two groups to be compared on their pesticide status. So, pesticide residues is the response variable and food type is the explanatory variable.

b. We can't compare the absolute numbers for each food type in Table 3.1 directly. However, by looking at relative frequencies, i.e., the proportions, a fair comparison can be made.

c. From Table 3.1, 29 out of 127 organic food samples contained pesticide residues. The proportion with pesticides is $29/127 = 0.228$. Likewise, 19,485 out of 26,571 conventionally grown food samples contained pesticide residues. The proportion is $19,485/26,571 = 0.733$, much higher than for organic foods. Since $0.733/0.228 = 3.2$, the relative occurrence of pesticide residues for conventionally grown produce is approximately three times that for organically grown produce.

d. The overall proportion of food samples with pesticide residues is the total number with pesticide residues out of the total number of food samples, or

$$(29 + 19,485)/(127 + 26,571) = 19,514/26,698 = 0.731.$$

We can find this result using the column totals of Table 3.1.

Insight

The value of 0.731 for the overall proportion of food samples with pesticide residues is close to the proportion for conventionally grown foods alone, which we found to be 0.733. This is because conventionally grown foods make up a high percentage of the sample. (From the row totals, the proportion of the sampled items that were conventionally grown was $26,571/26,698 = 0.995$.) In summary, pesticide residues occurred in more than 73% of the sampled items, and they were much more common (about three times as common) for conventionally grown than organic foods.

▶ *Try Exercise 3.3*

Did You Know?

Should we be alarmed that about 73% of the food tested contained pesticide residues? The study stated that the level is usually far below the limits set by the Environmental Protection Agency. Scientists did find that the pesticide residues on organic produce were generally less toxic. ◀

Contingency Tables

Table 3.1 has two categorical variables: food type and pesticide residues. We can analyze the categorical variables separately, through the column totals for pesticide residues and the row totals for food type. These totals are the category counts for the separate variables. For instance, 19,514 for the present and 7,184 for the not present categories of pesticide residues. We can also study the association between them, as we did by using the counts for the category combinations in the body of the table to find proportions, in Example 2, part c. Table 3.1 is an example of a **contingency table**.

> Contingency Table
>
> A **contingency table** is a display for **two categorical variables**. Its rows list the categories of one variable and its columns list the categories of the other variable. Each entry in the table, called a **cell**, gives the count for a particular pair of categories.

	Pesticide Residues		
Food Type	Present	Not Present	Total
Organic	29	98	127
Conven.	19,485	7,086	26,571
Total	19,514	7,184	26,698

A cell

For instance, the first cell in the second row of Table 3.1 (displayed again in the margin) shows the frequency 19,485. This is the number of conventional food types with pesticide residues present. The process of taking a data file and finding the frequencies for the cells of a contingency table is referred to as **cross-tabulation** or **cross-classification** of the data. Table 3.1 is formed by cross-tabulation of food type and pesticide status for the 26,698 sampled food items. When deciding which variable to use as the row and which as the column variable, we look for the role it plays. The response variable is typically used as the column variable, and the explanatory variable is used to form the rows of the contingency table.

Conditional Proportions

Consider the question, "Is there a difference between organically and conventionally grown foods in terms of their pesticide status?" To answer, we find the proportions of food samples with pesticides present within each category of food type and compare them. From Example 2, the proportions are $29/127 = 0.228$ for organic foods and $19,485/26,571 = 0.733$ for conventionally grown foods.

These proportions are called **conditional proportions** because their formation is **conditional** on (in this example) food type. Restricting our attention to organic foods, the proportion of organic food items with pesticides present equals 0.23. And focusing just on conventional food, the proportion of conventional food items with pesticides present equals 0.73. Table 3.2 shows the conditional proportions.

Recall

We obtain 0.23 from 29/127 and 0.77 from 98/127, the cell counts divided by the first row total. ◀

Table 3.2 Conditional Proportions on Pesticide Status for Two Food Types

These conditional proportions (using two decimal places) treat pesticide status as the response variable. The sample size n in the last column shows the total on which the conditional proportions are based.

	Pesticide Residues			
Food Type	Present	Not Present	Total	n
Organic	0.23	0.77	**1.00**	127
Conventional	0.73	0.27	**1.00**	26,571

The conditional proportions in each row sum to 1.0. The sample size n for each set of conditional proportions is listed so you can determine the frequencies on which the conditional proportions were based. *Whenever we distinguish between a response variable and an explanatory variable, it is natural to form conditional proportions (based on the explanatory variable) for categories of the response variable.*

By contrast, the proportion of *all* sampled food items with pesticide residues, which we found in part d of Example 2, is not a conditional proportion. It is not found for a particular food type. We ignored the information on food type and used the counts in the bottom margin of the table to form the proportion $19,514/26,698 = 0.731$. Such a proportion is called a **marginal proportion**. It is found using counts in the *margin* of the table.

Now that we know how to find conditional proportions numerically from a contingency table, let's study how we can represent them graphically. This will help us with visualizing the association between two categorical variables.

Caution

Conditional proportions refer to a particular row (a particular category of the explanatory variable) of the contingency table. **Marginal proportions** refer to the margins of the contingency table. ◀

Graphing Conditional ◄ Proportions

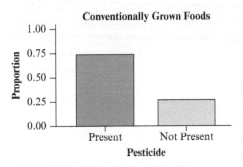

▲ Figure 3.1 Bar Graphs of Conditional Proportions on Pesticide Status. In these graphs, the conditional proportions are shown separately for each food type. **Question** Can you think of a way to construct a single graph that makes it easier to compare the food types on the pesticide status?

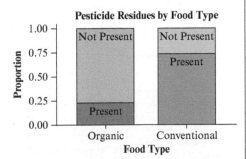

Stacked Bar Graph This type of graph stacks the proportions for pesticides present and not present on top of each other.

Example 3

Comparing Pesticide Residues for the Food Types

Picture the Scenario

For the food type and pesticide status, we've now seen two ways to display the data in a table. Table 3.1 showed cell frequencies in a contingency table, and Table 3.2 showed conditional proportions.

Questions to Explore

a. How can we use a single graph to show the association?

b. What does the graph tell us?

Think It Through

a. We've seen that a comparison of the two food types on the presence or absence of pesticide residues, the response variable, uses the conditional proportions for each food type (shown in Table 3.2). Figure 3.1 in the margin shows bar graphs of the conditional proportions, one graph for organic foods and another for conventionally grown foods. More efficiently, we can construct a single bar graph that shows the bars for the conditional proportions side by side, as in Figure 3.2. This is called a **side-by-side bar graph**. Because pesticide residues are either present or not present, one of these two categories is redundant, and we only show the conditional proportions for the "present" category for the two food types.

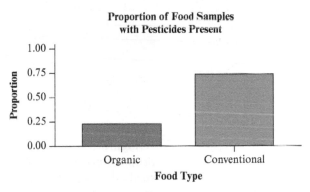

▲ Figure 3.2 Conditional Proportions for Pesticide Status, Given the Food Type. The graph shows the proportion of food samples with pesticides present for both organically and conventionally grown food. It is called a side-by-side bar graph and allows an easy and direct comparison of the conditional proportions. **Question** Using the information displayed in the graph, how would you describe the difference between organic and conventionally grown foods with regard to pesticide residues?

An alternative display, shown in the margin, compares the conditional proportions for each food type by **stacking** the proportion present and not present on top of each other. This graph is referred to as a stacked bar graph. The advantage of either graph is that it allows an easy comparison of the conditional proportions across the two food types.

b. Figure 3.2 clearly shows that the proportion of foods with pesticides present is much higher for conventionally grown food than for organically grown food.

Insight

Chapter 2 used bar graphs to display proportions for a single categorical variable. With two variables, bar graphs usually display conditional proportions, as in Figure 3.2. This display is useful for making comparisons, such as the way Figure 3.2 compares organic and conventionally grown foods in terms of the proportion of food samples with pesticide residues present.

To enter contingency tables when both variables have just two categories, use the *Association Between Two Categorical Variables* app. For contingency tables where one or both variables have more than two categories, use the *Explore Categorical Data* app and click on the Two Variables tab. Both apps provide conditional and marginal proportions and side-by-side or stacked bar graphs. We'll see a screenshot from this app in Example 4.

▶ **Try Exercise 3.4**

Looking for an Association

Studying the conditional proportions helps us judge whether there is an *association* between the variables. For instance, Table 3.2 suggests that there is a strong association between food type and pesticide status because the proportion of food items with pesticides present differs considerably (0.23 versus 0.73) between the two food types. There would be *no association* if, instead, the proportion with pesticides present had been the same for each food type. For instance, *suppose* that for **either food type**, 40% of the food samples had pesticides present, as shown in Table 3.3; the conditional proportions would then be the same for each food type. This would indicate that pesticide status is not associated with, or **independent** of, food type.

In Practice

When forming a contingency table, determine whether one variable should be the response variable. If there is a clear explanatory/response distinction, that dictates which way the conditional proportions are computed. In some cases, either variable could be the response variable, such as in cross-tabulating belief in heaven (yes, no) with belief in hell (yes, no). Then conditional proportions can be computed, with either variable playing the role of the explanatory variable.

Table 3.3 Hypothetical Conditional Proportions on Pesticide Status for Each Food Type, Showing No Association

The conditional proportions for the response variable (pesticide residues) categories are the same for each food type.

Food Type	Pesticide Residues		Total
	Present	**Not Present**	**Total**
Organic	0.40	0.60	**1.00**
Conventional	0.40	0.60	**1.00**

Figure 3.3 shows a side-by-side bar graph for the hypothetical conditional proportions from Table 3.3. The figure in the margin shows the corresponding stacked version. Compare Figure 3.3, no association, with Figure 3.2, which shows an association. In Figure 3.3, for both food types, 40% of the samples had pesticides present. This indicates **no association** between food type and pesticide status. The conditional proportions are **the same** (40% present, 60% not present), whether the food type is organic or conventional. By contrast, the distribution of pesticide status looks quite different for the two food types in Figure 3.2

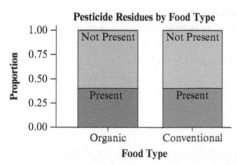

Stacked Bar Graph showing identical distributions.

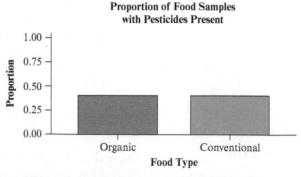

▲ **Figure 3.3** Hypothetical Conditional Proportions on Pesticide Status, Given Food Type, Showing No Association. **Question** What's the difference between Figures 3.2 and 3.3 in the pattern shown by the bars in the graph?

(23% present, 77% not present for organic food and 73% present, 27% not present for conventional food), indicating an association.

We will discuss the association between two categorical variables much more in Chapter 11, including inferential methods. For now, it is important that you can describe the association in a contingency table by computing conditional proportions and interpreting a plot comparing them, such as Figure 3.2. The numerical summaries mentioned in the next paragraph will help you with this task.

Comparing Two Conditional Proportions

We saw from Figure 3.2 that the proportion of foods with pesticides present is much higher for conventionally grown food than for organically grown food. How can we describe this difference numerically? For tables such as Table 3.2 that have two categories for the response and explanatory variables, there are two important statistics that we can use:

- **The Difference of Proportions**   We have seen from Figure 3.2 and the conditional proportions in Table 3.2 that a proportion of 0.73 of conventionally grown food samples had pesticide residues present, compared to only 0.23 for organic food samples. The difference between these two conditional proportions is $0.73 - 0.23 = 0.50$. It is called the **difference of proportions**. When interpreting this difference, we almost always use percentages instead of proportions. Expressed using percentages, the difference is $73\% - 23\% = 50\%$. We say that the percentage of conventionally grown food samples with pesticide residues present is **50 percentage points higher** than the one for organic food samples. We are careful not to say that the percentage of conventionally grown food samples with pesticide residues present is *50% higher*. This distinction between "50 percentage points" and "50%" often gets blurred in everyday language (and the popular media). But the two food percentages (73% and 23%) differ by 50 percentage points, not by 50%. If they differed by 50%, one would be half of the other, which is not the case. So, whenever you are computing the difference of two conditional proportions, that difference is expressed in percentage points. The next measure, called the ratio of proportions, allows for the interpretation as one being a certain percent of the other.

  A difference of 50 percentage points is a substantial difference and indicates a strong association between the two variables. When there is no association, as in hypothetical Table 3.3 and Figure 3.3, the two conditional proportions would be identical (or, in practice, nearly identical) and the difference of proportions would be 0 (or, in practice, very close to 0).

  We will learn much more about the difference of two proportions, e.g., how to find its margin of error, in Chapter 10. But we are sure you have seen it before in the media, e.g., when results from election polls comparing two candidates or parties are described. Then, we often hear that one candidate leads the other by a certain number of percentage points. For instance, if according to the latest poll one candidate gets 35% of the vote and the other 29%, then the first candidate leads the second by 6 percentage points.

- **The Ratio of Proportions**   Another way to compare two conditional proportions is through their ratio, given by $0.73/0.23 = 3.2$. How do we interpret this ratio? We say that the proportion of food with pesticide residues present is 3.2 times larger for conventionally grown food than for organic food. Again, this indicates a rather strong association. What would that ratio be if the variables were not associated? In that case, the two proportions would be identical (or, in practice, nearly identical), as in Table 3.3. Then, their ratio would be equal to 1 (or, in practice, very close to 1).

Caution

"Don't say the percentage of food samples with residues present is 50% higher for conventionally grown food. Say it is 50 percentage points higher. When comparing two percentages through their difference, we express the units of that difference as percentage points." ◄

The ratio of proportions is often preferred over the difference of proportions when the proportions to compare are both small. You may remember the study we mentioned in Chapter 1 that compared two treatments (aspirin vs. placebo) in terms of the proportion of elderly patients suffering a heart attack. The conditional proportion of a heart attack for patients on placebo was 0.054 (or 5.4%) and for those on aspirin 0.050 (or 5.0%). The ratio of these two proportions equals $0.054/0.050 = 1.08$. How do we interpret this ratio? We could say that the proportion of patients suffering a heart attack is 1.08 times larger in the placebo group compared to the aspirin group. However, when a ratio falls between 1 and 2, it is more common to speak of a **percent increase**. A ratio of 1.08 implies an 8% increase. Consequently, when interpreting the ratio of 1.08, we say that the proportion of a heart attack was **8% higher** for patients in the placebo group compare to patients in the aspirin group.

In Practice Interpreting the Ratio of Proportions

It is easier to interpret the ratio of proportions when putting the larger conditional proportion in the numerator. If the ratio is between 1 and 2, we commonly interpret it as a percent increase (such as a ratio of 1.23 indicating a 23% higher proportion), whereas if the ratio is larger than 2, we commonly interpret it as a multiplicative increase (such as a ratio of 2.8 indicating a 2.8 times larger proportion). Instead of saying "2.8 times larger," we also often say "2.8 times more likely," depending on the context.

The ratio of proportions is often referred to as the risk ratio or the relative risk in the medical, public health or psychological literature. For instance, it is a popular measure for describing the association between a drug and a control treatment in clinical trials.

Difference and Ratio of Proportions ◄

	Recovery		
Treatment	Yes	No	Total
Remdesivir	177	45	**222**
Placebo	128	71	**199**

Example 4

Treating COVID-19 Infections

Picture the Scenario

In December 2019, a novel coronavirus (later designated COVID-19) was identified that would soon spread around the world. An existing drug called Remdesivir was identified early on as a potential treatment against the symptoms of COVID-19, which include severe respiratory infections. In the spring of 2020, a clinical trial assessed the efficacy of Remdesivir versus a placebo treatment in terms of the recovery of patients infected and hospitalized with the COVID-19 virus.[3] Here, we look at data from this trial concerning patients with severe COVID-19 (those that needed oxygen supply). Of 222 such patients randomly assigned to the Remdesivir treatment group, 177 recovered after 28 days. Of 199 such patients randomly assigned to the placebo group, 128 recovered after 28 days. The contingency table in the margin shows these results.

Questions to Explore

a. Identify the response and explanatory variable. Then, find the conditional proportions of the response variable for each category of the explanatory variable, plot them, convert them to percentages and interpret.

---

[3]Beigel, J.H., Tomashek, K.M., Dodd, L.E. et al. (May 22, 2020). *Remdesivir for the Treatment of COVID-19 - Preliminary Report,* New England Journal of Medicine. DOI: 10.1056/NEJMoa2007764.

b. Compute the difference between the proportions of recovery for Remdesivir and placebo and interpret this difference in context.

c. Compute the ratio between the proportions of recovery for Remdesivir and placebo and interpret this ratio in context.

Think It Through

a. The response variable is whether a patient recovered, and the explanatory variable is the treatment a patient received (Remdesivir or placebo). Of the 222 patients in the Remdesivir group, a proportion of $177/222 = 0.797$, or 79.7%, recovered after 28 days. Of the 199 patients in the placebo group, a proportion of $128/199 = 0.643$, or 64.3% recovered after 28 days. You can easily obtain these conditional proportions and a corresponding side-by-side bar graph with the *Association Between Two Categorical Variables* app. The screenshot in Figure 3.4 shows the output of the app, which displays the contingency table with marginal totals and the table of conditional sample proportions (also with marginal totals), as well as a side-by-side bar graph. While the data for this example are preloaded in the app, you can also enter your own data by selecting Contingency Table under Enter Data.

▶ **Figure 3.4** Screenshot from *Association Between Two Categorical Variables* app. The top two tables in the app show the contingency table with row and column totals added, and a table of the conditional (row) proportions. A side-by-side bar graph compares the two conditional proportions graphically. The app can compute the difference and ratio of proportions. In this screenshot, we show results for the ratio of proportions, which is shown in the table below the bar graph.

b. The difference of the proportions between patients taking Remdesivir and placebo is $0.797 - 0.643 = 0.154$, or 15.4 percentage points. The proportion of patients recovering from COVID-19 is 15.4 percentage points higher for those patients taking Remdesivir compared to those taking a placebo.

c. The ratio of the two proportions equals $0.797/0.643 = 1.24$, as shown in the screenshot. This ratio implies that the proportion of patients recovering on Remdesivir is 1.24 times larger than the proportion of patients recovering on placebo. Another way to express this is to say that the proportion of patients recovering is 24% higher for those on Remdesivir than for those on placebo.

> **Insight**
>
> The difference (or ratio) of proportions are descriptive measures for the association, comparing the conditional proportions in the two groups. In Chapter 10, we will learn how to attach a margin of error to the difference, which will help us estimate the efficiency of Remdesivir in the larger population. Based on such considerations, Remdesivir was approved for emergency use for treating severe COVID-19 patients in May 2020.
>
> ▶ *Try Exercise 3.8*

You will see both the difference and the ratio of proportions quoted almost daily in the popular media, presenting the results of various research studies (such as the one on Remdesivir mentioned in Example 4) or opinion surveys (such as comparing two candidates in terms of the proportion of votes they will get). Chapter 10 and Section 11.3 in Chapter 11 discusses both of these measures further. For now, you can use the difference or the ratio of proportions to add to your description of the association in contingency tables.

3.1 Practicing the Basics

3.1 Which is the response/explanatory variable? For the following pairs of variables, which more naturally is the response variable and which is the explanatory variable?

a. Carat (= weight) and price of a diamond

b. Dosage (low/medium/high) and severity of adverse event (mild/moderate/strong/serious) of a drug

c. Top speed and construction type (wood or steel) of a roller coaster

d. Type of college (private/public) and graduation rate

3.2 Sales and advertising Each month, the owner of Fay's Tanning Salon records in a data file the monthly total sales receipts and the amount spent that month on advertising.

a. Identify the two variables.

b. For each variable, indicate whether it is quantitative or categorical.

c. Identify the response variable and the explanatory variable.

3.3 Does higher income make you happy? Every General Social Survey (GSS) includes the question, "Taken all together, would you say that you are very happy, pretty happy, or not too happy?" The table below uses the 2010 survey (GSS filter variable YEAR(2010)) to cross-tabulate happiness (row GSS variable HAPPY) with family income (column GSS variable FINRELA), measured as the response to the question, "Compared with American families in general, would you say that your family income is below average, average, or above average?"

	Happiness			
Income	**Not Too Happy**	**Pretty Happy**	**Very Happy**	**Total**
Above Average	21	213	126	**360**
Average	96	506	248	**850**
Below Average	143	347	114	**604**
Total	**260**	**1,066**	**488**	**1,814**

a. Identify the response variable and the explanatory variable.

 b. Find the conditional proportions of happiness at each level of income. Interpret and summarize the association between these variables by comparing some of the conditional proportions across income levels. (The *Explore Categorical Data* app, under the Two Categorical Variables tab has this data set preloaded. It is one of the options for data from the textbook. The app provides side-by-side bar graphs and a table of conditional and marginal proportions.)

c. Overall, what proportion of people reported being very happy?

3.4 Diamonds The clarity and cut of a diamond are two 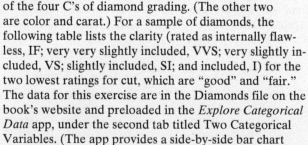 of the four C's of diamond grading. (The other two are color and carat.) For a sample of diamonds, the following table lists the clarity (rated as internally flawless, IF; very very slightly included, VVS; very slightly included, VS; slightly included, SI; and included, I) for the two lowest ratings for cut, which are "good" and "fair." The data for this exercise are in the Diamonds file on the book's website and preloaded in the *Explore Categorical Data* app, under the second tab titled Two Categorical Variables. (The app provides a side-by-side bar chart and computes conditional and marginal proportions automatically.).

	Clarity					
Cut	**IF**	**VVS**	**VS**	**SI**	**I**	**Total**
Good	2	4	16	55	3	**80**
Fair	1	3	8	30	2	**44**

a. Find the conditional proportions for the five categories of clarity, given cut.

b. Sketch (or access and download via the app) a side-by-side (or stacked) bar graph that compares the two cuts on clarity. Summarize findings in a paragraph.

c. Based on these data, is there evidence of an association between the cuts and clarity? Explain. (*Hint:* Are the conditional proportions very close across the two cuts?)

3.5 **Alcohol and college students** The Harvard School of Public Health, in its College Alcohol Study Survey, surveyed college students in about 200 colleges. The survey asked students questions about their drinking habits. Binge drinking was defined as five drinks in a row for males and four drinks in a row for females. The table shows results from the 2001 study, cross-tabulating subjects' gender by whether they have participated in binge drinking.

	Binge Drinking Status		
Gender	Binge Drinker	Non-Binge Drinker	Total
Male	1,908	2,017	**3,925**
Female	2,854	4,125	**6,979**
Total	**4,762**	**6,142**	**10,904**

a. Identify the response variable and the explanatory variable.

b. Report the cell counts of subjects who were (i) male and a binge drinker, (ii) female and a binge drinker.

c. Can you compare the counts in part b to answer the question, "Is there a difference between male and female students who binge drink?" Explain.

d. Construct a contingency table that shows the conditional proportions of sampled students who do or do not binge drink, given gender. Interpret.

e. Based on part d, does it seem that there is an association between binge drinking and gender? Explain by comparing the conditional proportions.

3.6 **How to fight terrorism?** A survey of 1,000 adult Americans (*Rasmussen Reports*, April 15, 2004) asked each whether the best way to fight terrorism is to let the terrorists know we will fight back aggressively or to work with other nations to find an international solution. The first option was picked by 53% of the men but by only 36% of the women in the sample. Assume there were 600 men and 400 women in the sample.

a. Identify the response variable and the explanatory variable and their categories.

b. Construct a contingency table that shows the counts for the different combination of categories.

c. Use a contingency table to display the percentages for the two options, separately for females and for males.

d. Explain why the percentages reported here are *conditional* percentages.

e. Sketch a graph (or use the *Association Between Two Categorical Varibales* app to enter the contingency table and download a graph) that compares the proportions for men and women.

f. Compute the difference of proportions and the ratio of proportions and interpret each.

g. Give an example of how results would have to differ from these for you to conclude that there's *no* evidence of association between these variables.

3.7 **Heaven and hell** Two questions on the General Social Survey read, "Do you believe in heaven?" (variable HEAVEN) and "Do you believe in hell?" (variable HELL). 955 subjects answered "yes" to both questions, 188 answered "no" to both, 162 answered "yes" to heaven but "no" to hell, and 9 answered "no" to heaven but "yes" to hell.

a. For these two variables, is it clear which should be the response and which the explanatory variable?

b. Display the data as a contingency table, labeling the variables and the categories.

c. Find the conditional proportions that treat opinion about heaven as the response variable and opinion about hell as the explanatory variable. Interpret.

d. Find the conditional proportions that treat opinion about hell as the response variable and opinion about heaven as the explanatory variable. Interpret.

e. Find the marginal proportion who (i) believe in heaven, (ii) believe in hell.

3.8 **Eyewitness Testimony** To evaluate how eyewitness testimonies may affect jurors in reaching a verdict, researchers recorded two mock murder trials: one with weak and one with strong eyewitness testimonies.[4] They then asked jurors to come to a verdict of either guilty or not guilty based on the version of the recording they were shown. (The data file for this experiment, which includes additional variables, is on the book's website under EyewitnessTestimony.) You can enter the counts from the contingency table below in the *Association Between Two Categorical Variables* app to answer the following questions.

	Verdict	
Eyewitness Testimony	Guilty	Not Guilty
Strong	42	148
Weak	38	145

a. How many jurors were shown the recording with the strong and how many jurors were shown the recording with the weak testimony?

b. What is the response variable, and what is the explanatory variable?

c. Find the conditional proportions (convert them to percentages) of a guilty verdict given eyewitness testimony. Interpret and sketch a plot comparing the conditional proportions.

d. Find the difference of the conditional proportions and interpret this difference in context.

e. Is it true that the proportion of jurors watching the recording with the strong testimony is 6% higher than the proportion of jurors watching the recording with the weak testimony? Explain.

3.9 **Surviving the Titanic** Was the motto "Women and Children First" followed on the fateful journey of the Titanic? Refer to the following table on surviving the sinking of the Titanic. You can access this table, a corresponding plot, and relevant conditional proportions via the *Association Between Two Categorical Variables* app.

---

[4] Papailiou, A., Yokum, D. V., & Robertson, C. T. (December 9, 2015). *The Novel New Jersey Eyewitness Instruction Induces Skepticism but Not Sensitivity.* PLoS ONE 10(12): e0142695.

Passenger	Survived	
	Yes	No
Children & Female Adult	373	161
Male Adult	338	1,329

a. What's the percentage of children and female adult passengers who survived? What's the percentage of male adults who survived?

b. Compute the difference in the proportion of children and female adult passengers who survived and male adult passengers who survived. Interpret.

c. Compute the ratio of the proportion between children and female adult passengers and male adult passengers who survived. Interpret.

3.10 GSS **Gender gap in party ID** In recent election years, political scientists have analyzed whether a gender gap exists in political beliefs and party identification. The table shows data collected from the 2010 General Social Survey on gender (variable SEX) and party identification (variable PARTYID).

Gender	Party Identification			Total
	Democrat	Independent	Republican	
Male	111	155	89	**355**
Female	237	205	95	**537**
Total	**348**	**360**	**184**	**892**

a. Identify the response and explanatory variables.

b. What proportion of sampled individuals is (i) male and Republican, (ii) female and Republican?

c. What proportion of the overall sample is (i) male, (ii) Republican?

d. Are the proportions you computed in part c conditional or marginal proportions?

e. The two bar graphs, one for each gender, display the proportion of individuals identifying with each political party. What are these proportions called? Is there a difference between males and females in the proportions that identify with a particular party? Summarize whatever gender gap you observe.

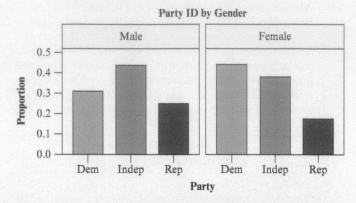

3.11 GSS **Use the GSS** Go to the GSS website (sda.berkeley.edu), click Archive near the top, and scroll down to the most current General Social Survey (GSS) Cumulative Datafile, or access it directly via this book's website. Type SEX for the row variable and HAPPY for the column variable. Type YEAR(2018) in the Selection Filter(s) box to only see results for the 2018 survey and select No Weights for the Weight option. Put a check next to Row in the Percentaging box under the Output Options menu. Click Run the Table.

a. Report the contingency table of counts.

b. Report the conditional proportions (or percentages) to compare the genders on reported happiness.

c. Are females and males similar, or quite different, in their reported happiness? Compute and interpret the difference and ratio of the proportion of being not too happy between the two sexes.

3.2 The Relationship Between Two Quantitative Variables

In practice, when we investigate the association between two variables, there are three types of cases:

Recall

Figure 2.16 in Chapter 2 used **side-by-side box plots** to compare heights for females and males. ◄

In Words

We use the term association to study how two categorical variables relate, and the term relationship to study how two quantitative variables relate.

- The variables could be *categorical* as food type and pesticide status are. In this case, as we have already seen, the data are displayed in a contingency table, and we can explore the association by comparing conditional proportions.

- One variable could be *quantitative* and the other could be *categorical* such as analyzing height and gender or income and race. As we saw in Chapter 2, we can compare the categories (such as females and males) using summaries of center and variability for the quantitative variable (such as the mean and standard deviation of height) and graphs such as side-by-side box plots.

- Both variables could be *quantitative*. In this case, we analyze how the outcome on the response variable tends to change as the value of the explanatory variable changes. When studying two quantitative variables, it is common to use the term **relationship** instead of association, although these two terms are often used interchangeably. The next few sections deal with describing such a relationship through plots and statistics.

In exploring the relationship between two quantitative variables, we'll use the principles introduced in Chapter 2 for exploring the data of a single variable. We first use graphs to look for an overall pattern. We follow up with numerical summaries and check also for unusual observations that deviate from the overall pattern and may affect results.

Numerical and Graphical Summaries

Example 5

Worldwide Internet and Facebook Use

Picture the Scenario

The number of worldwide Internet users and the number of users of social networking sites such as Facebook have grown significantly over the past decade. This growth though has not been distributed evenly throughout the world. In 2012, countries such as Australia, Sweden, and the Netherlands have achieved an Internet penetration of more than 85%, whereas only 13% of India's population used the Internet. The story with Facebook is similar. More than 50% of the populations of countries such as the United States and Australia used Facebook, compared to fewer than 6% of the populations of countries such as China, India, and Russia.

The Internet Use data file on the book's website contains data for 32 countries on Internet penetration, Facebook penetration, broadband subscription percentage, and other variables related to Internet use for the year 2012. In this example, we'll investigate the relationship between Internet penetration and Facebook penetration in the year 2012. Note that we will often say "use" instead of "penetration" in these two variable names. Table 3.4 displays the values of these two variables for each of the 32 countries.

Table 3.4 Internet and Facebook Penetration Rates for 32 Countries

Country	Internet Penetration	Facebook Penetration
Argentina	55.8%	48.8%
Australia	82.4%	51.5%
Belgium	82.0%	44.2%
Brazil	49.9%	29.5%
Canada	86.8%	51.9%
Chile	61.4%	55.5%
China	42.3%	0.1%
Colombia	49.0%	36.3%
Egypt	44.1%	15.1%
France	83.0%	39.0%
Germany	84.0%	30.9%
Hong Kong	72.8%	56.4%
India	12.6%	5.1%

(Continued)

Country	Internet Penetration	Facebook Penetration
Indonesia	15.4%	20.7%
Italy	58.0%	38.1%
Japan	79.1%	13.5%
Malaysia	65.8%	46.5%
Mexico	38.4%	31.8%
Netherlands	93.0%	45.1%
Peru	38.2%	31.2%
Philippines	36.2%	30.9%
Poland	65.0%	25.6%
Russia	53.3%	5.6%
Saudi Arabia	54.0%	20.7%
South Africa	41.0%	12.3%
Spain	72.0%	38.1%
Sweden	94.0%	52.0%
Thailand	26.5%	26.5%
Turkey	45.1%	43.4%
United Kingdom	87.0%	52.1%
United States	81.0%	52.9%
Venezuela	44.1%	32.6%

Source: Data from the World Bank (data.worldbank.org) and www.internetworldstats.com for the year 2012.

Question to Explore

Use numerical and graphical summaries to describe the shape, center, and variability of the distributions of Internet use and Facebook use.

Think It Through

Using many of the statistics from Chapter 2, we obtain the following numerical summaries to describe center and variability for each variable:

Variable	N	Mean	StDev	Minimum	Q1	Median	Q3	Maximum	IQR
Internet Use	32	59.2	22.4	12.6	43.6	56.9	81.3	94.0	37.7
Facebook Use	32	33.9	16.0	0.0	24.4	34.5	47.1	56.4	22.7

Figure 3.5 portrays the distributions using histograms. We observe that the shape for Internet use is bimodal, with one mode around 45% and the other around 85%. We also see that Internet use has a wide range, from a minimum of just over 10% to a maximum of just under 95%. Facebook use ranges between 0% and about 55%, with most nations above 20%. Its distribution seems left-skewed.

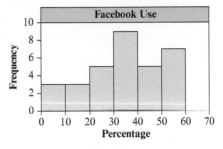

▲ **Figure 3.5** Histograms of Internet Use and Facebook Use for the 32 Countries. **Question** Which nations, if any, might be outliers in terms of Internet use? Facebook use? Which graphical display would more clearly identify potential outliers?

Insight

The histograms portray each variable separately but give no clue about their relationship. Is it true that countries with higher Internet use tend to have higher Facebook use? How can we picture the association between the two variables on a single display? We'll study how to do that next.

▶ *Try Exercise 3.13, part a*

Looking for a Trend: The Scatterplot

With two quantitative variables, it is common to denote the response variable y and the explanatory variable x. We use this notation because graphical plots for examining the association use the y-axis for values of the response variable and the x-axis for values of the explanatory variable. This graphical plot is called a *scatterplot*.

> Scatterplot
>
> A *scatterplot* is a graphical display for **the relationship between two quantitative variables,** using the horizontal (x) axis for the explanatory variable x and the vertical (y) axis for the response variable y. Each point (x, y) in the scatterplot represents an observation with value x for the explanatory and value y for the response variable. With a total of n observations, the scatterplot has n points.

Scatterplots ◀

Example 6

Internet and Facebook Use

Picture the Scenario

We return to the data from Example 5 for 32 countries on Internet and Facebook use.

Questions to Explore

a. Display the relationship between Internet use and Facebook use with a scatterplot.

b. What can we learn about the association by inspecting the scatterplot?

Think It Through

a. The first step is to identify the response variable and the explanatory variable. We'll study how Facebook use depends on Internet use. A temporal relationship exists between when individuals become Internet users and when they become Facebook users; the former precedes the latter. We will treat Internet use as the explanatory variable and Facebook use as the response variable. Thus, we use x to denote Internet use and y to denote Facebook use. We plot Internet use on the horizontal axis and Facebook use on the vertical axis. Figure 3.6 shows the scatterplot for the data in Table 3.4. Can you find the observation (dot) representing the United States on the scatterplot? It has Internet use $x = 81\%$ and Facebook use $y = 52.9\%$.

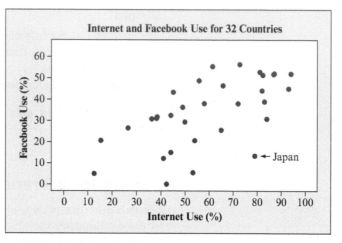

▲ **Figure 3.6** Scatterplot for Internet and Facebook Use (in % of the total population). The point for Japan is labeled and has coordinates $x = 79\%$ and $y = 13\%$. **Question** Is there any point that you would identify as standing out in some way? Which country does it represent, and how is it unusual in the context of these variables?

b. Here are some things we learn by inspecting the scatterplot:

- There is a clear trend. Nations with larger percentages of Internet use generally have larger percentages of Facebook use.

- The point for Japan seems unusual. Its Internet use is among the highest of all countries (79%), but its Facebook use is among the lowest (13%). Based on values for other countries with similarly high Internet use, we might expect Facebook use to be between 30% and 50% rather than 13%. Although not as unusual as Japan, Facebook use for Russia (RU, 6%, see margin figure) and China (CN, 0.1%) are much lower than we'd expect, based on what we see for other countries with similar Internet use of around 50%.

- Setting these three countries aside, the variability in Facebook use is similar across the whole range of Internet use. For countries with Internet use below about 50%, Facebook use varies from about 5% to 40%. For countries with Internet use larger than about 50%, it varies from about 20% to 60%.

Insight

Although the points for Japan and, to less extent, Russia and China, can be considered atypical, there is a clear overall relationship. The countries with lower Internet use tend to have lower Facebook use, and the countries with higher Internet use tend to have higher Facebook use.

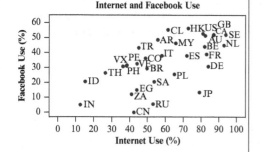

Scatterplot with two-letter country code

You can create interactive scatterplots with the *Scatterplots & Correlation* app. The internet use data is preloaded, and you can hover over points to see which country they correspond to. Example 7 will show a screenshot of the app.

▶ *Try Exercise 3.13, parts b and c*

How to Examine a Scatterplot

We examine a scatterplot to study the **relationship** between two quantitative variables. How do values on the response variable change as values of the explanatory variable change? As Internet use rises, for instance, we see that Facebook use rises. When there's a trend in a scatterplot, what's the direction? Is the relationship **positive** or **negative?**

> ### Positive Relationship and Negative Relationship
>
> Two quantitative variables x and y are said to have a positive relationship when high values of x tend to occur with high values of y, and when low values of x tend to occur with low values of y. **Positive relationship:** As x goes up, y tends to go up.
>
> Two quantitative variables have a negative relationship when high values of one variable tend to pair with low values of the other variable, and low values of one variable pair with high values of the other. **Negative relationship:** As x goes up, y tends to go down.

Figure 3.6 displays a positive relationship, because high values of Internet use tend to occur with high values of Facebook use, and low values of Internet use tend to occur with low values of Facebook use. If we were to study the relationship between $x = $ weight of car (in kg) and $y = $ gas mileage (in miles per gallon), we'd expect a negative relationship: Heavier cars would tend to get poorer gas mileage, i.e., drive fewer miles per gallon of gas. The scatterplot below shows such a negative relationship, using data from the Car Weight and Mileage data file on the book's website.

Once you have determined whether there is a positive or a negative relationship (or neither!), look for the type of trend. Is any noticeable trend reasonably approximated by a straight line? If yes, we speak of a **linear relationship** between the two variables.

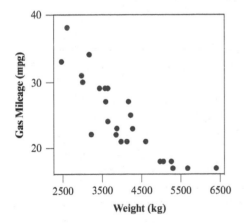

> ### Linear Relationship
>
> A relationship between two quantitative variables is called linear if the scatterplot reveals a trend that is well approximated by a straight line.

Figure 3.7 on the next page shows several linear and nonlinear relationships and one scatterplot of no relationship. To aid with the visualization, a smooth trend line is superimposed over each scatterplot.

A third point to look out for when describing a scatterplot (in addition to determining if the relationship is positive, negative, or neither, and whether it is approximately linear) is whether some observations are unusual, falling well apart from the overall trend of the relationship. An extreme example follows next.

► **Figure 3.7 Various Types of Linear and Nonlinear Relationships.** The depiction of the relationships are idealized in this figure. In practice, a scatterplot often doesn't reveal such a clear linear or nonlinear trend as shown here.

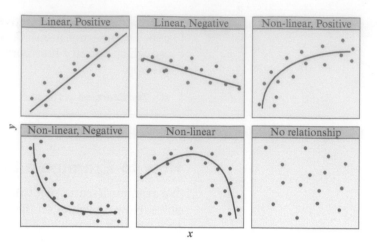

Example 7

Examining Scatterplots ◄

The Butterfly Ballot and the 2000 U.S. Presidential Election

Picture the Scenario

Al Gore and George W. Bush were the Democratic and Republican candidates in the 2000 U.S. presidential election. In Palm Beach County, Florida, initial election returns reported 3,407 votes for the Reform Party candidate, Pat Buchanan. Political analysts thought this total seemed surprisingly large. They felt that most of these votes may have actually been intended for Gore (whose name was next to Buchanan's on the ballot) but were wrongly cast for Buchanan because of the design of the butterfly ballot used in that county, which some voters found confusing. On the butterfly ballot, Bush appeared first in the left column, followed by Buchanan in the right column, and Gore in the left column (see the photo in the margin).

For each of the 67 counties in Florida, the Buchanan and the Butterfly Ballot data file on the book's website includes the Buchanan vote and the vote for the Reform party candidate in 1996 (Ross Perot).

Questions to Explore

Describe the relationship between the number of votes for the Reform Party candidate in 1996 and 2000. How can we explore graphically whether the Buchanan vote in Palm Beach County in 2000 was in fact surprisingly high, given the Reform Party voting totals in 1996?

Think It Through

Figure 3.8 on the next page is a screenshot of the *Scatterplots & Correlation* app, which shows a scatterplot between the number of votes for Perot in 1996 (on the *x*-axis) and the number of votes for Buchanan in 2000 (on the *y*-axis). Each point represents a county. (In the app, hover over a point to see the county it refers to.) The scatterplot shows a positive linear relationship: Counties with a high Perot vote in 1996 tended to have a high Buchanan vote in 2000, and counties with a low Perot vote in 1996 tended to have a low Buchanan vote in 2000.

However, one point in the scatterplot falls well above the others. This severe outlier is the observation for Palm Beach County, the county that had

▶ **Figure 3.8** Screenshot of the *Scatterplots & Correlation* App, Showing the Relationship Between the Florida Countywide Vote for Reform Party Candidates Pat Buchanan in 2000 and Ross Perot in 1996. **Question** Why is the top point in the scatterplot, but not each of the two rightmost points, considered an outlier relative to the overall trend of the data points?

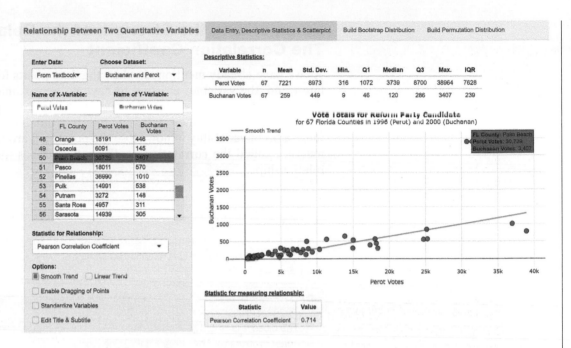

the butterfly ballot. It is far removed from the overall trend (indicated by the smooth line in the app) for the other 66 data points, which follow an approximately linear relationship.

Insight

Alternatively, you could plot the Buchanan vote against the Gore vote or against the Bush vote (Exercise 3.24). These and other analyses conducted by statisticians[5] predicted that fewer than 900 votes were truly intended for Buchanan in Palm Beach County, compared to the 3,407 votes he actually received. Bush won the state by 537 votes and, with it, the Electoral College and the election. So, this vote may have been a pivotal factor in determining the outcome of that election. Other factors that played a role were 110,000 disqualified overvote ballots in which people mistakenly voted for more than one presidential candidate (with Gore marked on 84,197 ballots and Bush on 37,731), often because of confusion from names being listed on more than one page of the ballot, and 61,000 undervotes caused by factors such as hanging chads from manual punch-card machines in some counties.

▶ **Try Exercise 3.24**

Except for the data point representing Palm Beach County, the relationship displayed in Figure 3.8 is approximately linear. We call this relationship a **strong** linear relationship in the sense that we can predict the *y*-value quite well from knowing the *x*-value. The next step in analyzing a relationship is to find a numerical summary that measures how strong the linear relationship is.

---

[5]For further discussion of these and related data, see the article "Misvotes, Undervotes and Overvotes: The 2000 Presidential Election in Florida" by A. Agresti and B. Presnell, *Statistical Science*, vol. 17, pp. 1–5, 2002.

Summarizing the Strength of the Relationship: The Correlation Coefficient

As we have already mentioned, when the data points follow a roughly straight-line trend, the variables are said to have an approximately **linear** relationship. But there often is quite a bit of variation in terms of how close the points fall to the trend line. Are they clustering tightly around it or, as is more common, is there a bit of variability in how close the points fall around the line? A summary measure called the **correlation coefficient** describes the strength of the linear relationship.

Correlation Coefficient

The **correlation coefficient** summarizes the strength and direction of the **linear** (straight-line) relationship between two quantitative variables. Denoted by r, it takes values between -1 and $+1$.

- A positive value for r indicates a positive relationship, and a negative value for r indicates a negative relationship.
- The closer r is to ± 1, the closer the data points fall to a straight line, and the stronger the linear relationship. The closer r is to 0, the weaker the linear relationship.

Let's get a feel for the correlation coefficient r by looking at its values for the scatterplots shown in Figure 3.9:

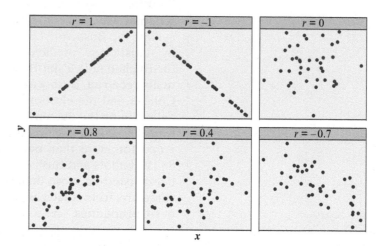

▲ **Figure 3.9** Some Scatterplots and Their Correlation Coefficient. The correlation coefficient gets closer to ± 1 when the data points fall closer to a straight line. **Question** Why are the cases in which the data points are closer to a straight line considered to represent a stronger relationship?

The correlation coefficient r takes the extreme values of $+1$ and -1 only when the data points follow a straight-line pattern *perfectly*, as seen in the first two graphs in Figure 3.9. When $r = +1$ occurs, the line slopes upward. The relationship is positive because higher values of x tend to occur with higher values of y. The value $r = -1$ occurs when the line slopes downward, corresponding to a negative relationship.

In practice, don't expect the data points to fall perfectly on a straight line. However, the closer they come to that ideal, the closer the correlation coefficient is to $+1$ or -1. For instance, the scatterplot in Figure 3.9 with $r = 0.8$ shows a stronger relationship than the one with $r = 0.4$, for which the data points fall farther from a straight line.

Properties of the Correlation Coefficient

Recall

The **absolute value** of a number gives the distance the number falls from zero on the number line. The correlation values of −0.9 and 0.9 both have an absolute value of 0.9. They both represent a stronger relationship than correlation values of −0.6 and 0.6, for example. ◄

- The correlation coefficient r always **falls between −1 and +1.** The closer the value to 1 in absolute value (see the margin comments), the stronger the linear (straight-line) relationship as the data points fall nearer to a straight line.
- A positive correlation coefficient indicates a **positive relationship**, and a negative correlation coefficient indicates a **negative relationship**.
- The correlation coefficient **does not depend on** which variable is treated as the response and which as the explanatory variable.
- The correlation coefficient **does not depend on the variables' units.** For example, suppose one variable is the income of a subject, in dollars. If we change the observations to units of euros or to units of thousands of dollars, we'll get the same correlation coefficient. The correlation coefficient is **not affected by a linear transformation** of the response or explanatory variable.
- And just to make sure, the correlation coefficient is only appropriate to calculate for quantitative variables which show an approximate linear relationship.

Example 8

▸ Finding and Interpreting the Correlation Coefficient

Internet Use and Facebook Use

Picture the Scenario

In Example 6, we looked at the relationship between Internet use and Facebook use. The screenshot in the margin is taken from the *Scatterplots & Correlation* app and shows the scatterplot again, this time with a smooth trend line superimposed.

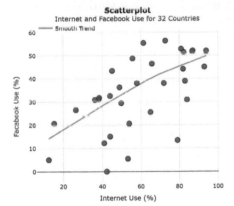

Questions to Explore

a. What is the value of the correlation coefficient r?

b. How can we interpret the value of the correlation coefficient r?

Think It Through

a. The scatterplot reveals an approximately linear relationship, so computing the correlation coefficient r is sensible. (It would not be sensible if the relationship were nonlinear.) The relationship is also positive, so we expect r to be larger than 0. The app displays the value of the correlation coefficient r right underneath the scatterplot as "Pearson's Correlation Coefficient," and it is equal to $r = 0.614$.

b. A value of $r = 0.614$ confirms the positive linear relationship that we see in the scatterplot but also that the points don't cluster too tightly around a linear trend line, in which case r would have been closer to 1. In summary, the relationship between a country's Facebook and Internet use is approximately linear and moderately strong ($r = 0.614$), with higher Internet use tending to occur with higher Facebook use.

Insight

We get exactly the same correlation coefficient if we treat Facebook use as the explanatory variable and Internet use as the response variable. Also, it doesn't matter whether we use the proportions or the percentages when computing the correlation coefficient. Both sets of units result in $r = 0.614$.

The identifier *Pearson* in the label "Pearson Correlation Coefficient" refers to British statistician Karl Pearson. In 1896, he provided the formula used to compute the correlation value from sample data. This formula is shown next.

▸ *Try Exercise 3.16*

Formula for the Correlation Coefficient

Recall

From Section 2.5, the **z-score** for an observation indicates the number of standard deviations and the direction (above or below) that the observation falls from the overall mean. ◀

Although software can compute the correlation coefficient for us, it helps to understand it if you see its formula. Let z_x denote the z-score for an observation x on the explanatory variable. Remember that z_x represents the number of standard deviations that x falls above or below the overall mean. That is,

$$z_x = \frac{\text{observed value} - \text{mean of all } x}{\text{standard deviation of all } x} = \frac{(x - \bar{x})}{s_x},$$

where s_x denotes the standard deviation of the x-values. Similarly, let z_y denote the number of standard deviations that an observation y on the response variable falls above or below the mean of all y. To obtain r, you calculate the product $z_x z_y$ for each observation and then find a typical value (a type of average) of those products.

In Practice Using Technology to Calculate r

Hand **calculation of the correlation coefficient** r is tedious. You should rely on our app, software, or a calculator.

Calculating the Correlation Coefficient r

$$r = \frac{1}{n-1} \Sigma z_x z_y = \frac{1}{n-1} \Sigma \left(\frac{x - \bar{x}}{s_x} \right) \left(\frac{y - \bar{y}}{s_y} \right)$$

where n is the number of observations (points in the scatterplot), $\bar{x}$ and $\bar{y}$ are means, and s_x and s_y are standard deviations for x and y. The sum is taken over all n observations.

For $x =$ Internet use and $y =$ Facebook use, we found a correlation coefficient of $r = 0.614$, using statistical software. To visualize how the formula works, let's revisit the scatterplot, reproduced in Figure 3.10, with a vertical line at the mean of x and a horizontal line at the mean of y. These lines divide the scatterplot into four **quadrants.** The summary statistics are:

In Words

A **quadrant** is any of the four regions created when a plane is divided by a horizontal line and a vertical line.

$$\bar{x} = 59.2 \qquad \bar{y} = 33.9$$
$$s_x = 22.4 \qquad s_y = 16.0$$

The point for Japan ($x = 79, y = 13$) has as its z-scores $z_x = 0.89, z_y = -1.27$. This point is labeled in Figure 3.10. Because $x = 79$ is to the right of the mean for x and $y = 13$ is below the mean for y, it falls in the lower-right quadrant. This makes Japan somewhat atypical in the sense that all but seven of the 32 countries have points that fall in the upper-right or lower-left quadrants. The product of the z-scores for Japan equals $0.89(-1.27) = -1.13$, indicating its negative contribution to r.

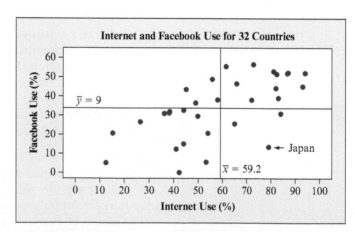

▲ **Figure 3.10** Scatterplot of Internet Use and Facebook Use Divided into Quadrants at $(\bar{x}, \bar{y})$. Of the 32 data points, 25 lie either in the upper-right quadrant (above the mean on each variable) or the lower-left quadrant (below the mean on each variable). **Question** Do the points in these two quadrants make a positive or a negative contribution to the correlation coefficient? (*Hint:* Is the product of z-scores for these points positive or negative?)

> ## SUMMARY: Product of z-Scores and the Correlation Coefficient r
>
> - The product of the z-scores for any point in the upper-right quadrant is positive. The product is also positive for each point in the lower-left quadrant. Such points make a positive contribution to the correlation coefficient.
> - The product of the z-scores for any point in the upper-left and lower-right quadrants is negative. Such points make a negative contribution to the correlation coefficient.

The overall correlation coefficient reflects the number of points in the various quadrants and how far they fall from the means. For example, if all points fall in the upper-right and lower-left quadrants, the correlation coefficient must be positive.

Graph Data to See If Computing r Is Appropriate

The correlation coefficient r is an efficient way to summarize the relationship shown by lots of data points with a single number. But be careful to use it only when it is appropriate. Figure 3.11 illustrates why. It shows a scatterplot in which the data points follow a U-shaped curve. There is a relationship because as x increases, y first tends to decrease and then tends to increase. For example, this might happen if x = age of person and y = annual medical expenses. Medical expenses tend to be high for newly born and young children, then they tend to be low until the person gets old, when they become high again. However, r = 0 for the data in Figure 3.11.

The correlation coefficient is designed for approximately linear relationships. For Figure 3.11, r = 0, and judging by that number alone, one would assume there is no relationship, when in fact there is a strong relationship. It is just not linear. The correlation coefficient is not valid for describing the strength of nonlinear relationships.

This figure highlights an important point to remember about *any* data analysis:

- **Always plot the data.**

If we merely used software to calculate the correlation coefficient for the data in Figure 3.11 without looking at the scatterplot, we might mistakenly conclude that the variables have no relationship. They *do* have one (and a fairly strong one), but it is not linear.

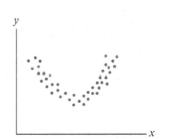

▲ **Figure 3.11** The Correlation Coefficient Poorly Describes the Association When the Relationship Is Curved. For this U-shaped relationship, r is equal to 0, even though the variables are strongly associated. **Question** Can you use the formula for r, in terms of how points fall in the quadrants, to reason why the correlation coefficient would be 0?

> **In Practice** Always Construct a Scatterplot
>
> Always **construct a scatterplot** to display a relationship between two quantitative variables. The correlation coefficient is only meaningful for describing the direction and strength of an approximate *linear* relationship.

3.2   Practicing the Basics

3.12   Used cars and direction of association   For the 100 cars on the lot of a used-car dealership, would you expect a positive relationship, negative relationship, or no relationship between each of the following pairs of variables? Explain why.

a. The age of the car and the number of miles on the odometer

b. The age of the car and the resale value

c. The age of the car and the total amount that has been spent on repairs

d. The weight of the car and the number of miles it travels on a gallon of gas

e. The weight of the car and the number of liters it uses per 100 km.[*]

_____

[*]liters/100 km rather than miles/gallon is a more common measure for the fuel efficiency in many countries.

3.13 Broadband and GDP The Internet Use data file on the book's website contains data on the number of individuals with broadband access and Gross Domestic Product (GDP) for 32 nations. Let x represent GDP (in billions of U.S. dollars) and y = number of broadband users (in millions). The *Scatterplots & Correlation* app has this dataset preloaded, and you can answer all questions below using it or some other software.

a. Give the five-number summary for each variable.

b. The figure below shows a scatterplot. Describe this plot in terms of the relationship between broadband subscribers and GDP.

c. Give the approximate x- and y-coordinates for the nation that has the highest number of broadband subscribers.

d. Use the app or other software to calculate the correlation coefficient between the two variables. What is the sign of the coefficient? Explain what the sign means in the context of the problem.

e. Identify one nation that appears to have fewer broadband subscribers than you might expect, based on that nation's GDP, and one that appears to have more.

f. If you recalculated the correlation coefficient after changing GDP from U.S. dollar to euro, would the correlation coefficient change? Explain.

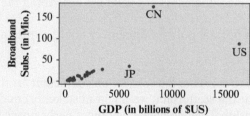

Broadband Subscribers and GDP for 32 Countries

3.14 Economic development based on GDP The previous problem discusses GDP, which is a commonly used measure of the overall economic activity of a nation. For this group of nations, the GDP data have a mean of 1,909 and a standard deviation of 3,136 (in billions of U.S. dollars).

a. The five-number summary of GDP is minimum = 204, Q1 = 378, median = 780, Q3 = 2,015, and maximum = 16,245. Construct (e.g., by copying and pasting the data for GDP into the *Explore Quantitative Data* app) or otherwise sketch a box plot.

b. Based on these statistics and the graph in part a, describe the shape of the distribution of GDP values.

c. The data set also contains per capita GDP, or the overall GDP divided by the nation's population size. Construct a scatterplot of per capita GDP and GDP and explain why no clear trend emerges.

d. Your friend, Joe, argues that the correlation coefficient between the two variables must be 1 since they are both measuring the same thing. In reality, the actual correlation coefficient between per capita GDP and GDP is only 0.32. Identify the flaw in Joe's reasoning.

3.15 Politics and newspaper reading For the FL Student Survey data file on the book's website, the correlation coefficient between y = political ideology (scored 1 = very liberal to 7 = very conservative) and x = number of times a week reading a newspaper is −0.07.

a. Would you call this relationship strong or weak? Explain.

b. The correlation coefficient between political ideology and religiosity (how often attend religious services) is 0.58. For this sample, which explanatory variable, newspaper reading or religiosity, seems to have a stronger relationship with y? Explain.

3.16 Carbon footprint of sandwiches The article "Understanding the impact on climate change of convenience food: Carbon footprint of sandwiches"[6] analyzed data of 24 commercially available (i.e., ready-made) sandwiches with regard to their carbon footprint (measured in grams of carbon dioxide equivalent, g CO_2e and encompassing everything from the agricultural production to packaging and waste management) and how the carbon footprint depends on the energy content (measured in kCal) of the sandwich. The data are available on the book's website and are preloaded in the *Scatterplots & Correlation* app. Describe the relationship between energy content and carbon footprint by

a. visualizing the relationship with a scatterplot and

b. writing a paragraph about the relationship that quotes the correlation coefficient.

3.17 Match the scatterplot with r Match the following scatterplots with the correlation coefficients.

1. $r = -0.9$ **2.** $r = -0.5$ **3.** $r = 0$ **4.** $r = 0.6$

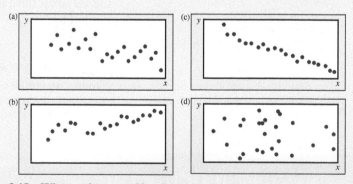

3.18 What makes $r = 1$? Consider the data:

x	3	4	5	6	7
y	8	13	12	14	16

a. Sketch a scatterplot. (You can also enter these data in the *Scatterplots & Correlation* app by selecting Own Data for Data Entry.)

---

[6]https://www.sciencedirect.com/science/article/pii/S2352550917300635

b. If one pair of (x, y) values is removed, the correlation coefficient for the remaining four pairs equals 1. Which pair is it?

c. If one y value is changed, the correlation coefficient for the five pairs equals 1. Identify the y value and how it must be changed for this to happen.

3.19   Gender and chocolate preference   The following table shows data on gender (coded as 1 = female, 2 = male) and preferred type of chocolate (coded as 1 = white, 2 = milk, 3 = dark) for a sample of 10 students.

Preferred Chocolate Type					
Name	Gender	Type	Name	Gender	Type
Anna	1	2	Josef	2	3
Franz	2	3	Eva	1	3
Hans	2	2	Doris	1	2
Lisl	1	1	Sophie	1	1
Michael	2	3	Kathi	1	1

The students' teacher enters the data into software and reports a correlation coefficient of 0.640 between gender and type of preferred chocolate. He concludes that there is a moderately strong positive linear relationship between someone's gender and chocolate preference. What's wrong with this analysis?

3.20 $r = 0$ Sketch a scatterplot for which $r > 0$, but $r = 0$ after one of the points is deleted.

3.21   Correlation inappropriate   Describe a situation in which it is inappropriate to use the correlation coefficient to measure the relationship between two quantitative variables.

3.22   Attractiveness and performance   The abstract of a study (Postma, 2014, "A relationship between attractiveness and performance in professional cyclists." Biol. Lett., doi: 10:20130966) reads: "Females often prefer to mate with high quality males, and one aspect of quality is physical performance. Although a preference for physically fitter males is therefore predicted, the relationship between attractiveness and performance has rarely been quantified. Here, I [...] ask whether variation in (endurance) performance is associated with variation in facial attractiveness within elite professional cyclists that finished the 2012 Tour de France[...]." The data from this study are available on the book's website and contain a column called "Performance" that is a composite score of the time it took each rider to complete the Tour de France prologue, the two individual timed trials, and the complete race. *Smaller* values indicate faster, i.e., better, performing riders. The data also contains a variable called "Attractiveness." To obtain this attractiveness score, the portrait of each rider was rated by several persons on a scale from 1 to 5, and the average rating is reported in this column.

a. In the context of this study, which variable plays the role of the (i) explanatory variable, (ii) response variable?

b. Construct an appropriate plot to analyze the relationship between performance and attractiveness. (The *Scatterplots & Correlation* app has this data set preloaded under the name "Tour de France".)

c. Based on the scatterplot, do you expect the correlation coefficient r to be positive or negative? Why?

d. Find the correlation coefficient r and write a short paragraph describing the relationship. (Comment on whether the relationship is approximately linear and its direction and strength.)

e. Do you think performance is a good predictor for attractiveness for these riders?

3.23   Prices and protein revisited   Is there a relationship between the protein content and the cost of Subway sandwiches (as observed in a store in North Carolina in August 2019)? Use software to analyze the data in the following table, which are also available in the *Scatterplots & Correlation* app.:

Sandwich	Cost ($)	Protein (g)
Black Forest Ham	3.89	19
Chicken & Bacon Ranch Melt	4.99	36
Cold Cut Combo	3.89	16
Italian B.M.T.®	4.39	19
Meatball Marinara	3.99	20
Oven Roasted Chicken	4.39	23
Roast Beef	5.09	25
Rotisserie-Style Chicken	4.89	29
Spicy Italian	3.99	18
Steak & Cheese (with American)	4.89	23
Subway Club®	4.89	24
Sweet Onion Chicken Teriyaki	4.89	25
Tuna	4.39	19
Turkey Breast	4.49	18
Veggie Delite®	3.89	9

a. Construct a scatterplot to show how protein depends on cost. Is the relationship positive or negative? Do you notice any unusual observations?

b. Would you describe the relationship as linear?

c. Obtain the correlation coefficient (i) using the data on all 15 sandwiches and (ii) using all but the Veggie Delite and the Chicken & Bacon Ranch Melt sandwich. (In the app, after clicking on Enable Dragging of Points, you can drag a point outside the graph to remove it.)

d. Using data on all 15 sandwiches, write a short paragraph describing the relationship, mentioning the correlation coefficient.

3.24 **Buchanan vote** Refer to Example 7 and the Buchanan and the Butterfly Ballot data file on the book's website. Let y = Buchanan vote and x = Gore vote. (If you open these data in a spreadsheet, you can copy and paste columns, such as the Buchanan and Gore vote totals, into the *Explore Quantitative Variables* app for part a and the *Scatterplots & Correlation* app for part b, after selecting Your Own under Enter Data in each app.)

TRY
APP

a. Construct a box plot for each variable. Summarize what you learn.

b. Construct a scatterplot. Identify any unusual points. What can you learn from a scatterplot that you cannot learn from box plots?

c. For the county represented by the most outlying observation, about how many votes would you have expected Buchanan to get if the point followed the same pattern as the rest of the data?

d. Repeat parts a and b using y = Buchanan vote and x = Bush vote.

3.3 Linear Regression: Predicting the Outcome of a Variable

Recall

Computing the correlation coefficient r does not require one variable to be designated as response and the other as explanatory. ◄

We've seen how to explore the relationship between two quantitative variables graphically with a scatterplot. When the relationship is approximately linear, the correlation coefficient describes its strength numerically. We can analyze the data further by finding an equation for the line that bests describes this relationship. The equation for this line can be used to **predict** the value of the response variable from the value of the explanatory variable.

In Words

The **symbol** $\hat{y}$, which denotes the predicted value of y, is pronounced *y-hat*.

Regression Line: An Equation for Predicting the Response Outcome

The **regression line** predicts the value for the response variable y as a straight-line function of the value x of the explanatory variable. Let $\hat{y}$ denote the **predicted value** of y. The equation for the regression line has the form

$$\hat{y} = a + bx.$$

In this formula, a denotes the **y-intercept** and b denotes the **slope** of the regression line.

Predict an Outcome ◄

Example 9

Height Based on Human Remains

Picture the Scenario

Anthropologists can reconstruct information using partial human remains at burial sites. For instance, after finding a femur (thighbone), they can predict how tall an individual was. They do this using the regression line $\hat{y} = 61.4 + 2.4x$, where $\hat{y}$ is the predicted height and x is the length of the femur, both in centimeters.

Questions to Explore

a. What is the response and what is the explanatory variable?

b. How can we graph the line that depicts how the predicted height depends on the femur length?

c. A femur found at a particular site has a length of 50 cm. What is the predicted height of the person who had that femur?

Think It Through

It is natural here to treat the length of the femur as the explanatory variable to predict the height of a person, the response variable. The formula $\hat{y} = 61.4 + 2.4x$ has y-intercept 61.4 and slope 2.4. It has the straight-line form $\hat{y} = a + bx$ with $a = 61.4$ and $b = 2.4$.

Each number x, when substituted into the formula $\hat{y} = 61.4 + 2.4x$, yields a value for $\hat{y}$. For simplicity in plotting the line, we start with $x = 0$, although in practice this would not be an observed femur length. The value $x = 0$ has $\hat{y} = 61.4 + 2.4(0) = 61.4$. This is called the **y-intercept** and is located 61.4 units up the y-axis at $x = 0$, at coordinates (0, 61.4). The value $x = 50$ has $\hat{y} = 61.4 + 2.4(50) = 181.4$. When the femur length is 50 cm, the predicted height of the person is 181.4 cm. The coordinates for this point are (50, 181.4). We can plot the line by connecting the points (0, 61.4) and (50, 181.4). Figure 3.12 plots the straight line for x between 0 and 50. In summary, the predicted height $\hat{y}$ increases from 61.4 to 181.4 as x increases from 0 to 50.

In Practice Notation for the Regression Line

The formula $\hat{y} = a + bx$ uses slightly different notation from the traditional formula you may have seen previously, which is $y = mx + b$. In that equation, $m = $ the slope (the coefficient of x) and $b = $ y-intercept. Regardless of the notation, the interpretation of the y-intercept and slope remain the same.

▲ **Figure 3.12** Graph of the Regression Line for $x = $ Femur Length and $y = $ Height of Person. **Question** At what point does the line cross the y-axis? How can you interpret the slope of 2.4?

Insight

A regression line is often called a **prediction equation** since it predicts the value of the response variable y at any value of x. Sadly, this particular prediction equation had to be applied to bones found in mass graves in Kosovo, to help identify Albanians who had been executed by Serbians in 1998.[7]

▶ **Try Exercises 3.26, part a, and 3.27, part a**

---

[7]"The Forensics of War," by Sebastian Junger in *Vanity Fair*, October 1999.

Interpreting the y-Intercept and Slope

The **y-intercept** is the predicted value of y when x = 0. This fact helps us plot the line, but it may not have any interpretative value if no observations had x values near 0. It does not make sense for femur length to be 0 cm, so the y-intercept for the equation $\hat{y} = 61.4 + 2.4x$ is not a relevant predicted height. This is also why the x-axis of the graph in Figure 3.13 starts with a femur length of 40, which is close to the smallest femur length observed.

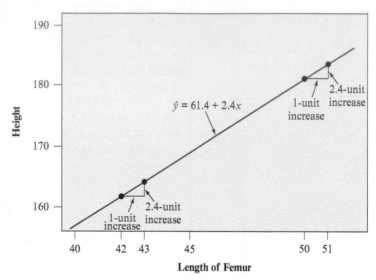

▲ **Figure 3.13 The Slope of a Straight Line.** The slope is the change in the predicted value $\hat{y}$ of the response variable for a 1-unit increase in the explanatory variable x. For an increase in femur length from 50 cm to 51 cm, the predicted height increases by 2.4 cm. **Questions** What is the change in the predicted height when the femur length changes from 42 cm to 43 cm? What does a slope of 0 imply?

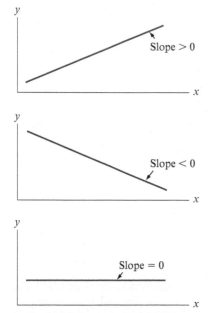

▲ **Figure 3.14** Three Regression Lines Showing Positive Relationship (Slope > 0), Negative Relationship (Slope < 0) and No Relationship (Sope = 0). **Question** Would you expect a positive or negative slope when y = annual income and x = number of years of education?

The **slope** b in the equation $\hat{y} = a + bx$ equals the amount that $\hat{y}$ changes when x increases by one unit. For the line $\hat{y} = 61.4 + 2.4x$, we've seen that $\hat{y} = 181.4$ at x = 50. If x increases by 1.0 to x = 51, we get $\hat{y} = 61.4 + 2.4(51) = 183.8$. The increase in $\hat{y}$ is from 181.4 to 183.8, which is 2.4, the slope value. **For every 1-cm increase in the length of the femur, the height is predicted to increase by 2.4 cm.** Figure 3.13 portrays this interpretation.

When the slope is negative, the predicted value $\hat{y}$ *decreases* as x increases. The straight line then goes downward, and the relationship is *negative*.

When the slope = 0, the regression line is horizontal (parallel to the x-axis). The predicted value $\hat{y}$ of y stays constant at the y-intercept for any value of x. Then the predicted value $\hat{y}$ does not change as x changes, and the variables do not exhibit an association. Figure 3.14 in the margin illustrates the three possibilities for the sign of the slope.

The absolute value of the slope describes the *magnitude* of the change in $\hat{y}$ for a 1-unit change in x. The larger the absolute value, the steeper the regression line. A line with b = 4.8, such as $\hat{y} = 61.4 + 4.8x$, is steeper than one with b = 2.4. A line with b = −0.7 is steeper than one with b = −0.4.

Depending on the units of measurement, a 1-unit increase in a predictor x could be a trivial amount, or it could be huge. We will gain a better feel for how to interpret the slope in context as we explore upcoming examples.

Finding a Regression Equation

How can we use the data to find the equation for the regression line? We should first construct a scatterplot to make sure that the relationship is approximately linear. If so, then the *Linear Regression* app or other statistical software or calculators can easily find the straight line that best fits the data.

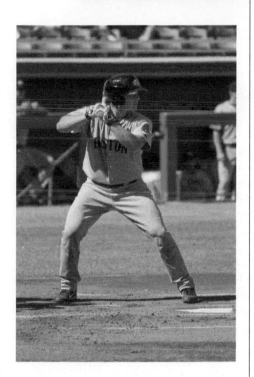

Example 10

Regression Equation ◀

Predicting Baseball Scoring Using Batting Average

Picture the Scenario

In baseball, two summaries of a team's offensive ability are the team batting average (the proportion of times the team's players get a hit, out of the times they are officially at bat) and team scoring (the team's mean number of runs scored per game). Table 3.5 shows the 2010 statistics for the American League teams, from the AL Team Statistics data file on the book's website.

Scoring runs is a result of hitting, so team scoring is the response variable y and team batting average is the explanatory variable x. Figure 3.15 shows a screenshot of the *Linear Regression* app, which has these data preloaded. The scatterplot shown in the app reveals an approximately linear and positive relationship, with a correlation coefficient of $r = 0.568$, also shown in the app.

Table 3.5 Team Batting Average and Team Scoring (Mean Number of Runs per Game) for American League Teams in 2010[8]

Team	Batting Average	Team Scoring
NY Yankees	0.267	5.30
Boston	0.268	5.05
Tampa Bay	0.247	4.95
Texas	0.276	4.86
Minnesota	0.273	4.82
Toronto	0.248	4.66
Chicago Sox	0.268	4.64
Detroit	0.268	4.64
LA Angels	0.248	4.20
Kansas City	0.274	4.17
Oakland	0.256	4.09
Cleveland	0.248	3.99
Baltimore	0.259	3.78
Seattle	0.236	3.17

[8]*Source:* Data from www.espn.com/mlb/statistics

▶ **Figure 3.15**
Screenshot of the *Linear Regression* App, Showing Scatterplot, Regression Line, and Intercept and Slope of the Regression Equation. The correlation coefficient *r* is shown under Model Summary. **Question** How can you find the prediction error that results when you use the regression line to predict team scoring for a team?

Questions to Explore

a. According to the app, what is the regression equation?

b. If a team has a batting average of 0.27 next year, what is its predicted mean number of runs per game, based on the model for the 2010 data?

c. How do you interpret the slope in this context?

Think It Through

a. The *Linear Regression* app shows the *y*-intercept and slope in the table right below the scatterplot. We see that the intercept equals $a = -2.32$ and the slope equals $b = 26.1$ (rounded to one decimal place, which is sufficient here). The app mentions "Batting Average" in parentheses next to the slope to remind the user that the slope refers to the coefficient for the explanatory variable "Batting Average." With these two numbers, the regression equation becomes

$$\hat{y} = a + bx = -2.32 + 26.1x.$$

The app shows this equation in the top left corner of the scatterplot. If we replace *y* and *x* with the names of the response and explanatory variables, we obtain as the regression equation:

$$\text{Predicted Team Scoring} = -2.32 + 26.1(\text{Batting Average})$$

b. We predict that an American League team with a team batting average of 0.27 will score an average of $\hat{y} = -2.32 + 26.1(0.27) = 4.72$ runs per game. (If you check the box Find Predicted Value in the app under Regression Options, you can enter 0.27 as the value for *x* and the app provides the predicted value 4.72, see Figure 3.15.)

c. Because the slope $b = 26.1$ is positive, the relationship is positive: The predicted team scoring increases as team batting average increases. The slope refers to the change in $\hat{y}$ for a 1-unit change in *x*. However,

x = team batting average is a proportion. In Table 3.5, the team batting averages fall between about 0.23 and 0.28, a range of 0.05. So, a more meaningful increase to look at is a 0.01 unit increase instead of a 1-unit increase. A 0.01 increase in x corresponds to a $26.1(0.01) = 0.261$ increase in the predicted team score, leading to the following interpretation of the slope: **For every 0.01 increase in the batting average, we predict team scoring to increase by 0.261 runs per game.**

If we consider the 0.05 difference in the batting average between the worst and best hitting teams, such a 0.05 increase in the batting average corresponds to an increase of $21.6(0.05) = 1.3$ in predicted team scoring. The mean number of runs scored per game is predicted to be about 1.3 higher for the best hitting teams than for the worst hitting teams.

Insight

Figure 3.15 shows the regression line superimposed over the scatterplot. Note that it only applies over the range of observed batting averages. For instance, it's not sensible to predict that a team with batting average of 0.0 will average -2.32 runs per game.

▶ *Try Exercises 3.26, part b, and 3.33. To get a feel for fitting a regression line, use the* **Explore Linear Regression** *app discussed in Exercise 3.114*

Residuals

The regression equation $\hat{y} = -2.32 + 26.1x$ predicts team scoring for a given value of x = team batting average. Once we have found the regression equation, we can compare the predicted values to the actual team scoring to check the accuracy of those predictions.

For example, New York had $y = 5.3$ and $x = 0.267$. The prediction for y = mean number of runs per game at 0.267 is $-2.32 + 26.1x = -2.32 + 2.61(0.267) = 4.65$. The prediction error is the difference between the actual y value of 5.3 and the predicted value of 4.65, which is $y - \hat{y} = 5.3 - 4.65 = 0.65$. For New York, the regression equation underestimates y by 0.65 runs per game. For Seattle, $x = 0.236$ and $y = 3.17$. The regression line yields a predicted value of $-2.32 + 26.1(0.236) = 3.84$, so the prediction is too high. The prediction error is $3.17 - 3.84 = -0.67$. These prediction errors are called **residuals.**

Each observation has a residual. As we just saw, some are positive and some are negative. A positive residual occurs when the actual y is larger than the predicted value $\hat{y}$, so that $y - \hat{y} > 0$. A negative residual results when the actual y is smaller than the predicted value $\hat{y}$, so that $y - \hat{y} < 0$. The smaller the absolute value of a residual, the closer the predicted value is to the actual value, and the better is the prediction. If the predicted value is the same as the actual value, the residual is zero.

Graphically in the scatterplot, *for an observation, the vertical distance between the point and the regression line is the absolute value of the residual.* Figure 3.16 illustrates this fact for the positive residual for New York (0.65) and the negative residual for Seattle (-0.67). The residuals are vertical distances because the regression equation predicts y, the variable on the vertical axis, at a given value of x.

Residual

In a scatterplot, the vertical distance between the point and the regression line is the absolute value of the residual. The residual is denoted as the difference $y - \hat{y}$ between the actual value and the predicted value of the response variable.

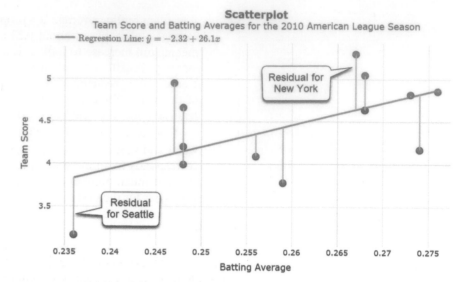

▲ **Figure 3.16** Scatterplot of Team Batting Average and Team Scoring, with the Residuals for New York and Seattle. Screenshot from the second tab of the *Scatterplots & Correlation* app. The residual is the prediction error, which is represented by the vertical distance of the point from the regression line. **Question** Why is a residual represented by a *vertical* distance from the regression line?

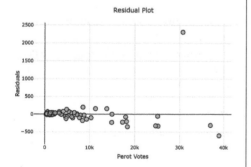

Example 11

Residual for Palm Beach County

Picture the Scenario

Example 7 investigated whether the vote total in Palm Beach County, Florida, in the 2000 presidential election was unusually high for Pat Buchanan, the Reform Party candidate. We did this by plotting, for all 67 counties in Florida, Buchanan's vote against the Reform Party candidate (Ross Perot) vote in the 1996 election.

Question to Explore

For the regression line with y = Buchanan vote and x = Perot vote for the 67 counties, what is the residual for Palm Beach County?

Think It Through

With the *Linear Regression* app, it is easy to find the regression line and the residuals for all 67 counties. For Palm Beach County, the actual Buchanan vote was $y = 3,407$ and the predicted vote was $\hat{y} = 1,100$. Its residual is $y - \hat{y} = 3,407 - 1,100 = 2,307$. The first plot in the margin shows the original scatterplot with the regression line superimposed and visualizes the residual for each county. The one for Palm Beach County is clearly visible as the one with the largest vertical distance. (This distance equals 2,307.) The second plot shows a scatterplot of the residuals (on the y-axis) against the explanatory variable (Perot vote). Again, the residual for Palm Beach County clearly stands out. While most residuals are relatively close to zero across the entire range of the x-axis, the one for Palm Beach County clearly stands apart as an outlier in the scatterplot. The third plot in the margin (on the next page) shows a histogram of the 67 residuals. All but one of the residuals are close to zero. The one in the right tail is the one for Palm Beach County, a clear outlier. All three plots are obtained with the *Linear Regression* app, which also provides the fitted values and residuals for the 67 counties under the

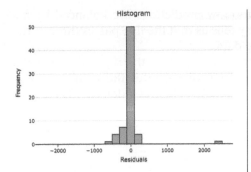

second tab titled Fitted Values & Residual Analysis. In summary, the residual for Palm Beach County is very unusual, indicating that Buchanan's vote was much higher than predicted by the linear regression equation.[9]

Insight

As we'll discuss in the next section, an extreme outlier can pull the regression line toward it. Because of this, it's a good idea to fit the data *without* the Palm Beach County observation and see how well that line predicts results for Palm Beach County. In the app, check the box called Click to Remove Points, then go to the scatterplot and click on the point for Palm Beach County to remove it from the data set. Observe how the slope of the regression line changes when you do this. The app now displays the regression equation $\hat{y} = 45.7 + 0.0241x$ for the remaining 66 counties. Since the Perot vote in Palm Beach County was 30,739, this line would predict a Buchanan vote there of $\hat{y} = 45.7 + 0.0241(30,739) = 787$. This compares to the actual Buchanan vote of 3,407 in Palm Beach County, for a residual of $3,407 - 787 = 2,620$. Again, the actual Buchanan vote seems surprisingly high.

▶ *Try Exercises 3.27, part d and 3.34, part c*

The Method of Least Squares Yields the Regression Line

We've used the *Linear Regression* app to find the equation for the regression line. But how is it done? The software behind the app chooses the optimal line to fit through the data points by making the residuals as small as possible. This process involves compromise because a line can perfectly predict one point (resulting in a residual of 0) but poorly predict many other points (resulting in larger residuals). The actual summary measure used to evaluate regression lines is called the

$$\text{Residual sum of squares} = \Sigma(\text{residual})^2 = \Sigma(y - \hat{y})^2.$$

This formula squares each vertical distance between a point and the line and then adds up these squared values. The better the line, the smaller the residuals tend to be, and the smaller the residual sum of squares tends to be. For each potential line, we have a set of predicted values, a set of residuals, and a residual sum of squares. The line that the app reports is the one that has the *smallest* residual sum of squares. This way of selecting a line is called the **least squares method.**

Least Squares Method

Among the many possible lines that could be drawn through data points in a scatterplot, the **least squares method** gives what we call the regression line. This method produces the line that has the smallest value for the residual sum of squares using $\hat{y} = a + bx$ to predict y.

Besides making the errors as small as possible, this regression line

- Has some positive residuals and some negative residuals, and the sum (and mean) of the residuals equals 0.
- Passes through the point $(\bar{x}, \bar{y})$.

---

[9]A more complex analysis accounts for larger counts tending to vary more. However, our analysis is adequate for highlighting data points that fall far from the linear trend.

The first property tells us that the too-low predictions are balanced by the too-high predictions. The second property tells us that the line passes through the center (as measured by the mean) of the data.

Even though we usually rely on software to compute the regression line, the method of least squares does provide explicit formulas for the y-intercept and slope, based on summary statistics for the sample data. Let $\bar{x}$ denote the mean of x, $\bar{y}$ the mean of y, s_x the standard deviation of the x values, and s_y the standard deviation of the y values.

Regression Formulas for y-Intercept and Slope

The **slope** equals $b = r\left(\dfrac{s_y}{s_x}\right)$.

The **y-intercept** equals $a = \bar{y} - b(\bar{x})$.

Notice that the slope b is directly related to the correlation coefficient r, and the y-intercept depends on the slope. Let's return to the baseball data in Example 10 to illustrate the calculations. For that data set, we have $\bar{x} = 0.2597$ for batting average, $\bar{y} = 4.45$ for team scoring, $s_x = 0.01257$, and $s_y = 0.577$. The correlation coefficient is $r = 0.568$, so

$$b = r\left(\frac{s_y}{s_x}\right) = 0.568(0.577/0.01257) = 26.1$$

$$\text{and } a = \bar{y} - b(\bar{x}) = 4.45 - 26.07(0.2597) = -2.32$$

The regression line to predict team scoring from batting average is $\hat{y} = -2.32 + 26.1x$, which is exactly what the *Linear Regression* app reported.

> **In Practice**
>
> The formulas for a and b help us interpret the regression line $\hat{y} = a + bx$, but you should rely on software for calculations. Software doesn't round during the different steps of the calculation, so it will give more accurate results.

The Slope, the Correlation, and the Units of the Variables

We've used the correlation coefficient r to describe the strength of the relationship. Why can't we use the *slope* to do this, with bigger slopes representing stronger relationships? The reason is that the numerical value of the slope depends on the units for the variables.

For example, the slope of the regression equation in Example 9 between $y = $ height and $x = $ femur length (measured in centimeters) was equal to $b = 2.4$. For every 1-unit ($= 1$ cm) increase in the length of the femur, the predicted height increases by 2.4 cm. If femur length is recorded in millimeters instead of centimeters, the slope of the regression equation will change from $b = 2.4$ to $b = 0.24$, i.e., $1/10$ of the original slope. If femur length is recorded in meters, the slope would change to $b = 240$. So the numerical value of the slope b can't tell us whether the relationship is strong or weak since we can make b as large or as small as we want by changing the units. By contrast, *the correlation coefficient r does not change when the units of measurement change*. It is the same whether we measure femur length in centimeters, millimeters, meters, or inches.

In summary, we've learned that the correlation coefficient describes the strength of a linear relationship. We've also seen how the regression line predicts the response variable y by using the explanatory variable x. Although correlation and regression methods serve different purposes, there are strong connections between them:

- They are both appropriate when the relationship between two quantitative variables is approximately linear.
- The correlation coefficient and the slope of the regression line have the same sign. If one is positive, so is the other one. If one is negative, so is the other one. If one is zero, the other is also zero.

However, there are some differences between correlation and regression methods. With regression, we must identify response and explanatory variables. We get a different line if we use x to predict y than if we use y to predict x. By contrast, the correlation coefficient is the same either way and there is no need to identify a response and explanatory variable. Also, the values for the y-intercept and slope of the regression line depend on the units, whereas the correlation coefficient does not. Finally, the correlation coefficient falls between -1 and $+1$, whereas the regression slope can equal any real number.

r-Squared (r^2)

When we predict a value of y, why should we use the regression line? We could instead predict y using the center of its distribution, such as the sample mean, $\bar{y}$. The reason for using the regression line is that if x and y have an approximate linear relationship, then we can predict most y values more accurately by substituting x values into the regression equation, $\hat{y} = a + bx$, than by using the sample mean $\bar{y}$ for prediction. For instance, if there is a positive linear relationship between x and y, it would be unwise to predict each y value with the sample mean $\bar{y}$, regardless of the value of x. Rather, we would want our predictions of y to increase with x, as indicated by the linear relationship. The stronger the relationship, the more accurate these predictions based on the regression equation become.

To judge how much better the predictions become, we can compare the residual sum of squares resulting from either type of prediction. The overall prediction error when using $\hat{y}$ to predict y is given by $\Sigma(y - \hat{y})^2$. The overall prediction error when using $\bar{y}$ to predict y is given by $\Sigma(y - \bar{y})^2$. The smaller the first sum is relative to the second, the better the regression model is able to predict the response, in an overall sense.

The measure that compares these two prediction errors is called r-squared (r^2). Expressed as a percentage, it tells us by how much the overall prediction error decreases when using $\hat{y}$ instead of $\bar{y}$ to predict y. For instance, from the screenshot of the app in Figure 3.15, under Model Summary, we see that $r^2 = 32\%$. This means that the overall prediction error decreases by 32% when using the regression equation (i.e., a team's batting average) to predict a team's scoring compared to just using the overall mean team score of 4.45 to predict each team's scoring. (Note that this latter prediction simply ignores a team's batting average when predicting a team's scoring.)

A simple way to compute r^2, as you have probably guessed by the notation, is to square the correlation coefficient r. In Example 10, $r = 0.57$, and $(0.57)^2 = 0.32$, or 32%, labeled as "Coefficient of Determination" in the *Linear Regression* app.

The r^2 measure has a second important interpretation based on the fact that $\Sigma(y - \bar{y})^2$ measures the variability of the response variable y. (Remember the derivation and formula of the variance and standard deviation in Section 2.4?) In this interpretation, r^2 tells us how much of the overall variability in the response variable y can be explained by its linear relationship with x. For instance, with $r^2 = 32\%$ in Example 10, 32% of the variability in team scoring (i.e., the fact that some teams have higher or lower scoring than others) can

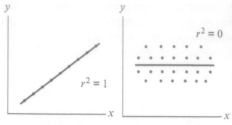

be explained by the linear relationship between a team's batting average and a team's scoring. A percentage of 32% does not seem like very much, and in fact the majority (i.e., 100% − 32% = 68%) of the variability in team scoring *cannot* be explained by the relationship with team batting averages. Many other variables besides batting averages apparently contribute to team scoring. Batting averages only account for 32% of the variability in team scoring.

Both interpretations of r^2 judge how accurate the regression equation is. The larger r^2, the more accurate our predictions resulting from the regression equation. Also, the larger r^2, the larger the proportion of the variability in the response variable that can be explained by the linear relationship with the explanatory variable.

When the data points follow an exact linear relationship, as in the scatterplot in the margin, y and $\hat{y}$ are identical for all points, which results in $r = 1$. Then, $r^2 = 1$ and all (100%) of the variability in the y-values can be explained by the linear relationship between x and y. When $r = 0$, there is no linear relationship between x and y, as in the second scatterplot in the margin. Then r^2 is also equal to 0, and none (0%) of the variability we see in the response variable y can be explained by the linear relationship between x and y (because there is no linear relationship). In practice, r^2 falls somewhere between these two extremes.

We'll give further explanation of r^2 and related measures in Chapter 12. We mention r^2 here because you'll often see it listed on regression software output or quoted together with the regression equation as an indicator of its accuracy, so we want you to know what it represents.

Associations with Quantitative and Categorical Variables

In this chapter, we've learned how to explore associations between categorical variables and between quantitative variables. It's also possible to mix the variable types or add other variables. For example, with two quantitative variables, we can identify points in the scatterplot according to their values on a third categorical variable. This is done by using different symbols or colors on the scatterplot to portray the different categories. When exploring the relationship between just two variables, we speak of a **bivariate** analysis. With three or more variables involved, this becomes a **multivariate** analysis.

Exploring Multivariate Relationships ◄

Example 12

The Gender Difference in Winning Olympic High Jumps

Picture the Scenario

The summer Olympic Games occur every four years, and one of the track and field events is the high jump. Men have competed in the high jump since 1896 and women since 1928. The High Jump data file on the book's website contains the winning heights (in meters) for each year and gender.[10]

Questions to Explore

a. How can we graphically explore the relationship between the two quantitative variables Winning Height and Year, accounting for the categorical variable Gender?

b. How have the winning heights changed over time? How different are the winning heights for men and women in a typical year?

---

[10]From www.olympic.org/medallists-results.

▶ **Figure 3.17**
Scatterplot for the
Winning High Jumps
(in Meters) in the
Olympics as Obtained
via the *Multivariate
Relationships* App. The
red dots represent men
and the blue squares
represent women.
Question In a typical year,
what is the approximate
difference between the
winning heights for men
and for women?

Think It Through

a. Figure 3.17 shows a screenshot from the *Multivariate Relationship* app with x = Year and y — Winning Height. The data points arc displayed with a red circle for men and a blue square for women, obtained by selecting Gender as the grouping variable in the app. There were no Olympic Games during World War II, so no observations appear for 1940 or 1944.

b. The scatterplot shows that for each gender the winning heights have an increasing, approximately linear trend over time. Men have consistently jumped higher than women, between about 0.3 and 0.4 meters in a given year. The women's winning heights are similar to those for the men about 60 years earlier—for instance, about 2.0 meters in 1990–2012 for women and in 1930–1940 for men.

Insight

We could describe these trends by fitting a regression line to the points for men and a separate regression line to the points for women. Figure 3.17 indicates these lines and gives the regression equation for each gender below the scatterplot. The slopes are nearly identical, indicating a similar rate of improvement over the years for both genders. However, note that since about 1980 the winning heights have leveled off somewhat. We should be cautious in using regression lines to predict future winning heights.

▶ *Try Exercise 3.43*

3.3 Practicing the Basics

3.25 **Sketch plots of lines** Identify the values of the y-intercept a and the slope b, and sketch the following regression lines, for values of x between 0 and 10.
  a. $\hat{y} = 7 + 0.5x$
  b. $\hat{y} = 7 + x$
  c. $\hat{y} = 7 - x$
  d. $\hat{y} = 7$

3.26 **Sit-ups and the 40-yard dash** Is there a relationship between how many sit-ups you can do and how fast you can run 40 yards? The scatterplot shows the relationship between these variables for a study of female athletes to be discussed in Chapter 12.

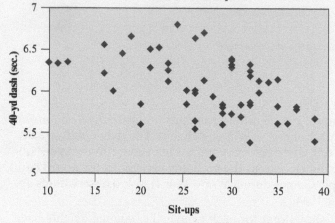

Scatterplot of Time to Run 40-Yard Dash by Number of Sit-Ups

  a. The regression equation is $\hat{y} = 6.71 - 0.024x$. Find the predicted time in the 40-yard dash for a subject who can do (i) 10 sit-ups, (ii) 40 sit-ups. Based on these times, explain how to sketch the regression line over this scatterplot.
  b. Interpret the y-intercept and slope of the equation in part a, in the context of the number of sit-ups and time for the 40-yard dash.
  c. Based on the slope in part a, is the correlation coefficient positive or negative? Explain.

3.27 **Home selling prices** The House Selling Prices FL data file, preloaded in the *Linear Regression* app and also on the book's website, lists selling prices of homes in Gainesville, Florida, in 2003 and some predictors for the selling price. For the response variable y = selling price in thousands of dollars and the explanatory variable x = size of house in thousands of square feet, $\hat{y} = 9.2 + 77.0x$.
  a. How much do you predict a house would sell for if it has (i) 2,000 square feet, (ii) 3,000 square feet?
  b. Using results in part a, explain how to interpret the slope.
  c. Is the correlation between these variables positive or negative? Why?
  d. One home that is 3,000 square feet sold for $300,000. Find the residual, and interpret.

3.28 **Rating restaurants** Zagat restaurant guides publish ratings of restaurants for many large cities around the world (see www.zagat.com). The review for each restaurant gives a verbal summary as well as a 0- to 30-point rating of the quality of food, décor, service, and the cost of a dinner with one drink and tip. For 31 French restaurants in Boston in 2014, the food quality ratings had a mean of 24.55 and standard deviation of 2.08 points. The cost of a dinner (in U.S. dollars) had a mean of $50.35 and standard deviation of $14.92. The equation that predicts the cost of a dinner using the rating for the quality of food is $\hat{y} = -70 + 4.9x$. The correlation coefficient between these two variables is 0.68. (Data available in the Zagat_Boston file.)
  a. Predict the cost of a dinner in a restaurant that gets the (i) lowest observed food quality rating of 21, (ii) highest observed food quality rating of 28.
  b. Interpret the slope in context.
  c. Interpret the correlation coefficient.
  d. Show how the slope can be obtained from the correlation coefficient and other information given.

3.29 **Predicting cost of meal from rating** Refer to the previous exercise. The correlation coefficient with the cost of a dinner is 0.68 for food quality rating, 0.69 for service rating, and 0.56 for décor rating. According to the definition of r^2 as a measure for the reduction in the prediction error, which of these three ratings can be used to make the most accurate predictions for the cost of a dinner: quality of food, service, or décor? Why?

3.30 **Internet in Indonesia** For the 32 nations in Example 8, we found a correlation coefficient of 0.614 between Internet Use and Facebook Use (both as percentages of population). The regression equation as given by the *Linear Regression* app is $\hat{y} = 7.90 + 0.439x$.
  a. Based on the correlation coefficient, the slope had to be positive. Why?
  b. Indonesia had an Internet use of 15.4% and Facebook use of 20.7%. Find its predicted Facebook use based on the regression equation.
  c. Find the residual for Indonesia. Interpret.

3.31 **Broadband subscribers and population** The Internet Use data file in the *Linear Regression* app and on the book's website contains data on the number of individuals in a country with broadband access and the population size for each of 32 nations. When using population size as the explanatory variable, x, and broadband subscribers as the response variable, y, the regression equation is $\hat{y} = 5,530,203 + 0.0761x$.
  a. Interpret the slope of the regression equation. (Make sure to use a meaningful increase.) Is the association positive or negative? Explain what this means.
  b. Predict broadband subscribers at the (i) minimum population size x value of 7,154,600, (ii) at the maximum population size x value of 1,350,695,000.

c. For the United States, broadband subscribers = 88,520,000, and population = 313,914,040. Find the predicted broadband use and the residual for the United States. Interpret the value of this residual.

3.32 SAT reading and math scores The SAT2018 data file on the book's website contains average reading and math SAT scores for each of the 50 states, Washington D.C., Puerto Rico, and the Virgin Islands for the test in 2018. Let the explanatory variable x = reading and the response variable y = math. The regression equation is $\hat{y} = -20.7 + 1.016x$.

a. California had an average reading score of 531. Use the regression equation to predict the average math score for California.

b. Calculate the residual associated with California and explain what it means in the context of the problem.

c. Does it appear that a state's average reading score is a reliable predictor of its average math score? Explain. Use the *Linear Regression* app (you can upload the data into the app by choosing Upload File under Enter Data) or other software to obtain an appropriate statistic.

3.33 How much do seat belts help? A study in 2000 by the National Highway Traffic Safety Administration estimated that failure to wear seat belts led to 9,200 deaths in the previous year, and that the number of deaths would decrease by 270 for every 1 percentage point gain in seat belt usage. Let $\hat{y}$ = predicted number of deaths in a year and x = percentage of people who wear seat belts.

a. Report the slope b for the equation $\hat{y} = a + bx$.

b. If the y-intercept equals 28,910, then predict the number of deaths in a year if (i) no one wears seat belts, (ii) 73% of people wear seat belts (the value in 2000), (iii) 100% of people wear seat belts.

3.34 Regression between cereal sodium and sugar The following figure, taken from the *Linear Regression* app, shows the result of a regression analysis of the explanatory variable x = sugar and the response variable y = sodium for the breakfast cereal data set discussed in Chapter 2 (the Cereal data file on the book's website).

a. What criterion is used in finding the line?

b. Can you draw a line that will result in a smaller sum of the squared residuals?

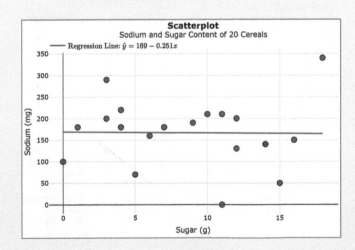

c. Now let's look at a histogram of the residuals. Explain what the two short bars on the far right of the histogram mean in the context of the problem. Which two brands of cereal do they represent? Can you find them on the scatterplot? (*Hint:* In the app, you can hover over a point in the scatterplot to see which cereal it represents.)

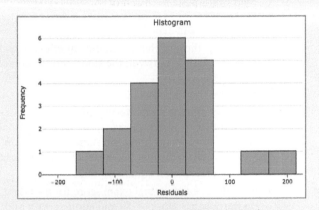

3.35 Regression and correlation between cereal sodium and sugar Refer to the previous exercise.

a. For this example, it seems that the average sodium content is as good a predictor as the one resulting from the regression equation. Do you expect r^2 to be large or small? Why?

b. For this data, $r = -0.017$. Interpret r^2.

c. Show the algebraic relationship between the correlation coefficient of -0.017 and the slope of the regression equation $b = -0.25$, using the fact that the standard deviations are 5.32 g for sugar and 77.3 mg for sodium.

3.36 Advertising and sales Each month, the owner of Fay's Tanning Salon records in a data file y = monthly total sales receipts and x = amount spent that month on advertising, both in thousands of dollars. For the first three months of operation, the observations are as shown in the table.

Advertising	Sales
0	4
1	6
2	8

a. Sketch a scatterplot.

b. From inspection of the scatterplot, state the correlation coefficient and the regression line. (*Note:* You should be able to figure them out without using software or formulas.)

c. Find the mean and standard deviation for each variable.

d. Using part c, find the regression line, using the formulas for the slope and the y-intercept. Interpret the y-intercept and the slope.

3.37 Midterm–final correlation For students who take Statistics 101 at Lake Wobegon College in Minnesota, both the midterm and final exams have mean = 75 and standard deviation = 10. The professor explores using the midterm exam score to predict the final exam score. The regression equation relating y = final exam score to x = midterm exam score is $\hat{y} = 30 + 0.60x$.

a. Find the predicted final exam score for a student who has (i) midterm score = 100, (ii) midterm score = 50. Note that in each case the predicted final exam score *regresses toward the mean* of 75. (This is a property of the regression equation that is the origin of its name, as Chapter 12 will explain.)

b. Show that the correlation coefficient equals 0.60 (*Hint:* Use the relation between the slope and the correlation coefficient.)

c. Interpret the slope in context.

3.38 Predict final exam from midterm In an introductory statistics course, x = midterm exam score and y = final exam score. Both have mean = 80 and standard deviation = 10. The correlation coefficient between the exam scores is 0.70.

a. Find the regression equation.

b. Find the predicted final exam score for a student with midterm exam score = 80 and another with midterm exam score = 90.

3.39 NL baseball Example 10 related y = team scoring (per game) and x = team batting average for American League teams. For National League teams in 2010, $\hat{y} = -6.25 + 41.5x$. (Data available on the book's website in the NL team statistics file.)

a. The team batting averages varied between 0.242 and 0.272. Explain how to interpret the slope in context.

b. Software reports $r^2 = 0.81$. Explain how to interpret this measure.

3.40 Study time and college GPA A graduate teaching assistant (Euijung Ryu) for Introduction to Statistics (STA 2023) at the University of Florida collected data from one of her classes to investigate the relationship between using the explanatory variable x = study time per week (average number of hours) to predict the response variable y = college GPA. For the eight males in her class, the data were as shown in the following table.

a. Use the *Linear Regression* app or other software to obtain a scatterplot and the correlation coefficient. Use these to describe the relationship. (When using the app, select Your Own under Enter Data, provide names for the x and y variables, enter the data appearing below, and press Submit.)

b. Find and interpret the prediction equation by reporting the predicted GPA for a student who studies (i) 5 hours per week, (ii) 25 hours per week.

c. Interpret the slope in context.

Student	Study Time	GPA
1	14	2.8
2	25	3.6
3	15	3.4
4	5	3.0
5	10	3.1
6	12	3.3
7	5	2.7
8	21	3.8

3.41 Oil and GDP An article in the September 16, 2006, issue of *The Economist* showed a scatterplot for many nations relating the response variable y = annual oil consumption per person (in barrels) and the explanatory variable x = gross domestic product (GDP, per person, in thousands of dollars). The values shown on the plot were approximately as shown in the table.

a. Use the *Linear Regression* app or other software to obtain a scatterplot and the correlation coefficient. Use these to describe the relationship. (When using the app, select Your Own under Enter Data, provide names for the x and y variables, enter the data into the table, and press Submit.)

b. Find the prediction equation and interpret the slope.

c. Find and interpret the residual for Canada.

Nation	GDP	Oil Consumption
India	3	1
China	8	2
Brazil	9	4
Mexico	10	7
Russia	11	8
S. Korea	20	18
Italy	29	12
France	30	13
Britain	31	11
Germany	31	12
Japan	31	16
Canada	34	26
U.S.	41	26

3.42 Mountain bikes Is there a relationship between the weight of a mountain bike and its price? A lighter bike is often preferred, but do lighter bikes tend to be more expensive? The following table, from the Mountain Bike data file on the book's website, gives data on price, weight, and type of suspension (FU = full, FE = front end) for 12 brands.

Mountain Bikes			
Brand and Model	Price($)	Weight(LB)	Type
Trek VRX 200	1000	32	FU
Cannondale Super V400	1100	31	FU
GT XCR-4000	940	34	FU
Specialized FSR	1100	30	FU
Trek 6500	700	29	FE
Specialized Rockhop	600	28	FE
Haro Escape A7.1	440	29	FE
Giant Yukon SE	450	29	FE
Mongoose SX 6.5	550	30	FE
Diamondback Sorrento	340	33	FE
Motiv Rockridge	180	34	FE
Huffy Anorak 36789	140	37	FE

Source: Data from *Consumer Reports,* June 1999.

a. Use the *Linear Regression* app (or, better yet, the *Multivariate Relationships* app if you are also completing the next exercise) or other software to obtain a scatterplot. (You can upload the data file, after you have downloaded it to your computer, to either app by selecting Upload File under Enter Data.)

b. Find the regression equation. Interpret the slope in context. Does the *y*-intercept have contextual meaning?

c. You decide to purchase a mountain bike that weighs 30 pounds. What is the predicted price of the bike?

3.43 **Mountain bike and suspension type**   Refer to the previous exercise. In addition to weight and price, the data file also contains information on the type of suspension of the bike (FU = full, FE = front-end).

a. The following scatterplot, obtained via the *Multivariate Relationships* app, colors the dots by suspension type. Is the single regression line fitted in the previous exercise the best way to describe the relationship between weight and price?

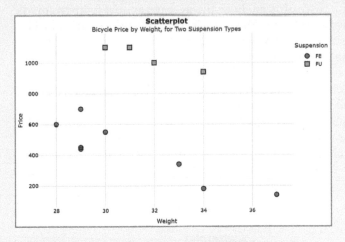

b. Using the app or other software, find separate regression equations for the two suspension types. Summarize your findings.

c. The correlation coefficient for all 12 data points is $r = -0.32$. If the correlation coefficients for the full and front-end suspension bikes are found separately, how do you believe they will compare to $r = -0.32$? Find them and interpret. (*Hint:* The *Multivariate Relationships* app allows you to find r and r^2 for each suspension type separately.)

d. You see a mountain bike advertised for $700 that weighs 28.5 lb. The type of suspension is not given. Would you predict that this bike has a full or a front-end suspension? Statistically justify your answer.

3.44 **Fuel consumption**   Most cars are fuel efficient when running at a steady speed of around 40 to 50 mph. A scatterplot relating fuel consumption (measured in mpg) and steady driving speed (measured in mph) for a mid-sized car is shown below. The data are available in the Fuel file on the book's website.[11]

a. The correlation coefficient equals 0.106. Comment on the use of the correlation coefficient as a measure for the strength of the relationship between fuel consumption and steady driving speed.

b. Comment on the use of the regression equation as a tool for predicting fuel consumption from the velocity of the car.

c. Over what subrange of steady driving speed might fitting a regression equation be appropriate? Why?

3.4 Cautions in Analyzing Associations

This chapter has introduced ways to explore **associations** between variables. When using these methods, you need to be cautious about certain potential pitfalls.

Extrapolation Is Dangerous

Extrapolation refers to using a regression line to predict *y* values for *x* values outside the observed range of data. This is riskier as we move farther from that range. If the trend changes, extrapolation gives poor predictions. For example, regression analysis is often applied to observations of a quantitative response variable over time. The regression line describes the time trend. But it is dangerous to use the line to make predictions far into the future.

---

[11]*Source:* Berry, I. M. (2010). *The Effects of Driving Style and Vehicle Performance on the Real-World Fuel Consumption of U.S. Light-Duty Vehicles*. Masters thesis, Massachusetts Institute of Technology, Cambridge, MA.

Extrapolation ◄

Example 13

Forecasting Future Global Warming

Picture the Scenario

In Chapter 2, we explored trends in temperatures over time using time plots. Let's use regression with the Central Park Yearly Temps data file on the book's website to describe the trend over time of the average annual temperatures from 1869–2018 for Central Park, New York City.

Questions to Explore

a. What does a regression line tell us about the trend over the 20th century?

b. What does it predict about the average annual temperature in the year (i) 2025 (ii) 3000? Are these extrapolations sensible?

Think It Through

a. Figure 3.18 shows a time plot of the Central Park average annual temperatures. For a regression analysis, the average annual temperature is the response variable. Time (the year) is the explanatory variable. The *Linear Regression* app (after uploading this file under Enter Data) tells us that the regression line is $\hat{y} = -2.45 + 0.029x$.

The positive slope reflects an increasing trend: The average annual temperature tended upward over the century. The slope b = 0.029 indicates that **for each one-year increase, the predicted average annual temperature increases by 0.029 degrees Fahrenheit.** The slope value of 0.029 seems close to 0, indicating little warming. However, 0.029 is the predicted change *per year*. Over a century, the predicted change is $0.029(100) = 2.9$ degrees, which is quite significant.

Scatterplot
Average Annual Temperature in Central Park, New York, from 1869 - 2018
— Regression Line: $\hat{y} = -2.45 + 0.029x$

▲ **Figure 3.18** Screenshot from the *Linear Regression* App Showing a Time Plot of Central Park Average Annual Temperature, with Fitted Regression Line Superimposed. **Question** If the present trend continues, what would you predict for the annual mean temperature for 2025?

b. Using the trend line, the predicted average annual temperature for the year 2025 is

$$\hat{y} = -2.45 + 0.029(2025) = 56.3 \text{ degrees Fahrenheit.}$$

Further into the future we see more dramatic increases. At the next millennium, for the year 3000, the forecast is $\hat{y} = -2.45 + 0.029(3000) = 84.6$ degrees. If this is accurate, it would be exceedingly uncomfortable to live in New York!

Insight

It is dangerous to extrapolate far outside the range of observed x values. There's no guarantee that the relationship will have the same trend outside that range. It seems reasonable to predict for 2025. That's not looking too far into the future from the last observation in 2018. However, it is foolhardy to predict for 3000. It's not sensible to assume that the same straight-line trend will continue for the next 982 years. As time moves forward, the average annual temperatures may increase even faster or level off or even decrease.

▶ *Try Exercise 3.47*

Predictions about the future using time series data are called **forecasts.** When we use a regression line to forecast a trend for future years, we must make the assumption that the past trend will remain the same in the future. This is risky.

Be Cautious of Influential Outliers

One reason to plot the data before you do a correlation or regression analysis is to check for unusual observations. Such an observation can tell you something interesting, as in Examples 7 and 11 about the Buchanan vote in the 2000 U.S. presidential election. Furthermore, a data point that is an outlier on a scatterplot can have a substantial effect on the regression line and correlation coefficient, especially with small data sets.

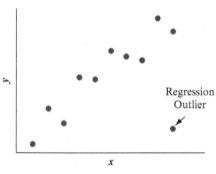

Regression Outlier

What's relevant here is not whether an observation is an outlier in its x value, relative to the other x values, or in its y value, relative to the other y values. Instead, we search for observations that are **regression outliers,** being well removed from the trend that the rest of the data follow. The margin figure shows an observation that is a regression outlier, although it is not an outlier on x alone or on y alone.

When an observation has a large effect on results of a regression analysis, it is said to be **influential**. For an observation to be influential, two conditions must hold:

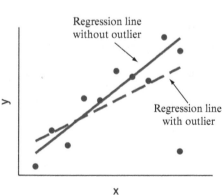

Regression line without outlier

Regression line with outlier

- Its x value is relatively low or high compared to the rest of the data.
- The observation is a regression outlier, falling quite far from the trend that the rest of the data follow.

When both of these happen, the line tends to be pulled toward that data point and away from the trend of the rest of the points as the margin figure illustrates.

Figure 3.19 shows two regression outliers. The correlation coefficient without these two points equals 0.00. The first regression outlier is near the middle of the range of x. It does not have much potential for tilting the line up or down. It has little influence on the slope or the correlation coefficient. The correlation coefficient changes only to 0.03 when we add it to the data set. The second regression outlier is at the high end of the range of x-values. It is influential. The correlation coefficient changes to 0.47 when we add it to the data set.

▲ **Figure 3.19 An Observation Is a Regression Outlier If It Is Far Removed from the Trend That the Rest of the Data Follow.** The top two points are regression outliers. Not all regression outliers are influential in affecting the correlation coefficient or slope. **Question** Which regression outlier in this figure is influential?

Example 14

Influential Outliers ◀

Higher Education and Higher Murder Rates

Picture the Scenario

Table 3.6 shows data[12] for the 50 states and the District of Columbia on

Violent crime rate: The annual number of murders, forcible rapes, robberies, and aggravated assaults per 100,000 people in the population.

Murder rate: The annual number of murders per 100,000 people in the population.

Poverty: Percentage of the residents with income below the poverty level.

High school: Percentage of the adult residents who have at least a high school education.

College: Percentage of the adult residents who have a college education.

Single parent: Percentage of families headed by a single parent.

The data are in the U.S. Statewide Crime data file on the book's website. and preloaded in the *Linear Regression* app. Let's look at the relationship between y = murder rate and x = college. We'll look at other variables in the exercises.

Questions to Explore

a. Use the *Linear Regression* app or other software to construct the scatterplot between y = murder rate and x = college. Does any observation look like it could be influential in its effect on the regression line?

b. Find the regression line. Check whether the observation identified in part a actually is influential by finding the line again without that observation.

---

[12]From *Statistical Abstract of the United States, 2003.*

Table 3.6 Statewide Data on Several Variables

State	Violent Crime	Murder Rate	Poverty	High School	College	Single Parent
Alabama	486	7.4	14.7	77.5	20.4	26.0
Alaska	567	4.3	8.4	90.4	28.1	23.2
Arizona	532	7.0	13.5	85.1	24.6	23.5
Arkansas	445	6.3	15.8	81.7	18.4	24.7
California	622	6.1	14.0	81.2	27.5	21.8
Colorado	334	3.1	8.5	89.7	34.6	20.8
Connecticut	325	2.9	7.7	88.2	31.6	22.9
Delaware	684	3.2	9.9	86.1	24.0	25.6
District of Columbia	1508	41.8	17.4	83.2	38.3	44.7
Florida	812	5.6	12.0	84.0	22.8	26.5
Georgia	505	8.0	12.5	82.6	23.1	25.5
Hawaii	244	2.9	10.6	87.4	26.3	19.1
Idaho	253	1.2	13.3	86.2	20.0	17.7
Illinois	657	7.2	10.5	85.5	27.1	21.9
Indiana	349	5.8	8.3	84.6	17.1	22.8
Iowa	266	1.6	7.9	89.7	25.5	19.8
Kansas	389	6.3	10.5	88.1	27.3	20.2
Kentucky	295	4.8	12.5	78.7	20.5	23.2
Louisiana	681	12.5	18.5	80.8	22.5	29.3
Maine	110	1.2	9.8	89.3	24.1	23.7
Maryland	787	8.1	7.3	85.7	32.3	24.5
Massachusetts	476	2.0	10.2	85.1	32.7	22.8
Michigan	555	6.7	10.2	86.2	23.0	24.5
Minnesota	281	3.1	7.9	90.8	31.2	19.6
Mississippi	361	9.0	15.5	80.3	18.7	30.0
Missouri	490	6.2	9.8	86.6	26.2	24.3
Montana	241	1.8	16.0	89.6	23.8	21.4
Nebraska	328	3.7	10.7	90.4	24.6	19.6
Nevada	524	6.5	10.1	82.8	19.3	24.2
New Hampshire	175	1.8	7.6	88.1	30.1	20.0
New Jersey	384	3.4	8.1	87.3	30.1	20.2
New Mexico	758	7.4	19.3	82.2	23.6	26.6
New York	554	5.0	14.7	82.5	28.7	26.0
North Carolina	498	7.0	13.2	79.2	23.2	24.3
North Dakota	81	0.6	12.8	85.5	22.6	19.1

State	Violent Crime	Murder Rate	Poverty	High School	College	Single Parent
Ohio	334	3.7	11.1	87.0	24.6	24.6
Oklahoma	496	5.3	14.1	86.1	22.5	23.5
Oregon	351	2.0	12.9	88.1	27.2	22.5
Pennsylvania	420	4.9	9.8	85.7	24.3	22.8
Rhode Island	298	4.3	10.2	81.3	26.4	27.4
South Carolina	805	5.8	12.0	83.0	19.0	27.1
South Dakota	167	0.9	9.4	91.8	25.7	20.7
Tennessee	707	7.2	13.4	79.9	22.0	27.9
Texas	545	5.9	14.9	79.2	23.9	21.5
Utah	256	1.9	8.1	90.7	26.4	13.6
Vermont	114	1.5	10.3	90.0	28.8	22.5
Virginia	282	5.7	8.1	86.6	31.9	22.2
Washington	370	3.3	9.5	91.8	28.6	22.1
West Virginia	317	2.5	15.8	77.1	15.3	22.3
Wisconsin	237	3.2	9.0	86.7	23.8	21.7
Wyoming	267	2.4	11.1	90.0	20.6	20.8

Think It Through

a. Figure 3.20 shows the scatterplot produced with the *Linear Regression* app, which has the data set preloaded. The observation out by itself in the top right corner is D.C. with $x = 38.3$ and $y = 41.8$, which is the largest observation on both these variables. It satisfies both conditions for an observation to be influential: It has a relatively extreme value

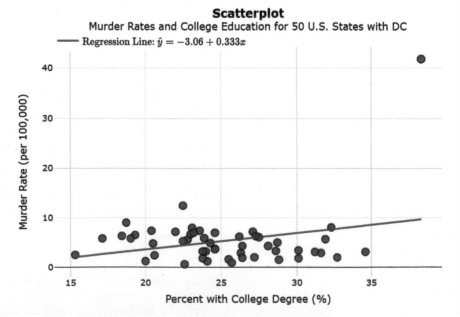

▲ **Figure 3.20** Scatterplot Relating Murder Rate to Percentage with College Education. Screenshot from the *Linear Regression* app. **Question** How would you expect the slope to change if D.C. is excluded from the regression analysis?

on the explanatory variable (college), and it is a regression outlier, falling well away from the linear trend of the other points.

b. Using information from the app, the regression line fitted to all 51 observations, including D.C., equals $\hat{y} = -3.06 + 0.333x$. The slope is *positive*, as shown in Figure 3.20. You can check that the predicted murder rate *increases* from 1.9 to 10.1 as the percentage with a college education increases from $x = 15\%$ to $x = 40\%$, roughly the range of observed x values. By contrast, when we fit the regression line only to the 50 states, excluding the observation for D.C., $\hat{y} = 8.04 - 0.138x$. The slope of -0.138 reflects a *negative* trend, as shown in Figure 3.21. Now, the predicted murder rate *decreases* from 5.9 to 2.4 as the percentage with a college education increases from 15% to 40%. (In the app, check the option Click to Remove Points to remove points from the scatterplot by clicking on them and observing how the fitted regression line changes.)

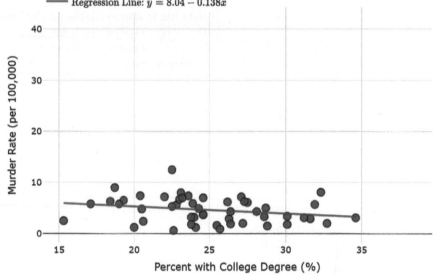

Scatterplot
Murder Rates and College Education for 50 U.S. States (without DC)
—— Regression Line: $\hat{y} = 8.04 - 0.138x$

▲ **Figure 3.21** Scatterplot Relating Murder Rate to Percentage with College Education Without the Observation for D.C. **Question** Which line better describes the trend for the 50 states, the one obtained with or without D.C?

Insight

Including D.C. in the regression analysis has the effect of pulling the slope of the regression line upward. The regression line then makes it seem, misleadingly, as if the murder rate tends to *increase* when the percentage with a college education increases. In fact, for the rest of the data, the predicted murder rate tends to *decrease*. The regression line including D.C. distorts the relationship for the other 50 states. In summary, the D.C. data point is highly influential. The regression line for the 50 states alone better represents the overall negative trend. In reporting these results, we should show this line and then note that D.C. is a regression outlier that falls well outside this trend.

▶ *Try Exercise 3.45*

Caution

Always construct a scatterplot before finding a correlation coefficient or fitting a regression line. ◀

This example shows the correlation coefficient and the regression line are **nonresistant:** They are prone to distortion by outliers. *Investigate any regression outlier.* Was the observation recorded incorrectly, or is it merely different from the rest of the data in some way? It is often a good idea to refit the regression line without it to see if it has a large effect, as we did in this last example.

Correlation Does Not Imply Causation

In a regression analysis, suppose that as x goes up, y also tends to go up (or go down). Can we conclude that there's a *causal* connection, with changes in x causing changes in y?

The concept of causality is central to science. We are all familiar with it, at least in an informal sense. We know, for example, that exposure to a virus can cause the flu or heating air will cause air to rise. But just observing an association between two variables is not enough to imply a causal connection. There may be some alternative explanation for the association.

Example 15

Correlation and Causation ◄

Education and Crime

Picture the Scenario

Figure 3.22 shows a scatterplot of data on y = crime rate and x = education for 67 Florida counties, obtained via the *Multivariate Relationships* app. (The data file is also available on the book's website.) Education was measured as the percentage of residents aged at least 25 in the county who had at least a high school degree. Crime rate was measured as the number of crimes in that county in the past year per 1,000 residents.

As the scatterplot with the superimposed regression line shows, these variables have a positive relationship. You can check that the correlation coefficient is $r = 0.47$. Unlike the previous example, there is no obvious influential observation causing the positive correlation between education and higher crime rate. (The one county, Miami-Dade, that stands out with the highest crime rate is not influential because its x-value is not extreme.) Another variable measured for these counties is urbanization, measured as the percentage of the residents who live in metropolitan areas. It has a correlation coefficient of 0.68 with crime rate and 0.79 with education. (Scatterplots not shown.)

► **Figure 3.22** Scatterplot of Crime Rate and Percentage with at Least a High School Education. This is a screenshot from the *Multivariate Relationships* app. **Questions** Does more education cause more crime, or does more crime cause more education, or possibly neither? Is it correct to say that every 10 percentage point increase in the percentage with a high school education causes the crime rate to increase by 14.9 more crimes per thousand?

Simple Linear Regression Model
$\hat{y} = -50.9 + 1.49 \cdot$ (Percent with high school education)

Correlation r	Coefficient of Determination r²
0.4670	21.8%

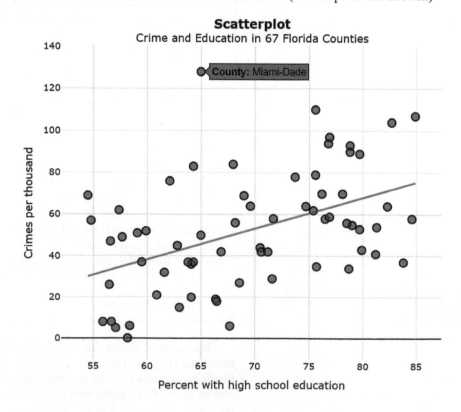

Scatterplot
Crime and Education in 67 Florida Counties

Question to Explore

From the positive correlation coefficient (and positive slope) between crime rate and education, can we conclude that having a more highly educated populace causes the crime rate to go up?

Think It Through

The strong correlation between urbanization and education (correlation coefficient $r = 0.79$) tells us that highly urban counties tend to have higher education levels. The moderately strong correlation between urbanization and crime rate ($r = 0.68$) tells us that highly urban counties also tend to have higher crime. So, perhaps the reason for the positive correlation between education and crime rate is that education tends to be greater in more highly urbanized counties, but crime rates also tend to be higher in such counties. So, counties with higher education tend to be more urban, and more urban counties tend to have more crime. We can illustrate this by coloring the dots in the scatterplot according to their level of urbanization, as in Figure 3.23. (In the *Multivariate Relationships* app, select Urbanization (%) as the Grouping Variable to reproduce this plot.)

The coloring of the dots reveals a pattern: The brighter (i.e., more urban) dots tend to occur in the upper right corner, where counties with high education and high crime rate are located. The darker dots tend to occur in the lower left corner, where counties with lower education and lower crime rates are located.

The correlation between education and crime rate occurs because each one is correlated with urbanization. Therefore, it would be wrong to conclude a causal relationship between education and crime rate. More likely, a higher level of urbanization is responsible for elevated crime rates, not a higher level of education.

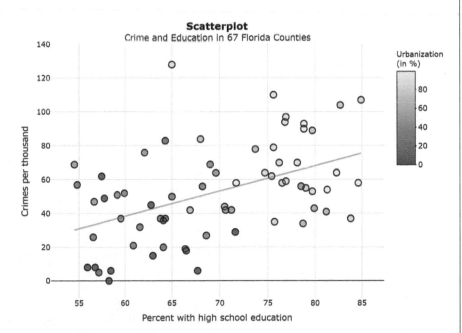

▲ **Figure 3.23** Scatterplot of Crime Rate and Percentage with at Least a High School Education, with Dots Colored According to the Percentage of Urbanization of a County. Screenshot from the *Multivariate Relationships* app. Brighter dots correspond to counties with higher percentage of urbanization. Darker dots correspond to counties with lower urbanization. **Question** If urbanization were not related with either education or the crime rate, how would the color of the dots be distributed?

Insight

For counties with similar levels of urbanization, the relationship between crime rate and education may look quite different. To illustrate, we grouped all counties with zero urbanization into a group called "rural," counties with urbanization ranging between 15% and 50% into a group called "mixed," and counties with urbanization between 50% and 100% (like Miami-Dade) into a group called "urban." Figure 3.24 shows the scatterplot with dots colored according to these three groups, with a regression line fitted to the counties in each group separately. (In the app, you can select to show the regression equation and correlation coefficient for the observations within each of the three groups.)

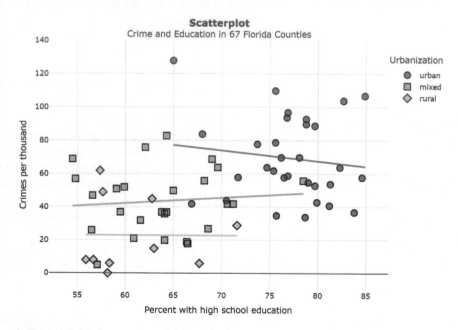

▲ **Figure 3.24** Scatterplot of Crime Rate and Percentage with at Least a High School Education, with Dots Colored According to Whether the County is Rural, Mixed, or Urban. Screenshot from the *Multivariate Relationships* app.

Now, the correlation coefficient between education and crime rate is $r = 0.00$ for rural counties, $r = 0.09$ for mixed counties, and $r = -0.13$ for urban counties. These results show a very different picture: In each group, the correlation coefficient is either zero or very close to zero, indicating no relationship at all. This is also shown by the regression lines, which are essentially flat, indicating no relationship.

Summing up, if we ignored urbanization, we would have, somewhat counter-intuitively, reported a positive correlation between education and crime rates. However, if we take urbanization into account, e.g., by grouping counties with similar levels of urbanization together, we see that there really isn't much of a relationship between education and crime rates, which goes along with our intuition.

This discussion shows the difference between a **bivariate** analysis, which only considers the two variables crime rate and education, and a **multivariate** analysis, which takes additional variables, such as urbanization, into account when analyzing the relationship. An extension of the regression equation that considers two or more (instead of just one) explanatory variables is an example of such a multivariate analysis. Called Multiple Linear Regression, it is the topic of Chapter 14.

▶ *Try Exercises 3.53 and 3.57*

Whenever two variables are related, other variables may have influenced that relationship. In Example 15, urbanization influenced the relationship between crime rate and education. This illustrates an important point: **Correlation does not imply causation.**

In Example 15, crime rate and education were positively correlated, but that does not mean that having a high level of education causes a county's crime rate to be high. In fact, we showed that the likely reason for the higher crime rates is the higher level of urbanization in those counties. Whenever we observe a correlation between variables x and y, there may be a third variable correlated with both x and y that is responsible for their association. Then, a multivariate analysis that takes this third variable into account is more appropriate than a bivariate analysis that ignores it. Let's look at another example to illustrate this point.

Lurking Variable ◄

Example 16

Ice Cream and Drowning

Picture the Scenario

The Gold Coast of Australia, south of Brisbane, is famous for its beaches. Because of strong rip tides, however, each year many people drown. Data collected monthly show a positive relationship between y = number of people who drowned in that month and x = number of gallons of ice cream sold in refreshment stands along the beach in that month.

Question to Explore

Clearly, the high sales of ice cream don't cause more people to drown. Identify another variable that could be responsible for this relationship.

Think It Through

In the summer in Australia (especially January and February), the weather is hot. People tend to buy more ice cream in those months. They also tend to go to the beach and swim more in those months, and more people drown. In the winter, it is cooler. People buy less ice cream, fewer people go to the beach, and fewer people drown. So, the monthly temperature is a variable that could be responsible for the correlation. As the monthly temperature goes up, so do ice cream sales and so does the number of people who drown.

Insight

If we looked only at months having similar monthly temperatures, probably we would not observe any relationship between ice cream sales and the number of people who drown. A multivariate analysis that adjusts for the temperature is more appropriate than a bivariate analysis that ignores it.

► *Try Exercise 3.54*

A third variable that is not measured in a study but that influences the relationship between the response variable and the explanatory variable is referred to as a **lurking variable.**

Lurking Variable

A **lurking variable** is a variable, usually unobserved, that influences the association between the variables of primary interest.

In interpreting the positive correlation between crime rate and education for Florida counties, we'd be remiss if we failed to recognize that the correlation could be due to a lurking variable. This could happen if we observed those two variables but not urbanization, which would then be a lurking variable. Likewise, if we got excited by the positive correlation between ice cream sales and the number drowned in a month, we'd fail to recognize that the monthly temperature is a lurking variable. The difficulty in practice is that often we have only a vague understanding what the lurking variables may be.

Simpson's Paradox

We can express the statement that *correlation does not imply causation* more generally as **association does not imply causation.** This warning holds whether we analyze two quantitative variables or two categorical variables.

The direction of an association between two variables can change after we include a third variable and analyze the data at separate levels of that variable; this is known as **Simpson's paradox.**[13] We observed Simpson's paradox in Figure 3.24 in Example 15, where the positive correlation coefficient between crime rate and education changed to a correlation coefficient of zero or even a negative correlation coefficient when data were considered at separate levels of urbanization. This example serves as a warning: *Be cautious about interpreting an association.* Always be wary of lurking variables that may influence the association.

Let's illustrate by revisiting Example 1, which presented a study indicating that smoking could apparently be beneficial to your health. Could a lurking variable be responsible for this association?

Reversal in Direction of Association

Example 17

Smoking and Health

Picture the Scenario

Example 1 mentioned a survey[14] of 1,314 women in the United Kingdom that asked each woman whether she was a smoker. Twenty years later, a follow-up survey observed whether each woman was dead or still alive. Table 3.7 is a contingency table of the results. The response variable is survival status after 20 years. Of the 582 smokers, 139 died, which is 24%. Of the 732 nonsmokers, 230 died, which is 31%. The proportion of women who died was larger for the nonsmokers.

Table 3.7 Smoking Status and 20-Year Survival in Women

Smoker	Survival Status		Total
	Dead	**Alive**	
Yes	139	443	**582**
No	230	502	**732**
Total	**369**	**945**	**1,314**

---

[13]The paradox is named after a British statistician who in 1951 investigated conditions under which this flip-flopping of association can happen.

[14]Described by D. R. Appleton et al., *American Statistician*, vol. 50, pp. 340–341 (1996).

Could the age of the woman at the beginning of the study explain the association? Presumably it could if the smokers tended to be younger than the nonsmokers. For this reason, Table 3.8 shows four contingency tables relating smoking status and survival status for these 1,314 women, separated into four age groups.

Table 3.8 Smoking Status and 20-Year Survival for Four Age Groups

| | Age Group | | | | | | | |
| | 18–34 | | 35–54 | | 55–64 | | 65+ | |
Smoker	Dead	Alive	Dead	Alive	Dead	Alive	Dead	Alive
Yes	5	174	41	198	51	64	42	7
No	6	213	19	180	40	81	165	28

Questions to Explore

a. Show that the counts in Table 3.8 are consistent with those in Table 3.7.
b. For each age group, find the (marginal) percentage of women who smoked.
c. For each age group, find the (marginal) percentage of women who died.
d. For each age group, compute the conditional percentage of dying for smokers and nonsmokers. To describe the association between smoking and survival status for each age group, find the difference in the percentages.
e. How can you explain the association in Table 3.7, whereby smoking seems to help women live a longer life? How can this association be so different from the one shown in the partial tables of Table 3.8?

Think It Through

a. If you add the counts in the four separate parts of Table 3.8, you'll get the counts in Table 3.7. For instance, from Table 3.7, we see that 139 of the women who smoked died. From Table 3.8, we get this from $5 + 41 + 51 + 42 = 139$, taking the number of smokers who died from each age group. Doing this for each cell, we see that the counts in the two tables are consistent with each other.
b. Of the 398 women in age group 1, 179 ($= 45\%$) were smokers. In age group 2, 55% were smokers. In age group 3, 49%. But in age group 4, only 20% were smokers. So the oldest age group had the fewest smokers among them.
c. Of the 398 women in age group 1, 11 ($= 3\%$) died. In age group 2, 14% died and in age group 3, 39%. As we would expect, the most women, 86%, died in age group 4 after a period of 20 years.
d. Table 3.9 shows the conditional percentages who died, for smokers and nonsmokers in each age group. Figure 3.25 plots them. The difference (in percentage points) is shown in the last row. For each age group, a higher percentage of smokers than nonsmokers died.
e. Could age explain the association? The proportion of smokers is higher in the younger age group (e.g., 45% and 55% for age groups 1 and 2, 20% in age group 4). Naturally, these younger women are less likely to die after 20 years (3% and 14% in age groups 1 and 2, 85% in age group 4). Overall, when ignoring age, this leads to fewer smokers dying compared

Table 3.9 Conditional Percentages of Deaths for Smokers and Nonsmokers, by Age.

For instance, for smokers of age 18–34, from Table 3.8 the proportion who died was $5/(5 + 174) = 0.028$, or 2.8%.

	Age Group			
Smoker	18–34	35–54	55–64	65+
Yes	2.8%	17.2%	44.3%	85.7%
No	2.7%	9.5%	33.1%	85.5%
Difference	0.1%	7.7%	11.2%	0.2%

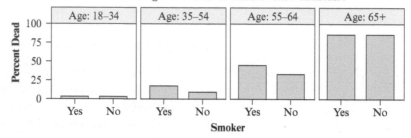

▲ **Figure 3.25** Bar Graph Comparing Percentage of Deaths for Smokers and Nonsmokers, by Age. This side-by-side bar graph shows the conditional percentages from Table 3.9.

to nonsmokers, as observed in Table 3.7. Although the association for this table indicates that overall, smokers had a *lower* chance of dying than nonsmokers, it merely reflects the fact that younger women were more likely to be smokers and hence less likely to die during the study time frame compared to the nonsmokers, who were predominately older.

When we looked at the data separately for each age group in Table 3.8, we saw the reverse: For each age group, smokers had a *higher* chance of dying than nonsmokers. The analysis using Table 3.7 did not account for age, which strongly influences the association.

Insight

Because of the reversal in the association after taking age into account, the researchers did *not* conclude that smoking is beneficial to your health. This example illustrates the dramatic influence that a lurking variable can have, which would be unknown to researchers if they fail to include a certain variable in their study. An association can look quite different after adjusting for the effect of a third variable by grouping the data according to its values.

▶ *Try Exercise 3.58*

The Effect of Lurking Variables on Associations

Lurking variables can affect associations in many ways. For instance, a lurking variable may be a **common cause** of both the explanatory and response variable. In Example 16, the monthly temperature is a common cause of both ice cream sales and the number of people who drown.

In practice, there's usually not a single variable that causally explains a response variable or the association between two variables. More commonly, there are **multiple causes.** When there are multiple causes, the association among them makes it difficult to study the effect of any single variable. For example, suppose someone claims that growing up in poverty causes crime. Realistically, probably lots of things contribute to crime. Many variables that you might think of as possible causes, such as a person's educational level, whether the person grew up in a stable family, and the quality of the neighborhood in which the person lives, are themselves likely to be associated with whether a person grew up in poverty. Perhaps people growing up in poverty tend to have poorly educated parents, grow up in high-crime neighborhoods, and achieve low levels of education. Perhaps all these factors make a person more likely to become a criminal. Growing up in poverty may have a direct effect on crime but also an indirect effect through these other variables.

It's especially tricky to study cause and effect when two variables are **measured over time.** The variables may be associated merely because they both have a *time trend.* Suppose that both the divorce rate and the crime rate have an increasing trend over a 10-year period. They will then have a positive correlation: Higher crime rates occur in years that have higher divorce rates. Does this imply that an increasing divorce rate *causes* the crime rate to increase? Absolutely not. They would also be positively correlated with all other variables that have a positive time trend over this period, such as annual average house price and the annual use of cell phones. There are likely to be other variables that are themselves changing over time and have causal influences on the divorce rate and the crime rate.

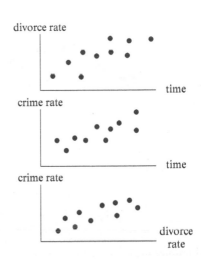

A relationship between the *crime rate* and *divorce rate* may merely reflect a common time trend.

Confounding

When two explanatory variables are both associated with a response variable but are also associated with each other, **confounding** occurs. It is difficult to determine whether either of them truly causes the response because a variable's effect could be at least partly due to its association with the other variable. Example 15 illustrated a study with confounding. For the 67 Florida counties, educational level and crime rate had a positive relationship. However, urbanization was a confounding variable since it also had a positive relationship with educational level and the crime rate. Counties with high urbanization also had high education and vice versa. Once we adjusted for urbanization by forming groups of counties with similar levels of urbanization, the relationship between educational level and the crime rate vanished. Example 17 is another example of a study where confounding occurs. Over the 20-year study period, smokers had a lower rate of dying than nonsmokers. However, age was a confounding variable. Older subjects were less likely to be smokers, and older subjects were more likely to die. Once we adjusted for age by forming age groups, smokers had a *higher* rate of dying than nonsmokers in every age group. Age had a dramatic influence on the association between smoking and survival status.

What's the difference between a confounding variable and a lurking variable? A lurking variable is not measured in the study. It has the *potential* for confounding. If it were included in the study and if it were associated both with the response variable and the explanatory variable, it would become a confounding variable. It would affect the relationship between the response and explanatory variables.

The potential for lurking variables to affect associations is the main reason it is difficult to study many issues of importance, whether for medical issues such as the effect of smoking on cancer or social issues such as what causes crime, what causes the economy to improve, or what causes students to succeed in school. It's not impossible—statistical methods can analyze the effect of an explanatory variable after adjusting for confounding variables (as we adjusted for age in Example 17)—but there's always the chance that an important variable was not included in the study.

3.4 Practicing the Basics

3.45 Outliers and extrapolations The screenshot from the *Linear Regression* app shows the data and regression line for the 50 states plus D.C. in Table 3.6 relating

x = percentage of single-parent families to

y = annual murder rate (number of murders per 100,000 people in the population).

a. Is D.C. an influential observation? Explain why or why not.

b. Using the app or other software, remove D.C. and confirm that the regression line for the remaining 50 observations is given by $\hat{y} = -8.25 + 0.56x$. By how much did the slope change when removing this single observation? (*Hint:* When using the app, check the box for Click to Remove Points and then click on the observation for D.C. to remove it.)

c. Using the regression equation from part b, find the predicted murder rate at $x = 0$. Why is it not sensible to make a prediction at $x = 0$ based on these data?

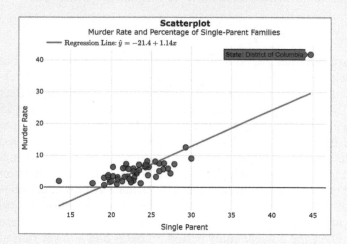

3.46 Men's Olympic long jumps The Olympic winning men's long jump distances (in meters) from 1896 to 2016 and the fitted regression line for predicting them using x = year are displayed in the following graph. (This is a screenshot from the *Linear Regression* app, where we uploaded the data set available on the book's website.)

a. Identify an observation that may influence the fit of the regression line. Why did you identify this observation?

b. Which do you think is a better prediction for the year 2020—the sample mean of the y values in this plot or the value obtained by plugging 2020 into the fitted regression equation?

c. Would you feel comfortable using the regression line shown to predict the winning long jump for men in the year 2060? Why or why not?

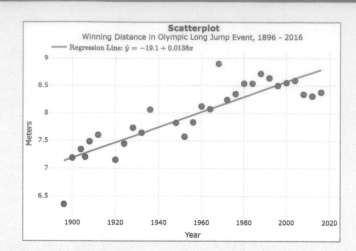

3.47 U.S. average annual temperatures Use the U.S. Temperatures data file available on the book's website. (*Source:* National Climatic Data Center).

a. Use the *Linear Regression* app (upload the data) or other software to construct a scatterplot of average annual temperature versus year, fit a linear trend line, and interpret the slope.

b. Predict the annual average U.S. temperature for the year (i) 2020 and (ii) 2200.

c. In which prediction in part b do you have more faith? Why?

d. Use the feature to overlay a smooth trend over the scatterplot (check the box for Smooth Trend in the *Linear Regression* app). How does the smooth trend differ from the linear trend?

3.48 Murder and poverty For Table 3.6, the regression equation for the 50 states and D.C. relating y = murder rate and x = percent of people who live below the poverty level is $\hat{y} = -4.1 + 0.81x$. For D.C., $x = 17.4$ and $y = 41.8$.

a. When the observation for D.C. is removed from the data set, $\hat{y} = 0.4 + 0.36x$. Does D.C. have much influence on this regression analysis? Explain.

b. If you were to look at a scatterplot, based on the information given, do you think that the poverty value for D.C. would be relatively large or relatively small? Explain.

c. Use the *Linear Regression* app, which has this dataset preloaded, to construct the scatterplot, overlay the regression line and then remove the D.C. observation to see how the regression line changes.

3.49 TV watching and the birth rate The following graph shows data on x = the number of televisions per 100 people and y = the birth rate (number of births per 1,000 people) for six African and Asian nations. The regression line, $\hat{y} = 29.8 - 0.024x$, applies to the data for these six countries. For illustration, another point is added at (81, 15.2), which is the observation for the United States. The regression line for all seven points is $\hat{y} = 31.2 - 0.195x$. The figure shows this line and the one without the U.S. observation.

a. Does the U.S. observation appear to be (i) an outlier on x, (ii) an outlier on y, or (iii) a regression outlier relative to the regression line for the other six observations?

b. State the two conditions under which a single point can have a dramatic effect on the slope and show that they apply here.

c. This one point also drastically affects the correlation coefficient, which is $r = -0.051$ without the United States but $r = -0.935$ with the United States. Explain why you would conclude that the relationship between birth rate and number of televisions is (i) very weak without the U.S. point and (ii) very strong with the U.S. point.

d. Explain why the U.S. residual for the line fitted using that point is very small. This shows that a point can be influential even if its residual is not large.

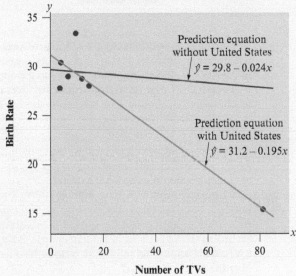

Regression Equations for Birth Rate and Number of TVs per 100 People

Prediction equation without United States
$\hat{y} = 29.8 - 0.024x$

Prediction equation with United States
$\hat{y} = 31.2 - 0.195x$

Birth Rate

Number of TVs

3.50 **College education and single parents** Using the *Linear Regression* app or other software, analyze the relationship between x = college education and y = percentage single-parent families, for the data in Table 3.6, which are in the U.S. Statewide Crime data file on the book's website but also preloaded with the app.

a. Construct a scatterplot. Based on your plot, identify two observations that seem quite different from the others, having a y value relatively large in one case and somewhat small in the other case.

b. Find the regression equation (i) for the entire data set, (ii) deleting only the first of the two outlying observations, and (iii) deleting only the second of the two outlying observations.

c. Is either deleted observation influential on the slope? Summarize the influence.

d. Including D.C., $\hat{y} = 21.2 + 0.089x$, whereas deleting that observation, $\hat{y} = 28.1 - 0.206x$. Find $\hat{y}$ for D.C. in the two cases. ($x = 38.3$ for D.C.) Does the predicted value for D.C. depend much on which regression equation is used?

3.51 **Regression between cereal sodium and sugar** Let x = sodium and y = sugar for the breakfast cereal data in the Cereal data file on the book's website and preloaded in the *Linear Regression* app.

a. Construct a scatterplot. Do any points satisfy the two criteria for a point to be potentially influential on the regression? Explain.

b. Find the regression line and correlation coefficient, using all the data points, and then using all except a potentially influential observation. Summarize the influence of that point.

3.52 **Gestational period and life expectancy** Does the life expectancy of animals depend on the length of their gestational period? The data in the Animals file on the book's website and preloaded in the *Linear Regression* app show observations on the average longevity (in years) and average gestational period (in days) for 21 animals. (*Source:* Wildlife Conservation Society)

a. Use the scatterplot below to describe the relationship. Are there any unusual observations?

b. Using the app or other software, verify the given numbers for the slope of the regression line and r^2 shown on the plot.

c. Are there any outliers? If so, are they regression outliers? Explain.

d. Find the regression line and r^2 (i) without the elephant or (ii) without the hippo. Compare your results to those in part b. Was the observation influential? Explain.

Scatterplot of Average Life Expectancy vs. Gestational Period for 21 Animals

Elephant

Hippopotamus

Longevity (years)

Cow

$\hat{y} = 6.29 + 0.045x$
$r^2 = 0.73$

Gestational Period (days)

3.53 **Height and vocabulary** Do tall students tend to have better vocabulary skills than short students? We might think so looking at a sample of students from Grades 1, 6, and 12 of the Lake Wobegon school district. The correlation coefficient was 0.81 between their height and their vocabulary test score: Taller students tended to have higher vocabulary test scores.

a. Is there a causal relationship, whereby being taller gives you a better vocabulary?

b. Explain how a student's age could be a lurking variable that might be responsible for this relationship, being a common cause of both height and vocabulary test score.

c. Sketch a hypothetical scatterplot (similar to Figure 3.24), labeling or coloring points by the child's grade (1, 6, and 12), such that overall there is a positive trend, but the slope would be about 0 when we consider only children in a given grade. How does the child's age play a role in the relationship between height and test score?

3.54 More firefighters cause worse fires? Data are available for all fires in Chicago last year on x = number of firefighters at the fire and y = cost of damages due to the fire.

a. If the correlation coefficient is positive, does this mean that having more firefighters at a fire causes the damage to be worse? Explain.

b. Identify a third variable that could be a common cause of x and y. Construct a hypothetical scatterplot (such as Figure 3.23 or 3.24), identifying points according to their value on the third variable, to illustrate your argument.

3.55 Antidrug campaigns An Associated Press story (June 13, 2002) reported, "A survey of teens conducted for the Partnership for a Drug Free America found kids who see or hear antidrug ads at least once a day are less likely to do drugs than youngsters who don't see or hear ads frequently. When asked about marijuana, kids who said they saw the ads regularly were nearly 15 percent less likely to smoke pot."

a. Discuss at least one lurking variable that could affect these results.

b. Explain how multiple causes could affect whether a teenager smokes pot.

3.56 What's wrong with regression? Explain what's wrong with the way regression is used in each of the following examples:

a. Winning times in the Boston marathon (at www.bostonmarathon.org) have followed a straight-line decreasing trend from 160 minutes in 1927 (when the race was first run at the Olympic distance of about 26 miles) to 128 minutes in 2014. After fitting a regression line to the winning times, you use the equation to predict that the winning time in the year 2300 will be about 13 minutes.

b. Using data for several cities on x = % of residents with a college education and y = median price of home, you get a strong positive correlation (correlation coefficient $r = 0.93$). You conclude that having a college education causes you to buy a more expensive house.

c. A regression between x = number of years of education and y = annual income for 100 people shows a modest positive trend, except for one person who dropped out after 10th grade but is now a multimillionaire. It's wrong to ignore any of the data, so we should report all results including this point. For this data, the correlation coefficient $r = -0.28$.

3.57 Pay teachers less? The screenshot below, taken from the *Multivariate Relationships* app, shows a scatterplot of the average teacher salary (in USD) and the average SAT score (both from 2016) in the 50 U.S. states, with a regression line superimposed. (*Data Sources:* nces.ed.gov and www.collegeboard.org.)

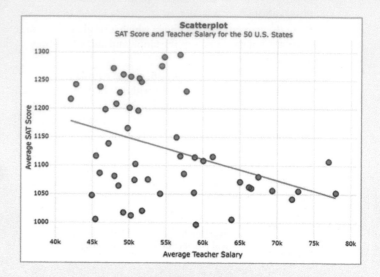

a. The correlation coefficient between the average teacher salary and the average SAT score is given by $r = -0.23$, and the regression line has a slope of $b = -0.0037$. For the states with higher average teacher salaries, should these results be used to argue for a decrease in the teacher's salary, as this may lead to better SAT performance?

b. An important variable recorded with this data is the SAT participation rate, measured as the percentage of students who take the SAT in a state. This may vary from as low as 10% to as high as 100%. The following screenshot (reproducible via the *Multivariate Relationships* app) colors the dots of the scatterplot according to the percent of students participating in the SAT. What additional information does this provide over the first scatterplot?

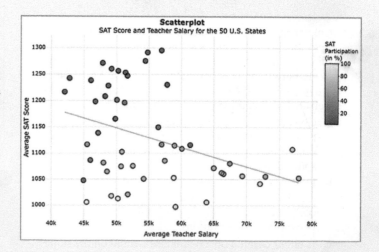

c. When grouping states into three groups ("low," "medium," and "high") according to their SAT participation rate, we obtain the following scatterplot with superimposed regression lines for each group (reproducible via the *Multivariate Relationships* app). The correlation coefficient *r* between teacher salary and SAT score now equals 0.11 for states with low participation, 0.18 for states with medium participation, and 0.71 for states with high SAT participation rates. How did adjusting for the confounding variable SAT Participation affect the association? (Background information: For states with low participation rates, typically only the top students tend to take the SAT as a means to get into good colleges, leading to relatively high average SAT scores for those states. For states with high participation rates, almost all students take the SAT, resulting in relatively lower average SAT scores.)

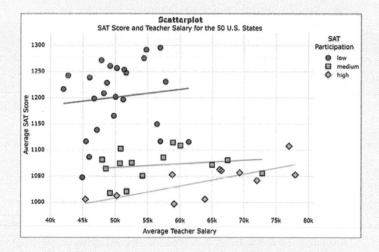

Scatterplot
SAT Score and Teacher Salary for the 50 U.S. States

3.58   Death penalty and race   The following table shows results of whether the death penalty was imposed in murder trials in Florida between 1976 and 1987. For instance, the death penalty was given in 53 out of 467 cases in which a white defendant had a white victim.

Death Penalty, by Defendant's Race and Victim's Race				
Victim's Race	Defendant's Race	Death Penalty		
		Yes	No	Total
White	White	53	414	**467**
	Black	11	37	**48**
Black	White	0	16	**16**
	Black	4	139	**143**

Source: Originally published in *Florida Law Review*. Michael Radelet and Glenn L. Pierce, Choosing Those Who Will Die: Race and the Death Penalty in Florida, vol. 43, *Florida Law Review* 1 (1991).

a. First, consider only those cases in which the victim was white. Find the conditional proportions that got the death penalty when the defendant was white and when the defendant was black. Describe the association.

b. Repeat part a for cases in which the victim was black. Interpret.

c. Now add these two tables together to get a summary contingency table that describes the association between the death penalty verdict and defendant's race, ignoring the information about the victim's race. Find the conditional proportions. Describe the association and compare to parts a and b.

d. Explain how these data satisfy Simpson's paradox. How would you explain what is responsible for this result to someone who has not taken a statistics course?

e. In studying the effect of defendant's race on the death penalty verdict, would you call victim's race a confounding variable? What does this mean?

3.59   NAEP scores   Eighth-grade math scores on the National Assessment of Educational Progress had a mean of 277 in Nebraska compared to a mean of 271 in New Jersey (H. Wainer and L. Brown, *American Statistician*, vol. 58, 2004, p. 119).

a. Identify the response variable and the explanatory variable.

b. For white students, the means were 281 in Nebraska and 283 in New Jersey. For black students, the means were 236 in Nebraska and 242 in New Jersey. For other nonwhite students, the means were 259 in Nebraska and 260 in New Jersey. Identify the third variable given here. Explain how it is possible for New Jersey to have the higher mean for each race, yet for Nebraska to have the higher mean when the data are combined. (This is a case of Simpson's paradox for a quantitative response.)

3.60   Age a confounder?   A study observes that the subjects in the study who say they exercise regularly reported only half as many serious illnesses per year, on the average, as those who say they do not exercise regularly. One paragraph in the results section of an article about the study starts out, "We next analyzed whether age was a confounding variable in studying this association."

a. Explain what this sentence means and how age could potentially explain the association between exercising and illnesses.

b. If age was not actually measured in the study and the researchers failed to consider its effects, could it be a confounding variable or a lurking variable? Explain the difference between a lurking variable and a confounding variable.

Chapter Review

SUMMARY OF NOTATION

Correlation Coefficient: $r = \dfrac{1}{n-1}\Sigma z_x z_y = \dfrac{1}{n-1}\Sigma\left(\dfrac{x-\bar{x}}{s_x}\right)\left(\dfrac{y-\bar{y}}{s_y}\right)$ where n is the number of points, $\bar{x}$ and $\bar{y}$ are means, s_x and s_y are standard deviations for x and y.

Regression equation: $\hat{y} = a + bx$, for predicted response $\hat{y}$, y-intercept a, slope b.

Formulas for the slope and y-intercept are

$$b = r\left(\frac{s_y}{s_x}\right) \text{ and } a = \bar{y} - b(\bar{x}).$$

r^2: Percent reduction in overall prediction error. Also, the percent of the variability in y explained by the linear relationship with x.

CHAPTER SUMMARY

This chapter introduced descriptive statistics for studying the **association** between two variables. We explored how the value of a **response variable** (the outcome of interest) is related to the value of an **explanatory variable**.

- For two *categorical variables*, **contingency tables** summarize the counts of observations at the various combinations of categories of the two variables. Bar graphs can plot **conditional proportions** or percentages for the response variable, at different given values of the explanatory variable. For contingency tables with two rows and two columns, the **difference** and the **ratio of proportions** are two important measures that describe the association numerically.

- For two *quantitative variables*, **scatterplots** display the relationship and show whether it is **positive** (upward trend) or **negative** (downward trend) and whether it is **linear** or not. The **correlation coefficient**, r, describes the direction and strength of a linear relationship. It satisfies $-1 \le r \le 1$. The closer r is to -1 or 1, the stronger the linear relationship.

- When a relationship between two quantitative variables is approximately linear it can be described by a **regression line**, $\hat{y} = a + bx$ where $\hat{y}$ is the predicted response, a is the intercept, b the slope, and x the explanatory variable. The slope b describes the direction of the relationship (positive or negative, like the correlation coefficient) but in addition estimates the effect on $\hat{y}$ for a one-unit increase in x. The regression line can be used to predict a value of the response variable y for a given value of the explanatory variable x. The square of the correlation coefficient, r^2, is used to judge the overall accuracy of predictions.

- The correlation coefficient and the regression equation can be strongly affected by an **influential observation**. This observation takes a relatively small or large value on x and is a **regression outlier**, falling away from the straight-line trend of the rest of the data points. Be cautious of **extrapolating** a regression line to predict y at values of x that are far above or below the observed x-values.

- **Association does not imply causation.** A **lurking variable** may influence the association. It is possible that an apparent association vanishes after adjusting for a third variable. This can be detected by graphical procedures such as coloring dots in a scatterplot or forming groups based on the third variable and analyzing each group separately. It is even possible for the association to reverse in direction after we adjust for a third variable. This phenomenon is called **Simpson's paradox.**

LEARNING OBJECTIVES

1. Explain what is meant by the association of two variables.
2. Identify which of two variables is the response variable and which is the explanatory variable.
3. Construct and interpret a contingency table for two categorical variables.
4. Compute conditional proportions from a contingency table and interpret side-by-side or stacked bar graphs.
5. Compare two conditional proportions through their difference or ratio and interpret the difference or ratio of proportions in context. Understand that a difference close to 0 or a ratio close to 1 indicates weak or no association.
6. Describe the form, direction, and strength of a relationship between two quantitative variables based on a scatterplot.
7. Define and interpret the correlation coefficient r.
8. Formulate the equation for the regression line and interpret the y-intercept and slope in context.
9. Predict values of a quantitative response variable with a regression line, using a quantitative explanatory variable.
10. Compute and interpret residuals (prediction errors).
11. Understand the two ways to interpret r^2.
12. Understand the dangers of extrapolation.
13. Identify and understand the effect of regression outliers and/or influential observation.
14. Understand that association does not necessarily imply causation.
15. Distinguish between a bivariate and a multivariate analysis of two quantitative variables through adjusting for a third variable. (Separate regression lines for groups defined by a third categorical variable.)
16. Understand that the correlation coefficient or the regression line can change once adjusted for by a third variable.
17. Explain the impact of a lurking variable and a confounding variable.
18. Understand that associations between two categorical variables can change once adjusted for by a third variable (Simpson's paradox).

ANSWERS TO FIGURE QUESTIONS

Figure 3.1 Construct a single graph with side-by-side bars (as in Figure 3.2) to compare the conditional proportions of pesticide residues in the two types of food.

Figure 3.2 The proportion of foods having pesticides present is much higher for conventionally grown food than for organically grown food.

Figure 3.3 The bars in Figure 3.2 have different heights, in contrast to Figure 3.3 for which the bars have the same height. For Figure 3.3, the proportion of foods having pesticides present is the same for both types of food.

Figure 3.5 There are no apparent outliers for either variable. A box plot would more clearly identify potential outliers.

Figure 3.6 The point for Japan appears atypical. All of the other countries with comparable Internet use have at least 25% Facebook use, whereas Japan has 13% Facebook use.

Figure 3.8 The top point is far above the overall straight-line trend of the other 66 points on the graph. The two rightmost points fall in line with the overall increasing trend.

Figure 3.9 If data points are closer to a straight line, there is a smaller amount of variability around the line; thus, we can more accurately predict one variable knowing the other variable, indicating a stronger association.

Figure 3.10 These 25 points make a positive contribution to the correlation coefficient because the product of their z-scores will be positive.

Figure 3.11 Yes, the points fall in a balanced way in the quadrants. The positive cross products in the upper-right quadrant are roughly counterbalanced by the negative cross products in the upper-left quadrant. The positive cross products in the lower-left quadrant are roughly counterbalanced by the negative cross products in the lower-right quadrant.

Figure 3.12 The line crosses the y-axis at 61.4. For each femur length increase of 1 cm, the height is predicted to increase 2.4 cm.

Figure 3.13 When femur length changes from 42 cm to 43 cm, the predicted height increases by 2.4 cm. The height is predicted to be the same for each femur length.

Figure 3.14 We would expect a positive slope.

Figure 3.15 The error from predicting with the regression line is represented by a vertical line from the regression line to the observation. The distance between the point and line is the prediction error.

Figure 3.16 The absolute values of the residuals are vertical distances because the regression equation predicts y, the variable on the vertical axis.

Figure 3.17 The difference in winning heights for men and women is typically about 0.3 to 0.4 meters.

Figure 3.18 $\hat{y} = a + bx = -2.45 + 0.029(2025) = 56.3$

Figure 3.19 The observation in the upper-right corner will influence the tilt of the straight-line fit.

Figure 3.20 The slope will decrease if D.C. is excluded from the regression analysis.

Figure 3.21 The line fitted to the data that does not include D.C.

Figure 3.22 Possibly neither. There may be another variable influencing the positive relationship between crime rate and amount of education. No. While it's correct that we predict a 14.9 increase in the crime rate, it's wrong to conclude that this is *caused* by the increase in the education percentage.

Figure 3.23 If urbanization did not have any relationship with either education or crime rate, then the colors of the dots would be distributed randomly across the graph, not revealing any pattern.

STATISTICAL SOFTWARE

Art of Stat Web Apps

- **Explore Categorical Data** This app, under the second tab titled Two Categorical Variables, finds joint, conditional, and marginal proportions for contingency tables. It constructs side-by-side or stacked bar graphs which you can customize and download. You can enter data as counts in a contingency table, or provide the raw observations on two categorical variables, e.g., by copying and pasting from a spreadsheet. Several data sets from the book are preloaded.

- **Association Between Two Categorical Variables** For 2×2 contingency tables with two outcomes on the response variable (e.g., Success and Failure) and two outcomes on the explanatory variable (e.g., Group 1 and Group 2), this app provides bar graphs of the conditional proportions and computes the difference or ratio of proportions, based on contingency table counts or raw observations you enter. Several data sets from the book are preloaded.

- **Scatterplots & Correlation** This app constructs interactive scatterplots and finds the correlation coefficient r. It can overlay a smooth or linear trend line and provides an option to move points around to see how this affects the correlation coefficient. You can also plot the corresponding z-scores to see the distribution of points in the four quadrants. In the scatterplot, you can interactively change the range of the axes or zoom in and out; change the title, subtitle, or axis labels; and download the plot as a .png file to include in your homework. The app comes with several data sets from the book preloaded, but you can provide your own data by copying and pasting the variables from a spreadsheet into the app.

- **Explore Linear Regression** This app lets you add points to an empty scatterplot to explore the form of the regression equation and how it may be affected by outliers. As you click to add or remove points from the scatterplot, the app updates statistics such as the correlation coefficient r and the slope b. You can also generate scatterplots that show no, a linear, or a quadratic relationship to explore when linear regression is appropriate.

- **Linear Regression** This app constructs interactive scatterplots and fits a regression equation. In the scatterplot, you can hover over points (to identify outliers) or overlay a smooth or linear trend line. The app provides the regression equation in the plot and prints out a table with the values for the intercept and slope, the correlation coefficient r, and r^2. There are options for clicking on a point to remove it from the data set or showing residuals on the scatterplot, as well as finding the predicted value for a given x-value. A second tab titled Fitted Values & Residual Analysis gives the fitted values and the residuals, as well as a scatterplot, histogram or boxplot of the residuals, with hovering information showing the fitted value and residual for each point. The app comes with several data sets from the book preloaded, but you can upload your own .csv file (the first row needs to contain the variable names) or provide data by copying values from a spreadsheet into the app. You can change title, subtitle, or axis labels on the scatterplot and download it as a .png file to include in your homework.

R

Check out the sample R scripts posted on ArtofStat.com (go to the tab titled R Code), which replicate the analysis from many examples in this chapter. Here is just a short summary.

- **Contingency Tables and Bar Graphs:** To read in a 2×2 contingency table, create a matrix and give it row and column names:

```
> counts <- c(29, 98, 19485, 7086)
> mytable <- matrix(counts, nrow=2, ncol=2,
byrow=TRUE, dimnames=list('Food Type'
= c('Organic', 'Conventional'), 'Pesticides'
= c('Present', 'Absent')))
> mytable
              Pesticides
Food Type       Present Absent
  Organic            29     98
  Conventional    19485   7086
```

Then, find the conditional proportions for pesticide status through

```
> cond.props <- prop.table(mytable,1)
> cond.props
              Pesticides
Food Type        Present     Absent
  Organic      0.2283465  0.7716535
  Conventional 0.7333183  0.2666817
```

Plot the ones for the presence of pesticides in a bar graph like this:

```
> barplot(cond.props[,1], xlab='Food Type',
ylab='Proportion', ylim=c(0,1), main=
'Proportion of Food Samples \n with Pesticide
Present', col=c('green4', 'orange2'))
```

- **Scatterplots:** To create a scatterplot in R, provide the *x*- and *y*-variable and use the plot() command, illustrated here with the Subway Sandwich data:

```
> protein <- c(19, 36, 16, 19, 20, 23, 25,
29, 18, 23, 24, 25, 19, 18, 9)
> cost <- c(3.89, 4.99, 3.89, 4.39, 3.99,
4.39, 5.09, 4.89, 3.99, 4.89, 4.89, 4.89,
4.39, 4.49, 3.89)
```

```
> plot(protein, cost, xlab='Protein Content
(g)', ylab='Cost of Sandwich', main=
'Scatterplot of 15 Sandwiches', col='red')
```

- **Correlation Coefficient r and r^2:** To obtain 'the correlation coefficient r, use the cor() command. Square it to get r^2:

```
> cor(protein, cost)
[1] 0.7824487
> cor(protein, cost)^2
[1] 0.6122259
```

- **Intercept and Slope for Regression Equation:** To obtain the intercept and slope for the linear regression equation, and to overlay the regression line over the scatterplot constructed above, use:

```
> lin.reg <- lm(cost ~ protein)
> lin.reg
Coefficients:
(Intercept)        protein
    3.23228        0.05717
> abline(lin.reg, col='blue')
```

- **Loading .csv Data File into R and Fitting Regression Model:** Now, we illustrate loading a .csv data file (the Internet Use data) into R, creating a scatterplot, overlaying the regression line, and obtaining the intercept and slope. (*Note:* Any text after the # symbol is a comment. It is not part of the R command and only serves to explain what the command is doing. You don't have to type it into R.)

-
```
> myfile <- file.choose()  #point to where
your .csv file is located
> InternetUse <- read.csv(myfile)  #reads in
the file
> colnames(InternetUse)  #to see the names of
variables in dataset
> attach(InternetUse)  #so you can refer to
variable names
> plot(Internet.Penetration,
Facebook.Penetration, col='red')
>  lin.reg  <-  lm(Facebook.Penetration  ~
Internet.Penetration)
> lin.reg
Coefficients:
       (Intercept)  Internet.Penetration
            7.8980                 0.4389
> abline(lin.reg, col='blue')
```

CHAPTER EXERCISES

Practicing the Basics

3.61 **Choose explanatory and response** For the following pairs of variables, identify the response variable and the explanatory variable.

   a. Number of square feet in a house and assessed value of the house.

   b. Political party preference (Democrat, Independent, Republican) and gender.

   c. Annual income and number of years of education.

   d. Number of pounds lost on a diet and type of diet (low-fat, low-carbohydrate).

3.62 **Graphing data** For each case in the previous exercise,

   a. Indicate whether each variable is quantitative or categorical.

   b. Describe the type of graph that could best be used to portray the results.

3.63 **Life after death for males and females** In a recent General Social Survey, respondents answered the question, "Do you believe in a life after death?" The following table shows the responses cross-tabulated with gender. (The data are also available in the *Association Between Two Categorical Variables* app.)

Opinion About Life After Death by Gender		
	Opinion About Life After Death	
Gender	Yes	No
Male	621	187
Female	834	145

a. Construct a table of conditional proportions.

b. Summarize results. Is there much difference between responses of males and females? Compute the difference and ratio of proportions and interpret each.

3.64 **God and happiness** Go to the GSS website (sda.berkeley .edu), click Archive, and scroll down to the most current General Social Survey (GSS) Cumulative Datafile, or access it directly via the book's website. Type GOD for the row variable, HAPPY for the column variable, and YEAR(2018) for the Selection Filter. Select No Weights for the Weight option, then click on Run the Table. (*Source:* General Social Survey © 2011-2019 NORC; SDA UC Berkely © 2020 UC Regents)

a. Report the contingency table of counts.

b. Treating reported happiness as the response variable, find the conditional proportions. (You can do this manually with a calculator; by entering the contingency table into the second tab of the *Explore Categorical Data* app, which will also give you a bar graph; or by a feature on the GSS website by selecting Row under Percentaging under Output Options.) For which opinion about God are subjects most likely to be very happy?

c. To analyze the association, is it more informative to view the proportions in part b or the frequencies in part a? Why?

3.65 **Degrees and income** The mean annual salaries earned in 2005 by year-round workers with various educational degrees are given in the table:

Degree	Mean Salary
No diploma	$19,964
High school diploma	$29,448
Bachelor's degree	$54,689
Master's degree	$67,898
Doctoral degree	$92,863
Professional degree	$119,009

Source: U.S. Census Bureau, U.S. Department of Commerce

a. Identify the response variable. Is it quantitative or categorical?

b. Identify the explanatory variable. Is it quantitative or categorical?

c. Explain how a bar graph could summarize the data.

3.66 **Bacteria in ground turkey** *Consumer Reports* magazine (June 2013) reported purchasing samples of ground turkey from different brands to test for the presence of bacteria. The table below shows the number of samples that tested positive for Enterococcus bacteria for packages that claimed no use of antibiotics in the processing of the meat

and for packages in which no such claim was made. (The data are also available in the *Association Between Two Categorical Variables* app.)

Bacteria in Ground Turkey		
	Test result for Enterococcus	
Package Claim	Positive	Negative
No claim	26	20
No antibiotics	23	5

a. Find the difference in the proportion of packages that tested positive and interpret.

b. Find the ratio of the proportion of packages that tested positive and interpret.

3.67 **Women managers in the work force** The following side-by-side bar graph appeared in a 2003 issue of the *Monthly Labor Review* about women as managers in the work force. The graph summarized the percentage of managers in different occupations who were women, for the years 1972 and 2002.

Source: Monthly Labor Review, vol. 126, no. 10, 2003, p. 48. Bureau of Labor Statistics, U.S Department of Labor.

a. Consider the first two bars in this graph. Identify the response variable and explanatory variable.

b. Express the information from the first two bars in the form of conditional proportions in a contingency table for two categorical variables, year and gender.

c. Based on part b, does it seem as if there's an association between these two variables? Explain.

d. The entire graph shows two explanatory variables. What are they?

3.68 **RateMyProfessor.com** The website RateMyProfessors .com reported a correlation coefficient of 0.62 between the quality rating of the professor (on a simple 1 to 5 scale with higher values representing higher quality) and the rating of how easy a grader the professor is. This correlation coefficient is based on ratings of nearly 7,000 professors.

a. Describe the direction of the relationship.

b. What would you expect this correlation coefficient to equal if the quality rating did not tend to depend on the easiness rating of the professor?

3.69 **Alcohol and calories** The data set Beers available on the book's website contains information on 227 domestic and international beers regarding their alcohol content (in %) and the amount of calories per 12-ounce serving. (*Source:* beer100.com.)

APP

a. Use the *Linear Regression* app (upload the data from the book's website into the app) or other software to create a scatterplot and obtain a correlation coefficient. Write a paragraph about the relationship.

b. Does the correlation coefficient depend on whether you treat calories or alcohol content as the response variable?

c. Treating calories as the response variable and alcohol content as the explanatory variable, find the regression equation and interpret the slope in context.

d. Does the slope depend on whether you treat calories or alcohol content as the response variable?

3.70 **African droughts and dust** Is there a relationship between the amount of dust carried over large areas of the Atlantic and the Caribbean and the amount of rainfall in African regions? In an article (*Source:* J. M. Prospero and P. J. Lamb, *Science*, vol. 302, 2003, pp. 1024–1027), the following scatterplots were given. The precipitation index is a measure of rainfall.

Source: J. M. Prospero and P. J. Lamb, *Science*, vol. 302, 2003, pp. 1024–1027.

a. Match the following regression equations and correlation coefficients with the appropriate graph.

   (i) $\hat{y} = 14.05 - 7.18x$; $r = -0.75$

   (ii) $\hat{y} = 16.00 - 2.36x$; $r = -0.44$

   (iii) $\hat{y} = 12.80 - 9.77x$; $r = -0.87$

b. Based on the scatterplots and information in part a, what would you conclude about the relationship between dust amount and rainfall amounts?

3.71 **Crime rate and urbanization** For the data in Example 15 on crime in Florida, the regression line between y = crime rate (number of crimes per 1,000 people) and x = percentage living in an urban environment is $\hat{y} = 24.5 + 0.56x$.

a. Using the slope, find the difference in predicted crime rates between counties that are 100% urban and counties that are 0% urban. Interpret.

b. What is the difference in the predicted crime rate for two counties that differ by 20 percentage points in the percentage living in an urban environment?

3.72 **Gestational period and life expectancy revisited** The data in the Animals file on the book's website and preloaded in the *Linear Regression* app hold observations on the average longevity (in years) and gestational period (in days) for a variety of animals. Exercise 3.52 showed the scatterplot together with the regression equation with intercept 6.29 and slope 0.045 and an r^2 value of 73%.

a. Interpret the slope.

b. A leopard has a gestational period of about 98 days. What is its predicted average longevity?

c. Interpret the value of r^2.

d. Show that extrapolating from animals to humans (with gestational period of about 40 weeks) grossly underestimates average human longevity.

3.73 **Height and paycheck** The headline of an article in the *Gainesville Sun* (October 17, 2003) stated, "Height can yield a taller paycheck." It described an analysis of four large studies in the United States and Britain by a University of Florida professor on subjects' height and salaries. The article reported that for each gender, "an inch is worth about $789 a year in salary. So, a person who is 6 feet tall will earn about $5,523 more a year than a person who is 5 foot 5."

a. For the interpretation in quotes, identify the response variable and explanatory variable.

b. State the slope of the regression equation, when height is measured in inches and income in dollars.

c. Explain how the value $5,523 relates to the slope.

3.74 **Predicting college GPA** An admissions officer claims that at his college the regression equation $\hat{y} = 0.5 + 7x$ approximates the relationship between y = college GPA and x = high school GPA, both measured on a four-point scale.

a. Sketch this equation between $x = 0$ and 4, labeling the x- and y-axes. Is this equation realistic? Why or why not?

b. Suppose that actually $\hat{y} = 0.5 + 0.7x$. Predict the GPA for two students having GPAs of 3.0 and 4.0. Interpret and explain how the difference between these two predictions relates to the slope.

3.75 **College GPA = high school GPA** Refer to the previous exercise. Suppose the regression equation is $\hat{y} = x$. Identify the y-intercept and slope. Interpret the line in context.

3.76 **What's a college degree worth?** In 2002, a census bureau survey reported that the mean total earnings that a full-time worker in the United States can expect to earn between ages 25 and 64 is $1.2 million for those with only a high-school education and $2.1 million for those with a college degree but no advanced degree.

a. Assuming four years for a college degree and a straight-line regression of y = total earnings on x = number years of education, what is the slope? Interpret it.

b. If y instead measures earnings per year (rather than for 40 years), then what is the slope? Interpret.

3.77 Car weight and gas hogs The table shows a short excerpt from the Car Weight and Mileage data file on the book's website. That file lists several cars with automatic transmission and their x = weight (in pounds) and y = mileage (miles per gallon of gas). The prediction equation is $\hat{y} = 47.32 - 0.0052x$.

Automobile Brand	Weight	Mileage
Honda Accord Sedan LX	3,164	34
Toyota Corolla	2,590	38
Dodge Dakota Club Cab	3,838	22
Jeep Grand Cherokee Laredo	3,970	21
Hummer H2	6,400	17

Sources: auto.consumerguide.com, honda.com, toyota.com, landrover.com, ford.com.

a. Interpret the slope in terms of a 1,000-pound increase in the vehicle weight.

b. Find the predicted mileage and residual for a Hummer H2. Interpret.

3.78 Rotten Tomatoes The website rottentomatoes.com publishes two kinds of ratings for movies released in theaters or on streaming services: a critics score and an audience score. The critics score equals the percentage of professional movie critics registered with Rotten Tomatoes who have given a movie a positive review (a rating of 3.5 and above). The audience score equals the percentage of regular users of the website who have given the movie a positive review. The data file Rotten Tomatoes on the book's website lists these two scores for 74 movies reviewed in June and July 2019. For instance, the movie *Shazam!* received a critics score of 91% and an audience score of 84%. The following scatterplot, obtained via the *Linear Regression* app, shows these data and other information.

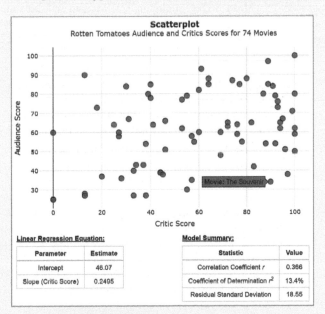

Scatterplot
Rotten Tomatoes Audience and Critics Scores for 74 Movies

Linear Regression Equation:

Parameter	Estimate
Intercept	46.07
Slope (Critic Score)	0.2495

Model Summary:

Statistic	Value
Correlation Coefficient r	0.366
Coefficient of Determination r^2	13.4%
Residual Standard Deviation	18.55

a. Describe the relationship.

b. State the prediction equation and find the predicted audience score and the residual for the movie *Shazam!*.

c. Is the regression equation overestimating or underestimating the audience score for the movie *Shazam!* based on its critics score?.

d. The scatterplot identifies the movie *The Souvenir*. Is the regression equation over- or underestimating it's audience score based on its critics score?

e. Do you think critics score is a good predictor of audience score? Cite and interpret an appropriate statistic.

3.79 Domestic and international beer Exercise 3.69 analyzed the relationship between the alcohol content (in %) and the amount of calories in 12-ounce servings of various beer brands. The scatterplot below, obtained via the *Multivariate Relationships* app, colors the points according to whether the beer was domestic or international and shows a regression line for each group.

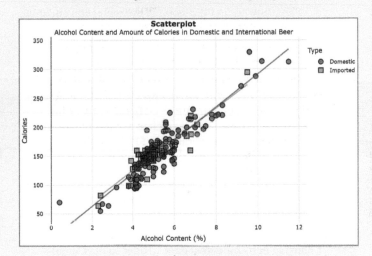

Scatterplot
Alcohol Content and Amount of Calories in Domestic and International Beer

a. Judging from the plot, does the relationship between alcohol content and amount of calories depend on which type of beer (domestic or international) is considered?

b. Is the type of beer a confounding variable for the relationship between alcohol content and amount of calories?

3.80 Fertility and GDP Refer to the Human Development data file, which is preloaded in the *Linear Regression* app and also available on the book's website. Use x = GDP and y = fertility (mean number of children per adult woman).

a. Using the app or other software, construct a scatterplot and indicate whether regression seems appropriate.

b. Find the correlation coefficient r and the regression equation.

c. With x = percent using contraception, $\hat{y} = 6.7 - 0.065x$. Can you compare the slope of this regression equation with the slope of the equation with GDP as a predictor to determine which has the stronger relationship with y? Explain.

d. Contraception has a correlation coefficient of $r = -0.887$ with fertility. Which variable has a stronger relationship with fertility: GDP or contraception?

3.81 Women working and birth rate Using data from several nations, a regression analysis of y = crude birth rate (number of births per 1,000 population size) on women's economic activity (female labor force as a percentage of the male labor force) yielded the equation $\hat{y} = 36.3 - 0.30x$ and a correlation coefficient of $r = -0.55$.

a. Describe the effect by comparing the predicted birth rate for countries with $x = 0$ and countries with $x = 100$.

b. Suppose that the correlation coefficient between the crude birth rate and the nation's GNP equals -0.35. Which variable, GNP or women's economic activity, seems to have the stronger relationship with birth rate? Explain.

3.82 Education and income The regression equation for a sample of 100 people relating x = years of education and y = annual income (in dollars) is $\hat{y} = -20,000 + 4000x$, and the correlation coefficient equals 0.50. The standard deviations were 2.0 for education and 16,000 for annual income.

a. Show how to find the slope in the regression equation from the correlation coefficient.

b. Suppose that now we let x = annual income and y = years of education. Will the correlation coefficient or the slope change in value? If so, show how.

3.83 Income in euros Refer to the previous exercise. Results in the regression equation $\hat{y} = -20,000 + 4000x$ for y = annual income were translated to units of euros at a time when the exchange rate was $1.25 per euro.

a. Find the intercept of the regression equation. (*Hint*: What does 20,000 dollars equal in euros?)

b. Find the slope of the regression equation.

c. What is the correlation coefficient r when annual income is measured in euros? Why?

3.84 Changing units for cereal data Refer to the Cereal data file, preloaded in the *Linear Regression* app and available on the book's website, with x = sugar (g) and y = sodium (mg), for which $\hat{y} = 169 - 0.25x$.

a. Convert the sugar measurements to mg, upload the new data file to the app or other software, and calculate the line obtained from regressing sodium (mg) on sugar (mg). Which statistics change and which remain the same? Clearly interpret the slope coefficient.

b. Suppose we instead convert the sugar measurements to ounces. How would this effect the slope of the regression line? Can you determine the new slope just from knowing that 1 ounce equals 28.35 grams?

3.85 Murder and single-parent families For Table 3.6 on the 50 states and D.C., the figure below shows the relationship between the murder rate and the percentage of single-parent families.

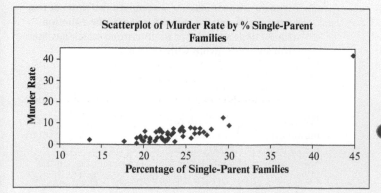

Scatterplot of Murder Rate by % Single-Parent Families

a. For D.C., the percentage of single-parent families = 44.7 and the murder rate = 41.8. Identify D.C. on the scatterplot and explain the effect you would expect it to have on a regression analysis.

b. The regression line fitted to all 51 observations is $\hat{y} = -21.4 + 1.14x$. The regression line fitted only to the 50 states is $\hat{y} = -8.2 + 0.56x$. Summarize the effect of including D.C. in the analysis.

3.86 Violent crime and college education For the U.S. Statewide Crime data file, preloaded in the *Linear Regression* app and available on the book's website, let y = violent crime rate and x = percent with a college education.

a. Construct a scatterplot. Identify any points that you think may be influential in a regression analysis.

b. Fit the regression line, using all 51 observations. Interpret the slope.

c. Fit the regression line after deleting the observation identified in part a. Interpret the slope and compare results to part b.

3.87 Violent crime and high school education Repeat the previous exercise using x = percent with at least a high school education. This shows that an outlier is not especially influential if its x-value is not relatively large or small.

3.88 Crime and urbanization For the U.S. Statewide Crime data file, preloaded in the *Linear Regression* app and available on the book's website, selecting y = violent crime rate and x = urbanization (percentage of the residents living in metropolitan areas) gives the following results (check the option for Summary Statistics in the app):

Variable	N	Mean	StDev	Minimum	Q1	Median	Q3	Maximum
violent	51	442	241	81	282	384	550	1,508
urban	51	68	21	28	51	70	84	100

Regression Equation: $\hat{y} = 36 + 5.93x$

a. Using the five-number summary, sketch a box plot for y (or use the *Explore Quantitative Data* app). What does your graph and the reported mean and standard deviation of y tell you about the shape of the distribution of violent crime rate?

b. Use the *Linear Regression* app or other software to construct a scatterplot. Does it show any potentially influential observations? Would you predict that the slope would be larger, or smaller, if you delete that observation? Why?

c. Fit the regression without the observation highlighted in part b. Describe the effect on the slope. (In the *Linear Regression* app, check the option Click to Remove Points to click on a point in the scatterplot and remove it.)

3.89 High school graduation rates and health insurance Access the HS Graduation Rates file on the book's website, which contains statewide data on x = high school graduation rate and y = percentage of individuals without health insurance. Upload the file to the *Linear Regression* app or other software.

a. Construct a scatterplot. Describe the relationship.

b. Find the correlation coefficient *r*. Interpret.

c. Find the regression equation for the data. Interpret the slope, and summarize the relationship.

3.90 Women's Olympic high jumps Example 12 discussed how the winning height in the Olympic high jump changed over time. You can use the *Multivariate Relationships* app to confirm (see also Figure 3.17)

$$\text{Predicted Height} = -0.36 + 0.0057 \,(\text{Year})$$

for predicting the **women's** winning height (in meters) using the year number.

a. Predict the winning Olympic high jump distance for women in (i) 2020 and (ii) 3000.

b. Do you feel comfortable making either prediction in part a? Explain.

3.91 Income and height A survey of adults revealed a positive correlation between the height of the subjects and their income in the previous year.

a. Explain how gender could be a potential lurking variable that could be responsible for this relationship.

b. If gender had actually been one of the variables measured in the study, would it be a lurking variable or a confounding variable? Explain.

3.92 More TV watching goes with fewer babies? For United Nations data from several countries, there is a strong negative correlation between the birth rate and the per capita television ownership.

a. Does this imply that having higher television ownership causes a country to have a lower birth rate?

b. Identify a lurking variable that could provide an explanation for this relationship.

3.93 More sleep causes death? An Associated Press story (February 15, 2002) quoted a study at the University of California at San Diego that reported, based on a nationwide survey, that those who averaged at least 8 hours sleep a night were 12% more likely to die within six years than those who averaged 6.5 to 7.5 hours of sleep a night.

a. Explain how the subject's age could be positively associated both with time spent sleeping and with an increased death rate and, hence, could be a lurking variable responsible for the observed relationship between sleeping and the death rate.

b. Explain how the subject's age could be a common cause of both variables.

3.94 Ask Marilyn Marilyn vos Savant writes a column for *Parade* magazine to which readers send questions, often puzzlers or questions with a twist. In the April 28, 1996, column, a reader asked, "A company decided to expand, so it opened a factory generating 455 jobs. For the 70 white-collar positions, 200 males and 200 females applied. Of the people who applied, 20% of the females and only 15% of the males were hired. Of the 400 males applying for the blue-collar positions, 75% were hired. Of the 100 females applying, 85% were hired. A federal Equal Employment Opportunity Commission (EEOC) enforcement official noted that many more males were hired than females and decided to investigate. Responding to charges of irregularities in hiring, the company president denied any discrimination, pointing out that in both the white-collar and blue-collar fields, the percentage of female applicants hired was greater than it was for males. But the government official produced his own statistics, which showed that a female applying for a job had a 58% chance of being denied employment whereas male applicants had only a 45% denial rate. As the current law is written, this constituted a violation. . . . Can you explain how two opposing statistical outcomes are reached from the same raw data?" (Copyright 1996 Marilyn vos Savant. Initially published in *Parade* Magazine. All rights reserved.)

a. Construct two contingency tables giving counts relating gender to whether hired (yes or no), one table for white-collar jobs and one table for blue-collar jobs.

b. Construct a single contingency table for gender and whether hired, combining all 900 applicants into one table. Verify that the percentages not hired are as quoted above by the government official.

c. Comparing the data in the tables constructed in parts a and b, explain why this is an example of Simpson's paradox.

Concepts and Investigations

3.95 NL baseball team ERA and number of wins Is a baseball team's earned run average (ERA = the average number of earned runs they give up per game) a good predictor of the number of wins that a team has for a season? The data for the National League teams in 2010 are available in the NL Team Statistics file on the book's website. Conduct a correlation and regression analysis, including graphical and numerical descriptive statistics. Summarize results in a two-page report.

3.96 Time studying and GPA Is there a relationship between the amount of time a student studies and a student's GPA? Access the Georgia Student Survey file on the book's website or use your class data to explore this question using appropriate graphical and numerical methods. Write a brief report summarizing results.

3.97 Harvest date in Burgundy Access the Wine Harvest file on the book's website and upload it to the *Linear Regression* app. This data set holds, for each year and starting as early as 1354, the number of days past August 31 that the wine harvest began for vineyards in the Burgundy region of France. A negative value implies that the harvest occurred before August 31. Fit a regression line to these data and interpret the time trend. Which year gave the largest residual in absolute value? Research what was special about that year in terms of the summer temperature.

3.98 Regression for dummies You have conducted a regression analysis for the catalog sales company you work for, using monthly data for the last year on *y* = total sales in the month and *x* = number of catalogs mailed in preceding month. You are asked to prepare a 200-word summary of what regression does under the heading "Regression for Dummies," to give to fellow employees who have never taken a statistics course. Write the summary, being careful not to use any technical jargon with which the employees may not be familiar.

3.99 Fluoride and AIDS An Associated Press story (August 25, 1998) about the lack of fluoride in most of the water supply in Utah quoted antifluoride activist Norma Sommer as claiming that fluoride may be responsible for AIDS, since the water supply in San Francisco is heavily fluoridated and that city has an unusually high incidence of AIDS. Describe how you could use this story to explain to someone who has never studied statistics that association need not imply causation.

3.100 Fish consumption fights Alzheimer's An AP story (July 22, 2003) described a study conducted over four years by Dr. Martha Morris and others from Chicago's Rush-Presbyterian-St. Luke's Medical Center involving 815 Chicago residents aged 65 and older (*Archives of Neurology*, July 21, 2003). Those who reported eating fish at least once a week had a 60% lower risk of Alzheimer's than those who never or rarely ate fish. However, the story also quoted Dr. Rachelle Doody of Baylor College of Medicine as warning, "Articles like this raise expectations and confuse people. Researchers can show an association, but they can't show cause and effect." She said it is not known whether those people who had a reduced risk had eaten fish most of their lives, and whether other dietary habits had an influence. Using this example, describe how you would explain to someone who has never taken statistics (a) what a lurking variable is, (b) how there can be multiple causes for any particular response variable, and (c) why they need to be skeptical when they read new research results.

3.101 Dogs make you healthier A study published in the *British Journal of Health Psychology* (D. Wells, vol. 12, 2007, pp. 145–156) found that dog owners are physically healthier than cat owners. The author of the study was quoted as saying, "It is possible that dogs can directly promote our well being by buffering us from stress. The ownership of a dog can also lead to increases in physical activity and facilitate the development of social contacts, which may enhance physiological and psychological human health in a more indirect manner." Identify lurking variables in this explanation and use this quote to explain how lurking variables can be responsible for an association.

Multiple Choice or True/False

3.102 Correlate GPA and GRE In a study of graduate students who took the Graduate Record Exam (GRE), the Educational Testing Service reported a correlation coefficient of $r = 0.37$ between undergraduate grade point average (GPA) and graduate first-year GPA.[15] This indicates that

a. As undergraduate GPA increases by one unit, graduate first-year GPA increases by 0.37 unit.

b. Because the correlation coefficient is not 0, we can predict a person's graduate first-year GPA perfectly if we know their undergraduate GPA.

c. The relationship between undergraduate GPA and graduate first-year GPA follows a curve rather than a straight line.

d. As one of these variables increases, there is a weak tendency for the other variable to increase also.

3.103 Properties of r Which of the following is *not* a property of r?

a. r is always between -1 and 1.

b. r depends on which of the two variables is designated as the response variable.

c. r measures the strength of the linear relationship between x and y.

d. r does not depend on the units of y or x.

e. r has the same sign as the slope of the regression equation.

3.104 Interpreting r One can interpret $r = 0.30$ as

a. a weak, positive linear relationship

b. 30% of the time $\hat{y} = y$

c. $\hat{y}$ changes 0.30 units for every one-unit increase in x

d. a stronger linear relationship than two variables with $r = -0.70$

3.105 Correct statement about r Which one of the following statements is correct?

a. The correlation coefficient r is always the same as the slope of the regression line.

b. The mean of the residuals from the least-squares regression line is 0 only when $r = 0$.

c. The correlation coefficient r is the percentage of points that lie in the quadrants where x and y are both above the mean or both below the mean.

d. The correlation coefficient r is inappropriate if a U-shaped relationship exists between x and y.

3.106 Describing association between categorical variables You can summarize the data for two categorical variables x and y by

a. drawing a scatterplot of the x- and y-values.

b. constructing a contingency table for the x- and y-values.

c. calculating the correlation coefficient r between x and y.

d. constructing a box plot for each variable.

3.107 Slope and correlation The slope of the regression equation and the correlation coefficient are similar in the sense that

a. they do not depend on the units of measurement.

b. they both must fall between -1 and $+1$.

c. they both have the same sign.

d. neither can be affected by severe regression outliers.

3.108 Interpretation of r^2 An r^2 measure of 0.85 implies that

a. the correlation coefficient r between x and y equals 0.85.

b. for a one-unit increase in x, we predict y to increase by 85%.

[15]*Source:* GRE Guide to the Use of Scores, 1998–1999, www.gre.org.

c. 85% of the response variable y can be explained by the linear relationship between x and y.

d. 85% of the variability we observe in the response variable y can be explained by its linear relationship with x.

3.109 True or false The variables y = annual income (thousands of dollars), x_1 = number of years of education, and x_2 = number of years experience in job are measured for all the employees having city-funded jobs in Knoxville, Tennessee. Suppose that the following regression equations and correlations apply:

(i) $\hat{y} = 10 + 1.0x_1$, $r = 0.30$.

(ii) $\hat{y} = 14 + 0.4x_2$, $r = 0.60$.

The correlation coefficient is -0.40 between x_1 and x_2. Which of the following statements are true?

a. The weakest relationship is between x_1 and x_2.

b. The regression equation using x_2 to predict x_1 has negative slope.

c. Each additional year on the job corresponds to a $400 increase in predicted income.

d. The predicted mean income for employees having 20 years of experience is $4,000 higher than the predicted mean income for employees having 10 years of experience.

Advanced Exercises

3.110 Suppose you convert y = income from British pounds to dollars, and suppose a pound equals 2.00 dollars.

a. Explain why the y values double, the mean of y doubles, the deviations $(y - \bar{y})$ double, and the standard deviation s_y doubles.

b. Using the formula for calculating the correlation coefficient r, explain why it would not change value.

3.111 When correlation = slope Consider the formula $b = r(s_y/s_x)$ that expresses the slope in terms of the correlation coefficient. Suppose the data are equally spread out for each variable. That is, suppose the data satisfy $s_x = s_y$. Show that the correlation coefficient r and the slope are the same. (In practice, the standard deviations are not usually identical unless the variables are standardized. However, this provides an interpretation for the correlation coefficient as representing what we would get for the slope of the regression line if the two variables were equally spread out.)

3.112 Center of the data Consider the formula $a = \bar{y} - b\bar{x}$ for the y-intercept.

a. Show that $\bar{y} = a + b\bar{x}$. Explain why this means that the predicted value of the response variable is $\hat{y} = \bar{y}$ when $x = \bar{x}$.

b. Show that an alternative way of expressing the regression model is as $(\hat{y} - \bar{y}) = b(x - \bar{x})$. Interpret this formula.

3.113 Final exam "regresses toward mean" of midterm Let y = final exam score and x = midterm exam score. Suppose that the correlation coefficient is 0.70 and that the standard deviation is the same for each set of scores.

a. Using part b of the previous exercise and the relation between the slope and correlation coefficient r, show that $(\hat{y} - \bar{y}) = 0.70(x - \bar{x})$.

b. Explain why this indicates that the predicted difference between your final exam grade and the class mean is 70% of the difference between your midterm exam score and the class mean. Your score is predicted to "regress toward the mean." (The concept of *regression toward the mean*, which is responsible for the name of regression analysis, will be discussed in Section 12.2.)

Student Activities

3.114 Effect of moving a point The *Explore Linear Regression* app lets you add and delete points on a scatterplot. The regression line is automatically calculated for the points you provide.

a. Select the option Draw Own and add 5 points to the empty scatterplot that have an approximate linear relationship between x and y but a slope near 0.

b. Add a sixth observation that is influential. What did you have to do to get the slope to change noticeably from 0?

c. Now consider the effect of sample size on the existence of influential points. Start by creating 50 points with a similar pattern as in part a. You can create this from scratch, point by point, or simply select Random Scatter from the drop down menu for the initial relationship and select 50 for the number of points. Is it now harder to add a single point that makes the slope change noticeably from 0? Why?

d. Try this activity, now exploring the effect of adding or deleting points on the correlation coefficient r. (Check the box to display r.) Repeat parts a–c in terms of the correlation coefficient instead of the slope.

3.115 Guess the correlation The *Guess the Correlation* app lets you guess the correlation coefficient r from randomly generated scatterplots. How close are your guesses to the actual correlation coefficients? Find the correlation coefficient between your guesses and the actual value after 10 guesses.

3.116 Analyze your data Refer to the data file the class created in Exercise 1.50 of Chapter 1. For variables chosen by your instructor, conduct a regression and correlation analysis. Prepare a one-page report summarizing your analyses, interpreting your findings.

In Chapter 1, we emphasized that the statistical investigative process begins with formulating questions to be answered with data. In Chapters 2 and 3, we used data to describe distributions of and relationships between variables. In later chapters, data will form the basis of inferences about populations. But how do we actually collect data in the first place to obtain valid results? This chapter discusses two major types of study designs and related issues for the purpose of gathering useful data.

Gathering Data

Example 1

Cell Phones and Your Health

Picture the Scenario

How safe are cell phones to use? Cell phones emit electromagnetic radiation, and a cell phone's antenna is the main source of this energy. The closer the antenna is to the user's head, the greater the exposure to radiation. With the increased use of cell phones, there has been a growing concern over the potential health risks. Several studies have explored the possibility of such risks:

Study 1 A German study (Stang et al., 2001) compared 118 patients with a rare form of eye cancer called uveal melanoma to 475 healthy patients who did not have this eye cancer. The patients' cell phone use was measured using a questionnaire. On average, the eye cancer patients used cell phones more often.

Study 2 A British study (Hepworth et al., 2006) compared 966 patients with brain cancer to 1,716 patients without brain cancer. The patients' cell phone use was measured using a questionnaire. Cell phone use for the two groups was similar.

Study 3 A study published in *The Journal of the American Medical Association* (Volkow et al., 2011)

indicates that cell phone use speeds up activity in the brain. As part of a randomized crossover study, 47 participants were fitted with a cell phone device on each ear and then underwent two positron emission topography, or PET, scans to measure brain glucose metabolism. During one scan, the cell phones were both turned off. During the other scan, an automated 50-minute muted call was made to the phone on the right ear. The order of when the call was received (for the first or second scan) was randomized. Comparison of the PET scans showed a significant increase in activity in the part of the brain closest to the antenna during the transmission of the automated call.

Studies 1 and 3 found potential physiological responses to cell phone use. Study 2 did not.

Question to Explore

- Why do results of different medical studies sometimes disagree?

- Consider the different study designs to explore whether cell phone use is associated with various types of physiological activities in our bodies. For each study,

a. Does the study design establish a causal link between cell phone use and potential health risks?

b. Is the study ethically feasible?

c. How can you design the study to be efficient?

d. What types of biases or lurking variables might exist?

Thinking Ahead

A knowledge of different **study designs for gathering data** helps us understand how contradictory results can happen in scientific research studies and determine which studies

deserve our trust. In this chapter, we'll learn that the study design can have a major impact on its results. Unless the study is well designed and implemented, the results may be meaningless or, worse yet, misleading. Throughout Chapter 4, we will return to the cell phone studies introduced in Example 1 to ask more questions and understand how study design can affect what are appropriate conclusions to infer from an analysis of the data.

Chapters 2 and 3 introduced graphical and numerical ways of describing data. We described shape, center, and variability, looked for patterns and unusual observations, and explored associations between variables. For these and other statistical analyses to be useful, we must have "good data." But what's the best way to gather data to ensure they are "good"? The studies described in Example 1 used two methods. The first two studies merely *observed* subjects, whereas the third study *conducted an experiment* with them. We'll now learn about such methods, study their pros and cons, and see both good and bad ways to use them. This will help us understand when we can trust the conclusions of a study and when we need to be skeptical.

4.1 Experimental and Observational Studies

Recall

From Section 1.2, the **population** consists of *all* the subjects of interest. We collect data on a subset of the population, which we call the **sample.**

From the beginning of Chapter 3, the **response variable** measures the outcome of interest. Studies investigate how that outcome is related to the **explanatory variable.** ◄

We use statistics to learn about a **population.** The German and British studies in Example 1 examined subjects' cell phone use and whether the subjects had brain or eye cancer. Since it would be too costly and time-consuming to seek out *all* individuals in the populations of Germany or Great Britain, the researchers used **samples** to gather data. These studies, like many, have two variables of primary interest—a **response variable** and an **explanatory variable.** The response variable is whether a subject has cancer (eye or brain). The explanatory variable is the amount of cell phone use.

Types of Studies: Experimental and Observational

Some studies, such as Study 3 in Example 1, perform an **experiment.** Subjects are assigned to experimental conditions, such as the "on" and "off" condition of cell phones, that we want to compare on the response outcome. These experimental conditions are called **treatments.** They correspond to different values of the explanatory variable.

> **Experimental Study**
>
> A researcher conducts an experimental study, or more simply, an **experiment,** by assigning subjects to certain experimental conditions and then observing outcomes on the response variable (or variables). The experimental conditions, which correspond to assigned values of the explanatory variable, are called **treatments.**

For example, Study 3 used 47 participants as the subjects. In this experimental study, each participant was assigned to both treatments. These are the categories of the explanatory variable, whether the cell phone is off or on. The purpose of the experiment was to examine the association between this variable and the response variable—the amount of brain activity changes—to determine whether it increased.

An experiment assigns each subject to a treatment (or to both treatments as in the design employed in Study 3) and then observes the response. By contrast, many studies merely *observe* the values on the response variable and the explanatory variable for the sampled subjects without doing anything to them. Such studies are called **observational studies.** They are **nonexperimental.**

> ### Observational Study
>
> In an **observational study,** the researcher observes values of the response variable and explanatory variables for the sampled subjects, without anything being done to the subjects (such as imposing a treatment).

In short, an **observational study** merely *observes* rather than *experiments* with the study subjects. An **experimental study** assigns each subject to one or more treatments and then observes the outcome on the response variable.

Identifying Experimental Versus Observational Studies ◄

Example 2

Cell Phone Use

Picture the Scenario

Example 1 described three studies about whether relationships might exist between cell phone use and physiological activity in the human body. We've seen that Study 3 was an experiment. Studies 1 and 2 both examined the amount of cell phone use for cancer patients and for noncancer patients using a questionnaire.

Questions to Explore

a. Were Studies 1 and 2 experimental or observational studies?

b. How were Studies 1 and 2 fundamentally different from Study 3 in terms of how the treatments were determined for each subject?

Think It Through

a. In Studies 1 and 2, information on the amount of cell phone use was gathered by giving a questionnaire to the sampled subjects. The subjects (people) decided how much they would use a cell phone and thus determined their amount of radiation exposure. The studies merely observed this exposure. No experiment was performed. So, Studies 1 and 2 were *observational* studies.

b. In Study 3, each subject was given both treatments (the "off" condition and the "on" condition). The researchers did not merely observe the subjects for the amount of brain activity but exposed the subjects to both treatments and determined which treatment each would receive first: Some received the call during the first PET scan and some during the second scan. The researchers imposed the treatments on the subjects. So, Study 3 was an *experimental* study.*

---

*The researchers noted that "Results of this study provide evidence that acute cell phone exposure affects brain metabolic activity. However, these results provide no information about their relevance to potential carcinogenic effects (or lack thereof) from chronic cell phone use."

Insight

One reason that results of different medical studies sometimes disagree is that they are not the same *type* of study. Properly designed experimental studies allow direct causal inference to be made, whereas observational studies do not allow causal inference. As we'll see, there are different types of both observational and experimental studies, and some are more trustworthy than others.

▶ *Try Exercises 4.1 and 4.3*

Let's consider another study. From its description, we'll try to determine whether it is an experiment or an observational study.

Example 3

Experiment or Observational Study ◀

	Drug Use		
Drug Tests?	**Yes**	**No**	**Total**
Yes	2,092	3,561	5,653
No	6,452	10,985	17,437

Bar Graph of Drug Use

Drug Testing and Student Drug Use

Picture the Scenario

"Student Drug Testing Not Effective in Reducing Drug Use" was the headline in a news release from the University of Michigan. It reported results from a study of 76,000 students in 497 high schools and 225 middle schools nationwide.[1] Each student in the study filled out a questionnaire. One question asked whether the student used drugs. The study found that drug use was similar in schools that tested for drugs and in schools that did not test for drugs. For instance, the table in the margin shows the frequency of drug use for sampled twelfth graders from the two types of schools. In addition, the figure in the margin shows the conditional proportions of drug use for these students. (You can replicate the graph by entering the contingency table in the *Association Between Two Categorical Data* app.)

Questions to Explore

a. What were the response and explanatory variables?

b. Was this an observational study or an experiment?

Think It Through

a. The study compared the percentage of students who used drugs in schools that tested for drugs and in schools that did not test for drugs. Whether the student used drugs was the response variable. The explanatory variable was whether the student's school tested for drugs. Both variables were categorical, with categories "yes" and "no." For each grade, the data were summarized in a contingency table, as shown in the margin for twelfth graders.

b. For each student, the study merely observed whether the student's school tested for drugs and whether the student used drugs. So this was an observational study.

Insight

An experiment would have assigned schools to use or not use drug testing rather than leaving the decision to the schools. For instance, the study could have randomly selected half the schools to perform drug testing and half not to perform it and then, a year later, measured the student drug use in each school.

▶ *Try Exercise 4.7*

[1]Study by R. Yamaguchi et al., reported in *Journal of School Health*, vol. 73, pp. 159–164, 2003.

As we will soon discuss, an experimental study gives the researcher more control over outside influences. This control can allow more accuracy in studying the association.

Advantage of Experiments Over Observational Studies

Recall

From Section 3.4, a **lurking variable** is a variable not observed in the study that influences the association between the response and explanatory variables due to its own association with each of those variables. ◄

In an observational study, lurking variables can affect the results. Study 1 in Example 1 found an association between cell phone use and eye cancer. However, there could be lifestyle, genetic, or health differences between the subjects with eye cancer and those without it, and between those who use cell phones a lot and those who do not. A lurking variable could affect the observed association. For example, a possible lifestyle lurking variable is computer use. Perhaps those who use cell phones often also use computers frequently. Perhaps high exposure to computer screens increases the chance of eye cancer. In that case, the higher prevalence of eye cancer for heavier users of cell phones could be due to their higher use of computers, not their higher use of cell phones.

By contrast, an experiment reduces the potential for lurking variables to affect the results. Why? We'll see that with a type of "random" selection to determine which subjects receive each treatment, we are attempting to form and balance groups of subjects receiving the different treatments; that is, the groups have similar distributions on other variables, such as lifestyle, genetic, or health characteristics. For instance, suppose the researchers in cell phone Study 3 decided to have 24 subjects receive the "on" condition and 23 subjects receive the "off" condition instead of having each subject receive both treatments. The health of the subjects could be a factor in how the brain responds to the treatments and the amount of brain activity that appears on the scans. If we randomly determine which subjects receive the "on" condition and which do not, the two groups of subjects are expected to have similar distributions on health. One group will not be much healthier, on average, than the other group. When the groups are balanced on a lurking variable, there is no association between the lurking variable and the explanatory variable (for instance, between health of the subject and whether the subject receives the "on" condition). Then, the lurking variable will not affect how the explanatory variable is associated with the response variable. One treatment group will not tend to have more brain activity because of health differences, on the average.

In Study 3, described in Example 1, by using the same subjects for both treatments, the researchers were attempting to further control the variability from the subject's health. In this experimental study, it was important to randomize the order in which the subject received the treatment.

Establishing **cause and effect** is central to science. But it's not possible to establish cause and effect definitively with observational studies. There's always the possibility that some lurking variable could be responsible for the association. If people who make greater use of cell phones have a higher rate of eye cancer, it may be because of some variable that we failed to measure in our study, such as computer use. As we learned in Section 3.4, **association does not imply causation**.

Because it's easier to address the potential impact of lurking variables in an experiment than in an observational study, *we can study the effect of an explanatory variable on a response variable more accurately with an experiment than with an observational study.* With an experiment, the researcher has control over which treatment each subject receives. If we find an association between the explanatory variable and the response variable, we can be more sure that we've discovered a causal relationship than if we merely find an association in an observational study. Consequently, the best method for determining causality is to conduct an experiment.

Caution

In Example 3, it would be premature to conclude that drug testing in schools has *no effect* on drug use. This was only an observational study. Perhaps the schools employing drug testing were the ones which had much higher drug use to begin with. Initial drug use of students could be a lurking variable. ◄

Determining Which Type of Study Is Possible

If experiments are preferable, why ever conduct an observational study? Why bother to measure whether cell phone usage was greater for those with cancer than for those not having it? Why not instead conduct an experiment, such as the following: Pick half the students from your school at random and tell them to use a cell phone each day for the next 50 years. Tell the other half of the student body never to use cell phones. Fifty years from now, analyze whether cancer was more common for those who used cell phones.

There are obvious difficulties with such an experiment:

- It's not ethical for a study to expose over a long period of time some of the subjects to something (such as cell phone radiation) that we suspect may be harmful.
- It's difficult in practice to make sure that the subjects behave as told. How can you monitor them to ensure that they adhere to their treatment assignment over the 50-year experimental period?
- Who wants to wait 50 years to get an answer?

For these reasons, medical experiments are often performed over a short time period or often with exposure to treatments that would not be out of the ordinary (such as a one-time exposure to cell phone activity). To measure the effects on people of longer exposure to potentially harmful treatments, often the experiment uses animals such as mice instead of people. Because inferences about human populations are more trustworthy when we use samples of human subjects than when we use samples of animal subjects, scientists often resort to observational studies. Then we are not deliberately placing people in harm's way, but observing people who have chosen on their own to take part in the activity of interest. We'll study methods for designing a good observational study in Section 4.4. This can yield useful information when an experiment is not practical or ethical.

Another reason nonexperimental studies are common is that many questions of interest do not involve trying to assess causality. For instance, if we want to gauge the public's opinion on some issue, or if we want to conduct a marketing study to see how people rate a new product, it's completely adequate to use a study that samples (appropriately) the population of interest.

Finally, as we have mentioned in Section 1.3 of Chapter 1, the digital revolution now enables researchers (or social media platforms and other global, mostly tech companies) to gather data on millions of people, measuring hundreds of variables simultaneously. These data are, in essence, massive observational studies, called **Big Data**. The hope is that by the sheer number of variables recorded, lurking variables that would have gone unnoticed otherwise can be identified (often through machine learning algorithms) and adjusted for when studying associations.

Using Data Already Available

Of course, you will not conduct a study every time you want to answer some question, such as whether cell phone use is dangerous. It's human nature to rely instead on already available data. The most readily available data come from your personal observations. Perhaps a friend recently diagnosed with brain cancer was a frequent user of cell phones. Is this strong evidence that frequent cell phone use increases the likelihood of getting brain cancer?

Informal observations of this type are called **anecdotal evidence.** Unfortunately, there is no way to tell whether they are representative of what happens for an entire population. Sometimes you hear people give anecdotal evidence to attempt to disprove causal relationships. "My Uncle Geoffrey is 85 years old and he's smoked a pack of cigarettes a day for his entire adult life, yet he's as healthy as a horse." An association does not need to be perfect, however, to be causal. Not all people who smoke a pack of cigarettes each day will get lung cancer, but a much higher proportion of them will do so than people who are nonsmokers. Perhaps Uncle Geoffrey is lucky to be in good health, but that should not encourage you to smoke regularly.

Did You Know?

Examples of sources for available data:

- www.google.com/publicdata (hundreds of public databases)
- data.worldbank.org (lots of economic and political indicators)
- www.data.gov, www.statcan.ca, www.inegi.org.mx, data.europa.eu, www.gov.uk/government/statistics, www.abs.gov.au, www.mospi.gov.in (Government data from the United States, Canada, Mexico, the European Union, the United Kingdom, Australia and India) ◄

A famous saying is, "The plural of anecdote is not data." Instead of using anecdotal evidence to draw conclusions, you should rely on data from reputable research studies. You can find research results on topics of interest by entering keywords in Internet search engines. This search directs you to published results, such as in medical journals for medical studies.[2] Results from well-designed studies are more trustworthy than anecdotal evidence. We listed some of the sources of available data in Chapter 1, Section 1.3, and point out some more in the margin of the previous page.

The Census and Other Sample Surveys

The General Social Survey (GSS) is an example of a **sample survey.** It gathers information by interviewing a sample of subjects from the U.S. adult population to provide a snapshot of that population. The study in Example 3 on student drug use in schools also used a sample survey.

> ### Sample Survey
>
> A **sample survey** selects a sample of subjects from a population and collects data from them. In the field of statistics a survey does not just indicate an opinion poll or a questionnaire; it includes any information gathered from or about the subject.

A sample survey is a type of nonexperimental study. The subjects provide data on the variable or variables measured. There is no assignment of subjects to different treatments.

Most countries conduct a regular **census.** A census attempts to count the number of people in the population and to measure certain characteristics about them. It is different from a sample survey, which selects only a small part of the entire population.

In Article 1, Section 2, the U.S. Constitution states that a complete counting of the U.S. population is to be done every 10 years. The first census was taken in 1790. It counted 3.9 million people; today the U.S. population is estimated to be more than 300 million (308,745,538 by the 2010 U.S. census). Other than counting the population size, here are three key reasons for conducting the U.S. census:

- The Constitution mandates that seats in the House of Representatives be apportioned to states based on their portion of the population measured by the census. When the 1910 census was completed, Congress fixed the number of seats at 435. With each new census, states may gain or lose seats, depending on how their population size compares with other states.
- Census data are used in the drawing of boundaries for electoral districts.
- Census data are used to determine the distribution of federal dollars to states and local communities.

Although it's the intention of a census to sample *everyone* in a population, in practice this is not possible. Some people do not have known addresses for the census bureau to send a census form. Some people are homeless or transient. Because data are needed regularly on economic variables, such as the unemployment rate, the U.S. Census Bureau continually takes samples of the population rather than relying solely on the complete census. An example is the monthly Current Population Survey, which surveys about 60,000 U.S. households and is the primary source of labor force statistics for the population of the United States, including the unemployment rate. It is usually more practical, in terms of time and money, to take a sample rather than to try to measure everyone in a population.

---

[2]Most surveys of research about cell phones suggest that there is no convincing evidence yet of adverse radiation effects (e.g., D. R. Cox, *J. Roy. Statist. Soc., Ser. A*, vol. 166, pp. 241–246, 2003). The primary danger appears to be people using cell phones while driving!

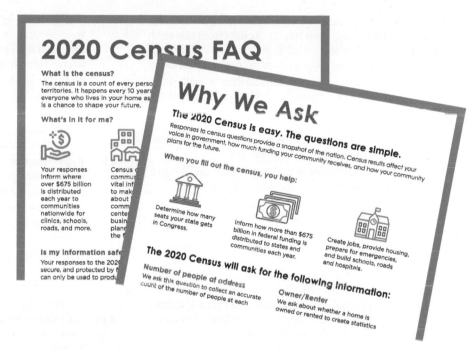

Two flyers sent out by the U.S. Census Bureau to encourage households to fill in the 2020 Census.

For a sample survey to be informative, it is important for the sample to reflect the population well. As we'll discuss next, random selection—letting chance determine which subjects are in the sample—is the key to getting a good sample.

4.1 Practicing the Basics

4.1 **Cell phones** Consider the cell phone Study 3 described in Example 1.
[TRY]
    a. Identify the response variable and the explanatory variable.
    b. Was this an observational study or an experiment? Explain why.

4.2 **High blood pressure and binge drinking** Many studies have demonstrated that high blood pressure increases the risk of developing heart disease or having a stroke. It is also safe to say that the health risks associated with binge drinking far outweigh any benefits. A study published in *Health Magazine* in 2010 suggested that a combination of the two could be a lethal mix. As part of the study that followed 6,100 South Korean men aged 55 and over for two decades, men with high blood pressure who binge drank even occasionally had double the risk of dying from a stroke or heart attack when compared to teetotalers with normal blood pressure.
    a. Is this an observational or experimental study?
    b. Identify the explanatory and response variable(s).
    c. Does the study prove that a combination of high blood pressure and binge drinking causes an increased risk of death by heart attack or stroke? Why or why not?

4.3 **Low-fat versus low-carb diet?** One hundred forty-eight men and women without heart disease or diabetes enrolled in a study. Half of the subjects were randomly assigned to a low-carb diet (<40 g/d), and the others were
[TRY]
given a low-fat diet ($<30\%$ of daily energy intake from total fat). Subjects on the low-carb diet lost more weight after one year compared with those on the low-fat diet (an average of 8 pounds more). (L. A. Bazzano et al., *Ann Intern Med* 2014; 161(5): 309–318. doi:10.7326/M14-0180)
    a. Identify the response variable and the explanatory variable.
    b. Was this study an observational study or an experimental study? Explain.
    c. Based on this study, is it appropriate to recommend that everyone who wishes to lose weight should prefer a low-carb diet over a low-fat diet? Explain your answer.

4.4 **Experiments versus observational studies** When either type of study is feasible, an experiment is usually preferred over an observational study. Explain why, using an example to illustrate. Also explain why it is not always possible for researchers to carry out a study in an experimental framework. Give an example of such a situation.

4.5 **School testing for drugs** Example 3 discussed a study comparing high schools that tested for drugs with high schools that did not test for drugs, finding similar levels of student drug use in each. State a potential lurking variable that could affect the results of such a study. Describe what the effect could be.

4.6 **Hormone therapy and heart disease** Since 1976 the Nurses' Health Study has followed more than 100,000 nurses. Every two years, the nurses fill out a questionnaire about their habits and their health. Results from this study indicated that postmenopausal women have a reduced risk of heart disease if they take a hormone replacement drug.

a. Suppose the hormone-replacement drug actually has no effect. Identify a potential lurking variable that could explain the results of the observational study. (*Hint:* Suppose that the women who took the drug tended to be more conscientious about their personal health than those who did not take it.)

b. Recently a randomized experiment called the Women's Health Initiative was conducted by the National Institutes of Health to see whether hormone therapy is truly helpful. The study, planned to last for eight years, was stopped after five years when analyses showed that women who took hormones had 30% more heart attacks. This study suggested that rather than reducing the risk of heart attacks, hormone replacement drugs actually increase the risk.[3] How is it that two studies could reach such different conclusions? (For attempts to reconcile the studies, see a story by Gina Kolata in *The New York Times*, April 21, 2003.)

c. Explain why randomized experiments, when feasible, are preferable to observational studies.

4.7 **Speaking foreign languages** A 2014 study (http://www.futurity.org/foreign-languages-make-us-less-moral/) examined the relationship between using a foreign language and acting for the common good. They examined two groups of people, one that used their native language and one that used a foreign language. Each group was presented with a moral dilemma that required the subject to make a choice about saving himself or herself versus sacrificing his or her life for the sake of saving others. Those using a foreign language chose saving others at a higher rate than those using their native language.

a. Identify the response variable and the explanatory variable.

b. Is this study an observational study or an experiment? Explain.

c. Can we conclude that speaking a foreign language causes one to act morally? Explain.

4.8 **Breast-cancer screening** A study published in 2010 in the *New England Journal of Medicine* discusses a breast-cancer screening program that began in Norway in 1996 and was expanded geographically through 2005. Women in the study were offered mammography screening every two years. The goal of the study was to compare incidence-based rates of death from breast cancer across four groups:

1. Women who from 1996 through 2005 were living in countries with screening.

2. Women who from 1996 through 2005 were living in countries without screening.

3. A historical-comparison group who lived in screening countries from 1986 through 1995.

4. A historical-comparison group who lived in nonscreening countries from 1986 through 1995.

Data were analyzed for 40,075 women. Rates of death were reduced in the screening group as compared to the historical screening group and in the nonscreening group as compared to the historical nonscreening group.

a. Is this an observational or experimental study?

b. Identify the explanatory and response variable(s).

c. Does the study prove that being offered mammography screening causes a reduction in death rates associated with breast cancer? Why or why not?

4.9 **Experiment or observe?** Explain whether an experiment or an observational study would be more appropriate to investigate the following:

a. Whether smoking has an effect on coronary heart disease

b. Whether higher SAT scores tend to be positively associated with higher college GPAs

c. Whether a special coupon attached to the outside of a catalog makes recipients more likely to order products from a mail-order company

4.10 **Baseball under a full moon** During a baseball game between the Boston Brouhahas and the Minnesota Meddlers, the broadcaster mentions that the away team has won "13 consecutive meetings between the two teams played on nights with a full moon."

a. Is the broadcaster's comment based on observational or experimental data?

b. The current game is being played in Boston. Should the Boston Brouhahas be concerned about the recent full moon trend?

4.11 **Seat belt anecdote** Andy once heard about a car crash victim who died because he was pinned in the wreckage by a seat belt he could not undo. As a result, Andy refuses to wear a seat belt when he rides in a car. How would you explain to Andy the fallacy behind relying on this anecdotal evidence?

4.12 **Poker as a profession?** Tony's mother is extremely proud that her son will graduate college in a few months. She expresses concern, however, when Tony tells her that following graduation, he plans to move to Las Vegas to become a professional poker player. He mentions that his friend Nick did so and is now earning more than a million dollars per year. Should Tony's anecdotal evidence about Nick soothe his mother's concern?

4.13 **What's more to blame for obesity?** In a study published in the July 7, 2014, edition of the *American Journal of Medicine*, it was suggested that lack of exercise contributed more to weight gain than eating too much. The study examined the current exercise habits and caloric intake of a sample of both males and females. (Source: http://www.cbsnews.com/news/whats-more-to-blame-for-obesity-lack-of-exercise-or-eating-too-much/)

a. Was this an observational study or an experimental study? Explain why.

b. Identify the response variable and the explanatory variable(s).

c. Does this study prove that lack of exercise causes weight gain more often than eating too much?

d. It was reported that women younger than 40 are quite vulnerable to the risks of a sedentary lifestyle.

[3]See article by H. N. Hodis et al., *New England Journal of Medicine*, August 7, 2003.

Name a lurking variable that might explain this risk of a sedentary lifestyle for these younger women that in turn leads to little exercise and/or eating more.

4.14 Census every 10 years?   A nationwide census is conducted in the United States every 10 years.

   a. Give at least two reasons the United States takes a census only every 10 years.

b. What are reasons for taking the census at all?

c. The most commonly discussed characteristic learned from a census is the size of the population. However, other characteristics of the population are measured during each census. Using the Internet, report two such characteristics recorded during the 2020 U.S. census. (*Hint:* Visit the following website: www.census.gov.)

4.2 Good and Poor Ways to Sample

The sample survey is a common type of nonexperimental study. The first step of a sample survey is to define the population targeted by the study. For instance, the Gallup organization (news.gallup.com) conducts a monthly survey of about 1,000 adult Americans. Gallup then reports the percentage of those sampled who respond "approve" when asked, "Do you approve or disapprove of the way [the current president of the United States] is handling his job as president?" If the sampling is conducted properly, this provides a good estimate of the approval rate within the entire population. The population consists of all adults living in the United States.

Sampling Frame and Sampling Design

Once you've identified the population, the second step is to compile a list of subjects so you can sample from it. This list is called the **sampling frame.**

> ### Sampling Frame
> The **sampling frame** is the list of subjects in the population from which the sample is taken.

Ideally, the sampling frame lists the entire population of interest. In practice, as in a census, it's usually hard to identify every subject in the population.

Suppose you plan to sample students at your school, asking students to complete a questionnaire about various issues. The population is all students at the school. One possible sampling frame is the school's student directory. Another one is a list of registered students at the school.

Once you have a sampling frame, you need to specify a method for selecting subjects from it. The method used is called the **sampling design.** Here's one possible sampling design: As you go through the sampling frame using the registrar's list of students, select all those that happen to be in your statistics class. This will give you easy access to them. Do you think such a sample is necessarily reflective of the entire student body? Is there a representative mixture of freshmen through seniors, gender representation, athletes and nonathletes, working and nonworking students, political party affiliations, and so on? With this sampling design, it's doubtful.

When you pick a sample merely by convenience, the results may not be representative of the population. Some response outcomes may occur much more frequently than in the population, and some may occur much less. Consider a survey question about the number of hours a week that you work at an outside job. If your class is primarily juniors and seniors, they may be more likely to work than freshmen or sophomores. The mean response in the sample may be much larger than in the overall student population. Information from the sample may be misleading.

Simple Random Sampling

Recall

In Chapter 1, we defined the margin of error as a measure of how close an estimate falls to the true population parameter. ◄

You're more likely to obtain a representative sample if you let *chance*, rather than *convenience*, determine the sample. The sampling design should give each student listed in the sampling frame an equal chance to be in the sample. It should also enable the data analyst to find a margin of error for the statistic that is computed from the sample, such as a sample proportion or mean. With the margin of error, the analyst can express how close the statistic is likely to fall to the corresponding population parameter. These are reasons for using **random sampling.**

You may have been part of a selection process in which your name was put in a box or hat along with many other names, and someone blindly picked a name for a prize. If the names were thoroughly mixed before the selection, this emulates a *random* type of sampling called a **simple random sample.**

Recall

As in Chapters 2 and 3, *n* denotes the *number* of observations in the sample, called the **sample size.** ◄

> **Simple Random Sample**
>
> A **simple random sample** of n subjects from a population is one in which each possible sample of that size has the same chance of being selected.

A *simple random sample* is often just called a **random sample.** The "simple" adjective distinguishes this type of sampling from more complex random sampling designs presented in Section 4.4.

Example 4

Simple Random Samples ◄

Drawing Prize Winners

Picture the Scenario

A student club decides to raise money for a local charity by selling 60 raffle tickets to a dinner banquet. The Athletic Department has donated two football season tickets as prizes. The winners for the season tickets will be drawn randomly from the 60 raffle tickets sold. To select the two winners, the organizers choose a simple random sample of size $n = 2$ from the 60 raffle tickets. The 60 raffle tickets, which contain the numbers 1 through 60, are placed in a container and mixed. Then, the student club president reaches into the container and randomly draws two raffle tickets from it. The owners of the raffle tickets selected are the winners of the season tickets.

Questions to Explore

a. What are the possible samples of size 2 that could be drawn? That is, what are all the possible combinations of two raffle ticket numbers that could be drawn by the student president?

b. What is the chance that a particular sample of size 2 will be drawn?

c. Ann is in attendance at the banquet and owns raffle ticket number 1. What is the chance that her ticket will be chosen? Bob owns raffle ticket number 55. What is the chance that his ticket will be chosen?

Think It Through

a. The entire collection of possible samples is too long to list, but we can visualize the possibilities by listing certain pairs of ticket numbers:

(1,2), (1,3), (1,4), . . ., (1,58), (1,59), (1,60)
(2,3), (2,4), . . ., (2,58), (2,59), (2,60)
. . .

(57,58), (57,59), (57,60)
(58,59), (58,60)
(59,60)

b. The first row listed contains 59 possible samples, the second row contains 58, and so forth. There are thus $59 + 58 + \ldots + 3 + 2 + 1$ samples, which equals 1,770 possible samples. The process of randomly selecting two unique tickets ensures that each possible sample of size 2 has an equal chance of occurring. Since there are 1,770 possible samples of two numbers, the chance of any one sample being selected is 1 out of 1,770. (More on this in Chapter 5.)

c. Looking at the first row in part a, we see that 1 shows up in 59 of the samples (all of the samples listed in the top row), but not in any other row. So the chance that Ann wins a season ticket is 59 out of 1,770, or 3.3%. Bob's ticket number of 55 also shows up in 59 of all the possible samples listed in part a: the number 55 paired with every other number from 1 to 60, except the number 55. So, Bob's chances for winning a season ticket are also 3.3%.

Insight

The chance of 59/1,770 for Ann is the same as that of Bob and every other of the 60 ticket holders. In a simple random sample, every ticket has the same chance of being selected. What's more, each of the 1,770 two-number combinations listed in part a has the same chance of being selected, which fits our definition of a simple random sample above. (This is ensured by the process of the president reaching into the container and selecting two raffle tickets at random.)

The type of random sampling in this example is called sampling **without replacement**. This means that once a single raffle ticket is randomly selected, it becomes ineligible for further selection. If instead the president reaches in the container, randomly selects a single ticket, puts it back into the container, mixes the tickets, and selects a second ticket at random, the process is called **sampling with replacement**. Then, the list of all possible samples in part a would need to be augmented by (1,1), (2,2), . . ., (59,59), (60,60) because the same ticket could be selected twice. If one of these samples happens to be selected, e.g., (1,1), then Ann wins both season tickets!

In practice, especially with larger populations and larger sample sizes, it is difficult to mix and select tickets from a container so that each sample truly has an equal chance of being selected. There are better ways of selecting simple random samples, as we'll learn next.

▶ *Try Exercise 4.15*

Selecting a Simple Random Sample

What's a better way to take a simple random sample than blindly drawing slips of paper out of a hat? You first number the subjects in the sampling frame consecutively. You then generate a subset of size *n* of those numbers randomly. Finally, you sample the subjects whose numbers were generated. In practice, a computer is used to generate the sample. This could be through an app or a statistical software program. The following example demonstrates how a random sample is selected using the *Random Numbers* app from the book's website.

▲ Figure 4.1 Screenshot of *Random Numbers* app for selecting 10 numbers at random and without replacement from the numbers 1 through 67. Note: When you replicate this process with the app, you will likely get a different set of 10 numbers, unless you check the option for Fix Random Seed.

Selecting a Simple Random Sample ◄

Example 5

Auditing a School District

Picture the Scenario

Local school districts must be prepared for annual visits from state auditors whose job is to verify the dollar amount of the accounts within the school district and determine whether the money is being spent appropriately. It is too time-consuming and expensive for auditors to review all accounts, so they typically review only some of them. In order for a school district not being able to anticipate which accounts will be reviewed, the auditors take a simple random sample of the accounts.

Questions to Explore

a. How can the auditors use random numbers to select 10 accounts to audit in a school district that has 67 accounts?

b. Why is it important for the auditors not to use personal judgment in selecting the accounts to audit?

Think It Through

a. The sampling frame consists of the 67 accounts. We first number the accounts from 1 to 67 by setting the maximum to 67 in the *Random Numbers* app (and keeping the minimum at 1), see the screenshot in Figure 4.1. Because we want to sample 10 accounts, we set the numbers to generate to 10 in the corresponding box, which means the app will randomly select 10 numbers from the numbers 1 through 67. Since we don't want to sample any account twice, we sample without replacement (the default in the app).

On pressing the Generate button, we obtained the following 10 numbers selected at random and without replacement from the numbers 1 through 67: 5, 58, 12, 39, 36, 66, 40, 43, 31, and 8. These correspond to the account numbers being randomly selected for auditing.

b. By using simple random sampling, the auditors hold the school district responsible for all accounts. If the auditors personally chose the accounts to audit, they might select certain accounts each year. A school district would soon learn which accounts they need to have in order and which accounts can be given less attention.

Insight

Likewise, the Internal Revenue Service (IRS) randomly selects some tax returns for audit, so taxpayers cannot predict ahead of time whether they will be audited. For efficiency, the IRS samples a small proportion of tax returns with small amounts owed and a larger proportion of tax returns with high amounts owed. It does this because it cares about the total amount of tax revenue brought in.

▶ *Try Exercise 4.16*

Methods of Collecting Data in Sample Surveys

In Example 5, the subjects sampled were accounts. More commonly, they are people. For any survey, it is difficult to get a good sampling frame since a list of all adults in a population typically does not exist. So, it's necessary to pick a place where almost all people can be found—a person's place of residence.

Once we identify the desired sample for a survey, how do we contact the people to collect the data? The three most common methods are personal interview, telephone interview, and self-administered questionnaire (either in person or online).

Personal interview   In a personal (face-to-face) interview, an interviewer asks prepared questions and records the subject's responses. An advantage is that subjects are more likely to participate. A disadvantage is the cost. Also, some subjects may not answer sensitive questions pertaining to opinions or lifestyle, such as alcohol and drug use, whether they have been victims of sexual abuse, or their HIV status that they might otherwise answer on a printed questionnaire.

Telephone interview   A telephone interview is like a personal interview but conducted over the phone. A main advantage is lower cost because no travel is involved. A disadvantage is that the interview might have to be short. Subjects generally aren't as patient on the phone and may hang up before starting or completing the interview. Nonetheless, phone surveys are the most common methods used by polling agencies.

Self-administered questionnaire   Subjects are requested to fill out a questionnaire mailed, e-mailed, or otherwise available online. With services such as Google Forms or Survey Monkey, or with social media sites such as Twitter or Facebook, you can now easily create your own survey and invite people to participate. An advantage is that it is cheaper than a personal interview. A disadvantage is that fewer people tend to participate.

Most major national polls that survey regularly to measure public opinion use the telephone interview. An example is the polls conducted by the Gallup organization. The General Social Survey is an exception, using personal interviews for its questionnaire, which is quite long.

For telephone interviews, since the mid-1980s, many sample surveys have used **random digit dialing** to select households. The survey can then obtain a sample without having a sampling frame. In the United States, typically the area code and the 3-digit exchange are randomly selected from the list of all such codes and exchanges. Then, the last four digits are dialed randomly, and an adult is selected randomly within the household. Although this sampling design incorporates randomness, it is not a simple random sample because each sample of households is not equally likely to be chosen. (Do you see why not? Does everyone have a telephone, or exactly one telephone?)

Sources of Potential Bias in Sample Surveys

A variety of problems can cause responses from a sample to favor some parts of the population over others. Then, results from the sample are not representative of the population and are said to exhibit **bias.**

Sampling bias   Bias may result from the sampling method. The main way this occurs is if the sample is not a random sample from the population. Another way it can occur is due to **undercoverage**—having a sampling frame that lacks representation from parts of the population. A phone survey using landlines will not reach homeless people, prison inmates, or people who don't have landline phones. If its sampling frame consists of the names in a phone directory, it will not reach those who are not listed, such as students. Responses by those who are not in the sampling frame might be quite different from those who are in the frame. Bias resulting from the sampling method, such as nonrandom sampling or undercoverage, is called **sampling bias.** Trying to avoid this bias, polling agencies are spending considerable efforts to reach those not sufficiently represented by the available sampling frame, but also use statistical methods (so called sample weights) to adjust results.

Nonresponse bias   A second type of bias occurs when some sampled subjects cannot be reached or refuse to participate. This is called **nonresponse bias.** The subjects who are willing to participate may be different from the overall sample in some systematic way, perhaps having strong emotional convictions about the issues being surveyed. Even those who do participate may not respond to some

Did You Know?

Besides Gallup, there are other polling groups that conduct national surveys, such as the Pew Research Center (www .pewresearch.org). TV stations and newspapers commonly use such polling organizations to conduct polls. ◀

In Words

There is **bias** if the way in which the study was designed or the data were gathered made certain outcomes occur more or less often in the sample than they do in the population. For example, consider the population of adults in your home town. The results of an opinion survey asking about raising the sales tax to support public schools may be biased in the direction of raising taxes if you sample only educators or biased in the direction of lowering taxes if you sample only business owners. Alternatively, the results could be biased toward raising taxes if a higher proportion of educators responded than business owners.

questions, resulting in nonresponse bias due to **missing data.** All major surveys suffer from some nonresponse bias. The General Social Survey has a nonresponse rate of about 20–30%. The nonresponse rate is much higher for many telephone surveys. By contrast, government-conducted surveys often have lower nonresponse rates. The Current Population Survey has a nonresponse rate of only about 7%. To reduce nonresponse bias, investigators try to make follow-up contact with the subjects who do not return questionnaires.

Results have dubious worth when there is substantial nonresponse. For instance, in her best-selling and controversial book *Women and Love* (1987), author and feminist Shere Hite presented results of a survey of adult women in the United States. One of her conclusions was that 70% of women who had been married at least five years have extramarital affairs. She based this conclusion on responses to questionnaires returned from a sample of 4,500 women. This sounds impressively large. However, the questionnaire was mailed to about 100,000 women. We cannot know whether this sample of 4.5% of the women who responded is representative of the 100,000 who received the questionnaire, much less the entire population of adult American women. In fact, Hite was criticized for her research methodology of using a nonrandom sample and the large nonresponse rate.

Response bias   A third type of potential bias is in the actual responses made. This is called **response bias.** An interviewer might ask the questions in a leading way, such that subjects are more likely to respond a certain way. Or, subjects may lie because they think their true response is socially unacceptable, or they may give the response that they think the interviewer prefers.

If you design an interview or questionnaire, you should strive to construct questions that are clear and understandable. *Avoid questions that are confusing, long, or leading*. The wording of a question can greatly affect the responses. For example, a Roper poll was designed to determine the percentage of Americans who express some doubt that the Holocaust occurred in World War II. In response to the question, "Does it seem possible or does it seem impossible to you that the Nazi extermination of the Jews *never* happened?" 22% said it was possible the Holocaust never happened. The Roper organization later admitted that the question was worded in a confusing manner. When it asked, "Does it seem possible to you that the Nazi extermination of the Jews never happened, or do you feel certain that it happened?" only 1% said it was possible it never happened.[4]

Even the order in which questions are asked can dramatically influence results. One study[5] asked, during the Cold War, "Do you think the U.S. should let Russian newspaper reporters come here and send back whatever they want?" and "Do you think Russia should let American newspaper reporters come in and send back whatever they want?" For the first question, the percentage of yes responses was 36% when it was asked first and 73% when it was asked second.

In Practice Be Alert for Potential Bias

With any sample survey, carefully scrutinize the results. Look for information about how the sample was selected, how large the sample size was, the nonresponse rate, how the questions were worded, and who sponsored the study. The less you know about these details, the less you should trust the results.

SUMMARY: Types of Bias in Sample Surveys

- **Sampling bias** occurs from using nonrandom samples or having undercoverage.
- **Nonresponse bias** occurs when some sampled subjects cannot be reached or refuse to participate or fail to answer some questions.
- **Response bias** occurs when the subject gives an incorrect response (perhaps lying) or the way the interviewer asks the questions (or wording of a question in print) is confusing or misleading.

[4]*Newsweek*, July 25, 1994.
[5]Described in Crossen (1994).

Poor Ways to Sample

How the sample is obtained can also result in bias. Two sampling methods that may be necessary but are not ideal are a convenience sample and a volunteer sample.

Convenience samples   Have you ever been stopped on the street or at a shopping mall to participate in a survey? Such a survey is likely not a random sample but rather a **convenience sample.** It is easy for the interviewer to obtain data relatively cheaply. But the sample may poorly represent the population. Biases may result because of the time and location of the interview and the judgment of the interviewer about whom to interview. For example, working people might be underrepresented if the interviews are conducted on workdays between 9 A.M. and 5 P.M. Poor people may be underrepresented if the interviewer conducts interviews at an upscale shopping mall.

Volunteer samples   Have you ever answered a survey you've seen posted on the Internet, such as at the home page for a news organization? A sample of this type, called a **volunteer sample,** is the most common type of convenience sample. As the name implies, subjects *volunteer* to be in the sample. One segment of the population may be more likely to volunteer than other segments because they have stronger opinions about the issue or are more likely to visit that Internet site. This results in sampling bias. For instance, a survey by the Pew Research Center (January 6, 2003) estimated that 46% of Republicans said they like to register their opinions in online surveys, compared with only 28% of Democrats. (Why? One possible lurking variable is time spent on the Internet. Perhaps Republicans spend more time on the Internet than Democrats do.) Thus, results of online surveys may be more weighted in the direction of Republicans' beliefs than the general population.

Convenience samples are not ideal. Sometimes, however, they are necessary, both in observational studies and in experiments. This is often true in medical studies. Suppose we want to investigate how well a new drug performs compared to a standard drug for subjects who suffer from high blood pressure. We won't find a sampling frame of all who suffer from high blood pressure and take a simple random sample of them. We may, however, be able to sample such subjects at medical centers or by using volunteers. Even then, randomization should be used wherever possible. For the study patients, we can randomly select who is given the new drug and who is given the standard one.

Some samples are poor not only because of their convenience but also because they use a sampling frame that does not reflect the population. An example of this was a poll in 1936 to predict the result of a presidential election.

Example 6

A Biased Sample ◀   ## The *Literary Digest* Poll

Picture the Scenario

The *Literary Digest* magazine conducted a poll to predict the result of the 1936 presidential election between Franklin Roosevelt (Democrat and incumbent) and Alf Landon (Republican). At the time, the magazine's polls were famous because they had correctly predicted three successive elections. In 1936, *Literary Digest* mailed questionnaires to 10 million people and asked how they planned to vote. The sampling frame was constructed from telephone directories, country club memberships, and automobile registrations. Approximately 2.3 million people returned the questionnaire. The *Digest* predicted that Landon would win, getting 57% of the vote. Instead, Landon actually got only 36%, and Roosevelt won in a landslide.

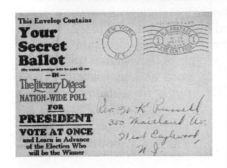

Questions to Explore

a. What was the population?

b. How could the *Literary Digest* poll make such a large error, especially with such a huge sample size? What type of bias occurred in this poll?

Think It Through

a. The population was all registered voters in the United States in 1936.

b. This survey had two severe problems:

- Sampling bias due to undercoverage of the sampling frame and a nonrandom sample: In 1936, the United States was in the Great Depression. Those who had cars and country club memberships and thus received questionnaires tended to be wealthy. The wealthy tended to be primarily Republican, the political party of Landon. Many potential voters were not on the lists used for the sampling frame. There was also no guarantee that a subject in the sampling frame was a registered voter.

- Nonresponse bias: Of the 10 million people who received questionnaires, 7.7 million did not respond. As might be expected, those individuals who were unhappy with the incumbent (Roosevelt) were more likely to respond.

Insight

For this same election, a pollster who was getting his new polling agency off the ground surveyed 50,000 people and predicted that Roosevelt would win. Who was this pollster? George Gallup. The Gallup organization is still with us today. However, the *Literary Digest* went out of business soon after the 1936 election.[6]

▶ *Try Exercise 4.24*

A Large Sample Size Does Not Guarantee an Unbiased Sample

Many people think that as long as the sample size is large, it doesn't matter how the sample was selected. This is incorrect, as illustrated by the *Literary Digest* poll. A sample size of 2.3 million did not prevent poor results. The sample was not representative of the population, and the sample percentage of 57% who said they would vote for Landon was far from the actual population percentage of 36% who voted for him. As another example, consider trying to estimate the average grade point average (GPA) on your campus. If you select 10 students from the library, you can produce an estimate that is biased toward higher GPAs (assuming those students who go to the library are studying more than those who don't). If you, instead, gather a larger sample of 30 students from the library, you still have an estimate that is biased toward higher GPAs. The larger sample size did not fix the problem of sampling in the library. Many Internet surveys have thousands of respondents, but a volunteer sample of thousands is not as good as a random sample, even if that random sample is much smaller. *We're almost always better off with a simple random sample of 100 people than with a volunteer sample of thousands of people.*

---

[6]Bryson, M. C. (1976), *American Statistician*, vol. 30, pp. 184–185.

> **SUMMARY: Key Parts of a Sample Survey**
>
> - Identify the **population** of all the subjects of interest.
> - Define a **sampling frame,** which attempts to list all the subjects in the population.
> - Use a **random sampling design,** implemented using random numbers, to select n subjects from the sampling frame.
> - Be cautious about **sampling bias** due to nonrandom samples (such as volunteer samples) and sample undercoverage, **response bias** from subjects not giving their true response or from poorly worded questions, and **nonresponse bias** from refusal of subjects to participate.

In Section 4.1 we learned that *experimental* studies are preferable to *nonexperimental* studies but are not always possible. Some types of nonexperimental studies have fewer potential pitfalls than others. For a sample survey with random sampling, we can make inferences about the population of interest. By contrast, with a study using a convenience sample, results apply only to those subjects actually observed. For this reason, some researchers use the term *observational study* to refer only to studies that use available subjects (such as a convenience sample) and not to sample surveys that randomly select their sample.

4.2 Practicing the Basics

4.15 Choosing officers A campus club consists of five officers: president (P), vice president (V), secretary (S), treasurer (T), and activity coordinator (A). The club can select two officers to travel to New Orleans for a conference; for fairness, they decide to make the selection at random. In essence, they are choosing a simple random sample of size $n = 2$.
  a. What are the possible samples of two officers?
  b. What is the chance that a particular sample of size 2 will be drawn?
  c. What is the chance that the activity coordinator will be chosen?

4.16 Simple random sample of tickets In Example 4, the club president randomly draws two tickets out of a container holding 60 tickets. Replicate this process by using the *Random Numbers* app (or some other statistical software or the website random.org) to select two numbers at random (and without replacement) from the numbers 1 through 60. (See Figure 4.1.)

4.17 Random sample of classmates Suppose 74 students are present in a statistics class. Use the *Random Numbers* app (or other software or the website random.org) to show how the teacher can select five students at random. (For instance, to check if they have completed the assigned homework.)

4.18 Sampling from a directory A local telephone directory has 50,000 names, 100 per page for 500 pages. Explain how you can find and use random numbers (e.g., with the *Random Numbers* app) to select 10 names for a simple random sample from the telephone directory.

4.19 Bias due to perceived race A political scientist at the University of Chicago studied the effect of the race of the interviewer.[7] Following a phone interview, respondents were asked whether they thought the interviewer was Black or White (all were actually Black). Perceiving a White interviewer resulted in more conservative opinions. For example, 14% agreed that "American society is fair to everyone" when they thought the interviewer was Black, but 31% agreed to this statement when posed by an interviewer that the respondent thought was White. Which type of bias does this illustrate: Sampling bias, nonresponse bias, or response bias? Explain.

4.20 Confederates Some southern states in the United States have wrestled with the issue of a state flag that is sensitive to African Americans and not divisive. Suppose a survey asks, "Do you oppose the present state flag that contains the Confederate symbol, a symbol of past slavery in the South and a flag supported by extremist groups?"
  a. Explain why this is an example of a leading question.
  b. Explain why a better way to ask this question would be, "Do you favor or oppose the current state flag containing the Confederate symbol?"

4.21 Instructor ratings The website www.ratemyprofessors .com provides students an opportunity to view ratings for instructors at their universities. A group of students planning to register for a statistics course in the upcoming semester are trying to identify the instructors who receive the

---

[7]Study by Lynn Sanders, as reported by the *Washington Post*, June 26, 1995.

highest ratings on the site. One student decides to register for Professor Smith's course because she has the best ratings of all statistics instructors. Another student comments:

a. The website ratings are unreliable because the ratings are from students who voluntarily visit the site to rate their instructors.

b. To obtain reliable information about Professor Smith, they would need to take a simple random sample (e.g., of size 20) of the 78 ratings left by students on the site and compile new overall ratings based on those in the random sample.

Which, if either, of the student's comments are valid?

4.22 Job trends The 2013–2014 Recruiting Trends report, produced each year by Michigan State University, reports that hiring over the past year of people with a bachelor's degree increased 7%, for people with a PhD increased 26%, and for people with an MBA decreased 25%. This was based on a voluntary poll of all employers who interacted with at least one of 300 career service centers on college campuses. The survey was answered by 6,500 employers.

a. What is the population for this survey?

b. We cannot calculate the nonresponse rate. Explain what other information is needed to calculate this rate.

c. Describe two potential sources of bias with this survey.

4.23 Gun control More than 75% of Americans answer yes when asked, "Do you favor cracking down against illegal gun sales?" but more than 75% say no when asked, "Would you favor a law giving police the power to decide who may own a firearm?"

a. Which statistic would someone who opposes gun control prefer to quote?

b. Explain what is wrong with the wording of each of these statements.

4.24 Violent video games and family closeness A recent study (*J Child Fam Stud*, doi:10.1007/s10826-014-9949-9) found that children in Singapore who had a closer relationship with their parents played fewer hours of video games per week and had fewer pathological symptoms of video-gaming.

a. What is the population of interest for this survey?

b. Describe why this is an observational study.

c. Identify a lurking variable in this study.

4.25 Fracking The journal *Energy Policy* (2014, 65: 57–67) presents a survey of opinions about fracking. Hydraulic fracturing, or fracking, is the process of drilling through rock and injecting a pressurized mixture of sand, water, and chemicals that fractures the rock and releases oil and gas. There has been much debate in the media about its impact on the environment, on land owners, and on the economy. The survey involved contacting a nationally representative sample of 1,960 adults in 2012. Of the 1,960 people contacted, 1,061 adults responded to the survey. The study reported that those more familiar with fracking, women, and those holding egalitarian worldviews were more likely to oppose fracking.

a. Describe the population of interest for this study.

b. Explain why a census is not practical for this study. What advantages does sampling offer?

c. Explain how nonresponse bias might be an issue in this study.

4.26 Teens buying alcohol over Internet In August 2006, a trade group for liquor retailers put out a press release with the headline, "Millions of Kids Buy Internet Alcohol, Landmark Survey Reveals." Further details revealed that in an Internet survey of 1,001 teenagers, 2.1% reported that they had bought alcohol online. In such a study, explain how there could be

a. Sampling bias. (*Hint:* Are all teenagers equally likely to respond to the survey?)

b. Nonresponse bias, if some teenagers refuse to participate.

c. Response bias, if some teenagers who participate are not truthful.

4.27 Cheating spouses and bias In a survey conducted by vouchercloud.net and reported in the *Palm Beach Post*, it was found that of 2,645 people who had participated in an extramarital affair, the average amount spent per month on the affair was $444. (*Source:* http://www.palmbeachpost.com/news/news/cheating-spouses-spend-444-month-affair-survey-fin/ngbgy/?__federated=1)

a. No information was given on how the surveyed individuals were selected. What type of bias could result if the 2,645 individuals were not randomly selected? How would this type of bias potentially affect the responses and the sample mean amount spent per month on the affair?

b. The concern was raised in the article that the individuals' answers could not be validated. What type of bias could result from untruthful answers? How would this type of bias affect the responses and the sample mean amount spent per month on the affair?

4.28 Online dating A story titled "Personals, Sex Sites Changing the Rules of Love" reported results of a study about online dating by the MSNBC network. The study used online responses of 15,246 people. Of those who responded, three fourths were men and about two thirds had at least a bachelor's degree. One reported finding was that "29% of men go online intending to cheat." Identify the potential bias in this study that results from

a. Sampling bias due to undercoverage.

b. Sampling bias due to the sampling design.

c. Response bias.

4.29 Identify the bias A newspaper designs a survey to estimate the proportion of the population willing to invest in the stock market. It takes a list of the 1,000 people who have subscribed to the paper the longest and sends each of them a questionnaire that asks, "Given the extremely volatile performance of the stock market as of late, are you willing to invest in stocks to save for retirement?" After analyzing result from the 50 people who reply, they report that only 10% of the local citizens are willing to invest in stocks for retirement. Identify the bias that results from the following:

a. Sampling bias due to undercoverage

b. Sampling bias due to the sampling design

c. Nonresponse bias

d. Response bias due to the way the question was asked

4.30 Types of bias Give an example of a survey that would suffer from

a. Sampling bias due to the sampling design

b. Sampling bias due to undercoverage

c. Response bias

d. Nonresponse bias

4.3 Good and Poor Ways to Experiment

Just as there are good and poor ways to gather a sample in an observational survey, there are good and poor ways to conduct an experiment. First, let's recall the definition of an experimental study from Section 4.1: We assign each subject to an experimental condition, called a **treatment.** We then observe the outcome on the response variable. The goal of the experiment is to investigate the association—how the treatment affects the response. An advantage of an experimental study over a nonexperimental study is that it provides stronger evidence for causation.

In an experiment, subjects are often referred to as **experimental units.** This name emphasizes that the objects measured need not be human beings. They could, for example, be schools, stores, mice, or computer chips.

The Elements of a Good Experiment

Let's consider another example to help us learn what makes a good experiment. It is common knowledge that smoking is a difficult habit to break. Studies have reported that regardless of what smokers do to quit, most relapse within a year. Some scientists have suggested that smokers are less likely to relapse if they take an antidepressant regularly after they quit. How can you design an experiment to study whether antidepressants help smokers to quit?

For this type of study, as in most medical experiments, it is not feasible to randomly sample the population (all smokers who would like to quit) because they cannot be readily identified. We need to use a convenience sample. For instance, a medical center might advertise to attract volunteers from the smokers who would like to quit.

Control comparison group   Suppose you have 400 volunteers who would like to quit smoking. You could ask them to quit, starting today. You could have each start taking an antidepressant and then a year from now check how many have relapsed. Perhaps 42% of them would relapse. But this is not enough information. You need to be able to compare this result to the percentage who would relapse if they were *not* taking the antidepressant.[8]

An experiment normally has a primary treatment of interest, such as receiving an antidepressant. But it should also have a second treatment for comparison to help you analyze the effectiveness of the primary treatment. So the volunteers should be split into two groups: One group receives the antidepressant, and the other group does not. You could give the second group a pill that looks like the antidepressant but that does not have any active ingredient—a placebo. This second group, using the placebo treatment, is called the **control group.** After subjects are assigned to the treatments and observed for a certain period of time, the relapse rates are compared. Because the only distinction between the two groups, at least by design, is taking the antidepressant, the difference between the relapse rate of two groups can be attributed to the treatment.

Why bother to give the placebo to the control group if the pill doesn't contain any active ingredient? This is partly so that the two treatments appear identical to the subjects. (As we'll discuss, subjects should not know which treatment they are receiving.) This is also because people who take a placebo tend to respond better than those who receive nothing, perhaps for psychological reasons. This is called the **placebo effect.** For instance, of the subjects not receiving the antidepressant, perhaps 75% would relapse within a year, but if they received a placebo pill perhaps 55% of them would relapse. If the relapse rate was 42% for subjects who received antidepressants, then in comparing relapse rates for the antidepressant

---

[8]Chapter 12 explains another reason a control group is needed. The regression effect implies that, over time, poor subjects tend to improve and good subjects tend to get worse, in relative terms.

and control groups, it makes a big difference how you define the control group. Using these numbers, you would say the reduction in the relapse rate was 33 percentage points (75% − 42%) when comparing it to nothing, but 13 percentage points (55% − 42%) when compared to the placebo group.

In some experiments, *a control group may receive an existing treatment rather than a placebo.* For instance, a smoking cessation study might analyze whether an antidepressant works better than a nicotine patch in helping smokers to quit. It may be unethical not to provide the standard of care, in this case a nicotine patch, if it has already been shown in previous studies to be more effective than a placebo. Or the experiment could compare all three treatments: antidepressant, nicotine patch, and a placebo.

Randomization   In the smoking cessation experiment, how should the 400 study subjects be assigned to the treatment groups? Should you personally decide which treatment each subject receives? This could result in bias. If you are conducting the study to show that the antidepressant is effective, you might consciously or subconsciously place smokers you believe will be more likely to succeed into the group that receives the antidepressant.

It is better to use **randomization** to assign the subjects: Randomly assign 200 of the 400 subjects to receive the antidepressant and the other 200 subjects to form the control group. Randomization helps to prevent bias from one treatment group tending to be different from the other in some way, such as having better health or being younger. In using randomization, we attempt to *balance the treatment groups* by making them similar with respect to their distribution on potential lurking variables. This enables us to attribute any difference in their relapse rates to the treatments they are receiving, not to lurking variables or to researcher bias.

You might think you can do better than randomization by using your own judgment to assign subjects to the treatment groups. For instance, when you identify a potential lurking variable, you could try to balance the groups according to its values. If age is that variable, every time you put someone of a particular age in one treatment group, you could put someone of the same age in the other treatment group. There are two problems with this: (1) *many* variables are likely to be important, and it is difficult to balance groups on *all* of them at once, and (2) you may not have thought of other relevant lurking variables. Even if you can balance the groups on the variables you identified, the groups could be unbalanced on these other variables, causing the overall results to be biased in favor of one treatment.

You can feel more confident about the worthiness of new research findings if they come from a randomized experiment with a control group rather than from an experiment without a control group, from an experiment that did not use randomization to assign subjects to the treatments, or from an observational study. An analysis[9] of published medical studies about treatments for heart attacks indicated that the new therapy provided improved treatment 58% of the time in studies without randomization and control groups but only 9% of the time in studies having randomization and control groups. This suggests that studies conducted without randomization or without other ways to reduce bias may produce results that tend to be overly optimistic.

SUMMARY: The Role of Randomization in Experiments

Use randomization for assigning subjects to the treatments

- To eliminate bias that may result if you (the researchers) assign the subjects
- To balance the groups on variables that you know affect the response
- To balance the groups on lurking variables that may be unknown to you

---

[9]See Crossen (1994), p. 168.

Blinding the study   It is important that the treatment groups be treated as equally as possible. Ideally, the subjects are **blind** to the treatment to which they are assigned. In the smoking cessation study, the subjects should not know whether they are taking the antidepressant or a placebo. Whoever has contact with the subjects during the experiment, including the data collectors who record the subjects' response outcomes, should also be blind to the treatment information. Otherwise they could intentionally or unintentionally provide extra support to one group or make different decisions for subjects, depending on which treatment they received, including whether they have relapsed. (Does just one cigarette count? What about two? etc.) When neither the subject nor those having contact with the subject know the treatment assignment, the study is called **double-blind.** That's ideal.

Example 7

Study Design ◀

Antidepressants for Quitting Smoking

Picture the Scenario

To investigate whether antidepressants help people quit smoking, one study[10] used 429 men and women who were 18 or older and had smoked 15 cigarettes or more per day for the previous year. The subjects were highly motivated to quit and in good health. They were assigned to one of two groups: One group took 300 mg daily of an antidepressant that has the brand name bupropion. The other group did not take an antidepressant. At the end of a year, the study observed whether each subject had successfully abstained from smoking or had relapsed.

Questions to Explore

a. Identify the response and explanatory variables, the treatments, and the experimental units.

b. How should the researchers assign the subjects to the two treatment groups?

c. Without knowing more about this study, what would you identify as a potential problem with the study design?

Think It Through

a. This experiment has

Response variable: Whether the subject abstains from smoking for one year (yes or no)
Explanatory variable: Whether the subject received bupropion (yes or no)
Treatments: bupropion, no bupropion
Experimental units: The 429 volunteers who are the study subjects

b. The researchers should randomize to assign subjects to the two treatments. They could use random numbers to randomly assign half (215) of the subjects to form the group that uses bupropion and 214 subjects to the group that does not receive bupropion (the control group). Using the *Random Numbers* app, the procedure would be as follows:

■ Number the study subjects from 1 to 429.

■ In the *Random Numbers* app, keep the minimum at 1, set the maximum to 429 and the number of random numbers to generate to 215, select Sampling Without Replacement, and press Generate.

---

[10]*Annals of Internal Medicine* 2001; 135: 423–433.

■ The 215 random numbers displayed by the app determine the 215 subjects who will receive bupropion. (For instance, if one of the numbers is 392, then the subject numbered 392 is put in the bupropion group.) The remaining 214 of the 429 subjects will form the control group.

c. The description of the experiment in Picture the Scenario did not say whether the subjects who did *not* receive bupropion were given a placebo or whether the study was blinded. If not, these would be potential sources of bias. In addition, the definition of what it means to relapse or abstain from smoking needs to be clearly defined.

Insight

In the actual reported study, the subjects were randomized to receive bupropion or a placebo for 45 weeks. The study *was* double-blinded. This experimental study was well designed. The study results showed that at the end of one year, 55% of the subjects receiving bupropion were not smoking, compared with 42% in the placebo group. After 18 months, 48% of the bupropion subjects were not smoking compared to 38% for the placebo subjects. However, after two years, the percentage of nonsmokers was similar for the two groups, 42% versus 40%.

▶ *Try Exercise 4.32*

In Practice The Randomized Experiment in Medicine

In medicine, the randomized experiment (clinical trial) has become the gold standard for evaluating new medical treatments. The Cochrane Collaboration (www.cochrane .org) is an organization devoted to synthesizing evidence from medical studies all over the world. According to this organization, there have been hundreds of thousands of randomized experiments comparing medical treatments. In most countries, a company cannot get a new drug approved for sale unless it has been tested in a randomized experiment.
Source: Background information from S. Senn (2003), *Dicing with Death.* Cambridge University Press, p. 68.

Generalizing Results to Broader Populations

We've seen that random samples are preferable to convenience samples, yet convenience samples are more feasible than many experiments. When an experiment uses a convenience sample, be cautious about the extent to which results generalize to a larger population. Look carefully at the characteristics of the sample. Do they seem representative of the overall population? If not, the results have dubious worth.

Many medical studies use volunteers at *several* medical centers to try to obtain a broad cross section of subjects. But some studies mistakenly try to generalize to a broader population than the one from which the sample was taken. A psychologist may conduct an experiment using a sample of students from an introductory psychology course. For the results to be of wider interest, however, the psychologist might claim that the conclusions generalize to *all* college students, to all young adults, or even to all adults. Such generalizations may be wrong since the sample may differ from those populations in fundamental ways such as in average socioeconomic status, race, gender, or attitudes.

SUMMARY: Key Parts of a Good Experiment

■ A good experiment has a **control comparison group**, **randomization** in assigning experimental units to treatments, and **blinding**.

■ The **experimental units** are the subjects—the people, animals, or other objects to which the treatments are applied.

■ The **treatments** are the experimental conditions imposed on the experimental units. One of these may be a **control** (for instance, either a placebo or an existing treatment) that provides a basis for determining whether a particular treatment is effective. The treatments correspond to values of an explanatory variable.

■ Randomly assign the experimental units to the treatments. This tends to balance the comparison groups with respect to lurking variables.

■ Replication of studies increases confidence in the conclusions.

Carefully assess the scope of conclusions in research articles, mass media, and advertisements. Evaluate critically the basis for the conclusions by noting the experimental design or the sampling design upon which the conclusions are based.

4.3 Practicing the Basics

4.31 Smoking affects lung cancer? You would like to investigate whether smokers are more likely than nonsmokers to get lung cancer. From the students in your class, you pick half at random to smoke a pack of cigarettes each day and half not ever to smoke. Fifty years from now, you will analyze whether more smokers than nonsmokers got lung cancer.

   a. Is this an experiment or an observational study? Why?

   b. Summarize at least three practical difficulties with this planned study.

4.32 Never leave home without duct tape There have been anecdotal reports of the ability of duct tape to remove warts. In an experiment conducted at the Madigan Army Medical Center in the state of Washington (*Archives of Pediatric and Adolescent Medicine* 2002; 156: 971–974), 51 patients between the ages of 3 and 22 were randomly assigned to receive either duct-tape therapy (covering the wart with a piece of duct tape) or cryotherapy (freezing a wart by applying a quick, narrow blast of liquid nitrogen). After two months, the percentage successfully treated was 85% in the duct tape group and 60% in the cryotherapy group.

   a. Identify the response variable, the explanatory variable, the experimental units, and the treatments.

   b. Describe the steps of how you could randomize in assigning the 51 patients to the treatment groups.

4.33 More duct tape In a follow-up study, 103 patients in the Netherlands having warts were randomly assigned to use duct tape or a placebo, which was a ring covered by tape so that the wart itself was kept clear (*Arch. Pediat. Adoles. Med.* 2006; 160: 1121–1125).

   a. Identify the response variable, the explanatory variable, the experimental units, and the treatments.

   b. After six weeks, the warts had disappeared for 16% of the duct tape group and 6% of the placebo group. Find the difference of the two proportions and interpret it in the context of this study. (Section 3.1 in Chapter 3 introduced the difference of proportions.)

4.34 Vitamin B A *New York Times* article (March 13, 2006) described two studies in which subjects who had recently had a heart attack were randomly assigned to one of four treatments: placebo and three different doses of vitamin B. In each study, after years of study, the differences among the proportions having a heart attack were reported. Identify the (a) response variable, (b) explanatory variable, (c) experimental units, and (d) the treatments in this study.

4.35 Facebook study During the one-week period of January 11–18, 2012, Facebook conducted an experiment to research whether emotional states can be transferred to others via emotional contagion. Facebook users were randomly selected to be part of two parallel studies in which Facebook manipulated the exposure to emotional expressions in the user's news feed. Two parallel experiments were conducted. In one study, it reduced the positive emotional content; in the other study, the negative emotional content was reduced. For each study, there was a control group (where the users' news feed was not manipulated), and an experimental group (where the users' news feed was manipulated—either positively or negatively). Two variables were measured in each study after the manipulation by Facebook: the percentage of all words produced by a person that was positive and the percentage of all words produced by a person that was negative. There were 689,003 Facebook users in the study. (Source: *PNAS*, June 17, 2014, vol. 111, no. 24, www.pnas.org/cgi/doi/10.1073/pnas.1320040111)

   a. Explain why this study is an experiment.

   b. Identify the experimental units.

   c. For the study in which exposure to friends' positive emotional content was reduced, identify the explanatory variable and the two response variables.

   d. The Facebook users randomly selected for the study were unaware they were part of this experiment. Provide a reason Facebook elected not to inform the selected users that they were part of an experiment. Provide a reason the users selected for the study may have felt not informing them about the study was unethical.

4.36 Science faculty selection of grad students In an experimental study, science faculty ($n = 127$) from research universities rated application materials of a student. The 127 application folders were identical except that some were labeled male and some were labeled female. A folder was randomly assigned to each faculty member. The application was for a laboratory manager position. The science faculty rated their application folder on the competency of the applicant, how employable the applicant was, and the recommended starting salary of the applicant. It was found that the faculty rated the male application folders higher on competency, being employable, and starting salary. (Source: www.pnas.org/cgi/doi/10.1073/pnas.1211286109)

   a. What is a reasonable statistical question for this experiment?

   b. Identify the explanatory variable, treatments, response variables (there are more than one), and experimental units.

   c. Explain why it was important to assign the folders randomly.

4.37 **Pain reduction medication** Consider an experiment being designed to study the effectiveness of an experimental pain reduction medication. The plan includes recruiting 100 individuals suffering from moderate to severe pain to participate. One half of the group will be assigned to take the actual experimental drug, and the other half will be assigned a placebo. The study will be blind in the sense that the individuals will not know which treatment they are receiving. At the end of the study, individuals will be asked to record, using a standardized scale, how much pain relief they experienced. Why is it important to use a placebo in such a study?

4.38 **Pain reduction medication, continued** Consider the same setting as that of Exercise 4.37. Of the 100 participants, 45 are male and 55 are female. During the design of the study, one member of the research team suggests that all males be given the active drug and all females be given the placebo. Another member of the team wants to randomly assign each of the total group of 100 participants to one of the two treatments.

a. Which researcher's plan is the best experimental design for measuring the effectiveness of the medication if the results of the experiment are to be generalized to the entire population, which consists of both females and males?

b. Does the fact that the participants of the study were recruited rather than selected at random prohibit generalization of the results?

4.39 **Pain reduction medication, yet again** Revisit the setting of Exercise 4.37. Suppose that in addition to the participants being blinded, the researchers responsible for recording the results of the study are also blinded. Why does it matter whether the researchers know which participants receive which treatment?

4.40 **Colds and vitamin C** For some time there has been debate about whether regular large doses of vitamin C reduce the chance of getting a common cold.

a. Explain how you could design an experiment to test this. Describe all parts of the experiment, including (i) what the treatments are, (ii) how you assign subjects to the treatments, and (iii) how you could make the study double-blind.

b. An observational study indicates that people who take vitamin C regularly get fewer colds, on the average. Explain why these results could be misleading.

4.41 **Reducing high blood pressure** A pharmaceutical company has developed a new drug for treating high blood pressure. The company would like to compare the drug's effects to those of the most popular drug currently on the market. Two hundred volunteers with a history of high blood pressure and who are currently not on medication are recruited to participate in a study.

a. Explain how the researchers could conduct a randomized experiment. Indicate the experimental units, the response and explanatory variables, and the treatments.

b. Explain what would have to be done to make this study double-blind.

4.4 Other Ways to Conduct Experimental and Nonexperimental Studies

In this chapter, we've learned the basics of ways to conduct nonexperimental and experimental studies. This final section shows ways these methods are often extended in practice so they are even more powerful. We'll first learn about alternatives to simple random sampling in sample surveys and then about types of observational studies that enable us to study questions for which experiments with humans are not feasible. Finally, we'll learn how to study the effects of two or more explanatory variables with a single experiment.

Sample Surveys: Other Random Sampling Designs Useful in Practice

Simple random sampling gives every possible sample the same chance of selection. In practice, more complex random sampling designs are often easier to implement or are more efficient, requiring a smaller sampling size for the same precision. Sometimes they are even preferable to simple random sampling.

Cluster random sampling To use simple random sampling, we need a sampling frame—the list of all, or nearly all, subjects in the population. In some cases, this information is not available. It may be easier to identify **clusters** of subjects. A study of residents of a country can identify counties or census tracts. A study of students can identify schools. A study of the elderly living in institutions can identify nursing homes. We can obtain a sample by randomly selecting the clusters and observing each subject in the clusters chosen.

For instance, suppose you would like to sample about 1% of the families in your city. You could use city blocks as clusters. Using a map to label and number city blocks, you could select a simple random sample of 1% of the blocks and then select every family on each of those blocks for your observations.

Cluster Random Sample

Divide the population into a large number of **clusters,** such as city blocks. Select a simple random sample of the clusters. Use the subjects in those clusters as the sample. This is a **cluster random sample.**

For personal interviews, when the subjects within a cluster are close geographically, cluster sampling is less expensive per observation than simple random sampling. By interviewing every family in a particular city block, you can obtain many observations quickly and with little travel.

SUMMARY: Advantages and Disadvantages of a Cluster Random Sample

Cluster random sampling is a preferable sampling design if

- A reliable sampling frame is not available, or
- The cost of selecting a simple random sample is excessive.

The disadvantages are:

- We usually require a larger sample size with cluster sampling for the same level of precision.
- Selecting a small number of clusters might result in a sample that is more homogeneous than the population.

Stratified random sampling   Suppose we are interested in estimating the mean number of hours a week that students in your school work on outside employment. The plan is to use the student directory to take a simple random sample of $n = 40$ students and analyze how the mean compares for freshmen, sophomores, juniors, and seniors. Merely by chance, you may get only a few observations from one of the classes, making it hard to accurately estimate the mean for that class. If the student directory also identifies students by their class, you could amend the sampling scheme to take a simple random sample of 10 students from each class, still having an overall $n = 40$. The four classes are called **strata** of the population. This type of sample is called a **stratified random sample.**

Stratified Random Sample

A **stratified random sample** divides the population into separate groups, called **strata**, based on some attribute or characteristic about the subjects, and then selects a simple random sample from each stratum.

Stratified sampling is particularly useful when the typical values of the response variable differ substantially across the strata. A limitation of stratification is that you must have a sampling frame and know the stratum into which each subject in the sampling frame belongs. You might want to stratify students in your school by whether the student has a job, to make sure you get enough students who work and who don't work. However, this information may not be available for each student.

> **SUMMARY: Advantages and Disadvantages of a Stratified Random Sample**
>
> Stratified random sampling has the
>
> - Advantage that you can include in your sample enough subjects in each group (stratum) you want to evaluate.
> - Disadvantage that you must have a sampling frame and know the stratum into which each subject belongs.

What's the difference between a stratified sample and a cluster sample? A stratified sample *uses every stratum.* By contrast, a cluster sample *uses a sample of the clusters* rather than all of them. Figure 4.2 illustrates the distinction among sampling subjects (simple random sample), sampling clusters of subjects (cluster random sample), and sampling subjects from within strata (stratified random sample).

Simple Random Sampling

12 observations chosen randomly

Stratified Sampling

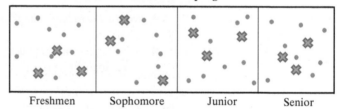

3 observations chosen from each of 4 strata

Cluster Sampling

3 clusters chosen randomly

Multistage Sampling

1 cluster chosen randomly from within each stratum

▲ **Figure 4.2** Selecting 12 observations through (i) random sampling, (ii) stratified sampling, (iii) cluster sampling, and (iv) multistage sampling. The x's represent observations selected, the dots observations not selected. **Question** What's the difference between clustering and stratifying?

Table 4.1 Summary of Random Sampling Methods

Method	Description	Advantages
Simple random sample	Each possible sample is equally likely	Sample tends to be a good reflection of the population
Cluster random sample	Identify clusters of subjects, take simple random sample of the clusters	Do not need a sampling frame of subjects, less expensive to implement
Stratified random sample	Divide population into groups (strata), take simple random sample from each stratum	Ensures enough subjects in each group that you want to compare

In addition, a cluster sample uses predetermined groups to create a single sampling frame, whereas a stratified sample creates multiple sampling frames by strata based on a subject characteristic. In the previous examples, city blocks already exist and can be listed as the sampling frame. The sampling frames for class year have to be defined separately before random selection is performed.

Comparison of different random sampling methods   A good sampling design ensures that each subject in a population has an opportunity to be selected. The design should incorporate randomness. Table 4.1 summarizes the random sampling methods we've presented.

In practice, sampling designs often have two or more stages. When carrying out a large survey for predicting national elections, the Gallup organization often (1) identifies election districts as clusters and takes a simple random sample of them, and (2) takes a simple random sample of households within each selected election district rather than sampling every household in a district, which might be infeasible.

Marketing companies also commonly use *two-stage cluster sampling*, first randomly selecting test market cities (the clusters) and then randomly selecting consumers within each test market city. Many major surveys, such as the General Social Survey, Gallup polls, and the Current Population Survey, incorporate both stratification and clustering at various stages, called multistage sampling.

In future chapters, when we use the term *random sampling*, we'll mean *simple random sampling*. The formulas for most statistical methods assume simple random sampling. Similar formulas exist for other types of random sampling, but they are complex and beyond the scope of this text.

Retrospective and Prospective Observational Studies

We've seen that an experiment can investigate cause and effect better than an observational study. With an observational study, it's possible that an observed association may be due to some lurking variable. However, observational studies do have advantages. It's often not practical to conduct an experiment. For instance, with human subjects it's not ethical to design an experiment to study the long-term effect of cell phone use on getting cancer. Nevertheless, it is possible to design an observational study that controls for identified lurking variables.

Rather than taking a cross section of a population at some time, such as with a sample survey, some studies are *backward looking* (**retrospective**) or *forward looking* (**prospective**). Observational studies in medicine are often retrospective. How can we study whether there is an association between long-term cell phone use and brain cancer if we cannot perform an experiment? We can form a sample of subjects who have brain cancer and a similar sample of subjects who do not and then compare the past use of cell phones for the two groups. This approach was first applied to study smoking and lung cancer.

Example 8

Lung Cancer and Smoking

Picture the Scenario

In 1950 in London, England, medical statisticians Austin Bradford Hill and Richard Doll conducted one of the first studies linking smoking and lung cancer. In 20 hospitals, they matched 709 patients admitted with lung cancer in the preceding year with 709 noncancer patients at the same hospital of the same gender and within the same five-year grouping on age. All patients were queried about their smoking behavior. A smoker was defined as a person who had smoked at least one cigarette a day for at least a year. The study used a *retrospective* design to look into the past in measuring the patients' smoking behavior.

Table 4.2 shows the results. The 709 *cases* in the first column of the table were the patients with lung cancer. The 709 *controls* in the second column were the matched patients without lung cancer.

Table 4.2 Results of Retrospective Study of Smoking and Lung Cancer

The cases had lung cancer. The controls did not. The *retrospective* aspect refers to studying whether subjects had been smokers in the past.

Smoker	Lung Cancer	
	Yes (case)	No (control)
Yes	688	650
No	21	59
Total	**709**	**709**

Question to Explore

Compare the proportions of smokers for the lung cancer cases and the controls. Interpret.

Think It Through

For the lung cancer cases, the proportion who were smokers was $688/709 = 0.970$, or 97%. For the controls (not having lung cancer), the proportion who were smokers was $650/709 = 0.917$, or about 92%. The lung cancer cases were more likely than the controls to have been smokers.

Insight

An inferential analysis of these data (see Section 11.3 in Chapter 11) provides evidence for an association between smoking and lung cancer.

▶ *Try Exercise 4.46*

In Words

In Example 8, the response outcome of interest was having lung cancer. The cases had lung cancer, the controls did not have lung cancer, and they were compared on the explanatory variable—whether the subject had been a smoker (yes or no).

Case-control studies The type of retrospective study used in Example 8 to study smoking and lung cancer is called a **case-control study**.

Case-Control Study

A **case-control study** is a retrospective observational study in which subjects who have a response outcome of interest (the cases) and subjects who have the other response outcome (the controls) are compared on an explanatory variable.

This is a popular design for medical studies in which it is not practical or ethical to perform an experiment. We can't randomly assign subjects into a smoking group and a nonsmoking group—this would involve asking some subjects to start smoking. Since we can't use randomization to balance effects of potential lurking variables, usually the cases and controls are matched on such variables. In Example 8, cases and controls were matched on their age, gender, and hospital.

In a case-control study, the number of cases and the number of controls is fixed. The random part is observing the outcome for the explanatory variable. For instance, in Example 8, for the 709 patients of each type, we looked back in time to see whether they smoked. We found percentages for the categories of the explanatory variable (smoker, nonsmoker) given lung cancer status (cases or control). It is not meaningful to form a percentage for a category of the response variable. For example, we cannot estimate the population percentage of subjects who have lung cancer, for smokers or nonsmokers. By the study design, *half* the subjects had lung cancer. This does not mean that half the population had lung cancer.

Case-Control Studies ◄

Example 9

Cell Phone Use

Picture the Scenario

Studies 1 and 2 about cell phone use in Example 1 were both case-control studies. In Study 2, the cases were brain cancer patients. The controls were randomly sampled from general practitioner lists and were matched with the cases on age, sex, and place of residence. In Study 1, the cases had a type of eye cancer. In forming a sample of controls, Study 1 did not attempt to match subjects with the cases.

Question to Explore

Why might researchers decide to match cases and controls on characteristics such as age?

Think It Through

We've seen that one way to balance groups on potential lurking variables such as age is to randomize in assigning subjects to groups. However, these were observational studies, not experiments. So it was not possible for the researchers to use randomization to balance treatments on potential lurking variables. Matching is an attempt to achieve the balance that randomization provides.

When researchers fail to use relevant variables to match cases with controls, those variables could influence the results. They could mask the true relationship. The results could suggest an association when actually there is not one, or the reverse. Without matching, results are more susceptible to effects of lurking variables.

Insight

The lack of matching in Study 1 may be one reason that the results from the two studies differed, with Study 2 not finding an association and Study 1 finding one. For example, in Study 1 suppose the eye cancer patients tended to be older than the controls, and suppose older people tend to be heavier users of cell phones. Then, age could be responsible for the observed association between cell phone use and eye cancer.

▶ *Try Exercise 4.47*

Prospective studies A *retrospective* study, such as a case-control study, looks into the past. By contrast, a *prospective* study follows its subjects into the future.

◄ Prospective Studies

Example 10

Nurses' Health

Picture the Scenario

The Nurses' Health Study, conducted by researchers at Harvard University,[11] began in 1976 with 121,700 female nurses age 30 to 55 years. The purpose of the study was to explore relationships among diet, hormonal factors, smoking habits, and exercise habits, and the risk of coronary heart disease, pulmonary disease, and stroke. Since the initial survey in 1976, the nurses have filled out a questionnaire every two years.

Question to Explore

What does it mean for this observational study to be called *prospective*?

Think It Through

The retrospective smoking study in Example 8 looked to the past to learn whether its lung cancer subjects had been smokers. By contrast, at the start of the Nurses' Health Study, it was not known whether a particular nurse would eventually have an outcome such as lung cancer. The study followed each nurse into the future to see whether she developed that outcome and to analyze whether certain explanatory variables (such as smoking) were associated with it.

Insight

Over the years, several analyses have been conducted using data from the Nurses' Health Study. One finding (reported in *The New York Times*, February 11, 2003) was that nurses in this study who were highly overweight 18-year-olds were five times as likely as young women of normal weight to need hip replacement later in life.

▶ *Try Exercise 4.48*

SUMMARY: Types of Nonexperimental Studies

- A **retrospective** study looks into the past.
- A **prospective** study identifies a group (cohort) of people and observes them in the future. In research literature, prospective studies are often referred to as cohort studies.
- A **sample survey** takes a **cross section** of a population at the current time. Sample surveys are sometimes called **cross-sectional** studies.

Observational Studies and Causation

Can we ever *definitively* establish causation with an observational study? No, we cannot. For example, because the smoking and lung cancer study in Example 8 was observational, cigarette companies argued that a lurking variable could have caused this association. So why are doctors so confident in declaring that

---

[11]More information on this study can be found at www.nurseshealthstudy.org.

smoking causes lung cancer? For a combination of reasons: (1) Experiments conducted using animals have shown an association, (2) in many countries, over time, female smoking has increased relative to male smoking, and the incidence of lung cancer has increased in women compared to men. Other studies, both retrospective and prospective, have added more evidence. For example, when a prospective study begun in 1951 with 35,000 doctors ended in 2001, researchers[12] estimated that cigarettes took an average of 10 years off the lives of smokers who never quit. This study estimated that at least half the people who smoke from youth are eventually killed by their habit.

Most important, studies carried out on different populations of people have *consistently* concluded that smoking is associated with lung cancer, even after adjusting for all potentially confounding variables that researchers have suggested. As more studies are done that adjust for confounding variables, the chance that a lurking variable remains that can explain the association is reduced. As a consequence, although we cannot definitively conclude that smoking causes lung cancer, physicians will not hesitate to tell you that they believe it does.

Multifactor Experiments

Now let's learn about other ways of performing experiments. First, we'll learn how a single experiment can help us analyze the effects of two explanatory variables at once.

Categorical explanatory variables in an experiment are often referred to as **factors.** For example, consider the experiment described in Example 7 to study whether taking an antidepressant can help a smoker stop smoking. The factor measured whether a subject used the antidepressant bupropion (yes or no). Suppose the researchers also wanted to study a second factor, using a nicotine patch versus not using one. The experiment could then have four treatment groups that result from cross-classifying the two factors. See Figure 4.3. The four treatments are bupropion alone, nicotine patch alone, bupropion and nicotine patch, neither bupropion nor nicotine patch.

In Words

A **factor** is a categorical explanatory variable (such as whether the subject takes an antidepressant) having as categories the experimental conditions (the **treatments,** such as bupropion or no bupropion).

Nicotine Patch (Factor 1)

		Yes	No
Bupropion (Factor 2)	Yes	Treatment 1 Nicotine Patch Bupropion	Treatment 2 No Nicotine Patch Bupropion
	No	Treatment 3 Nicotine Patch Placebo	Treatment 4 No Nicotine Patch Placebo

▲ **Figure 4.3 An Experiment Can Use Two (or More) Factors at Once.** The treatments are the combinations of categories of the factors, as numbered in the boxes.

Why use both factors at once in an experiment? Why not do one experiment about bupropion and a separate experiment about the nicotine patch? The reason is that we can learn more from a two-factor experiment. For instance, the combination of using both a nicotine patch and bupropion may be more effective than using either method alone.

---

[12]See article by R. Doll et al., *British Med. J.*, June 26, 2004, p. 1519.

Multifactor Experiments ◄

Example 11

Antidepressants and/or Nicotine Patches

Picture the Scenario

Example 7 analyzed a study about whether bupropion helps a smoker quit cigarettes. Let's now also consider nicotine patches as another possible cessation aid.

Question to Explore

How can you design a single study to investigate the effects of nicotine patches and bupropion on whether a subject relapses into smoking?

Think It Through

You could use the two factors with four treatment groups shown in Figure 4.3. Figure 4.4 portrays the design of a randomized experiment, with placebo alternatives to bupropion and to the nicotine patch.

The study should be double-blind. After a fixed length of time, you compare the four treatments for the percentages who have relapsed.

Insight

In fact, a two-factor experiment *has* been conducted to study both these factors.[13] The most effective treatments were bupropion alone or in combination with a nicotine patch. We'll explore the results in

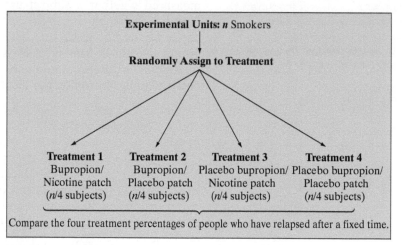

▲ **Figure 4.4** Diagram of a Randomized Experiment with Two Factors (Whether Use Bupropion and Whether Use a Nicotine Patch). **Question** A three-factor design could also incorporate whether a subject receives counseling to discourage smoking. What would such a diagram look like?

Exercise 4.72. If we included a third factor of whether the subject receives counseling, we would have three factors with $2 \times 2 \times 2 = 8$ treatments to compare.

► *Try Exercise 4.50*

Recall

This study is double-blind if both the subjects and the evaluator(s) of the subjects do not know whether the pill is active and whether the patch is active. ◄

---

[13]Jorenby, D. et al. (1999), *New England Journal of Medicine*, 340(9): 685–691.

Matched Pairs Designs

The experiments described in Examples 7 and 11 used **completely randomized designs:** The subjects were randomly assigned to one of the treatments. Sometimes we can use an alternative experimental design in which *each treatment is observed for each subject.* Medical experiments often do this to compare treatments for chronic conditions that do not have a permanent cure.

To illustrate, suppose a study plans to compare an oral drug and a placebo for treating migraine headaches. The subjects could take one treatment the first time they get a migraine headache and the other treatment the second time they get a migraine headache. The response is whether the subject's pain is relieved. The results for the first three subjects in the trial could look like this:

Subject	Drug	Placebo	
1	Relief	No relief	← first *matched pair*
2	Relief	Relief	
3	No relief	No relief	

Once the trial is finished, we would compare the proportion of subjects who experienced relief with the drug to the proportion (of the same subjects) that experienced relief with the placebo. The two observations for a particular subject are called a **matched pair** because they both come from the same person.

A matched-pairs design in which subjects cross over during the experiment from using one treatment to using another treatment is called a **crossover design.** Crossover design helps remove certain sources of potential bias. Using the same subjects for each treatment keeps potential lurking variables from affecting the results because those variables take the same values for each treatment. For instance, any difference observed between the drug and the placebo responses is not because subjects taking the drug had better overall health. Another example of a matched pair, crossover design is Study 3 discussed in Example 1.

An additional application of a matched-pairs design occurs in agricultural experiments that compare the crop yield for two fertilizer types. In each field, two plots are marked, one for each fertilizer. Two plots in the same field are likely to be more similar in soil quality and moisture than two plots from different fields. If we instead used a completely randomized design to assign entire fields to each fertilizer treatment, there's the possibility that by chance one fertilizer will be applied to fields that have better soil. This is especially true when the experiment can't use many fields.

Blocking in an Experiment

The matched-pairs design extends to the comparison of more than two treatments. The migraine headache crossover study could investigate relief for subjects who take a low dose of an oral drug, a high dose of that drug, and a placebo. The crop yield study could have several fertilizer types.

In experiments with matching, a set of matched experimental units is referred to as a **block.** A block design with random assignment of treatments to units within blocks is called a **randomized block** design. In the migraine headache study, each person is a block. In the crop yield study, each field is a block. A purpose of using blocks is to provide similar experimental units for the treatments, so they're on an equal footing in any subsequent comparisons.

To reduce possible bias, treatments are usually randomly assigned within a block. In the migraine headache study, the order in which the treatments are taken would be randomized. Bias could occur if all subjects received one treatment before another. An example of potential bias in a crossover study is a positive carry-over effect if the first drug taken has lingering effects that can help improve results for the second drug taken. Likewise, in a crop yield study, the fertilizers are randomly assigned to the plots in a field.

On the Shoulders of . . . Austin Bradford Hill (1897–1991) and Richard Doll (1912–2005)

How did statisticians become pioneers in examining the effects of smoking on lung cancer?

In the mid-20th century, Austin Bradford Hill was Britain's leading medical statistician. In 1946, to assess the effect of streptomycin in treating pulmonary tuberculosis, he designed what is now regarded as the first controlled randomized medical experiment. About that time, doctors noticed the alarming increase in the number of lung cancer cases. The cause was unknown but suspected to be atmospheric pollution, particularly coal smoke. In 1950, Bradford Hill and medical doctor and epidemiologist Richard Doll published results of the case-control study (Example 8) that identified smoking as a potentially

important culprit. They were also pioneers in developing a sound theoretical basis for the case-control method. They followed their initial study with other case-control studies and with a long-term prospective study that showed that smoking was not only the predominant risk factor for lung cancer but also correlated with other diseases.

At first, Bradford Hill was cautious about claiming that smoking causes lung cancer. As the evidence mounted from various studies, he accepted the causal link as being overwhelmingly the most likely explanation. An influential article written by Bradford Hill in 1965 proposed criteria that should be satisfied before you conclude that an association reflects a causal link. For his work, in 1961 Austin Bradford Hill was knighted by Queen Elizabeth. Richard Doll was knighted in 1971.

4.4   Practicing the Basics

4.42   Student loan debt   A researcher wants to compare student loan debt for students who attend four-year public universities with those who attend four-year private universities. She plans to take a random sample of 100 recent graduates of public universities and 100 recent graduates of private universities. Which type of random sampling is used in her study design?

4.43   Club officers again   In Exercise 4.15, two officers were to be selected to attend a conference in New Orleans. Three of the officers are female and two are male. It is decided to send one female and one male to the convention.

   a.   Labeling the officers as 1, 2, 3, 4, 5, where 4 and 5 are male, draw a stratified random sample using random numbers (e.g., with the Random Numbers app). Explain how you did this. (*Hint:* You can use the Random Numbers app, where you first generate one random number from the numbers 1 through 4 and then, after pressing *Reset*, one random number from the numbers 5 and 6.)

   b.   Explain why this sampling design is not a simple random sample.

   c.   If the activity coordinator is female, what are her chances of being chosen? If male?

4.44   Security awareness training   Of 400 employees at a company, 25% work in production, 40% work in sales and marketing, and 35% work in new product development. As part of a security awareness training program, the group overseeing implementation of the program will randomly choose a sample of 20 employees to begin the training; the percentages of workers from each department in the sample are to align with the percentages throughout the company.

   a.   What type of sampling could be used to achieve this goal?

   b.   Using this sampling method, determine a sample of 20 employees to be chosen. (*Hint:* Use the Random Numbers app to select 5 numbers from the numbers 1 through 100 representing the employees working in production.)

4.45   Teaching and learning model   A school district comprises 24 schools. The numbers of students in each of the schools are as follows:

   455 423 399 388 348 344 308 299 297 272 266 260

   252 244 222 209 175 161 151 148 128 109 101 98

The district wants to implement an experimental teaching and learning model for approximately 20% of the 6,057 students in the district. Administrators want to choose the 20% randomly, but they will not be able to use simple random sampling throughout the entire district because the new model can be implemented only at the school level, not just for a select group of students at a school. The schools not selected will continue to use the current teaching and learning model.

a. Explain how one could use cluster random sampling to achieve the goal of choosing approximately 20% of the students in the district for the experimental model.

APP **b.** Use cluster random sampling and the *Random Numbers* app (or some other software) to determine which schools will be randomly selected to use the new model. How many schools are in your sample? How many students are in your sample?

c. Repeat part b, drawing a new sample. Did you obtain the same number of schools?

d. Would it be possible for the school district to implement stratified random sampling? Explain.

4.46 **German mobile study** The contingency table shows
TRY results from the German study about whether there was an association between mobile phone use and eye cancer (*Source:* Stang, A., et al. (2001). "The possible role of radio frequency radiation in the development of uveal melanoma." Epidemiology 12(1): 7–12).

a. The study was retrospective. Explain what this means.

b. Explain what is meant by cases and controls in the headings of the table.

c. What proportion had used mobile phones, of those in the study who (i) had eye cancer and (ii) did not have eye cancer?

Eye Cancer and Use of Mobile Phones

Mobile Phones	Cases	Controls
Yes	16	46
No	102	429
Total	118	475

4.47 **Smoking and lung cancer** Refer to the smoking
TRY case-control study in Example 8. Since subjects were not matched according to *all* possible lurking variables, a cigarette company can argue that this study does not prove a causal link between smoking and lung cancer. Explain this logic, using diet as the lurking variable.

4.48 **Smoking and death** Example 1 in Chapter 3 described a
TRY survey of 1,314 women during 1972–1974, in which each woman was asked whether she was a smoker. Twenty years later, a follow-up survey observed whether each woman was deceased or still alive. Was this study a retrospective study or a prospective study? Explain.

4.49 **Baseball under a full moon** Exercise 4.10 mentioned that the away team has won 13 consecutive games played between the Boston Brouhahas and Minnesota Meddlers during full moons. This is a statement based on retrospective observational data.

a. Many databases are huge, including those containing sports statistics. If you had access to the database, do you think you could uncover more surprising trends?

b. Would you be more convinced that the phase of the moon has predictive power if the away team were to win the *next* 13 games played under a full moon between Boston and Minnesota?

c. The results of which type of observational study are generally more reliable, retrospective or prospective?

4.50 **Two factors helpful?** A two-factor experiment
TRY designed to compare two diets and to analyze whether results depend on gender randomly assigns 20 men and 20 women to the two diets, 10 of each to each diet. After 3 months, the sample mean weight losses are as shown in the table.

Sample Mean Weight Loss by Diet Type and Gender

Diet	Gender Female	Male	Overall
Low-carb	12	0	6
Low-fat	0	12	6
Overall	6	6	6

a. Identify the two factors (explanatory variables) and the response variable.

b. What would the study have concluded if it did only a one-factor analysis on diet, looking at the overall results and not having the information about gender?

c. What could the study learn from the two-factor study that it would have missed by doing a one-factor study on diet alone or a one-factor study on gender alone?

4.51 **Growth Mind-Set** Carol Dweck is a noted psychologist from Stanford who believes that we should praise students' effort and not their intelligence. In her seminal study (2006), she gave students a test and then randomly divided the students into two groups. She praised the effort of one group and praised the intelligence of the other group. For their next exercise, the groups were given a choice of a challenging task or an easy task. Of those who were praised for their effort, 90% chose the challenging task, whereas fewer than half of the students who were praised for their intelligence chose the challenging task, fearful of losing their smart status.

a. Identify the response variable(s), explanatory variable, experimental units, and treatments.

b. What type of experimental design does this employ? Explain.

4.52 **Allergy relief** An experiment is being designed to compare relief from hay fever symptoms given by a low dose of a drug, a high dose of the drug, and a placebo. Each subject who suffers from hay fever and volunteers for the study is observed on 3 days, with a different treatment used each day. There are two days between treatments, so that a treatment does not have a carry-over effect for the next treatment assigned.

a. What are the blocks in this block design? What is this type of block design called?

b. Suppose the study is conducted as a double-blind study. Explain what this means.

c. Explain how randomization within blocks could be incorporated into the study.

4.53 Effect of partner smoking in smoking cessation study Smokers may have a more difficult time quitting smoking if they live with a smoker. How can an experiment explore this possibility in a study to compare bupropion with placebo? Suppose the researchers split the subjects into two groups: those who live with a smoker and those who do not live with smokers. Within each group, the subjects are randomly assigned to take bupropion or a placebo. The figure shows a flow chart of this design, when 250 of the 429 study subjects live with nonsmokers and 179 live with a smoker.

a. Is this design a *completely* randomized design? Why or why not? (*Hint:* Is the smoking status of the person a subject lives with randomly determined?)

b. Does this experiment have blocks? If so, identify them.

c. Is this design a randomized block design? Explain why or why not.

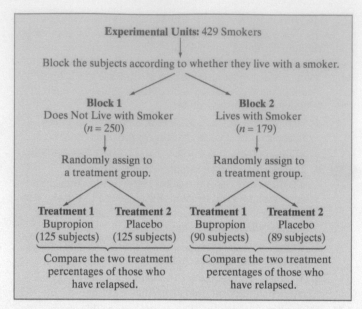

Diagram of an experiment to account for smoking status of partner

Chapter Review

CHAPTER SUMMARY

This chapter introduced methods for gathering data.

- An **experiment** assigns subjects to experimental conditions (such as drug or placebo) called **treatments**. These are categories of the explanatory variable. The outcome on the response variable is then observed for each subject.

- An **observational study** is a type of nonexperimental study that observes subjects on the response and explanatory variables. The study samples the population of interest, but merely observes rather than applies treatments to those subjects.

Since association does not imply causation, with observational studies we must be aware of potential **lurking variables** that influence the association. In an experiment, a researcher uses **randomization** in assigning experimental units (the subjects) to the treatments. This helps balance the treatments on lurking variables. A randomized experiment can provide support for causation. To reduce bias, experiments should be **double-blind**, with neither the subject nor the data collector knowing to which treatment a subject was assigned.

A **sample survey** is a type of nonexperimental study that takes a sample from a population. Good methods for selecting samples incorporate random sampling.

- A **simple random sample** of *n* subjects from a population is one in which each possible sample of size *n* has the same chance of being selected.

- A **cluster random sample** takes a simple random sample of clusters (such as city blocks) and uses subjects in those clusters as the sample.

- A **stratified random sample** divides the population into separate groups, called **strata**, and then selects a simple random sample from each stratum.

Be cautious of results from studies that use a convenience sample, such as a **volunteer sample**, which Internet polls use. Even with random sampling, **biases** can occur due to **sample undercoverage, nonresponse** by many subjects in the sample, and **responses that are biased** because of question wording or subjects' lying.

Most **sample surveys** take a cross section of subjects at a particular time. A **census** is a complete enumeration of an entire population. **Prospective** studies follow subjects into the future, as is true with many experiments. Medical studies often use **retrospective** observational studies, which look at subjects' behavior in the past.

- A **case-control study** is an example of a retrospective study. Subjects who have a response outcome of interest, such as cancer, serve as cases. Other subjects not having that outcome serve as controls. The cases and controls are compared on an explanatory variable, such as whether they had been smokers.

A categorical explanatory variable in an experiment is also called a **factor**. **Multifactor experiments** have at least two explanatory variables. With a **completely randomized design**, subjects are assigned randomly to categories of each explanatory variable. Some designs instead use **blocks**—sets of experimental units that are matched. **Matched-pairs designs** have two observations in each block. Often this is the same subject observed for each of two treatments, such as in a crossover study.

Data are only as good as the method used to obtain them. Unless we use a good study design, conclusions may be faulty.

LEARNING OBJECTIVES

1. Define an experiment.

2. Define explanatory variable, treatments, and response variable.

3. Define an observational study.

4. Compare the principles of an experiment to an observational study.

5. Identify the groups being compared in an experiment or observational study.

6. Define lurking variables and explain why they are problematic.

7. Identify the role of randomization in an experiment.

8. Describe how to use randomization in an experiment to assign treatments randomly, using random numbers generated with software.

9. Explain the meaning of the term "double-blind."

10. Define a sample survey.

11. Identify the role of randomization in selecting a sample.

12. Describe how to use randomization in selecting a sample using random numbers generated with software.

13. Contrast three types of random samples: simple random sample; cluster random sample; stratified random sample.

14. Identify potential biases in selecting samples, including sampling bias, undercoverage, nonresponse bias, response bias, and bias due to wording.

15. Explain the difference between a sample and a census.

16. Identify whether an observational study is prospective or retrospective.

17. Define a case-control study.

18. Identify when an experiment is a multifactor experiment.

19. Contrast completely randomized and matched-pairs designs

20. Identify the role of blocking in experiments.

ANSWERS TO THE CHAPTER FIGURE QUESTIONS

Figure 4.2 In a stratified sample, every stratum is used. A simple random sample is taken within each stratum. A cluster sample takes a simple random sample of the clusters. All the clusters are *not* used.

Figure 4.4 The diagram would look the same but have $2 \times 2 \times 2 = 8$ treatments.

STATISTICAL SOFTWARE

Art of Stat Web Apps

- **Random Numbers** The *Random Numbers* app is useful for generating a random sample. For instance, to select a random sample of $n = 5$ students from a class of 30 students, number the students from 1 to 30. In the app, set the minimum to 1 (which is the default) and the maximum to 30, and select 5 for "How many numbers do you want to generate?" Also, select Sampling Without Replacement (which is the default). Pressing the Generate button will provide five random numbers, which correspond to the students selected at random for this sample.

R

- **Random Samples:** The R command `sample` generates random numbers. For instance, > `sample(30, 5)` provides five numbers randomly selected from the numbers 1 through 30. For sampling with replacement, use > `sample (30, 5, replace=TRUE)`.

CHAPTER EXERCISES

Practicing the Basics

4.54 **Cell phones** If you want to conduct a study with humans to see whether cell phone use makes brain cancer more likely, explain why an observational study is more realistic than an experiment.

4.55 **Observational versus experimental study** Without using technical language, explain the difference between observational and experimental studies to someone who has not studied statistics. Illustrate with an example, using it also to explain the possible weaknesses of an observational study.

4.56 **Unethical experimentation** Give an example of a scientific question of interest for which it would be unethical to conduct an experiment. Explain how you could instead conduct an observational study.

4.57 **Spinal fluid proteins and Alzheimer's** A research study published in 2010 in the *Archives of Neurology* investigated the relationship between the results of a spinal fluid test and the presence of Alzheimer's disease. The study included 114 patients with normal memories, 200 with memory problems, and 102 with Alzheimer's disease. Each individual's spinal fluid was analyzed to detect the presence of two types of proteins. Almost everyone with Alzheimer's had the proteins in their spinal fluid. Nearly three quarters of the group with memory problems had the proteins, and each such member developed Alzheimer's within five years. About one third of those with normal memories had the proteins, and the researchers suspect that those individuals will develop memory problems and eventually Alzheimer's.

a. Identify the explanatory and response variable(s).

b. Was this an experimental or nonexperimental study? Why?

c. Would it be possible to design this study as an experiment? Explain why or why not.

4.58   Fear of asbestos   Your friend reads about a study in an epidemiology journal that estimates that the chance is 15 out of 1 million that a teacher who works for 30 years in a school with typical asbestos levels gets cancer from asbestos. However, she also knows about a teacher who died recently who may have had asbestos exposure. In deciding whether to leave teaching, should she give more weight to the study or to the story she heard about the teacher who died? Why?

4.59   NCAA men's basketball poll   The last four teams of the Southeast region of the 2011 NCAA Men's Basketball Tournament were Butler (located in Indiana), Brigham Young University (located in Utah), Florida, and Wisconsin. The sports website ESPN.com asked visitors of the site which team would win the Southeast region. Nationwide results are depicted on the map that follows. It was reported that 44% of the more than 3,300 Indiana resident respondents believed Butler would win the regional, and 78% of the more than 5,600 Wisconsin resident respondents believed Wisconsin would win.

a. Explain why the percentages within Indiana and Wisconsin vary so drastically from the nationwide percentages displayed in the figure.

b. It was reported that between 42.3% and 45.7% of Indiana residents believed Butler was likely to win. What type of potential bias prevented these results from being representative of the entire population of Indiana residents?

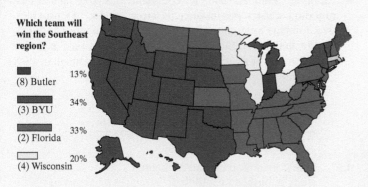

Which team will win the Southeast region?

- (8) Butler — 13%
- (3) BYU — 34%
- (2) Florida — 33%
- (4) Wisconsin — 20%

© ESPN.com (2012). Graphic feature used with permission.

4.60   Sampling your fellow students   You are assigned to direct a study on your campus to discover factors that are associated with strong academic performance. You decide to identify 20 students who have perfect GPAs of 4.0 and then measure explanatory variables for them that you think may be important, such as high school GPA and average amount of time spent studying per day.

a. Explain what is wrong with this study design.

b. Describe a study design that would provide more useful information.

4.61   Beware of Internet polling   An Internet survey at a newspaper website reports that only 14% of respondents believe in gun control. Mention a lurking variable that could bias the results of such an online survey, and explain how it could affect the results.

4.62   Comparing female and male students   You plan to sample from the 3,500 undergraduate students who are enrolled at the University of Rochester to compare the proportions of female and male students who would like to see the United States elect a female president.

a. Describe the steps for how you would proceed if you plan a simple random sample of 80 students. Illustrate by picking the first three students for the sample.

b. Suppose that you use random numbers to select students but stop selecting females as soon as you have 40, and you stop selecting males as soon as you have 40. Is the resulting sample a simple random sample? Why or why not?

c. What type of sample is the sample in part b? What advantage might it have over a simple random sample?

4.63   Football discipline   A large southern university had problems with 17 football players being disciplined for team rule violations, arrest charges, and possible NCAA violations. The online *Atlanta Journal Constitution* ran a poll with the question, "Has the football coach lost control over his players?" having possible responses, "Yes, he's been too lenient," and "No, he can't control everything teenagers do."

a. Was there potential for bias in this study? If so, what types of bias?

b. The poll results after two days were

Yes	6,012	93%
No	487	7%

Does this large sample size guarantee that the results are unbiased? Explain.

4.64   Obesity in metro areas   A Gallup poll tracks obesity in the United States for the most and least obese metro areas in the United States. The poll, based on more than 200,000 responses between January and December 2010, reported that certain chronic conditions are more prevalent in the most obese metro areas. The table that follows presents a summary of the findings.

Chronic Condition	10 Most Obese Metro Areas	10 Least Obese Metro Areas
Diabetes	14.6%	8.5%
High blood pressure	35.8%	25.6%
High cholesterol	28.5%	24.1%
Heart attack	5.9%	3.4%

Source: www.gallup.com/poll/146669/Adults-Obese-Metro-Areas-Nationwide.aspx © 2020 Gallup, Inc.

a. Are we able to conclude from the Gallup poll that obesity causes a higher incidence of these conditions?

b. What is a possible variable other than obesity that may be associated with these chronic conditions?

4.65 Voluntary sports polls In 2014, the Pittsburgh Penguins were ahead of the New York Rangers three games to one in the first round of the National Hockey League play-offs. ESPN.com conducted a voluntary, online poll that asked respondents to predict the outcomes of the rest of the series. Of all 1,094 respondents, 52% said Penguins in 5 games, 34% said Penguins in 6 games, 5% said Penguins in 7 games, and 9% said Rangers in 7 games.

a. Was this a simple random sample? Explain.

b. If ESPN.com wanted to determine the true proportions for all sports fans, how could it do so more reliably?

Source: http://espn.go.com/sportsnation/polls/ /category/5239/ your-nhl-playoff-predictions

4.66 Video games mindless? "Playing video games not so mindless." This was the headline of a news report[14] about a study that concluded that young adults who regularly play video games demonstrated better visual skills than young adults who do not play regularly. Sixteen young men volunteered to take a series of tests that measured their visual skills; those who had played video games in the previous six months performed better on the tests than those who hadn't played.

a. What are the explanatory and response variables?

b. Was this an observational study or an experiment? Explain.

c. Specify a potential lurking variable. Explain your reasoning.

4.67 Physicians' health study Read about the first Physicians' Health Study at phs.bwh.harvard.edu.

a. Explain whether it was (i) an experiment or an observational study and (ii) a retrospective or prospective study.

b. Identify the response variable and the explanatory variable(s) and summarize results.

4.68 Aspirin prevents heart attacks? During the 1980s approximately 22,000 physicians over the age of 40 agreed to participate in a long-term study called the Physicians' Health Study. One question investigated was whether aspirin helps lower the rate of heart attacks. The physicians were randomly assigned to take aspirin or take a placebo.

a. Identify the response variable and the explanatory variable.

b. Explain why this is an experiment and identify the treatments.

c. There are other explanatory variables, such as the amount of exercise a physician got, that we would expect to be associated with the response variable. Explain how such a variable is dealt with by the randomized nature of the experiment.

4.69 Exercise and heart attacks Refer to Exercise 4.68. One potential confounding variable was the amount of exercise the physicians got. The randomization should have balanced the treatment groups on exercise. The contingency table shows the relationship between whether the physician exercised vigorously and the treatments.

| Treatment | Exercise Vigorously? | | |
	Yes	No	Total
Aspirin	7,910	2,997	**10,907**
Placebo	7,861	3,060	**10,921**

a. Find the conditional proportions (recall Section 3.1) in the categories of this potential confounder (amount of exercise) for each treatment group. Are they similar?

b. Do you think that the randomization process did a good job of achieving balanced treatment groups in terms of this potential confounder? Explain.

4.70 Smoking and heart attacks Repeat the previous exercise, considering another potential confounding variable—whether the physicians smoked. The contingency table cross-classifies treatment group by smoking status.

| Treatment | Smoking Status | | | |
	Never	Past	Current	Total
Aspirin	5,431	4,373	1,213	**11,017**
Placebo	5,488	4,301	1,225	**11,014**

4.71 Aspirin, beta-carotene, and heart attacks In the study discussed in the previous three exercises, this completely randomized study actually used two factors: whether received aspirin or placebo and whether received beta-carotene or placebo. Draw a table or a flow chart to portray the four treatments for this study.

4.72 Bupropion and nicotine patch study results The subjects for the study described in Examples 7 and 11 were evaluated for abstinence from cigarette smoking at the end of 12 months. The table shows the percentage in each group that were abstaining.

Group	Abstinence Percentage	Sample Size
Nicotine patch only	16.4	244
Bupropion only	30.3	244
Nicotine patch with bupropion	35.5	245
Placebo only	15.6	160

a. Compare the abstinence proportion of 30.3% in the bupropion only group to the 16.4% in the Nicotine patch only group by finding and interpreting the difference of proportions. (See Section 3.1 in Chapter 3.)

---

[14]See www.freerepublic.com/focus/f-news/919978/posts.

b. Compare the abstinence proportion of 35.5% in the nicotine patch with bupropion group to the 15.6% in the placebo only group by finding and interpreting the ratio of proportions. (See Section 3.1 in Chapter 3.)

4.73   Prefer Coke or Pepsi?   You want to conduct an experiment with your class to see whether students prefer Coke or Pepsi.

a. Explain how you could do this, incorporating ideas of blinding and randomization, (i) with a completely randomized design, and (ii) with a matched pairs design.

b. Which design would you prefer? Why?

4.74   Comparing gas brands   The marketing department of a major oil company wants to investigate whether cars get better mileage using its gas (Brand A) than from an independent one (Brand B) that has cheaper prices. The department has 20 cars available for the study.

a. Identify the response variable, the explanatory variable, and the treatments.

b. Explain how to use a completely randomized design to conduct the study.

c. Explain how to use a matched-pairs design to conduct the study. What are the blocks for the study?

d. Give an advantage of using a matched-pairs design.

4.75   Samples not equally likely in a cluster sample?   In a cluster random sample with equal-sized clusters, every subject has the same chance of selection. However, the sample is not a simple random sample. Explain why not.

4.76   Nursing homes   You plan to sample residents of registered nursing homes in your county. You obtain a list of all 97 nursing homes in the county, and randomly select five of them. You obtain lists of residents from those five homes and interview all the residents in each home.

a. Are the nursing homes clusters or strata?

b. Explain why the sample chosen is not a simple random sample of the population of interest to you.

4.77   Multistage health survey   A researcher wants to study regional differences in dental care. He takes a multistage sample by dividing the United States into four regions, taking a simple random sample of ten schools in each region, randomly sampling three classrooms in each school, and interviewing all students in those classrooms about whether they've been to a dentist in the previous year. Identify each stage of this multistage sampling design, indicating whether it involves stratification or clustering.

4.78   Hazing   Hazing within college fraternities is a continuing concern. Before a national meeting of college presidents, a polling organization is retained to conduct a survey among fraternities on college campuses, gathering information on hazing for the meeting. The investigators from the polling organization realize that it is not possible to find a reliable sampling frame of all fraternities. Using a list of all college institutions, they randomly sample 30 of them and then interview the officers of each fraternity at each of these institutions that has fraternities. Would you describe this as a simple random sample,

cluster random sample, or stratified random sample of the fraternities? Explain.

4.79   Marijuana and schizophrenia   Many research studies focus on a link between marijuana use and psychotic disorders such as schizophrenia. Studies have found that people with schizophrenia are twice as likely to smoke marijuana as those without the disorder. Data also suggest that individuals who smoke marijuana are twice as likely to develop schizophrenia as those who do not use the drug. Contributing to the apparent relationship, a comprehensive review done in 2007 of the existing research reported that individuals who merely try marijuana increase their risk of developing schizophrenia by 40%. Meanwhile, the percentage of the population who has tried marijuana has increased dramatically in the United States over the past 50 years, whereas the percentage of the population affected by schizophrenia has remained constant at about 1%. What might explain this puzzling result?

4.80   Twins and breast cancer   Excessive cumulative exposure to ovarian hormones is believed to cause breast cancer. A study (*New England J. Medic.* 2003; 348: 2313–2322) used information from 1811 pairs of female twins, one or both of whom had breast cancer. Paired twins were compared with respect to age at puberty, when breast cancer was first diagnosed, and other factors. Their survey did not show an association between hereditary breast cancer and hormone exposure.

a. What type of observational study was used by the researchers?

b. Why do you think the researchers used this design instead of a randomized experiment?

Concepts and Investigations

4.81   Cell phone use   Using the Internet, find a study about cell phone use and its potential risk when used by drivers of automobiles.

a. Was the study an experiment or an observational study?

b. Identify the response and explanatory variables.

c. Describe any randomization or control conducted in the study as well as attempts to take into account lurking variables.

d. Summarize conclusions of the study. Do you see any limitations of the study?

4.82   Read a medical journal   Go to a website for an online medical journal, such as *British Medical Journal* (www.bmj.com). Pick an article in a recent issue.

a. Was the study an experiment or an observational study?

b. Identify the response variable and the primary explanatory variable(s).

c. Describe any randomization or control conducted in the study as well as attempts to take into account lurking variables.

d. Summarize conclusions of the study. Do you see any limitations of the study?

4.83 **Internet poll** Find an example of results of an Internet poll. (You can also include the social media sites you use.) Do you trust the results of the poll? If not, explain why not.

4.84 **Search for an observational study** Find an example of an observational study from a newspaper, journal, the Internet, a social media site, or some other medium.

   a. Identify the explanatory and response variables and the population of interest.

   b. What type of observational study was conducted? Describe how the data were gathered.

   c. Were lurking variables considered? If so, discuss how. If not, can you think of potential lurking variables? Explain how they could affect the association.

   d. Can you identify any potential sources of bias? Explain.

4.85 **Search for an experimental study** Find an example of a randomized experiment from a newspaper, journal, the Internet, a social media site, or some other media.

   a. Identify the explanatory and response variables.

   b. What were the treatments? What were the experimental units?

   c. How were the experimental units assigned to the treatments?

   d. Can you identify any potential sources of bias? Explain.

4.86 **Judging sampling design** In each of the following situations, summarize negative aspects of the sample design.

   a. A newspaper asks readers to vote at its Internet site to determine whether they believe government expenditures should be reduced by cutting social programs. Based on 1,434 votes, the newspaper reports that 93% of the city's residents believe that social programs should be reduced.

   b. A congresswoman reports that letters to her office are running 3 to 1 in opposition to the passage of stricter gun control laws. She concludes that approximately 75% of her constituents oppose stricter gun control laws.

   c. An anthropology professor wants to compare attitudes toward premarital sex of physical science majors and social science majors. She administers a questionnaire to her Anthropology 437, Comparative Human Sexuality class. She finds no appreciable difference in attitudes between the two majors, so she concludes that the two student groups are about the same in their views about premarital sex.

   d. A questionnaire is mailed to a simple random sample of 500 household addresses in a city. Ten are returned as bad addresses, 63 are returned completed, and the rest are not returned. The researcher analyzes the 63 cases and reports that they represent a "simple random sample of city households."

4.87 **More poor sampling designs** Repeat the previous exercise for the following scenarios:

   a. A principal in a large high school wants to sample student attitudes toward a proposal that seniors must pass a general achievement test to graduate. She lists all of the first-period classes. Then, using a random number table, she chooses a class at random and interviews every student in that class about the proposed test.

   b. A new restaurant opened in January. In June, after six months of operation, the owner applied for a loan to improve the building. The loan application asked for the annual gross income of the business. The owner's record book contains receipts for each day of operation since opening. She decides to calculate the average daily receipt based on a sample of the daily records and multiply that by the number of days of operation in a year. She samples every Friday's record. The average daily receipt for this sample was then used to estimate the yearly receipts.

4.88 **Age for legal alcohol** You want to investigate the opinions students at your school have about whether the age for legal drinking of alcohol should be 18.

   a. Write a question to ask about this in a sample survey in such a way that results would be biased. Explain why it would be biased.

   b. Now write an alternative question that should result in unbiased responses.

4.89 **Quota sampling** An interviewer stands at a street corner and conducts interviews until obtaining a quota in various groups representing the relative sizes of the groups in the population. For instance, the quota might be 50 factory workers, 100 housewives, 60 elderly people, 30 Hispanics, and so forth. This is called **quota sampling**. Is this a random sampling method? Explain and discuss potential advantages or disadvantages of this method. (The Gallup organization used quota sampling until it predicted, incorrectly, that Dewey would easily defeat Truman in the 1948 presidential election.)

4.90 **Smoking and heart attacks** A Reuters story (*Smoking and heart attacks*, April 2, 2003) reported that "the number of heart attack victims fell by almost 60% at one hospital six months after a smoke-free ordinance went into effect in the area (Helena, Montana), a study showed, reinforcing concerns about second-hand smoke." The number of hospital admissions for heart attack dropped from just under seven per month to four a month during the six months after the smoking ban.

   a. Did this story describe an experiment or an observational study?

   b. In the context of this study, describe how you could explain to someone who has never studied statistics that association does not imply causation. For instance, give a potential reason that could explain this association.

4.91 **Issues in clinical trials** A randomized clinical trial is planned for AIDS patients to investigate whether a new treatment provides improved survival over the current standard treatment. It is not known whether it will be better or worse.

a. Why do researchers use randomization in such experiments rather than letting the subjects choose which treatment they will receive?

b. When patients enrolling in the study are told the purpose of the study, explain why they may be reluctant to be randomly assigned to one of the treatments.

c. If a researcher planning the study thinks the new treatment is likely to be better, explain why the researcher may have an ethical dilemma in proceeding with the study.

4.92 Compare smokers with nonsmokers Example 8 and Table 4.2 described a case-control study on smoking and lung cancer. Explain carefully why it is not sensible to use the study's proportion of smokers who had lung cancer (that is, $688/(688 + 650)$) and proportion of nonsmokers who had lung cancer $(21/(21 + 59))$ to estimate corresponding proportions of smokers and nonsmokers who have lung cancer in the overall population.

4.93 Is a vaccine effective? A vaccine is claimed to be effective in preventing a rare disease that occurs in about one of every 100,000 people. Explain why a randomized clinical trial comparing 100 people who get the vaccine to 100 people who do not get it is unlikely to be worth doing. Explain how you could use a case-control study to investigate the efficacy of the vaccine.

4.94 Helping and hindering among infants Researchers at Yale University's Infant Cognition Center were interested in determining whether infants had the ability to distinguish between the actions of helping and hindering. Each infant in the study was shown two videos. One video included a figure performing a helping action and the other included a figure performing a hindering action. Infants were presented with two toys resembling the helping and hindering figures from the videos and allowed to choose one of the toys to play with. The researchers conjectured that, even at a very young age, the infants would tend to choose the helpful object.

a. How might the results of this study been biased had each infant been shown the video with the helpful figure before being shown the video with the hindering figure?

b. How could such a potential bias be eliminated?

4.95 Helping and hindering among infants, continued In the previous exercise, we considered how showing each baby in the study the two videos in the same order might create a bias. In fact, of the 16 babies in the study, half were shown the videos in one order while the other half was shown the videos in the opposite order. Explain how to use the *Random Numbers* app to randomly divide the 16 infants into two groups of 8.

APP

4.96 Helping and hindering among infants, continued Fourteen of the 16 infants in the Yale study elected to play with a toy resembling the helpful figure as opposed to one resembling the hindering figure. Is this convincing evidence that infants tend to prefer the helpful figure?

APP

Use the *Random Numbers* app on the book's website to investigate the approximate likelihood of the observed results of 14 out of 16 infants choosing the helpful figure, if in fact infants are indifferent between the two figures. To perform a simulation with this app, click on the Coin Flips tab and set the number of flips to generate equal to 16. Click on Generate and determine the number of heads in the generated sequence. This represents the number of times the child selects the helpful toy if they choose at random. Repeat this simulation for a total of 10 simulations. Out of the 10 simulations, how often did you obtain 14 or more heads out of 16 tosses? Are your results convincing evidence that infants actually tend to exhibit a preference?

Multiple Choice

4.97 What's a simple random sample? A simple random sample of size n is one in which

a. Every nth member is selected from the population.

b. Each possible sample of size n has the same chance of being selected.

c. There is *exactly* the same proportion of women in the sample as is in the population.

d. You keep sampling until you have a fixed number of people having various characteristics (e.g., males, females).

4.98 Be skeptical of medical studies? An analysis of published medical studies about heart attacks (Crossen, 1994, p. 168) noted that in the studies having randomization and strong controls for bias, the new therapy provided improved treatment 9% of the time. In studies without randomization or other controls for bias, the new therapy provided improved treatment 58% of the time.

a. This result suggests it is better not to use randomization in medical studies because it is harder to show that new ideas are beneficial.

b. Some newspaper articles that suggest a particular food, drug, or environmental agent is harmful or beneficial should be viewed skeptically unless we learn more about the statistical design and analysis for the study.

c. This result shows the value of case-control studies over randomized studies.

d. The randomized studies were poorly conducted, or they would have found the new treatment to be better much more than 9% of the time.

4.99 Opinion and question wording A recent General Social Survey asked subjects whether they supported legalized abortion in each of seven circumstances. The percentage who supported legalization varied between 44.6% (if the woman is not married) to 88.6% (if the woman's health is seriously endangered by the pregnancy). This indicates that

a. Responses can depend greatly on the question wording.

b. Nonexperimental studies can never be trusted.

c. The sample must not have been randomly selected.

d. The sample must have had problems with response bias.

4.100 Campaign funding When the Yankelovich polling organization asked, "Should laws be passed to eliminate all possibilities of special interests giving huge sums of money to candidates?" 80% of the sample answered yes. When they posed the question, "Should laws be passed to prohibit interest groups from contributing to campaigns, or do groups have a right to contribute to the candidate they support?" only 40% said yes (*Source: A Mathematician Reads the Newspaper,* by J. A. Paulos, New York: Basic Books, 1995, p. 15). This example illustrates problems that can be caused by

a. Nonresponse

b. Bias in the way a question is worded

c. Sampling bias

d. Undercoverage

4.101 Emotional health survey An Internet poll conducted in the United Kingdom by Netdoctor.co.uk asked individuals to respond to an "emotional health survey" (see www.hfienberg.com/clips/pollspiked.htm). There were 400 volunteer respondents. Based on the results, the British Broadcasting Corporation (BBC) reported that "Britons are miserable—it's official." This conclusion reflected the poll responses, of which one quarter feared a "hopeless future," one in three felt "downright miserable," and nearly one in ten thought "their death would make things better for others." Which of the following is *not* correct about why these results may be misleading?

a. Many people who access a medical website and are willing to take the time to answer this questionnaire may be having emotional health problems.

b. Some respondents may not have been truthful or may have been Internet surfers who take pleasure in filling out a questionnaire multiple times with extreme answers.

c. The sample is a volunteer sample rather than a random sample.

d. It's impossible to learn useful results about a population from a sample of only 400 people.

4.102 Sexual harassment In 1995 in the United Kingdom, the Equality Code used by the legal profession added a section to make members more aware of sexual harassment. It states that "research for the Bar found that over 40 percent of female junior tenants said they had encountered sexual harassment during their time at the Bar." This was based on a study conducted at the University of Sheffield that sent a questionnaire to 334 junior tenants at the Bar, of whom 159 responded. Of the 159, 67 were female. Of those females, 3 said they had experienced sexual harassment as a major problem, and 24 had experienced it as a slight problem. (*Source: Equality Code, 1995. The Bar Council.*)

a. The quoted statement might be misleading because the nonresponse was large.

b. No one was forced to respond, so everyone had a chance to be in the sample, which implies it was a simple random sample.

c. This was an example of a completely randomized experiment, with whether a female junior tenant experienced sexual harassment as the response variable.

d. This was a retrospective case-control study, with those who received sexual harassment as the cases.

4.103 Effect of response categories A study (N. Schwarz et al., *Public Opinion Quarterly*, vol. 49, 1985, p. 388) asked German adults how many hours a day they spend watching TV on a typical day. When the possible responses were the six categories (up to $\frac{1}{2}$ hour, $\frac{1}{2}$ to 1 hour, 1 to $1\frac{1}{2}$ hours, . . ., more than $2\frac{1}{2}$ hours), 16% of respondents said they watched more than $2\frac{1}{2}$ hours per day. When the six categories were (up to $2\frac{1}{2}$ hours, $2\frac{1}{2}$ to 3 hours, . . ., more than 4 hours), 38% said they watched more than $2\frac{1}{2}$ hours per day.

a. The samples could not have been random, or this would not have happened.

b. This shows the importance of question design, especially when people may be uncertain what the answer to the question really is.

c. This study was an experiment, not an observational study.

Advanced Exercises

4.104 Systematic sampling A researcher wants to select 1% of the 10,000 subjects from the sampling frame. She selects subjects by picking one of the first 100 on the list at random, skipping 100 names to get the next subject, skipping another 100 names to get the next subject, and so on. This is called a **systematic random sample**.

a. With simple random sampling, (i) every subject is equally likely to be chosen, and (ii) every possible sample of size n is equally likely. Indicate which, if any, of (i) and (ii) are true for systematic random samples. Explain.

b. An assembly-line process in a manufacturing company is checked by using systematic random sampling to inspect 2% of the items. Explain how this sampling process would be implemented.

4.105 Mean family size You'd like to estimate the mean size of families in your community. Explain why you'll tend to get a smaller sample mean if you sample n families than if you sample n individuals (asking them to report their family size). (*Hint:* When you sample individuals, explain why you are more likely to sample a large family than a small family. To think of this, it may help to consider the case $n = 1$ with a population of two families, one with 10 people and one with only 2 people.)

4.106 Capture–recapture Biologists and naturalists often use sampling to estimate sizes of populations, such as deer or fish, for which a census is impossible. Capture–recapture is one method for doing this. A biologist wants to count the deer population in a certain region.

She captures 50 deer, tags each, and then releases them. Several weeks later, she captures 125 deer and finds that 12 of them were tagged. Let N = population size, M = size of first sample, n = size of second sample, and R = number tagged in second sample. The table shows how results can be summarized.

		In First Sample?		
		Yes (tagged)	No (not tagged)	Total
In Second	Yes	R		n
Sample?	No			
	Total	M		N

a. Identify the values of M, n, and R for the biologist's experiment.

b. One way to estimate N lets the sample proportion of tagged deer equal the population proportion of tagged deer. Explain why this means that

$$\frac{R}{n} = \frac{M}{N}$$

and, hence, that the estimated population size is $N = (M \times n)/R$

c. Estimate the number of deer in the deer population using the numbers given.

d. The U.S. Census Bureau uses capture–recapture to make adjustments to the census by estimating the undercount. The capture phase is the census itself (persons are "tagged" by having returned their census form and being recorded as counted), and the recapture phase (the second sample) is the postenumerative survey (PES) conducted after the census. Label the table in terms of the census application.

Student Activities

4.107 Munchie capture–recapture Your class can use the capture–recapture method described in the previous exercise to estimate the number of goldfish in a bag of Cheddar Goldfish. Pour the Cheddar Goldfish into a paper bag, which represents the pond. Sample 10 of them. For this initial sample, use Pretzel Goldfish to replace them, to represent the tagged fish. Then select a second sample and derive an estimate for N, the number of Cheddar Goldfish in the original bag. See how close your estimate comes to the actual number of fish in the bag. (Your teacher will count the population of Cheddar Goldfish in the bag before beginning the sampling.) If the estimate is not close, what could be responsible, and what would this reflect as difficulties in a real-life application such as sampling a wildlife population?

4.108 Sampling the states This activity illustrates how sampling bias can result when you use a nonrandom sample, even if you attempt to make it representative: You are in a geography class, discussing how the area covered by each of the 48 states in the contiguous United States varies from state to state. The teacher asks for your best guess of the average (as measured by the mean) area covered for these 48 states. A map and a list of the states

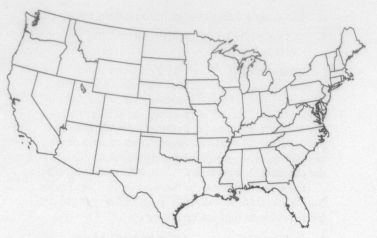

Map of the contiguous United States.

Areas of the 48 States in the Contiguous U.S.	
State	Area (square miles)
Alabama	52,419
Arizona	113,998
Arkansas	53,179
California	163,696
Colorado	104,094
Connecticut	5,543
Delaware	2,489
Florida	65,755
Georgia	59,425
Idaho	83,570
Illinois	57,914
Indiana	36,418
Iowa	56,272
Kansas	82,277
Kentucky	40,409
Louisiana	51,840
Maine	35,385
Maryland	12,407
Massachusetts	10,555
Michigan	96,716
Minnesota	86,939
Mississippi	48,430
Missouri	69,704
Montana	147,042
Nebraska	77,354
Nevada	110,561
New Hampshire	9,350
New Jersey	8,721
New Mexico	121,589
New York	54,556
North Carolina	53,819
North Dakota	70,700
Ohio	44,825
Oklahoma	69,898
Oregon	98,381
Pennsylvania	46,055
Rhode Island	1,545
South Carolina	32,020
South Dakota	77,116
Tennessee	42,143
Texas	268,581
Utah	84,899
Vermont	9,614
Virginia	42,774
Washington	71,300
West Virginia	24,230
Wisconsin	65,498
Wyoming	97,814
U.S. TOTAL	**3,119,819**

with their areas (in square miles) are shown in the figure and table. Area for a state includes dry land and permanent inland water surface.

Although we could use these data to calculate the actual mean area, let's explore *how well sampling performs in estimating the mean area* by sampling five states and finding the sample mean.

a. The most convenient sampling design is to use our eyes to pick five states from the map that we think have areas representative of all the states. Do this, picking five states that you believe have areas representative of the actual mean area of the states. Compute their sample mean area (e.g., by entering the data into the *Explore Quantitative Data* app).

b. Collect the sample means for all class members. Construct a dot plot of these means (e.g., by entering them into the *Explore Quantitative Data* app). Describe the distribution of sample means. Note the shape, center, and variability of the distribution.

c. Another possible sampling design is simple random sampling. Randomly select five states (e.g., using the *Random Numbers* app by generating five random numbers from the numbers 1 to 48) and compute the sample mean area.

d. Collect the sample means from part c of all class members. Construct a dot plot of the sample means using the same horizontal scale as in part b. (You can use the *Explore Quantitative Data* app for this: Go to the Several Groups tab, select Your Own for Enter Data and enter the data from part b as the first group and from part c as the second group.) Describe this distribution of sample means. Note the shape, center, and variability of the distribution.

e. The true mean total land area for the 48 states can be calculated from the accompanying table by dividing the total at the bottom of the table by 48. Which sampling method, using your eyes or using random selection, tended to be better at estimating the true population mean? Which method seems to be less biased? Explain.

f. Write a short summary comparing the two distributions of sample means.

BIBLIOGRAPHY

Burrill, G., C. Franklin, L. Godbold, and L. Young (2003). *Navigating through Data Analysis in Grades 9–12*, NCTM.

Crossen, C. (1994). *Tainted Truth: The Manipulation of Fact in America*. New York: Simon & Schuster.

Dweck, C. (2006). *Mindset: The New Psychology of Success*. New York: Random House Publishing Group.

Hepworth, S. J., et al. (2006). "Mobile phone use and risk of glioma in adults: case control study." *BMJ* 332: 883–887.

Leake, J. (2001) "Scientists Link Eye Cancer to Mobile Phones," *The London Times*, Jan. 14. www.emf-health .com/reports-eyecancer.htm.

Stang, A., et al. (2001). "The possible role of radio frequency radiation in the development of uveal melanoma." *Epidemiology* 12(1): 7–12.

Volkow, N. (2011). "Effects of Cell Phone Radiofrequency Signal Exposure on Brain Glucose Metabolism." *JAMA* 305(8): 808–813.

Probability, Probability Distributions, and Sampling Distributions

Using the concept of probability, we can quantify uncertainty and randomness that we experience in our daily lives. In this chapter we will define what we mean by probability and show how we can compute basic probabilities by following certain rules. Understanding probability and uncertainty is also necessary for understanding the inferential procedures that we will discuss in later chapters.

Probability in Our Daily Lives

Example 1

Failing a Test for Illegal Drug Use

Picture the Scenario

Many employers require potential employees to take a diagnostic test for illegal drug use. Such tests are also used to detect drugs used by athletes. For example, at the 2018 Winter Olympics in Pyeongchang South Korea, 3,149 anti-doping tests were conducted, resulting in four disqualifications (among them a bronze medalist) because of the use of a banned substance.

But diagnostic and other medical tests have a broader use. They can be used to detect certain medical conditions. For example, anyone can now buy a pregnancy test in a pharmacy or order genetic tests from companies like 23andMe, which try to predict the probability of developing diabetes, Alzheimer's, or Parkinson's disease.

Questions to Explore

■ Given that a person recently used drugs, how can we estimate the likelihood that a diagnostic test will correctly predict drug use?

■ Suppose a diagnostic test predicts that a person has a certain disease. How likely is it that the person actually has the disease?

Thinking Ahead

We'll learn how to answer the preceding questions by using probability methods. The answers, especially to the second question, are often surprising and a main reason why, for instance, mammography, a test to detect breast cancer, is controversial for younger-aged women. In Example 8, we'll look at data on the performance of a diagnostic test for detecting Down syndrome in pregnant women using the triple test that is routinely administered. In Example 13, we'll analyze results of random drug tests for air traffic controllers.

Learning how to find probabilities and how to interpret them will help you, as a consumer of information, understand how to assess probabilities in many uncertain aspects of your life.

In everyday life, often you must make decisions when you are uncertain about the outcome. Should you invest money in the stock market? Should you get extra collision insurance on your car? Should you start a new business, such as opening a pizza place across from campus? Daily, you face even mundane decisions, such as whether to carry an umbrella with you in case it rains.

This chapter introduces **probability**—the way we quantify uncertainty. You'll learn how to measure the chances of the possible outcomes for **random phenomena**—everyday situations for which the outcome is uncertain. Using probability, for instance, you can find the chance of winning the lottery or the likelihood that an employer's drug test correctly detects whether you've used drugs. But, you also need probability to measure the uncertainty in results from experiments that employ randomization or surveys that employ random sampling. The margin of error we emphasized in Chapter 1 as a measure for the precision of estimating population parameters is a probability statement. The ideas in this chapter set the foundation for how we'll use probability in the rest of the book to make inferences based on data.

Recall

The margin of error states how close an estimate is *likely* to fall to the true population parameter. ◄

5.1 How Probability Quantifies Randomness

As we discovered in Chapter 4, statisticians rely on an essential component to avoid bias in gathering data. This is **randomness**—randomly assigning subjects to treatments or randomly selecting people for a sample. Randomness also applies to the outcomes of a response variable. The possible outcomes are known, but it's uncertain which outcome will occur for any given observation.

We've all employed randomization in games. Some popular randomizers are rolling dice, spinning a wheel, and flipping a coin. Randomization helps to make a game fair, each player having the same chances for the possible outcomes. Rolls of dice and flips of coins are simple ways to represent the randomness of randomized experiments and sample surveys. For instance, the head and tail outcomes of a coin flip can represent drug and placebo when a medical study randomly assigns a subject to receive one of these two treatments.

With a *small* number of observations, outcomes of *random phenomena* may look quite different from what you expect. For instance, you may expect to see a random pattern with different outcomes; instead, exactly the same outcome may happen a few times in a row. That's not necessarily a surprise; unpredictability for any given observation is the essence of randomness. We'll discover, however, that with a *large* number of observations, summary statistics settle down and get increasingly closer to particular numbers. For example, with 4 tosses of a coin, we wouldn't be surprised to find all 4 tosses resulting in heads. However, with 100 tosses, we would be surprised to find the number of heads equal to 100. As we make more observations, the proportion of times that a particular outcome occurs gets closer and closer to a certain number we would expect. This long-run proportion provides the basis for the definition of *probability*.

In Words

Phenomena are any observable occurrences.

Randomness ◄

Example 2

The Fairness of Rolling Dice

Picture the Scenario

The board game you've been playing has a die that determines the number of spaces moved on the board. After you've rolled the die 100 times, the number 6 has appeared 23 times, more frequently than each of the other 5 numbers, 1 through 5. At one point, it turns up three times in a row, resulting in you winning a game. Your opponent then complains that the die favors the number 6 and is not a fair die.

Did You Know?

The singular of *dice* is *die*. For a proper die, numbers on opposite sides add to 7, and when 4 faces up, the die can be turned so that 2 faces the player, 1 is at the player's right, and 6 is at the player's left. (*Ainslie's Complete Hoyle,* New York: Simon & Schuster, 2003) ◄

Questions to Explore

a. If a fair die is rolled 100 times, how many 6s do you expect?
b. Would it be unusual for a 6 to be rolled 23 times in 100 rolls? Would it be surprising to roll three 6s in a row at some point?

Think It Through

a. With many rolls of a fair die, each of the six numbers would appear about equally often. A 6 should occur about one sixth of the time. In 100 rolls, we expect a 6 to come up about $(1/6)100 = 16.7 \approx 17$ times.
b. How can we determine whether it is unusual for 6 to come up 23 times out of 100 rolls or three times in a row at some point? One way uses simulation. We could roll the die 100 times and see what happens, roll it another 100 times and see what happens that time, and so on. Does a 6 appear 23 (or more) times in many of the simulations? Does a 6 occur three times in a row in many simulations?

   This simulation using a die would be tedious. Fortunately, we can use the *Random Numbers* app (or other software) to simulate rolling a fair die. Each simulated roll of a die is called a **trial**. After each trial, we record whether a 6 occurred. We will keep a running record of the proportion of times that a 6 has occurred. At each value for the number of trials, this is called a **cumulative proportion**. Table 5.1 shows partial results of one simulation of 100 rolls. To find the cumulative proportion

Table 5.1 Simulation Results of Rolling a Fair Die 100 Times

Each trial is a simulated roll of the die, with chance 1/6 of a 6. At each trial, we record whether a 6 occurred as well as the cumulative proportion of 6s by that trial.

Trial	Die Result	6 Occurs?	Cumulative Proportion of 6s	
1	6	yes	1/1	= 1.0
2	2	no	1/2	= 0.500
3	6	yes	2/3	= 0.667
4	5	no	2/4	= 0.500
5	6	yes	3/5	= 0.600
6	2	no	3/6	= 0.500
7	2	no	3/7	= 0.429
8	3	no	3/8	= 0.375
⋮	⋮	⋮	⋮	⋮
30	1	no	9/30	= 0.300

Trial	Die Result	6 Occurs?	Cumulative Proportion of 6s	
31	1	no	9/31	= 0.290
32	6	yes	10/32	= 0.313
33	6	yes	11/33	= 0.333
34	6	yes	12/34	= 0.353
35	2	no	12/35	= 0.343
⋮	⋮	⋮	⋮	⋮
99	5	no	22/99	= 0.220
100	6	yes	23/100	= 0.230

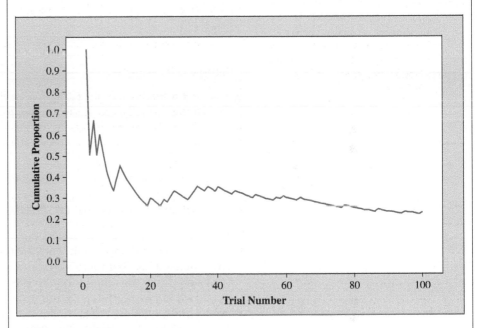

▲ **Figure 5.1** The Cumulative Proportion of Times a 6 Occurs, for a Simulation of 100 Rolls of a Fair Die. The horizontal axis of this figure reports the number of the trial, and the vertical axis reports the cumulative proportion of 6s observed by then. **Question** The first four rolls of the die were 6, 2, 6, and 5. How can you find the cumulative proportion of 6s after each of the first four trials?

after a certain number of trials, divide the number of 6s at that stage by the number of trials. For example, by the eighth roll (trial), there had been three 6s in eight trials, so the cumulative proportion is $3/8 = 0.375$. Figure 5.1 plots the cumulative proportions against the trial number.

In this simulation of 100 rolls of a die, a 6 occurred 23 times, different from the expected value of about 17. From Table 5.1, a 6 appeared three times in a row for trials 32 through 34.

Insight

One simulation does not prove anything. It suggests, however, that rolling three 6s in a row out of 100 rolls may not be highly unusual. It also shows that 23 rolls with a 6 out of 100 trials can occur. To find out whether 23 rolls with a 6 is unusual, we need to repeat this simulation many times (see Activity 1 on the next page). In Chapter 6, we will learn about the binomial distribution, which allows us to compute the likelihood for observing 23 (or more) 6s out of 100 trials.

▶ *Try Exercise 5.10*

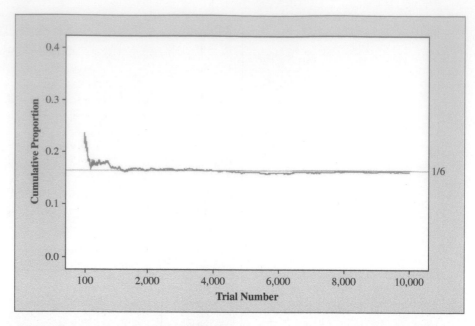

▲ **Figure 5.2 The Cumulative Proportion of Times That a 6 Occurs for a Simulation of 10,000 Rolls of a Fair Die.** Figure 5.1 showed the first 100 trials, and this figure shows results of trials 100 through 10,000. As the trial number gets larger, the cumulative proportion gets closer to 1/6. The probability of a 6 on any single roll is defined to be this *long-run* value. **Question** What would you expect for the cumulative proportion of heads after you flipped a balanced coin 10,000 times?

Long-Run Behavior of Random Outcomes

The number of 6s in 100 rolls of a die can vary. One time we might get 19 rolls with 6s, another time we might get 22, another time 13, and so on. So what do we mean when we say that there's a one-in-six chance of a 6 on any given roll?

Let's continue the simulation from Example 2 and Table 5.1. In that example we stopped after only 100 rolls, but now let's continue simulating for a very large number of rolls. Figure 5.2 shows the cumulative proportion of 6s plotted against the trial number for a total of 10,000 rolls, beginning where we left off with the 100th trial. As the simulation progresses, with the trial number increasing, the cumulative proportion of 6s gradually settles down. After 10,000 simulated rolls, Figure 5.2 shows that the cumulative proportion is *very* close to the value of 1/6.

With a relatively short run, such as 10 rolls of a die, the cumulative proportion of 6s can fluctuate a lot. It need not be close to 1/6 after the final trial. However, as the number of trials keeps increasing, the proportion of times the number 6 occurs becomes more predictable and less random: It gets closer and closer to 1/6. *With random phenomena, the proportion of times that something happens is highly random and unpredictable in the short run but very predictable in the long run.*

► Activity 1

Simulate Many Rolls of a Die

Because one simulation is insufficient to tell us what is typical, go to the *Random Numbers* app at the book's website. Set the minimum to 1, the maximum to 6, and the numbers to generate to 100, then click on Generate. How many 6s do you observe out of the 100 simulated rolls? In the app, under Options, check the boxes for Show Percent and Frequency Table to see the exact number or simply hover over the bar chart. (In our simulation,

shown in the screenshot on the next page, we obtained 18 6s.) For the 100 rolls you generated, what proportion of rolls were 6s? Repeat this simulation a few more times (hit the Reset button after each simulation) to get a feel for how the proportion of 6s in the 100 simulated rolls compares to the expected value of 1/6 (=16.7%).

You'll probably see that it's possible for 23 or more of the 100 rolls (that is, at least 23%) to result in 6s. If you keep doing this simulation over and over again, about 6.3% of the time you'll get 23 or more 6s out of the 100 rolls. Also, about 30% of the time, you'll see at least three 6s in a row

somewhere out of the 100 rolls. This shows that either of these scenarios is not that unusual.

Now, click the Reset button but then click on the Generate button 10 times, without hitting Reset in between. This will generate a total of $10 \times 100 = 1,000$ rolls. After each click, the proportion of 6s in the rolls generated so far (you can watch this proportion update in the bar chart after each click, but before that select Show Percent under Options to display percentages on the y-axis) will tend to fall *closer and closer* to its expected value of 1/6 (=16.7%). For 1,000 (instead of 100) rolls, we would be very surprised if at least 23% of them resulted in 6s. This proportion should now be close to 1/6 (or 16.7%).

Probability Quantifies Long-Run Randomness

In 1689, the Swiss mathematician Jacob Bernoulli proved that as the number of trials increases, the proportion of occurrences of any given outcome approaches a particular number (such as 1/6) in the long run. To show this, he assumed that the outcome of any one trial does not depend on the outcome of any other trial, something we will later define as independence. Bernoulli's result is known as the **law of large numbers.**

We will interpret the **probability** of an outcome to represent long-run results. Imagine a very long sequence of independent observations on some random phenomenon, like rolling a die. Each observation results or does not result in the outcome under investigation. We define the probability of the outcome as the proportion of times that it occurs in the long run.

> **Probability**
>
> With any random phenomenon, the **probability** of a particular outcome is the proportion of times that the outcome would occur in a long run of observations of the phenomenon.

When we say that the probability of rolling a 6 is 1/6, this means that the proportion of times that a 6 would occur in a long run of observations of rolling a fair die is 1/6. The probability would also be 1/6 for each of the other possible outcomes: 1, 2, 3, 4, or 5.

A weather forecaster might say that the probability of rain today is 0.70. This means that in a large number of days with atmospheric conditions like those today, the proportion of days in which rain occurs is 0.70. Since a probability is a *proportion*, it takes a value between 0 and 1. Sometimes probabilities are expressed as percentages, such as when the weather forecaster reports the probability of rain as 70%.

Why does probability refer to the *long run*? Because we can't accurately assess a probability with a small number of trials. If you randomly sample 10 people and they are all right-handed, you can't conclude that the probability of being right-handed equals 1.0. As we've seen, there can be a lot of unpredictability in the cumulative proportion for small samples. It takes a much larger sample of people to predict accurately the proportion of people in the population who are right-handed.

Independent Trials

With random phenomena, many believe that when some outcome has not happened in a while, it is *due* to happen: Its probability goes up until it happens. In many rolls of a fair die, if a particular value (say, 5) has not occurred in a long time, some think it's due and that the chance of a 5 on the next roll is greater than 1/6. If a family has four girls in a row and is expecting another child, are they due to get a boy? Does the next child have a different probability of being a boy than each of the first four children did?

Example 2 showed that over a short run, observations may deviate from what is expected. (Remember three 6s in a row?) But with many random phenomena, such as outcomes of rolling a die or having children, what happens on previous trials does not affect the trial that's about to occur. The trials are **independent** of each other.

> **Independent Trials**
>
> Different trials of a random phenomenon are **independent** if the outcome of any one trial is not affected by the outcome of any other trial.

With independent trials, whether you get a 5 on one roll of a fair die does not affect whether you get a 5 on the following roll. It doesn't matter if you had 20 rolls in a row that are not 5s, the next roll still has probability 1/6 of being a 5. The die has no memory and can't remember the previous outcomes it produced. If you have lost many bets in a row (such as betting on red in Roulette), don't assume that you are due to win if you continue to place your bets on red. The *law of large numbers*, which gamblers invoke as the *law of averages*, only guarantees *long-run* performance. In the short run, the unpredictability of results may well exceed what you expect, which is why some people win at the casino and some people lose. However, the house (casino) can rely on the law of large numbers to win in the long run.

Finding Probabilities

In practice, we sometimes can find probabilities by making assumptions about the nature of the random phenomenon. For instance, by symmetry, it may be reasonable to assume that the possible outcomes of that phenomenon are *equally likely*. In rolling a die, we might assume that based on the physical makeup of the die, each of the six sides has an equal chance. Then the probability of rolling any particular number equals 1/6. If we flip a coin and assume that the coin is balanced, then the probability of flipping a tail (or a head) equals 1/2.

> **In Practice** The Sample Proportion Estimates the Actual Probability
>
> In theory, we could observe several trials of a random phenomenon and use the proportion of times an outcome occurs as its probability. In practice, this is imperfect. The sample proportion merely *estimates* the actual probability, and only for a *very large* number of trials is it necessarily close. In Chapters 7 and 8, we'll see how the sample size determines just how accurate that estimate is.

Types of Probability: Relative Frequency and Subjective Probability

We've defined the probability of an outcome as a long-run proportion (relative frequency) of times that the outcome occurs in a very large number of trials. However, this definition is not always helpful. Before the Apollo 11 mission, how could NASA scientists estimate the probability of successfully landing someone on the moon? No results were available on long-run observations of past landings. If you are trying to decide whether to buy any type of insurance, how can you find the probability that you will actually ever use it? You won't have a long run of trials available on which to base any probability calculations.

In such situations, you must rely on **subjective** information rather than solely on **objective** information such as data. You assess the probability of an outcome by taking into account all the information you have. Such probabilities are not based on a long run of trials. In this **subjective definition of probability,** the probability of an outcome is defined to be a *personal probability*—your degree of belief that the outcome will occur, based on the available information. For instance, in a report published in 1965, NASA estimated the probability of a successful landing as 73% using information they had about various parts of the mission. This uses a subjective definition of probability. Neil Armstrong himself is said to have estimated the probability of a successful landing closer to 50%.

One branch of statistics uses subjective probability as its foundation. It is called **Bayesian statistics**, in honor of Thomas Bayes, a British clergyman who discovered a probability rule on which it is based. The subjective approach is less common than the approach we discuss in this book. We'll merely warn you to be wary of anyone who gives a subjective probability of 1 (certain occurrence) or of 0 (certain nonoccurrence) for some outcome. As Benjamin Franklin said, nothing in life is certain but death and taxes!

5.1 Practicing the Basics

5.1 Probability Explain what is meant by the long-run relative frequency definition of probability.

5.2 Testing a coin Your friend decides to flip a coin repeatedly to analyze whether the probability of a head on each flip is 1/2. He flips the coin 10 times and observes a head 7 times. He concludes that the probability of a head for this coin is $7/10 = 0.70$.

a. Your friend claims that the coin is not balanced, since the probability is not 0.50. What's wrong with your friend's claim?

b. If the probability of flipping a head is actually 1/2, what would you have to do to ensure that the cumulative proportion of heads falls very close to 1/2?

5.3 Vegetarianism You randomly sample 10 people in your school, and none of them is a vegetarian. Does this mean that the probability of being a vegetarian for students at your school equals 0? Explain.

5.4 Flight delay Over the month of January 2017, 29,495 flights took off from Atlanta International Airport. Of these, 8,512 had a departure delay of more than 5 minutes.

a. What is the random phenomenon we are interested in, in the context of this example?

b. What is a trial in the context of this example?

c. Can you consider the 29,495 flights as a long run or short run of trials? Explain.

d. Estimate the probability of a flight being delayed by more than 5 minutes, assuming flight delays are independent of each other.

e. Write down the definition of independence of trials in the context of this example. Do you think trials are independent?

5.5 World Cup 2014 The Power Rank website (thepower rank.com) listed the probability of each team to win the 2014 World Cup in soccer as follows:

1. Brazil, 35.9%	17. Croatia, 0.9%
2. Argentina, 10.0%	18. Ecuador, 0.8%
3. Spain, 8.9%	19. Nigeria, 0.8%
4. Germany, 7.4%	20. Switzerland, 0.7%
5. Netherlands, 5.7%	21. Greece, 0.6%
6. Portugal, 3.9%	22. Iran, 0.6%
7. France, 3.4%	23. Japan, 0.6%
8. England, 2.8%	24. Ghana, 0.6%
9. Uruguay, 2.5%	25. Belgium, 0.4%
10. Mexico, 2.5%	26. Honduras, 0.3%
11. Italy, 2.3%	27. South Korea, 0.3%
12. Ivory Coast, 2.0%	28. Bosnia-Herzegovina, 0.3%
13. Colombia, 1.5%	29. Costa Rica, 0.3%
14. Russia, 1.5%	30. Cameroon, 0.2%
15. United States, 1.1%	31. Australia, 0.2%
16. Chile, 1.0%	32. Algeria, 0.1%

a. Interpret Brazil's probability of 35.9%, which was based on computer simulations of the tournament under various assumptions. Is it a relative frequency or a subjective interpretation of probability?

b. Germany would emerge as the actual winner of the 2014 World Cup. Does this indicate that the 7.4% chance of Germany winning, which was calculated before the tournament, should have been 100% instead?

5.6   **Random numbers**   Consider a random number generator designed for equally likely outcomes, such as the random numbers you can generate with the *Random Numbers* app. For each part, explain why the statement is true or false.

a. When generating a random number between 1 and 10, each number has a probability of 0.10 of being selected.

b. When generating 20 random numbers between 1 and 10, each number between 1 and 10 must occur exactly twice.

c. When generating a random number between 1 and 10, the proportion of times that an 8 is generated tends to get closer to 0.10 as the number of random numbers generated gets larger and larger.

d. When generating a large set of random numbers between 1 and 10, each number between 1 and 10 occurs close to 10% of the time in this set.

5.7   **Polls and sample size**   A pollster agency wants to estimate the proportion of citizens of the European Union who support same-sex unions. She claims that if the sample size is large enough, she does not need to worry about the method of selecting the sample. Do you agree with the pollster's comments? Explain.

5.8   **Heart transplant**   Before the first human heart transplant, Dr. Christiaan Barnard of South Africa was asked to assess the probability that the operation would be successful. Did he need to rely on the relative frequency definition or the subjective definition of probability? Explain.

5.9   **Nuclear war**   You are asked to use your best judgment to estimate the probability that there will be a nuclear war within the next 10 years. Is this an example of relative frequency or subjective definition of probability? Explain.

5.10   **Simulate coin flips**   Use the *Random Numbers* app (go to the tab that says Coin Flips) on the book's website or other software (such as random.org/coin) to illustrate the long-run definition of probability by simulating short-term and long-term results of flipping a balanced coin.

a. Keep the probability of a head at the default value of 50% and set the number of flips to generate in a simulation to 10. Click on Simulate and record the proportion of heads for this simulation. Do this a total of 10 times by repeatedly clicking Simulate.

b. Now set the number of flips to 100. Click Simulate 10 times, and record the 10 proportions of heads for each simulation. Do they vary much?

c. Now set the number of flips to 1,000. Click Simulate 10 times, and record the 10 proportions of heads for each simulation. Do they vary more, or less, than the proportions in part b based on 100 flips?

d. Summarize the effect of the number of flips on the variability of the proportion. How does this reflect what's implied by the law of large numbers?

5.11   **Unannounced pop quiz**   A teacher announces a pop quiz for which the student is completely unprepared. The quiz consists of 100 true-false questions. The student has no choice but to guess the answer randomly for all 100 questions.

a. Simulate taking this quiz by random guessing. Number a sheet of paper 1 to 100 to represent the 100 questions. Write a T (true) or F (false) for each question, by predicting what you think would happen if you repeatedly flipped a coin and let a tail represent a T guess and a head represent an F guess. (Don't actually flip a coin; merely write down what you think a random series of guesses would look like.)

b. How many questions would you expect to answer correctly simply by guessing?

c. The table shows the 100 correct answers. The answers should be read across rows. How many questions did you answer correctly?

Pop Quiz Correct Answers

T	F	T	T	F	F	T	T	T	T	T	F	T	F	F	T	T	F	T	F
F	F	F	F	F	F	F	T	F	F	T	F	T	F	F	T	T	F	T	T
T	F	F	F	F	T	F	T	T	F	T	T	T	F	F	F	F	F	T
T	F	T	F	F	T	T	T	T	F	F	F	F	F	F	F	T	F	F
F	F	T	F	F	T	T	F	F	T	F	T	F	T	T	T	T	F	F

d. The preceding answers were actually randomly generated. What percentage were true, and what percentage would you expect? Why are they not necessarily identical?

e. Are there groups of answers within the sequence of 100 answers that appear nonrandom? For instance, what is the longest run of Ts or Fs? By comparison, which is the longest run of Ts or Fs within your sequence of 100 answers? (There is a tendency in guessing what randomness looks like to identify too few long runs in which the same outcome occurs several times in a row.)

5.12   **Stock market randomness**   An interview in an investment magazine (*In the Vanguard*, Autumn 2003) asked mathematician John Allen Paulos, "What common errors do investors make?" He answered, "People tend not to believe that markets move in random ways. Randomness is difficult to recognize. If you have people write down 100 Hs and Ts to simulate 100 flips of a coin, you will always be able to tell a sequence generated by a human from one generated by real coin flips. When humans make up the sequence, they don't put in enough consecutive Hs and Ts, and they don't make the lengths of those runs long enough or frequent enough. And that is one of the reasons people look at patterns in the stock market and ascribe significance to them." (Used with permission from John Allen Paulos, 2020.)

a. Suppose that on each of the next 100 business days the stock market has a 1/2 chance of going up and a 1/2 chance of going down, and its behavior one day is independent of its behavior on another day. Use the *Random Numbers* app or other software (such as random.org/coin) to simulate whether the market goes up or goes down for each of the next 100 days. What is the longest sequence of consecutive moves up or consecutive moves down that you observe? (*Hint:* In the *Random Numbers* app, go to the Coin Flip tab and type in 100 for the number of flips. The box below will show the outcomes of these many flips, which you can inspect for runs.)

b. Run the simulation nine more times, with 100 observations for each run, and each time record the longest sequence of consecutive moves up or consecutive moves down that you observe. For the 10 runs, summarize the proportion of times that the longest sequence was 1, 2, 3, 4, 5, 6, 7, 8, or more. (Your

class may combine results to estimate this more precisely.)

c. Based on your findings, explain why if you are a serious investor you should not get too excited if sometime in the next few months you see the stock market go up for five days in a row or go down for five days in a row.

5.2 Finding Probabilities

We've learned that probability enables us to quantify uncertainty and randomness. Now, let's explore some basic rules that help us find probabilities.

Sample Spaces

The first step is to list all the possible outcomes of the random phenomenon under investigation. The set of possible outcomes is called the **sample space.**

> ### Sample Space
> For a random phenomenon, the **sample space** is the set of all possible outcomes.

For example, when you roll a die once, the sample space consists of the six possible outcomes, $\{1,2,3,4,5,6\}$. When you flip a coin twice, the sample space consists of the four possible outcomes, $\{HH,HT,TH,TT\}$, where, for instance, TH represents a tail on the first flip and a head on the second flip.

Example 3

Sample Space ◀

Multiple-Choice Pop Quiz

Picture the Scenario

Your statistics instructor decides to give an unannounced pop quiz with three multiple-choice questions. Each question has five options, and the student's answer is either correct (C) or incorrect (I). If a student answered the first two questions correctly and the last question incorrectly, the student's outcome on the quiz can be symbolized by CCI.

Question to Explore

What is the sample space for the possible answers on this pop quiz?

Think It Through

One technique for listing the outcomes in a sample space is to draw a **tree diagram,** with branches showing what can happen on subsequent trials. For a student's performance on three questions, the tree has three sets of branches, as Figure 5.3 shows.

From the tree diagram, a student's performance has eight possible outcomes and the sample space is given by {CCC, CCI, CIC, CII, ICC, ICI, IIC, III}.

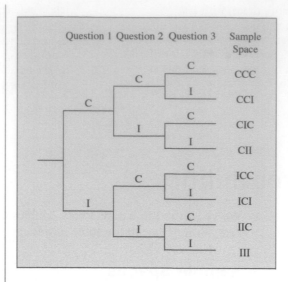

◀ **Figure 5.3** Tree Diagram for Student Performance on a Three-Question Pop Quiz. Each path from the first set of two branches to the third set of eight branches determines an outcome in the sample space. **Question** How many possible outcomes would there be if the quiz had four questions?

Insight

The number of branches doubles at each stage. There are 2 branches for question 1, $2 \times 2 = 4$ branches at question 2, and $2 \times 2 \times 2 = 8$ branches at question 3.

▶ *Try Exercise 5.14*

Figure 5.3 showed a tree diagram of the sample space. Another way to find out about the size of the sample space with repeated trials (such as flipping a coin) multiplies the number of possible outcomes on each trial with each other. For instance, a pop quiz with three questions (= trials) has $2 \times 2 \times 2 = 8$ possible outcomes in the sample space when denoting each answer as correct or incorrect. With four questions, there are $2 \times 2 \times 2 \times 2 = 16$ possible outcomes in the sample space.

Now, instead of measuring whether a question is answered correctly or incorrectly, suppose we want to record the actual choice made out of the 5 multiple-choice options for each question. Then, how big is the sample space? With 5 possible outcomes on each question (= trial), and 3 questions, there are $5 \times 5 \times 5 = 125$ possible outcomes in the sample space. With 4 questions, this increases to $5 \times 5 \times 5 \times 5 = 625$ possible outcomes. As you can see, drawing a tree diagram would be impractical in such situations, as there simply are too many options. The tree diagram is ideal for visualizing a small number of outcomes. As the number of trials or the number of possible outcomes on each trial increases, it becomes impractical to construct a tree diagram, so we'll also learn about methods for finding probabilities without having to list the entire sample space.

Events

We'll sometimes need to specify a particular group of outcomes in a sample space, that is, a *subset* of the outcomes. An example is the subset of outcomes for which a student passes the pop quiz by answering at least two of the three questions correctly. A subset of a sample space is called an **event**.

Event

An **event** is a subset of the sample space. An **event** corresponds to a particular outcome or a group of possible outcomes.

Events are usually denoted by letters from the beginning of the alphabet, such as A and B, or by a letter or string of letters that describes the event. For a student taking the three-question pop quiz, some possible events are

A = student answers all three questions correctly = {CCC}

B = student passes (at least two correct) = {CCI, CIC, ICC, CCC}.

Finding Probabilities of Events

Each outcome in a sample space has a probability. So does each event. To find such probabilities, we list the sample space and specify plausible assumptions about its outcomes. Sometimes, for instance, we can assume that the outcomes are equally likely. In any case, the probabilities for the outcomes in a sample space must follow two basic rules:

- The probability of each individual outcome is between 0 and 1.
- The sum of the probabilities of the individual outcomes in a sample space equals 1.

Probability for a Sample Space With ◄ Equally Likely Outcomes

Example 4

Treating Colds

Picture the Scenario

The University of Wisconsin is conducting a randomized experiment[1] to compare an herbal remedy (echinacea) to a placebo for treating the common cold. The response variables are the cold's severity and its duration. Suppose a particular clinic in Madison, Wisconsin, has four volunteers, of whom two are men (Jamal and Ken) and two are women (Linda and Mei). Two of these volunteers will be randomly chosen to receive the herbal remedy, and the other two will receive the placebo.

Questions to Explore

a. Identify the possible samples to receive the herbal remedy. For each possible sample, what is the probability that it is the one chosen?

b. What's the probability of the event that the sample chosen to receive the herbal remedy consists of one man and one woman?

Think It Through

a. To find the sample space, here it is best to think about all possible two-person groups that can be formed from the four volunteers. These are the 6 possible samples: {(Jamal, Ken), (Jamal, Linda), (Jamal, Mei), (Ken, Linda), (Ken, Mei), (Linda, Mei)}. Randomly choosing 2 out of the 4 participants means that each of these 6 samples in the sample space is equally likely to be chosen. Since there are six possible samples, each one has probability 1/6. These probabilities fall between 0 and 1, and their sum equals 1, as is necessary for probabilities for a sample space.

b. The event in which the sample chosen has one man and one woman consists of the outcomes {(Jamal, Linda), (Jamal, Mei), (Ken, Linda), (Ken, Mei)}. These are the possible pairings of one man with one woman. Each outcome has probability 1/6, so the probability of this event is 4(1/6) = 4/6 = 2/3.

[1]See www.fammed.wisc.edu/research/news0503d.html.

This example shows that to find the probability for an event, we can (1) find the probability for each outcome in the sample space and (2) add the probabilities of the outcomes that the event comprises.

SUMMARY: Probability of an Event

■ The probability of an event A, denoted by P(A), is obtained by adding the probabilities of the individual outcomes in the event.
■ When all the possible outcomes are equally likely,

$$P(A) = \frac{\text{number of outcomes in event A}}{\text{number of outcomes in the sample space}}.$$

In Example 4, to find the probability of choosing one man and one woman, we first determined the probability of each of the six possible outcomes. Because the probability is the same for each, 1/6, and because the event contains four of those outcomes, the probability is 1/6 added four times. The answer equals 4/6, the number of outcomes in the event divided by the number of outcomes in the sample space.

In Practice Equally Likely Outcomes Are Unusual

Except for simplistic situations such as random sampling or flipping balanced coins or rolling fair dice, different outcomes are not usually equally likely. Then, probabilities are often estimated, using sample proportions from simulations or from large samples of data.

Probabilities for a Sample Space With Outcomes That Are Not Equally Likely

Example 5

Tax Audit

Picture the Scenario

April 15 is tax day in the United States—the deadline for filing federal income tax forms. The main factor in the amount of tax owed is a taxpayer's income level. Each year, the IRS audits a sample of tax forms to verify their accuracy. Table 5.2 is a contingency table that cross-tabulates the nearly 150 million long-form federal returns received in 2017 by the taxpayer's income level and whether the tax form was audited.

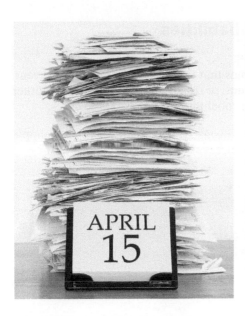

Recall

Section 3.1 introduced **contingency tables** to summarize the relationship between two categorical variables. ◄

Did You Know?

Most people find it easier to interpret probabilities, especially very small ones, by using their reciprocal. Thus, "there is a one in 1.9 million chance of being struck by lightning in the United States" is more accessible to most people than "the probability is 0.00000053," which is 1/1,900,000. (*Source:* http://www .lightningsafety.noaa.gov/odds.htm) ◄

Table 5.2 Contingency Table Cross-Tabulating Tax Forms by Income Level and Whether Audited

There were 149.9 million returns filed. The frequencies in the table are reported in thousands. For example, 839 represents approximately 839,000 tax forms that reported income under $200,000 and were audited.

Income Level	Audited		Total
	Yes	No	
Under $200,000	839	141,686	**142,525**
$200,000–$1,000,000	72	6,803	**6,875**
More than $1,000,000	23	496	**519**
Total	**934**	**148,986**	**149,919**

Source: https://www.irs.gov/pub/irs-news/fy_2017_enforcement_and_services_results_final.pdf, U.S. Department of Treasury

Questions to Explore

a. Consider, for each return, the income level and whether it was audited. If we draw a return at random, what are the possible outcomes that define the sample space?

b. What is the probability of each outcome in the sample space? Are they equally likely?

c. For a randomly selected return in 2017, what is the probability of (i) an audit, (ii) the return showing an income of more than $1,000,000?

Think It Through

a. The sample space is the set of all possible outcomes for a tax return. For each return, we recorded the income level (3 possibilities) and whether it was audited (2 possibilities), resulting in a total of 6 possible outcomes: (Under $200,000, Yes), (Under $200,000, No), ($200,000–$1,000,000, Yes), and so forth.

b. The probabilities for the 6 outcomes in the sample space are not equally likely. For instance, it is far more likely for a return to be not audited. Those outcomes that include a "No" for auditing are therefore far more likely than those that include a "Yes." To find the probability for each of the 6 outcomes, we divide the number of returns that fall in the corresponding cell of Table 5.2 by the total number of returns; e.g., the probability for the outcome (Under $200,000, Yes) equals 839/149,919 = 0.005596, about 0.56% or a chance of 1 in 179.

c. (i) The event of being audited consists of the three outcomes (Under $200,000, Yes), ($200,000 – $1,000,000, Yes) and (Over $1,000,000, Yes), with estimated probabilities of 839/149,919, 72/149,919, and 23/149,919, for a total of (839 + 72 + 23)/149,919 = 934/149,919 = 0.0062, or about a 1 in 161 chance.

  (ii) The event of a return showing an income of more than $1,000,000 consists of the outcomes (Over $1,000,000, No) and (Over $1,000,000, Yes), with probability (23 + 496)/149,919 = 519/149,919 = 0.0035, or about a 1 in 289 chance.

Insight

The event of a randomly selected return being audited consists of three of the possible six outcomes. If we wrongly assumed that the six possible outcomes are equally likely, then the probability for this event would be calculated as 3/6 = 0.5, vastly different from 0.0062.

▶ *Try Exercise 5.23, parts a and b*

Basic Rules for Finding Probabilities About a Pair of Events

Some events are expressed as the outcomes that (a) are *not* in some other event, or (b) are in one event *and* in another event, or (c) are in one event *or* in another event. We'll next learn how to calculate probabilities for these three cases.

The Complement of an Event   For an event A, all outcomes of the sample space that are *not* in A are called the **complement** of A.

Complement of an Event

The **complement** of an event A consists of all outcomes in the sample space that are *not* in A. It is denoted by A^C. The probabilities of A and of A^C add to 1, so

$$P(A^C) = 1 - P(A).$$

In Example 5, for instance, the event of having an income *less than* $200,000 is the complement of the event of having an income of $200,000 or more. Because the probability that a randomly selected taxpayer had an income of under $200,000 is $142,525/149,919 = 0.951$, the probability of income at least $200,000 is $1 - 0.951 = 0.049$.

Figure 5.4 illustrates the complement of an event. The box represents the entire sample space. The event A is the oval in the box. The complement of A, which is shaded, is everything else in the box that is not in A. Together, A and A^C cover the sample space. Because an event and its complement contain all possible outcomes, their total probability is 1, and the probability of either one of them is 1 minus the probability of the other. A diagram like Figure 5.4 that uses areas inside a box to represent events is called a **Venn diagram.**

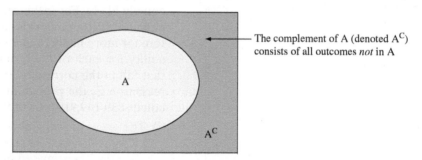

The complement of A (denoted A^C) consists of all outcomes *not* in A

▲ **Figure 5.4** Venn Diagram Illustrating an Event A and Its Complement A^C. **Question** Can you sketch a Venn diagram of two events A and B such that they share some common outcomes, but some outcomes are only in A or only in B?

To find the probability of an event, it's sometimes easier to find the probability of its complement and then subtract that probability from 1. An example is when we need to find the probability that *at least one* of several events will occur. It's usually easier to first find the probability of its complement, that *none* of these events will occur and then subtract it from 1.

Complement of an Event ◄

Example 6

Women on a Jury

Picture the Scenario

A jury of 12 people is chosen for a trial. The defense attorney claims it must have been chosen in a biased manner because 50% of the city's adult residents are female, yet the jury contains no women.

Questions to Explore

If the jury were randomly chosen from the population, what is the probability that the jury would have (a) no females, (b) at least one female?

Think It Through

Let's use 12 letters, with F for female and M for male, to represent a possible jury selection. For instance, MFMMMMMMMMMM denotes the jury in which only the second person selected is female. The number of possible outcomes is $2 \times 2 \times 2 \times \ldots \times 2$, that is, 2 multiplied 12 times, which is $2^{12} = 4,096$. This is a case in which listing the entire sample space is not practical. Since the population is 50% male and 50% female, these 4,096 possible outcomes are equally likely.

a. Only 1 of the 4,096 possible outcomes corresponds to a no-female jury, namely, MMMMMMMMMMMM. Based on what we learned about equally likely outcomes, the probability of this outcome is 1/4,096, or 0.00024. So, if a jury is truly chosen by random sampling, the event of having no women in it is extremely unlikely (0.02%).

b. As noted previously, it would be tedious to list all possible outcomes in which at least one female is on the jury. But this is not necessary. The event that the jury contains *at least one* female is the complement of the event that it contains *no* females. Thus,

$$P(\text{at least one female}) = 1 - P(\text{no females}) = 1 - 0.00024 = 0.99976.$$

Insight

You might instead let the sample space be the possible values for the *number* of females on the jury, namely 0, 1, 2, . . . 12. But these outcomes are not equally likely. For instance, only one of the 4,096 possible samples has 0 females, but 12 of them have 1 female: The female could be the first person chosen, or the second (as in MFMMMMMMMMMM), or the third, and so on. Chapter 6 will show a formula (binomial) that gives probabilities for this alternative sample space and will allow for cases when the outcomes are not equally likely.

► *Try Exercise 5.17*

Disjoint Events   Events that do not share any outcomes in common are said to be **disjoint**.

Disjoint Events

Two events, A and B, are **disjoint** if they do not have any common outcomes.

Did You Know?

Disjoint events are also referred to as **mutually exclusive** events. We will use only the term "disjoint." ◄

Example 3 discussed a pop quiz with three questions. The event that the student answers exactly one question correctly is {CII, ICI, IIC}. The event that the student answers exactly two questions correctly is {CCI, CIC, ICC}. These two events have no outcomes in common, so they are disjoint. In a Venn diagram, they have no overlap (Figure 5.5). By contrast, neither is disjoint from the event that the student answers the first question correctly, which is {CCC, CCI, CIC, CII}, because this event has outcomes in common with each of the other two events.

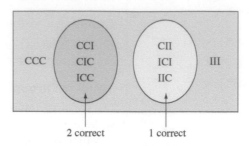

▲ **Figure 5.5 Venn Diagram Illustrating Disjoint Events.** The event of a student answering exactly one question correctly is disjoint from the event of answering exactly two questions correctly. **Question** Identify on this figure the event that the student answers the first question correctly. Is this event disjoint from either of the two events identified in the Venn diagram?

Consider an event A and its complement, A^C. They share no common outcomes, so they are disjoint events.

Intersection and Union of Events Some events are composed from other events. For instance, for two events A and B, the event that *both* occur is also an event. Called the **intersection** of A and B, it consists of the outcomes that are in both A and B. By contrast, the event that the outcome is in A *or* B or both is the **union** of A and B. It is a larger set, containing the intersection as well as outcomes that are in A but not in B and outcomes that are in B but not in A. Figure 5.6 shows Venn diagrams illustrating the intersection and union of two events.

In Words

Intersection means A *and* B (the "overlap" of the events). **Union** means A *or* B or both.

Intersection and Union of Two Events

The **intersection** of A and B consists of outcomes that are in both A *and* B.

The **union** of A and B consists of outcomes that are in A *or* B or both. In probability, "A *or* B" denotes that A occurs or B occurs or both occur.

 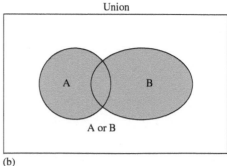

(a)   (b)

▲ **Figure 5.6 The Intersection and the Union of Two Events.** Intersection means A occurs *and* B occurs, denoted "A and B." The intersection consists of the shaded "overlap" part in Figure 5.6 (a). Union means A occurs *or* B occurs *or* both occur, denoted "A or B." It consists of all the shaded parts in Figure 5.6 (b). **Question** How could you find P(A or B) if you know P(A), P(B), and P(A and B)?

For instance, for the three-question pop quiz, consider the events:

$$A = \text{student answers first question correctly} = \{CCC, CCI, CIC, CII\}$$

$$B = \text{student answers two questions correctly} = \{CCI, CIC, ICC\}.$$

Then the intersection, A *and* B, is $\{CCI, CIC\}$, the two outcomes common to A and B. The union, A *or* B, is $\{CCC, CCI, CIC, CII, ICC\}$, the outcomes that are in A or in B or in both A and B.

How do we find probabilities of intersections and unions of events? Once we identify the possible outcomes, we can use their probabilities. For instance, for Table 5.2 (shown in the margin) for 149.9 million tax forms, let

A denote $\{\text{audited} = \text{yes}\}$

B denote $\{\text{income} \geq \$1,000,000\}$

The intersection A and B is the event that a taxpayer is audited *and* has income $\geq \$1,000,000$. This probability is simply the proportion of the 149.9 million tax forms for which these two events occurred, namely $P(A \text{ and } B) = 23/149,919 = 0.00015$. The union of A and B consists of all forms that either were audited or had income greater than $1,000,000 or both. From the table, these are $(839 + 72 + 23 + 496) = 1,430$ thousand forms, so the probability is $1,430/149,919 = 0.0095$. We can formalize rules for finding the union and intersection of two events, as we'll see in the next two subsections.

	Audited	
Income	**Yes**	**No**
Under $200,000	839	141,686
$200,000–$1,000,000	72	6,803
More than $1,000,000	23	496

Counts refer to thousands of taxpayers

Addition Rule: Finding the Probability That Event A or Event B Occurs

Since the union A or B contains outcomes from A and from B, we can add $P(A)$ to $P(B)$. However, this sum counts the outcomes that are in *both* A and B (their intersection) twice (Figure 5.7). We need to subtract the probability of the intersection from $P(A) + P(B)$ so that it is only counted once. If there is no overlap, that is, if the events are disjoint, no outcomes are common to A and B. Then we can simply add the probabilities.

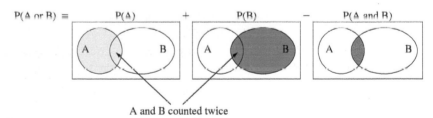

A and B counted twice

▲ **Figure 5.7** The Probability of the Union, Outcomes in A or B or Both. Add P(A) to P(B) and subtract P(A and B) to adjust for outcomes counted twice. **Question** When does $P(A \text{ or } B) = P(A) + P(B)$?

> **Addition Rule: Probability of the Union of Two Events**
>
> For the **union** of two events, $P(A \text{ or } B) = P(A) + P(B) - P(A \text{ and } B)$.
> If the events are **disjoint**, then $P(A \text{ and } B) = 0$, so $P(A \text{ or } B) = P(A) + P(B)$.

For example, consider a family with two children. The sample space possibilities for the genders of the two children are $\{FF, FM, MF, MM\}$, where the first letter in a symbol is the first child's gender and the second letter is the second child's gender (F = female, M = male). Let the event $A = \{\text{first child a girl}\}$ and the event $B = \{\text{second child a girl}\}$. Then, assuming the four possible outcomes in the sample space are equally likely, $P(A) = P(\{FF, FM\}) = 0.50$,

$P(B) = P(\{FF, MF\}) = 0.50$, and $P(A \text{ and } B) = P(\{FF\}) = 0.25$. The event A or B is the event that the first child is a girl, or the second child is a girl, or both, that is, *at least* one child is a girl. Its probability is

$$P(A \text{ or } B) = P(A) + P(B) - P(A \text{ and } B) = 0.50 + 0.50 - 0.25 = 0.75.$$

Multiplication Rule: Finding the Probability That Events A and B Both Occur

The probability of the intersection of events A and B has a formula that we will introduce in the next section. Here, we will just look at an important special case, that of two independent events.

Consider playing two rounds of roulette in a casino, and let R1 denote the event of a red number in the first round and R2 the event of a red number in the second round. In U.S. casinos, the roulette wheel has 38 equally likely numbers, of which 18 are red, so the probability of a red number in any given round is 18/38 = 47.4%. This means $P(R1) = 47.4\%$ and $P(R2) = 47.4\%$. What is the probability of the event R1 and R2, the event of getting a red number in the first *and* second round? In the long run over many two-round games, of the 47.4% of games that had a red number in the first round, another 47.4% will have a red number in the second round. So, in the long run, 47.4% of 47.4% of games will have a red number in both the first and second round. This is a proportion of $0.474 \times 0.474 = 0.225$, or 22.5%. The probability of two red numbers is therefore $P(R1 \text{ and } R2) = 22.5\%$, which we obtained by multiplying $P(R1)$ and $P(R2)$.

This multiplication calculation is valid only under the assumption of **independent trials**. In this context, independent trials means the chance of a red number in the second round is independent of whether the number was red in the first round. The chance of a red number in the second round is 47.4%, regardless of the number obtained in the first round. This is true since the outcomes of successive spins of the roulette wheel don't depend on each other.

Summing up, to find the probability of the intersection of two events, we can multiply their probabilities whenever the events are independent.

Recall

Independent trials means that what happens on one trial is not influenced by what happens on any other trial. ◄

> ### Multiplication Rule: Probability of the Intersection of Independent Events
>
> For the **intersection** of two **independent** events, A and B,
>
> $$P(A \text{ and } B) = P(A) \times P(B).$$

The paradigm for independent events is repeatedly flipping a coin, spinning a wheel, or rolling a die, where what happens on one trial does not affect what happens on another. For instance, for two rolls of a die,

$$P(6 \text{ on roll } 1 \text{ and } 5 \text{ on roll } 2) = P(6 \text{ on roll } 1) \times P(5 \text{ on roll } 2) = \frac{1}{6} \times \frac{1}{6} = \frac{1}{36}.$$

This multiplication rule extends to more than two independent events.

Example 7

Multiplication Rule ◄

Guessing Yet Passing a Pop Quiz

Picture the Scenario

For a three-question multiple-choice pop quiz, a student is totally unprepared and randomly guesses the answer to each question. If each question has five options, then the probability of selecting the correct answer for any given question is 1/5, or 0.20. With guessing, the response on one question is not influenced by the response on another question. Thus, whether one question is answered correctly is independent of whether another question is answered correctly.

Questions to Explore

a. Find the probabilities of the possible student outcomes for the quiz, in terms of whether each response is correct (C) or incorrect (I).

b. Find the probability that the student passes, answering *at least two* questions correctly.

Think It Through

a. For each question $P(C) = 0.20$ and $P(I) = 1 - 0.20 = 0.80$. The probability that the student answers all three questions correctly is
$$P(CCC) = P(C) \times P(C) \times P(C) = 0.20 \times 0.20 \times 0.20 = 0.008.$$
This would be unusual. Similarly, the probability of answering the first two questions correctly and the third question incorrectly is
$$P(CCI) = P(C) \times P(C) \times P(I) = 0.20 \times 0.20 \times 0.80 - 0.032.$$
This is the same as P(CIC) and P(ICC), the other possible ways of getting two correct. Figure 5.8 is a tree diagram showing how to multiply probabilities to find the probabilities for all eight possible outcomes.

▲ **Figure 5.8** Tree Diagram for Guessing on a Three-Question Pop Quiz. Each path from the first set of branches to the third set determines one sample space outcome. Multiplication of the probabilities along that path gives its probability when trials are independent. **Question** Would you expect trials to be independent if a student is *not* merely guessing on every question? Why or why not?

b. The probability of *at least* two correct responses is
$$P(CCC) + P(CCI) + P(CIC) + P(ICC) = 0.008 + 3(0.032) = 0.104.$$
In summary, there is only about a 10% chance of passing when a student randomly guesses the answers.

Insight

As a check, you can see that the probabilities of the eight possible outcomes sum to 1.0. The probabilities indicate that it is in a student's best interests not to rely on random guessing.

▶ *Try Exercise 5.16*

Events Often Are Not Independent

In practice, events need not be independent. For instance, on a quiz with only two questions, the instructor found the following proportions for the actual responses of her students (I = incorrect, C = correct):

Outcome:	II	IC	CI	CC
Probability:	0.26	0.11	0.05	0.58

Recall

From Section 3.1, the proportions expressed in contingency table form

1st Question	2nd Question	
	C	**I**
C	0.58	0.05
I	0.11	0.26

A and B

◄

Let A denote {first question correct} and let B denote {second question correct}. Based on these probabilities,

$$P(A) = P(\{CI, CC\}) = 0.05 + 0.58 = 0.63$$
$$P(B) = P(\{IC, CC\}) = 0.11 + 0.58 = 0.69$$

and

$$P(A \text{ and } B) = P(\{CC\}) = 0.58.$$

If we (wrongly) assumed that A and B are independent and used the multiplication rule for independent events, then

$$P(A \text{ and } B) = P(A) \times P(B) = 0.63 \times 0.69 = 0.43.$$

This would provide a wrong answer, since P(A and B) actually equals 0.58, not 0.43.

Responses to different questions on a quiz are typically not independent. Most students do not guess randomly. Students who get the first question correct may have studied more than students who do not get the first question correct, and thus they may also be more likely to get the second question correct.

In Practice Make Sure That Assuming Independence Is Realistic

Don't assume that events are independent unless you have given this assumption careful thought and it seems plausible. In Section 5.3, you will learn more about how to find probabilities when events are not independent.

Probability Rules

In this section, we have developed several rules for finding probabilities. Let's summarize them.

SUMMARY: Rules for Finding Probabilities

- The sample space lists the individual outcomes of a random phenomenon. The probability of each individual outcome in the sample space is between 0 and 1, and the sum of all the individual probabilities equals 1.
- The probability of an event is the sum of the probabilities of the individual outcomes from the sample space that make up the event.
- For an event A and its **complement** A^C (not in A), $P(A^C) = 1 - P(A)$.
- The **union** of two events (that is, A occurs or B occurs or both) has
$$P(A \text{ or } B) = P(A) + P(B) - P(A \text{ and } B).$$
- When A and B are **independent,** the **intersection** of two events has
$$P(A \text{ and } B) = P(A) \times P(B).$$
- Two events A and B are **disjoint** when they have no common elements. Then
$$P(A \text{ and } B) = 0, \text{ and thus } P(A \text{ or } B) = P(A) + P(B).$$

5.2 | Practicing the Basics

5.13 Blood types   There are four major types of blood: A, B, AB, and O. Suppose 40% of a certain population has Type A, 10% Type B, 5% Type AB, and 45% Type O blood. The blood type of a randomly selected person from this population is determined as part of an experiment.

   a. List all the potential outcomes in the sample space.

   b. List the probabilities for each outcome in the sample space. Are they equally likely?

   c. Check that the probabilities for the outcomes in the sample space are (i) between 0 and 1 and (ii) sum to 1.

5.14 Student union poll   Part of a student opinion poll at a university asks students what they think of the quality of the existing student union building on the campus. The possible responses were great, good, fair, and poor. Another part of the poll asked students how they feel about a proposed fee increase to help fund the cost of building a new student union. The possible responses to this question were in favor, opposed, and no opinion.

   a. List all potential outcomes in the sample space for someone who is responding to both questions.

   b. Show how a tree diagram can be used to display the outcomes listed in part a.

5.15 Random digit   A single random number between 1 and 10 is generated using the *Random Numbers* app or other software, such as random.org.

   a. State the sample space for the possible outcomes.

   b. State the probability for each possible outcome, assuming the app or software generates equally likely outcomes.

   c. Each outcome in a sample space must have probability between 0 and 1, and the sum of the probabilities must equal 1. Show that your assignment of probabilities in part b satisfies this rule.

5.16 Pop quiz   A teacher gives a four-question unannounced true-false pop quiz, with two possible answers to each question.

   a. Use a tree diagram to show the possible response patterns in terms of whether any given response is correct or incorrect. How many outcomes are in the sample space?

   b. An unprepared student guesses all the answers randomly. Find the probabilities of the possible outcomes on the tree diagram.

   c. Refer to part b. Using the tree diagram, evaluate the probability of passing the quiz, which the teacher defines as answering *at least* three questions correctly.

5.17 More true-false questions   Your teacher gives a true-false pop quiz with 10 questions.

   a. Show that the number of possible outcomes for the sample space of possible sequences of 10 answers is 1,024.

   b. What is the complement of the event of getting *at least* one of the questions wrong?

   c. With random guessing, show that the probability of getting *at least* one question wrong is approximately 0.999.

5.18 Rolling two dice   Some friends are playing a game in which two six-sided dice are rolled (craps, Settlers of Catan, etc.). One of them exclaims, "Since the sum of the dice can be any of the 11 numbers between 2 and 12, there is a 1 in 11 chance that each result will occur." Do you agree or disagree with his assessment of the probabilities? Explain.

5.19 Three children   A couple plans to have three children. Suppose that the probability of any given child being female is 0.5, and suppose that the genders of each child are independent events.

   a. Write out all outcomes in the sample space for the genders of the three children.

   b. What should be the probability associated with each outcome?

Using the sample space constructed in part a, find the probability that the couple will have

   c. two girls and one boy.

   d. at least one child of each gender.

5.20 Wrong sample space   A couple plans to have four children. The father notes that the sample space for the number of girls the couple can have is 0, 1, 2, 3, and 4. He goes on to say that since there are five outcomes in the sample space, and since each child is equally likely to be a boy or girl, all five outcomes must be equally likely. Therefore, the probability of all four children being girls is 1/5. Explain the flaw in his reasoning.

5.21 Insurance   Every year the insurance industry spends considerable resources assessing risk probabilities. To accumulate a risk of about one in a million of death, you can drive 100 miles, take a cross-country plane flight, work as a police officer for 10 hours, work in a coal mine for 12 hours, smoke two cigarettes, be a nonsmoker but live with a smoker for two weeks, or drink 70 pints of beer in a year (Wilson and Crouch, 2001, pp. 208–209). Show that a risk of about one in a million of death is also approximately the probability of flipping 20 heads in a row with a balanced coin.

5.22 Cell phone and case   At the local cell phone store, the probability that a customer who walks in will purchase a new cell phone is 0.2. The probability that the customer will purchase a new cell phone protective case is 0.25. Is this information sufficient to determine the probability that a customer will purchase a new cell phone and a new cell phone protective case? If so, find the probability. If not, explain why not. (*Hint:* Considering the buying practices of consumers in this context, is it reasonable to assume these events are independent?)

5.23 Seat belt use and auto accidents   Based on records of automobile accidents in a recent year, the Department of Highway Safety and Motor Vehicles in Florida reported the counts who survived (S) and died (D), according to whether they wore a seat belt (Y = yes, N = no). The data are presented in the contingency table shown. (*Source:* Department of Highway Safety and Motor Vehicles in Florida; *255*: J. Haddow et al., New England Journal of Medicine, vol. 330, pp. 1114–1118, 1994)

Outcome of Auto Accident			
Wore Seat Belt	Survived (S)	Died (D)	Total
Yes (Y)	412,368	510	**412,878**
No (N)	162,527	1,601	**164,128**
Total	**574,895**	**2,111**	**577,006**

a. What is the sample space of possible outcomes for a randomly selected individual involved in an auto accident? Use a tree diagram to illustrate the possible outcomes. (*Hint:* One possible outcome is YS.)

b. Using these data, estimate (i) P(D), (ii) P(N).

c. Estimate the probability that an individual did not wear a seat belt and died.

d. Based on part a, what would the answer to part c have been if the events N and D were independent? So, are N and D independent, and if not, what does that mean in the context of these data?

5.24 Protecting the environment When the General Social Survey most recently asked subjects whether they are a member of an environmental group (variable GRNGROUP) and whether they would be willing to pay higher prices to protect the environment (variable GRNPRICE), the results were as shown in the table.

		Pay Higher Prices		
		Yes	Not Sure	No
Environmental Group	Yes	293	71	66
Member	No	2,211	1,184	1,386

For a randomly selected American adult:

a. Estimate the probability of being (i) a member of an environmental group and (ii) willing to pay higher prices to protect the environment.

b. Estimate the probability of being both a member of an environmental group *and* willing to pay higher prices to protect the environment.

c. Given the probabilities in part a, show that the probability in part b is larger than it would be if the variables were independent. Interpret.

d. Estimate the probability that a person is a member of an environmental group *or* willing to pay higher prices to protect the environment. Do this (i) directly using the counts in the table and (ii) by applying the appropriate probability rule to the estimated probabilities found in parts a and b.

5.25 Global warming and trees A survey asks subjects whether they believe that global warming is happening (yes or no) and how much fuel they plan to use annually for automobile driving in the future, compared to their past use (less, about the same, more).

a. Show the sample space of possible outcomes by drawing a tree diagram that first gives the response on global warming and then the response on fuel use.

b. Let A be the event of a "yes" response on global warming and let B be the event of a "less" response on future fuel use. Suppose P(A and B) > P(A)P(B). Indicate whether A and B are independent events and explain what this means in nontechnical terms.

5.26 Newspaper sales You are the director of newspaper sales for the local paper. Each customer has signed up for either weekday delivery or weekend delivery. You record whether he or she received the delivery as Y for yes and N for no. The probabilities of the customer receiving the newspaper are as follows.

Outcome (Weekday, Weekend):	YY	YN	NY	NN
Probability:	0.25	0.05	0.20	0.5

a. Display the outcomes in a contingency table, using the rows as the weekend event and the columns as the weekday event.

b. Let W denote the event that the customer bought a newspaper during the week and S be the event that he or she got it on the weekend (S for Saturday/Sunday). Find P(W) and P(S).

c. Explain what the event W and S means and find P(W and S).

d. Are W and S independent events? Explain why you would not normally expect customer choices to be independent.

5.27 Arts and crafts sales A local downtown arts and crafts shop found from past observation that 20% of the people who enter the shop actually buy something. Three potential customers enter the shop.

a. How many outcomes are possible for whether the clerk makes a sale to each customer? Construct a tree diagram to show the possible outcomes. (Let Y = sale, N = no sale.)

b. Find the probability of at least one sale to the three customers.

c. What did your calculations assume in part b? Describe a situation in which that assumption would be unrealistic.

5.3 Conditional Probability

As Example 1 explained, many employers require potential employees to take a diagnostic test for drug use. The diagnostic test has two categorical variables of interest: (1) whether the person has recently used drugs (yes or no), and (2) whether the diagnostic test shows that the person has used them (yes or no). Suppose the diagnostic test predicts that the person has recently used drugs. What's the probability that the person truly did use drugs?

This section introduces **conditional probability**, which deals with finding the probability of an event when you know that the outcome was in some particular part of the sample space. Most commonly, it is used to find a probability about a category for one variable (for instance, a person being a drug user), when we know the outcome on another variable (for instance, a test result showing drug use).

Finding the Conditional Probability of an Event

Income Level	Audited		
	Yes	**No**	**Total**
Under $200,000	839	141,686	**142,525**
$200,000–$1,000,000	72	6,803	**6,875**
More than $1,000,000	23	496	**519**
Total	**934**	**148,986**	**149,919**

Counts refer to thousands of taxpayers

Example 5 showed a contingency table on income and whether a taxpayer is audited by the IRS. The table is shown again in the margin. We found that the probability that a randomly selected taxpayer was audited equaled $934/149,919 = 0.0062$, or 0.6%. Were the chances higher if a taxpayer was at the highest income level? From the table in the margin, the number having income $\geq \$1,000,000$ was 519 (all counts refer to thousands of taxpayers). Of them, 23 were audited, for a probability of $23/519 = 0.0443$, or 4.4%. This is substantially higher than 0.6%, indicating that those earning the most are the most likely to be audited.

We call 4.4% a **conditional probability** because it doesn't refer to all 149,919 taxpayers, but only to those with income higher than one million (the condition). For taxpayers with more than 1 million income, the probability of being audited is 4.4%. The clause (= condition) "For taxpayers with more than 1 million income" makes it a conditional probability.

To indicate a conditional probability, we introduce new notation. Let A denote the event that a taxpayer is audited, and let B denote the event that the taxpayer had income higher than 1 million. Then $P(A|B)$ denotes the conditional probability of event A, given event B has occurred, i.e., the conditional probability that a taxpayer is audited, given that the taxpayer had income higher than 1 million. The " | " symbol in "A|B" stands for "given." For the tax example, $P(A|B) = 0.044$.

We can compute the conditional probability of A given B from the counts in a contingency table, as we just did with 23/519 using the taxpayer table. A more formal definition expresses the conditional probability $P(A|B)$ in terms of $P(A)$ and $P(A \text{ and } B)$.

> **Conditional Probability**
>
> For events A and B, the **conditional probability** of event A, given that event B has occurred, is
>
> $$P(A|B) = \frac{P(A \text{ and } B)}{P(B)}.$$
>
> $P(A|B)$ is read as "the probability of event A given event B." The vertical slash represents the word "given." Of the times that B occurs, $P(A|B)$ is the proportion of times that A also occurs.

From the contingency table of tax returns, we see that $P(B) = 519/149,919 = 0.003462$ and $P(A \text{ and } B) = 23/149,919 = 0.000153$. Of the proportion of 0.003462 taxpayers with income larger than 1 million, a fraction of 0.000153/0.003462 = 0.044, or 4.4% were audited. Expressed using the formula:

$$P(A|B) = \frac{P(A \text{ and } B)}{P(B)} = \frac{0.000153}{0.003462} = 0.044.$$

Given that a taxpayer has income larger than 1 million, the chance of being audited are 4.4%.

Does this concept of a conditional probability sound familiar? In Section 3.1, when learning about contingency tables, we saw that we could find **conditional proportions** for a categorical variable at any particular category of a second categorical variable. These enabled us to study how the outcome of a response variable (e.g. the presence of pesticides) depends on the outcome of an explanatory variable (e.g., the food type). The conditional probabilities just found are merely conditional proportions. They refer to the population of taxpayers, treating audit status as a response variable and income level as an explanatory variable.

We could find similar conditional probabilities on audit status at each given level of income. We'd then get the results shown in Table 5.3. For instance, what is the probability of being audited given that a taxpayer has income below 200,000? Table 5.3 shows a conditional probability of only 0.006, or 0.6%. How did we get this? Of all the 142,525 taxpayers with income less than 200,000, 839 were audited, for a conditional probability of 839/142,525 = 0.006, or 0.6%. Or, we could use the formula, with event A representing being audited and event B representing income below 200,000. Then, P(A|B) = P(A and B) / P(B) = (839/149,919) / (142,525/149,919) = 0.0056/0.9507 = 0.006.

Note that in each row of Table 5.3, the conditional probabilities sum to 1.0. This is because for a given income level (row), the conditional probabilities of being audited and not being audited cover all the possible outcomes.

Table 5.3 Conditional Probabilities on Audited Given the Income Level

Each cell count in Table 5.2 was divided by the row marginal total to obtain the conditional probabilities shown here, such as 0.006 = 839/142,525.

Income Level	Audited Yes	Audited No	Total
Under $200,000	0.006	0.994	**1.000**
$200,000–$1,000,000	0.010	0.990	**1.000**
More than $1,000,000	0.044	0.956	**1.000**

Figure 5.9 is a graphical illustration of the definition of conditional probability. "Given event B" means that we restrict our attention to the outcomes in that

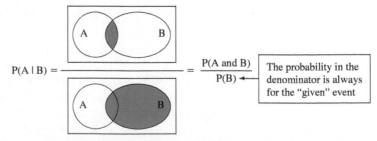

▲ **Figure 5.9** Venn Diagram of Conditional Probability of Event A Given Event B. Of the cases in which B occurred, P(A|B) is the proportion in which A also occurred. **Question** Sketch a representation of P(B|A). Is P(A|B) necessarily equal to P(B|A)?

event. This is the set of outcomes in the denominator. The proportion of those cases in which A occurred are those outcomes that are in event A as well as B. So the intersection of A and B is in the numerator.

Example 8

The Triple Blood Test for Down Syndrome

Picture the Scenario

A diagnostic test for a condition is said to be **positive** if it states that the condition is present and **negative** if it states that the condition is absent. How accurate are diagnostic tests? One way to assess accuracy is to measure the probabilities of two types of possible errors:

False positive: Test states the condition is present, but it is actually absent.

False negative: Test states the condition is absent, but it is actually present.

The Triple Blood Test screens a pregnant woman and provides an estimated risk of her baby being born with the genetic disorder Down syndrome. This syndrome is caused when abnormal cell division in a fetus results in extra genetic material from chromosome 21. It is the most common genetic cause of mental impairment. The chance of having a baby with Down syndrome increases after a woman is 35 years old.

A study[2] of 5,385 women aged 35 or over analyzed the Triple Blood Test to test its accuracy. It reported that of the 5,385 women, "48 of the 54 cases of Down syndrome would have been identified using the test and 25 percent of the unaffected pregnancies would have been identified as being at high risk for Down syndrome (these are false positives)."

Questions to Explore

a. Construct the contingency table that shows the counts for the possible outcomes of the blood test and whether the fetus has Down syndrome.

b. Assuming the sample is representative of the population, estimate the probability of a positive test for a randomly chosen pregnant woman 35 years or older.

c. Given that the diagnostic test result is positive, estimate the probability that Down syndrome is actually present.

Think It Through

a. We'll use the following notation for the possible outcomes of the two variables:

Down syndrome status: D = Down syndrome present, D^C = unaffected

Blood test result: POS = positive, NEG = negative.

Table 5.4 shows the four possible combinations of outcomes. From the article quote, there were 54 cases of Down syndrome. This is the first row total. Of them, 48 tested positive, so $54 - 48 = 6$ tested negative. These are the counts in the first row. There were 54 Down cases out of $n = 5,385$, so $5,385 - 54 = 5,331$ cases were unaffected, event D^C. That's the second row total. Now, 25% of those 5,331, or $0.25 \times 5,331 = 1,333$, would have a positive test. The remaining $5,331 - 1,333 = 3,998$ would have a negative test. These are the counts for the two cells in the second row.

[2]J. Haddow et al., *New England Journal of Medicine*, vol. 330, pp. 1114–1118, 1994.

Table 5.4 Contingency Table for Triple Blood Test of Down Syndrome

Down Syndrome Status	Blood Test		Total
	POS	NEG	
D (Down)	48	6	54
D^C (unaffected)	1,333	3,998	5,331
Total	1,381	4,004	5,385

b. From Table 5.4, the estimated probability of a positive test is $P(POS) = 1,381/5,385 = 0.256$.

c. The probability of Down syndrome, given that the test is positive, is the conditional probability $P(D|POS)$. Conditioning on a positive test means we consider only the cases in the first column of Table 5.4. Of the 1,381 who tested positive, 48 cases actually had Down syndrome, so $P(D|POS) = 48/1,381 = 0.035$. Let's see how to get this from the definition of conditional probability,

$$P(D|POS) = \frac{P(D \text{ and } POS)}{P(POS)}.$$

Since $P(POS) = 0.256$ from part b and $P(D \text{ and } POS) = 48/5,385 = 0.0089$, we get that $P(D|POS) = 0.0089/0.256 = 0.035$. In summary, of the women who tested positive, fewer than 4% actually had fetuses with Down syndrome.

Insight

So why should a woman undergo this test, as most positive test results are false positives? From Table 5.4, $P(D) = 54/5,385 = 0.010$, so we estimate a 1 in 100 chance of Down syndrome for women aged 35 or over. Also from Table 5.4, $P(D|NEG) = 6/4,004 = 0.0015$, a bit more than 1 in 1,000. A woman can have much less worry about Down syndrome if she has a negative test result because the chance of Down is then a bit more than 1 in 1,000, compared to 1 in 100 overall. On the other hand, a positive test result may lead to a lot of unnecessary stress, given that for only 4% of the positive tests Down syndrome is actually present.

▶ *Try Exercises 5.34 and 5.37*

Did You Know?

One way to follow up a positive test result is an Amniocentesis, a procedure in which amniotic fluid is removed from the uterus. The result of this genetic test can reliably rule out Down syndrome, but it comes with its own sets of risks. ◀

In Practice Conditional Probabilities in the Media

When you read or hear a news report that uses a probability statement, be careful to distinguish whether it is reporting a conditional probability. Most statements are conditional on some event and must be interpreted in that context. For instance, probabilities reported by opinion polls are often conditional on a person's gender, race, or age group.

Multiplication Rule for Finding P(A and B)

From Section 5.2, when A and B are independent events, $P(A \text{ and } B) = P(A) \times P(B)$. The definition of conditional probability provides a more general formula for P(A and B) that holds regardless of whether A and B are independent. We can multiply the equation $P(A|B) = P(A \text{ and } B)/P(B)$ on both sides by $P(B)$, to get the following formula for the probability of events A and B both occurring:

$$P(A \text{ and } B) = P(B) \times P(A|B).$$

Multiplication Rule for Evaluating P(A and B)

For events A and B, the probability that A and B both occur equals

$$P(A \text{ and } B) = P(B) \times P(A|B).$$

Applying the conditional probability formula to $P(B|A)$, we also see that

$$P(A \text{ and } B) = P(A) \times P(B|A).$$

Multiplication Rule ◄

Example 9

Double Faults in Tennis

Picture the Scenario

In a tennis match, on a given point, the player who is serving has two chances to hit the ball in play. The ball must fall in the correct marked box area on the opposite side of the net. A serve that misses that box is called a *fault*. Most players hit the first serve very hard, resulting in a fair chance of making a fault. If they do make a fault, they hit the second serve less hard and with some spin, making it more likely to be successful. Otherwise, with two misses—a *double fault*—they lose the point.

Question to Explore

The 2019 men's champion in the Wimbledon tournament was Novak Djokovic of Serbia. During the final match versus Roger Federer, he faulted on his first serve 38% of the time. Given that he made a fault with his first serve, he faulted on his second serve 10.8% of the time. Assuming these percentages are typical of his serving performance, what is the probability that he makes a double fault when he serves?

Think It Through

Let F1 be the event that Djokovic makes a fault with the first serve, and let F2 be the event that he makes a fault with the second serve. We know $P(F1) = 0.38$ and $P(F2|F1) = 0.108$, as shown in the margin figure. The event that Djokovic makes a double fault is "F1 and F2." From the multiplication rule, its probability is

$$P(F1 \text{ and } F2) = P(F_1) \times P(F_2|F_1) = 0.38 \times 0.108 = 0.041.$$

Insight

Djokovic makes a fault on his first serve 38% of the time, and in 10.8% of those cases, he makes a fault on his second serve. So, he makes a double fault in 10.8% of the 38% of points in which he faults on the first serve, which overall is 0.041 (or 4.1%) of all his service points.

► *Try Exercise 5.40*

F2(0.108)
F1(0.38)
(0.892)
Make Second Serve
(0.62)
Make First Serve

Did You Know?

In tennis, you only serve a second time if you fault on the first serve. ◄

Independent Events Defined Using Conditional Probability

Two events A and B are **independent** if the probability that one occurs is not affected by whether the other event occurs. This is expressed more formally using conditional probabilities.

Recall

Two events A and B are also independent if $P(A \text{ and } B) = P(A) \times P(B)$. ◄

For instance, let's consider the genders of two children in a family (F = female, M = male). The sample space is {FF, FM, MF, MM}. Suppose these four outcomes are equally likely, which is approximately true in practice. Let A denote {first child is female} and let B denote {second child is female}. Then $P(A) = 1/2$, since two of the four possible outcomes have a female for the first child. Likewise, $P(B) = 1/2$. Also, $P(A \text{ and } B) = 1/4$, since this corresponds to the single outcome, FF. So, from the definition of conditional probability,

$$P(B|A) = P(A \text{ and } B)/P(A) = (1/4)/(1/2) = 1/2.$$

Thus, $P(B|A) = 1/2 = P(B)$, so A and B are independent events. Given A (that the first child is female), the probability that the second child was female is 1/2 since one outcome (FF) has this out of the two possibilities (FF, FM). Intuitively, the gender of the second child does not depend on the gender of the first child.

Checking for Independence ◄

Example 10

Two Events from Diagnostic Testing

Picture the Scenario

Table 5.4 showed a contingency table relating the result of a diagnostic blood test (POS = positive, NEG = negative) to whether a woman's fetus has Down syndrome (D = Down syndrome, D^C = unaffected). Based on the counts in that table, the table in the margin shows the estimated conditional probabilities.

	Blood Test		
Status	**POS**	**NEG**	**Total**
D	0.889	0.111	**1.000**
D^C	0.250	0.750	**1.000**
Total	**0.256**	**0.744**	**1.000**

Questions to Explore

a. Are the events POS and D independent or dependent?
b. Are the events POS and D^C independent or dependent?

Think It Through

a. The probability of a positive test result is 0.256 because 1,381 out of 5,385 tested positive. However, the probability of a positive result, given Down syndrome, is

$$P(POS|D) = 0.889.$$

Since $P(POS|D) = 0.889$ differs from $P(POS) = 0.256$, the events POS and D are dependent.

b. Likewise,

$$P(POS|D^C) = 0.250.$$

This differs slightly from $P(POS) = 0.256$, so POS and D^C are also dependent events.

Insight

As we'd expect, the probability of a positive result depends on whether the fetus has Down syndrome, and it's much higher if the fetus does (88.9% vs. 25%). The diagnostic test would be worthless if the disease status and the test result were independent. However, the conditional probability $P(POS \mid D^C)$

reveals a serious issue with the test. Given the fetus does not have Down syndrome, the probability that the test gives a positive test result is 25%, which is quite larger. This is the probability of a false positive result known as the **false positive rate**. A consequence is that many women taking the test may be emotionally stressed by receiving a positive test result that eventually will turn out to be false.

▶ *Try Exercise 5.41*

Generally, if A and B are dependent events, then so are A and B^C, and so are A^C and B, and so are A^C and B^C. For instance, if A depends on whether B occurs, then A also depends on whether B does not occur. So, once we find that POS and D are dependent events, we know that POS and D^C are dependent events also.

We can now justify the formula given in Section 5.2 for the probability of the intersection of two independent events, namely $P(A \text{ and } B) = P(A) \times P(B)$. This is a special case of the multiplication rule for finding $P(A \text{ and } B)$,

$$P(A \text{ and } B) = P(A) \times P(B|A).$$

If A and B are independent, then $P(B|A) = P(B)$, so the multiplication rule simplifies to

$$P(A \text{ and } B) = P(A) \times P(B).$$

SUMMARY: Checking for Independence

There are three ways to determine if events A and B are independent:

- Is $P(A|B) = P(A)$?
- Is $P(B|A) = P(B)$?
- Is $P(A \text{ and } B) = P(A) \times P(B)$?

If any of these is true, then the others are also true and the events A and B are independent.

Disjoint Events versus Independent Events

Students often struggle to distinguish between the concepts of disjoint events and independent events. This is because the words seem to have a similar connotation. In fact, two events A and B that are disjoint can never be independent. Once we know event B has happened, it is impossible for event A to happen. This is because no outcomes of the sample space that are in B are also in A since A and B are disjoint. The probability of A, whatever it is initially, changes to zero once we know event B has happened. So, the probability of A depends on whether event B happened, making A and B dependent events.

As an example, let A be the event of rolling an even number and B be the event of rolling an odd number on a single roll of a die. A and B are disjoint events because no number on the die is both even and odd. However, they are not independent. Initially, $P(A) = 1/2$. But once we are told that event B has happened, $P(A|B) = 0$. Because $P(A) \neq P(A|B)$, A and B are not independent.

5.3 Practicing the Basics

5.28 Recidivism rates A 2014 article from *Business Insider* (http://www.businessinsider.com/department-of-justice-report-shows-high-recidivism-rate-2014-4) discusses recidivism rates in the United States. Recidivism is defined as being reincarcerated within five years of being sent to jail initially. Among the data reported, *Business Insider* cites that the recidivism rate for blacks is 81% compared to 73% among whites. Using notation, express each of these as a conditional probability.

5.29 Spam Because of the increasing nuisance of spam e-mail messages, many start-up companies have emerged to develop e-mail filters. One such filter was recently advertised as being 95% accurate. The way the advertisement is worded, 95% accurate could mean that (a) 95% of spam is blocked, (b) 95% of valid e-mail is allowed through, (c) 95% of the e-mail allowed through is valid, or (d) 95% of the blocked e-mail is spam. Let S denote {message is spam}, and let B denote {filter blocks message}. Using these events and their complements, identify each of these four possibilities as a conditional probability.

5.30 Tax audit and income Refer to Table 5.2 in Example 5, shown below again, on audit status and income of all 149,919 million tax returns filed in 2018.

a. Find the probability that a randomly selected return has income below 200,000 and is not audited.

b. Given that a return has income below 200,000, what is the probability it was not audited?

c. Given that a return is not audited, what is the probability that it had income below 200,000?

| | Audited | | |
Income Level	Yes	No	Total
Under $200,000	839	141,686	**142,525**
$200,000–$1,000,000	72	6,803	**6,875**
More than $1,000,000	23	496	**519**
Total	**934**	**148,985**	**149,919**

5.31 Religious affiliation The 2012 Statistical Abstract of the United States[3] provides information on individuals' self-described religious affiliations. The information for 2008 is summarized in the following table (all numbers are in thousands).

Christian	
Catholic	57,199
Baptist	36,148
Christian (no denomination specified)	16,834
Methodist/Wesleyan	11,366
Other Christian	51,855

Jewish	2,680
Muslim	1,349
Buddhist	1,189
Other non-Christian	3,578
No Religion	34,169
Refused to Answer	11,815
Total Adult Population in 2008	**228,182**

a. Find the probability that a randomly selected individual is identified as Christian.

b. Given that an individual identifies as Christian, find the probability that the person is Catholic.

c. Given that an individual answered, find the probability the individual is identified as following no religion.

5.32 Cancer deaths Current estimates are that about 25% of all deaths are due to cancer, and of the deaths that are due to cancer, 30% are attributed to tobacco, 40% to diet, and 30% to other causes.

a. Define events and identify which of these four probabilities refer to conditional probabilities.

b. Find the probability that a death is due to cancer and tobacco.

5.33 Revisiting seat belts and auto accidents The following table is from Exercise 5.23 classifying auto accidents by survival status (S = survived, D = died) and seat belt status of the individual involved in the accident.

| | Outcome | | |
Belt	S	D	Total
Yes	412,368	510	**412,878**
No	162,527	1,601	**164,128**
Total	**574,895**	**2,111**	**577,006**

a. Estimate the probability that the individual died (D) in the auto accident.

b. Estimate the probability that the individual died, given that the person (i) wore and (ii) did not wear a seat belt. Interpret results.

c. Are the events of dying and wearing a seat belt independent? Justify your answer.

5.34 Go Celtics! Larry Bird, who played pro basketball for the Boston Celtics, was known for being a good shooter. In games during 1980–1982, when he missed his first free throw, 48 out of 53 times he made the second one, and when he made his first free throw, 251 out of 285 times he made the second one.

a. Form a contingency table that cross tabulates the outcome of the first free throw (made or missed) in the rows and the outcome of the second free throw (made or missed) in the columns.

---

[3]*Source:* Data from www.census.gov, U.S. Department of Commerce.

b. For a given pair of free throws, estimate the probability that Bird (i) made the first free throw and (ii) made the second free throw. (*Hint:* Use counts in the (i) row margin and (ii) column margin.)

c. Estimate the probability that Bird made the second free throw, given that he made the first one. Does it seem as if his success on the second shot depends strongly, or hardly at all, on whether he made the first?

5.35 **Identifying spam** An article[4] on www.networkworld .com about evaluating e-mail filters that are designed to detect spam described a test of MailFrontier's Anti-Spam Gateway (ASG). In the test, there were 7,840 spam messages, of which ASG caught 7,005. Of the 7,053 messages that ASG identified as spam, they were correct in all but 48 cases.

a. Set up a contingency table that cross classifies the actual spam status (with the rows "spam" and "not spam") by the ASG filter prediction (with the columns "predict message is spam" and "predict message is not spam"). Using the information given, enter counts in three of the four cells.

b. For this test, given that a message is truly spam, estimate the probability that ASG correctly detects it.

c. Given that ASG identifies a message as spam, estimate the probability that the message truly was spam.

5.36 **Homeland security** According to an article in *The New Yorker* (March 12, 2007), the Department of Homeland Security in the United States is experimenting with installing devices for detecting radiation at bridges, tunnels, roadways, and waterways leading into Manhattan. The New York Police Department (NYPD) has expressed concerns that the system would generate too many false alarms.

a. Form a contingency table that cross classifies whether a vehicle entering Manhattan contains radioactive material and whether the device detects radiation. Identify the cell that corresponds to the false alarms the NYPD fears.

b. Let A be the event that a vehicle entering Manhattan contains radioactive material. Let B be the event that the device detects radiation. Sketch a Venn diagram for which each event has similar (not the same) probability but the probability of a false alarm equals 0.

c. For the diagram you sketched in part b, explain why $P(A|B) = 1$, but $P(B|A) < 1$.

5.37 **Down syndrome again** Example 8 discussed the Triple Blood Test for Down syndrome, using data summarized in a table shown again below.

Status	Blood Test POS	NEG	Total
D	48	6	**54**
D^c	1,333	3,998	**5,331**
Total	**1,381**	**4,004**	**5,385**

a. Given that a test result is negative, show that the probability the fetus actually has Down syndrome is $P(D|NEG) = 0.0015$.

b. Is $P(D|NEG)$ equal to $P(NEG|D)$? If so, explain why. If not, find $P(NEG|D)$.

5.38 **Obesity in America** A 2014 Gallup poll reported that 27% of people in the United States are obese (having a body mass index score of 30 or more). Blacks have the highest obesity rate at 35%, whereas Asians have the lowest, at 9%.

a. Of the three percentages (estimated probabilities) reported, which are conditional? Explain.

b. These results are based on telephone interviews of 272,347 adults aged 18 or older. Of these adults, 24,131 were Black and 5,752 were Asian. Create a contingency table showing estimated counts for race (Black, Asian, Other) and obesity (Yes, No).

c. Create a tree diagram with the first branching representing race and the second branching representing obesity. Be sure to include the appropriate percentages on each branch.

5.39 **Happiness in relationship** Are people happy in their romantic relationships? The table shows results from the 2012 General Social Survey for adults classified by gender and happiness. (*Source:* 2012 General Social Survey © 2011–2019 NORC.)

Gender	Level of Happiness Very Happy	Pretty Happy	Not Too Happy	Total
Male	69	73	4	**146**
Female	78	80	13	**171**
Total	**147**	**153**	**17**	**317**

a. Estimate the probability that an adult is very happy in their romantic relationship.

b. Estimate the probability that an adult is very happy (i) given that the adult identifies as male and (ii) given that the adult identifies as female.

c. For these subjects, are the events being very happy and identifying as female independent? (Your answer will apply merely to this sample. Chapter 11 will show how to answer this for the population of all adults.)

5.40 **Serena Williams serves** In her loss in the 2019 Wimbledon finals (against Simona Halep), Serena Williams made 32 of her 47 first serves and committed one double fault.

a. Find the probability that her first serve is good.

b. Find the conditional probability of double faulting, given that her first serve resulted in a fault.

c. On what percentage of her service points does she double fault?

---

[4]www.networkworld.com/reviews/2003/0915spamstats.html.

5.41 Free throws Pro basketball player Shaquille O'Neal was a poor free-throw shooter. Consider situations in which he shoots a pair of free throws. The probability that he makes the first free throw is 0.50. Given that he makes the first, suppose the probability that he makes the second is 0.60. Given that he misses the first, suppose the probability that he makes the second one is 0.40.

a. What is the probability that he makes both free throws?

b. Find the probability that he makes *one* of the two free throws (i) using the multiplicative rule with the two possible ways he can do this and (ii) by defining this as the complement of making neither or both of the free throws.

c. Are the results of the free throws independent? Explain.

5.42 Conditional probability? Which of the four statements refers to a conditional probability when selecting an adult person from the U.S population at random? (The probabilities are estimated based on a representative sample.)

a. There is a 93% probability that the person favors universal background checks for gun sales.

b. There is a 43% probability that the person owns a gun.

c. Given that the person is a gun owner, there is an 87% chance that the person favors universal background checks.

d. There is a 37% chance that the person is a gun owner and supports universal background checks.

5.43 Conditional or not conditional? For a randomly selected passenger on the Titanic, which of the following statements refers to a conditional probability?

a. There is an 8% chance that the passenger was booked in third class and survived the sinking.

b. If the passenger was booked in third class, there is a 25% chance the passenger survived the sinking.

c. If the passenger survived, there is a 28% chance the passenger was booked in first class.

d. There is a 32% chance that the passenger survived.

5.44 Disjoint or independent A roulette wheel has 18 even-numbered slots, 18 odd-numbered slots, a slot numbered zero, and a double zero slot. The zero and double zero slots are considered neither even nor odd. On each spin of the wheel, one of these 38 slots is selected at random. Are the two events {even number} and {uneven number} from one spin of the roulette wheel

a. disjoint or not disjoint events?

b. independent or dependent events?

Explain why.

5.45 Family with two children For a family with two children, let A denote {first child is female}, let B denote (at least one child is female}, and let C denote {both children are female}.

a. Show that $P(C|A) = 1/2$.

b. Are A and C independent events? Why or why not?

c. Find $P(C|B)$.

d. Describe what makes $P(C|A)$ different than $P(C|B)$.

5.46 Checking independence In three independent flips of a balanced coin, let A denote {first flip is a head}, B denote {second flip is a head}, C denote {first two flips are heads}, and D denote {three heads on the three flips}.

a. Find the probabilities of A, B, C, and D.

b. Which, if any, pairs of these events are independent? Explain.

5.4 Applying the Probability Rules

Probability relates to many aspects of your daily life—for instance, when you make decisions that affect your financial well being and when you evaluate risks due to lifestyle decisions. Objectively or subjectively, you need to consider questions such as: What's the chance that the business you're thinking of starting will succeed? What's the chance that the extra collision insurance you're thinking of getting for your car will be needed?

We'll now apply the basics of probability to coincidence in our lives.

Is a Coincidence Truly an Unusual Event?

Some events in our lives seem to be coincidental. One of the authors, who lives in Georgia, once spent a summer vacation in Newfoundland, Canada. One day during that trip, she made an unplanned stop at a rest area and observed a camper with a Georgia license tag from a neighboring county to her hometown. She discovered that the camper's owner was a patient of her physician husband. Was this meeting as coincidental as it seemed?

Events that seem coincidental are often not so unusual when viewed in the context of *all* the possible random occurrences at all times. Lots of topics can trigger an apparent coincidence—the person you meet having the same last name as yours, the same birth place, the same high school or college, the same profession, the same birthday, and so on. It's really not so surprising that in your travels you will sometime have a coincidence, such as seeing a friend or meeting someone who knows somebody you know.

With a large enough sample of people or times or topics, seemingly surprising things are actually quite sure to happen. Events that are rare per person occur rather commonly with large numbers of people. If a particular event happens to one person in a million each day, then in the United States, we expect about 300 such events a day and more than 100,000 every year. The one in a million chance regularly occurs, however surprised we may be if it should happen to us.

If you take a coin now and flip it 10 times, you would probably be surprised to get 10 heads. But if you flipped the coin for a long time, would you be surprised to get 10 heads in a row at some point? Perhaps you would, but you should not be. For instance, if you flip a balanced coin 2,000 times, then you can expect the longest run of heads during those flips to be about 10. When a seemingly unusual event happens to you, think about whether it is like seeing 10 heads on the next 10 flips of a coin, or more like seeing 10 heads in a row sometime in a long series of flips. If the latter, it's really not such an unusual occurrence.

Coincidence and Seemingly Unusual Patterns

Once we have data, it's easy to find patterns: 10 heads in a row, 10 tails in a row, 5 tails followed by 5 heads, and so forth. Our minds are programmed to look for patterns. Out of the huge number of things that can happen to us and to others over time, it's not surprising to occasionally see patterns that seem unusual.

To illustrate that an event you may perceive as a coincidence is actually not that surprising, let's answer the question, "What is the chance that at least two people in your class have the same birthday?"

Coincidence ◄

Example 11

Matching Birthdays

Picture the Scenario

Suppose a class has 25 students. Since there are 365 possible birth dates (without counting February 29), our intuition tells us that the probability of two or more students sharing the same birthday is small. Assume that the birth date of a student is equally likely to be any one of the 365 days in a year and that students' birth dates are independent (for example, there are no twins in the class).

Question to Explore

What is the probability that *at least* two of the 25 students have the same birthday? Is our intuition correct that the probability of a match is small?

Think It Through

The event of *at least one* birthday match includes one match, two matches, or more. To find the probability of *at least one* match, it is simpler to find the complement probability of *no* matches. Then

$$P(\text{at least one match}) = 1 - P(\text{no matches}).$$

To begin, suppose a class has only two students. The first student's birthday could be any of 365 days. Given that student's birthday, the chance that the second student's birthday is different is 364/365 because 364 of the possible 365 birthdays are different. The probability is $1 - 364/365 = 1/365$ that the two students share the same birthday.

Now suppose a class has three students. The probability that all three have different birthdays is

$P(\text{no matches}) = P(\text{students 1 and 2 and 3 have different birthdays}) =$

$P(\text{students 1 and 2 different}) \times P(\text{student 3 different} | \text{students 1 and}$

$2 \text{ different}) = (364/365) \times (363/365).$

The second probability in this product equals 363/365 because there are 363 days left for the third student that differ from the different birthdays of the first two students.

For 25 students, similar logic applies. By the time we get to the 25th student, for that student's birthday to differ from the other 24, there are 341 choices left out of 365 possible birthdays. So

$P(\text{no matches}) = P(\text{students 1 and 2 and 3 \dots and 25 have different birthdays})$

$= (364/365) \times (363/365) \times (362/365) \times \ \dots \ \dots \ \dots \ \times (341/365).$

student 2,	student 3,	student 4,	next 20 students	student 25,
given 1	given 1,2	given 1,2,3		given 1,...,24

This product equals 0.43. Using the probability for the complement of an event,

$P(\text{at least one match}) = 1 - P(\text{no matches}) = 1 - 0.43 = 0.57.$

The probability exceeds 1/2 of at least one birthday match in a class of 25 students.

Insight

Is this probability higher than you expected? It should not be once you realize that with 25 students, there are 300 *pairs* of students who can share the same birthday (see Exercise 5.49). Remember that with lots of opportunities for something to happen, coincidences are really not so surprising.

Did you have a birthday match in your class? Was it coincidence? If the number of students in your class is at least 23, the probability of at least one match is greater than 1/2. For a class of 50 students, the probability of at least one match is 0.97. For 100 students, it is 0.9999997 (there are then 4,950 different *pairs* of students). Here are a couple of other facts about matching birthdays that may surprise you:

- With 88 people, there's a 1/2 chance that at least three people have the same birthday.

- With 14 people, there's a 1/2 chance that at least two people have a birthday within a day of each other in the calendar year.

▶ *Try Exercise 5.47*

Sampling With or Without Replacement

In many sampling processes, once subjects are selected from a population, they are not eligible to be selected again. This is called *sampling without replacement*. At any stage of such a sampling process, probabilities of potential outcomes depend on the previous outcomes. Conditional probabilities are then used in finding probabilities of the possible samples.

Sampling Without Replacement ◄

Example 12

Winning Lotto

Picture the Scenario

The biggest jackpot in state lotteries, typically millions of dollars, comes from the Lotto game. In Lotto South, available in Georgia, Kentucky, and Virginia, six numbers are randomly sampled without replacement from the integers 1 to 49. For example, a possible sample is (4, 9, 23, 26, 40, 46). Their order of selection is not important.

Question to Explore

You buy a Lotto South ticket. What is the probability that it is a winning ticket, matching the six numbers chosen?

Think It Through

The probability of winning is the probability that the six numbers chosen are the six that you have on your ticket. Since your ticket has 6 of the 49 numbers that can be selected for the first number, P(you have 1st number) = 6/49. Given that you have the first number, for the second trial there are 5 numbers left that you hold out of 48 possible, so P(have 2nd number | have 1st number) = 5/48. Given that you have the first two, for the third trial there are 4 numbers left that you hold out of 47 possible, so P(have 3rd number | have 1st and 2nd numbers) = 4/47. Continuing with this logic, using an extension of the multiplication rule with conditional probabilities,

P(have all 6 numbers) = P(have 1st and 2nd and 3rd and 4th and 5th and 6th)

= P(have 1st) × P(have 2nd | have 1st) × P(have 3rd | have 1st and 2nd) . . .

. . . × P(have 6th | have 1st and 2nd and 3rd and 4th and 5th)

= (6/49) × (5/48) × (4/47) × (3/46) × (2/45) × (1/44)

= 720/10,068,347,520 = 0.00000007.

This is about 1 chance in 14 million.

Insight

Note that it would be wrong to write P(have 2nd number) = 5/48 without indicating that this probability assumes that you already matched the first number. In fact, P(have 2nd number) is much larger than 5/48 because it also considers all the cases where you did not match the first number. So, be careful that you use conditional probabilities whenever you assume some event has already occurred.

► *Try Exercise 5.50*

Lotto South uses *sampling without replacement*. Once a number is chosen, it cannot be chosen again. If, by contrast, Lotto South allowed numbers to be picked more than once, the sampling scheme would be *sampling with replacement*.

After each observation without replacement, the population remaining is reduced by one and the conditional probability of a particular outcome changes. It can change considerably when the population size is small, as we saw in the Lotto example. However, with large population sizes, reducing the population by one does not much affect the probability from one trial to the next. In practice,

Recall

From Chapter 4, Section 4.1, a simple random sample of *n* subjects from a population is one in which each possible sample of that size has the same chance of being selected. ◄

when selecting samples, we usually sample without replacement. With populations that are large (in the millions) compared to the sample size (in the thousands), the probability of any given observation depends little on the previous observations. Probabilities of possible samples are then practically equivalent for sampling without replacement and sampling with replacement. Why is this important? Remember, we defined a random sample as one for which each possible sample is equally likely. When the population is large in comparison to the sample, then it really doesn't matter whether we sample with or without replacement.

Multiplication Rule for Several Events

The birthday example and the Lotto example both used an extension of the multiplicative rule $P(A \text{ and } B) = P(A)P(B|A)$ that applies when more than two events are involved.

For three events A, B, and C, the probability that all three occur equals

$$P(A \text{ and } B \text{ and } C) = P(A)P(B|A)P(C|A \text{ and } B)$$

If the events are independent of each other, then

$$P(A \text{ and } B \text{ and } C) = P(A)P(B)P(C)$$

This rule extends to more than three events. For instance, with four events, $P(A \text{ and } B \text{ and } C \text{ and } D) = P(A)P(B|A)P(C|A \text{ and } B)P(D|A \text{ and } B \text{ and } C)$. If you go back to the Lotto South example, you'll see how we used the rule with six events, one for each of our six selected numbers matching the winning numbers.

In Practice, Probability Models Approximate Reality

We've now found probabilities in many idealized situations. In practice, it's often not obvious when different outcomes are equally likely or different events are independent. When calculating probabilities, it is advisable to specify a **probability model** that spells out all the assumptions made.

> ### Probability Model
>
> A **probability model** specifies the possible outcomes for a sample space and provides assumptions on which the probability calculations for events composed of those outcomes are based.

We will see examples of simple probability models in Chapter 6 for various random phenomena. In practice, though, probability models merely *approximate* reality. They are rarely *exactly* satisfied. For instance, in the matching birthday example, our probability model ignored February 29, assumed each of the other 365 birthdays are equally likely, and assumed that students' birth dates are independent. So, the answer found is only approximate. Whether probability calculations using a particular probability model are accurate depends on whether assumptions in that model are close to the truth or unrealistic.

Diagnostic Testing and Bayes' Rule

We've seen the important role that probability plays in diagnostic testing, illustrated in Section 5.3 (Example 8) with the pregnancy test for Down syndrome. Table 5.5 summarizes conditional probabilities about the result of a diagnostic test, given whether some condition or state (such as Down syndrome) is present. We let S denote that the state is present and S^C denote that it is not present.

Table 5.5 Probabilities of Correct and Incorrect Results in Diagnostic Testing

The probabilities in the body of the table refer to the test result, conditional on whether the state (S) is truly present. The sensitivity and specificity are the probabilities of the two types of correct diagnoses.

State Present?	Diagnostic Test Result		Total Probability
	Positive (POS)	Negative (NEG)	
Yes (S)	Sensitivity $P(POS|S)$	False negative rate $P(NEG|S)$	**1.0**
No (S^C)	False positive rate $P(POS|S^C)$	Specificity $P(NEG|S^C)$	**1.0**

In Table 5.5, **sensitivity** and **specificity** refer to correct test results, given the actual state. For instance, given that the state tested for is present, sensitivity is the probability the test detects it by giving a positive result, that is, sensitivity = $P(POS|S)$.

Medical journal articles or diagnostic tests offered via the Internet commonly report the sensitivity and specificity. However, what's more relevant to you once you take a diagnostic test are the conditional probabilities that condition on the test result. If you know the sensitivity and specificity and how often the state occurs, can you find $P(S|POS)$ by using the rules of probability?

It turns out that there is a formula known as **Bayes' Rule** that will allow you to compute this probability. However, instead of giving that formula, it is actually easier to find this probability with a tree diagram, as shown in the margin. The first branches show the probabilities of the two possible states, $P(S)$ and $P(S^C)$. The next set of branches show the known conditional probabilities, such as $P(POS|S)$, for which we are given the true state. Then, according to our multiplication rule from Section 5.3, the products $P(S)P(POS|S)$ and $P(S^C)P(POS|S^C)$ give intersection probabilities $P(S \text{ and } POS)$ and $P(S^C \text{ and } POS)$, which can be used to get probabilities such as

$$P(POS) = P(S \text{ and } POS) + P(S^C \text{ and } POS).$$

Then you can find $P(S|POS) = P(S \text{ and } POS)/P(POS)$.

Example 13

Bayes' Rule ◄

Random Drug Testing of Air Traffic Controllers

Picture the Scenario

Air traffic controllers monitor the flights of aircraft and help to ensure safe takeoffs and landings. In the United States, air traffic controllers are required to undergo periodic random drug testing. A urine test is used as an initial screening due to its low cost and ease of implementation. One such urine test, the *Triage Panel for Drugs of Abuse plus TCA*,[5] detects the presence of drugs. Its sensitivity and specificity have been reported[6] as 0.96 and 0.93. Based on past drug testing of air traffic controllers, the FAA reports that the probability of drug use at a given time is approximately 0.007 (less than 1%). This is called the **prevalence** of drug use.

---

[5]Screening assay from Biosite Diagnostics, San Diego, California.
[6]M. Peace et al., *Journal of Analytical Toxicology*, vol. 24 (2000).

Questions to Explore

a. A positive test result puts the air traffic controller's job in jeopardy. What is the probability of a positive test result?

b. Find the probability an air traffic controller truly used drugs, given that the test is positive.

Think It Through

a. We've been given the probability of drug use, $P(S) = 0.007$, the sensitivity $P(POS|S) = 0.96$, and the specificity $P(NEG|S^C) = 0.93$. Figure 5.10 shows a tree diagram that is useful for visualizing these probabilities and for finding P(POS).

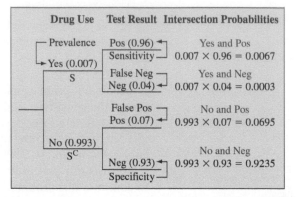

▲ **Figure 5.10** Tree Diagram for Random Drug Testing of Air Traffic Controllers. The first set of branches shows the probabilities for drug use. The second set of branches shows the conditional probabilities for the test result, given whether the person used drugs or not. Multiplication of the probabilities along each path gives the probabilities of intersections of the events.

From the tree diagram and the multiplication rule from Section 5.3,

$$P(S \text{ and } POS) = P(S)P(POS|S) = 0.007 \times 0.96 = 0.0067.$$

The other path with a positive test result has probability

$$P(S^C \text{ and } POS) = P(S^C)P(POS|S^C) = 0.993 \times 0.07 = 0.0695.$$

To find P(POS), we add the probabilities of these two possible positive test paths. Thus,

$$P(POS) = P(S \text{ and } POS) + P(S^C \text{ and } POS)$$
$$= 0.0067 + 0.0695 = 0.0762.$$

There's nearly an 8% chance of the test suggesting that the person used drugs. Why can we simply add the probabilities here in the last step? Because the two events "S and POS" and "S^C and POS" are disjoint (an air traffic controller can either use drugs and test positive or not use drugs and test positive), and we can use the simple addition rule.

b. The probability of drug use, given a positive test, is $P(S|POS)$. From the definition of conditional probability,

$$P(S|POS) = P(S \text{ and } POS)/P(POS) = 0.0067/0.0762 = 0.0880.$$

When the test is positive, only 9% of the time had the person actually used drugs.

If you're uncertain about how to answer part a and part b with a tree diagram, you can construct a contingency table, as shown in Table 5.6. Assume 10,000 controllers are tested. We are told that 0.7% of them use drugs, which is 70. This is the total for the first row. The remaining $10,000 - 70 = 9,930$ do not use drugs. This is the total of the second row in Table 5.6. We are also told that of those 70 who use drugs, 96% test positive, which is 67, which leaves 3 who test negative. These are the counts in the first row. Finally, we know that of those 9,930 who do not use drugs, 93% test negative, which is 9,235. The remaining 9,930 − 9,235 = 695 test positive. These two counts form the second row of Table 5.6. Finally, fill in the last row of Table 5.6, which shows the column totals. With this table, we see that out of the 762 controllers who tested positive, 67 actually used drugs, for a proportion of 67/762 = 0.0880, or about 9%.

We started with a hypothetical group of 10,000 controllers here to get the numerical accuracy we needed for the low probabilities involved, especially the fact that only 0.7% use drugs. You can build a similar table assuming a group of 1,000 controllers or, for even higher numerical accuracy, 100,000 controllers.

Table 5.6 Contingency Table for a Hypothetical Group of 10,000 Air Controllers

Use Drugs?	Drug Test Result		Total
	POS	**NEG**	
Yes (S)	67	3	70
No (S^C)	695	9,235	9,930
Total	**762**	**9,238**	**10,000**

Insight

If the prevalence rate is truly near 0.007, the chances are low that an individual who tests positive is actually a drug user. Does a positive test mean the individual will automatically lose his or her job? No, if the urine test comes back positive, the individual is given a second test that is more accurate but more expensive than the urine test.

▶ *Try Exercise 5.57*

Are you surprised that $P(S \mid POS)$ is so small (only 9%) for the air controllers? To help understand the logic behind this, it's a good idea to show on a tree diagram what you'd expect to happen with a hypothetical group of air controllers, just as we did with the contingency table. Figure 5.11 shows the result for a group of 10,000 air controllers.

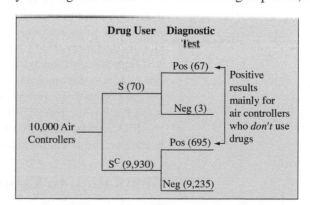

▲ **Figure 5.11 Expected Results of Drug Tests for 10,000 Air Controllers.** This diagram shows typical results when 0.7% (70 in 10,000) are drug users (event S), a positive result has a probability of 96% for those who use drugs, and a negative result has a probability of 93% for those who do not use drugs. Most positive results occur with individuals who are *not* using drugs because there are so many such individuals (more than 99% of the population). **Question** How would results change if a higher percentage of the population were using drugs?

Since 0.7% (which is 70 in 10,000) of the target population uses drugs, the tree diagram shows 70 drug users and 9,930 nondrug users out of the 10,000 air controllers. For the 70 drug users, there's a 96% chance the test detects the drug use. So we'd expect $0.96 \times 70 = 67$ to be detected with the test. For the 9,930 nondrug users, there's a 93% chance the test is negative. So we'd expect about $0.93 \times 9,930 = 9,235$ individuals to have a negative result and the other $9,930 - 9,235 = 695$ nondrug users to have a positive result, as shown in Figure 5.11.

In summary, Figure 5.11 shows $67 + 695 = 762$ individuals having a positive test result, but only 67 who truly were drug users, for a proportion of $67/762 = 0.09$ (rounded to two decimals). What's happening is that the 7% (= 695/9,930) of positive test results for the large majority of individuals who *do not* use drugs is much larger (in terms of number of individuals affected) than the 96% (= 67/70) of correct test results for the very small number of individuals who *do* use drugs.

If the prevalence rate were $P(S) = 0.15$ (let's hope it's not really this high!) instead of 0.007, you can verify that $P(S|POS) = 0.71$ rather than 0.09. The probability that the person truly used drugs is then much higher, 71%. In fact, the chance that a positive test result is truly correct depends very much on the prevalence rate. The lower the prevalence rate, the lower the chance. The more drug free the population, the less likely an individual who tests positive for drugs truly used them.

In Example 13, we started with probabilities of the form $P(POS|S)$ and used them to find a conditional probability $P(S|POS)$ that reverses what is given and what is to be found. The method used to find this reverse conditional probability can be summarized in a single formula (see Exercise 5.116), known as **Bayes' Rule**. We have not shown that formula here because it is easier to understand the logic behind it using tree diagrams or contingency tables.

Probability Answers to Questions Can Be Surprising

The results in Example 13 on drug testing of air traffic controllers may seem surprising, but actually they are not uncommon. As another example, consider the mammogram for detecting breast cancer in women. One study[7] estimated a sensitivity of 86% and a specificity of 88%. When a randomly selected woman receives a positive mammogram result, what are the chances she actually has breast cancer? In Exercise 5.57 you can work out that it may be only about 7%.

These diagnostic testing examples point out that when probability is involved, answers to questions about our daily lives are sometimes not as obvious as you may think. Consider the question, "Should a woman have an annual mammogram?" Medical choices are rarely between certainty and risk but, rather, between different risks. If a woman fails to have a mammogram, this is risky—she may truly have breast cancer. If she has a mammogram, there's the risk of a false positive or false negative, such as the risk of needless worry and additional invasive procedures (often biopsy and other treatments) due to a false positive.

Likewise, with the Triple Blood Test for Down syndrome, most positive results are false, yet the recommendation after receiving a positive test may be to follow up the test with an amniocentesis, a procedure that gives a more definitive diagnosis but has the risk of causing a miscarriage. With some diagnostic tests (such as the PSA test for prostate cancer), testing can detect the disease, but the evidence is unclear about whether early detection has much, if any, effect on life expectancy.

Simulation to Estimate a Probability

Some probabilities are very difficult to find with ordinary reasoning. In such cases, one way to approximate an answer is to use simulations with the help of a

---

[7]W. Barlow et al., *J. Natl. Cancer Inst.*, 2002, vol. 94, p. 1151.

computer. We have carried out simulations in previous chapters, in chapter exercises, and in Activity 1 in this chapter. The steps for a simulation are as follows:

- Identify the random phenomenon to be simulated.
- Describe how to simulate observations of the random phenomenon.
- Carry out the simulation many times.
- Summarize results and state the conclusion.

Using Computer Simulations to Approximate Probabilities ◄

Example 14

Estimating Probabilities

Picture the Scenario

At carnivals and entertainment parks, there is a popular game of horseracing. Each player has a movable horse on the display whose number corresponds to his or her alley number. The game consists of rolling a ball up an alley, where it can land in one of 15 holes. The holes are colored according to the graphic in the margin.

If your ball lands in a red hole, your horse advances one space. If it lands in yellow, your horse advances two spaces, and if it lands in green, your horse gallops ahead three spaces. After your ball goes in the hole, it returns to you for your next roll. The first horse that moves 12 spaces is the winner.

You look over the game and estimate that you have a 40% chance of getting the ball in a red hole, a 30% chance of getting it in a yellow hole, and a 20% chance of getting it in a green hole. There is also a 10% chance that you miss the holes and your ball returns to you without advancing the horse.

Question to Explore

Based on your estimates of the probabilities for hitting the holes, what is the chance you will win the game with 8 rolls or fewer?

Think It Through

Listing the sample space, finding probabilities for each outcome in it and then finding all outcomes that define an event such as "8 rolls or fewer" seems hopelessly complex for this scenario. We proceed using computer simulations according to the following steps:

Step 1: *Identify the random phenomenon to be simulated.* We want to simulate each roll of the ball to determine how far the horse advances. We then want to determine the number of rolls it takes to win the game.

Step 2: *Describe how to simulate observations of the random phenomenon.* There are a number of ways to carry out a simulation. For this example, we will use the *Random Numbers* app so you can replicate what we are doing. Because this is a simulation, when you try to replicate what we did here, you will get different outcomes, but the overall conclusion will be approximately the same.

In the app, keep the minimum at 1 and set the maximum to 10. This will allow you to generate one number at random from the numbers 1 to 10. If the number generated is 1, 2, 3, or 4, which happens 40% of the time since all 10 numbers are equally likely, we say that the ball landed in a red hole and the horse advances 1 space. If the number generated is 5, 6, or 7 (which happens 3/10 = 30% of the time), we say that the ball landed in a yellow hole and the horse advances

Did You Know?

You can also simulate the rolls by using random numbers from 1 to 10 from *random.org*. A generated number between 1 and 4 corresponds to red, numbers 5 and 6 to yellow, 8 and 9 to green, and a 10 means a miss. ◄

2 spaces. If the number generated is 8 or 9 (which happens 2/10 = 20% of the time), we say that the ball landed in a green hole and the horse advances 3 spaces. Finally, if the number generated is a 10 (which happens 1/10 = 10% of the time), we say that the ball missed the holes and the horse doesn't advance. With this setup, press the Generate button a couple of times to see what number you get and keep track of

(i)   how often you pressed Generate (this is the number of your rolls),

(ii) the random number generated,

(iii) the color of the hole represented by that random number,

(iv) how many spaces your horse advances, and

(v)   the total number of spaces it advances over all current simulations.

As soon as the number in (v) is 12 or more spaces, you stop the simulation and count how often you pressed Generate, which represents the number of rolls that were necessary to win the game.

When we ran the simulation, the very first number we generated was a 5, which meant the hole was yellow and the horse moved forward 2 spaces. The next number we generated was a 3, a red hole, and the horse moved forward 1 space, for a total of now 3 spaces. We then got the number 9, meaning the horse moved forward an additional 3 spaces, then the numbers 7, another 7, 2, and 5. The screenshot from the *Random Numbers* app in the margin shows the history of all numbers generated up to that point, and the following table summarizes all results and actions.

Roll Number	Number Generated	Hole	Horse Advances	Horse on Space #
1	5	yellow	2	2
2	3	red	1	3
3	9	green	3	6
4	7	yellow	2	8
5	7	yellow	2	10
6	2	red	1	11
7	5	yellow	2	13

We stopped generating numbers after obtaining the number 5, because by then the horse has moved forward from a total of 11 spaces to a new total of 13 spaces, and the game is over since the horse reached 12 spaces. For this one simulation of the game, we needed to generate 7 random numbers, which means we needed 7 rolls to win the game.

Step 3: *Carry out the simulation of the game many times.* We need many more game simulations of the type in Step 2 to say anything meaningful about the probability of finishing the game in 8 rolls or fewer. So, we carried out another (press *Reset* to start a new simulation) and generated the sequence of numbers 4, 1, 1, 10, 6, 5, 8, 4, 10, and 5, which correspond to moving the horse forward 1, 1, 0, 2, 2, 3, 1, 0, and 2 spaces, for a total of 12 spaces. We needed to generate 10 numbers (the two misses, represented by the number 10, cost us), which means we finished this game after 10 rolls. Now repeat this simulation of a game many more times. The following table shows the results from a total of 20 such simulations. (For the one where we needed 11 rolls, the 5th simulated game, we missed three times in a row.)

Choose Minimum: **Choose Maximum:**

1   10

How many numbers do you want to generate?   **Sample with Replacement?**   ◉ No ○ Yes

1

↻ Generate   Reset

Current Simulation: **All Simulations:**

5   5 3 9 7 7 2 5

Screenshot from the *Random Numbers* app

Game	# Rolls to Finish Game	8 Rolls or Fewer?	Game	# Rolls to Finish Game	8 Rolls or Fewer?
1	7	Yes	11	7	Yes
2	10	No	12	10	No
3	10	No	13	6	Yes
4	8	Yes	14	7	Yes
5	11	No	15	7	Yes
6	7	Yes	16	9	No
7	6	Yes	17	7	Yes
8	7	Yes	18	8	Yes
9	8	Yes	19	6	Yes
10	8	Yes	20	8	Yes

Step 4: *Summarize results and state conclusions.* For 15 of the 20 simulated games, it took us 8 rolls or fewer to finish the game. So we estimate the probability of finishing the game in 8 rolls or fewer as 15/20, or 75%.

Insight

Simulation is a powerful tool in that we can estimate probabilities without having to use and understand more complex mathematical probability rules. In fact, many probabilities that are calculated these days in science and business are quite complex and are done using simulations.

   If you are not satisfied with the precision of our estimate, you can increase the number of games simulated. Exercise 5.64 explores simulating more games. Exercise 5.65 extends this problem by thinking about alternative strategies for playing the game.

▶ *Try Exercises 5.63 and 5.64*

Probability Is the Key to Statistical Inference

The concepts of probability hold the key to methods for conducting statistical inference–making conclusions about populations by using sample data. To help preview this connection, let's consider an opinion poll. Suppose a poll indicates that 45% of those sampled favor legalized gambling. What's the probability that this sample percentage falls within a certain margin of error, say plus or minus 3%, of the true population percentage? The next two chapters will build on the probability foundation of this chapter and enable us to answer such a question. We will study how to evaluate the probabilities of all the possible outcomes in a survey sample or an experiment. This will then be the basis of the statistical infer ence methods we'll learn about in Chapters 8–10.

5.4 Practicing the Basics

5.47 Birthdays of presidents   Of the first 44 presidents of the United States (George Washington through Barack Obama), two had the same birthday (Polk and Harding). Is this highly coincidental? Answer by finding the probability of at least one birthday match among 44 people.

5.48 Matching your birthday   You consider your birth date to be special since it falls on January 1. Suppose your class has 25 students.

a. Is the probability of finding at least one student with a birthday that matches yours greater, the same, or less than the probability found in Example 11 of a match for at least two students? Explain.

b. Find that probability.

5.49 **Lots of pairs** Show that with 25 students, there are 300 *pairs* of students who can have the same birthday. So it's really not so surprising if at least two students have the same birthday. (*Hint:* You can pair 24 other students with each student, but how can you make sure you don't count each pair twice?)

5.50 **Big loser in Lotto** Example 12 showed that the probability of having the winning ticket in Lotto South was 0.00000007. Find the probability of holding a ticket that has zero winning numbers out of the 6 numbers selected (without replacement) for the winning ticket out of the 49 possible numbers.

5.51 **Drawing cards without replacement** Cards are drawn without replacement from a standard deck of 52 cards, of which 13 are hearts. What is the probability that the first three cards drawn are all hearts?

5.52 **Horrible 11 on 9/11** The digits in 9/11 add up to $11 (9 + 1 + 1)$, American Airlines flight 11 was the first to hit the World Trade Towers (which took the form of the number 11), there were 92 people on board $(9 + 2 = 11)$, September 11 is the 254th day of the year $(2 + 5 + 4 = 11)$, and there are 11 letters in Afghanistan, New York City, the Pentagon, and George W. Bush (see article by L. Belkin, *New York Times*, August 11, 2002). How could you explain to someone who has not studied probability that, because of the way we look for patterns out of the huge number of things that happen, this is not necessarily an amazing coincidence?

5.53 **Coincidence in your life** State an event that has happened to you or to someone you know that seems highly coincidental (such as seeing a friend while on vacation). Explain why that event may not be especially surprising, once you think of all the similar types of events that could have happened to you or someone that you know, over the course of several years.

5.54 **Monkeys typing Shakespeare** Since events of low probability eventually happen if you observe enough trials, a monkey randomly pecking on a typewriter could eventually write a Shakespeare play just by chance. Let's see how hard it would be to type the title of *Macbeth* properly. Assume 50 keys for letters and numbers and punctuation. Find the probability that the first seven letters that a monkey types are macbeth. (Even if the monkey can type 60 strokes a minute and never sleeps, if we consider each sequence of seven keystrokes as a trial, we would wait on the average over 100,000 years before seeing this happen!)

5.55 **Drawing cards** A standard card deck has 52 cards consisting of 26 black and 26 red cards. Three cards are dealt from a shuffled deck, *without replacement*.

a. True or false: The probability of being dealt three black cards is $(1/2) \times (1/2) \times (1/2) = 1/8$. If true, explain why. If false, show how to get the correct probability.

b. Let A = first card red and B = second card red. Are A and B independent? Explain why or why not.

c. Answer parts a and b if each card is replaced in the deck after being dealt.

5.56 **Rosencrantz and Guildenstern** In the opening scene of Tom Stoppard's play *Rosencrantz and Guildenstern Are Dead*, about two Elizabethan contemporaries of Hamlet, Guildenstern flips a coin 91 times and gets a head each time. Suppose the coin was balanced.

a. Consider the sample space for 91 coin flips, such that all outcomes in the sample space are equally likely. How many outcomes are in the sample space?

b. What's the probability of the event of getting a head 91 times in a row?

c. What's the probability of at least one tail in the 91 flips?

d. State the probability model on which your solutions in parts b and c are based.

5.57 **Mammogram diagnostics** Breast cancer is the most common form of cancer in women, affecting about 10% of women at some time in their lives. There is about a 1% chance of having breast cancer at a given time (that is, $P(S) = 0.01$ for the state of having breast cancer at a given time). The chance of breast cancer increases as a woman ages, and the American Cancer Society recommends an annual mammogram after age 40 to test for its presence. Of the women who undergo mammograms at any given time, about 1% are typically estimated to actually have breast cancer. The likelihood of a false test result varies according to the breast density and the radiologist's level of experience. For use of the mammogram to detect breast cancer, typical values reported are sensitivity = 0.86 and specificity = 0.88.

a. Construct a tree diagram in which the first set of branches shows whether a woman has breast cancer and the second set of branches shows the mammogram result. At the end of the final set of branches, show that $P(S \text{ and } POS) = 0.01 \times 0.86 = 0.0086$ and report the other intersection probabilities also.

b. Restricting your attention to the two paths that have a positive test result, show that $P(POS) = 0.1274$.

c. Of the women who receive a positive mammogram result, what proportion actually have breast cancer?

d. The following tree diagram illustrates how $P(S|POS)$ can be so small, using a typical group of 100 women who have a mammogram. Explain how to get the frequencies shown on the branches and why this suggests that $P(S|POS)$ is only about 0.08.

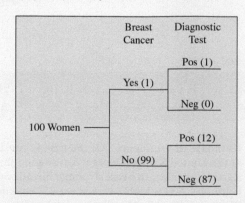

Typical results of mammograms for 100 women

5.58 **More screening for breast cancer**   Refer to the previous exercise. For young women, the prevalence of breast cancer is lower. Suppose the sensitivity is 0.86 and the specificity is 0.88, but the prevalence is only 0.001.

  a. Given that a test comes out positive, find the probability that the woman truly has breast cancer.

  b. Show how to use a tree diagram with frequencies for a typical sample of 1,000 women to explain to someone who has not studied statistics why the probability found in part a is so low.

  c. Of the cases that are positive, explain why the proportion in error is likely to be larger for a young population than for an older population.

5.59 **Conditional probabilities in court**   Former pro football star O.J. Simpson was accused of murdering his wife. In the trial, a defense attorney pointed out that although Simpson had been guilty of earlier spousal abuse, annually only about 40 women are murdered per 100,000 incidents of partner abuse. This means that P(murdered by partner | partner abuse) = 40/100,000. More relevant, however, is P(murdered by partner | partner abuse and women murdered). Every year it is estimated that 5 of every 100,000 women in the United States who suffer partner abuse are killed by someone other than their partner. Part of a tree diagram is shown starting with a hypothetical set of 100,000 women who suffer partner abuse. (*Source:* Gigerenzer, G. (2002). Calculated Risks. New York: Simon &Schuster, p.14.)

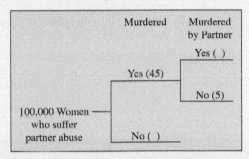

  a. Based on the results stated, explain why the numbers 45 and 5 are entered as shown on two of the branches.

  b. Fill in the two blanks shown in the tree diagram.

  c. Conditional on partner abuse and the woman being murdered (by someone), explain why the probability the woman was murdered by her partner is 40/45. Why is this so dramatically different from P(murdered by partner | partner abuse) = 40/100,000?

5.60 **Convicted by mistake**   In criminal trials (e.g., murder, robbery, driving while impaired, etc.) in the United States, it must be proven that a defendant is guilty beyond a reasonable doubt. This can be thought of as a very strong unwillingness to convict defendants who are actually innocent. In civil trials (e.g., breach of contract, divorce hearings for alimony, etc.), it must only be proven by a preponderance of the evidence that a defendant is guilty. This makes it easier to prove a defendant guilty in a civil case than in a murder case. In a high-profile pair of cases in the mid-1990s, O. J. Simpson was found to be not guilty of murder in a criminal case against him. Shortly thereafter, however, he was found guilty in a civil case and ordered to pay damages to the families of the victims.

  a. In a criminal trial by jury, suppose the probability the defendant is convicted, given guilt, is 0.95 and the probability the defendant is acquitted, given innocence, is also 0.95. Suppose that 90% of all defendants truly are guilty. Given that a defendant is convicted, find the probability he or she was actually innocent. Draw a tree diagram or construct a contingency table to help you answer.

  b. Repeat part a, but under the assumption that 50% of all defendants truly are guilty.

  c. In a civil trial, suppose the probability the defendant is convicted, given guilt is 0.99, and the probability the defendant is acquitted, given innocence, is 0.75. Suppose that 90% of all defendants truly are guilty. Given that a defendant is convicted, find the probability he or she was actually innocent. Draw a tree diagram or construct a contingency table to help you answer.

5.61 **DNA evidence compelling?**   DNA evidence can be extracted from biological traces such as blood, hair, and saliva. "DNA fingerprinting" is increasingly used in the courtroom as well as in paternity testing. Given that a person is innocent, suppose that the probability of his or her DNA matching that found at the crime scene is only 0.000001, one in a million. Further, given that a person is guilty, suppose that the probability of his or her DNA matching that found at the crime scene is 0.99. Jane Doe's DNA matches that found at the crime scene.

  a. Find the probability that Jane Doe is actually innocent, if absolutely her probability of innocence is 0.50. Interpret this probability. Show your solution by introducing notation for events, specifying probabilities that are given, and using a tree diagram to find your answer.

  b. Repeat part a if the unconditional probability of innocence is 0.99. Compare results.

  c. Explain why it is very important for a defense lawyer to explain the difference between P(DNA match | person innocent) and P(person innocent | DNA match).

5.62 **HIV testing**   A company called Oraquick offers in-home oral HIV testing. According to their website,[8] out of 4,999 persons who were unaware of their HIV status, 96 persons were HIV positive and 4,903 persons were HIV negative (as determined by an independent lab test). For 4,902 out of the 4,903 persons who were HIV negative, Oraquick's test correctly predicted such a negative result, but incorrectly predicted a positive result for the one remaining person. Of the 96 persons who were HIV positive, Oraquick's test correctly predicted a positive result for 88 of them and a negative result for the others.

  a. Construct a contingency table useful for displaying the information from Oraquick's reporting.

  b. Estimate the (i) sensitivity and (ii) specificity of Oraquick's test for the population that the sample of 4,999 persons represents.

  c. Estimate (i) P(HIV | POS) and (ii) P(No HIV | NEG) for the population that the sample of 4,999 people represents. (Note: These two probabilities are called the **positive and negative predictive** value, respectively.)

---

[8]http://www.oraquick.com/Taking-the-Test/Understanding-Your-Results.

5.63   Simulating donations to local blood bank   The director of a local blood bank is in need of a donor with type AB blood. The distribution of blood types for Americans is estimated by the American Red Cross to be

Type	A	B	O	AB
Probability	40%	10%	45%	5%

The director decides that if more than 20 donors are required before the first donor with AB blood appears, she will need to issue a special appeal for AB blood.

a. Using simulation via the *Random Numbers* app (or other software), estimate the probability that a special appeal for AB blood has to be made. Show all 4 steps of the simulation, including any assumptions that you make. Refer to Example 14 as a model for carrying out this simulation, but now you will need to generate from numbers 1 to 100, with (as an example) the first 40 representing drawing someone with type A blood and numbers 96 to 100 as drawing someone with type AB blood.

b. In practice, you would do at least 1,000 simulations to estimate this probability well. You'd then find that the probability of exceeding 20 donors before finding a type AB donor is 0.36. However, simulation is actually not needed. Show how to find this probability by using the methods of this chapter.

5.64   Probability of winning   In Example 14, we estimated the probability of winning the game in 8 rolls or fewer as 75%. If you conducted another 20 simulations of this game, what is your updated estimate of this probability?

(We know that as the number of repetitions increases, the estimated probability of winning will get closer to the actual probability of winning.)

5.65   Probability of winning   In Example 14, we explored the number of rolls it takes to win the game. In reality, it's not the number of rolls but rather the time it takes to move 12 spaces that dictates who wins the game. Consider two alternative strategies for playing the game. The first strategy, let's call it the aiming strategy, uses the probabilities given in Example 14 and takes 4 seconds to roll each ball. A second strategy is to roll the ball in rapid succession. Under the rapid-succession strategy it takes only 3 seconds to roll each ball; however, the probabilities of landing in the holes become 50% for red, 20% for yellow, 10% for green, and 20% for no holes.

a. Using the random numbers 5, 3, 9, 7, 7, 2, 5, 8, and 2, generated with the *Random Numbers* app, find the time the game is completed with the (i) aiming strategy and (ii) rapid-succession strategy.

b. Use the *Random Numbers* app to generate another 19 sets of random numbers. (Note: You may have to press Generate a couple more times to get to 12 spaces with the rapid-succession strategy.) There is no need to generate separate random numbers for evaluating the time needed with each strategy. The same set of numbers can be used to evaluate the time for both strategies, just as you did in part a. For each simulation of a game, keep track of which of the two strategies is faster. Based on the 20 simulations of a game, what is the estimated probability that the rapid-succession strategy is faster?

Chapter Review

SUMMARY OF NOTATION

A, B, C   Events
A^C Complement of event A (the outcomes *not* in A)
P(A)   Probability of event A
P(A or B)   Probability that A occurs or B occurs or both occur

P(A and B)   Probability that both A and B occur
P(A|B)   Conditional probability of event A, given event B (| denotes "given")

CHAPTER SUMMARY

In this chapter, we've seen how to quantify uncertainty and randomness. With many independent trials of random phenomena, outcomes do show certain regularities. The proportion of times an outcome occurs in the long run is its **probability**.

The **sample space** is the set of all possible outcomes of a random phenomenon. An **event** is any subset of the sample space. Two events A and B are **disjoint** if they have no common elements.

We find probabilities by using basic rules:

- The **probability** of each individual outcome falls between 0 and 1, and the sum of all the individual probabilities in the sample space equals 1.

- The **probability of an event** is the sum of the probabilities of the individual outcomes that make up the event.

- For an event A and its **complement A^C** (the outcomes not in A),
$$P(A^C) = 1 - P(A).$$

- $P(A \text{ or } B) = P(A) + P(B) - P(A \text{ and } B)$. This simplifies to $P(A \text{ or } B) = P(A) + P(B)$ when the events are disjoint.

- $P(A \text{ and } B) = P(A) \times P(B|A)$, where $P(B|A)$ denotes the **conditional probability** of event B, given that event A occurs. Equivalently, the conditional probability satisfies
$$P(B|A) = \frac{P(A \text{ and } B)}{P(A)}.$$

- Likewise, $P(A \text{ and } B) = P(B)P(A|B)$, and $P(A|B) = P(A \text{ and } B)/P(B)$.

- When A and B are **independent**, $P(A|B) = P(A)$ and $P(B|A) = P(B)$. Then, and only then, $P(A \text{ and } B) = P(A) \times P(B)$.

It's easiest to find **conditional probabilities** by organizing counts in a contingency table, or by imagining what would happen to a hypothetical population of 10,000 individuals, either in a contingency table or a tree diagram.

A **probability model** states certain assumptions and, based on them, finds the probabilities of events of interest.

Understanding probability helps us to make informed decisions in our lives. In the next four chapters, we'll see how an understanding of probability gives us the basis for making statistical inferences about a population.

LEARNING OBJECTIVES

1. Understand that probability is the tool that quantifies randomness.

2. Understand that the probability of an outcome is defined as the long-run relative frequency of that outcome in repeated trials.

3. Understand when this definition is not useful and subjective probabilities have to be used that express beliefs.

4. Construct the sample space for a random phenomenon and define an event in terms of outcomes from this sample space.

5. Know that the probability of each outcome listed in the sample space is between 0 and 1, and that they sum to 1.

6. Identify when two events are disjoint.

7. Identify when two events are independent.

8. Employ the basic probability rules: Addition rule and Multiplication rule.

9. Calculate, explain, and understand how conditional probabilities are used and the role they play for making informed decisions daily in our lives.

10. Understand that probability models with their assumptions often only approximate reality.

11. Understand that simulation is a powerful tool that can be used to estimate probabilities instead of using complex mathematics.

ANSWERS TO THE CHAPTER FIGURE QUESTIONS

Figure 5.1 The cumulative proportion after each roll is evaluated as the frequency of 6s rolled through that trial (roll) divided by the total number of trials (rolls). The cumulative proportions are $1/1 = 1$ for roll 1, $1/2 = 0.50$ for roll 2, $2/3 = 0.67$ for roll 3, and $2/4 = 0.50$ for roll 4.

Figure 5.2 It should be very, very close to 1/2.

Figure 5.3 $2 \times 2 \times 2 \times 2 = 16$ branches.

Figure 5.4 Venn diagrams will vary. One possible Venn diagram follows.

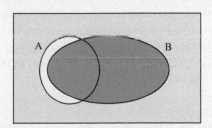

Figure 5.5 The favorable outcomes to the event that the student answers the first question correctly are {CCC,CCI,CIC,CII} This event is not disjoint from either of the two labeled events in the Venn diagram.

Figure 5.6 $P(A \text{ or } B) = P(A) + P(B) - P(A \text{ and } B)$

Figure 5.7 $P(A \text{ or } B) = P(A) + P(B)$ when the events A and B are disjoint.

Figure 5.8 We would not expect the trials to be independent if the student is not guessing. If the student is using prior knowledge, the probability of getting a correct answer on a question, such as question 3, may be more likely if the student answers questions 1 and 2 correctly.

Figure 5.9 $P(A|B)$ is not necessarily equal to $P(B|A)$. They have the same numerator, $P(A \text{ and } B)$, but different denominators, $P(B)$ and $P(A)$ respectively, which may not be equal.

Figure 5.11 As the prevalence rate increases, of the individuals that test positive, a higher percentage of positive test results will occur with individuals that actually use drugs. For example, if 5% of the population uses drugs, of the 115 individuals out of 1,000 who would be expected to test positive, 48 would be actual drug users, whereas 67 would not be drug users.

STATISTICAL SOFTWARE

Art of Stat Web Apps

- **Random Numbers** As illustrated in Activity 1, the *Random Numbers* app can be used to simulate rolling a die, or, switching to the Coin Flips tab, flipping a balanced or unbalanced coin, while keeping track of long-run proportions. The app offers generating numbers with and without replacement. Example 14 shows how to use the app for more complicated simulation scenarios.

R

- **Random Samples:** The R command `sample()` generates random numbers. For instance, `> sample(30, 5)` provides five numbers randomly selected from the numbers 1 through 30. For sampling with replacement, use `> sample(30, 5, replace=TRUE)`. The simple command `> sample(30)` provides a random permutation of the first 30 numbers.

CHAPTER EXERCISES

Practicing the Basics

5.66 Peyton Manning completions As of the end of the 2010 NFL season, Indianapolis Colts quarterback Peyton Manning, throughout his 13-year career, completed 65% of all of his pass attempts. Suppose that each pass attempted in the next season has probability 0.65 of being completed.

   a. Does this mean that if we watch Manning throw 100 times in the upcoming season, he would complete exactly 65 passes? Explain.

   b. Explain what this probability means in terms of observing him over a longer period, say for 1,000 passes over the course of the next two seasons, assuming Manning is still at his typical playing level. Would it be surprising if his completion percentage over a large number of passes differed significantly from 65%?

5.67 Due for a boy? A couple has five children, all girls. They are expecting a sixth child. The father tells a friend that by the law of large numbers the chance of a boy is now much greater than 1/2. Comment on the father's statement.

5.68 P(life after death) Explain the difference between the relative frequency and subjective definitions of probability. Illustrate by explaining how it is possible to give a value for (a) the probability of life after death, (b) the probability that in the morning you remember at least one dream that you had in the previous night's sleep, based on what you observe every morning for the next year.

5.69 Choices for lunch For the set lunch at Amelia's Restaurant, customers can select one meat dish, one vegetable, one beverage, and one dessert. The menu offers two meats (beef and chicken), three vegetables (corn, green beans, or potatoes), three beverages (cola, ice tea, or coffee), and one dessert (Amelia's apple pie).

   a. Use a tree diagram to list the possible meals and to determine how many there are.

   b. In practice, would it be sensible to treat all the outcomes in the sample space as equally likely for the customer selections we'd observe? Why or why not?

5.70 Enron scandal After the major accounting scandals with Enron, a large energy company that was caught hiding billions of dollars in debt and fooled a big auditing company, both of which eventually went bankrupt, the question may be posed, "Was there any way to examine Enron's accounting books to determine if they had been doctored?" One way uses Benford's law, which states that in a variety of circumstances, numbers as varied as populations of small towns, figures in a newspaper or magazine, and tax returns and other business records begin with the digit 1 more often than other digits. (See also Exercise 11.66)

This law states that the probabilities for the digits 1 through 9 are approximately:

Digit	1	2	3	4	5	6	7	8	9
Probability	0.30	0.18	0.12	0.10	0.08	0.07	0.06	0.05	0.04

   a. If we were to randomly pick one of the digits between 1 and 9 using, for example, the *Random Numbers* app, what is the probability for each digit?

   b. When people attempt to fake numbers, there's a tendency to use 5 or 6 as the initial digit more often than predicted by Benford's law. What is the probability of 5 or 6 as the first digit by (i) Benford's law and (ii) random selection?

5.71 Life after death In a General Social Survey, in response to the question "Do you believe in life after death?" 1,455 answered yes and 332 answered no.

   a. Based on this survey, estimate the probability that a randomly selected adult in the United States believes in life after death.

   b. A married couple is randomly selected. Estimate the probability that both subjects believe in life after death.

   c. What assumption did you make in answering part b? Explain why that assumption is probably unrealistic, making this estimate unreliable.

5.72 Death penalty jury In arguing against the death penalty, Amnesty International has pointed out supposed inequities, such as the many times a Black person has been given the death penalty by an all-White jury. If jurors are selected randomly from an adult population, find the probability that all 12 jurors are White when the population is (a) 90% White and (b) 50% White.

5.73 Driver's exam Three 15-year-old friends with no particular background in driver's education decide to take the written part of the Georgia Driver's Exam. Each exam was graded as a pass (P) or a failure (F).

   a. How many outcomes are possible for the grades received by the three friends together? Using a tree diagram, list the sample space.

   b. If the outcomes in the sample space in part a are equally likely, find the probability that all three pass the exam.

   c. In practice, the outcomes in part a are not equally likely. Suppose that statewide, 70% of 15-year-olds pass the exam. If these three friends were a random sample of their age group, find the probability that all three pass.

   d. In practice, explain why probabilities that apply to a random sample are not likely to be valid for a sample of three friends.

5.74 Independent on coffee? Students in a geography class are asked whether they've visited Europe in the past 12 months and whether they've flown on a plane in the past 12 months.

   a. For a randomly selected student, would you expect these events to be independent or dependent? Explain.

   b. How would you explain to someone who has never studied statistics what it means for these events to be either independent or dependent?

   c. Students in a different class were asked whether they've visited Italy in the past 12 months and whether they've visited France in the past 12 months. For a randomly selected student, would you expect these events to be independent or dependent? Explain.

   d. Students in yet another class were asked whether they've been to a zoo in the past 12 months and whether they drink coffee. For a randomly selected student, would you expect these events to be independent or dependent? Explain.

   e. If you had to rank the pairs of events in parts a, c, and d in terms of the strength of any dependence, which pair of events is most dependent? Least dependent?

5.75 Health insurance According to a 2006 Census Bureau report, 59% of Americans have private health insurance, 25% have government health insurance (Medicare or Medicaid or military health care), and 16% have no health insurance.

   a. Estimate the probability that a patient has health insurance.

   b. Given that a subject has health insurance, estimate the probability it is private.

5.76 Teens and drugs In August 2006 the Center on Addiction and Substance Abuse (CASA) at Columbia University reported results of a survey of 1,297 teenagers about their views on the use of illegal substances. Twenty percent of the teens surveyed reported going to clubs for music or dancing at least once a month. Of them, 26% said drugs were usually available at these club events. Which of these percentages estimates a conditional probability? For each that does, identify the event conditioned on and the event to which the probability refers.

5.77 Teens and parents In the CASA teen survey described in the previous exercise, 33% of teens reported that parents are never present at parties they attend. Thirty-one percent of teens who say parents are never present during parties report that marijuana is available at the parties they attend, compared to only 1% of teens who say parents are present at parties reporting that marijuana is available at the parties they attend.

   a. Which of these percentages estimates a conditional probability? For each that does, identify the event conditioned on and the event to which the probability refers.

   b. For the variables parents present (yes or no) and marijuana available (yes or no), construct a contingency table showing counts for the 1,297 teenagers surveyed.

   c. Using the contingency table, given that marijuana is not available at the party, estimate the probability that parents are present.

5.78 Laundry detergent A manufacturer of laundry detergent has introduced a new product that it claims to be more environmentally sound. An extensive survey gives the percentages shown in the table.

Result of Advertising for New Laundry Product		
	Tried the New Product	
Advertising Status	**Yes**	**No**
Seen the ad	10%	25%
Have not seen ad	5%	60%

   a. Estimate the probability that a randomly chosen consumer would have seen advertising for the new product and tried the product.

   b. Given that a randomly chosen consumer has seen the product advertised, estimate the probability that the person has tried the product.

   c. Let A be the event that a consumer has tried the product. Let B be the event that a consumer has seen the product advertised. Express the probabilities found in parts a and b in terms of A and B.

   d. Are A and B independent? Justify your answer.

5.79 Board games and dice A board game requires players to roll a pair of balanced dice for each player's turn. Denote the outcomes by (die 1, die 2), such as (5, 3) for a 5 on die 1 and a 3 on die 2.

   a. List the sample space of the 36 possible outcomes for the two dice.

   b. Let A be the event that you roll doubles (that is, each die has the same outcome). List the outcomes in A and find its probability.

   c. Let B be the event that the sum on the pair of dice is 7. Find P(B).

   d. Find the probability of (i) A and B, (ii) A or B, and (iii) B given A.

   e. Are events A and B independent, disjoint, or neither? Explain.

5.80 Roll two more dice Refer to the previous exercise. Define event D as rolling an odd sum with two dice.

   a. B denotes a sum of 7 on the two dice. Find P(B and D). When an event B is contained within an event D, as here, explain why P(B and D) = P(B).

   b. Find P(B or D). When an event B is contained within an event D, explain why P(B or D) = P(D).

5.81 Conference dinner Of the participants at a conference, 50% attended breakfast, 90% attended dinner, and 40% attended both breakfast and dinner. Given that a participant attended breakfast, find the probability that she also attended dinner.

5.82 Waste dump sites A federal agency is deciding which of two waste dump projects to investigate. A top administrator estimates that the probability of federal law violations is 0.30 at the first project and 0.25 at the second project. Also, he believes the occurrences of violations in these two projects are disjoint.

a. What is the probability of federal law violations in the first project or in the second project?

b. Given that there is not a federal law violation in the first project, find the probability that there is a federal law violation in the second project.

c. In reality, the administrator confused disjoint and independent, and the events are actually independent. Answer parts a and b with this correct information.

5.83 A dice game Consider a game in which you roll two dice, and you win if the total is 7 or 11 and you lose if the total is 2, 3, or 12. You keep rolling until one of these totals occurs. Using conditional probability, find the probability that you win.

5.84 No coincidences Over time, you have many conversations with a friend about your favorite actress, favorite musician, favorite book, favorite TV show, and so forth for 100 topics. On any given topic, there's only a 0.02 probability that you agree. If you did agree on a topic, you would consider it to be coincidental.

a. If whether you agree on any two topics are independent events, find the probability that you and your friend *never* have a coincidence on these 100 topics.

b. Find the probability that you have a coincidence on at least one topic.

5.85 Amazing roulette run? A roulette wheel in Monte Carlo has 18 even-numbered slots, 18 odd-numbered slots, a slot numbered zero, and a double zero slot. On August 18, 1913, it came up even 26 times in a row.[9] As more and more evens occurred, the proportion of people betting on an odd outcome increased because they figured it was due.

a. Comment on this strategy.

b. Find the probability of 26 evens in a row if each slot is equally likely.

c. Suppose that over the past 100 years there have been 1,000 roulette wheels, each being used hundreds of times a day. Is it surprising if sometime in the previous 100 years one of these wheels had 26 evens in a row? Explain.

5.86 Death penalty and false positives For the decision about whether to convict someone charged with murder and give the death penalty, consider the variables reality (defendant innocent, defendant guilty) and decision (convict, acquit).

a. Explain what the two types of errors are in this context.

b. Jurors are asked to convict a defendant if they feel the defendant is guilty beyond a reasonable doubt.

Suppose this means that given the defendant is executed, the probability that he or she truly was guilty is 0.99. For the 1,234 people put to death from the time the death penalty was reinstated in 1977 until December 2010, find the probability that (i) they were all truly guilty, and (ii) at least one of them was actually innocent.

c. How do the answers in part b change if the probability of true guilt is actually 0.95?

5.87 Screening smokers for lung cancer An article about using a diagnostic test (helical computed tomography) to screen adult smokers for lung cancer warned that a negative test may cause harm by providing smokers with false reassurance, and a false-positive test results in an unnecessary operation opening the smoker's chest (Mahadevia et al., *JAMA*, vol. 289, pp. 313–322, 2003). Explain what false negatives and false positives mean in the context of this diagnostic test.

5.88 Screening for heart attacks Biochemical markers are used by emergency room physicians to aid in diagnosing patients who have suffered acute myocardial infarction (AMI), or what's commonly referred to as a heart attack. One type of biochemical marker used is creatine kinase (CK). Based on a review of published studies on the effectiveness of these markers (by E. M. Balk et al., *Annals of Emergency Medicine*, vol. 37, pp. 478–494, 2001), CK had an estimated sensitivity of 37% and specificity of 87%. Consider a population having a prevalence rate of 25%.

a. Explain in context what is meant by the sensitivity equaling 37%.

b. Explain in context what is meant by the specificity equaling 87%.

c. Construct a tree diagram for this diagnostic test. Label the branches with the appropriate probabilities.

5.89 Screening for colorectal cancer Gigerenzer reported that on the average, "Thirty out of every 10,000 people have colorectal cancer. Of these 30 people with colorectal cancer, 15 will have a positive hemoccult test. Of the remaining 9,970 people without colorectal cancer, 300 will still have a positive hemoccult test." (*Source:* Gigerenzer, G. (2002). Calculated Risks. New York: Simon & Schuster, p. 105.)

a. Sketch a tree diagram or construct a contingency table to display the counts.

b. Of the 315 people mentioned who have a positive hemoccult test, what proportion actually have colorectal cancer? Interpret.

5.90 Color blindness For genetic reasons, color blindness is more common in men than women: 5 in 100 men and 25 in 10,000 women suffer from color blindness.

a. Define events and identify in words these proportions as conditional probabilities.

b. If the population is half male and half female, what proportion of the population is color-blind? Use a tree diagram or contingency table with frequencies to portray your solution, showing what you would expect to happen with 20,000 people.

[9]*What Are the Chances?* by B. K. Holland (Johns Hopkins University Press, 2002, p. 10).

c. Given that a randomly chosen person is color-blind, what's the probability that person is female? Use the tree diagram or table from part b to find the answer.

5.91 HIV blood test For a combined ELISA-Western blot blood test for HIV-positive status, the sensitivity is about 0.999 and the specificity is about 0.9999 (Gigerenzer 2002, pp. 124, 126).

a. Consider a high-risk group in which 10% are truly HIV positive. Construct a tree diagram to summarize this diagnostic test.

b. Display the intersection probabilities from part a in a contingency table.

c. A person from this high-risk group has a positive test result. Using the tree diagram or the contingency table, find the probability that this person is truly HIV positive.

d. Explain why a positive test result is more likely to be in error when the prevalence is lower. Use tree diagrams or contingency tables with frequencies for 10,000 people with 10% and 1% prevalence rates to illustrate your arguments.

5.92 Prostate cancer A study of the PSA blood test for diagnosing prostate cancer in men (by R. M. Hoffman et al., *BMC Family Practice*, vol. 3, p. 19, 2002) used a sample of 2,620 men who were 40 years and older. When a positive diagnostic test result was defined as a PSA reading of at least 4, the sensitivity was estimated to be 0.86 but the specificity only 0.33.

a. Suppose that 10% of those who took the PSA test truly had prostate cancer. Given that the PSA was positive, use a tree diagram and/or contingency table to estimate the probability that the man truly had prostate cancer.

b. Illustrate your answer in part a by using a tree diagram or contingency table with frequencies showing what you would expect for a typical sample of 1,000 men.

c. Lowering the PSA boundary to 2 for a positive result changed the sensitivity to 0.95 and the specificity to 0.20. Explain why, intuitively, if the cases increase for which a test is positive, the sensitivity will go up but the specificity will go down.

5.93 U Win A fast-food chain is running a promotion to try to increase sales. Each customer who purchases a meal combo receives a game piece that contains one of the letters U, W, I, or N. If a player collects one of all four letters, that player is the lucky winner of a free milkshake. Suppose that of all game pieces, 10% contain the letter U, 30% contain W, 30% contain I, and 30% contain N. Use the *Random Numbers* app or other software to estimate the probability that you will collect enough game pieces with your next five combo meal purchases to receive the free shake. Clearly describe the steps of your simulation. Your simulation should consist of at least 20 repetitions.

5.94 Win again Referring to the previous exercise, conduct a simulation consisting of at least 20 repetitions, where for each repetition you keep track of *how many* combo meals you had to purchase to win the free shake. Clearly describe the steps of your simulation. After 20 (or more, if you have the time) repetitions, average the numbers you got from each repetition. This will estimate what is called the *expected value* of the number of meals you have to purchase in order to win the free shake.

Concepts and Investigations

5.95 Simulate law of large numbers Using the *Random Numbers* app (or other software), simulate the flipping of balanced and biased coins.

a. Report the proportion of heads after (i) 10 flips, (ii) 100 flips, (iii) 1,000 flips, and (iv) 10,000 flips. (Select the Coin Flips tab in the app. You can read off the proportions from the graph that appears after you press Generate in each case.) Explain how the results illustrate the law of large numbers and the long-run relative frequency definition of probability.

b. Use the *Random Numbers* app to simulate the roll of 3 or 4 with a die, using (i) 10 rolls, (ii) 100 rolls, (iii) 1,000 rolls, and (iv) 10,000 rolls. (*Hint:* What is the probability of rolling a 3 or 4? Use this to set up a biased coin, where you identify rolling a 3 or 4 as flipping a head.) Summarize your results.

5.96 Illustrate probability terms with scenarios

a. What is a sample space? Give an example of a sample space for a scenario involving (i) a designed experiment and (ii) an observational study.

b. What are disjoint events? Give an example of two events that are disjoint.

c. What is a conditional probability? Give an example of two events in your everyday life that you would expect to be (i) independent and (ii) dependent.

5.97 Short term versus long run Short-term aberrations do not affect the long run. To illustrate, suppose that you flip a coin 10 times and you get 10 heads. Find the cumulative proportion of heads, including these first 10 flips, if (a) in the 100 flips after those 10 you get 50 heads (so there are now 60 heads in 110 flips), (b) in the 1,000 flips after those 10 you get 500 heads, and (c) in the 10,000 flips after those 10 you get 5,000 heads. What number is the cumulative proportion tending toward as *n* increases?

5.98 Risk of space shuttle After the Columbia space shuttle disaster, a former NASA official who faulted the way the agency dealt with safety risk warned (in an AP story, March 7, 2003) that NASA workers believed, "If I've flown 20 times, the risk is less than if I've flown just once."

a. Explain why it would be reasonable for someone to form this belief from the way we use empirical evidence and margins of error to estimate an unknown probability.

b. Explain a criticism of this belief, using coin flipping as an analogy.

5.99 Mrs. Test Mrs. Test (see www.mrstest.com) sells diagnostic tests for various conditions. Its website gives only imprecise information about the accuracy of the tests. The test for pregnancy is said to be "over 99% accurate." Describe at least four probabilities to which this could refer.

5.100 Marijuana leads to heroin? Nearly all heroin addicts have used marijuana sometime in their lives. So, some argue that marijuana should be illegal because marijuana users are likely to become heroin addicts. Use a Venn diagram to illustrate the fallacy of this argument by sketching sets for M = marijuana use and H = heroin use such that $P(M|H)$ is close to 1 but $P(H|M)$ is close to 0.

5.101 Stay in school Suppose 80% of students finish high school. Of them, 50% finish college. Of them, 20% get a master's degree. Of them, 30% get a Ph.D.

a. What percentage of students get a Ph.D.?

b. Explain how your reasoning in part a used a multiplication rule with conditional probabilities.

c. Given that a student finishes college, find the probability of getting a Ph.D.

5.102 Hillary Clinton's Tweet During the 2016 presidential campaign, Hillary Clinton tweeted the following about background checks for gun ownership. It is an example of the wrong use of Venn diagrams and not using conditional probabilities.

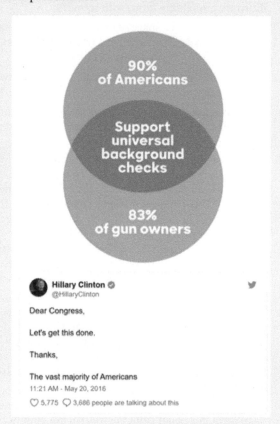

a. Define the two events A = {gun owner} and B = {support background checks} for a randomly selected American adult. Draw a correct Venn diagram (without including any percentages) that conveys the message that most gun owners support universal background checks.

b. According to polls,[10] 43% of Americans personally own guns. Of those personally owning guns, 87% favor universal background checks. Based on these numbers, state P(A) and P(B | A) and create a tweet (at most 280 characters) that describes these findings.

c. The polls also showed that overall, 93% of Americans favor universal background checks. Use this information and the information from part b to find $P(B|A^C)$. In words, what does this conditional probability tell us? (*Hint:* Construct a contingency table with a hypothetical sample of 100 Americans.)

d. Think of a better display than the one used by Hillary Clinton to compare conditional probabilities of favoring background checks for gun owners and for those who don't own guns.

5.103 Protective bomb Before the days of high security at airports, there was a legendary person who was afraid of traveling by plane because someone on the plane might have a bomb. He always brought a bomb himself on any plane flight he took, believing that the chance would be astronomically small that two people on the same flight would both have a bomb. Explain the fallacy in his logic, using ideas of independent events and conditional probability.

5.104 Streak shooter Sportscaster Maria Coselli claims that players on the New York Knicks professional basketball team are streak shooters. To make her case, she looks at the statistics for all the team's players over the past three games and points out that one of them (Joe Smith) made six shots in a row at one stage. Coselli argues, "Over a season, Smith makes only 45% of his shots. The probability that he would make six in a row if the shots were independent is $(0.45)^6 = 0.008$, less than one in a hundred. This would be such an unusual occurrence that we can conclude that Smith is a streak shooter."

a. Explain the flaws in Coselli's logic.

b. Use this example to explain how some things that look highly coincidental may not be so when viewed in a wider context.

5.105 Driving versus flying In the United States in 2002, about 43,000 people died in auto crashes and 0 people died in commercial airline accidents. G. Gigerenzer states, "The terrorist attack on September 11, 2001, cost the lives of some 3,000 people. The subsequent decision of millions to drive rather than fly may have cost the lives of many more." Explain the reasoning behind this statement. (*Source:* Gigerenzer, G. (2002). Calculated Risks. New York: Simon & Schuster, p. 31.)

5.106 Prosecutor's fallacy An eyewitness to a crime says that the person who committed it was male, between 15 and 20 years old, Hispanic, and drove a blue Honda. The prosecutor points out that a proportion of only 0.001 people living in that city match all those characteristics, and one of them is the defendant. Thus, the prosecutor argues that the probability that the defendant is not guilty is only 0.001. Explain what is wrong with this logic. (*Hint:* Is P(match) = P(not guilty | match)?)

—————
[10]*Sources:* Gallup's Gun "Topics A to Z" from a survey in October 2018 (https://news.gallup.com/poll/1645/Guns.aspx?g_source=link_newsv9&g_campaign=item_264932&g_medium=copy) and Quinnipiac University poll from March 2019 (https://poll.qu.edu/national/release-detail?ReleaseID=2604)

Multiple Choice or True/False

Problems 5.107–5.111 may have more than one correct answer.

5.107 Probability for independent or disjoint events I Choose ALL correct responses. For two events A and B, $P(A) = 0.5$ and $P(B) = 0.2$. Then $P(A \text{ or } B)$ equals

a. 0.10, if A and B are independent.

b. 0.70, if A and B are independent.

c. 0.60, if A and B are independent.

d. 0.70, if A and B are disjoint.

5.108 Probability for independent or disjoint events II Which of the following is always true?

a. If A and B are independent, then they are also disjoint.

b. $P(A|B) + P(A|B^C) = 1$

c. If $P(A|B) = P(B|A)$, then A and B are independent.

d. If A and B are disjoint, then A and B cannot occur at the same time.

5.109 Coin flip A balanced coin is flipped 100 times. By the law of large numbers:

a. There will almost certainly be *exactly* 50 heads and 50 tails.

b. If we got 100 heads in a row, almost certainly the next flip will be a tail.

c. For the 100 flips, the probability of getting 100 heads equals the probability of getting 50 heads.

d. It is absolutely impossible to get a head every time.

e. None of the above.

5.110 Dream come true You have a dream in which you see your favorite movie star in person. The very next day, you are visiting Manhattan and you see her walking down Fifth Avenue.

a. This is such an incredibly unlikely coincidence that you should report it to your local newspaper.

b. This is somewhat unusual, but given the many dreams you could have in your lifetime about people you know or know of, it is not an incredibly unlikely event.

c. If you had not had the dream, you would definitely not have seen the film star the next day.

d. This proves the existence of ESP.

5.111 Comparable risks Mammography is estimated to save about 1 life in every 1,000 women. "Participating in annual mammography screening ... has roughly the same effect on life expectancy as reducing the distance one drives each year by 300 miles" (Gigerenzer, G. (2002). Calculated Risks. New York: Simon & Schuster, pp. 60,73). Which of the following do you think has the closest effect on life expectancy as that of smoking throughout your entire life?

a. Taking a commercial airline flight once a year

b. Driving about 10 times as far every year as the average motorist

c. Drinking a cup of coffee every day

d. Eating a fast-food hamburger once a month

e. Never having a mammogram (if you are a woman)

5.112 True or false Answer true of false for each part.

a. When you flip a coin 10 times, you are more likely to get the sequence HHHHHTTTTT than the sequence HHHHHHHHHH.

b. When you flip a coin 10 times, you are more likely to get a sequence that contains five heads than a sequence that contains 10 heads.

5.113 True or false When you flip a balanced coin twice, three things can happen: 0 heads, 1 head, or 2 heads. Since there are three possible outcomes, they each have probability 1/3. (This was claimed by the French mathematician, Jean le Rond d'Alembert, in 1754. To reason this, write down the sample space for the possible sequence of results for the two flips.)

Advanced Exercises

5.114 Generalizing the addition rule For events A, B, and C such that each pair of events is disjoint, use a Venn diagram to explain why

$$P(A \text{ or } B \text{ or } C) = P(A) + P(B) + P(C).$$

5.115 Generalizing the multiplication rule For events A, B, and C, explain why $P(A \text{ and } B \text{ and } C) =$

$$P(A) \times P(B|A) \times P(C|A \text{ and } B).$$

5.116 Bayes' Rule Suppose we know $P(A), P(B|A)$, and $P(B^C|A^C)$, but we want to find $P(A|B)$.

a. Using the definition of conditional probability for $P(A|B)$ and for $P(B|A)$, explain why $P(A|B) = P(A \text{ and } B)/P(B) = [P(A)P(B|A)]/P(B)$.

b. Splitting the event that B occurs into two parts, according to whether A occurs, explain why

$$P(B) = P(B \text{ and } A) + P(B \text{ and } A^C).$$

c. Using part b and the definition of conditional probability, explain why

$$P(B) = P(A)P(B|A) + P(A^C)P(B|A^C).$$

d. Combining what you have shown in parts a–c, reason that

$$P(A|B) = \frac{P(A)P(B|A)}{P(A)P(B|A) + P(A^C)P(B|A^C)}.$$

This formula is called **Bayes' Rule**. It is named after a British clergyman who discovered the formula in 1763.

Student Activities

5.117 Simulating matching birthdays Do you find it hard to believe that the probability of at least one birthday match in a class of 25 students is 0.57? Let's simulate the answer. Using the *Random Numbers* app accessible from the book's website, each student in the class should simulate 25 numbers between 1 and 365. Observe whether there is at least one match of two numbers out of the 25 simulated numbers.

a. Combine class results. What proportion of the simulations had at least one birthday match?

b. Repeat part a for a birthday match in a class of 50 students. Again, combine class results. What is the simulated probability of at least one match?

5.118 **Simulate table tennis** In table tennis, the first person to get at least 21 points while being ahead of the opponent by at least two points wins the game. In games between you and an opponent, suppose successive points are independent and that the probability of your winning any given point is 0.40.

a. Do you have any reasonable chance to win a game? Showing all steps, simulate two games by generating random numbers between 1 and 10 using the *Random Numbers* app or other software; let numbers 1–4 represent winning a point and 5–10 losing a point.

b. Combining results for all students in the class, estimate the probability of winning.

5.119 **Which tennis strategy is better?** A tennis match can consist of a best of three sets (that is, the winner is the first to win two sets) or a best of five sets (the winner is the first to win three sets). Which would you be better off playing if you are the weaker player and have probability 0.40 of winning any particular set?

a. Simulate 10 matches of each type, using the *Random Numbers* app or other software. Show the steps of your simulation and specify any assumptions.

b. Combining results for all students in the class, estimate the probability of the weaker player winning the match under each type of match.

5.120 **Saving a business** The business you started last year has only $5,000 left in capital. A week from now, you need to repay a $10,000 loan or you will go bankrupt. You see two possible ways to raise the money you need. You can ask a large company to invest the $10,000, wooing it with the $5,000 you have left. You guess your probability of success is 0.20. Or you could ask, in sequence, several small companies each to invest $2,000, spending $1,000 on each to woo it. You guess your probability of success is 0.20 for each appeal. What's the probability you will raise enough money to repay the loan with each strategy? Which is the better strategy, to be bold with one large bet or to be cautious and use several smaller bets? With the bold strategy, the probability of success is simply 0.20. With the cautious strategy, we need to use simulation to find the probability of success.

a. Simulate the cautious strategy 10 times using the *Random Numbers* app or other software. Show the steps of the simulations and specify any assumptions.

b. Combining simulation results for all students in the class, estimate the probability of the cautious strategy being successful.

c. Which strategy would you choose? The bolder strategy or the cautious strategy? Explain.

BIBLIOGRAPHY

Against All Odds: Inside Statistics (1989). Produced by Consortium for Mathematics and Its Applications for PBS. See www.learner.org.

Gigerenzer, G. (2002). *Calculated Risks.* New York: Simon & Schuster.

Wilson, R., and E. A. C. Crouch (2001). *Risk-Benefit Analysis.* Cambridge, MA: Harvard Univ. Press.

CHAPTER 6

In Chapter 2, we introduced variables and studied how to describe their distribution using data from a sample or experiment. In this chapter, we learn how to describe the distribution of a variable in probabilistic terms and introduce two important special cases, the normal and the binomial distribution.

Random Variables and Probability Distributions

Example 1

Gender Discrimination

Picture the Scenario

A 2001 lawsuit by seven female employees claimed that Wal-Mart Stores Inc. promoted female workers less frequently than male workers. This lawsuit grew into the largest sex-discrimination class-action lawsuit in U.S. history, representing more than 1.5 million current and former female Wal-Mart employees, before it was eventually decided, in 2011, in favor of Wal-Mart by the Supreme Court.[1,2]

Question to Explore

Suppose that 10 individuals are chosen from a large pool of qualifying employees for a promotion program, and the pool has an equal number of female and male employees. When all 10 individuals chosen for promotion are male, the female employees claim that the program is gender-biased. How can we investigate statistically the validity of the women's claim?

Thinking Ahead

Other factors being equal, the probability of selecting a female for promotion is 0.50, as is the probability of selecting a male. If the employees are selected randomly in terms of gender, about half of the employees picked should be females and about half should be male. Due to ordinary sampling variation, however, it need not happen that exactly 50% of those selected are female. A simple analogy is in flipping a coin 10 times. We won't necessarily see exactly 5 heads.

Because none of the 10 employees chosen for promotion is female, we might be inclined to support the women's claim. The question we need to consider is, would these results be unlikely if there were no gender bias? An equivalent question is, if we flip a coin 10 times, would it be very surprising if we got 0 heads?

In this chapter, we'll apply the probability tools of the previous chapter to answer such questions. In Example 13, we'll revisit this gender discrimination question. In Example 14, we'll use probability arguments to analyze whether racial profiling may have occurred when police officers make traffic stops.

---

[1]*Source:* Background information taken from www.reuters.com/article/2010/12/06/us-walmart-lawsuit-discrimination-idUSTRE6B531W20101206.

[2]www.cnn.com/2011/US/06/20/scotus.wal.mart.discrimination/index.html?hpt=hp_t1.

We learned the basics of probability in Chapter 5. We'll next study tables, graphs, and formulas for finding probabilities that will be useful to us for the rest of the book. We'll see how possible outcomes and their probabilities are summarized in a **probability distribution.** Then, we'll study two commonly used probability distributions—the **normal** and the **binomial.** The normal distribution, which has a bell-shaped graph, plays a key role in statistical inference.

6.1 Summarizing Possible Outcomes and Their Probabilities

Recall
The characteristics we measure are called **variables** because their values vary from subject to subject. If the possible outcomes are a set of separate numbers, the variable is **discrete** (for example, a variable expressed as "the number of..." with possible values 0, 1, 2,...). If the variable can take any value in an interval, such as the sustained wind speed of a hurricane (any number larger than 74 mph), it is **continuous.** ◄

With proper methods of gathering data, the numerical values that a variable assumes should be the result of some random phenomenon. For example, the randomness may stem from selecting a random sample from a population or performing a randomized experiment. In such cases, we call the variable a **random variable.**

Random Variable

A **random variable** is a numerical measurement of the outcome of a random phenomenon. Often, the randomness results from the use of random sampling or a randomized experiment to gather the data. As a consequence, the values that a random variable takes on are determined by chance.

We've used letters near the end of the alphabet, such as x, to symbolize variables. We'll also use letters such as x for the possible values of a random variable. When we refer to the random variable itself, rather than a particular value, we'll use a capital letter, such as X. For instance, X = number of heads in three flips of a coin denotes the random variable, whereas $x = 2$ is one of its possible values as is $x = 3$ or $x = 0$.

Because a random variable refers to the outcome of a random phenomenon, each possible outcome has a specific probability of occurring. The **probability distribution** of a random variable specifies its possible values and their probabilities. An advantage of a variable being a random variable is that it's possible to specify such probabilities. Without randomness, we would not be able to predict the probabilities of the possible outcomes in the long run, and we would not be able to make long-run predictions for the values of the random variable.

Probability Distributions of Discrete Random Variables

When a random variable has separate possible values, such as 0, 1, 2, 3 for the number of heads in three flips of a coin, it is called **discrete.** The **probability distribution** of a discrete random variable assigns a probability to each possible value. Each probability falls between 0 and 1, and the sum of the probabilities of all possible values equals 1. We let $P(x)$ denote the probability of a possible value x, such as $P(2)$ for the probability that the random variable takes the value 2.

Recall
From Chapter 5, a **probability** is a long-run **proportion.** It can take any value in the interval from 0 up to 1. The probabilities for all the possible outcomes in the sample space add up to 1.0. ◄

Probability Distribution of a Discrete Random Variable

A **discrete** random variable X takes on values from a set of separate values (such as 0, 1, 2,...). Its **probability distribution** assigns a probability $P(x)$ to each possible value x.

- For each x, the probability $P(x)$ falls between 0 and 1.
- The sum of the probabilities for all the possible x values equals 1.

For instance, let X be a random number between 1 and 10, selected using software (such as the *Random Numbers* app) as part of the process of identifying subjects to include in a random sample. The possible values for X are $x = 1, 2, \ldots, 8, 9, 10$. Each number is equally likely, so the probability distribution is

$$P(1) = P(2) = P(3) = P(4) = P(5) =$$
$$P(6) = P(7) = P(8) = P(9) = P(10) = 0.10.$$

Each probability falls between 0 and 1, and the probabilities add up to 1.0. If X is the outcome of rolling a balanced die, then the possible values for X are $x = 1, 2, 3, 4, 5, 6$, and $P(1) = P(2) = P(3) = P(4) = P(5) = P(6) = 1/6$, again summing to 1.0.

Random variables can also be **continuous**, having possible values that form an interval rather than a set of separate numbers. We'll learn about continuous random variables and their probability distributions later in this section.

Example 2

Probability
Distribution for
a Discrete Random
Variable ◀

Best of Seven

Picture the Scenario

Many playoff and championship games in professional sports such as basketball, baseball, or hockey are decided by a best of seven series, in which the team that is the first to get four victories wins the series. This often adds drama because the number of games that actually need to be played is not fixed in advance. Let the random variable X represent the number of games needed to determine a winner in a best of 7 series, with possible outcomes 4 (when one teams wins the first four games, called a sweep), 5, 6, or 7. Table 6.1 shows the probability distribution of X when we assume that the chances for either team to win a game are 50% for all games played and that outcomes of games are independent of each other. (As you can see from the table, the most likely outcomes under this scenario are the need to play 6 or 7 games.)

Table 6.1 Probability Distribution of X = Number of Games Needed to Determine a Winner in a Best of Seven Series

Number of Games x	Probability $P(x)$
4	$1/8 = 0.125$
5	$1/4 = 0.25$
6	$5/16 = 0.3125$
7	$5/16 = 0.3125$

Questions to Explore

a. Why is X a random variable?

b. Show how Table 6.1 satisfies the two properties needed for a probability distribution.

c. What is the probability that a best of seven series will be decided by at least six games?

Think It Through

a. Before the start of the series, we are uncertain just how many games will be necessary to determine a winner. This number will be determined by a random phenomenon, the outcome of the games played, making X = number of games a random variable whose values are determined by chance.

Recall

P(6) denotes the probability that the random variable takes the value 6; that is, the probability that the number of games needed to be played to determine a winner is 6. ◄

b. In Table 6.1, the two conditions in the definition of a probability distribution are satisfied:

(i) For each x, the probability $P(x)$ falls between 0 and 1.

(ii) The sum of the probabilities for all the possible x values equals 1.

c. The probability of at least six games in a best of seven series is (using the addition rule for disjoint events)

$$P(6) + P(7) = 5/16 + 5/16 = 10/16 = 0.625.$$

Insight

We can display the probability distribution of a discrete random variable with a *graph* and sometimes with a *formula*. Figure 6.1 displays a graph for the probability distribution in Table 6.1.

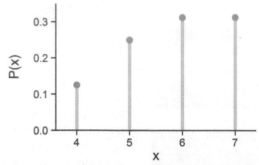

▲ **Figure 6.1** Graph of Probability Distribution of Number of Games Needed to Determine a Winner in a Best of Seven Series. The line for each possible value of X has a height equal to its probability. **Question** How would you describe the shape of the distribution?

▶ *Try Exercises 6.1 and 6.2*

In Chapter 2, we used graphs and numerical summaries to describe the three key components, shape, center, and variability, for the distribution of a quantitative variable. These summaries were calculated from observations on the variable obtained from a sample or experiment. For a probability distribution, a graph as in Figure 6.1 shows the shape, but how do we find corresponding summary measures for the center and variability of a probability distribution?

The Mean of a Probability Distribution

Recall

Section 1.2 defined a **parameter** to be a numerical summary of the population, such as a population mean or a population proportion. ◄

To describe characteristics of a probability distribution, we can use any of the numerical summaries defined in Chapter 2. These include mean, median, quartiles, and standard deviation. It is most common to use the *mean* to describe the center and the *standard deviation* to describe the variability. Recall that numerical summaries of populations are called **parameters**.

You can think of a **population distribution** as merely being a type of probability distribution—one that applies for selecting a subject at random from a population. Like numerical summaries of populations, numerical summaries of probability distributions are referred to as **parameters**. Typically, parameters are denoted by Greek letters. For example, the mean of a probability distribution is denoted by μ, and the standard deviation is denoted by σ.

In Words

μ is the Greek letter mu, pronounced "mew." σ is the lowercase Greek letter sigma. The corresponding Roman letter s is used for the standard deviation of *sample* data. Recall that the sample mean is denoted by $\bar{x}$.

Suppose we repeatedly observe values of a random variable, such as repeatedly noting the outcome when we roll a die. The mean μ of the probability distribution for that random variable is the value we would get, in the long run, for the average of those values. This long-run interpretation parallels the interpretation (in Section 5.1) of probability itself as a summary of the long-run behavior of a random phenomenon.

◄ **Mean of a Probability Distribution**

Probability Distribution for
X = Number of Games Needed to Win

Number of Games x	Probability $P(x)$
4	1/8 = 0.125
5	1/4 = 0.25
6	5/16 = 0.3125
7	5/16 = 0.3125

Did You Know?

In baseball, for the 73 World Series played between 1945 and 2018, 13 (or 18%) ended after 4 games, 14 (19%) after 5 games, 15 (20%) after 6 games, and 31 (42%) needed to go all the way to 7 games. (See Exercise 6.99.) ◄

Example 3

The Expected Number of Games Played in a Best of Seven Series

Picture the Scenario

Let's refer back to the probability distribution for the random variable X = number of games needed to determine a winner in a best of seven series, when we assume the chance for either team to win a game is 50% for all games played. The probability distribution for X is shown again in the margin.

Question to Explore

Find the mean of this probability distribution and interpret it.

Think It Through

Because $P(4) = 1/8$, over the long run we expect $x = 4$ (that is, a sweep) to occur in one-eighth (or 12.5%) of all series played. Likewise, we expect that $x = 5$ games are needed to determine a winner in one-fourth (25%) of all series played, $x = 6$ games in 31.25%, and $x = 7$ games also in 31.25% of all series played. Over 10,000 series played (i.e., in the long run), we would observe the number 4 about 1,250 times $(10,000 \times (1/8) = 1,250)$, the number 5 about 2,500 times, and the numbers 6 and 7 each about 3,125 times. Because the mean equals the sum of all observations divided by the total number of observations, we can calculate the mean as

$$\begin{array}{cccc} \textbf{1,250 terms} & \textbf{2,500 terms} & \textbf{3,125 terms} & \textbf{3,125 terms} \\ \downarrow & \downarrow & \downarrow & \downarrow \end{array}$$

$$\mu = \frac{(4 + 4 + \ldots + 4) + (5 + 5 + \ldots + 5) + (6 + 6 + \ldots + 6) + (7 + 7 + \ldots + 7)}{10,000}$$

$$= \frac{(1,250 \times 4) + (2,500 \times 5) + (3,125 \times 6) + (3,125 \times 7)}{10,000} = \frac{58,125}{10,000} = 5.8125$$

The mean of the probability distribution is 5.8125. Under the assumption above (50% chance of winning each game), we'd expect that on average about 5.8 games are needed to determine a winner in a best of seven series.

Insight

Because 1,250/10,000 = 0.125 and 2,500/10,000 = 0.25 and 3,125/10,000 = 0.3125, the calculation for the mean has the form

$$\mu = 4 \times \frac{1,250}{10,000} + 5 \times \frac{2,500}{10,000} + 6 \times \frac{3,125}{10,000} + 7 \times \frac{3,125}{10,000}$$

$$= 4 \times 0.125 + 5 \times 0.25 + 6 \times 0.3125 + 7 \times 0.3125$$

$$= 4 \times P(4) + 5 \times P(5) + 6 \times P(6) + 7 \times P(7).$$

Each possible value x is multiplied by its probability $P(x)$. In fact, for any discrete random variable, the mean of its probability distribution results from multiplying each possible value x by its probability $P(x)$ and then adding up these values.

► *Try Exercise 6.3*

Mean of a Discrete Probability Distribution

The **mean of a probability distribution** for a discrete random variable is

$$\mu = \Sigma x P(x),$$

where the sum is taken over all possible values of x.

For the number of games played in a best of seven series, as we saw in the example,

$$\mu = \Sigma x P(x) = 4P(4) + 5P(5) + 6P(6) + 7P(7)$$

$$= 4(0.125) + 5(0.25) + 6(0.3125) + 7(0.3125) = 5.8125.$$

The mean $\mu = \Sigma x P(x)$ is called a **weighted average**: Values of x that are more likely receive greater weight P(x). It does not make sense to take a simple average of the possible values of x, $(4 + 5 + 6 + 7)/4 = 5.5$, to obtain the mean because some outcomes are more likely than others and need to receive more weight.

Consider the special case in which the outcomes are *equally likely* such as the 6 possible outcomes when rolling a die, each occurring with probability 1/6. Then $\mu = \Sigma x P(x) = \Sigma x (1/6) = (1 + 2 + 3 + 4 + 5 + 6)/6 = 3.5$. Here, the formula $\Sigma x P(x)$ reduces to the ordinary mean of the 6 numbers, but this only happens for *equally likely* outcomes, such as the 6 faces of a die. The formula $\mu = \Sigma x P(x)$ for the mean of a probability distribution generalizes the ordinary formula for the mean to allow for outcomes that are not equally likely, such as the number of games played in a best of seven series.

The long-run average of observing some series with 4 games, some with 5 games, some with 6 games, and some with 7 games is 5.8125. This can be rounded to 5.8, but rounding it to 6, the closest integer, would be too crude and the mean doesn't need to equal any of the possible values.

There is also a general formula for the mean of a *continuous* probability distribution. It involves advanced material from calculus (an integral) so we will not present it here. However, we will discuss the mean for certain special and important continuous probability distributions, such as the normal distribution, in Section 6.2 (see also Exercise 6.14).

The mean μ of the probability distribution of a random variable X is also called the **expected value of X**. The expected value reflects not what we'll observe in a *single* observation, but rather what we expect for the *average* in a long run of observations. In the preceding example, the expected value of the number of games played in a best of seven series is $\mu = 5.8$. As with means of sample data, the mean of a probability distribution doesn't have to be one of the possible values for the random variable.

Expected Gain/Loss ◄

Example 4

Responding to Risk

Picture the Scenario

Are you a risk-averse person who prefers the sure thing to a risky action that could give you a better or a worse outcome? Or are you a risk taker, willing to gamble in hopes of achieving the better outcome?

Questions to Explore

a.   You are given $1,000 to invest. You must choose between (i) a sure gain of $500 and (ii) a 0.50 chance of a gain of $1,000 and a 0.50 chance to gain nothing. What is the expected gain with each strategy? Which do you prefer?

Probability Distribution for X = Gain on $1,000 Investment with Risk-Taking Strategy. (Part a)

Gain x	P(x)
0	0.50
1,000	0.50

Probability Distribution for X = Loss on $2,000 Investment with Risk-Taking Strategy. (Part b)

Loss x	P(x)
0	0.5
1,000	0.5

b. You are given $2,000 to invest. You must choose between (i) a sure loss of $500 and (ii) a 0.50 chance of losing $1,000 and a 0.50 chance of losing nothing. What is the expected loss with each strategy? Which do you prefer?

Think It Through

a. The expected gain is $500 with the sure strategy (i), since that strategy has gain $500 with probability 1.0. With the risk-taking strategy (ii), the probability distribution is shown in the margin (first table). The expected gain is $\mu = \Sigma x P(x) = \$0(0.50) + \$1,000(0.50) = \$500$.

b. The expected loss is $500 with the sure strategy (i). With the risk-taking strategy (ii), the expected loss is $\mu = \Sigma x P(x) = \$0(0.50) + \$1,000(0.50) = \$500$. (See the second table in the margin.)

Insight

In each scenario, the expected values are the same with each strategy. Yet most people prefer the sure-gain strategy (i) for the scenario in part a but the risk-taking strategy (ii) for the scenario in part b. They are risk averse in scenario a but risk taking in scenario b. This preference was explored in research by Daniel Kahneman and Amos Tversky, for which Kahneman won the Nobel Prize in 2002.

▶ *Try Exercise 6.8*

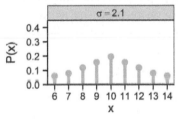

Two probability distributions with the same mean (10) but different standard deviations of 1.1 and 2.1.

Summarizing the Variability of a Probability Distribution: The Standard Deviation

As with distributions of sample data, it's useful to summarize both the *center* and the *variability* of a probability distribution. For instance, suppose two investment strategies have the same expected payout. Does one strategy have more variability in its payouts than the other?

The **standard deviation** of a probability distribution, denoted by σ, measures the variability from the mean. Larger values for σ correspond to greater variability. The margin figures show two distributions that have the same mean but different standard deviations. Roughly, σ describes how far values of the random variable fall, on the average, from the mean of the distribution. Similar to calculating the standard deviation for a sample, finding the standard deviation for the probability distribution is a two-step process. First, we find the variance, which is in terms of the squared deviations from the mean. Then we take the square root of the variance to find the standard deviation.

Variance and Standard Deviation of a Discrete Probability Distribution

The **variance of a probability distribution** for a discrete random variable is

$$\sigma^2 = \sum (x - \mu)^2 P(x),$$

where the sum is taken over all possible values of x. It is a weighted average of the squared distances between the possible values of the random variable X and its mean μ.

The **standard deviation of a probability distribution** for a discrete random variable is

$$\sigma = \sqrt{\sigma^2} = \sqrt{\sum (x - \mu)^2 P(x)}$$

and is the square root of the variance. It describes a typical distance for the values of the random variable X from their mean. The smaller the standard deviation, the closer the values of the random variable tend to fall to the mean.

Example 5

Risk Taking Entails More Variability

Picture the Scenario

Let's revisit the scenario from part a in Example 4. You are given $1,000 to invest and must choose between (i) a sure gain of $500 and (ii) a 0.50 chance of a gain of $1,000 and a 0.50 chance to gain nothing. Table 6.2 shows the probability distribution of the gain X for the two strategies.

Table 6.2 Probability Distribution of X = Gain for the Sure Strategy (Left Table) and the Risk-Taking Strategy (Right Table)

x	$P(x)$	x	$P(x)$
500	1.0	0	0.50
		1,000	0.50

Questions to Explore

Example 4 showed that both strategies have the same expected value, namely μ = $500. Which of the two probability distributions has the larger standard deviation?

Think It Through

There is *no* variability for the sure strategy because the gain is always $500, with no deviation. The standard deviation of this probability distribution is 0, the smallest possible value. Using the formula, since there is only one value of x, we get $\sigma = \sqrt{(500 - 500)^2} = \sqrt{(0)} = 0$.

 With the risk-taking strategy, no matter what the outcome (either $0 or $1,000), the result will be a distance of $500 away from the expected value of $500. Plugging in $x = 0$ and $x = 1,000$, $\mu = 500$, $P(0) = 0.5$ and $P(1,000) = 0.5$, the standard deviation is given by

$$\sigma = \sqrt{(0 - 500)^2\, 0.5 + (1,000 - 500)^2\, 0.5}$$
$$= \sqrt{(-500)^2\, 0.5 + (500)^2\, 0.5}$$
$$= \sqrt{(25,000)0.5 + (25,000)0.5}$$
$$= \sqrt{25,000} = 500.$$

The standard deviation for the probability distribution of the gain under the risk-taking strategy is σ = $500. With that strategy, there's much more variability in what can happen.

Insight

In practice, different investment strategies are often compared by their variability. Not only is an investor interested in the expected return of an investment but also the consistency of the return of the investment from year to year as measured by the standard deviation. Those investments with a larger standard deviation fluctuate more in their annual return and are considered riskier.

▶ **Try Exercises 6.9 and 6.10**

Did You Know?

In finance, the symbol σ is used to describe the volatility (= variability in the price) of financial instruments like stocks. It is one of the standard indicators printed in stock quotes next to highs and lows or the price-earning ratio. ◄

As another example, let's find the standard deviation for the random variable $X =$ the profit of a $5 bet on red in a game of roulette. Suppose we play the European version of roulette, which has outcomes red, black, or the number 0, with probabilities 18/37, 18/37, and 1/37, respectively. (There is no double-zero on European-type roulette wheels, which uniformly improves your chances of winning compared to the American version.) If red comes up, the bet is won and the profit is $5. However, if either black or the number 0 comes up, the bet is lost and the profit is −$5. The possible values for the random variable X are therefore $x = 5$ when the outcome is red, $x = -5$ when the outcome is black, and $x = -5$ when the outcome is the number 0. The probability distribution for X is shown in the margin.

To find the standard deviation, we first have to find the mean, which is

$$\mu = (5)\left(\frac{18}{37}\right) + (-5)\left(\frac{18}{37}\right) + (-5)\left(\frac{1}{37}\right) = -0.14$$

This shows that in the long run, we expect to lose 14 cents with this bet. The variance is given by

$$\sigma^2 = (5-(-0.14))^2\left(\frac{18}{37}\right) + (-5-(-0.14))^2\left(\frac{18}{37}\right) + (-5-(-0.14))^2\left(\frac{1}{37}\right)$$

$$= (5.14)^2\left(\frac{18}{37}\right) + (-4.86)^2\left(\frac{18}{37}\right) + (-4.86)^2\left(\frac{1}{37}\right) = 24.98.$$

The standard deviation is the square root of the variance and equals $\sigma = \sqrt{24.98} = 5.00$. This shows that a typical distance from the mean of −$0.14 is $5.00.

Suppose you are now betting on the outcome 0 instead of red. If you win this bet, your profit is $175. If you lose (i.e., either red or black come up), your profit is −$5. The expected profit (the mean) for this bet is also −$0.14, i.e., a loss of 14 cents. The payoff is larger, but the chances to lose the bet are also much larger, so that in the long run you are still expected to lose 14 cents. What about the standard deviation of the profit for this bet? Do you think it is smaller, larger, or about the same compared to the bet on red? Because there is now the possibility of a much larger deviation from the mean, the standard deviation is much larger and equals $\sigma = \$29.2$ for the bet on the outcome 0.

Probability Distributions of Continuous Random Variables

A random variable is called **continuous** when it can take on an infinite number of possible values in an interval. For instance, a recent study by the U.S. Census Bureau analyzed the time that people take to commute to work. Commuting time can be measured with real number values, such as any number between 0 and 150 minutes.

Probability distributions of continuous random variables assign probabilities to any interval of the possible values. For instance, a probability distribution for commuting time provides the probability that the travel time is less than 15 minutes or that the travel time is between 30 and 60 minutes. The probability that a random variable falls in any particular interval is between 0 and 1, and the probability of the interval that contains all the possible values equals 1.

When a random variable is continuous, the intervals that define the bars of a histogram can be chosen as desired. For instance, one possibility for commuting time is {0 to 30, 30 to 60, 60 to 90, 90 to 120, 120 to 150}, quite wide intervals. By contrast, using {0 to 1, 1 to 2, 2 to 3, . . . , 149 to 150} gives lots of very narrow intervals. As the number of intervals increases, with their width narrowing, the shape of the histogram gradually approaches a smooth curve. We'll use such

Probability Distribution for X = Profit of $5 Bet on Red

Outcome	x	$P(x)$
red	5	18/37
black	−5	18/37
0	−5	1/37

Many intervals

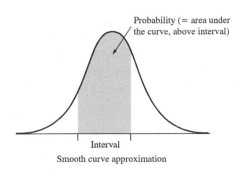

Probability (= area under the curve, above interval)

Interval

Smooth curve approximation

curves to portray probability distributions of continuous random variables. See the graphs in the margin on the previous page.

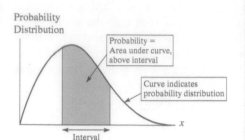

Probability
Distribution

Probability =
Area under curve,
above interval

Curve indicates
probability distribution

x

Interval

Probability Distribution of a Continuous Random Variable

A **continuous** random variable can take on an infinite number of possible values in an interval. Its **probability distribution** is specified by a curve that determines the probability that the random variable falls in any particular interval of values.

- Each interval has probability between 0 and 1. The probability for the interval is given by the area under the curve, above that interval. (See the figure in the margin.)

- The interval containing all possible values has probability equal to 1, so the total area under the curve equals 1.

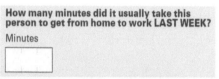

How many minutes did it usually take this person to get from home to work LAST WEEK?

Minutes

Snapshot of question from American
Community Survey

Figure 6.2 shows the curve for the probability distribution of X = commuting time to work for workers in the United States, based on information from the American Community Survey. This survey implied that the distribution of the commuting time is skewed to the right, with a mean of around 25 minutes,[3] and the shape of the curves reflects this. Historically, in surveys about travel to work, a commute of 45 minutes has been the maximum time that people would be willing to spend. The shaded area in Figure 6.2 refers to the interval of a commute longer than 45 minutes and the area above it to the probability of commuting longer than 45 minutes. This area equals 15% of the total area under the curve. So the probability of commuting longer than 45 minutes to work is 0.15, or 15%.

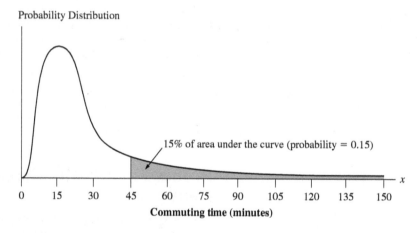

Probability Distribution

15% of area under the curve (probability = 0.15)

x

0   15   30   45   60   75   90   105   120   135   150

Commuting time (minutes)

▲ **Figure 6.2** Probability Distribution of Commuting Time. The area under the curve for values higher than 45 is 0.15. **Question** Identify the area under the curve representing the probability of a commute less than 15 minutes, which equals 0.27.

When observing continuous random variables, we need to round off our measurements. Probabilities are given for *intervals* of values rather than individual values. In measuring commuting time, the American Community Survey asked, "How many minutes did it usually take to get from home to work last week?" and respondents filled in a whole minute amount. Then, for instance, a commuting

---

[3]*Source:* McKenzie and Rapino, 2011. *Commuting in the United States: 2009,* American Community Survey Reports, ACS-15. U.S. Census Bureau, Washington, D.C. (www.census.gov/hhes/commuting/data/commuting.html), U.S. Department of Commerce.

Did You Know?

For continuous random variables, the area above a single value equals 0. For example, the probability that the commuting time equals 23.7693611045 ... minutes is 0, but the probability that the commuting time is between 23.5 and 24.5 minutes is positive. ◄

time of 24 minutes actually means the interval of real numbers that round to the integer value 24, which is the interval from 23.50 to 24.50. The corresponding probability is the area under the curve for this interval. In practice, the probability that the commuting time falls in some given interval, such as more than 45 minutes, less than 15 minutes, or between 30 and 60 minutes, is of greater interest than the probability it equals some particular single value.

> **In Practice** Continuous Variables Are Measured in a Discrete Manner
>
> In practice, **continuous** variables are measured in a **discrete** manner because of rounding.

Probability Distribution for a Continuous Random Variable ◄

Example 6

Height

Picture the Scenario

Figure 6.3 shows a histogram of heights for a sample of females at the University of Georgia, with a smooth curve superimposed. (*Source:* Data from University of Georgia.)

Question to Explore

What does the smooth curve represent?

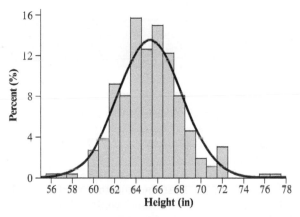

▲ **Figure 6.3** Histogram of Female Student Heights with Probability Distribution Curve Superimposed. Height is continuous but is measured as discrete by rounding to the nearest inch. The smooth curve approximates the probability distribution for height, treating it as a continuous random variable. Questions How would you describe the shape of the probability distribution? The probability for a female to be taller than 65 inches is approximately how much?

Think It Through

In theory, height is a continuous random variable. In practice, it is measured here by rounding to the nearest inch. For instance, the bar of the histogram above 64 represents heights between 63.5 and 64.5 inches, which were rounded to 64 inches. The histogram gives the data distribution for the discrete way height is actually measured in a sample. The smooth curve uses the data distribution to approximate the shape of the probability distribution (the population distribution) that height would have if we could actually measure all female heights precisely as a continuous random variable. The area under this curve between two points approximates the probability that height falls between those points. For instance, the area under the curve for the interval from 66 to 70 inches is 35% of the total area, so the probability of observing a height in this interval is 0.35, or 35%.

Insight

The histogram is a graphical representation of the distribution of the continuous variable in the sample. The smooth curve is a graphical representation of the distribution in the population. In Figure 6.3, the smooth curve has a bell shape. In the next section we'll study a particular probability distribution that has this shape and we'll learn how to find probabilities for it.

▶ *Try Exercise 6.15*

Sometimes we can use a sample space to help us find a probability distribution of a discrete random variable, as you'll see in Exercises 6.1, 6.4, and 6.11 and examples later in the chapter. Sometimes the probability distribution is available with a *formula*, a *table*, or a *graph*, as we'll see in the next two sections. Sometimes, though, it's helpful to use computer simulation to approximate the distribution, as shown in Activity 1 at the end of the chapter.

6.1   Practicing the Basics

6.1   Rolling dice

 a. State in a table the probability distribution for the outcome of rolling a balanced die. (This is called the **uniform distribution** on the integers 1, 2, . . . ,6.)

b. Two balanced dice are rolled. Show that the probability distribution for X = total on the two dice is as shown in the figure. (*Hint:* First construct the sample space of the 36 equally likely outcomes you could get. For example, you could denote the six outcomes where you get a 1 on the first die by $(1, 1), (1, 2), (1, 3), (1, 4),$

$(1, 5), (1, 6)$, where the second number in a pair is the number you get on the second die.)

c. Show that the probabilities in part b satisfy the two conditions for a probability distribution.

6.2   Dental insurance   You plan to purchase dental insurance for your three remaining years in school. The insurance makes a one-time payment of $1,000 in case of a major dental repair (such as an implant) or $100 in case of a minor repair (such as a cavity). If you don't need dental repair over the next 3 years, the insurance expires and you receive no payout. You estimate the chances of requiring a major repair over the next 3 years as 5%, a minor repair as 60%, and no repair as 35%.

a. Why is X = payout of dental insurance a random variable?

b. Is X discrete or continuous? What are its possible values?

c. Give the probability distribution of X.

d. How much should the insurance company expect to pay for this policy? (*Hint:* Find the mean for this probability distribution.)

6.3   **San Francisco Giants hitting**   The table shows the probability distribution of the number of bases for a randomly selected time at bat for a San Francisco Giants player in 2010 (excluding times when the player got on base because of a walk or being hit by a pitch). In 74.29% of the at-bats the player was out, 17.04% of the time the player got a single (one base), 5.17% of the time the player got a double (two bases), 0.55% of the time the player got a triple, and 2.95% of the time the player got a home run.

a.   Verify that the probabilities give a legitimate probability distribution.

b.   Find the mean of this probability distribution.

c.   Interpret the mean, explaining why it does not have to be a whole number, even though each possible value for the number of bases is a whole number.

San Francisco Giants Hitting	
Number of Bases	**Probability**
0	0.7429
1	0.1704
2	0.0517
3	0.0055
4	0.0295

6.4   **Best of three**   In a best out of three series played between teams A and B, the team that gets two wins first wins the entire series. Assuming that team A has a 70% chance of winning a game and that outcome of games are independent events, the probability that the series ends after two games is 58%.

a.   Find the probability distribution of X = number of games played in the series.

b.   Find the expected number of games to be played in the series.

c.   Verify that the probability that the series ends after two games is 58% by writing out the sample space of all possible sequences of wins and losses for team A in a best of three series. (A tree diagram may help.) Find the probability for each sequence and then add up those for which the series ends after two games. (Use what you learned in Section 5.2 about probabilities for intersections of independent events.)

6.5   **Grade distribution**   An instructor always assigns final grades such that 20% are A, 40% are B, 30% are C, and 10% are D. The grade point scores are 4 for A, 3 for B, 2 for C, and 1 for D.

a.   Specify the probability distribution for the grade point score of a randomly selected student of this instructor.

b.   Find the mean of this probability distribution. Interpret it.

6.6   **Selling houses**   Let X represent the number of homes a real estate agent sells during a given month. Based on previous sales records, she estimates that $P(0) = 0.68$, $P(1) = 0.19$, $P(2) = 0.09$, $P(3) = 0.03$, $P(4) = 0.01$, with negligible probability for higher values of x.

a.   Explain why it does not make sense to compute the mean of this probability distribution as

$(0 + 1 + 2 + 3 + 4)/5 = 2.0$ and claim that, on average, she expects to sell 2 homes.

b.   Find the correct mean and interpret.

6.7   **Playing the lottery**   The state of Ohio has several statewide lottery options. One is the Pick 3 game in which you pick one of the 1,000 three-digit numbers between 000 and 999. The lottery selects a three-digit number at random. With a bet of $1, you win $500 if your number is selected and nothing ($0) otherwise. (Many states have a very similar type of lottery.) (*Source:* Background information from www.ohiolottery.com.)

a.   With a single $1 bet, what is the probability that you win $500?

b.   Let X denote your winnings for a $1 bet, so $x = $0 or $x = $500. Construct the probability distribution for X.

c.   Show that the mean of the distribution equals 0.50, corresponding to an expected return of 50 cents for the dollar paid to play. Interpret the mean.

d.   In Ohio's Pick 4 lottery, you pick one of the 10,000 four-digit numbers between 0000 and 9999 and (with a $1 bet) win $5,000 if you get it correct. In terms of your expected winnings, with which game are you better off—playing Pick 4, or playing Pick 3? Justify your answer.

6.8   **Roulette**   A roulette wheel (the American version) consists of 38 equally likely numbers, 0 through 36 and 00. Of these, 18 numbers are red, 18 are black, and 2 are green (0 and 00). You are given $10 and told that you must pick one of two wagers: (1) Bet $10 on number 23. If the spin results in 23, you win $350 and also get back your $10 bet. If any other number comes up, you lose your $10 or (2) Bet $10 on black. If the spin results in any one of the black numbers, you win $10 and also get back your $10 bet. If any other color comes up, you lose your $10.

a.   Without doing any calculation, which wager would you prefer? Explain why. (There is no correct answer. Peoples' choices are based on their individual preferences and risk tolerances.)

b.   Let the random variable X = profit. Find the probability distribution of X for the bet in (1) and for the bet in (2). (*Hint:* It is sufficient if you just consider two values for the profit: the one if you win and the one if you lose.)

c.   Find the expected profit for each wager. Which wager is better in this sense?

6.9   **More roulette**   The previous exercise on roulette described two types of wagers: one on the single number 23 with profits of $350 if you win and −$10 if you lose and one on black with profits of $10 if you win and −$10 if you lose. Find the standard deviation for the profit for each type of wager. Which wager would you prefer? Explain.

6.10   **Ideal number of children**   Let X denote the response of a randomly selected person to the question, "What is the ideal number of children for a family to have?" The probability distribution of X in the United States is approximately as shown in the table, according to the gender of the person responding.

Probability Distribution of X = Ideal Number of Children

x	P(x) Females	P(x) Males
0	0.01	0.02
1	0.03	0.03
2	0.55	0.60
3	0.31	0.28
4	0.11	0.08

Note that the probabilities do not sum to exactly 1 due to rounding error. Probabilities for x larger than 4 are negligible.

a. Show that the means of the probability distributions are similar: 2.50 for females and 2.39 for males.

b. Show that the standard deviations for the probability distributions are 0.770 for females and 0.758 for males. Explain why a practical implication of the values for the standard deviations is that males hold slightly more consistent views than females about the ideal family size.

6.11 Profit and the weather   From past experience, a wheat farmer living in Manitoba, Canada, finds that his annual profit (in Canadian dollars) is $80,000 if the summer weather is typical, $50,000 if the weather is unusually dry, and $20,000 if there is a severe storm that destroys much of his crop. Weather bureau records indicate that the probability is 0.70 of typical weather, 0.20 of unusually dry weather, and 0.10 of a severe storm. Let X denote the farmer's profit next year.

a. Construct a table with the probability distribution of X.

b. What is the probability that the profit is $50,000 or less?

c. Find the mean of the probability distribution of X. Interpret.

d. Suppose the farmer buys insurance for $3,000 that pays him $20,000 in the event of a severe storm that destroys much of the crop and pays nothing otherwise. Find the probability distribution of his profit. Find the mean and summarize the effect of buying this insurance.

6.12 Buying on eBay   You are watching two items posted for sale on eBay and bid $30 for the first and $20 for the second item. You estimate that you are going to win the first bid with probability 0.1 and the second bid with probability 0.2, and you assume that winning the two bids are independent events. Let X denote the random variable denoting the total amount of money you will spend on the two items.

a. List the sample space of all possible outcomes of winning or losing the two bids. (It may help to draw a tree diagram.)

b. Find the probability of each outcome in the sample space. (Use the tree diagram.)

c. Find the probability distribution of X.

d. Find the mean of X.

e. Find the standard deviation of X.

6.13 Selling at the right price   Some companies, such as DemandTec, have developed software to help retail chains set prices that optimize their profits. An Associated Press story (April 28, 2007) about this software described a case in which a retail chain sold three similar power drills: one for $90, a better one for $120, and a top-tier one for $130. Software predicted that by selling the middle-priced drill for only $110, the cheaper drill would seem less a bargain and more people would buy the middle-price drill.

a. For the original pricing, suppose 50% of sales were for the $90 drill, 20% for the $120 drill, and 30% for the $130 drill. Construct the probability distribution of X = selling price for the sale of a drill, find its mean, and interpret.

b. For the new pricing, suppose 30% of sales were for the $90 drill, 40% for the $110 drill, and 30% for the $130 drill. Is the mean of the probability distribution of selling price higher with this new pricing strategy? Explain.

c. Find the standard deviation for each of the two pricing strategies. Which one results in prices closer to the mean in the long run?

6.14 Uniform distribution   A random number generator is used to generate a real number between 0 and 1, equally likely to fall anywhere in this interval of values. (For instance, 0.3794259832 . . . is a possible outcome.)

a. Sketch a curve of the probability distribution of this random variable, which is the continuous version of the **uniform distribution** (see Exercise 6.1).

b. The probability that the number falls in the interval from 0 to the mean is 50%. Find the mean. (Remember that the total area under the probability curve is 1.)

c. Find the probability that the random number falls between 0.35 and 0.75.

d. Find the probability that the random number is less than 0.8?

6.15 TV watching   A social scientist uses the General Social Survey (GSS) to study how much time per day people spend watching TV. The variable denoted by TVHOURS at the GSS Web site measures this using the discrete values 0, 1, 2, . . . , 24.

a. Explain how, in theory, TV watching is a continuous random variable.

b. An article about the study shows two histograms, both skewed to the right, to summarize TV watching for females and males. Since TV watching is in theory continuous, why were histograms used instead of curves?

c. If the article instead showed two curves, explain what they would represent.

6.2 Probabilities for Bell-Shaped Distributions: The Normal Distribution

German-born Carl Friedrich Gauss (1777–1855), shown here on a former German 10-Mark bill, was one of the first to use the normal distribution, with curve shown to his right.

Some probability distributions merit special attention because they are useful for many applications. They have formulas or tables that provide probabilities of the possible outcomes. We next learn about a probability distribution, called the **normal distribution,** that is commonly used for continuous random variables. It is characterized by a particular symmetric, bell-shaped curve with two parameters—the mean μ and the standard deviation σ.[4]

The Normal Distribution: A Probability Distribution with a Bell-Shaped Curve

Figure 6.3 at the end of the previous section showed that heights of female students at the University of Georgia have approximately a bell-shaped distribution. The approximating curve describes a probability distribution with a mean of 65.0 inches and a standard deviation of 3.5 inches. In fact, if we let the continuous random variable X = the height of a randomly selected adult female American, then the probability distribution for X is approximately normal, with mean $\mu = 65.0$ inches and standard deviation $\sigma = 3.5$ inches. Similarly, adult male heights have approximately a normal distribution with $\mu = 70.0$ inches and $\sigma = 4.0$ inches. Adult males tend to be a bit taller (since $70 > 65$) with heights varying from the mean a bit more (since $4.0 > 3.5$). Figure 6.4 shows the normal distribution for female heights and the one for male heights.

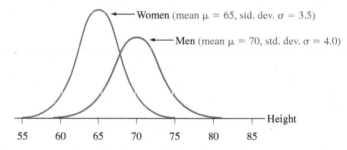

▲ **Figure 6.4** Normal Distributions for Women's Height and Men's Height. For each different combination of μ and σ values, there is a normal distribution with mean μ and standard deviation σ. **Questions** Why is the normal curve for women more peaked than the one for men? Given that $\mu = 70$ and $\sigma = 4$, within what interval do almost all of the men's heights fall?

▶ Activity 1

To get a feel for the parameters μ and σ and how they affect the shape of the distribution, access the *Normal Distribution* app. Take the slider for μ from left to right and observe how this changes the center of the distribution. For a given value for μ, take the slider for σ from left to right and observe how this changes the variability of the distribution.

Normal Distribution

The **normal distribution** is a symmetric, bell-shaped continuous probability distribution, characterized by its mean μ (expressing the center) and standard deviation σ (expressing the variability).

For a normal distribution, the probability of falling within 1, 2, or 3 standard deviations of the mean equals 0.68, 0.95, and 0.997, respectively. (See Figure 6.5.) This is true for any value of μ and any value of $\sigma > 0$.

---

[4]A mathematical formula specifies the precise shape of the curve for the probability distribution, but it is complex and we don't need to show the formula in this book.

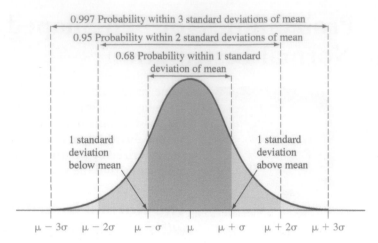

▲ **Figure 6.5** The Normal Distribution. The probability equals 0.68 for the interval within 1 standard deviation of the mean, 0.95 for the interval within 2 standard deviations, and 0.997 for the interval within 3 standard deviations. **Question** How do these probabilities relate to the empirical rule?

To illustrate, for adult female heights, $\mu = 65.0$ and $\sigma = 3.5$ inches and

$$\mu - 2\sigma = 65.0 - 2(3.5) = 58.0 \text{ and } \mu + 2\sigma = 65.0 + 2(3.5) = 72.0.$$

Assuming the normal distribution for female heights is accurate, 95% of female heights fall between 58 inches and 72 inches i.e., within two standard deviations from the mean. Expressed differently, for a randomly selected female, the probability of observing a height between 58 inches and 72 inches is 0.95, or 95%. For adult male heights, $\mu = 70.0$ and $\sigma = 4.0$ inches. Assuming the normal distribution for heights of males is accurate, 95% fall between $\mu - 2\sigma = 70.0 - 2(4.0) = 62$ inches and $\mu + 2\sigma = 70.0 + 2(4.0) = 78$ inches.

The property of the normal distribution in the definition tells us about probabilities within 1, 2, and 3 standard deviations of the mean. The multiples 1, 2, and 3 of the number of standard deviations from the mean are denoted by the symbol z in general. For instance, $z = 2$ for 2 standard deviations. For each fixed number z, the probability within z standard deviations of the mean is the area under the normal curve between $\mu - z\sigma$ and $\mu + z\sigma$, as shown in Figure 6.6. This probability is 0.68 for $z = 1$, so 68% of the area (probability) of a normal distribution falls between $\mu - \sigma$ and $\mu + \sigma$. Similarly, this probability is 0.95 for $z = 2$, and 0.997 (i.e., nearly 1.0) for $z = 3$. The entire area under the curve (i.e., from all the way to the left to all the way to the right) equals 1, or 100%.

The normal distribution is the most important distribution in statistics, partly because many variables have approximately normal distributions. The normal

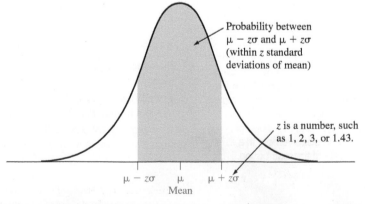

▲ **Figure 6.6** The Probability Between $\mu - z\sigma$ and $\mu + z\sigma$. This is the area highlighted under the curve. It is the same for every normal distribution and depends only on the value of z. Figure 6.5 showed this for $z = 1, 2,$ and 3, but z does not have to be an integer—it can be any number.

distribution is also important because it approximates many discrete distributions well when there are a large number of possible outcomes. However, the main reason for the prominence of the normal distribution is that many statistical methods rely on it for making inferences about a population. We'll see why in the next chapter.

Finding Probabilities for the Normal Distribution

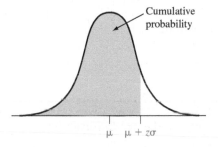

Cumulative probability

μ $\mu + z\sigma$

As we'll discuss, the probabilities 0.68, 0.95, and 0.997 for falling within 1, 2, and 3 standard deviations of the mean are no surprise, because of the empirical rule. But what if we wanted to find the probability within, say, 1.43 standard deviations? For such computations, we need software, or rely on a published table. We will discuss using a table from the back of the book first (in case you need it for exams or don't have access to technology), but then we'll show you how the *Normal Distribution* app finds such probabilities easily and conveniently.

Table A at the end of this book (reproduced in part in Table 6.3 below) allows us to find normal probabilities. It tabulates the normal **cumulative probability**, the probability of falling *below* the point $\mu + z\sigma$ (see the margin figure). The leftmost column of Table A lists the values for z to one decimal point, with the second decimal place listed above the columns. The tabulated probability for $z = 1.43$ falls in the row labeled 1.4 and in the column labeled 0.03. It equals 0.9236. For any given values for μ and σ of a normal distribution, the probability of falling below $\mu + 1.43\sigma$ equals 0.9236. Figure 6.7 illustrates.

Table 6.3 Part of Table A for Normal Cumulative (Left-Tail) Probabilities

The top of the table gives the second digit for z. The table entry is the probability of falling below $\mu + z\sigma$, for instance, 0.9236 below $\mu + 1.43\sigma$ for $z = 1.43$.

Second Decimal Place of z									
z	.00	.01	.02	.03	.04	.05	.06	.07	.08	.09
0.0	.5000	.5040	.5080	.5120	.5160	.5199	.5239	.5279	.5319	.5359
...									
1.3	.9032	.9049	.9066	.9082	.9099	.9115	.9139	.9147	.9162	.9177
1.4	.9192	.9207	.9222	.9236	.9251	.9265	.9278	.9292	.9306	.9319
1.5	.9332	.9345	.9357	.9370	.9382	.9394	.9406	.9418	.9429	.9441

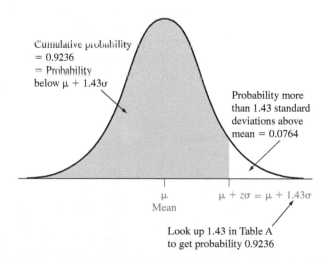

Cumulative probability
= 0.9236
= Probability
below $\mu + 1.43\sigma$

Probability more than 1.43 standard deviations above mean = 0.0764

μ
Mean

$\mu + z\sigma = \mu + 1.43\sigma$

Look up 1.43 in Table A to get probability 0.9236

▲ **Figure 6.7 The Normal Cumulative Probability, Less Than z Standard Deviations above the Mean.** Table A lists a cumulative probability of 0.9236 for $z = 1.43$, so 0.9236 is the probability of falling below $\mu + 1.43\sigma$ for any normal distribution. The complement probability of 0.0764 is the probability of falling *above* $\mu + 1.43\sigma$ in the right tail.

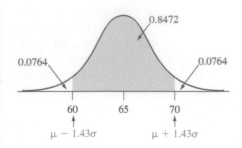

Since an entry in Table A is a probability *below* $\mu + z\sigma$, one minus that probability is the probability *above* $\mu + z\sigma$. For example, the right-tail probability above $\mu + 1.43\sigma$ equals $1 - 0.9236 = 0.0764$. By the symmetry of the normal curve, this probability also refers to the left tail below $\mu - 1.43\sigma$, which you'll find in Table A by looking up $z = -1.43$. The negative z-scores in the table refer to cumulative probabilities for random variable values *below* the mean.

Since the probability is 0.0764 in each tail, the probability of falling *more than* 1.43 standard deviations from the mean equals $2(0.0764) = 0.1528$. The total probability equals 1, so the probability falling *within* 1.43 standard deviations of the mean equals $1 - 0.1528 = 0.8472$, about 85%. This implies that the chances for a randomly selected woman in North America having height between $\mu - 1.43\sigma = 65.0 - 1.43(3.5) = 60$ inches and $\mu + 1.43\sigma = 65 + 1.43(3.5) = 70$ inches (that is, between 5 feet and 5 feet, 10 inches) equals 85%. When finding such probabilities, it is always advisable to draw a sketch similar to the one in the margin.

► **Finding Normal Probabilities with a Table or the App**

Example 7

Talk Time on Smartphones

Picture the Scenario

One of the defining features of a smartphone is how long one can talk on a single charge of the battery. Based on data from smartphones available from major cell phone carriers in the United States (and relying on the fact that a manufacturer's claim of the talk time is accurate), the distribution of the talk time approximately follows a normal distribution with a mean of $\mu = 330$ minutes and a standard deviation of $\sigma = 80$ minutes.

Questions to Explore

a. What percentage of smartphones have a talk time 1.25 standard deviations *below* the mean?

b. What percentage of smartphones have a talk time 1.25 standard deviations *above* the mean?

c. Find the probability of observing a talk time that is within 1.25 standard deviations of the mean.

Think It Through

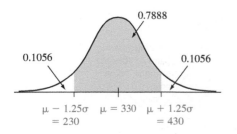

a. Because $\mu - 1.25\sigma = 330 - 1.25(80) = 230$, we are looking at the area under the normal curve (with mean 330 and standard deviation 80) that falls below 230 minutes. The figure in the margin illustrates. We can determine that area by finding the value in Table A for $z = -1.25$, which is 0.1056. So, 10.56% of smartphones have a talk time less than 1.25 standard deviations below the mean, i.e., shorter than 230 minutes.

b. By the symmetry of the normal distribution, the area above $\mu + 1.25\sigma = 330 + 1.25(80) = 430$ is also 0.1056. (If you want, you can look up the value for $z = 1.25$ in Table A, which is 0.8944, and subtract it from 1, which gives 0.1056 for the area in the upper tail, as expected.) So, 10.56% of smartphones have a talk time larger than 1.25 standard deviations above the mean, i.e., longer than 430 minutes.

c. Because the area below and above 1.25 standard deviations of the mean equals 0.1056 each, the area *outside* 1.25 standard deviations is $2(0.1056) = 0.2112$. Because the total area equals 1, the area *within* 1.25 standard deviations of the mean equals $1 - 0.2112 = 0.7888$. Therefore, the probability of observing a talk time that is within 1.25 standard deviations of the mean (i.e., between 230 and 430 minutes) equals about 79%.

Insight

The *Normal Distribution* app at www.ArtofStat.com and other (online) calculators can find normal probabilities without you having to use Table A. We will illustrate how to use the app below. However, no matter how you obtain the answer, drawing a quick **sketch** of the normal distribution and marking the area that you are looking for helps tremendously in avoiding mistakes.

To find probabilities with the *Normal Distribution* app, select the Find Probability tab and enter 330 for the mean μ and 80 for the standard deviation σ. This will display the corresponding normal curve. To find the probability in part a, enter 230 for the value of x, as shown in the first screenshot in the margin. The app displays the area to the left of 230, the required value, as 10.56%.

For part b, use the drop-down menu to change the type of probability to Upper Tail and then enter 430 as the value for x. This will display the normal curve with the area above 430 highlighted and marked as 10.56%. (Screenshot not shown.)

For part c, select Interval from the drop-down menu for the type of probability and then enter 230 for the value of a and 430 for the value of b. The app now highlights the area above this interval and shows that it equals 78.87%. (See the second screenshot in the margin.) Note that the app allows you to specify any values for the lower bound a and upper bound b for the interval, not necessarily values symmetric around the mean μ.

▶ *Try Exercises 6.16 and 6.17*

Screenshots from the *Normal Distribution* app.

Normal Probabilities and the Empirical Rule

The empirical rule states that for an approximately bell-shaped distribution, about 68% of observations fall within 1 standard deviation of the mean, 95% within 2 standard deviations, and nearly all within 3. In fact, those percentages came from probabilities calculated with the normal distribution: See Figure 6.8.

▲ **Figure 6.8** Normal Probability Within 2 Standard Deviations of the Mean. Probabilities in one tail determine probabilities in the other tail by symmetry. Subtracting the total two-tail probability from 1.0 gives probabilities within a certain distance of the mean. **Question** Can you do the analogous calculation for 3 standard deviations?

Recall

The empirical rule was introduced in Section 2.4. ◀

The probability falling more than 2 standard deviations from the mean in either tail is $2(0.0228) = 0.0456$, as you can check with Table A or the *Normal Distribution* app. (With the default $\mu = 0$ and $\sigma = 1$ in the app, select Two Tailed for the type of probability and enter 2 for the value of x.) Thus, the probability of falling *within* 2 standard deviations of the mean equals $1 - 0.0456 = 0.9544$. When a variable has a normal distribution, 95.44% of the distribution (95%, rounded) falls within 2 standard deviations of the mean.

The approximate percentages that the empirical rule lists are the percentages for the normal distribution, rounded. For instance, you can verify that the probability within 1 standard deviation of the mean of a normal distribution equals 0.68 (see Exercise 6.18). The probability within 3 standard deviations of the mean equals 0.997, or 1.00 rounded off. The empirical rule stated the probabilities as being *approximate* rather than *exact* because that rule referred to *all approximately* bell-shaped distributions, not just the normal.

How Can We Find the Value of z for a Given Cumulative Probability?

In practice, we'll sometimes need to find the value of z that corresponds to a certain normal cumulative probability. How can we do this? To illustrate, let's find the value of z for a cumulative probability of 0.025. We look up the cumulative probability of 0.025 in the body of Table A. It corresponds to $z = -1.96$, since it is in the row labeled −1.9 and in the column labeled 0.06. So a probability of 0.025 lies below $\mu - 1.96\sigma$. (You can also use the app to find this.)

By symmetry, a probability of 0.025 also lies above $\mu + 1.96\sigma$. A total probability of 0.050 lies more than 1.96σ from μ. Therefore, precisely $1 - 0.05 = 0.95$, or 95.0% of a normal distribution falls within 1.96 standard deviations of the mean. (See figure in margin.) We've seen previously that 95.44% falls within 2.00 standard deviations, and we now see that precisely 95.0% falls within 1.96 standard deviations.

95.0% (probability 0.95)

0.025   0.025

$\mu - 1.96\sigma$ μ $\mu + 1.96\sigma$

Example 8

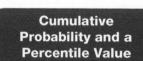

Cumulative Probability and a Percentile Value ◀

Mensa IQ Scores

Picture the Scenario

Mensa[5] is a society of high-IQ people whose members have IQ scores at the 98th percentile or higher. The Stanford-Binet IQ scores that are used as the basis for admission into Mensa are approximately normally distributed with a mean of 100 and a standard deviation of 16.

Question to Explore

What is the IQ score necessary for admission to Mensa?

Think It Through

For a value to represent the 98th percentile, its cumulative probability must equal 0.98, by the definition of a percentile. See Figure 6.9.

When looking up the cumulative probability of 0.980 in the body of Table A, we see it corresponds to $z = 2.05$. The 98th percentile is 2.05 standard deviations above the mean, at $\mu + 2.05\sigma$.

Since $\mu = 100$ and $\sigma = 16$, the 98th percentile of IQ scores equals

$$\mu + 2.05\sigma = 100 + 2.05(16) = 133.$$

In summary, 98% of the IQ scores fall below 133, and an IQ score of at least 133 is required to join Mensa.

---

[5]See www.mensa.org.

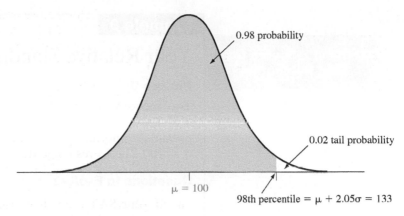

▲ **Figure 6.9** The 98th Percentile for a Normal Distribution. This is the value such that 98% of the distribution falls below it and 2% falls above. **Question** Where is the second percentile located?

Insight

About 2% of IQ scores are higher than 133. By symmetry, about 2% of IQ scores are lower than $\mu - 2.05\sigma = 100 - 2.05(16) = 67$. This is the second percentile. The remaining 96% of the IQ scores fall between 67 and 133, which is the region within 2.05 standard deviations of the mean.

   If you have access to technology, it is easier to obtain the answer via the *Normal Distribution* app. Select the Find Percentile/Quantile tab, enter 100 for the mean, 16 for the standard deviation, and 98 for the percent in the lower tail. The screenshot to the left shows the answer of 132.86, or 133 rounded.

▶ *Try Exercises 6.20 and 6.29, part b*

Screenshot from the *Normal Distribution* app.

Using z = Number of Standard Deviations to Find Probabilities

We've used the symbol z to represent the *number of standard deviations* a value falls from the mean. If we have a value x of a random variable, how can we figure out the number of standard deviations it falls from the mean μ of its probability distribution? The difference between x and μ equals $x - \mu$. The **z-score** expresses this difference as a number of standard deviations, using $z = (x - \mu)/\sigma$.

> **z-Score for a Value of a Random Variable**
>
> The **z-score** for a value x of a random variable is the number of standard deviations that x falls from the mean μ of the probability distribution. It is calculated as
>
> $$z = \frac{x - \mu}{\sigma}.$$

   The formula for the z-score is useful when we are given the value of x for some normal random variable and need to find a probability relating to that value. We convert x to a z-score and then use a normal table to find the appropriate probability. The next two examples illustrate this. However, note that z-scores can be used with any distributions, not just the normal distribution, to assess how many standard deviations an observation falls from the mean.

Using *z*-Scores to
Find Percentiles

Example 9

Your Relative Standing on the SAT

Picture the Scenario

Two sections on the SAT, a college entrance examination, are math and evidence-based reading and writing. The scores on each component are approximately normally distributed with mean $\mu = 500$ and standard deviation $\sigma = 100$. The scores range from 200 to 800 on each component.

Questions to Explore

a. If your SAT score from one of the components was $x = 650$, how many standard deviations from the mean was it?

b. What percentage of SAT scores was higher than yours?

Think It Through

a. The SAT score of 650 has a *z*-score of $z = 1.50$ because 650 is 1.50 standard deviations above the mean. We can find this directly using the formula for *z*-scores

$$z = \frac{x - \mu}{\sigma} = \frac{650 - 500}{100} = 1.50.$$

b. The percentage of SAT scores higher than 650 is the right-tail probability above 650, for a normal distribution with mean $\mu = 500$ and standard deviation $\sigma = 100$. From Table A, the *z*-score of 1.50 has cumulative probability 0.9332. That's the probability *below* 650, so the right-tail probability above it is $1 - 0.9332 = 0.0668$. (See figure in margin.) Only about 7% of SAT test scores fall above 650. In summary, a score of 650 was well above average, in the sense that relatively few students scored higher.

Insight

Positive *z*-scores occur when the value x falls *above* the mean μ. Negative *z*-scores occur when x falls *below* the mean. For instance, an SAT score of 350 has a *z*-score of

$$z = \frac{x - \mu}{\sigma} = \frac{350 - 500}{100} = -1.50.$$

The SAT score of 350 is 1.50 standard deviations *below* the mean. The probability that an SAT score falls below 350 is also 0.0668. Figure 6.10 on the next page illustrates.

If you have access to technology, the *Normal Distribution* app and other (online) calculators can find the answer to part b directly, without the need to convert to *z*-scores first. In the app, under the Find Probability tab, set the mean μ to 500, the standard deviation σ to 100, select Upper Tail for the type of probability, and enter 650 for the value of x. The screenshot in the margin shows the resulting probability of 6.68%. If you want to find the probability below 350, select Lower Tail for the type of probability and enter 350 for the value of x.

▶ ***Try Exercise 6.25***

The figure in the margin shows a normal curve with the area 0.9332 to the left and 0.0668 in the right tail, with x-axis values 200, 300, 400, 500, 600, 700, 800.

Screenshot from the *Normal Distribution* app.

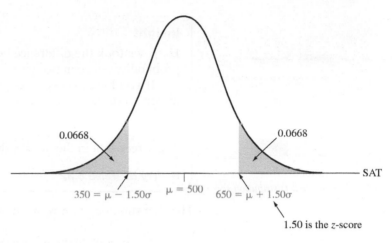

▲ **Figure 6.10 Normal Distribution for SAT.** The SAT scores of 650 and 350 have z-scores of 1.50 and −1.50 because they fall 1.50 standard deviations above and below the mean. **Question** Which SAT scores have $z = 3.0$ and $z = -3.0$?

Example 10

Using z-Scores to Find Interval Probabilities ◄

The Proportion of Students Who Get a B

Picture the Scenario

On the midterm exam in introductory statistics, an instructor always gives a grade of B to students who score between 80 and 90.

Question to Explore

One year, the scores on the exam have approximately a normal distribution with mean 83 and standard deviation 5. About what proportion of students earn a B?

Think It Through

A midterm exam score of 90 has a z-score of

$$z = \frac{x - \mu}{\sigma} = \frac{90 - 83}{5} = 1.40.$$

Its cumulative probability of 0.9192 (from Table A) means that about 92% of the exam scores were below 90. Similarly, an exam score of 80 has a z-score of

$$z = \frac{x - \mu}{\sigma} = \frac{80 - 83}{5} = -0.60.$$

Its cumulative probability of 0.2743 means that about 27% of the exam scores were below 80. See the normal curves that follow. Therefore about $0.9192 - 0.2743 = 0.6449$, or about 64%, of the exam scores were in the B range.

Screenshot from the *Normal Distribution* app.

Insight

Here, we took the difference between two cumulative probabilities to find a probability between two given values i.e., the probability for an interval.

If you have access to technology, finding the probability for an interval under a normal distribution is straightforward: In the *Normal Distribution* app, set the mean to 83, the standard deviation to 5, select Interval for the type of probability, and enter 80 for the value of *a* and 90 for the value of *b*. The screenshot in the margin shows the resulting probability of 64.5%.

▶ *Try Exercise 6.32*

Here's a summary of how we've used *z*-scores so far:

> ### Summary: Using *z*-Scores to Find Normal Probabilities or Random Variable *x* Values:
>
> - If you are given a value *x* and need to find a probability, convert *x* to a *z*-score using $z = (x - \mu)/\sigma$, use a table of normal probabilities to get a cumulative probability, and then convert it to the probability of interest.
> - If you are given a probability and need to find the value of *x*, convert the probability to the related cumulative probability, find the *z*-score using a normal table, and then evaluate $x = \mu + z\sigma$.
> - If you have access to the internet, the *Normal Distribution* app finds probabilities and percentiles for all kinds of situations easily.

In Example 8, we used the equation $x = \mu + z\sigma$ to find a percentile score (namely, 98th percentile $= \mu + 2.05\sigma = 100 + 2.05(16) = 133$). In Examples 9 and 10, we used the equation $z = (x - \mu)/\sigma$ to determine how many standard deviations certain scores fell from the mean, which enabled us to find probabilities (and hence percentiles) relating to those scores. With the *Normal Distribution* app, these tasks are more straightforward: You enter the mean and standard deviation of the normal distribution, and then supply the value of *x* to find probabilities. Conversely, you can also enter a value for the desired upper, lower, or two-tailed probability and obtain the corresponding percentile *x*.

Another use of *z*-scores is for comparing observations from different distributions in terms of their relative distances from the mean. If you studied Section 2.6, this is not a new concept. There, we used *z*-scores to compare observations from two different samples that used different measurement units. Here, we use *z*-scores to compare values from two different normal distributions.

Recall

In Section 2.6, we used *z*-scores to standardize a variable. This allowed us to compare observations that were measured on different scales, such as an athlete's performance in the Olympic 200 meters and javelin events. ◀

Example 11

Comparing z-Scores ◀

Comparing Test Scores That Use Different Scales

Picture the Scenario

There are two primary standardized tests used by college admissions, the SAT and the ACT.[6]

Question to Explore

When you applied to college, you scored 650 on an SAT exam, which had mean $\mu = 500$ and standard deviation $\sigma = 100$. Your friend took the comparable ACT, scoring 30. For that year, the ACT had $\mu = 21.0$ and $\sigma = 4.7$. How can we compare these scores to tell who performed better?

---

[6]See www.sat.org and www.act.org.

Think It Through

The test scores of 650 and 30 are not directly comparable because the SAT and ACT are evaluated on different scales with different means and different standard deviations. But we can convert them to z-scores and analyze how many standard deviations each falls from the mean.

With $\mu = 500$ and $\sigma = 100$, we saw in Example 9 that an SAT test score of $x = 650$ converts to a z-score of $z = (x - \mu)/\sigma = (650 - 500)/100 = 1.50$. With $\mu = 21.0$ and $\sigma = 4.7$, an ACT score of 30 converts to a z-score of

$$z = \frac{x - \mu}{\sigma} = \frac{30 - 21}{4.7} = 1.91.$$

The ACT score of 30 is a bit higher than the SAT score of 650, since an ACT score of 30 falls 1.91 standard deviations above its mean, whereas an SAT score of 650 falls 1.50 standard deviations above its mean. In this sense, the ACT score is better even though its numerical value is smaller.

Insight

The SAT and ACT test scores both have approximately normal distributions. From Table A, $z = 1.91$ (for the ACT score of 30) has a cumulative probability of 0.97. Of all students who took the ACT, only about 3% scored above 30. From Table A, $z = 1.50$ (for the SAT score of 650) has a cumulative probability of 0.93. Of all students who took the SAT, about 7% scored above 650.

▶ *Try Exercise 6.33*

The Standard Normal Distribution Has Mean = 0 and Standard Deviation = 1

Many statistical methods refer to a particular normal distribution called the **standard normal distribution**.

> ### Standard Normal Distribution
>
> The **standard normal distribution** is the normal distribution with mean $\mu = 0$ and standard deviation $\sigma = 1$. It is the distribution of normal z-scores.

For the standard normal distribution, the number falling z standard deviations above the mean is $\mu + z\sigma = 0 + z(1) = z$, simply the z-score itself. For instance, the value of 2.0 is two standard deviations above the mean, and the value of -1.3 is 1.3 standard deviations below the mean. As Figure 6.11 shows, for the standard normal distribution the original values are the same as the z-scores, since

$$z = \frac{x - \mu}{\sigma} = \frac{x - 0}{1} = x.$$

Recall

In Section 2.6, we learned that a z-score is a special linear transformation of the original observations resulting in a sample mean of 0 and a sample standard deviation of 1. The same is true if we use z-scores to transform the values of a random variable: The new (=transformed) probability distribution has mean 0 and standard deviation 1. ◀

Examples 9 and 11 dealt with SAT scores, having $\mu = 500$ and $\sigma = 100$. Suppose we convert each SAT score x to a z-score by using $z = (x - \mu)/\sigma = (x - 500)/100$. Then $x = 650$ converts to $z = 1.50$, and $x = 350$ converts to $z = -1.50$. When the values for any distribution are converted to z-scores, those z-scores have a mean of 0 and have a standard deviation of 1. If the original distribution was a normal distribution, then the entire set of z-scores has the standard normal distribution.

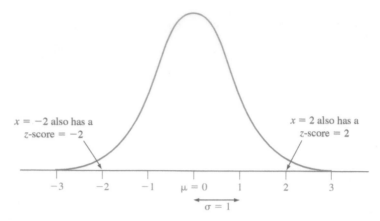

$x = -2$ also has a
z-score $= -2$

$x = 2$ also has a
z-score $= 2$

$\mu = 0$

$\sigma = 1$

▲ **Figure 6.11 The Standard Normal Distribution.** It has mean = 0 and standard deviation = 1. The random variable value x is the same as its z-score. **Question** What are the limits within which almost all z-scores fall?

> **z-Scores and the Standard Normal Distribution**
>
> When a random variable has a normal distribution and its values are converted to z-scores by subtracting the mean and dividing by the standard deviation, the z-scores have the **standard normal** distribution (the normal distribution with mean = 0, standard deviation = 1).

This result will be useful for statistical inference in upcoming chapters.

6.2 Practicing the Basics

For Exercises 6.16–6.23, it is easiest to obtain the answer when setting $\mu = 0$ and $\sigma = 1$ (the default setting in the *Normal Distribution* app), but note that the answer doesn't depend on what values you assume for μ and σ.

6.16 Probabilities in tails For a normal distribution, use Table A or the *Normal Distribution* app (or both) to find the probability that an observation is

a. at least 1 standard deviation above the mean.

b. at least 1 standard deviation below the mean.

c. within 1 standard deviation of the mean.

For each part, sketch the normal curve with mean μ and standard deviation σ and indicate the area corresponding to the probability, similar to the sketches on this page.

6.17 Probability in graph For the normal distributions shown below, use Table A or the *Normal Distribution* app (or both) to find the probability that an observation falls in the shaded region.

a.

μ $\mu + 0.67\sigma$

b.

$\mu - 0.5\sigma$ μ $\mu + 0.5\sigma$

6.18 Empirical rule Verify the empirical rule by using Table A or the *Normal Distribution* app (or both) to show that for a normal distribution, the probability (rounded to two decimal places) within

a. 1 standard deviation of the mean equals 0.68.

b. 2 standard deviations of the mean equals 0.95.

c. 3 standard deviations of the mean is very close to 1.00.

For each part, sketch a normal distribution similar to the sketches on this page, identifying on the sketch the probabilities you used to show the result.

6.19 Central probabilities For a normal distribution, use Table A or the *Normal Distribution* app (or both) to verify that the probability (rounded to two decimal places) within

a. 1.64 standard deviations of the mean equals 0.90.

b. 2.58 standard deviations of the mean equals 0.99.

c. Find the probability that falls within 0.67 standard deviations of the mean.

d. Sketch these three cases on a single graph.

6.20 z-score for given probability in tails For a normal distribution,

a. Find the z-score for which a total probability of 0.02 falls more than z standard deviations (in either direction) from the mean, that is, below $\mu - z\sigma$ or above $\mu + z\sigma$.

b. For this z, explain why the probability more than z standard deviations above the mean equals 0.01.

c. Explain why $\mu + 2.33\sigma$ is the 99th percentile.

6.21   Probability in tails for given z-score   For a normal
APP   distribution,

a. Show that a total probability of 0.01 falls more than
$z = 2.58$ standard deviations from the mean.

b. Find the z-score for which the two-tail probability that
falls more than that many standard deviations from
the mean in either direction equals (a) 0.05, (b) 0.10.
Sketch the two cases on a single graph.

6.22   z-score for right-tail probability
APP   a. For the normal distribution shown below, find the
z-score.

b. Find the value of z (rounding to two decimal places)
for right-tail probabilities of (i) 0.05 and (ii) 0.005.

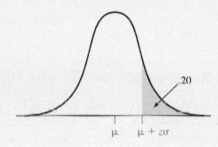

6.23   z-score and central probability   Find the z-score such
APP   that the interval within z standard deviations of the mean
(between $\mu - z\sigma$ and $\mu + z\sigma$) for a normal distribution
contains

a. 50% of the probability.

b. 90% of the probability.

c. Sketch the two cases on a single graph.

6.24   Female heights   The normal distribution for women's
APP   height in North America has $\mu = 65$ inches, $\sigma = 3.5$
inches. Most major airlines have height requirements
for flight attendants. Suppose that for a particular
airline, the minimum height requirement is 62 inches.
What proportion of adult females in North America are
not tall enough to be a flight attendant with that airline?

6.25   Blood pressure   A World Health Organization study (the
TRY   MONICA project) of health in various countries reported
that in Canada, systolic blood pressure readings have a
APP   mean of 121 and a standard deviation of 16. A reading
above 140 is considered high blood pressure.

a. What is the z-score for a blood pressure reading of
140?

b. If systolic blood pressure in Canada has a normal distribution, what proportion of Canadians suffers from
high blood pressure?

c. What proportion of Canadians has systolic blood pressures in the range from 100 to 140?

d. Find the 90th percentile of blood pressure
readings.

6.26   Coffee machine   Suppose your favorite coffee machine
APP   offers 12 ounce cups of coffee. The actual amount of
coffee put in the cup by the machine varies according to
a normal distribution, with mean equal to 13 ounces and
standard deviation equal to 0.6 ounces.

Answer parts a–e *without* the use of Table A or the
Normal Distribution app.

a. Approximately what percentage of cups will have between 12.4 and 13.6 ounces of coffee?

b. Approximately what percentage of cups will be filled
with less than 12.4 ounces?

c. Approximately what percentage of cups will be filled
with more than 14.2 ounces?

d. Approximately what percentage of cups will have between 13 and 13.6 ounces of coffee?

e. Approximately what percentage of cups will have between 13.6 and 14.2 ounces of coffee?

Answer parts f–h *using* Table A or the *Normal
Distribution* app (or both).

f. What percentage of cups will be filled with less than
12 ounces?

g. What percentage of cups will be filled with more than
12.5 ounces?

h. What percentage of cups will have between 12 and
13 ounces of coffee?

6.27   Energy use   An energy study in Gainesville, Florida,
APP   found that in March 2006, household use of electricity had a mean of 673 and a standard deviation of 556
kilowatt-hours. (*Source:* Data from Todd Kamhoot,
Gainesville Regional Utilities.)

a. Suppose the distribution of energy use was normal.
Using the *Normal Distribution* app or Table A, find the
proportion of households with electricity use greater
than 1,000 kilowatt-hours

b. Based on the mean and standard deviation given, do
you think that the distribution of energy use actually is
normal? Why or why not?

6.28   Birth weight for boys   In the United States, the mean
APP   birth weight for boys is 3.41 kg, with a standard deviation
of 0.55 kg. (*Source:* cdc.com.) Assuming that the distribution of birth weight is normal, find the following using the
Normal Distribution app or Table A.

a. A baby is considered of low birth weight if it weighs
less than 2.5 kg. What proportion of baby boys in the
United States are born with low birth weight?

b. What is the z score for a baby boy that weighs 1.5 kg
(defined as extremely low birth weight)?

c. Typically, birth weight is between 2.5 kg and 4.0 kg.
Find the probability a baby boy is born with typical
birth weight.

d. Matteo weighs 3.6 kg at birth. He falls at what percentile?

e. Max's parents are told that their newborn son falls at
the 96th percentile. How much does Max weigh?

6.29   MDI   The Mental Development Index (MDI) of the
TRY   Bayley Scales of Infant Development is a standardized mea-
sure used in observing infants over time. It is approximately
APP   normal with a mean of 100 and a standard deviation of 16.

a. What proportion of children has an MDI of (i) at least
120? (ii) at least 80?

b. Find the MDI score that is the 99th percentile.

c. Find the MDI score such that only 1% of the population has MDI below it.

6.30 Quartiles and outliers Refer to the previous exercise.

a. Find the z-score corresponding to the lower quartile (Q1) of a normal distribution.

b. Find and interpret the lower quartile and upper quartile of the MDI.

c. Find the interquartile range (IQR) of MDI scores.

d. Section 2.5 defined an observation to be a potential outlier if it is more than $1.5 \times$ IQR below Q1 or above Q3. Find the intervals of MDI scores that would be considered potential outliers.

6.31 April precipitation Over roughly the past 100 years, the mean monthly April precipitation in Williamstown, Massachusetts, equaled 3.6 inches with a standard deviation of 1.6 inches. (*Source:* http://web.williams.edu/weather/)

a. In April 1983, the wettest April on record, the precipitation equaled 8.4 inches. Find its z-score. If the distribution of precipitation were roughly normal, would this be unusually high? Explain.

b. Assuming a normal distribution, an April precipitation of 4.5 inches corresponds to what percentile?

c. Of the 119 measurements of April precipitation on record (reaching as far back as 1892), 66.5% fell within one, 97.5% within two, and 99.1% within three standard deviations of the mean. Do you think that the distribution of April precipitation is approximately normal? Why or why not?

6.32 Tall enough to ride? A new roller coaster at an amusement park requires individuals to be at least 4'8" (56 inches) tall to ride. It is estimated that the heights of 10-year-old boys are normally distributed with $\mu = 54.5$ inches and $\sigma = 4.5$ inches.

a. What proportion of 10-year-old boys is tall enough to ride the coaster?

b. A smaller coaster has a height requirement of 50 inches to ride. What proportion of 10 year-old-boys is tall enough to ride this coaster?

c. What proportion of 10-year-old boys is tall enough to ride the coaster in part b but not tall enough to ride the coaster in part a?

6.33 SAT versus ACT SAT math scores follow a normal distribution with an approximate $\mu = 500$ and $\sigma = 100$. Also ACT math scores follow a normal distribution with an approximate $\mu = 21$ and $\sigma = 4.7$. You are an admissions officer at a university and have room to admit one more student for the upcoming year. Joe scored 600 on the SAT math exam, and Kate scored 25 on the ACT math exam. If you were going to base your decision solely on their performances on the exams, which student should you admit? Explain.

6.34 Relative height Refer to the normal distributions for women's height ($\mu = 65$, $\sigma = 3.5$) and men's height ($\mu = 70$, $\sigma = 4.0$). A man's height of 75 inches and a woman's height of 70 inches are both 5 inches above their means. Which is relatively taller? Explain why.

6.3 Probabilities When Each Observation Has Two Possible Outcomes: The Binomial Distribution

We next study the most important probability distribution for discrete random variables. Learning about it helps us answer the questions we asked at the beginning of the chapter—for instance, whether there is strong evidence of discrimination against women in the selection of employees for management training.

The Binomial Distribution: Probabilities for Counts with Binary Data

In many applications, each observation is **binary:** It has one of two possible outcomes. For instance, a person may

- accept, or decline, an offer from a bank for a credit card,
- have, or not have, health insurance,
- vote yes or no in a referendum, such as whether to provide additional funds to the school district.

With a sample, we summarize such variables by counting the *number* or the *proportion* of cases with an outcome of interest. For instance, with a sample of size $n = 5$, let the random variable X denote the number of people who vote yes about some issue in a referendum. The possible values for X are 0, 1, 2, 3, 4, and 5. Under certain conditions, a random variable X that counts the number of observations of a particular type has a probability distribution called the **binomial distribution**.

Consider n cases, called **trials**, in which we observe a binary random variable. This is a *fixed number*, such as the $n = 5$ observations from a sample of five voters. The random variable X (representing the number of trials in which the outcome of interest occurs) can take any one of the integer values $0, 1, 2, \ldots, n$. The binomial distribution specifies probabilities for these possible values of X when the following three conditions hold:

Conditions for Binomial Distribution

- Each of n trials has two possible outcomes. The outcome of interest is called a success and the other outcome is called a failure.
- Each trial has the same probability of a success. The probability of a success is denoted by p and the probability of a failure is then $1 - p$.
- The n trials are independent. That is, the result for one trial does not depend on the results of any other trials.

The **binomial random variable** X counts the number of successes in the n trials.

Flipping a coin n times, where n is determined in advance, is a perfect example for the binomial distribution:

- Each trial is a flip of the coin. There are two possible outcomes for each flip, head or tail. Let's identify (arbitrarily) head as a success.
- If head or tail are equally likely, the probability of head (a success) equals $p = 0.50$. This success probability is the same for each flip.
- The flips are independent, since the result for any specific flip does not depend on the results of any other flips.

The binomial random variable X counts the number of heads (the outcome of interest) in the n flips. With $n = 3$ coin flips, the random variable $X =$ number of heads could equal $0, 1, 2,$ or 3.

Example 12

Speed Dating

Picture the Scenario

You are planning to attend a local speed dating event where you will meet three randomly selected candidates. The rules dictate that you talk to each one for five minutes before moving on to the next. A match is established if both you and the candidate you met liked each other. Going into the event, you assume your chances of establishing a match with any given candidate are 20% and that meetings with different candidates are independent.

Question to Explore

What is the probability that you will match with two of the three candidates you meet?

Think It Through

Each of your three meetings with a candidate is a trial, with binary outcome whether it results in a match or not. Let the random variable $X =$ number of matches when meeting $n = 3$ candidates. Then $X = 0, 1, 2,$ or 3. Let p denote the probability of a match, which you assume is 0.2. Then, the probability of not establishing a match is $1 - p = 0.8$. Denote the outcome of a trial

(= meeting) by S or F, representing success or failure based on you matching with the candidate or not. Table 6.4 shows the eight possible outcomes when meeting 3 candidates. For instance, FSS represents no match with the first but successful matches with the second and third candidate. Table 6.4 also shows the probabilities for each outcome by using the multiplication rule for independent events. We can use this rule because we assume that outcomes of meetings with different candidates are independent events. The three ways in which we can get two matches are SSF, SFS, and FSS. Each of these has probability equal to $(0.2)^2(0.8) = 0.032$. The total probability of two matches is $3(0.2)^2(0.8) = 3(0.032) = 0.096$.

Recall

From Section 5.2, for two independent events, $P(A \text{ and } B) = P(A)P(B)$ and from the extended multiplication rule in Section 5.4, for three independent events, $P(A \text{ and } B \text{ and } C) = P(A)P(B)P(C)$. Thus, $P(F \text{ and } S \text{ and } S) = P(F)P(S)P(S) = 0.8 \times 0.2 \times 0.2$. ◄

Table 6.4 Sample Space and Probabilities in Three Meetings

For each of the three meetings, the probability of a match is 0.2.

Outcome	Probability	Outcome	Probability
SSS	$0.2 \times 0.2 \times 0.2 = (0.2)^3$	SFF	$0.2 \times 0.8 \times 0.8 = (0.2)^1(0.8)^2$
SSF	$0.2 \times 0.2 \times 0.8 = (0.2)^2(0.8)^1$	FSF	$0.8 \times 0.2 \times 0.8 = (0.2)^1(0.8)^2$
SFS	$0.2 \times 0.8 \times 0.2 = (0.2)^2(0.8)^1$	FFS	$0.8 \times 0.8 \times 0.2 = (0.2)^1(0.8)^2$
FSS	$0.8 \times 0.2 \times 0.2 = (0.2)^2(0.8)^1$	FFF	$0.8 \times 0.8 \times 0.8 = (0.8)^3$

Insight

With general probability of a match denoted by p, the solution for $x = 2$ matches in $n = 3$ trials equals $P(2) = 3(p)^2(1 - p)^1$. The multiple of 3 represents the number of ways that two successes can occur in three trials (SSF or SFS or FSS). You can use similar logic to evaluate the probability that $x = 0$, or 1, or 3. Try $x = 1$, for which you should get $P(1) = 0.384$.

► *Try Exercise 6.35, part a*

The formula for binomial probabilities When the number of trials n is large, it's tedious to write out all the possible outcomes in the sample space. Then, we can use a formula to find binomial probabilities for *any* n and p. We alluded to it when we wrote for $n = 3$ and $x = 2$ above that $P(2) = 3(p)^2(1 - p)^1$, which follows the formula $P(x) = 3(p)^x(1 - p)^{(n-x)}$.

Probabilities for a Binomial Distribution

Denote the probability of success on a trial by p. For n independent trials, the probability of x successes equals

$$P(x) = \frac{n!}{x!(n - x)!}p^x(1 - p)^{n-x}, \text{ for } x = 0, 1, 2, \ldots, n.$$

The symbol $n!$ is called **n factorial**. It represents $n! = 1 \times 2 \times 3 \times \ldots \times n$, the product of all integers from 1 to n. That is, $1! = 1, 2! = 1 \times 2 = 2, 3! = 1 \times 2 \times 3 = 6, 4! = 1 \times 2 \times 3 \times 4 = 24$, and so forth. Also, 0! is defined to be 1. For given values for p and n, you can find the probabilities of the possible outcomes by substituting values for x into this binomial formula.

Let's use this formula to find the answer for Example 12 about speed dating:

- The random variable X represents the number of matches (successes) in $n = 3$ meetings (trials).
- The probability of a match in a particular trial is $p = 0.2$.
- The probability of exactly two matches in three meetings is the binomial probability with $n = 3, x = 2$ and success probability $p = 0.2$,

$$P(2) = \frac{n!}{x!(n-x)!} p^x (1-p)^{n-x} = \frac{3!}{2!1!}(0.2)^2(0.8)^1 = 3(0.04)(0.8) = 0.096.$$

What's the role of the different terms in this binomial formula?

- The factorial term tells us the number of possible outcomes that have $x = 2$ successes. Here, $3!/(2!1!) = (3 \times 2 \times 1)/[(2 \times 1)(1)] = 3$ tells us there were three possible outcomes with two successful matches, namely SSF, SFS, and FSS.
- The term $(0.2)^2(0.8)^1$ with the exponents gives the probability for each such sequence. Here, the probability is $(0.2)^2(0.8) = 0.032$ for each of the three sequences having $x = 2$ successful matches and $n - x = 3 - 2 = 1$ unsuccessful match, for a total probability of $3(0.032) = 0.096$.

Try to calculate $P(1)$ by letting $x = 1$ in the binomial formula with $n = 3$ and $p = 0.2$. You should get 0.384. You'll see that there are again three possible sequences, now each with probability $(0.2)^1(0.8)^2 = 0.128$. Table 6.5 summarizes the calculations for all four possible x values. The screenshot next to it shows the output from the *Binomial Distribution* app when setting (via the sliders) $n = 3$ and $p = 0.2$. This app provides a convenient way to compute binomial probabilities for any n and p.

APP

Screenshot from the *Binomial Distribution* app.

Table 6.5 The Binomial Distribution for $n = 3, p = 0.20$

When $n = 3$, the binomial random variable X can take any integer value between 0 and 3. As always, the individual probabilities sum to 1.

x	$P(x) = [n!/(x!(n-x)!)]\, p^x(1-p)^{n-x}$
0	$0.512 = [3!/(0!3!)](0.2)^0(0.8)^3$
1	$0.384 = [3!/(1!2!)](0.2)^1(0.8)^2$
2	$0.096 = [3!/(2!1!)](0.2)^2(0.8)^1$
3	$0.008 = [3!/(3!0!)](0.2)^3(0.8)^0$

Example 13

Binomial Distribution ◄

Testing for Gender Bias in Promotions

Picture the Scenario

Example 1 introduced a case involving possible discrimination against female employees. A group of women employees has claimed that female employees are less likely than male employees of similar qualifications to be promoted.

Question to Explore

Suppose the large employee pool that can be tapped for management training is half female and half male. In a group recently selected for promotion, none of the 10 individuals chosen were female. What would be the probability of 0 females in 10 selections, if there truly were no gender bias?

Think It Through

If there is no gender bias, other factors being equal, at each choice the probability of selecting a female equals 0.50 and the probability of selecting a male equals 0.50. Let X denote the number of females selected for promotion in a random sample of 10 employees. Then, the possible values for X are $0, 1, \ldots, 10$, and X has the binomial distribution with $n = 10$ and $p = 0.50$. Entering these values for n and p, the *Binomial Distribution* app displays the probability that X equals 0 (or any other number between 0 and 10) by hovering over the corresponding bar. The screenshot in Figure 6.12 shows that P(0), the probability of no women being selected, equals 0.001, or 0.1%.

▶ **Figure 6.12**
Screenshot from the *Binomial Distribution* app. In the app, under the Find Probabilities tab, enter 10 for the number n of trials and 0.5 for the probability p of success (selecting a female). Then, enter 0 for the value of x. The subtitle of the graph then shows the desired probability, which is also printed in a table below the graph. (Not shown in this screenshot.) Hovering over each bar reveals the corresponding probabilities for the number of successes.

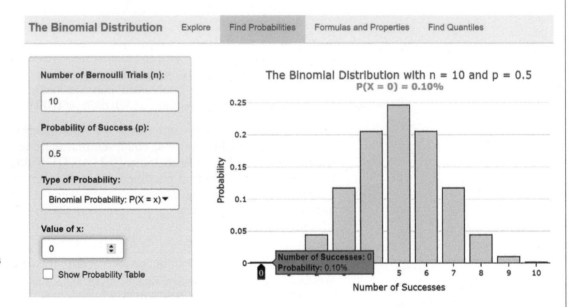

We can also use the binomial formula

$$P(x) = \frac{n!}{x!(n - x)!} p^x (1 - p)^{n-x}$$

$$= \frac{10!}{x!(10 - x)!} (0.50)^x (0.50)^{10-x}, \text{ for } x = 0, 1, 2, \ldots, 10.$$

The probability that no females are chosen ($x = 0$) equals

$$P(0) = \frac{10!}{0!10!} (0.50)^0 (0.50)^{10} = (0.50)^{10} = 0.001 = 0.1\%.$$

Any number raised to the power of 0 equals 1. Also, 0! = 1, and the 10! terms in the numerator and denominator divide out, leaving $P(0) = (0.50)^{10}$. If the employees were chosen randomly, it is very unlikely (one chance in a thousand) that none of the 10 selected for promotion would have been female.

Insight

In summary, because this probability is so small, seeing no women chosen would make us highly skeptical that the choices were random with respect to gender.

▶ *Try Exercise 6.46*

Binomial Probability Distribution for
n = 10 and p = 0.5

x	P(x)	x	P(x)
0	0.001	6	0.205
1	0.010	7	0.117
2	0.044	8	0.044
3	0.117	9	0.010
4	0.205	10	0.001
5	0.246		

In this example, we found the probability that $x = 0$ female employees would be chosen for promotion. To get a more complete understanding of just which outcomes are likely, you can find the probabilities of *all* the possible x values. The table in the margin lists the entire binomial distribution for $n = 10$ and $p = 0.50$. You can get this from the *Binomial Distribution* app by checking the box for Show Probability Table. In the table, the least likely values for x are 0 and 10. If the employees were randomly selected, it is highly unlikely that 0 females or 10 females would be selected.

Let's explore the shape of the binomial distribution. The left graph in Figure 6.13 shows the binomial distribution with $n = 10$ and $p = 0.50$. It has a symmetric appearance around $x = 5$. For instance, $x = 3$ has the same probability as $x = 7$. The binomial distribution is perfectly symmetric only when $p = 0.50$. When $p \neq 0.50$, the binomial distribution has a skewed appearance. The degree of skew increases as p gets closer to 0 or 1. To illustrate, the graph on the right in Figure 6.13 shows the binomial distribution for $n = 10$ when $p = 0.15$. If 15% of the people who might be promoted were female, it would not be especially surprising to observe 3, 2, 1, or even 0 females in the selection, but the probabilities drop sharply for larger x-values.

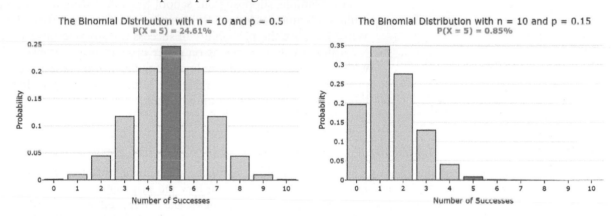

▲ **Figure 6.13** Binomial Distributions When $n = 10$ for $p = 0.5$ (left graph) and for $p = 0.15$ (right graph). Screenshots from the *Binomial Distribution* app. The binomial probability distribution is symmetric when $p = 0.5$, but it can be quite skewed for p near 0 or near 1. **Question** How do you think the distribution would look if $p = 0.85$?

Check to See If Binomial Conditions Apply

Caution

A binomial random variable counts the **number of successes out of n trials**. Its possible values are 0 to n. In Example 2, where X was equal to the number of games played in a best out of seven series, X is **not** binomial. There, we didn't count successes but rather how many games are played in order to reach 4 wins, with possible values ranging from 4 to 7. ◀

Before you use the binomial distribution, check that its three conditions apply. These are (1) binary observations (success or failure), (2) the same probability of success for each trial (denoted by p), and (3) a fixed number n of independent trials. To judge this, ask yourself whether the observations resemble coin flipping, the simple prototype for the binomial. For instance, it seems plausible to use the binomial distribution for Example 13 on gender bias in selecting employees for promotion. In this instance,

■ The observations are binary because (female, male) plays the role of (head, tail).
■ If employees are randomly selected, the probability p of selecting a female on any given trial is 0.50.
■ With random sampling of 10 employees, the outcome for one trial does not depend on the outcome of another trial.

One scenario where the assumptions do not apply is when sampling from a small population without replacement. To illustrate, suppose we are randomly drawing 10 cards from a standard deck of 52 cards without replacement and we define a success as drawing spades. In that case, the trials (=drawing a card) are not independent, as the probability of drawing spades on the second trial depends on whether spades was drawn on the first trial. Therefore, the random variable

X = number of spades in n = 10 draws (although it has possible values ranging from 0 to n) does **not** follow a binomial distribution. This is because the trials are not independent and the probability of drawing spades does not stay the same from trial to trial. Therefore, we cannot use the formula for binomial probabilities to figure out the chances of drawing, e.g., x = 4 spades. However, suppose we had 100 decks, each of 54 cards, for a total of 5,400 cards, and we randomly sampled, without replacement, 10 cards, which is less than 1% of all cards. Then, the binomial probabilities provide a good approximation for the probability of observing x successes (spades).

> **In Practice** Required Population and Sample Sizes to Use the Binomial
>
> When sampling n separate subjects from a population (i.e., when sampling without replacement), the exact probability distribution of the number of successes is too complex to discuss in this book. However, the binomial distribution provides a good approximation to this distribution when n is less than 10% of the population size. In practice, the sample size n is usually small compared to the population size, and this guideline is satisfied.

For example, suppose your school has 4,000 students. Then the binomial formula is adequate as long as the sample size is less than 10% of 4,000, which is 400. Why? Because the probability of success for any one observation will be similar regardless of what happens on other observations. Likewise, Example 13 dealt with the selection of 10 employees for promotion when the employee pool for promotion was very large. Again, the sample size was less than 10% of the population size, so using the binomial is valid.

► Activity 2

To **visualize the binomial distribution**, in the *Binomial Distribution* app, under the Explore tab, move the slider for the probability p from left to right to see how the shape of the binomial distribution changes from right skewed to left skewed, for given n. Then, set the slider for p to 0.3 and now move the slider for n from left (n = 2) to right (n = 100) to see how the shape changes from right skewed to almost symmetric and bell shaped. For n = 100, the shape resembles which continuous probability distribution?

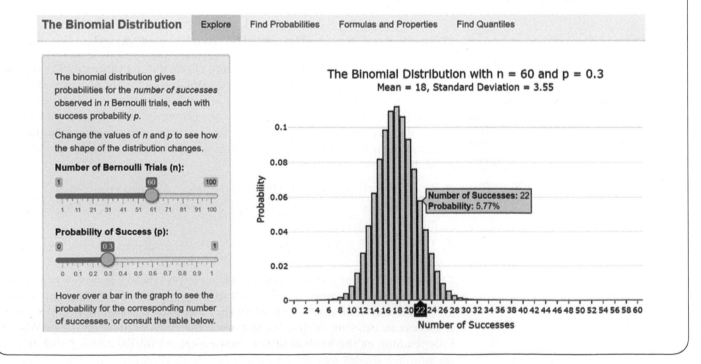

Mean and Standard Deviation of the Binomial Distribution

Recall

Section 6.1 presented the formula for the mean and standard deviation of a discrete random variable. ◀

As with any discrete probability distribution, we can use the formula $\mu = \Sigma x P(x)$ and $\sigma = \sqrt{\Sigma (x - \mu)^2 P(x)}$ to find the mean and standard deviation. However, these expressions simplify considerably for the binomial distribution and they can be written entirely in terms of the number of trials n and the probability of success p.

> ### Binomial Mean and Standard Deviation
>
> The binomial probability distribution for n trials with probability p of success on each trial has mean μ and standard deviation σ given by
>
> $$\mu = np, \quad \sigma = \sqrt{np(1 - p)}.$$

The formula for the mean makes sense intuitively. If the probability of success is p for a given trial, then we expect about a proportion p of the n trials to be successes, or about np total. If we flipped a fair coin $(p = 0.50)$ 100 times, we expect that about $np = 100(0.50) = 50$ flips come up heads.

Normal Approximation of the Binomial Distribution

When the number of trials n is large, it can be tedious to calculate binomial probabilities of all the possible outcomes. Often, it's adequate merely to use the mean and standard deviation to describe the most likely values for the number of successes. For large n, the binomial distribution has an approximate bell shape (as you can see from the screenshot in Activity 2), so in that case, we can use the normal distribution to approximate the binomial distribution and conclude that nearly all the possibilities for the number of successes fall between $\mu - 3\sigma$ and $\mu + 3\sigma$.

Normal Approximation of the Binomial Distribution ◀

Example 14

Checking for Racial Profiling

Picture the Scenario

In 2006, the New York City Police Department (NYPD) confronted approximately 500,000 pedestrians for suspected criminal violations. Of those confronted, 88.9% were non-White. Meanwhile, according to the 2006 American Community Survey conducted by the U.S. Census Bureau, of the more than 8 million individuals living in New York City, 44.6% were White.

Question to Explore

Are the data presented above evidence of racial profiling in police officers' decisions to confront particular individuals?

Think It Through

We'll treat the 500,000 confrontations as $n = 500,000$ trials. From the fact that 44.6% of the population was White, we can deduce that the other 55.4% was non-White. Then, if there is no racial profiling, the probability that any given confrontation should involve a non-White suspect is $p = 0.554$ (other things being equal, such as the rate of engaging in criminal activity). Suppose also that successive confrontations are independent. (They would not be, for example, if police confronted certain groups of pedestrians at the same time or repeatedly stopped a pedestrian they engaged with before.) Under these assumptions, for the 500,000 police confrontations, the number of non-Whites confronted has a binomial distribution with $n = 500,000$ and $p = 0.554$.

Recall

From Section 6.2, when a distribution has a normal distribution, nearly 100% of the observations fall within 3 standard deviations of the mean. ◀

275,947 277,000 278,053   444,500

The Binomial Distribution with n = 500000 and p = 0.554
P(X ≥ 444500) = 0.00%

Screenshot from the *Binomial Distribution* app.

The binomial distribution with $n = 500{,}000$ and $p = 0.554$ has mean

$$\mu = np = 500{,}000(0.554) = 277{,}000, \text{ and standard deviation}$$

$$\sigma = \sqrt{np(1-p)} = \sqrt{500{,}000(0.554)(0.446)} = 351.$$

As we'll argue below, this binomial distribution is approximated reasonably well by the normal distribution because the number of trials is so large. Then, the probability that the number of non-Whites falls within 3 standard deviations of the mean is close to 1.0, or 100%. This is the interval between

$$\mu - 3\sigma = 277{,}000 - 3(351) = 275{,}947 \text{ and}$$

$$\mu + 3\sigma = 277{,}000 + 3(351) = 278{,}053.$$

If no racial profiling is taking place, we would not be surprised if between about 275,947 and 278,053 of the 500,000 people stopped were non-White. See the smooth curve approximation for the binomial in the first graph in the margin. However, 88.9% of all stops, or $500{,}000(0.889) = 444{,}500$ stops, involved non-Whites. This suggests that the number of non-Whites stopped is much higher than we would expect if the probability of confronting a pedestrian were the same for each resident, regardless of race.

Insight

By this approximate analysis, we would not expect to see this many non-Whites stopped if there were truly a 0.554 chance that each confrontation involved a non-White. Using the *Binomial Distribution* app, the exact probability of 444,500 or more confrontations when $n = 500{,}000$ and $p = 0.544$ equals 0.00%, as you can see from the subtitle in the screenshot. The graph in the screenshot clearly shows that the shape of the binomial distribution for such a large n very closely resembles that of a normal distribution.

▶ *Try Exercise 6.45*

The solution in Example 14 used the normal distribution to approximate the binomial distribution. This is valid when the number of trials n is sufficiently large.

▶ Activity 3

From the screenshot in Activity 2, $p = 0.3$ and $n = 60$ in the *Binomial Distribution* app. Under these settings, you can see the normal shape of the binomial distribution, because $60(0.3) = 18$ and $60(0.7) = 42$, both larger than 15. Now, move the slider for p to 0.05, and watch how the normal shape breaks down and gives rise to a right-skewed distribution. When $p = 0.05$, $np = 60(0.05) = 3$, which is not larger than 15.

In Practice When the Binomial Distribution Is Approximately Normal

The binomial distribution can be approximated well by the normal distribution when n is large enough so that the expected number of successes, np, and the expected number of failures, $n(1 - p)$, are both at least 15.[7]

In Example 14, of those stopped, the expected number who were non-White was $np = 500{,}000(0.554) = 277{,}000$. The expected number who were White was $n(1 - p) = 500{,}000(0.446) = 223{,}000$. Both exceed 15 by far, so this binomial distribution has approximately a normal distribution which we can use to find the probability for any given interval.

---

[7]A lower bound of 15 is actually a bit higher than needed. The binomial is bell shaped even when both np and $n(1 - p)$ are about 10. We use 15 here because it ties in better with a guideline in coming chapters for using the normal distribution for inference about proportions.

6.3 Practicing the Basics

6.35 Kidney transplants In kidney transplantations, compatibility between donor and receiver depends on such factors as blood type and antigens. Suppose that for a randomly selected donor from a large national kidney registry, there is a 10% chance that the donor is compatible with a specific receiver. Three donors are randomly selected from this registry. Find the probability that 0, 1, 2, or all 3 selected donors are compatible.

   a. Do this by constructing the sample space and finding the probability for each possible outcome of choosing three donors. Use these probabilities to construct the probability distribution for the number of matching donors.

   b. Do this using the formula for the binomial distribution.

   c. Check your results using the *Binomial Distribution* app.

6.36 Compatible donors Refer to the previous exercise. Let the random variable X = number of compatible donors. Check the conditions for X to be binomial by answering parts a–c.

   a. What constitutes a trial, how many trials are there, and how many outcomes does each trial have?

   b. Does each trial have the same probability of success? Explain

   c. Are the trials independent?

6.37 Symmetric binomial Use the *Binomial Distribution* app to study the graph and shape for each of the following binomial distributions:

   a. $n = 4$ and $p = 0.50$.

   b. $n = 4$ and $p = 0.30$.

   c. $n = 4$ and $p = 0.10$.

   d. Which if any of the graphs in parts a–c are symmetric? Without actually constructing the graph, would the case $n = 20$ and $p = 0.50$ be symmetric or skewed?

   e. Which of the graphs in parts a–c is the most heavily skewed? Without actually constructing the graph, would the case $n = 4$ and $p = 0.01$ exhibit more or less skewness than the graph in part c?

6.38 Number of girls in a family Each newborn baby has a probability of approximately 0.49 of being female and 0.51 of being male. For a family with four children, let X = number of children who are girls.

   a. Explain why the three conditions are satisfied for X to have the binomial distribution.

   b. Identify n and p for the binomial distribution.

   c. Find the probability that the family has two girls and two boys.

6.39 Bidding on eBay You are bidding on four items available on eBay. You think that for each bid, you have a 25% chance of winning it, and the outcomes of the four bids are independent events. Let X denote the number of winning bids out of the four items you bid on.

   a. Explain why the distribution of X can be modeled by the binomial distribution.

   b. Find the probability that you win exactly 2 bids.

   c. Find the probability that you win 2 bids or fewer.

   d. Find the probability that you win more than 2 bids.

6.40 More eBay bidding For each of the following situations, explain whether the binomial distribution applies for X.

   a. You are bidding on four items available on eBay. You think that you will win the first bid with probability 25% and the second through fourth bids with probability 30%. Let X denote the number of winning bids out of the four items you bid on.

   b. You are bidding on four items available on eBay. Each bid is for $70, and you think there is a 25% chance of winning a bid, with bids being independent events. Let X be the total amount of money you pay for your winning bids.

6.41 Passing by guessing A quiz in a statistics course has four multiple-choice questions, each with five possible answers. A passing grade is three or more correct answers to the four questions. Allison has not studied for the quiz. She has no idea of the correct answer to any of the questions and decides to guess at random for each.

   a. Find the probability she lucks out and answers all four questions correctly.

   b. Find the probability that she passes the quiz.

6.42 NBA free throws In the National Basketball Association, the top free-throw shooters usually have probability of about 0.90 of making any given free throw.

   a. During a game, one such player (Dirk Nowitzki) shot 10 free throws. Let X = number of free throws made. What must you assume for X to have a binomial distribution? (Studies have shown that such assumptions are well satisfied for this sport.)

   b. Specify the values of n and p for the binomial distribution of X in part a.

   c. Find the probability that he made (i) all 10 free throws (ii) 9 free throws and (iii) more than 7 free throws.

6.43 Season performance Refer to the previous exercise. Over the course of a season, this player shoots 400 free throws.

   a. Find the mean and standard deviation of the probability distribution of the number of free throws he makes.

   b. By the normal distribution approximation, within what range would you expect the number made almost certainly to fall? Why?

   c. Within what range would you expect the *proportion* made to fall?

6.44 Is the die balanced? A balanced die with six sides is rolled 60 times.

   a. For the binomial distribution of X = number of 6s, what is n and what is p?

   b. Find the mean and the standard deviation of the distribution of X. Interpret.

   c. If you observe $x = 0$, would you be skeptical that the die is balanced? Explain why, based on the mean and standard deviation of X.

   d. Show that the probability that $x = 0$ is 0.0000177.

6.45 **Exit poll** An exit poll is taken of 3,000 voters in a state-wide election. Let X denote the number who voted in favor of a special proposition designed to lower property taxes and raise the sales tax. Suppose that in the population, exactly 50% voted for it.

a. Explain why this scenario would seem to satisfy the three conditions needed to use the binomial distribution. Identify n and p for the binomial.

b. Find the mean and standard deviation of the probability distribution of X.

c. Using the normal distribution approximation, give an interval in which you would expect X almost certainly to fall, if truly $p = 0.50$. (*Hint:* You can follow the reasoning of Example 14 on racial profiling.)

d. Now, suppose that the exit poll had $x = 1,706$. What would this suggest to you about the actual value of p?

6.46 **Jury duty** The juror pool for the upcoming murder trial of a celebrity actor contains the names of 100,000 individuals in the population who may be called for jury duty. The proportion of the available jurors on the population list who are Hispanic is 0.40. A jury of size 12 is selected at random from the population list of available jurors. Let $X = $ the number of Hispanics selected to be jurors for this jury.

a. Is it reasonable to assume that X has a binomial distribution? If so, identify the values of n and p. If not, explain why not.

b. Find the probability that no Hispanic is selected.

c. If no Hispanic is selected out of a sample of size 12, does this cast doubt on whether the sampling was truly random? Explain.

6.47 **Poor, poor, Pirates** On September 7, 2008, the Pittsburgh Pirates lost their 82nd game of the 2008 season and tied the 1933–1948 Philadelphia Phillies major sport record (baseball, football, basketball, and hockey) for most consecutive losing seasons at 16. In fact, their losing streak continued until 2012 with 20 consecutive losing seasons. A Major League Baseball season consists of 162 games, so for the Pirates to end their streak, they need to win at least 81 games in a season (which they did in 2013).

a. Over the course of the streak, the Pirates have won approximately 42% of their games. For simplicity, assume the number of games they win in a given season follows a binomial distribution with $n = 162$ and $p = 0.42$. What is their expected number of wins in a season?

b. What is the probability that the Pirates will win at least 81 games in a given season? Use (i) the *Binomial Distribution* app to find the exact binomial probability and (ii) the *Normal Distribution* app to find the approximate area under a normal distribution.

c. Can you think of any factors that might make the binomial distribution an inappropriate model for the number of games won in a season?

6.48 **Checking guidelines** For Example 13 on the gender distribution of promotions, the population size was more than one thousand, half of whom were female. The sample size was 10.

a. Check whether the guideline was satisfied about the relative sizes of the population and the sample, thus allowing you to use the binomial for the probability distribution for the number of females selected.

b. Check whether the guideline was satisfied for this binomial distribution to be approximated well by a normal distribution.

6.49 **Class sample** Four of the 20 students (20%) in a class are fraternity or sorority members. Five students are picked at random. Does $X = $ the number of students in the sample who are fraternity or sorority members have the binomial distribution with $n = 5$ and $p = 0.20$? Explain why or why not.

6.50 **Binomial needs fixed n** For the binomial distribution, the number of trials n is a fixed number. Let X denote the number of girls in a randomly selected family in Canada that has three children. Let Y denote the number of girls in a randomly selected family in Canada (that is, the number of children could be any number). A binomial distribution approximates well the probability distribution for one of X and Y, but not for the other.

a. Explain why.

b. Identify the case for which the binomial applies and identify n and p.

6.51 **Binomial assumptions** For the following random variables, explain why at least one condition needed to use the binomial distribution is unlikely to be satisfied.

a. $X = $ number of people in a family of size 4 who go to church on a given Sunday, when any one of them goes 50% of the time in the long run (binomial, $n = 4$, $p = 0.50$). (*Hint:* Is the independence assumption plausible?)

b. $X = $ number voting for the Democratic candidate out of the 100 votes in the first precinct that reports results, when 60% of the population voted for the Democrat in that state (binomial, $n = 100$, $p = 0.60$). (*Hint:* Is the probability of voting for the Democratic candidate the same in each precinct?)

c. $X = $ number of females in a random sample of four students from a class of size 20, when half the class is female (binomial, $n = 4$, $p = 0.50$).

Chapter Review

SUMMARY OF NOTATION

X	A random variable taking on values determined by chance	σ	Standard deviation of the random variable, probability or population distribution
$P(x)$	Probability that a discrete random variable takes on the particular value x	σ^2	Variance of the random variable, probability or population distribution
μ	Mean of the random variable, probability or population distribution	$p, 1 - p$	Probabilities of the two possible outcomes (e.g., success or failure) of a binary random variable, and the probability of success in a binomial distribution

CHAPTER SUMMARY

■ A **random variable** is a numerical measurement of the outcome of a random phenomenon. It takes on values determined by chance. As with ordinary variables, random variables can be **discrete** (taking separate values) or **continuous** (taking values in an interval).

■ A **probability distribution** specifies probabilities for the possible values of a random variable. Probability distributions have summary measures of the center and the variability, most notably the **mean** μ and **standard deviation** σ. The mean (also called **expected value**) for a discrete random variable is

$$\mu = \Sigma x P(x),$$

where $P(x)$ is the probability of the outcome x and the sum is taken over all possible outcomes and the standard deviation is.

$$\sigma = \sqrt{\sum (x - \mu)^2 P(x)},$$

describing the expected distance from the mean.

■ The **normal distribution** is the probability distribution of a continuous random variable that has a symmetric bell-shaped graph specified by the parameters μ (the mean) and σ (the standard deviation). For $z = 1, 2,$ and 3, the probability of falling within z standard deviations of the mean are 68%, 95%, and almost 100%, for any given value of μ and σ. More

generally, the area under the normal distribution between two points a and b gives the probability of falling in this interval.

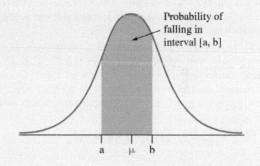

Probability of falling in interval [a, b]

■ The **z-score** for a value x of a random variable with mean μ and standard deviation σ equals

$$z = (x - \mu)/\sigma.$$

It measures the number of standard deviations that x falls from the mean μ. For a normal distribution, the z-scores have the **standard normal distribution**, which has mean = 0 and standard deviation = 1.

■ The **binomial distribution** is the probability distribution of the discrete random variable that measures the **number of successes** X in n independent trials, with probability p of a success on a given trial. It has probabilities

$$P(x) = \frac{n!}{x!(n-x)!} p^x (1-p)^{n-x}, x = 0, 1, 2, \ldots, n.$$

The mean is $\mu = np$, and the standard deviation is

$$\sigma = \sqrt{np(1-p)}.$$

LEARNING OBJECTIVES

1. Define a random variable.

2. Determine whether a random variable is discrete or continuous.

3. Define a probability distribution and understand what properties are necessary for a discrete probability distribution to be valid.

4. Find and interpret the mean of a discrete probability distribution and understand that it is typically used to measure the center of a probability distribution.

5. Find the standard deviation of a discrete probability distribution and understand that it is typically used to measure the variability of a probability distribution.

6. Describe the normal distribution and find probabilities associated with it. Understand the important role of the normal distribution in statistics.

7. Understand that the standard normal distribution has mean 0 and standard deviation 1.

8. Understand how the z-score is used to find how far a particular value x of the random variable falls from the mean μ.

9. Identify the conditions for a discrete random variable to be classified as binomial.

10. Understand that a binomial random variable measures the number of successes in n independent trials. Find binomial probabilities associated with these counts.

11. Find and interpret the mean and standard deviation for a binomial random variable.

12. Understand that for large n, the binomial distribution can be approximated by the normal distribution with the same mean and standard deviation.

ANSWERS TO THE CHAPTER FIGURE QUESTIONS

Figure 6.1 The shape of the distribution is skewed to the left.

Figure 6.2 The area under the curve from 0 to 15 should be shaded.

Figure 6.3 The shape of the distribution is bell shaped. The probability for a female to be taller than 65 inches is about 50%.

Figure 6.4 The distribution for women has a smaller standard deviation. It is more peaked (and its curve is higher) because it extends over a smaller range. We evaluate $70 \pm 3(4)$, which gives an interval for the men's heights from 58 inches to 82 inches.

Figure 6.5 These probabilities are similar to the percentages stated for the empirical rule. The empirical rule states that for an approximately bell-shaped distribution, approximately 68% of the observations fall within 1 standard deviation of the mean, 95% within 2 standard deviations of the mean, and nearly all within 3 standard deviations of the mean.

Figure 6.8 For 3 standard deviations, the probability in one tail is 0.0013. By symmetry, this is also the probability in the other tail. The total tail area is 0.0026, which subtracted from 1 gives an answer of 0.997.

Figure 6.9 The second percentile is the value located on the left side of the curve such that 2% of the distribution falls below it and 98% falls above.

Figure 6.10 The SAT score with $z = -3$ is $500 - 3(100) = 200$. The SAT score with $z = 3$ is $500 + 3(100) = 800$.

Figure 6.11 The values of -3 and 3.

Figure 6.13 The distribution with $p = 0.85$ is skewed to the left.

STATISTICAL SOFTWARE

Art of Stat Web Apps

- **Normal Distribution** This app explores and visualizes the normal distribution and finds probabilities (for a given value of x) or percentiles (for a given probability) for different scenarios that use the normal distribution. In particular, after entering the mean and standard deviation (which default to 0 and 1, respectively, i.e., the standard normal distribution) the app can find probabilities in the lower or upper tail, or for an interval. Similarly, the app can find percentiles (z-scores) corresponding to probabilities in either or both tails. All probabilities and percentiles computed are clearly shown and highlighted on the normal distribution graph.

- **Binomial Distribution** This app explores and visualizes the binomial distribution and finds binomial probabilities $P(x)$ for given values of the number of trials n and the success probability p. It draws the graph of the binomial distribution and users can hover over bars to obtain the corresponding probability. The app can find various cumulative probabilities (e.g., the probability for the number of successes to fall between two bounds) and clearly visualize these on the graph. The first tab of the app allows users to explore the shape of the binomial distribution with sliders for n and p.

R

- **Normal Distribution:** The R command `pnorm` finds probabilities under the normal curve. From Example 7,

```
> pnorm(230, mean=330, sd=80)
[1] 0.1056498
```

tells us that the probability of falling below 230 in a normal distribution with mean 330 and standard deviation 80 is 0.1056, or 10.56%. The command > `pnorm(430, mean=330,`

`sd=80, lower=FALSE)` gives the probability of falling above 430. To get the probability of falling within 230 and 430, use > `pnorm(430, mean=330, sd=80) - pnorm(230, mean=330, sd=80)`, or, for the answer to the question in Example 10, > `pnorm(90, mean=83, sd=5) - pnorm(80, mean=83, sd=5)`.

To find a percentile, for instance the 98th percentile for Mensa membership in Example 8, use

```
> qnorm(0.98, mean=100, sd=16)
[1] 132.86
```

to find that the required IQ score is 133. When you don't specify a mean and standard deviation, R automatically assumes a mean of 0 and standard deviation of 1, i.e., the standard normal distribution, so that > `pnorm(1.96)` returns 0.975 or > `qnorm(0.025)` returns -1.96. Finally, to draw a normal distribution in R, let

```
> mu <- 0
> sigma <- 1
> x <- mu + seq(-3.2, 3.2, 0.01)*sigma
> plot(x, dnorm(x, mean=mu, sd=sigma), type='l',
ylab="")
```

You can set your own values for `mu` and `sigma` in the first two lines.

- **Binomial Distribution:** The R command `dbinom` finds probabilities for the binomial distribution, such as the probability of 2 matches $P(2) = 0.096$ when $n = 3$ (specified using `size`) and $p = 0.2$ (specified using `prob`) in Example 12:

```
> dbinom(2, size=3, prob=0.2)
[1] 0.096
```

To find the probability for the number of successes to be *less than or equal* to 2, use > pbinom(2, size=3, prob=0.2). To draw the binomial distribution in R, such as in Figure 6.13 use

```
> n <- 10
> p <- 0.15
```

```
> plot(0:n,dbinom(0:n,size=n,prob=p),type='h',
ylab='Probability')
```

You can set your own values for n and p in the first two lines.

CHAPTER EXERCISES

Practicing the Basics

6.52 Grandparents Let X denote the number of living grandparents that a randomly selected adult American has. According to recent General Social Surveys, its probability distribution is approximately $P(0) = 0.71$, $P(1) = 0.15$, $P(2) = 0.09$, $P(3) = 0.03$, $P(4) = 0.02$.

   a. Does this refer to a discrete or a continuous random variable? Why?

   b. Show that the probabilities satisfy the two conditions for a probability distribution.

   c. Find the mean of this probability distribution.

6.53 Straight or boxed? Consider a Pick-3 lottery in which the lottery selects one of the 1,000 three-digit numbers between 000 and 999 at random. Suppose your birthday is May 14, and like many people, you decide to bet $1 on your birthday number (i.e., 514). There are two options to play, straight or boxed. If you choose to play straight, you win $500 if and only if the number chosen is 514. If you choose to play boxed, you win $80 if the number chosen contains the digits 5, 1, and 4 in any order. Which option would you prefer to play and why?

   a. Define the random variable X as the profit from that bet. (The profit equals the winnings minus the $1 you paid to play.) Give the probability distribution for X for each option (i.e., list the possible profits and their probabilities).

   b. Find the expected profit for each option.

   c. Based on the expected profit alone, which option would you prefer to play and why?

   d. If you had to guess which of the two options has the larger standard deviation, which one would you choose? Why?

   e. Find the standard deviation of the profits for each option.

6.54 Auctioning paintings A collector is interested in two paintings by the same artist available at an auction. She plans to bid $3,000 for the first painting auctioned off and $2,000 for the second. She estimates that the probability she will win the bid for the first painting (and spend $3,000) is 30%. If she gets that first painting, she thinks there is an 80% chance she will also win the bid for the second painting (and spend another $2,000). If she does not win the bid for the first painting, she thinks there is only a 10% chance she will win the bid for the second painting. Let the random variable X denote the amount of money the collector will spend at the auction.

   a. List the sample space of all possible outcomes of winning or losing the bids for the two paintings. (It may help to draw a tree diagram.)

   b. Are the events of winning the bid for the first painting and winning the bid for the second painting independent events? Explain.

   c. Find the probability of each outcome in the sample space. (Use the tree diagram.)

   d. Find the probability distribution of X.

   e. Find the mean of X.

   f. Find the standard deviation of X.

6.55 NJ lottery New Jersey has a six-way combination lottery game in which you pick three digits (each can be any of 0, 1, 2, ..., 9) and you win if the digits the lottery picks are the same as yours in any of the six possible orders. For a dollar bet, a winner receives $45.50. Two possible strategies are (a) to pick three different digits, or (b) to pick the same digit three times. Let X = winnings for a single bet.

   a. Find the probability distribution of X and its mean for strategy a.

   b. Find the probability distribution of X and its mean for strategy b.

   c. Which is the better strategy? Why?

6.56 Are you risk averse? You need to choose between two alternative programs for dealing with the outbreak of a deadly disease. In program 1, 200 people are saved. In program 2, there is a 2/3 chance that no one is saved and a 1/3 chance that 600 people are saved.

   a. Find the expected number of lives saved with each program.

   b. Now you need to choose between program 3, in which 400 people will die, and program 4, in which there is a 1/3 chance that no one will die and a 2/3 chance that 600 people will die. Find the expected number of deaths with each program.

   c. Explain why programs 1 and 3 are similar and why 2 and 4 are similar. (If you had to choose, would you be like most people and be risk averse in part a, choosing program 1, and risk taking in part b, choosing program 4?)

6.57 Flyers' insurance An insurance company sells a policy to airline passengers for $1. If a flyer dies on a given flight (from a plane crash), the policy gives $100,000 to the chosen beneficiary. Otherwise, there is no return. Records show that a passenger has about a one in a million chance of dying on any given flight. You buy a policy for your next flight.

a. Specify the probability distribution of the amount of money the beneficiary makes from your policy.

b. Find the mean of the probability distribution in part a. Interpret.

c. Explain why the company is very likely to make money in the long run.

6.58 **Mean and standard deviation for a binary random variable** One of the simplest discrete random variables is a binary random variable (sometimes called a Bernoulli random variable). It takes on only two distinct values, 1 and 0, with probabilities p and $1 - p$, respectively. Let X denote a binary random variable, with possible values $x = 1$ or 0 and $P(1) = p$ and $P(0) = 1 - p$.

a. Show that the mean of X is equal to p.

b. Show that the variance of X is equal to $p(1 - p)$ and the standard deviation is equal to $\sqrt{p(1 - p)}$.

c. Show that the mean and standard deviation result from setting $n = 1$ in the formulas for the mean and standard deviation of the binomial distribution.

6.59 **Standard deviation for best out of seven** The table below shows the probability distribution for the number of games played in a best of seven series when each team has a 50% (taken from Example 2) or 99% chance of winning a game.

# Games	50% Chance	99% Chance
4	0.1250	0.9606
5	0.2500	0.0384
6	0.3125	0.0001
7	0.3125	$2(10^{-5})$

a. Find the standard deviation of X = number of games played to determine a winner when each team has a 50% chance of winning a game. (In Example 3, the mean was found to be equal to 5.8125.)

b. The table also shows the probability distribution when one team has a 99% chance of winning each game. Would you expect the standard deviation for this distribution to be smaller or larger than the one in part a? (*Hint:* Note how almost all the time the game will end after 4 games.)

6.60 **Normal probabilities** For a normal distribution, find the probability that an observation is

a. Within 1.96 standard deviations of the mean.

b. More than 2.33 standard deviations from the mean.

6.61 **z-scores** Find the z-score such that the interval within z standard deviations of the mean contains probability (a) 0.95 and (b) 0.99 for a normal distribution. Sketch the two cases on a single graph.

6.62 **Normal probabilities without technology** The distribution of test scores on a certain test is normal, with mean 85 and standard deviation 5. Find approximate probabilities for the following events without any help from

technology (such as the *Normal Distribution* app) or a table (such as Table A):

a. Scores between 80 and 90.

b. Scores less than 80.

c. Scores higher than 95.

d. Scores between 75 and 80.

e. Scores lower than 75 or higher than 95.

6.63 **z-score and tail probability**

a. Find the z-score for the number that is less than only 1% of the values of a normal distribution. Sketch a graph to show where this value is.

b. Find the z-scores corresponding to the (i) 90th and (ii) 99th percentiles of a normal distribution.

6.64 **Boys and girls birth weight** Exercise 6.28 mentioned that in the United States, birth weight of boys is approximately normal, with mean 3.41 kg and standard deviation 0.55 kg. For girls, the birth weight is also approximately normal with mean 3.29 kg and standard deviation 0.52 kg.

a. A weight below 2.5 kg is considered low birth weight. 2.5 kg corresponds to which percentile for boys and to which percentile for girls?

b. Is a birth weight of 2.5 kg more extreme for boys or girls? Why?

6.65 **Cholesterol** The American Heart Association reports that a total cholesterol score of 240 or higher represents high risk of heart disease. A study of postmenopausal women reported a mean of 220 and standard deviation of 40. If the total cholesterol scores have a normal distribution, what proportion of the women fall in the high-risk category? (*Source:* Data from *Clin. Drug. Invest.,* 2000, vol. 20, pp. 207–214. The American Heart Association.)

6.66 **Female heights** Female heights in North America follow a normal distribution with $\mu = 65$ inches and $\sigma = 3.5$ inches. Find the proportion of females who are

a. under five feet.

b. over six feet.

c. between 60 and 70 inches.

d. Repeat parts a–c for North American males, the heights of whom are normally distributed with $\mu = 70$ inches and $\sigma = 4$ inches.

6.67 **Cloning butterflies** The wingspans of recently cloned monarch butterflies follow a normal distribution with mean 9 cm and standard deviation 0.75 cm. What proportion of the butterflies has a wingspan

a. less than 8 cm?

b. wider than 10 cm?

c. between 8 and 10 cm?

d. Ten percent of the butterflies have a wingspan wider than how many cm?

6.68 **Gestation times** For 5,459 pregnant women using Aarhus University Hospital in Denmark in a two-year period who reported information on length of gestation until birth, the mean was 281.9 days, with standard deviation 11.4 days. A baby is classified as premature if the gestation time is 258 days or fewer. (*Source:* Data from *British Medical Journal*, July 24, 1993, p. 234.) If gestation times are normally distributed, what's the proportion of babies born in that hospital prematurely?

6.69 Used car prices   Data from the Web site carmax.com compiled in July 2014 show that prices for used Audi A4 cars advertised on the Web site have a mean of $23,800 and a standard deviation of $4,380. Assume a normal distribution for the price.

a. What percent of used Audi A4s cost more than $25,000?

b. What percent of used Audi A4s cost between $18,000 and $22,000?

c. The least expensive 10% of used Audi A4s offered on the Web site cost at most how much?

6.70 Used car deals   Refer to the previous exercise. Suppose carmax.com decides to highlight any used car that is priced 1.5 standard deviations below the mean price as a special deal on its Web site.

a. If the distribution of used-car prices is normal, what percentage of used Audi A4s will be highlighted?

b. If the distribution of used-car prices is normal, what percentage of used Honda Civics will be highlighted? (Do you need to know the mean and standard deviation for used Honda Civics?)

c. If the distribution of used-car prices is in fact skewed to the right, will the percentage of used Audi A4s that are highlighted most likely be smaller or larger than the one from part a? Explain.

6.71 Metric height   A Dutch researcher reads that male height in the Netherlands has a normal distribution with $\mu = 72.0$ inches and $\sigma = 4.0$ inches. She prefers to convert this to the metric scale (1 inch = 2.54 centimeters). The mean and standard deviation then have the same conversion factor.

a. In centimeters, would you expect the distribution still to be normal? Explain.

b. Find the mean and standard deviation in centimeters. (*Hint:* What does 72.0 inches equal in centimeters?)

c. Find the probability that height exceeds 200 centimeters.

6.72 Manufacturing tennis balls   According to the rules of tennis, a tennis ball is supposed to weigh between 56.7 grams (2 ounces) and 58.5 grams (2 1/16 ounces). A machine for manufacturing tennis balls produces balls with a mean of 57.6 grams and a standard deviation of 0.3 grams when it is operating correctly. Suppose that the distribution of the weights is normal.

a. If the machine is operating properly, find the probability that a ball manufactured with this machine satisfies the rules.

b. After the machine has been used for a year, the process still has a mean of 57.6, but because of wear on certain parts, the standard deviation increases to 0.6 grams. Find the probability that a manufactured ball satisfies the rules.

6.73 Bride's choice of surname   According to a study done by the *Lucy Stone League* and reported by *ABC News* [8] in February 2011, 90% of brides take the surname of their new husband. Ann notes that of her four best friends who recently married, none kept her own name. If they had been a random sample of brides, how likely would this have been to happen?

6.74 ESP   Jane Doe claims to possess extrasensory perception (ESP). She says she can guess more often than not the outcome of a flip of a balanced coin in another room. In an experiment, a coin is flipped three times. If she does not actually have ESP, find the probability distribution of the number of her correct guesses.

a. Do this by constructing a sample space, finding the probability for each point, and using it to construct the probability distribution.

b. Do this using the formula for the binomial distribution.

6.75 More ESP   In another experiment with Jane Doe from the previous exercise, she had to predict which of five numbers was chosen in each of three trials. Jane Doe does not actually have ESP and is just randomly guessing. Explain why this experiment satisfies the three conditions for the binomial distribution by answering parts a–c.

a. For the analogy with coin flipping, what plays the role of (head, tail)?

b. Explain why it is sensible to assume the same probability of a correct guess on each trial. What is this probability?

c. Explain why it is sensible to assume independent trials.

6.76 Yale babies   In a study carried out at the Infant Cognition Center at Yale University, researchers showed 16 infants two videos: One featured a character that could be perceived as helpful, and the other featured a character that could be perceived as hindering. After the infants viewed the videos, the researchers presented the infants with two objects that resembled the figures from the videos and allowed the infants to choose one to play with. The researchers assumed that the infants would not exhibit a preference and would make their choices by randomly choosing one of the objects. Fourteen of the 16 infants chose the helpful object. If the assumption that infants choose objects randomly were true, what is the probability that 14 or more of the infants would have chosen the helpful object? Could this be considered evidence that the infants must actually be exhibiting a preference for the helpful object? (*Hint:* Use the binomial distribution.)

6.77 Weather   A weather forecaster states, "The chance of rain is 50% on Saturday and 50% again on Sunday. So there's a 100% chance of rain sometime over the weekend." If whether it rains on Saturday is independent of whether it rains on Sunday, find the actual

---

[8]*Source:* Background information from abcnews.go.com/Health/change-bride-marriage-uproar-judgment/story?id=12860570&page=1.

probability of rain *at least once* during the weekend as follows:

a. Answer using methods from Chapter 5, such as by listing equally likely sample points or using the formula for the probability of a union of two events.

b. Answer using the binomial distribution.

6.78 **Dating success** Based on past experience, Julio believes he has a 60% chance of success when he calls a woman and asks for a date.

a. State assumptions needed for the binomial distribution to apply to the number of times he is successful on his next five requests.

b. If he asks the same woman each of the five times, is it sensible to treat these requests as independent trials?

c. Under the binomial assumptions, state *n* and *p* and the mean of the distribution.

d. Under the binomial assumptions, find the probability that he is successful exactly twice.

e. Under the binomial assumptions, find the probability that he is successful more than 3 times.

6.79 **Likes on Facebook** A large retail chain sends out an ad about a new product to 15 million users on Facebook and asks them to like the message. Assume the probability that a user will like the message (instead of ignoring it) is 0.00001.

a. State assumptions for a binomial distribution to apply for X = the number of likes the message will receive. Identify *n* and *p* for that distribution.

b. Suppose the assumptions are met. Find the mean and standard deviation of X.

c. Is it reasonable to approximate the binomial distribution with the normal one? Why? (Assume the assumptions are met.)

d. Based on the normal approximation of the binomial distribution, find the interval for the possible numbers of likes that are within three standard deviations of the mean.

e. Refer to the assumptions for the analysis in part a. Explain at least one way they may be violated.

6.80 **Likes with online credit** The retail chain from the previous exercise decides to follow up its first ad with a second one, again to 15 million Facebook users. This time it gives away a $1 online credit for every user who likes the ad. Now, assume the probability is 0.0005 that a user will like it.

a. Find the mean and standard deviation for the number of likes this second ad will receive.

b. Find the interval for the possible number of likes that covers almost all possible values, using the normal approximation.

c. How much money would you advise the retail company to set aside for covering these $1 online credits? Why?

6.81 **Which distribution for sales?** A salesperson uses random digit dialing to call people and try to interest them in applying for a charge card for a large department store chain. From past experience, she is successful on 2% of

her calls. In a typical working day, she makes 200 calls. Let X be the number of calls on which she is successful.

a. What type of distribution does X have: normal, binomial, discrete probability distribution but not binomial, or continuous probability distribution but not normal?

b. Find the mean and standard deviation of X. Interpret the mean.

c. Find the probability that on a given day she has 0 successful calls.

Concepts and Investigations

6.82 **Quartiles** If z is the positive number such that the interval within z standard deviations of the mean contains 50% of a normal distribution, then

a. Explain why this value of z is about 0.67.

b. Explain why for any normal distribution the first and third quartiles equal $\mu - 0.67\sigma$ and $\mu + 0.67\sigma$.

c. The interquartile range, IQR, relates to σ by IQR = $2 \times 0.67\sigma$. Explain why.

6.83 **Best of five** Example 2 gave the probability distribution for the number of games played in a best out of seven series between teams A and B. Let's derive the probability distribution for a best of five series, in which the team that gets 3 wins first wins the entire series.

a. Write out the sample space of all possible sequences of wins and losses. (There are 20 such sequences. Constructing a [partial] tree diagram and stopping as soon as either 3 wins or 3 losses are observed may help in finding all 20.)

b. For each sequence in part a, determine its length. These are the distinct values of the random variable X = number of games played.

c. Find the probability of each sequence in part a when team A has a 50% chance of winning each game.

d. For each value x of the random variable X, find P(x) by adding up the probabilities for those sequences that end after x games.

6.84 **More best of five** Refer to the previous exercise which asked for the distribution of the number of games played in a best of 5 series when team A wins with probability 50%.

a. Find the expected number of games played in a best of five series.

b. Find the expected number of games played when team A has an 80% chance of winning each game.

6.85 **Family size in Gaza** The Palestinian Central Bureau of Statistics (www.pcbs.gov.ps) asked mothers ages 20–24 about the ideal number of children. For those living on the Gaza Strip, the probability distribution is approximately P(1) = 0.01, P(2) = 0.10, P(3) = 0.09, P(4) = 0.31, P(5) = 0.19, and P(6 or more) = 0.29. Because the last category is open-ended, it is not possible to calculate the mean exactly. Explain why you can find the *median* of the distribution, and find it. (*Source:* Data from www.pcbs.gov.ps.)

6.86 **Global warming** Suppose that weekly use of gasoline
for motor vehicle travel by adults in North America
has approximately a normal distribution with a mean of
20 gallons and a standard deviation of 6 gallons. Many
people who worry about global warming believe that
Americans should pay more attention to energy conservation. Assuming that the standard deviation and
the normal shape are unchanged, to what level must
the mean reduce so that 20 gallons per week is the third
quartile rather than the mean?

6.87 **Fast-food profits** Mac's fast-food restaurant finds that
its daily profits have a normal distribution with mean
$140 and standard deviation $80.

   a. Find the probability that the restaurant loses money
on a given day (that is, daily profit less than 0).

   b. Find the probability that the restaurant makes money
for the next seven days in a row. What assumptions
must you make for this calculation to be valid? (*Hint:*
Use the binomial distribution.)

6.88 **Airline overbooking** For the Boston to Chicago route,
an airline flies a Boeing 737–800 with 170 seats. Based on
past experience, the airline finds that people who purchase
a ticket for this flight have 0.80 probability of showing up
for the flight. They routinely sell 190 tickets for the flight,
claiming it is unlikely that more than 170 people show
up to fly.

   a. Provide statistical reasoning they could use for this
decision.

   b. Describe a situation in which the assumptions on
which their reasoning is based may not be satisfied.

6.89 **Babies in China** The sex distribution of new babies is
close to 50% each, with the percentage of males usually
being just slightly higher. In China in recent years, the
percentage of female births seems to have dropped, a
combination of policy limiting family size, the desire of
most families to have at least one male child, the possibility of determining sex well before birth, and the availability of abortion. Suppose that historically 49% of births in
China were female but birth records in a particular town
for the past year show 800 females born and 1200 males.
Conduct an investigation to determine whether the current probability of a female birth in this town is less than
0.49, by using the mean and standard deviation of the
probability distribution of what you would observe with
2,000 births if it were still 0.49.

Multiple Choice or True/False

6.90 **IQR for normal distribution** For a normally distributed
random variable, the IQR is

   a. twice the standard deviation

   b. less than twice the standard deviation

   c. larger than twice the standard deviation

   d. Can't tell because this will depend on the specific mean and standard deviation of the normal
distribution.

6.91 **Guess answers** A question has four possible answers,
only one of which is correct. You randomly guess the
correct response. With 20 such questions, the distribution
of the number of incorrect answers

   a. is binomial with $n = 20$ and $p = 0.25$.

   b. is binomial with $n = 20$ and $p = 0.50$.

   c. has mean equal to 10.

   d. has probability $(.75)^{20}$ that all 20 guesses are
incorrect.

6.92 **Terrorist coincidence?** On 9/11/2002, the first anniversary of the terrorist destruction of the World Trade
Center in New York City, the winning three-digit New
York State Lottery number came up 9-1-1. The probability of this happening was

   a. 1/1000.

   b. $(1/1000)^2 = 0.000001$.

   c. 1 in a billion.

   d. 3/10.

6.93 **True or false:** For a random variable following the normal distribution with mean $\mu = 50$ and $\sigma = 10$, the probability of having values in the interval [41, 47] equals the
area under the normal curve over the interval [41, 47].

6.94 **True or false:** A random variable following the normal
distribution is an example of a discrete random variable
with mean computed as $\mu = \Sigma = xP(x)$.

Advanced Concepts

6.95 **Linear transformations: Taxes and fees** Assume prices
for used Audi A4s available on carmax.com follow a
normal distribution with mean $23,800 and standard
deviation $4,380.

   a. Prices quoted on carmax.com are without sales tax.
To account for a 6% sales tax, you multiply each
price by 1.06. What is the distribution of these new
prices that include tax? (*Hint:* When multiplying values of a random variable by a constant [such as multiplying all prices by 1.06], the mean and the standard
deviation of this new random variable are simply the
mean and the standard deviation of the original variable multiplied by that same constant. The shape of
the distribution is not affected by multiplying.)

   b. Carmax.com adds a $199 processing fee when a vehicle
is sold through its Web page. What is the distribution
of the prices when this fee is added to all prices? (*Hint:*
When adding a constant to values of a random variable
[such as adding 199 to all prices], the mean of this new
random variable is obtained by simply adding the same
constant to the original mean. The standard deviation,
however, is unaffected by the addition, so the standard
deviation of the new variable is the same as the standard
deviation of the old variable, regardless of how much is
added [or subtracted]. The shape of the distribution is
also not affected by adding a constant to all values.)

6.96 **Binomial probabilities** Justify the $p^x(1 - p)^{n-x}$ part of
the binomial formula for the probability $P(x)$ of a particular sequence with x successes, using what you learned in
Section 5.2 about probabilities for intersections of independent events.

6.97 **Waiting time for doubles** Most discrete random variables can take on a finite number of values. Let X = the number of rolls of two dice necessary until doubles (the same number on each die) first appears. The possible values for this discrete random variable (called the **geometric**) are 1, 2, 3, 4, 5, 6, 7, and so on, still separate values (and discrete) but now an infinite number of them.

a. Using intersections of independent events, explain why $P(1) = 1/6, P(2) = (5/6)(1/6)$, and $P(3) = (5/6)^2(1/6)$.

b. Find $P(4)$ and explain how to find $P(x)$ for an arbitrary positive integer x.

6.98 **Geometric mean** Exercise 6.47 discussed the record losing streak of the Pittsburgh Pirates. In particular, if the Pirates' chance of winning any single game is 0.42, then at the beginning of a new season, the probability of them winning at least 81 games, and hence not adding another losing season to the streak, is about 0.024. The previous exercise mentions a type of random variable called the *geometric random variable*. A simple formula exists for calculating the mean of a geometric variable; if the probability of success on any given trial is p, then the expected number of trials required for the first success to occur is $1/p$. If the first such trial is taken to be the 2000 Major League Baseball season (i.e., 5 years into their losing streak), during what year would we expect the Pirates to break their streak?

6.99 **World Series in baseball** For the 73 World Series played between 1945 and 2018, 13 (18%) ended after 4 games, 14 (19%) after 5 games, 15 (21%) after 6 games, and 31 (42%) needed to go all the way to 7 games.

a. Find the average number of games played based on these data. (Remember from Section 6.1 that the mean for the theoretical distribution given in Example 2 is 5.8125.)

b. Draw a histogram for these observations and compare it to the theoretical distribution in Table 6.1. What could be responsible for the differences?

c. A 2003 *New York Times* article mentioned that series going to seven games are unusually common. Is this true? Of 73 series, if the theoretical distribution given in Table 6.1 holds true, how many series do we expect to be decided in seven games? Compare this to the observed frequency.

Student Activities

6.100 **Best of seven games** In professional baseball, basketball, and hockey in North America, the final two teams in the playoffs play a best of seven series of games. The first team to win four games is the champion. Use simulation with the *Random Numbers* app to approximate the probability distribution of the number of games needed to declare a champion when (a) the teams are evenly matched and (b) the better team has probability 0.90 of winning any particular game. In each case, conduct 10 simulations. Then combine results with other students in your class and estimate the mean number of games needed in each case. In which case does the series tend to be shorter? (*Hint:* For part a, generate random numbers between 1 and 10, where 1–5 represents a win for team A and 6–10 a win for team B. With the app, keep on generating a single random number until one team reaches 4 wins. For part b, again generate random numbers between 1 and 10, but now let 1–9 represent a win for team A and 10 a win for team B. Keep on generating a single random number until one team reaches 4 wins. Then repeat the entire process 9 more times to get a total of 10 simulations. The exact probabilities for part a are given in Example 2; the exact probabilities for part b are $P(4) = 0.6562, P(5) = 0.2628, P(6) = 0.0664$, and $P(7) = 0.0146$, resulting in a mean of 4.4. Your approximations should be close to these.)

▶ Activity 4

What Hot Streaks Should We Expect in Basketball?

In basketball games, TV commentators and media reporters often describe players as being hot if they make several shots in a row. Yet statisticians have shown that for players at the professional level, the frequency and length of streaks of good (or poor) shooting are similar to what we'd expect if the success of the shots were random, with the outcome of a particular shot being independent of previous shots.[9]

Shaquille O'Neal was one of the top players in the National Basketball Association, but he was a poor free-throw shooter. He made about 50% of his free-throw attempts over the

---

[9]For instance, see articles by A. Tversky and T. Gilovich, *Chance*, vol. 2 (1989), pp. 16–21 and 31–34.

course of a season. Let's suppose that he had probability 0.50 of making any particular free throw that he took in a game. Suppose also whether or not he made any particular free throw was independent of his previous ones. He took 20 free throws during the game. Let X denote the longest streak he made in a row during the game. This is a discrete random variable, taking the possible values $x = 0, 1, 2, 3, \ldots, 20$. Here, $x = 0$ if he made none of the 20, $x = 1$ if he never made more than 1 in a row, $x = 2$ if his longest streak was 2 in a row, and so forth.

What is the probability distribution of X? This is difficult to find using probability rules, so let's approximate it by simulating 10 games with $n = 20$ free throws. Representing each of O'Neal's shots by the flip of a coin, we treat a head as making a shot and a tail as missing it. We simulate O'Neal's 20 free throws by flipping a coin 20 times. We did this and got

TTHHHTHTTTHTIIIITHTTHT

This corresponds to missing shots 1 and 2, then making shots 3, 4, and 5, missing shot 6, and so forth. The simulated value of X = the longest streak of shots made is the longest sequence of heads in a row. In the sequence just shown, the longest streak made is $x = 3$, corresponding to the heads on flips 3, 4, and 5.

You would do the 20 coin flips 10 times to simulate what would happen in 10 games with 20 free throws in each. This would be a bit tedious. Instead, we suggest that you use your own judgment to write down quickly 10 sets of 20 H and T symbols (as shown above for one set) on a sheet of paper to reflect the sort of results you would expect for 10 games with 20 free throws in each. After doing this, find the 10 values of X = longest streak of Hs, using each set of 20 symbols. Do you think your instructor would be able to look at your results and figure out that you did not actually flip the coin?

A more valid way to do the simulation uses actual coins or software, such as the *Random Numbers* app on the book's web site. Click on the second tab in that app, called Coin Flips, and enter 20 for the number of flips to generate. Then, press Generate. The screenshot shows one such simulation of 20 coin flips (highlighted underneath the Generate button), which resulted in a longest streak of 6. Use this to simulate 10 games with $n = 20$ free throws in each. When we did this, we got the following results for the first three simulations:

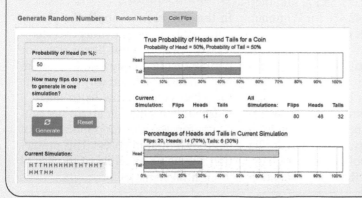

Random numbers	longest streak
T H T H T H H T H T T H T H H T H T H H	4
H H H T H T H T H H T H H T T H T T T T	4
H H H T H H H H H T T H T T T H T H H H	5

In practice, to get accurate results you have to simulate a *huge* number of games (at least a thousand), for each set of 20 free throws observing the longest streak of successes in a row. Your results for the probability distribution would then approximate those shown in the table[10].

Probability Distribution of X = Longest Streak of Successful Free Throws

The distribution refers to 20 free throws with a 0.50 chance of success for each. All potential x values higher than 9 had a probability of 0.00 to two decimal places and a total probability of only 0.006.

x	$P(x)$	x	$P(x)$
0	0.00	5	0.13
1	0.02	6	0.06
2	0.20	7	0.03
3	0.31	8	0.01
4	0.23	9	0.01

The probability that O'Neal never made more than four free throws in a row equals $P(0) + P(1) + P(2) + P(3) + P(4) = 0.76$. This would usually be the case. The mean of the probability distribution is $\mu = 3.7$.

The longest streak of successful shots tends to be longer, however, with a larger number of total shots. With 200 shots, the distribution of the longest streak has a mean of $\mu = 7$. Although it would have been a bit unusual for O'Neal to make his next seven free throws in a row, it would not have been at all unusual if he made seven in a row sometime in his next 200 free throws. Making seven in a row was then not really a hot streak but merely what we expect by random variation. Sports announcers often get excited by streaks that they think represent a hot hand but merely represent random variation.

With 200 shots, the probability is only 0.03 that the longest streak equals four or fewer. Look at the 10 sets of 20 H and T symbols that you wrote on a sheet of paper to reflect the results you expected for 10 games of 20 free throws each. Find the longest streak of Hs out of the string of 200 symbols. Was your longest streak four or fewer? If so, your instructor could predict that you faked the results rather than used random numbers, because there's only a 3% chance of this if they were truly generated randomly. Most students underestimate the likelihood of a relatively long streak.

This concept relates to the discussion in Section 5.4 about coincidences. By itself, an event may seem unusual. But when you think of all the possible coincidences and all the possible times they could happen, it is probably not so unusual.

---

[10] *Source:* Background material from M. F. Schilling, "The longest run of heads," *The College Mathematics Journal,* vol. 21, 1990, pp. 196–207.

We rely on statistics computed from random samples for inference about populations. In this chapter, we use what we learned about probability distributions to investigate the possible values of two important statistics, the sample proportion and the sample mean. We will see the central role the normal distribution plays in statistics. We will also explore the distribution of statistics through a computer-intensive technique called the Bootstrap. One of the fundamental insights of this chapter is that often we can predict quite well how close a statistic falls to the population value.

Sampling Distributions

Example 1

Predicting Election Results Using Exit Polls

Picture the Scenario

An exit poll is an opinion poll in which voters are randomly sampled after leaving the voting booth. Using exit polls, polling organizations predict winners after learning how a small number of people voted, often only a few thousand out of possibly millions of voters. What amazes many people is that these predictions almost always turn out to be correct.

In California in November 2010, the gubernatorial race pitted the Republican candidate Meg Whitman against the Democratic candidate, Jerry Brown. The exit poll on which TV networks relied for their projections on election night found that, after sampling 3,889 voters, 53.1% said they voted for Brown, 42.4% for Whitman, and 4.5% for other candidates or gave no answer (*Source:* www.cnn.com). At the time of the exit poll, the percentage of the entire voting population (nearly 9.5 million people) that voted for Brown was unknown. In determining whether they could predict a winner, the TV networks had to decide whether the exit polls gave enough evidence to predict that the population percentage voting in favor of Brown was enough to win the election.

Questions to Explore

- How close can we expect a sample percentage to be to the population percentage? For instance, if 53.1% of 3,889 sampled voters supported Brown, how close is 53.1% to the actual percentage in the entire population of 9.5 million voters who voted for him?

- How does the sample size influence our analyses? For instance, could we just sample 100 voters instead of 3,889 voters and make an accurate inference about the population percentage voting for Brown? On the other hand, are 3,889 voters enough, or do we need tens of thousands of voters in our sample?

Thinking Ahead

In this chapter, we apply the probability tools of the previous two chapters to analyze how likely it is for sample results to be close to population values. You'll see why the results for 3,889 voters allow us to make a reasonable prediction about the outcome for the entire population of nearly 9.5 million voters. This prediction will be an example of the use of inferential statistics.

Recall

From Section 1.2, a **statistic** is a numerical summary of sample data, such as the proportion in an exit poll who voted for Brown. A **parameter** is a numerical summary of a population, such as the proportion of all California voters who voted for Brown. ◄

We learned about probability in Chapter 5 and about probability distributions such as the normal distribution in Chapter 6. We'll next study how probability, and in particular the normal probability distribution, provides the basis for making statistical inferences. As Chapter 1 explained, inferential methods use statistics computed from samples to make decisions and predictions about a population. The population summaries are called parameters and are typically unknown. Inferential methods, which try to estimate these unknown parameters, are the main focus of the rest of this book.

7.1 How Sample Proportions Vary Around the Population Proportion

In Chapter 6, we used probability distributions with known parameter values to find probabilities of possible outcomes of a random variable. In practice, we seldom know the values of parameters. They are estimated using data from surveys, observational studies, or experiments. However, elections provide a context in which we eventually know the population parameter (after election day). Before election day, candidates are interested in gauging where they stand with voters, so they rely on surveys (polls) to help predict whether they will receive the necessary percentage to win. On election day, TV networks rely on exit polls to assist in making early evening predictions before all the votes are counted.

Let's consider the California gubernatorial election mentioned in Example 1. Before all the votes were counted, the proportion of the population of voters who voted for Jerry Brown was an unknown parameter. An exit poll of 3,889 voters reported that the sample proportion who voted for him was 0.531. This statistic *estimates* the unknown parameter in this scenario, the population proportion that voted for Jerry Brown. How do we know whether the sample proportion from the California exit poll is a good estimate, falling close to the population proportion? The total number of voters was over nine million, and the poll sampled a minuscule portion of them. This section introduces a type of probability distribution called the **sampling distribution** that helps us determine how close to the population parameter a sample statistic is likely to fall.

A Sampling Distribution Shows How Statistics Vary

Recall

Section 6.1 introduced the term **random variable** as a variable that takes on different values determined by chance. An uppercase letter, such as X, refers to the random variable. A lowercase letter, such as x, refers to particular values of the random variable. ◄

For a randomly selected voter in an exit poll, whether or not that voter voted for Brown is a random variable. Let X = vote outcome denote this random variable, with possible values $x = 1$ if the voter voted for Brown and $x = 0$ if the voter did not vote for Brown (i.e., voted for Meg Whitman, some other candidate, or provided an empty or invalid ballot). Such a variable, a special case of a categorical random variable, is called a **binary** variable because it has only two different values (1 or 0), corresponding to whether the voter voted for Brown or not.

When we specify the probabilities for each of these two outcomes, we specify the **population distribution** for this binary random variable. For example, the official final results for this election showed that Brown received 53.8% of the votes. So, for the population of voters on election day, the population distribution for the binary random variable X equals $P(1) = 53.8\%$ and $P(0) = 46.2\%$. The table in the margin shows this population distribution, and its graph is shown in the left panel of Figure 7.1.

In practice, we typically don't know the values for the population distribution. (Election polls are an exception, where we eventually know the true proportion of voters who voted for a candidate.) Let p denote the (unknown) proportion of times that $x = 1$ in the entire population, called the **population proportion**. Then, $1 - p$ is the proportion of times that $x = 0$ in the entire population. The first table

Population Distribution of X:

Outcome x	$P(x)$
1	0.538
0	0.462
Total	**1.000**

Population Distribution of X With (Unknown) Population Proportion p:

Outcome x	P(x)
1	p
0	1−p
Total	**1**

Data Distribution of X based on a Sample of Size 3,889:

Outcome x	P(x)
1	0.531
0	0.469
Total	**1.000**

in the margin shows this population distribution. We call p a **population parameter** and try to estimate its value by taking a sample from the population.

The exit poll consisted of such a sample of 3,889 voters from the population of all voters. The proportion of times $x = 1$ and $x = 0$ in this sample forms what we call the **data distribution**. In the sample, 53.1% of the 3,889 voters voted for Brown, so the data distribution has $P(1) = 53.1\%$ and $P(0) = 46.9\%$. The second table in the margin and the right panel of Figure 7.1 show the data distribution for this particular exit poll of 3,889 voters. Since the data here are observations of a categorical variable, we draw a bar graph to represent its distribution.

For each sample drawn from the population, we will get a different data distribution. For instance, if some other news agency also conducts an exit poll of 3,889 voters, the resulting data distribution will be (slightly) different from the one shown in the right panel of Figure 7.1.

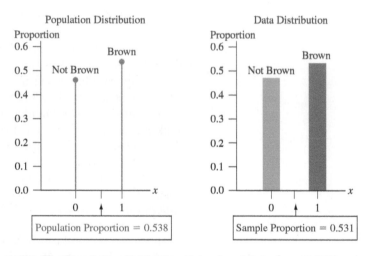

▲ **Figure 7.1** The Population (9.5 Million Voters) and Data ($n = 3,889$) Distributions of Vote Outcome (0 = Not Brown, 1 = Brown). **Question** Why do these look so similar?

As we learned in Chapter 2, we summarize results from a sample by computing statistics. Here, the relevant statistic to estimate the population proportion is the **sample proportion** of the 3,889 voters who voted for Brown, which equaled 53.1%. An exit poll run by another agency and based on a different sample of voters will result in a different sample proportion, and a third agency will get yet another different sample proportion. In that regard, sample proportions can be viewed as random variables because they vary from sample to sample. Before any exit poll was ever taken, the sample proportion voting for Brown was unknown. It was a random variable. We observed one value for it (53.1%) from the exit poll described in Example 1. We can observe other values for it from other exit polls. Since different exit polls use different voters, the sample proportion varies from one poll (sample) to another. (You see this in practice when various news outlets predict different proportions for the same candidate, each based on their own poll.) Because the sample proportion is a random variable, we can describe its possible values using a probability distribution. We call this distribution the **sampling distribution** because it describes how the values for the statistic vary from sample to sample.

Sampling Distribution

The **sampling distribution** of a statistic describes all potential values that could be observed for the statistic when taking a random sample of size n from the population.

For sampling 3,889 voters in an exit poll, imagine *all* the distinct samples of 3,889 voters (out of the 9.5 million voters) you could possibly get. Each such sample has a value for the sample proportion voting for Brown. Suppose you could look at each possible sample, find the sample proportion for each one, and then construct the frequency distribution of those sample proportion values. (Graphically, construct a histogram, since sample proportions are numerical values.) This would be the sampling distribution of the sample proportion, and the frequencies would tell you how likely it is to observe certain values for the proportion. The histogram in the margin shows a likely shape for this distribution. In practice, even for a moderate sample size n, figuring out all the possible samples and finding the sample proportion for each is an impossible task, as there are simply too many possibilities to consider. Fortunately, in this section you will learn what the sampling distribution of the sample proportion looks like without having to actually consider any of the samples you could possibly get.

A sampling distribution is merely a type of probability distribution. Rather than giving probabilities for the outcome of the vote of an individual subject (as in a population distribution), it gives probabilities for the values of a statistic computed from a sample. The concept that is sometimes hard to understand is that a statistic, when computed from a random sample, can be regarded as a random variable. When we compute a statistic (such as the sample proportion) from a random sample, we just happen to observe one of its possible values. Other samples will give different values, resulting in a whole distribution of values for the statistic, called the sampling distribution. Activity 1 shows how to use simulation to help us understand what a sampling distribution is and what its shape may look like.

In Words

Statistics are random variables with distributions called sampling distributions.

▶ **Activity 1**

Simulating the Sampling Distribution for a Sample Proportion

How much might a sample proportion vary from sample to sample? How would you describe the shape, center, and variability of the possible values for the sample proportion? What is the effect of the sample size n on the shape of the sampling distribution?

To answer these questions, we can simulate taking random samples of a given size from a population. To do this, we use the *Sampling Distribution for the Sample Proportion* app.

We'll carry out the simulation using the population proportion $p = 0.54$ that actually voted for Brown, rounded to two decimal places. First, we'll simulate what happens if we take a small sample of just $n = 40$ voters for the exit poll. Later, we will look at the actual sample size of 3,889 voters. In the app, as shown in Figure 7.2:

- Set the slider for the population proportion to 0.54. The top graph in the app updates to show this **population distribution**, where the orange half-circle on the x-axis (labeled p) marks the value of the population proportion between 0 and 1. (You can also provide labels for the two outcomes $x = 0$ and $x = 1$ in the population by clicking on the corresponding box and entering Not Brown for the outcome of 0 and Brown for the outcome of 1.)
- Set the slider for the sample size n to 40.

- Keep the default setting where you simulate drawing one sample (of size 40) from the population
- Press the Draw Sample(s) button once to generate this sample.

Figure 7.2 shows what the screen looks like after you have made these selections and draw one sample. Note that your screen may look somewhat different because your simulation may result in a different sample of 40 voters from the one shown here.

Just below the graph showing the population distribution, a bar graph appears that shows the **data distribution**, giving frequencies of the number of voters in the sample of size 40 voting (and not voting) for Brown. When we conducted this simulation, we had 23 people voting for Brown (generically called successes) and 17 not voting for him, as indicated in the title of that plot. In this simulation of one exit poll, the sample proportion voting for Brown was $23/40 = 0.575$, indicated by the blue triangle labeled $\hat{p}$. This particular estimate seems pretty good because it is relatively close to the actual population proportion of 0.54 (the orange half-circle). Were we simply lucky to be this close? You can repeat the process of drawing one sample of size $n = 40$ from the population by repeatedly clicking the Draw Sample(s) button. As you do this, the data distribution updates, showing the results of the current sample. In particular, pay attention to how the sample proportion (the blue triangle) jumps around the population proportions (the orange half-circle). This illustrates how the sample proportion varies from sample to sample and how close to or how far from the population proportion it can fall. This

▶ **Figure 7.2** Simulation Results when Taking One Sample of Size *n* = 40, Using the *Sampling Distribution for the Sample Proportion* App. The population proportion has been set as *p* = 0.54 and the sample size as *n* = 40. The top plot shows the **population distribution**. The middle plot shows the **data distribution** for the one sample drawn, which resulted in 23 successes (votes for Brown) and 17 failures (votes not for Brown), for a sample proportion of 23/40 = 0.575 of votes for Brown. The bottom plot marks the location for this sample proportion.

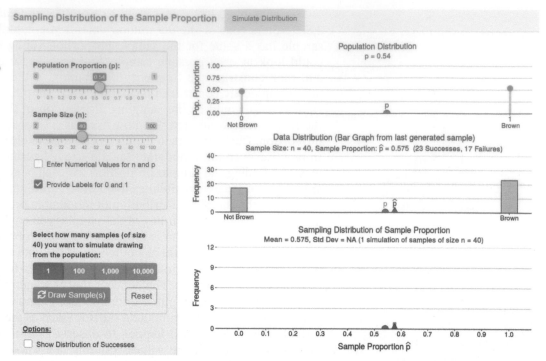

activity should enhance your understanding that the sample proportion can be regarded as a random variable, taking on certain values determined by chance (i.e., based on the voters included in the random sample).

The bottom graph, titled "Sampling Distribution of Sample Proportion," keeps track of the sample proportions you generate with each simulated sample and updates with each click. For the second sample generated, we obtained a sample proportion of 0.475, different but also pretty close to 0.54. Keep clicking on the Draw Sample(s) button (at least 50 times) and observe how the histogram depicting the distribution of the different values for the sample proportion keeps building up to form a particular shape. This histogram will eventually approximate the **sampling distribution** of the sample proportion of samples of size 40, when the population proportion equals 0.54.

To get a better feeling for the shape of the sampling distribution, we have to generate not only a few but several thousands of sample proportions. Rather than clicking the Draw Sample(s) button thousands of times, simply select the choice for 10,000 as the number of samples you want to simulate drawing. This will generate 10,000 samples of size *n* = 40 at once, compute the sample proportion for each, and add the results to the histogram in the bottom plot. Figure 7.3 shows the screen after first generating 50 samples by clicking Draw Sample(s) 50 times, but then switching to generate 10,000 samples at once with just one click on Draw Sample(s). With a total of 10,050 simulations, we now get a good idea about the shape of the sampling distribution. Apparently,

as the histogram in Figure 7.3 shows, with a sample size of 40 and a population proportion of 0.54, almost all sample proportions fall between 0.30 and 0.75, with many of them falling below 0.5.

For an exit poll trying to predict who will win, this is too much variability. Let's simulate the sampling distribution when the sample size is larger than 40. First, take the slider for the sample size and move it all the way up to *n* = 100. Observe how the range of the sampling distribution is now smaller, ranging from 0.4 to 0.7, but still too wide to be useful. Next, press Reset to start a new set of simulations and check the box for entering numerical values for *n* and *p* toward the top. In the field for the sample size, enter 3889, the actual sample size from the exit poll. Then, press Draw Sample(s) a couple of times and get a feel for how much the sample proportion varies from sample to sample with this larger sample size.

You will see that almost all sample proportions will be very close to the population proportion of 0.54. To be sure, select to generate 10,000 samples at once and press Draw Sample(s) one final time. Figure 7.4 shows the resulting histogram of sample proportions that will be similar to what's shown on your screen. Compared to *n* = 40 (or *n* = 100), with a sample size of *n* = 3,889, the variability of the sampling distribution is greatly reduced. Now the values for the sample proportion cluster very tightly around the population proportion of 0.54, and none of them are smaller than 0.5. (To get summary statistics on all the values simulated, including the minimum, check the box Summary Statistics of Samp. Dist. under Options.) Apparently, an exit poll with such a large sample size is much

▶ **Figure 7.3** Simulation Result when Taking 10,050 Samples, Each of Size 40, From a Population With $p = 0.54$. This screenshot shows results after a total of 10,050 simulations of taking a random sample of size 40 and computing the sample proportion for each. The bottom plot shows the histogram of the 10,050 sample proportions generated, approximating the sampling distribution of the sample proportion under these settings. **Question** With a mean of 0.542, a standard deviation of 0.079, and the bell shape of this distribution, find an interval in which almost all sample proportions will fall.

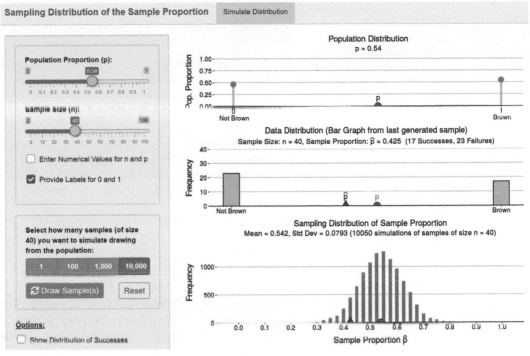

▶ **Figure 7.4** Simulated Sampling Distribution When Taking a Sample of Size $n = 3,889$. Screenshot taken from the *Sampling Distribution for the Sample Proportion* app. **Question** With a mean of 0.540 and standard deviation of 0.008, find an interval within which almost all sample proportions will fall when sampling $n = 3,889$ voters.

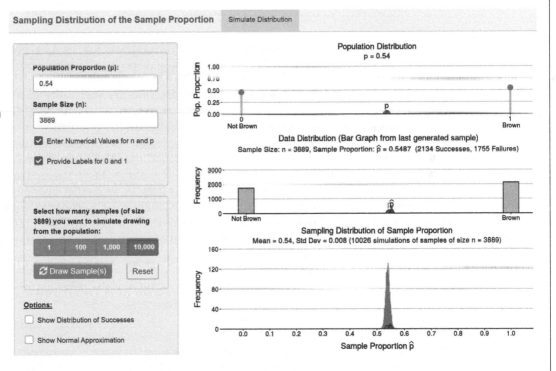

more useful, as it will allow you to estimate the population proportion much more accurately.

To get a feel for the sampling distribution, play around with this app, using different settings for n and p. Use the sliders for each one to see how changing their values affects the shape

of the sampling distribution. For instance, set the slider for p to 0.7 and the slider for n to 30 and simulate drawing 10,000 samples under these settings. Then, grab the slider of either n or p and see how the shape of the sampling distribution changes as you change n and p.

Try Exercises 7.1, 7.11, and 7.13 b ◀

Section 7.1 How Sampling Distributions ...

In Words

The population and data distributions give the distribution of a *variable* of interest in the population and sample, respectively. The sampling distribution gives the distribution of a *statistic* computed from a sample.

SUMMARY: Population Distribution, Data Distribution, Sampling Distribution

- **Population Distribution:** This is the distribution that describes the possible values of the variable of interest in the population. It depends on unknown parameters, such as the population proportion p for a binary variable. By taking a sample from the population, we hope to learn and make predictions about the unknown population parameter(s).
- **Data Distribution:** This is the distribution of the variable of interest based on the observations in the sample (the data). Its properties are described by statistics such as the sample proportion or the sample mean. With random sampling, the larger the sample size n, the more closely the data distribution resembles the population distribution.
- **Sampling Distribution:** This is the distribution of a statistic computed from observations in the sample, such as the sample proportion or the sample mean. Because the numerical value of a statistic varies from sample to sample, we get an entire distribution of possible values for it, which we call the sampling distribution. With random sampling, the sampling distribution provides probabilities (likelihood of occurrence) for all the possible values of the statistic. The sampling distribution holds the key for telling us how close a sample statistic, such as the sample proportion, falls to the corresponding unknown population parameter, such as the actual population proportion.

A Sampling Distribution Tells Us How Close a Statistic Falls to a Parameter

In Practice We Generally Use Only One Sample From a Population

Typically we would observe only *one* sample of the given size n, not many. But imagining the results of many samples of size n helps us conceptualize how much a statistic would vary from sample to sample.

Sampling distributions describe the variability in a sample statistic that occurs from sample to sample (or study to study). If different polling organizations each take a sample and estimate the population proportion that voted a certain way, they will get varying estimates because their samples have different people. Figures 7.3 and 7.4 portrayed the variability of the sample proportion when taking samples of size $n = 40$ and $n = 3,889$, respectively.

Sampling distributions help us to predict how close a statistic falls to the parameter it estimates. For instance, for a random sample of size 3,889, the simulation with the app showed that the probability is high that a sample proportion falls within a tiny interval of the (usually unknown) population proportion.

In Practice No Simulations Needed

We usually don't have to perform simulations to figure out the sampling distribution for many important statistics. We'll learn in the rest of this section and in the next section about results that tell us the expected shape of the sampling distribution and its mean and standard deviation.

These results will also show us how much the precision of an estimate improves with larger samples.

Every sample statistic is a random variable and, therefore has a sampling distribution. Besides the sample proportion, there is a sampling distribution of a sample mean, a sampling distribution of a sample median, a sampling distribution for the difference between two proportions or two means, a sampling distribution for the correlation coefficient r, and so forth. We'll focus in this section on the sample proportion and in the next section on the sample mean. In both cases, we will see that the sampling distribution can be described by a normal distribution when the sample size is large enough (something you might have suspected when looking at the histograms in Figures 7.3 and 7.4). Sampling distributions of statistics other than the proportion or the mean (such as the median or the correlation coefficient r) are more complicated and not as easily predictable. In Section 7.3, we'll learn about a general method that obtains the sampling distribution of a statistic via simulation. Let's first focus on the sample proportion as the statistic of interest.

Describing the Sampling Distribution of a Sample Proportion

We can describe the sampling distribution of a sample proportion by focusing on the key features of shape, center, and variability. We typically use the mean to describe center and the standard deviation to describe variability. For the sampling distribution of a sample proportion, the mean and standard deviation depend on the sample size n and the population proportion p.

Mean and Standard Deviation of the Sampling Distribution of the Sample Proportion

For a random sample of size n from a population with proportion p of outcomes in a particular category, the sampling distribution of the sample *proportion* in that category has

$$\text{mean} = p \quad \text{and} \quad \text{standard deviation} = \sqrt{\frac{p(1-p)}{n}}.$$

Example 2

Mean and Standard Deviation of a Sampling ◄ Distribution

Exit Poll of California Voters Revisited

Picture the Scenario

Example 1 discussed an exit poll of 3,889 voters for the 2010 California gubernatorial election.

Question to Explore

Election results showed that 53.8% of the population of all voters voted for Brown. What was the mean and standard deviation of the sampling distribution of the sample proportion who voted for him? Interpret these two measures.

Think It Through

For the sample of 3,889 voters, the sample proportion who voted for Brown could be any of the following values: 0, 1/3889, 2/3889, 3/3889,..., 3888/3889, or 1. But some of these values are more likely to occur than others, and the sampling distribution describes the frequency of these values. Now, if we know the population proportion, then we can describe the sampling distribution of the sample proportion more specifically by finding its mean and standard deviation. In this case, the population proportion is $p = 0.538$, so the sampling distribution of the sample proportion has mean $= p = 0.538$ and standard deviation $=$

$$\sqrt{p(1-p)/n} = \sqrt{\frac{(0.538)(0.462)}{3,889}} = 0.008.$$

On average, over many polls of the same size, we expect to observe a sample proportion of 0.538 (i.e., the population proportion), but there is variability around this mean. For example, we might observe a sample proportion of 0.531 or 0.548, both values falling approximately a standard deviation from the mean. In many exit polls of 3,889 voters each, the sample proportion voting for Brown would vary from poll to poll, and the standard deviation of those sample proportion would be 0.008. Figure 7.4 in Activity 1 on page 337 showed this graphically.

Insight

Why would we care about finding a sampling distribution? Because it shows us how close the sample proportion is likely to fall to the population proportion, which is the parameter that we are really interested in. Here, the standard deviation of the sampling distribution is very small (0.008). This small value tells us that with $n = 3,889$, the sample proportion is likely to fall very close to the population proportion.

▶ *Try Exercises 7.3 and 7.5*

Recall

The number of successes in n independent trials, where each trial (vote) can result in two outcomes (Brown, not Brown) and the probability of success is constant ($p = 0.538$) follows a binomial distribution. See Section 6.3. ◀

Recall

For large n, the binomial distribution is approximately normal when the expected number of successes and failures, np and $n(1 - p)$, are both at least 15. Here, $np = 3,889(0.538) = 2,092$, and $n(1 - p) = 3,889(0.462) = 1,797$ are both much larger than 15. ◀

Now that we know the mean and standard deviation of the sampling distribution, what can we say about its shape? Our simulations in Activity 1 show that the possible sample proportions pile up in a bell shape around the population proportion, suggesting a normal distribution. (Both the histogram in Figure 7.3 and the one in Figure 7.4 suggest a normal shape.) This is not surprising. As the margin note recalls, the number of people (out of n randomly sampled) who vote for Brown follows a binomial distribution. And in Section 6.3, we mentioned that for a large sample size n, (i.e., when both np and $n(1 - p)$ are at least 15) the binomial distribution can be well approximated by a normal distribution (see second margin note). Because for large n the *number of people* voting for Brown approximately follows a normal distribution, the *proportion of people* (i.e., the number divided by the sample size n) also approximately follows a normal distribution. The two histograms in Figure 7.5 illustrate this fact.

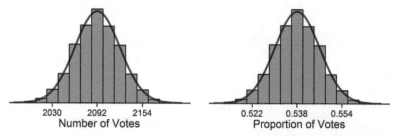

| 2030 | 2092 | 2154 |
| Number of Votes |

| 0.522 | 0.538 | 0.554 |
| Proportion of Votes |

▲ **Figure 7.5** Histogram of the Sampling Distribution for the Number and Proportion of Votes for Brown in Samples of Size $n = 3,889$, Assuming a Population Proportion of $p = 0.538$. Note the identical shape, which is approximately normal as indicated by the superimposed normal curve.

The histogram on the left summarizes the sampling distribution of the *number of people* voting for Brown in samples of size $n = 3,889$ when the population proportion is $p = 0.538$. It has an approximately normal shape. From Section 6.3, we know that the expected number of successes (here: votes for Brown) for a binomial distribution is $np = 3,889(0.538) = 2,092$, so it is no wonder that the distribution is centered at that value. When dividing each possible number of votes for Brown by the sample size 3,889, we obtain all possible proportions of votes. The histogram on the right summarizes the sampling distribution of these sample proportions. We see that the two distributions (one for the number, the other for the proportion of votes) are identical in shape. Note that the sampling distribution for the proportion of votes is centered at $2{,}092/3{,}889 = 0.538$, i.e., the population proportion. Summing up, for large n, **the sampling distribution of the sample proportion is approximately normal** and centered at the population proportion.

Example 3

> **Normal Shape of the Sampling Distribution** ◄

Predicting the Election Outcome

Picture the Scenario

In the exit poll on election day, 53.1% of the 3,889 voters sampled said they voted for Jerry Brown.

Questions to Explore

a. Is it reasonable to assume a normal shape for the sampling distribution of the sample proportion resulting from exit polls such as this one?

b. Given that the actual population proportion supporting Brown was 0.538, what are the values of the sample proportion we would expect to observe from exit polls such as this one? Find an interval in which you would expect about 95% of the possible sample proportions to fall. Almost all possible sample proportions fall within which distance from 0.538?

c. Based on the results of this exit poll, would you have been willing to predict Brown as the winner on election night while the votes were still being counted?

Think It Through

a. Yes. Both np and $n(1 - p)$ are larger than 15. Then, the sampling distribution of the number of votes for Brown and therefore the sampling distribution of the proportion of votes for Brown are approximately normal. In practice, we don't know that a proportion of exactly $p = 0.538$ voted for Brown. Then, it's not unreasonable to assume here that this proportion is about 0.5, in which case np and $n(1 - p)$ are still both much larger than 15.

b. When $p = 0.538$, the normal distribution has, as noted in Example 2, a mean of 0.538 and a standard deviation of 0.008. Figure 7.6 shows the graph for the sampling distribution. Nearly all possible sample proportions will fall within 3 standard deviations of the mean, or within about $3(0.008) = 0.024$ of the mean of 0.538. About 95% of all possible sample proportions fall within 2 standard deviations of the mean, or within the interval $0.538 \pm 2(0.008) = (0.522, 0.554)$.

c. On election night, the polling agency does not know the actual population proportion. However, we know that the expected variability in the sampling distribution of the sample proportion is given by $\sqrt{p(1 - p)/n}$. Our best estimate of the population proportion on election day is the sample proportion from the exit poll. Therefore, we could estimate the expected standard deviation in the sampling distribution by substituting the sample proportion of 0.531 for p and evaluating $\sqrt{(0.531)(0.469)/3{,}889}$, resulting in 0.008. We know that in a bell-shaped distribution, we expect to find nearly 100% of our values within 3 standard deviations of the mean (in this case, the population proportion). If we take the sample proportion 0.531 from the exit poll, then add and subtract 3 standard deviations, we can find a range of plausible values for the actual population proportion as $0.531 \pm 3(0.008)$, which gives 0.507 to 0.555. We observe that all the plausible values estimated for the population proportion of voters who will vote for Brown are above the value of 0.50 and give Brown a majority over

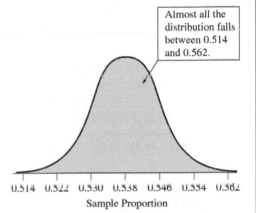

> Almost all the distribution falls between 0.514 and 0.562.

0.514 0.522 0.530 0.538 0.546 0.554 0.562
Sample Proportion

▲ **Figure 7.6** Sampling Distribution of Sample Proportion Voting for Brown in 2010 California Gubernatorial Election. This graph shows where we expect sample proportions to fall for random samples of size $n = 3{,}889$, when the population proportion that voted for Brown is $p = 0.538$. Nearly all the distribution falls between 0.514 and 0.562. We also observe that the likely range of values for the sample proportion lies completely above 0.5, indicating a majority of the votes for Brown. **Question** What would the sampling distribution look like if instead $p = 0.51$? Within what range would the sample proportion then be likely to fall?

any other candidate. Therefore, we would expect the polling agency to tell the TV network it can feel confident in predicting Brown as the winner.

Insight

In this election, when all 9.5 million votes were tallied, 53.8% voted for Brown. The exit poll prediction that he would win was correct. Jerry Brown was elected as California governor.

If the sample proportion favoring Brown had been closer to 0.50, we would have been unwilling to make a prediction. In such cases, TV networks declare the election "too close to call." Also, if the sample proportion of 0.531 were based on a poll of only $n = 800$ voters instead of $n = 3,889$, voters, the likely values for the population proportion would have included values both smaller and larger than 0.5. Then, the election would have also been too close to call. *A smaller sample size creates more variability in the sampling distribution and therefore creates less precision in making a prediction about the actual population proportion.*

▶ **Try Exercise 7.6**

SUMMARY: Sampling Distribution of a Sample Proportion

For a random sample of size n from a population with proportion p, the sampling distribution of the sample proportion has

$$\text{mean} = p \text{ and standard deviation} = \sqrt{\frac{p(1-p)}{n}}.$$

If n is sufficiently large so that the expected numbers of outcomes of the two types, np in the category of interest and $n(1-p)$ not in that category, are both at least 15, then the sampling distribution of a sample proportion is approximately normal.

When we simulated a sampling distribution in Activity 1 for a sample size of 3,889, we found that almost certainly the sample proportion falls within 0.024 of the population proportion $p = 0.538$. We now can see why this happens. We know that the standard deviation of this simulated sampling distribution is

$$\text{Standard deviation} = \sqrt{p(1-p)/n} = \sqrt{(0.538)(0.462)/3,889} = 0.008.$$

Because the simulated sampling distribution is approximately normal, the probability is very close to 1.0 that the sample proportions will fall within 3 standard deviations of 0.538, that is, within $3(0.008) = 0.024$ of 0.538.

In practice, we seldom know the population parameter. An election is an exception in that we eventually know the population parameter. This allows the luxury of being able to compare the actual population proportion to the estimated proportions from surveys before the votes were counted.

In the beginning of this section, we explored the shape of the sampling distribution and its mean and standard deviation by simulating thousands of potential samples and computing the statistic of interest. In practice, typically only **one sample** is taken from the population, not repeated samples. With the results for the sampling distribution developed in this section, this is all that's needed. The formulas for the mean and standard deviation of the sampling distribution only depend on the (unknown) population proportion p, and all we need to estimate p is the information contained in this one sample. We will explore exactly how to use the sampling distribution for making predictions about p in Chapters 8 and 9. Finally, it is important to remember that the results on the sampling distribution are only appropriate for a *randomly* selected sample.

In Practice Exit Polls Use a Multistage Type of Random Sampling

Exit polls use a multistage type of random sampling, not simple random sampling. The standard deviation formulas in this chapter technically apply only to simple random samples. However, they provide good approximations for the standard deviations with many multistage samples and are often used for such sampling schemes.

7.1   Practicing the Basics

7.1   Simulating the exit poll   Using the *Sampling Distribution for the Sample Proportion* app, simulate an exit poll for a referendum that only allowed for a "Yes" and "No" vote. Assume the true proportion of Yes votes in the population is 0.53. Refer to Activity 1 for guidance on using the app.

a. Simulate drawing one random sample of size 100. What sample proportion of Yes votes did you get? Why do you not expect to get exactly 0.53?

b. Simulate drawing 20 more random samples of size 100 by repeatedly clicking on Draw Sample(s). What was the smallest and what was the largest sample proportion you got? (Check Show Summary Statistics of Samp. Distb. to show statistics such as these.)

c. Press Reset and now simulate 10,000 samples of size 100 at once. Use the histogram of the 10,000 sample proportions you generated to describe the sampling distribution (shape, center, variability). (*Note:* The app allows you to save the graph to file.)

d. Use a formula from this section to predict the value of the standard deviation of the sample proportions that you generated in part c. Compare it to the standard deviation of the 10,000 simulated sample proportions stated in the title of the graph.

e. Now move the slider for the population proportion to 0.7, keeping the sample size n at 100. Based on the 10,000 simulations under this scenario, how does the sampling distribution differ from the one in part c?

7.2   Simulate condo solicitations   A company that is selling condos in Florida plans to send out an advertisement for the condos to 500 potential customers, in which they promise a free weekend at a resort on the Florida coast in exchange for agreeing to attend a four-hour sales presentation. The company would like to know how many people will accept this invitation. Its best guess is that 10% of customers will accept the offer. The company wants to use simulations to find the likely range for the proportion of the 500 customers who are actually going to accept the offer under this assumption. Simulate this scenario for the company, using the *Sampling Distribution for the Sample Proportion* app. Click on Enter Numerical Values and enter 500 for n. Refer to Activity 1 for guidance on using the app.

a. Perform one simulation. What sample proportion did you get? Why do you not expect to get exactly 0.10?

b. Now simulate at least 10,000 times. Describe the graph representing the simulated sampling distribution of the sample proportion values. Does it seem likely that the sample proportion will fall close to 10%, say within 5 percentage points of 10%? (*Note:* An option in the app allows you to zoom in on the *x*-axis.)

7.3   Condo sample distribution   Consider the sampling distribution you were simulating in parts a and b of the previous exercise, assuming a true proportion of $p = 0.10$. Using the appropriate formulas from this section, find the

mean and the standard deviation of the sampling distribution of the sample proportion:

a. For a random sample of size $n = 500$, as in that exercise.

b. For a random sample of size $n = 2,000$.

c. For a random sample of size $n = 125$. Summarize the effect of the sample size on the magnitude of the standard deviation.

7.4   iPhone apps   The iPhone maker Apple announces that 25% of iPhone owners use a certain app. Let X be a binary random variable that equals 1 if a randomly selected iPhone owner uses this particular app, and 0 otherwise.

a. State the population distribution of X using the information Apple provides. (That is, give the proportion of times that you expect a randomly selected owner to use or not use the app.)

b. For a random sample of 50 iPhone owners, 30 use the app. State the data distribution for X based on this sample.

c. Find the mean of the sampling distribution of the sample proportion who use the app in a random sample of 50 owners.

d. Find the standard deviation of the sampling distribution of the sample proportion who use the app in a random sample of 50 owners.

e. Explain what the standard deviation in part d describes.

7.5   Other scenario for exit poll   Refer to Examples 1 and 2 about the exit poll, for which the sample size was 3,889. In that election, 40.9% voted for Whitman.

a. Define a binary random variable X taking values 0 and 1 that represents the vote for a particular voter (1 = vote for Whitman and 0 = not a vote for Whitman). State the population distribution of X.

b. Find the mean and standard deviation of the sampling distribution of the proportion of the 3,889 people in the sample who voted for Whitman.

7.6   Exit poll and *n*   Refer to the previous exercise.

a. In part b, if the sampling distribution of the sample proportion had mean 0.409 and standard deviation 0.008, give an interval of values within which the sample proportion will almost certainly fall. (*Hint:* Use the fact that the sampling distribution is bell shaped.)

b. The sample proportion for Whitman from the exit poll was 0.424. Using part a, was this one of the plausible values expected in an exit poll? Why?

7.7   Delays at airport   During the month of January 2017, a total of 29,544 flights took off from the Atlanta International Airport. Of all these flights, 23.9% had a departure delay of more than 10 minutes. If we were to randomly sample just 100 of these flights:

a. What sample proportion should we expect to see in such a sample, and how much should we expect the proportion to vary from sample to sample in samples of size 100?

b. What is the approximate shape of the sampling distribution of the sample proportion of flights delayed by more than 10 minutes in samples of size 100? Why?

c. Would it be unusual for us to observe a sample proportion of 40% or higher of delayed flights? Why or why not?

d. Of all the flights scheduled to leave the airport in January 2017, 2% got canceled. If we were to randomly sample just 100 of all flights scheduled to leave the airport, would the sampling distribution of the sample proportion of canceled flights have an approximate normal shape? Why or why not?

7.8 **Relative frequency of heads** Construct the sampling distribution of the sample proportion of heads obtained in the experiment of flipping a balanced coin:

a. Once. (*Hint:* The possible sample proportion values are 0, if the flip is a tail, and 1 if the flip is a head. What are their probabilities?)

b. Twice. (*Hint:* The possible samples are {HH, HT, TH, TT}, so the possible sample proportion values are 0, 0.50, and 1.0, corresponding to 0, 1, or 2 heads. What are their probabilities?)

c. Three times. (*Hint:* There are 8 possible samples.)

d. Refer to parts a–c. Sketch the sampling distributions and describe how the shape is changing as the number of flips n increases.

7.9 **Experimental medication** As part of a drug research study, patients suffering from arthritis take an experimental pain relief medication. Suppose that 25% of all patients who take the new drug experience a certain side effect. For a given patient, let X be either 1 or 0, depending on whether the patient experienced the side effect, respectively.

a. If $n = 3$ patients take the drug, find the probability distribution of the proportion who will experience the side effect. (*Hint:* List all possible values for the sample proportion and their chances of occurring.)

b. Referring to part a, what are the mean and standard deviation of the sample proportion?

c. Repeat part b for a group of $n = 10$ patients and $n = 100$ patients. What happens to the mean and standard deviation of the sample proportion as n increases?

7.10 **Effect of n on sample proportion** The figure illustrates two sampling distributions for sample proportions when the population proportion $p = 0.50$.

a. Find the standard deviation for the sampling distribution of the sample proportion with (i) $n = 100$ and (ii) $n = 1,000$.

b. Explain why the sample proportion would be very likely (as the figure suggests) to fall (i) between 0.35 and 0.65 when $n = 100$, and (ii) between 0.45 and 0.55 when $n = 1,000$. (*Hint:* Recall that for an approximately normal distribution, nearly the entire distribution is within 3 standard deviations of the mean.)

c. Explain how the results in part b indicate that the sample proportion tends to estimate the population proportion more precisely when the sample size is larger.

7.11 **Syracuse full-time students** You'd like to estimate the proportion of the 14,201 undergraduate students at Syracuse University who are full-time students. You poll a random sample of 350 students, of whom 330 are fulltime. Unknown to you, the proportion of all undergraduate students who are full-time students is 0.951. Let X denote a random variable for which $x = 1$ denotes fulltime student and for which $x = 0$ denotes part-time student.

a. Describe the population distribution. Sketch a graph representing the population distribution.

b. Describe the data distribution. Sketch a graph representing the data distribution.

c. Find the mean and standard deviation of the sampling distribution of the sample proportion for a sample of size 350. Explain what this sampling distribution represents. Sketch a graph representing this sampling distribution.

d. Use the *Sampling Distribution for the Sample Proportion* app to check your answers from parts a through c. Set the population proportion equal to $p = 0.951$ and the sample size $n = 350$. Compare the population, data, and sampling distribution graph from the app with your graphs from parts a through c.

7.12 **Gender distributions** At a university, 60% of the 7,400 students identify as female. The student newspaper reports results of a survey of a random sample of 50 students about various topics involving alcohol abuse, such as participation in binge drinking. They report that in their sample, 26 students identified as female.

a. Explain how you can set up a binary random variable X to represent whether a student identifies as female.

b. Identify the population distribution of the random variable at this university. Sketch a graph.

c. Identify the data distribution of this variable for this sample. Sketch a graph.

d. Identify the sampling distribution of the sample proportion of students who identify as female in the sample. State its mean and standard deviation for a random sample of size 50. Sketch a graph.

e. Use the *Sampling Distribution for the Sample Proportion* app to check your answers from parts b through d. Set the population proportion equal to $p = 0.60$ and the sample size $n = 50$. Compare the population, data, and sampling distribution graph from the app with your graphs from parts b through d.

7.13 Shapes of distributions

a. With random sampling, does the shape of the data distribution tend to resemble more closely the sampling distribution or the population distribution? Explain.

b. Is the sampling distribution of the sample proportion always bell shaped? Investigate with the *Sampling Distribution for the Sample Proportion* app by setting $n = 30$ and increasing the population proportion p from 0.5 to 0.95. What do you observe?

c. Why is it inappropriate to assume a bell shape for the sampling distribution of the sample proportion when $p = 0.95$ and $n = 30$?

7.14 Student government election   A student running for a position in student government believes that 55% of the student body will vote for her. However, she is worried about low voter turnout.

a. Assuming she truly has 55% support in the entire student body, find the mean and standard deviation for the sampling distribution of the proportion of votes she will receive if only $n = 200$ students show up for voting.

b. Is it reasonable to assume a normal shape for this sampling distribution? Explain.

c. How likely is it that she will not get the majority of the vote, i.e., a sample proportion of 50% or lower from the 200 votes cast?

d. If instead $n = 1,000$ students show up for voting, how likely is it then that she will not win the majority?

7.2 How Sample Means Vary Around the Population Mean

Recall

Population Distribution: The distribution of the variable of interest in the population from which we sample.

Data Distribution: The distribution of the variable of interest computed from the sample and the distribution we see in practice.

Sampling Distribution: The distribution of the sample statistic (e.g., sample proportion or sample mean) we would get when repeatedly drawing samples of size n from the population. ◄

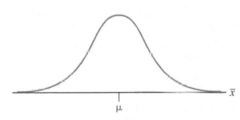

The sampling distribution of $\bar{x}$: The sample mean $\bar{x}$ fluctuates from sample to sample around the population mean μ.

The previous section discussed three types of distributions: the population distribution, the data distribution, and the sampling distribution (see the Recall box in the margin). The sampling distribution is a probability distribution for the possible values of a statistic. We learned how much a sample proportion can vary from sample to sample. Because the sample mean is another commonly used statistic to summarize numerical (quantitative) data, we'll now pay special attention to the sampling distribution of the sample mean. We'll discover results allowing us to predict how close a particular sample mean $\bar{x}$ falls to the population mean μ.

As with the sampling distribution of the sample proportion, there are two main results about the sampling distribution of the sample mean:

- One result provides formulas for the mean and standard deviation of the sampling distribution.
- The other indicates that for large n its shape is approximately a normal distribution, as we observed in the previous section for the sample proportion.

Let's use the *Sampling Distribution for the Sample Mean* app to investigate these properties. Now, the variable of interest is a quantitative variable (for which we want to find the mean), not a binary one (for which we found a proportion).

Simulating the Sampling Distribution of the Sample Mean

How much might a sample mean vary from sample to sample? How would you describe the shape, center, and variability of the possible values? To answer these questions, we'll again use simulations to see how the sampling distribution arises and what its shape could be, similar to Activity 1 in the previous section.

▶ Activity 2

Simulating the Sampling Distribution of the Sample Mean from a Bell-Shaped Population Distribution

We'll use the *Sampling Distribution for the Sample Mean (Continuous Population)* app from the book's website to simulate selecting random samples of a given size from a population. When you open this app, you can choose from a variety of different population distributions to sample from. For this activity, we are going to select the distribution of the height in the population of **all** 18,159 professional soccer players listed in FIFA19, a popular video game based on actual soccer player characteristics.

In the app, keep the default selection of Real Population Data for the type of population distribution in the first drop-down menu, but select Height of Soccer Players from the second drop-down menu. The app will now show the population distribution for the height of all 18,159 male soccer players listed in FIFA19[1] as a smooth curve. As you can see from the screenshot in Figure 7.7 (top plot), the distribution of heights is roughly bell shaped, with population mean $\mu = 181$ cm and population standard deviation $\sigma = 7$ cm, rounded to the nearest cm. (These are the mean and standard deviation for the heights of all 18,159 players in the population.)

What would happen if we take a random sample of just 20 of these 18,159 soccer players? In the app, keep the slider for the sample size n at 20 and the selection of generating one sample (of size 20) at a time. Figure 7.7 shows what happens if you press the Draw Sample(s) button once, thereby generating one random sample (of size 20) from the population of all soccer players. The data distribution (middle plot in Figure 7.7) shows the histogram of the 20 height values obtained from that sample, which had a sample mean of 184 cm, not too far from the population mean of 181 cm. (Your results will likely differ.)

Perform this simulation of drawing one sample of size 20 several (e.g., 50) times by repeatedly clicking the Draw Sample(s) button. Each time, a new random sample of 20 players is selected from the population of all players and the data distribution will update showing the last sample generated. With each click, observe how close (or far) the sample mean (indicated by the blue triangle) falls from the population mean (indicated by the orange half-circle). The bottom plot in the app keeps track of all the sample means you generate. Watch how a histogram for the generated sample means is slowly building up piece by piece as you repeatedly press the Generate Sample(s) button. This histogram will eventually show an approximation for the sampling distribution for the sample mean.

To get a better idea of the shape of this sampling distribution, we need to generate many thousands of samples. In the app, click the button for 10,000 for the number of samples to

▶ **Figure 7.7** Simulation Results when Taking One Sample of Size $n = 20$ from a Bell-Shaped Population Distribution of Soccer Player Heights. Screenshot from the *Sampling Distribution for the Sample Mean* app. The top plot shows the population distribution for the height of 18,159 soccer players listed in FIFA19, with a population mean height of 181 cm. The second plot shows a histogram displaying the data distribution for the heights obtained in one random sample of size 20 from the population. These 20 observations have a sample mean of $\bar{x} = 184$ cm. The third plot at the bottom keeps track of the sample means generated.

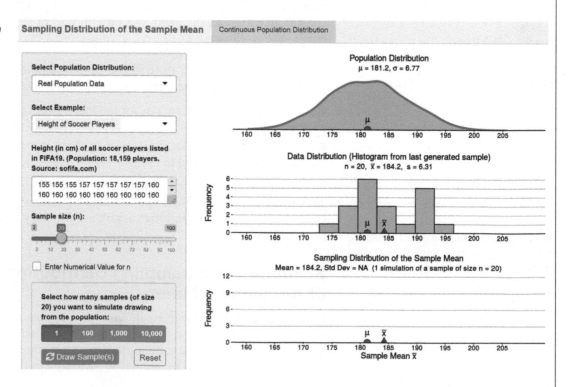

▶ **Figure 7.8** Simulation Results when Taking 10,050 Samples, Each of Size *n* = 20, from a Bell-Shaped Population Distribution of Soccer Player Heights. Screenshot from the *Sampling Distribution for the Sample Mean* app. The bottom plot shows the histogram of all 10,050 sample means generated. It represents the sampling distribution of the sample mean when taking random samples of size 20 from the population of soccer players. The 10,050 generated sample means have a mean of 181 cm and a standard deviation of 1.5 cm.

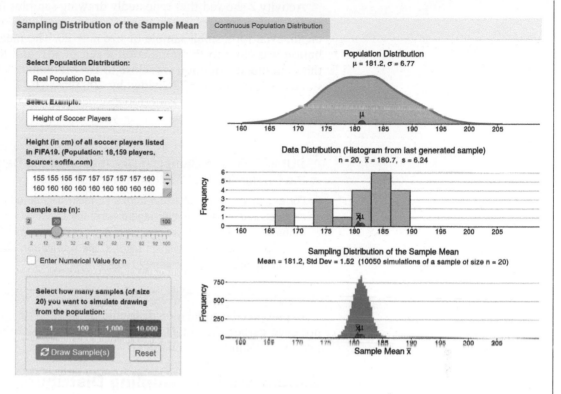

generate. When clicking Generate Sample(s) now, this will generate 10,000 random samples at once. Figure 7.8 shows the results we got. Judging from the histogram, the sampling distribution for the sample mean is bell shaped (roughly normal) and centered at the population mean of 181. In fact, as shown in the subtitle, the average of all the generated sample means equals 181. The variability of the sampling distribution (with a standard deviation of 1.5 cm and almost all values falling between about 177 cm and 187 cm) is noticeably smaller than the variability in the population distribution (with a population standard deviation of 7 cm and values ranging between about 160 cm and 200 cm). This illustrates that the sample mean varies much less than the population values.

Next, let's explore what happens when we take a sample of size *n* = 100 instead of 20. Move the slider for the sample size slowly from 20 to 100. Observe how the shape of the sampling distribution is changing as the sample size increases. Figure 7.9 shows the final result, where we superimposed the normal distribution to indicate that the shape of the sampling distribution is approximately normal.

For this activity, we used the soccer player heights for the population distribution. Try other examples for population distributions that are roughly bell shaped, such as the annual average cost of attending college for the population of 1,909

public and private four-year U.S. colleges, or the population distribution called "bell shaped," where you can enter your own population mean and standard deviation to create a bell-shaped distribution. After you generate thousands of samples from such a distribution, use the slider for the sample size *n* to see how the shape of the sampling distribution changes as the sample size increases.

▲ **Figure 7.9** Simulated Sampling Distribution of the Sample Mean When Taking Samples of Size 100. The simulations suggest an approximate normal shape for the sampling distribution. **Question** With a mean of 181 cm and a standard deviation of 0.7 cm, find an interval within which almost all sample means of size 100 will fall.

Try Exercises 7.15 and 7.30 b ◀

Activity 2 showed that repeatedly drawing samples from a bell-shaped population distribution results in a bell-shaped sampling distribution for the sample mean, even for a small sample of size $n = 20$. The mean of the sampling distribution was close to the population mean of 181, and the standard deviation of the sampling distribution was close to 1.5. Mathematically, this is the population standard deviation of 6.77 divided by $\sqrt{n}$; that is, $6.77/\sqrt{20} = 1.5$. Under the assumption that the bell-shaped population distribution is normal, we can state the following result in the next summary box.

SUMMARY: The Sampling Distribution of the Sample Mean When the Population Distribution is Normal

For a random sample of size n from a normally distributed population having mean μ and standard deviation σ, then regardless of the sample size n, the sampling distribution of the sample mean $\bar{x}$ is also normally distributed, with mean equal to the **population mean** μ and standard deviation equal to **the population standard deviation divided by the square root of the sample size,** $\sigma/\sqrt{n}$.

In practice, the population distribution of a variable is often not normal and may not even be bell-shaped. How will this affect the shape of the sampling distribution? Will it still have a bell shape?

Simulating the Sampling Distribution for a Sample Mean from a Non-Bell-Shaped Distribution

The simulation in Activity 2 for the sample mean with $n = 20$ showed a bell shape for the sampling distribution. This was not too surprising since we were sampling from a population distribution with a bell shape. Is it typical for sampling distributions of a sample mean to have bell shapes even if the population distribution is not bell shaped?

Example 4

Skewed Population Distribution ◄

Airbnb in New York City

Picture the Scenario

Let's look at a scenario in which the population distribution is highly skewed. Consider the price for renting a room in New York City via the popular platform Airbnb. At one point in 2019, there were a total of 47,660 rooms (including entire homes) listed for rent on this platform that were below $500 per day. The top graph in Figure 7.10 shows the population distribution of the room price for these 47,660 listings. The figure is a screenshot from the *Sampling Distribution for the Sample Mean (Continuous Population)* app, and you can access this population distribution by selecting New York Airbnb Prices for the examples under Real Population Data.[2]

Suppose we take a random sample of just 50 of the 47,660 listings for New York City from the Airbnb website. In the app, you can do this by setting the slider for the sample size to 50 and pressing the Generate Sample(s) button. The middle plot in Figure 7.10 shows the histogram for the price based on such a generated sample of size 50, which resulted in a sample mean of $133.

---

[2] Data from insideairbnb.com

▶ **Figure 7.10** Simulation Results when Taking 10,000 Samples, each of Size *n* = 50 From a Skewed Population Distribution of Airbnb Room Prices. Screenshot from the *Sampling Distribution for the Sample Mean (Continuous Population)* app. The top plot shows the population distribution with $\mu = 130$ (orange semicircle) and $\sigma = 85$. The middle plot shows the data distribution based on one sample of size 50, resulting in a sample mean of 133 (blue triangle). The blue histogram at the bottom shows the simulated sampling distribution of all 10,000 sample means. These 10,000 sample means have a mean of 13 and a standard deviation of 12.

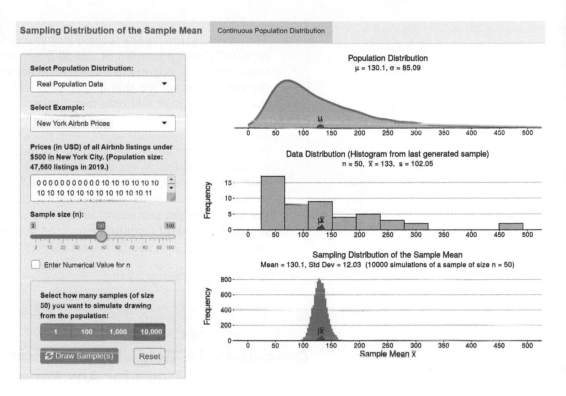

To get a feel for how the sample mean varies when taking samples of size 50 from such a population, we repeat this process of drawing a sample of size 50 and computing the sample mean many times (such as 10,000 times). The bottom plot in Figure 7.10 shows a histogram of the 10,000 generated sample means for samples of size 50. It represents an approximation of the sampling distribution of the sample mean.

Questions to Explore

a. Identify the population distribution and describe its shape, mean, and standard deviation.

b. Identify the data distribution and describe its shape, mean, and standard deviation.

c. Identify the sampling distribution of $\bar{x}$ and describe its shape, mean, and standard deviation.

Think It Through

a. The *population distribution* is the distribution of the room prices for all 47,660 listings on Airbnb (represented by the smooth curve in the first plot of Figure 7.10). You can think of it as the distribution of the random variable X = price of a room listed on Airbnb costing $500 or less. The distribution is skewed to the right with a very long tail for those relatively few listings that charge room prices in excess of $200. The mean population room price is μ = $130 (indicated by the orange semicircle) and the population standard deviation of the room prices is σ = $85.

b. The *data distribution* shows the distribution of the 50 values in one of the samples generated (here, the last sample generated). It is represented by the histogram for the 50 prices and similar in shape to the population distribution, being right skewed. The data distribution is described by a sample mean of $133 (indicated by the blue triangle in Figure 7.10) and a sample standard deviation of $102. These values are shown in the subtitle of the data distribution plot.

c. The *sampling distribution* is the distribution of the sample mean when repeatedly taking samples of size 50 from the population. It is represented by the histogram of the 10,000 generated sample means. From the simulation, we see that it is roughly bell shaped, despite the fact that the population and data distributions are right skewed. The histogram is centered at $130, which is the population mean (indicated by the orange semicircle in all three plots of Figure 7.10). It displays much less variability compared to the population distribution. The standard deviation in the population is $\sigma = \$85$, whereas the standard deviation of the 10,000 simulated sample means is $12, which is $\sigma/\sqrt{n} = 85/\sqrt{50} = 12$. All this suggests that the theoretical sampling distribution of the sample mean has (i) mean equal to the population mean, (ii) standard deviation equal to the population standard deviation divided by $\sqrt{n}$, and (iii) a bell shape.

▶ **Try Exercises 7.19 and 7.21**

Describing the Behavior of the Sampling Distribution of the Sample Mean for Any Population

Example 4 showed a surprising result: Even when a population distribution is not bell shaped but rather skewed, the *sampling distribution* of the sample mean $\bar{x}$ can have a bell shape. We also observe from our simulations that the mean of the sampling distribution appears to be the same as the population mean μ, and the standard deviation of the sampling distribution appears to be $\dfrac{\sigma}{\sqrt{n}}$.

These observations lead to the following result for the mean and standard deviation of the sampling distribution of the sample mean:

> ### Mean and Standard Deviation of the Sampling Distribution of the Sample Mean $\bar{x}$
>
> For a random sample of size n from a population having mean μ and standard deviation σ, the sampling distribution of the sample mean $\bar{x}$ has mean equal to the **population mean** μ and standard deviation equal to the **standard deviation of the population divided by the square root of the sample size,** i.e., $\dfrac{\sigma}{\sqrt{n}}$.

Sampling Distribution of the Sample Mean
Mean = 130.1, Std Dev = 12.03 (10000 simulations of a sample of size n = 50)

Screenshot from the *Sampling Distribution for the Sample Mean (Continuous Population)* app.

The bell shape of the sampling distribution the we observed in Example 4 is a consequence of the **Central Limit Theorem (CLT)**. It states that for a sufficiently large sample size n, the sampling distribution of the sample mean $\bar{x}$ has an approximate normal distribution. This result applies no matter what the shape of the population distribution from which the samples are taken, provided the sample size is large enough. We observed this in Example 4, where the population distribution of room prices was highly skewed, yet the sampling distribution of samples of size 50 was bell shaped. (See the margin figure, where we have overlaid the normal distribution over the histogram of the sampling distribution from Figure 7.10).

These observations lead to the following result about the shape of the sampling distribution of the sample mean:

> **The Central Limit Theorem (CLT): Describes the Shape of the Sampling Distribution for the Sample Mean $\bar{x}$**
>
> For a random sample of size n from a population having mean μ and standard deviation σ, as the sample size n increases, the sampling distribution of the sample mean $\bar{x}$ approaches a normal distribution.

What is amazing about the Central Limit Theorem is that *no matter what the shape of the population distribution*, the sampling distribution of the sample mean approaches a normal distribution as the sample size increases. In fact, for most population distributions, the normal distribution is approached very quickly as the sample size n increases. Thus, when the sample size is large enough, we don't need to worry about the shape of the population distribution in order to work with the sampling distribution of the sample mean.

Figure 7.11 displays sampling distributions of the sample mean $\bar{x}$ for five different shapes for the population distribution from which samples are taken. The population shapes are shown at the top of the figure; below them are portrayed the sampling distributions of $\bar{x}$ for random samples of sizes $n = 2, 5,$ and 30. Even if the population distribution itself is uniform (column 1 of the figure) or V shaped (column 2) or skewed (column 3) or bimodal (column 4), the sampling distribution of the sample mean has approximately a bell shape when n is at least 30 and sometimes for n as small as 5. In addition, the variability of the sampling distribution noticeably decreases as n increases, because the standard deviation of the sampling distribution decreases.

If the population distribution is normally distributed, then the sampling distribution is normally distributed no matter what the sample size. The rightmost column of Figure 7.11 shows this case.

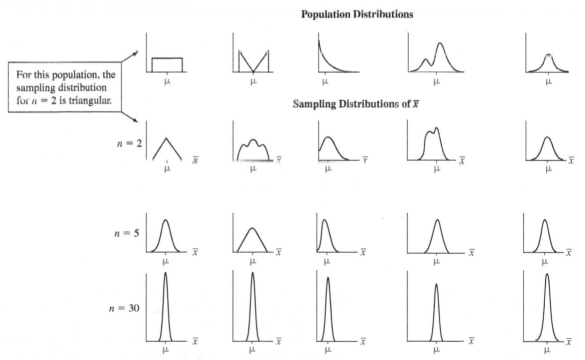

▲ **Figure 7.11** Five Population Distributions and the Corresponding Sampling Distributions of $\bar{x}$. Regardless of the shape of the population distribution, the sampling distribution becomes more bell shaped as the sample size n increases. You can use the *Sampling Distribution for the Sample Mean (Continuous Population)* app to choose various shapes for the population distribution (including the ones shown here) and simulate the shape of the sampling distribution. See Activity 3 and Exercises 7.28, 7.29, and 7.30.

> ▶ **Activity 3**

Exploring the Central Limit Theorem via Simulation

To see what we mean by the sampling distribution approaching a normal distribution as the sample size *n* increases, let's use the *Sampling Distribution for the Sample Mean (Continuous Population)* app with the scenario from Example 4. However, let's first just take a random sample of size *n* = 15 from the 47,660 listings on the Airbnb website. In the app, choose the New York Airbnb Prices for the example under Real Population Distributions, set the slider for *n* to 15, select to generate 10,000 random samples at once and press the Draw Sample(s) button. What is the shape of the resulting simulated sampling distribution?

As you can see from the app, it already looks bell shaped, although you can detect just a bit of a right skew. The first graph in Figure 7.12 shows a screenshot of this sampling distribution,

with a normal curve superimposed that doesn't quite fit. The Central Limit Theorem tells us that the sampling distribution approaches a normal distribution as the sample size gets larger, so let's move the slider for the sample size from 15 to 50. Do this slowly to see how the sampling distribution more and more resembles a normal distribution. The middle plot in Figure 7.12 shows the sampling distribution when *n* = 50, which now seems to follow the normal distribution quite closely. We say that the sampling distribution is **approximately normal**. As we increase the sample size further, let's say to 150, the approximation is getting even better. In the app, first bring the slider all the way to 100 to observe how the shape changes, then click on Enter Numeric Value for *n* and type in 150. The third graph in Figure 7.12 shows what you will see. The sampling distribution now almost perfectly follows that of a normal distribution. (In the app, you can click on Select Range of *x*-Axis (Zoom In) to further zoom into the graph.)

▲ **Figure 7.12 The Central Limit Theorem in Action.** Screenshots from the *Sampling Distribution for the Sample Mean* app for the New York Airbnb Prices example. As the sample size increases from *n* = 15 (left graph) to *n* = 50 (middle graph) to *n* = 150 (right graph), the sampling distribution of the sample mean approaches an approximate normal distribution.

Extremely skewed population distributions

For even more **extremely skewed** population distributions, we need a larger *n* for the sampling distribution to be approximately normal. In the app, select the example Delay of Flights Leaving ATL, which shows the departure delay of all 29,544 flights that left Atlanta International Airport in the month of January 2017. The population distribution of the delay time is extremely right skewed. The population mean is 15 minutes with a standard deviation of 55 minutes, but a few flights were delayed by an extremely long time, up to 1,470 minutes, which is approximately 24 hours. (In the app, you can scroll through all delay times, sorted from smallest to largest.) For this extremely skewed distribution, sampling 150 flights results in a sampling distribution that is still a bit skewed. Here, one needs a sample size of about 1,000 flights for the sampling distribution to become approximately normal. (Make sure you click on Select Range of *x*-Axis (Zoom In) to zoom into the graph.)

Discrete population distributions

Finally, the Central Limit Theorem does not just apply to continuous variables and populations, it also applies to **discrete**

ones. For instance, let *X* denote the number of Amazon stars (ranging from 1 to 5 stars) that the Fitbit Charge HR, a wireless activity wristband that measures heart rates, receives on Amazon.com. Consider the more than 40,000 reviewers who rated this product as the population. Then, based on their reviews, the population distribution of *X* is given by $P(1) = 0.23$, $P(2) = 0.11$, $P(3) = 0.11$, $P(4) = 0.13$, and $P(5) = 0.42$. This population distribution is preloaded in the *Sampling Distribution for the Sample Mean (Discrete Population)* app, as shown in the top graph of the screenshot in Figure 7.13. The mean, variance, and standard deviation of this population distribution are (using formulas from Section 6.1)

$$\mu = \sum xP(x) = 1(0.23) + 2(0.11) + 3(0.11) + 4(0.13) + 5(0.42) = 3.4,$$

$$\sigma^2 = \sum (x - \mu)^2 P(x) = (1 - 3.4)^2(0.23) + (2 - 3.4)^2(0.11) + (3 - 3.4)^2(0.11) + (4 - 3.4)^2(0.13) + (5 - 3.4)^2(0.42) = 2.68,$$

and

$$\sigma = \sqrt{\sigma^2} = \sqrt{2.68} = 1.64.$$

Suppose we take a random sample of just 30 of the more than 40,000 star reviews. Use the app to get an idea about the

► **Figure 7.13** The Central Limit Theorem for Discrete Variables. Screenshot from the *Sampling Distribution for the Sample Mean (Discrete Population)* app. Although the discrete population distribution of the number of stars has a U shape, the sampling distribution of the sample mean number of stars in a random sample of size 30 has an approximate normal shape.

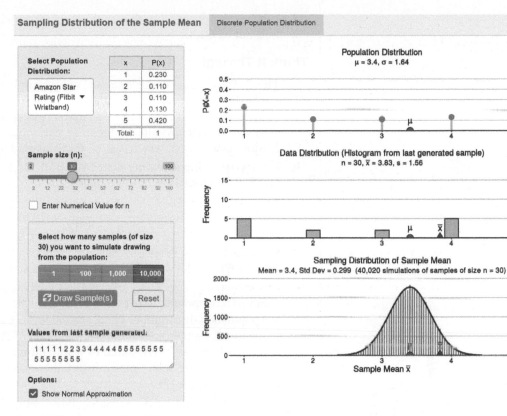

possible values for the sample mean number of stars for such a sample by moving the slider for the sample size to 30 and pressing Draw Sample(s) a couple of times. Then, select to generate 10,000 samples at once and press Draw Sample(s) a few more times. Look at the histogram of all the generated sample means that approximates the sampling distribution.

What is its shape? Figure 7.13 shows that it is approximately normal, centered at the population mean of 3.4 stars and with a standard deviation of $\sigma/\sqrt{n} = 1.64/\sqrt{30} = 0.299$ stars, exactly as predicted by the Central Limit Theorem.

Try Exercises 7.28 and 7.29 ◄

Example 5

Sampling Distribution ◄
of the Sample Mean

Average Salary

Picture the Scenario

Each winter season, Peter works numerous shifts as a waiter in a mountain resort in Austria. His salary (including tips) varies from shift to shift depending on the time (e.g., breakfast, lunch, dinner) or whether the shift falls on a weekday or weekend. The resort manager told Peter that he can expect to earn €150 per shift, but that the salary may vary a lot from shift to shift, as evidenced by a standard deviation of €60.

At the end of each season, Peter randomly selects pay stubs from 32 shifts he worked that season and computes the average salary per shift.

Questions to Explore

a. Around which euro value would you expect his average salary per shift to fluctuate?

b. How much variability would you expect in the average salaries from one season to the next? Find the standard deviation of the sampling distribution of the sample mean and interpret it.

c. Between what values do you expect about 95% of his average salaries to fall over many seasons?

d. What is the probability that there is a season when his average salary falls below €130?

Think It Through

a. The average salary Peter computes is a sample mean (a statistic), obtained from the random sample of $n = 32$ pay stubs for a particular season. We would expect these sample means (one for each winter season) to fluctuate around the mean (a parameter) of the assumed population distribution, which is $\mu = €150$, as told by the resort manager.

b. From part a, the sampling distribution of the sample mean has mean €150. Its standard deviation equals

$$\frac{\sigma}{\sqrt{n}} = \frac{60}{\sqrt{32}} = 10.6.$$

Over the seasons, Peter's average salary per shift would vary around the value of €150, with variability described by the standard deviation of €10.6.

c. For a sample of size 32, we expect the sampling distribution of a sample mean to be approximately bell shaped, regardless of the actual shape of the population distribution. Then, around 95% of the average salaries will fall within 2 standard deviations of the mean of that distribution, that is, within $2(10.6) = 21$ (rounded to whole numbers) of 150. So, we can expect his average salary per shift to fall between 150 ± 21, that is, between €129 and €171.

d. By the CLT, because 32 is a fairly large sample size, we may assume that the sampling distribution is approximately normal, with mean 150 and standard deviation 10.6. Then, the probability for a mean salary below 130 is the area below 130 under this normal distribution. As demonstrated in Chapter 6, we can use technology (such as the *Normal Distribution* app) or Table A in the appendix (with a z-score of $z = (130 - 150)/10.6 = -1.89$) to find that this area is equal to 2.94%. Note that we need to use the standard deviation of the sampling distribution (10.6) and not the standard deviation of the population distribution (60) for this calculation because the question is about where the average falls, not where an individual observation falls.

Insight

Figure 7.14 portrays a possible population distribution for Peter's salary per shift that is quite irregular, but right skewed and unimodal, centered at €150. The figure also indicates the sampling distribution of the average salary per

Sampling Distribution (mean = 150, standard deviation = 10.6)

Population Distribution ($\mu = 150$, $\sigma = 60$)

▲ **Figure 7.14** Salaries per Shift and the Sampling Distribution of Average Salaries Over 32 Shifts in a Season. There is more variability in the salaries from shift to shift (purple distribution) than in the average salaries from season to season (blue distribution).

shift over many seasons. Clearly, there is less variability in the average salary per shift from season to season than there is in the salary from shift to shift (as portrayed by the population distribution).

Even if you believe the graph depicted for the population distribution is unrealistic and should be more right skewed or even bimodal (after all, shifts on weekends or during holidays may bring in substantially more salary and tips), results will not change. This is because our sample size of 32 is large enough for the CLT to hold and we actually don't need to know the precise shape of the population distribution.

▶ *Try Exercises 7.16 and 7.22*

The Standard Deviation of the Sampling Distribution

Recall

From Section 1.2, the margin of error tells us how close we expect an estimate to fall to the true population parameter. ◀

One of the most useful results of this chapter on sampling distributions is that we now have a way to find the **variability** of a statistic such as the sample proportion or the sample mean. This will help us in our goal, articulated in Chapter 1, of assessing how close a statistic falls to the unknown population parameter and computing the margin of error. For sample proportions, the standard deviation of the sampling distribution is equal to $\sqrt{\dfrac{p(1-p)}{n}} = \dfrac{\sqrt{p(1-p)}}{\sqrt{n}}$, and for sample means, the standard deviation of the sampling distribution is given by $\dfrac{\sigma}{\sqrt{n}}$. For both cases, notice that as the sample size n increases, the denominator increases and the standard deviation becomes smaller. This relationship has an important practical implication: **With larger samples, a sample statistic tends to fall closer to the respective population parameter.** With the formulas above, once we estimate p or σ, we will know just how close the statistic will tend to fall.

In Practice We Rarely Know the Exact Characteristics of the Population Distribution

Rarely does a researcher know the exact characteristics of the population distribution (shape, mean, and standard deviation). With random sampling, we hope that the data distribution will look similar to the population distribution. In the next chapter, we show how in practice the statistician uses the data distribution to estimate the mean and standard deviation of the population distribution. In turn, we can use the sample standard deviation from the data distribution to estimate the standard deviation of the sampling distribution of the sample mean. This standard deviation helps us predict how close the sample mean falls to the population mean.

The Central Limit Theorem Helps Us Make Inferences

Sampling distributions are fundamental to statistical inference for making decisions and predictions about populations based on sample data. The Central Limit Theorem and the formula for the standard deviation of the sample mean $\bar{x}$ have many implications. These include the following:

- When the sampling distribution of the sample mean $\bar{x}$ is approximately normal, $\bar{x}$ falls within 2 standard deviations of the population mean μ with probability close to 0.95, and $\bar{x}$ almost certainly falls within 3 standard deviations of μ. Results of this type are vital to inferential methods that predict how close sample statistics fall to unknown population parameters, as expressed through the margin of error.

- For large n, the sampling distribution is approximately normal even if the population distribution is not. This enables us to make inferences about population means regardless of the shape of the population distribution. This is helpful in practice because usually we don't know the shape of the population distribution. Often, it is quite skewed, as in Example 4 (distribution of room prices) or Activity 3 (distribution of star ratings).

Using the fundamental concepts we have learned in this chapter for the sampling distribution of a sample proportion and for the sampling distribution of a sample mean will allow us to develop inference procedures for population proportions and population means in the upcoming chapters.

7.2 Practicing the Basics

7.15 **Simulate taking midterms** Assume that the distribution of the score on a recent midterm is bell shaped with population mean $\mu = 70$ and population standard deviation $\sigma = 10$. You randomly sample $n = 12$ students who took the midterm. Using the *Sampling Distribution for the Sample Mean (Continuous Population)* app, select Bell-Shaped as the population distribution from the top drop-down menu and

a. Simulate drawing one random sample of size 12. What sample mean score did you get? Why do you not expect to get exactly 70?

b. Now, press Reset and simulate drawing 10,000 samples of size 12 at once. Describe the simulated sampling distribution by using the histogram of the 10,000 sample means you generated. (*Note:* The app allows you to save the graph to a file.)

c. Suppose the population standard deviation actually is only half as much, e.g., 5 instead of 10. Change to this setting in the app. How does the simulated sampling distribution of the sample mean change?

7.16 **Education of the self-employed** According to a recent Current Population Reports, the population distribution of number of years of education for self-employed individuals in the United States has a mean of 13.6 and a standard deviation of 3.0.

a. Identify the random variable X whose population distribution is described here.

b. Find the mean and standard deviation of the sampling distribution of $\bar{x}$ for a random sample of size 100. Interpret the results.

c. Repeat part b for $n = 400$. Describe the effect of increasing n.

7.17 **Rolling one die** Let X denote the outcome of rolling a die.

a. Construct a graph of the (i) probability distribution of X and (ii) sampling distribution of the sample mean for $n = 2$. (You can think of (i) as the population distribution you would get if you could roll the die an infinite number of times.)

b. The probability distribution of X has mean 3.50 and standard deviation 1.71. Find the mean and standard deviation of the sampling distribution of the sample mean for (i) $n = 2$, (ii) $n = 30$. What is the effect of n on the sampling distribution?

c. Confirm your results from part b by accessing the *Sampling Distribution for the Sample Mean (Discrete Population)* app, selecting Fair Die as the population distribution and simulating the sampling distribution (with 10,000 simulations) when $n = 2$ and then $n = 30$. What is the reported mean and standard deviation of the 10,000 simulated means for each n?

7.18 **Playing roulette** A roulette wheel in Las Vegas has 38 slots. If you bet a dollar on a particular number, you'll win $35 if the ball ends up in that slot and $0 otherwise. Roulette wheels are calibrated so that each outcome is equally likely.

a. Let X denote your winnings when you play once. State the probability distribution of X. (This also represents the population distribution you would get if you could play roulette an infinite number of times.) It has mean 0.921 and standard deviation 5.603.

b. You decide to play once a minute for 12 hours a day for the next week, a total of 5,040 times. Show that the sampling distribution of your sample mean winnings has mean = 0.921 and standard deviation = 0.079.

c. Refer to part b. Using the Central Limit Theorem, find the probability that with this amount of roulette playing, your mean winnings is at least $1, so that you have not lost money after this week of playing. (*Hint:* Find the probability that a normal random variable with mean 0.921 and standard deviation 0.079 exceeds 1.0.)

7.19 **College debt** Access the *Sampling Distribution for the Sample Mean (Continuous Population)* app. Select College Debt as the example for the real population distribution. The app now shows the distribution of median college debt of graduates from colleges in the U.S. (This is based on data from almost all public and private four-year U.S. colleges. *Source:* collegescorecard.ed.gov.) Round all answers to the nearest $10.

a. Describe the shape of the population distribution, including its mean and standard deviation.

b. Suppose you plan to sample 30 colleges from all the colleges included in this population. Move the slider for the sample size to 30 and press Generate Sample(s) once. This will generate one random sample of size 30 from this population. Describe the distribution of median college debt in your sample of 30 values, including the sample mean and sample standard deviation. (Use the information displayed in the middle plot of the app.)

c. Repeat simulating samples of size 30 a few times by pressing the Generate Sample(s) button repeatedly to get an idea what values for the sample mean are possible. Then, select to simulate 10,000 samples at once. Using the resulting histogram of the generated sample means, describe the sampling distribution (shape, mean, standard deviation) of the sample mean.

d. Are the mean and standard deviation of the simulated sampling distribution as reported by the app close to the theoretical mean and standard deviation for this sampling distribution? Compute the theoretical values and compare.

e. Is the shape of the simulated sampling distribution as shown by the app close to the one predicted by the Central Limit Theorem? Explain.

7.20 **Canada lottery** In one lottery option in Canada (*Source:* Lottery Canada), you bet on a six-digit number between 000000 and 999999. For a $1 bet, you win $100,000 if you are correct. The mean and standard deviation of the probability distribution for the lottery winnings are $\mu = 0.10$ (that is, 10 cents) and $\sigma = 100.00$. Joe figures that if he plays enough times every day, eventually he will strike it rich, by the law of large numbers. Over the course of several years, he plays 1 million times. Let $\bar{x}$ denote his average winnings.

 a. Find the mean and standard deviation of the sampling distribution of $\bar{x}$.

 b. About how likely is it that Joe's average winnings exceed $1, the amount he paid to play each time? Use the Central Limit Theorem to find an approximate answer.

7.21 Shared family phone plan   A recent personalized information sheet from your wireless phone carrier claims that the mean duration of all your phone calls was $\mu = 2.8$ minutes with a standard deviation of $\sigma = 2.1$ minutes.

 a. Is the population distribution of the duration of your phone calls likely to be bell shaped, right skewed, or left skewed?

 b. You are on a shared wireless plan with your parents, who are statisticians. They look at some of your recent monthly statements that list each call and its duration and randomly sample 45 calls from the thousands listed there. They construct a histogram of the duration to look at the data distribution. Is this distribution likely to be bell shaped, right skewed, or left skewed, or is it impossible to tell?

 c. From the sample of $n = 45$ calls, your parents compute the mean duration. Is the sampling distribution of the sample mean likely to be bell shaped, right skewed, or left skewed, or is it impossible to tell? Explain.

7.22 Dropped from plan   The previous exercise mentions that the duration of your phone calls follows a distribution with mean $\mu = 2.8$ minutes and standard deviation $\sigma = 2.1$ minutes. From a random sample of $n = 45$ calls, your parents computed a sample mean of $\bar{x} = 3.4$ minutes and a sample standard deviation of $s = 2.9$ minutes.

 a. Give the likely shape of the population distribution for your phone calls. What are its mean and standard deviation?

 b. What are the mean and standard deviation of the data distribution?

 c. Find the mean and standard deviation of the sampling distribution of the sample mean.

 d. Is the sample mean of 3.4 minutes unusually high? Find its z-score and comment.

 e. Your parents told you that they will kick you off the plan when they find a sample mean larger than 3.5 minutes. How likely is this to happen?

7.23 Restaurant profit?   Jan's All You Can Eat Restaurant charges $8.95 per customer to eat at the restaurant. Restaurant management finds that its expense per customer, based on how much the customer eats and the expense of labor, has a distribution that is skewed to the right with a mean of $8.20 and a standard deviation of $3.

 a. If the 100 customers on a particular day have the characteristics of a random sample from their customer base, find the mean and standard deviation of the sampling distribution of the restaurant's sample mean expense per customer.

 b. Find the probability that the restaurant makes a profit that day, with the sample mean expense being less than $8.95. (*Hint:* Apply the Central Limit Theorem to the sampling distribution in part a.)

7.24 Survey accuracy   A study investigating the relationship between age and annual medical expenses randomly samples 100 individuals in Davis, California. It is hoped that the sample will have a similar mean age as the entire population.

 a. If the standard deviation of the ages of all individuals in Davis is $\sigma = 15$, find the probability that the mean age of the individuals sampled is within two years of the mean age for all individuals in Davis. (*Hint:* Find the sampling distribution of the sample mean age and use the Central Limit Theorem. You don't have to know the population mean to answer this, but if it makes it easier, use a value such as $\mu = 30$.)

 b. Would the probability be larger, or smaller, if $\sigma = 10$? Why?

7.25 Blood pressure   Vincenzo Baranello was diagnosed with high blood pressure. He was able to keep his blood pressure in control for several months by taking blood pressure medicine (amlodipine besylate). Baranello's blood pressure is monitored by taking three readings a day, in early morning, at midday, and in the evening.

 a. During this period, the probability distribution of his systolic blood pressure reading had a mean of 130 and a standard deviation of 6. If the successive observations behave like a random sample from this distribution, find the mean and standard deviation of the sampling distribution of the sample mean for the three observations each day.

 b. Suppose that the probability distribution of his blood pressure reading is normal. What is the shape of the sampling distribution? Why?

 c. Refer to part b. Find the probability that the sample mean exceeds 140, which is considered problematically high. (*Hint:* Use the sampling distribution, not the probability distribution.)

7.26 Household size   According to the 2010 U.S. Census Bureau Current Population Survey (www.census.gov/population/www/socdemo/hh-fam/cps2010.html), the average number of people in family households that contain both family and non-family members is 4.43 with a standard deviation of 2.02. This is based on census information for the population. Suppose the Census Bureau instead had estimated this mean using a random sample of 225 homes. Suppose the sample had a sample mean of 4.2 and standard deviation of 1.9.

 a. Identify the random variable X. Indicate whether it is quantitative or categorical.

 b. Describe the center and variability of the population distribution. What would you predict as the shape of the population distribution? Explain.

 c. Describe the center and variability of the data distribution. What would you predict as the shape of the data distribution? Explain.

 d. Describe the center and variability of the sampling distribution of the sample mean for 225 homes. What would you predict as the shape of the sampling distribution? Explain.

7.27 Average monthly sales   A large corporation employs 27,251 individuals. The average income in 2008 for all employees was $74,550 with a standard deviation of $19,872.

You are interested in comparing the incomes of today's employees with those of 2008. A random sample of 100 employees of the corporation yields $\bar{x} =$ \$75,207 and $s =$ \$18,901.

a. Describe the center and variability of the population distribution. What shape does it probably have? Explain.

b. Describe the center and variability of the data distribution. What shape does it probably have? Explain.

c. Describe the center and variability of the sampling distribution of the sample mean for $n = 100$. What shape does it have? Explain.

d. Explain why it would not be unusual to observe an individual who earns more than \$100,000, but it would be highly unusual to observe a sample mean income of more than \$100,000 for a random sample size of 100 people.

7.28 CLT for uniform population distributions Let's use the *Sampling Distribution for the Sample Mean (Continuous Population)* app to show that the sampling distribution approaches a normal distribution even when the population distribution is uniform. (Refer to the first distribution shown in Figure 7.11.) Select Uniform for the population distribution in the first drop-down menu and keep the default settings of 0 and 100 for the lower and upper bound.

a. Use the app to simulate the sampling distribution when the sample size $n = 2$. Run 10,000 simulations and look at the resulting histogram of the sample means. What shape does the simulated sampling distribution have?

b. Repeat part a, but now use a sample size of $n = 5$. Explain how the variability and the shape of the simulated sampling distribution changes as n increases from 2 to 5.

c. Repeat part a, but now use a sample size of $n = 30$. Explain how the variability and the shape of the simulated sampling distribution changes as n increases from 2 to 30. Compare results from parts a-c to the first column of Figure 7.11.

d. Explain how the Central Limit Theorem describes what you have observed.

7.29 CLT for left skewed population distributions Access the *Sampling Distribution for the Sample Mean (Continuous Population)* app, choose Skewed as the population distribution from the first drop-down menu and position the slider for the skewness to "extremely left." Repeat parts a–c of the previous exercise and explain how the variability and shape of the simulated sampling distribution of the sample mean changes as n changes from 2 to 5 to 30. Explain how the Central Limit Theorem describes what you have observed.

7.30 Sampling distribution for normal population distributions Access the *Sampling Distribution for the Sample Mean (Continuous Population)* app and select Bell-Shaped for the population distribution from the first drop-down menu, which looks similar to the last column in Figure 7.11. Select a value for the population mean and standard deviation. Is the sampling distribution normal even for $n = 2$? What does this tell you?

7.3 Using the Bootstrap to Find Sampling Distributions

In Section 7.1 we learned that the sampling distribution is the distribution of all possible values of a statistic when repeatedly taking samples of size n from a population. We have seen two important special cases: the sampling distribution for a sample proportion and the sampling distribution for a sample mean. These help us in assessing how close a statistic (the proportion or the mean) is likely to fall to the true population value (the population proportion or the population mean). When the sample size is large, both sampling distributions are approximately normal. Then, we expect the sample proportion or the sample mean to fall within about 2 or at most 3 standard deviations of their population values.

While the proportion and mean are two common statistics, there are others that describe important characteristics of the sample, such as the median or the standard deviation for a single sample or the correlation coefficient for describing the strength of a linear relationship between two variables (see Chapter 3). What can we say about the sampling distribution for such statistics?

Unfortunately, there is no theorem as general as the Central Limit Theorem that we could use to predict the sampling distribution or its standard deviation for such statistics without making further assumptions about the underlying population distribution. Typically, such assumptions amount to assuming a bell-shaped population distribution. However, in situations where, for instance, we would prefer the median over the mean as a measure for the center, the population distribution is skewed (e.g., a right-skewed distribution for income) and assuming a bell shape is not appropriate. How can we then assess how accurate

Recall

The standard deviation of the sampling distribution of the sample proportion is $\sqrt{p(1-p)/n}$ (where p is the population proportion). The standard deviation of the sampling distribution of the sample mean is $\sigma/\sqrt{n}$ (where σ is the population standard deviation). ◄

a statistic is in estimating a population value, and how can we obtain a margin of error without having a formula for the standard deviation? Fortunately, we can "pull ourselves up by our bootstraps"[3] to attack this problem by using computer simulations instead of mathematical formulas. A relatively recent innovation, called the **bootstrap**, does just that.

The previous two sections distinguished between the population distribution and the data distribution. One was the distribution of the variable of interest in the population, the other the distribution constructed with the observations from a random sample of size n from the population. In practice, we don't know the population distribution (e.g., in Activity 1 we wouldn't really know the true proportion of votes for Brown until a few days after the election), and so all we can work with is the data distribution. The bootstrap uses the data distribution to approximate the population distribution. It constructs an approximation of the sampling distribution by repeatedly simulating random samples from the data distribution.

Bootstrap Resampling

How exactly are we drawing random samples from the data distribution? Instead of simulating drawing a random sample from the population over and over again and constructing the sampling distribution along the way (as we have done in the simulation activities of the previous two sections), we now simulate drawing a random sample from the *observed data* (because we don't have all the population values). Such a random sample is called a **bootstrap sample** or, often, just a **resample**, and the entire process is known as **resampling** because we repeatedly take samples from the observed sample. The idea is that any sample taken from the observed sample—which, by virtue of being a random sample is representative of the population—is like taking a sample from the population.

You might pause here and ask how a bootstrap sample differs from the original sample. Aren't they just the same? The key is that a bootstrap sample is a sample taken **with replacement** from the original data and therefore can include a single observation multiple times and others not at all. The reason for sampling with replacement is that we want to mimic as close as possible the characteristics of taking a random sample from the population: For a random sample of size n taken from a population, every member of the population has the same chance of being included in the sample, and every possible group of n members has the same chance of being selected as the sample. To achieve these characteristics when sampling from the observed data (which now represent the population), we sample n times with replacement from the observed data. This will give us one bootstrap sample of size n. Sampling with replacement means that once a particular value is obtained, it is immediately eligible to be selected again. For example, if the random sample consists of the numbers {3, 8, 2}, then a bootstrap sample may be {8, 8, 3} or {2, 3, 2} or even {2, 2, 2}.

Recall

From Section 4.2, a random sample of n subjects from a population is one in which each possible sample of that size has the same chance of being selected. ◄

> **Bootstrap Sample**
>
> A bootstrap sample is a sample drawn *with replacement* from the original sample and of the *same size* as the original sample.

In practice, we need to use a computer to draw a bootstrap sample and to repeat the process of drawing bootstrap samples thousands of times. Activity 4 illustrates obtaining bootstrap samples using an app.

[3] This expression may originate from the fictional book character Baron Munchhausen who, riding his horse into a swamp, pulled the horse and himself out by his bootstraps just before drowning. (Actually, in the German version of the book that one author read as a child, the Baron used his ponytail to pull himself up, not his bootstraps.)

► Activity 4

Bootstrap Resampling

Open the *Bootstrap for One Sample* app, which allows drawing bootstrap samples. To illustrate, let's use data from Chapter 2 on the sugar content from a sample of 20 cereals that is preloaded by default. The app shows a dot plot of this sample (see the left graph in Figure 7.15). You can generate a bootstrap sample from this sample by pressing the Draw Bootstrap Sample(s) button once. This will take a random sample of size 20 from the original 20 observations, with

replacement. "With replacement" means that during the sampling process, once a particular sugar value is selected it immediately becomes available for selection again. As a consequence, some of the sugar values will end up being selected multiple times while others will not be selected at all for inclusion in the bootstrap sample. The app indicates this by coloring dots for observations that were selected once or more often in shades of orange while leaving blank dots corresponding to observations that were not selected. See the middle graph in Figure 7.15.

▲ **Figure 7.15 Dot Plot of Original and Bootstrapped Sample.** Screenshots from the *Bootstrap For One Sample* app. The first graph shows the dot plot of the original sample. The middle graph shows the same dot plot, but now the dots are colored according to how often each is included in the generated bootstrap sample of size 20, which is shown in the third dot plot.

For instance, the dot for the smallest observation of 0 is not colored in, indicating that it was not included in this bootstrap sample. Indeed, from the dot plot of the bootstrap sample shown in the right graph of Figure 7.15, the dot for 0 is missing. The next higher observation of 1 was included in the generated bootstrap sample multiple times, three times to be precise, as shown by the three dots in the dot plot for the bootstrap sample above the observation 1. Other original observations not included in the bootstrap sample are the two values of 3 or the value of 10. The highest value of 18 was included exactly once. Note that the dot plot of the bootstrap sample shows exactly 20 dots (i.e.,

observations), just as the dot plot of the original sample. The bootstrap sample is of the same size as the original sample.

To generate another bootstrap sample, press the Draw Bootstrap Sample(s) button again. This will update the dot plot of the original observations according to which observations are now included or not included in the newly generated bootstrap sample. The dot plot for the bootstrap sample will also get updated to reflect the distribution of this newly generated bootstrap sample.

Try Exercise 7.32 ◄

Bootstrap Distribution

For each bootstrap sample, we can compute a statistic of interest. Let's first do this with the sample mean. The sample mean of the original sample in Activity 1 was 8.75 g, as you can see from the subtitle of the first dot plot in Figure 7.15. The sample mean of the generated bootstrap sample depicted in the third dot plot in Figure 7.15 was equal to 9.55 g. This is the sample mean of the n observations included in the bootstrap sample. It differs from the sample mean of the original data because the bootstrap sample excluded some of the original observations and included some others, potentially multiple times, resulting in this new value for the sample mean. Remember that drawing a bootstrap sample mimics drawing a sample from the population. So 9.55 g represents one possible value for the sample mean sugar content in a random sample of size 20. If we draw another bootstrap sample and compute its sample mean, we obtain another possible value for it. Proceeding in this manner, we compute the sample mean from thousands of bootstrap samples. The distribution of all these means, called the **bootstrap distribution**, will give us information about the sampling distribution of the sample mean.

Constructing the Bootstrap Distribution of the Sample Mean

Using the *Bootstrap for One Sample* app from Activity 4 and the random sample of the sugar content in 20 cereals, let's find the sampling distribution of the sample mean as approximated via the bootstrap. The mean is the default statistic selected as the Statistic of Interest in the app. Note how the app, below the dot plot for the original sample, shows an empty plot titled "Bootstrap Sampling Distribution" where the location of the original sample mean (8.75) is marked as an orange triangle.

To generate one bootstrap sample and compute its mean, press the Draw Bootstrap Sample(s) button once. This will produce a dot plot of the generated bootstrap sample and show the mean of the generated bootstrap sample (marked as a blue triangle) in relation to the original sample mean (orange triangle). When we did this, we got a mean of 9.55 (see Figure 7.15). To generate another bootstrap sample, press the Draw Bootstrap Sample(s) button again, and observe where the sample mean of this new bootstrap sample falls in relation to the other two. This time, the sample mean of our generated bootstrap sample was equal to 8.60. Keep pressing the Draw Bootstrap Sample(s)

button to generate more bootstrap samples and observe how their sample means vary around the original sample mean. The first 10 "bootstrapped" sample means we obtained were 9.55, 8.60, 9.50, 9.85, 9.05, 7.50, 9.70, 9.15, 11.00 and 7.80.

You can see all generated sample means so far by checking Show Generated Bootstrap Statistics in the app. These numbers already give you an idea how much variability you can expect around the original sample mean (8.75), which is a stand-in for the population mean. As you generate more bootstrap samples, the histogram of the sampling distribution builds up. To see its shape more clearly, select to generate 10,000 bootstrap samples at once and then press the Draw Bootstrap Sample(s) button. Figure 7.16 shows the resulting histogram and summary statistics after a total of 20,025 simulations.

The histogram of the bootstrapped means is approximately normal, suggesting an approximately normal shape for the sampling distribution of the sample mean. This result should not come as a surprise. We know that by the Central Limit Theorem, the sampling distribution of the sample mean is approximately normal. Using the bootstrap to approximate the sampling distribution confirms this result for our sample of size 20.

► **Figure 7.16** Sampling Distribution of the Sample Mean Approximated via the Bootstrap. Screenshot from the *Bootstrap for One Sample* app. The original sample (first dot plot) acts as a stand-in for the population. The bootstrap sample (second dot plot) mimics a sample drawn from the population. The statistic (here, the sample mean) computed for each generated bootstrap sample is summarized in the bootstrap distribution, which approximates the sampling distribution of the statistic.

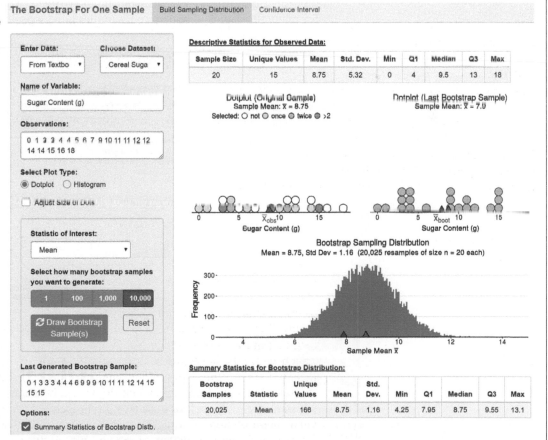

Note that the bootstrap distribution in Figure 7.16 is centered at the observed mean, which is a stand-in for the population mean. The standard deviation of the bootstrap distribution is equal to 1.16, as shown in the table underneath the histogram. This standard deviation is simply the standard deviation of the 20,025 bootstrapped sample means that were generated with the app. It tells us how much we expect sample means for such samples of size 20 to vary from sample to sample.

We learned in Section 7.2 that the standard deviation of the sample mean equals $\sigma/\sqrt{n}$, where σ is the standard deviation of sugar values in the population of all cereals that this sample is representative of. (Estimating σ from the sample and using it to compute the standard deviation is discussed in Chapter 8.) The bootstrap provides a direct way (without using a formula) of estimating this standard deviation. With the normal shape of the sampling distribution, we can be very confident that the sample mean will fall within 2 (or, at most, 3) standard deviations of the (unknown) population mean, i.e., within $2(1.16) = 2.32$ grams of the mean sugar value in the population of all cereals.

Bootstrap Distribution of the Median

In Activity 5, we focused on the sampling distribution of the sample mean, and therefore we computed the sample mean for each bootstrap sample. If we are interested in other statistics, such as the median sugar content, we can compute them instead. Without assumptions on the shape of the population distribution, such as assuming normality, which may be inappropriate, there is no Central Limit Theorem that would tell us about the shape of the sampling distribution, nor any formula for the standard deviation of the median. Using the bootstrap, we can approximate both. This makes the bootstrap a very powerful procedure. To approximate the sampling distribution of a particular statistic, all we need to do is to compute this statistic for many thousands of bootstrap resamples and inspect the resulting distribution.

► **Figure 7.17** Sampling Distribution of the Sample Median Approximated via the Bootstrap. Screenshot from the *Bootstrap for One Sample* app. The sampling distribution is discrete because the median in a sample of size 20 can equal only a handful of different values.

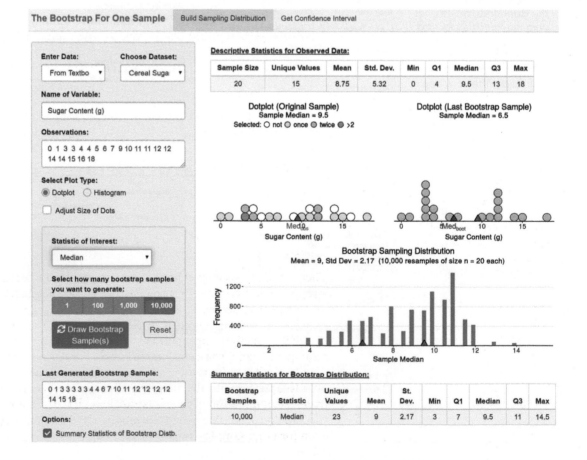

For example, in the *Bootstrap for One Sample* app, select the median instead of the mean as the Statistic of Interest and draw 10,000 bootstrap samples. Figure 7.17 on the previous page shows the bootstrap distribution of the median based on 10,000 bootstrap samples from the cereal data. The distribution is left skewed and seems far from normal. It is centered at the observed median of 9.5, and the standard deviation of 2.17 tells us how much we expect the sample median to vary from sample to sample. The distribution is discrete, concentrated on only a handful of values. This is expected because the median in a sample of size 20 can only equal a few different values. In Chapter 8, we will learn how to use this bootstrap distribution to conduct inference about a population median, such as giving an interval which we believe the population median will fall into.

If we are interested in the sampling distribution of the sample standard deviation of sugar values, we would simply compute the standard deviation for each generated bootstrap sample and look at the resulting distribution of values. (In the app, select Standard Deviation as the Statistic of Interest.) Summing up, the bootstrap can be used to obtain sampling distributions for all kinds of statistics.

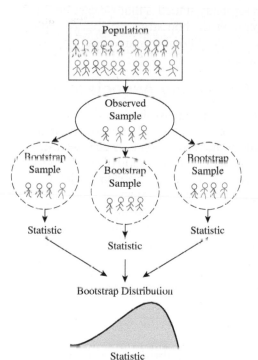

▲ **Figure 7.18** Illustration of the Bootstrap. Bootstrap samples are drawn with replacement from the original sample taken from the population. For each bootstrap sample, the statistic of interest is computed and the values are summarized in the bootstrap distribution. This process mimics taking actual samples from the population, and hence the bootstrap distribution is an approximation of the actual sampling distribution of the statistic.

> **SUMMARY: The Bootstrap**
>
> The bootstrap provides a way of approximating the sampling distribution of a statistic via simulation. The bootstrap distribution of a statistic is the distribution we get when we
>
> - repeatedly generate a random sample *with replacement* from the original sample. This is called a bootstrap sample. The bootstrap sample is of the same size as the original sample.
> - compute the statistic of interest for each generated bootstrap sample.
> - summarize the generated statistics graphically (e.g., by plotting a histogram) and numerically (e.g., by computing summary statistics).
>
> The bootstrap distribution can be used to obtain key properties of the true sampling distribution, such as its shape or standard deviation. These, in turn, can be used to conduct inference for population parameters, such as providing a margin of error or a range of plausible values for the parameter. Figure 7.18 summarizes how the bootstrap works.

The bootstrap is particularly valuable because no assumptions (such as assuming a bell shape) on the underlying population distribution are necessary. (This is also the case for the Central Limit Theorem, but it only applies for sample means and proportions.) For statistics where theoretical formulas for the shape and standard deviation of the sampling distribution don't exist without further assumptions, the bootstrap is a great way of obtaining approximations for both.

Limitations of the Bootstrap

There are a few issues you have to keep in mind when using the bootstrap to generate an approximation of the sampling distribution. Remember, the bootstrap uses the original sample as a surrogate for the population, and so it is paramount that the original sample is a random sample from the population of interest, or at least representative of it. If it is not, the sample may fail to capture the characteristics of the population and resampling from it will carry forward any biases that existed in the original sample.

In a similar vein, the larger your random sample, the better the bootstrap is able to approximate the sampling distribution because it has more information from the population. The bootstrap may not work for small samples, failing to capture the true shape and variability of the sampling distribution. However, even for large samples, sometimes the bootstrap can give results that are not very useful, especially for statistics such as the median (or the 25th or 75th percentile) that use only a few values in the sample.

As an example, consider the random sample (taken from the General Social Survey in 2016) of 438 U.S. adults who are employed full time and were asked how many hours they work in a typical week. This data set is preloaded in the *Bootstrap for One Sample* app under the name Weekly Work Hours. Based on the data, the distribution of the weekly work hours has a large mode at 40 hours, and several other smaller modes at 35, 45, 50, and 60 hours, but only a few values in between. Although the sample size is relatively large, taking a bootstrap resample (of size 438) from this sample almost always results in a median of 40 hours, as you can easily check with the app. Then, the bootstrap distribution basically consists of just the value 40. The reason for this strange behavior is that the sample of the 438 adults contains only 31 unique values for the number of hours worked, with 40 hours being by far the most common. (By contrast, you can check that the bootstrap distribution of the sample mean is approximately normal, despite the discrete nature and multimodality of the underlying population distribution.)

When the bootstrap distribution consists of only a few values and is highly discrete, it is of limited use and should not be used for the inferential procedures discussed in the next chapters. Fortunately, for many statistics that we care about, such as the ones mentioned in the next paragraph, the bootstrap distribution typically ranges over many different values. Then, we can use it to learn about important properties of the true sampling distribution.

The Bootstrap for Statistics Measuring Association

So far, we have use the bootstrap to obtain the sampling distribution for a statistic computed on observations from a single variable. In Chapter 3 we learned about important statistics that measure the strength of the association between two categorical or two quantitative variables, such as the difference and ratio of two proportions, the correlation coefficient r or the slope b of a linear regression model. For the correlation coefficient, for example, we mentioned that values of r close to 1 or –1 indicate a strong linear relationship, while values close to 0 indicate no linear relationship. The sampling distribution for the correlation coefficient r, as approximated via the bootstrap, will help us better quantify what we mean by "close to 0."

Example 6

Sampling Distribution for the Sample Correlation Coefficient ◀

Carbon Footprint of Sandwiches

Picture the Scenario

Ready-made sandwiches such as chicken or tuna sandwiches are a convenience food staple, sold prepackaged in many grocery stores. In the article "Understanding the impact on climate change of convenience food,"[4] researchers in the UK looked at the total environmental costs associated with the life cycle of such sandwiches, including costs arising in the agricultural production for the ingredients (from plants and animals), costs for transportation and cooling and costs for the production and disposal of the (plastic) packaging. For a representative sample of 24 different types of sandwiches, they summarized these costs in a popular measure called the **carbon footprint**, which is measured in grams of CO_2 equivalent. The carbon footprint of a sandwich may depend on its nutritional value, as measured by the energy content in calories. For instance, a veggie sandwich with low calories is expected to have a lower carbon footprint than an Egg & Bacon sandwich with a large caloric value.

To visualize the relationship between the carbon footprint and energy content in a scatterplot, we use the *Scatterplots & Correlation* app. This app can also carry out the bootstrap resampling, using the second tab of the app

---

[4] Espinoza-Orias, N., & Azapagic, A., "Understanding the impact on climate change of convenience food: Carbon footprint of sandwiches," *Sustainable Production and Consumption*, Vol. 15, July 2018.

▶ Figure 7.19 Bootstrap Distribution of the Sample Correlation. Screenshot from the *Scatterplots & Correlation* app, second tab. The bootstrap sample (shown in the right table and scatterplot) consists of repeatedly picking observations from the original sample (shown in the left table and scatterplot), with replacement. The correlation coefficient *r* computed from the generated bootstrap sample is summarized in the histogram at the bottom, which approximates the sampling distribution of the correlation coefficient.

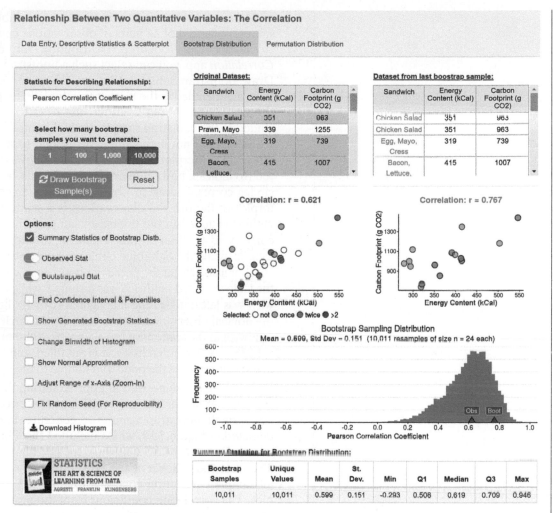

titled Bootstrap Distribution. Figure 7.19 shows a screenshot of this app, with the original data displayed in the top left table. The scatterplot below this table reveals an approximate linear relationship between the carbon footprint and the energy content for the 24 sandwiches.

Questions to Explore

a. What statistic describes the strength of the linear relationship between the carbon footprint and energy content of sandwiches? Find the numerical value of this statistic.

b. Describe how to take one bootstrap sample from the original data.

c. What statistic is computed for each bootstrap sample taken?

d. Find and describe the sampling distribution of the statistic, as approximated via the bootstrap.

Think It Through

a. We have data on two quantitative variables (carbon footprint, energy content) and their scatterplot reveals an approximate linear relationship, so the correlation coefficient *r* is an appropriate statistic to describe the strength of this relationship. As shown by the app, $r = 0.621$.

b. To obtain a bootstrap sample of size 24 (the number of sandwiches included in the study), we need to (re-)sample from the observed sample, with replacement. In the context of this study, this means that we need to randomly select 24 sandwiches from the original 24 sandwiches, with replacement. Here, once a particular sandwich is selected to be included in the bootstrap sample, we keep both its carbon footprint and its energy content, so that the final bootstrap sample consists of 24 pairs of observations on these two variables, just as the original sample consisted of 24 pairs of observations on these two variables.

Under the Bootstrap Distribution tab of the *Scatterplots & Correlation* app, you can select such a bootstrap sample by pressing the Draw Bootstrap Sample(s) button. The app indicates which observations are included in the bootstrap sample in two ways: In the table that shows the original observations, the rows for sandwiches that are included in the bootstrap sample are highlighted in red (see Figure 7.19). Rows that are not highlighted correspond to sandwiches not included. Also, the scatterplot of the original data shows circles filled in shades of red (to indicate how often an observation has been selected) and empty circles corresponding to observations not selected. Next to the scatterplot of the original observations is a scatterplot just for the observations included in the bootstrap sample. There, the dark blue circles correspond to observations appearing multiple times in the bootstrap sample, while the light blue circles are observations appearing once.

For instance, for the particular bootstrap sample shown in Figure 7.19, the Chicken Salad sandwich was included, while the Prawn & Mayo sandwich was left out. See the highlighted rows (in light red) in the table for the original observations. If you look for the circle for the Prawn & Mayo sandwich in the scatterplot below (energy content = 339, carbon footprint = 1,255), you'll see that its circle is not filled, and hence you will not find it in the scatterplot of the bootstrap sample to the right.

c. Because we are interested in approximating the sampling distribution for the sample correlation coefficient r, we compute this statistic for every single bootstrap sample we generate. For the bootstrap sample depicted in Figure 7.19, which included the Chicken Salad (twice) but not the Prawn & Mayo sandwich, the correlation coefficient $r = 0.767$. The histogram shown at the bottom of the screenshot keeps track of all sample correlation coefficient computed from the bootstrap samples. The correlation coefficient from the original sample (label: Orig) and the correlation coefficient computed from the current bootstrap sample (label: Boot) are highlighted.

d. After 10,011 bootstrap samples (we initially pressed the Draw Bootstrap Sample(s) button 11 times to get a feel for the potential correlation coefficients, and then selected to generate 10,000 bootstrap samples at once), the histogram at the bottom of Figure 7.19 shows the bootstrap distribution of the generated correlation coefficients. The distribution is left skewed, with a mean of 0.599 (close to the correlation coefficient of 0.62 from the original sample) and a standard deviation of 0.151, as you can see from the summary statistics below the graph. Don't be surprised by the fact that the distribution is not bell shaped. The Central Limit Theorem doesn't apply for the correlation coefficient r. Also, there is no general formula for the standard deviation of the correlation coefficient, so the information that the standard deviation among the 10,011 resampled correlation coefficients is equal to 0.151 is very valuable.

Insight

The bootstrap distribution approximates the sampling distribution for the correlation coefficient r. Because it is not bell shaped, we shouldn't be using the rule that the sample correlation is within 2 or at most 3 standard deviations (e.g., within about $2(0.15) = 0.3$) of the population correlation coefficient. Rather, we will use the 2.5th and 97.5th percentiles of the bootstrap distribution (which equal 0.25 and 0.84, respectively) to obtain an interval that contains the population correlation with high probability (see Chapter 8).

▶ *Try Exercise 7.38*

7.3 | Practicing the Basics

7.31 Bootstrap samples A random sample of 100 students is taken from a university with an enrollment of 10,000 students. Which part describes a bootstrap sample.

a. A sample of size 100 taken without replacement from all students enrolled.

b. A sample of size 100 taken with replacement from all students enrolled.

c. A sample of size 10,000 taken with replacement from all students enrolled.

d. A sample of size 100 taken without replacement from the students in the sample.

e. A sample of size 10,000 taken with replacement from the students in the sample.

f. A sample of size 100 taken with replacement from the students in the sample.

7.32 Social Security payments Open the *Bootstrap for One Sample* app and select Social Security Payments as the data set. This will display a dot plot of the Social Security payments that a random sample of 85 California residents reported receiving in 2017. (Data from the American Community Survey.)

a. Identify the numerical value of the largest observation. (*Hint:* Look at the table for the descriptive statistics or refer to all sample values shown in the box titled Observations.)

b. A bootstrap sample taken from these 85 observations is of what size?

c. Generate a bootstrap sample with the app by pressing the Draw Bootstrap Sample(s) button. Check the output to see if the largest observation was included in the bootstrap sample generated. Explain.

7.33 Mean Social Security payments Refer to exercise 7.32.

a. Take 5 bootstrap samples and report the mean payment obtained from each. (*Hint:* Write down the mean after each generation, or click Show Generated Bootstrap Statistics after 5 generations.)

b. Now, take an additional 10,000 bootstrap samples and describe the resulting bootstrap distribution of the sample mean.

c. Are you surprised by the shape of the bootstrap distribution? Explain.

d. Use the standard deviation of the bootstrap distribution to estimate how close the sample mean payment of $13,620 is likely to fall to the true mean Social Security payments for residents in California.

7.34 Median Social Security payments Refer to Exercise 7.32.

a. Based on the dot plot of the Social Security payments received by the 85 residents, is the distribution of payments received likely right skewed, symmetric, or left skewed?

b. Which statistic may be more appropriate to describe the typical payment received? The sample mean or the sample median? Explain.

c. Take 5 bootstrap samples and report the median payment obtained from each. (*Hint:* Write down the median after each generation or click Show Generated Bootstrap Statistics after 5 generations.)

d. Now, take an additional 10,000 bootstrap samples and check whether the resulting bootstrap distribution of the median looks bell shaped and continuous or is of no particular shape and discrete.

e. What's wrong with the argument that by the Central Limit Theorem, the sampling distribution of the sample median should be approximately normal?

7.35 Sampling distribution for s In Chapter 2, we introduced the sample standard deviation s as a statistic that measures the variability among observations. Explain conceptually how to obtain the sampling distribution of s via the bootstrap based on a random sample of size 100 from some population.

7.36 Variability in weekly work hours Open the *Bootstrap for One Sample* app and select Weekly Work Hours (2016) as the data set. This will display the distribution of the typical weekly work hours for a sample of 438 U.S. adults, obtained from the GSS.

a. State the sample mean and standard deviation for the weekly working hours in the sample of size 438. (*Hint:* Both are part of the descriptive statistics displayed on top of the app.)

b. Take 5 bootstrap samples and report the sample standard deviation s for each. (*Hint:* Write down the sample standard deviation obtained after each generation or click Show Generated Bootstrap Statistics after 5 generations.)

c. Now, take an additional 10,000 bootstrap samples and describe the resulting bootstrap distribution of the sample standard deviation.

d. At most, how far from the observed sample standard deviation of 9.9 hours do you expect the standard deviation of the weekly work hours in the U.S. adult population to fall?

7.37 CLT with outlier Open the *Bootstrap for One Sample* app and select Energy Consumption of OECD Countries as the data set. This will display a dot plot of the 2011 per capita energy consumption (in BTU) for a sample of 36 OECD countries (see Exercise 2.74). Iceland had the highest per capita consumption, with 665 million BTU. How does this outlier (which is also an outlier in the population of all OECD countries) affect the sampling distribution of the mean? The true population distribution may be rather skewed, in which case a sample of size 36 might not be large enough for the Central Limit Theorem to apply. In such cases, we can approximate the sampling distribution via the bootstrap.

a. Generate 10,000 bootstrap samples and find the bootstrap distribution of the sample mean via the app. Describe it.

b. Is the sample size of 36 large enough for the Central Limit Theorem to apply? (If not, we should rely on the sampling distribution as approximated by the bootstrap for inference.)

7.38 **Self-Esteem**   A study on a sample of 229 college freshmen investigated the relationship between their self-esteem based on how they think they appear to others and based on how they think others approve of them. Both of these psychological measures were obtained through various targeted questions on a survey. The score reported in the data for each of these two constructs (self-esteem based on appearance and self-esteem based on approval) is an average of the responses to the corresponding survey questions.

   a. Open this data set, called Self-Esteem, in the *Scatterplots & Correlation* app. Briefly describe the relationship between self-esteem based on appearance to others and self-esteem based on approval by others, using the output of the app.

   b. Take 5 bootstrap samples and report the sample correlation for each. (*Hint:* Write down the sample correlation obtained after each generation, or click Show Generated Bootstrap Statistics after 5 generations.)

   c. Now, take an additional 10,000 bootstrap samples and describe the resulting bootstrap distribution of the sample correlation.

   d. Can we use the rule that the true population correlation is within at most 3 standard deviations of the observed correlation of 0.53? Explain.

7.39 **Exercise hours**   A study on a random sample of 106 freshman entering college recorded how many hours per week they exercised at the beginning and towards the end of the fall semester.

   a. Open this data set, called Weekly Exercise Hours in the *Scatterplots & Correlation* app. Briefly describe the relationship shown in the scatterplot.

   b. Generate 10,000 bootstrap samples and describe the resulting bootstrap distribution of the sample correlation.

   c. Remove student 93, who is a potential outlier with 18 exercise hours per week at the beginning but only 4 hours at the end of the semester. Report the new correlation coefficient. (In the app, go to the first tab Data Entry, check Enable Dragging of Points, and drag this point outside the range to discard it.) Generate the bootstrap distribution using the remaining data using 10,000 resamples and check if the sampling distribution changed.

Chapter Review

SUMMARY OF NOTATION

p = population proportion
μ = mean of population distribution
σ = standard deviation of population distribution

CHAPTER SUMMARY

- The **population distribution** is the distribution of a variable of interest in the population. When the variable of interest is **binary**, measuring whether one out of *two possible outcomes* has occurred, the population distribution is described by the proportions p and $1-p$ of outcomes in these two categories. p is called the **population proportion**. When the variable of interest is quantitative, we summarize its population distribution by the **population mean** μ and the **population standard deviation** σ.

- The population proportion p or the population mean μ and the population standard deviation σ are called **population parameters**, and are typically **unknown**. By taking a sample from the population, we try to estimate these unknown population parameters.

- The **data distribution** is the distribution of the variable of interest in a **sample** of size n taken from the population. From it, we compute **sample statistics** such as the sample proportion or the sample mean that estimate the corresponding population parameters.

- The **sampling distribution** is the distribution that describes all potential values of a sample statistic that we might observe when taking a random sample of size n from the population. It is the key for telling us how close a sample statistic falls to the unknown population parameter we would like to estimate. We will use the sampling distribution to conduct inference, such as computing a margin of error or a range of plausible values for the unknown population parameter.

- The **sampling distribution of the sample proportion** has mean equal to the population proportion p and standard deviation equal to $\sqrt{p(1-p)/n}$.

- The **sampling distribution of the sample mean** $\bar{x}$ has mean equal to the population mean μ and standard deviation equal to $\sigma/\sqrt{n}$.

- The **Central Limit Theorem** states that for random samples of sufficiently large size (at least about 30 is usually enough), the **sampling distribution of the sample mean is approximately normal**. This theorem holds *no matter what the shape of the population distribution.*

- The **sampling distribution of the sample proportion is also approximately normal** whenever n is large enough so that both np and $n(1-p)$ are at least 15.

- The **approximate normality** of statistics involving the sample mean or the sample proportion is the reason the normal distribution plays such an important role in statistics.

- Other statistics such as the **sample median** or the **sample correlation coefficient** have sampling distributions, too. But unlike the sample mean or the sample proportion, there is no mathematical theorem like the CLT that can be used to predict the sampling distribution or standard deviations for these statistics without making further assumptions on the population distribution.

■ The **bootstrap** is a way to approximate the sampling distribution of many statistics through **resampling**. A bootstrap **resample** is a sample taken from the original observations, *with replacement* and of the *same* size as the original sample.

■ The bootstrap provides estimates of key quantities such as the **standard deviation of the sampling distribution** directly, without the use of formulas.

LEARNING OBJECTIVES

1. Define, recognize, and differentiate between the population distribution, data distribution, and sampling distribution.

2. Understand that a population distribution is described in terms of population parameters such as the population proportion (for binary variables) or the population mean and standard deviation (for continuous variables).

3. Understand that statistics computed from samples, such as the sample proportion or the sample mean, are random variables and have a distribution, called the sampling distribution.

4. State and understand how to use the mean and standard deviation for the sampling distribution of the sample proportion. Recognize the expected shape for this sampling distribution for large n.

5. State and understand how to use the mean and standard deviation for the sampling distribution of the sample mean. Recognize the expected shape for this sampling distribution for large n.

6. Identify the conditions needed for the Central Limit Theorem to hold and understand how to use the CLT.

7. Understand how the sample size influences the variability of the sampling distribution through the formula for the standard deviation of the sampling distribution.

8. Understand the role of the normal distribution with regard to sampling distributions.

9. Understand that not all statistics have a known sampling distribution, but that the sampling distribution often can be approximated via bootstrap resampling.

10. Define a bootstrap sample.

11. Carry out bootstrap resampling to construct the bootstrap distribution for statistics like the median or the correlation coefficient. Use summary statistics of the bootstrap distribution to learn about key properties of the sampling distribution.

ANSWERS TO FIGURE QUESTIONS

Figure 7.1   The larger the sample size, the more we expect the data distribution to resemble the population distribution.

Figure 7.3   Using the empirical rule, almost all sample proportions will fall within 3 standard deviations, so within $3(0.079) = 0.237$ of the mean of 0.542, which is the interval [0.305, 0.779].

Figure 7.4   Using the empirical rule, almost all sample proportions will fall within 3 standard deviations, so within $3(0.008) = 0.024$ of the mean of 0.54, which is the interval [0.516, 0.564].

Figure 7.6   With $p = 0.51$, the mean of the sampling distribution is 0.51 and the standard deviation is $\sqrt{0.51(1 - 0.51)/3{,}889} = 0.008$, so that almost all sample proportions will fall between $0.51 \pm 3(0.008)$, or in the interval [0.494, 0.526]. Then, there is a possibility that a particular exit poll does not indicate a Brown majority.

Figure 7.9   Using the empirical rule, almost all sample means will fall within 3 standard deviations, so within $3(0.7) = 2.1$, or roughly 2 cm of the mean of 181 cm, which is the interval [179, 183].

STATISTICAL SOFTWARE

Art of Stat Web Apps

■ **Sampling Distribution for the Sample Proportion**   As illustrated in Activity 1, you can use this app to simulate the sampling distribution for the sample proportion, for given population proportion p and sample size n. After simulating a sampling distribution, use the sliders for p and n to learn how the sampling distribution reacts to changes in these two parameters. The app can also display the generated number of successes (in addition to the proportion of successes) and you can overlay a normal distribution to visually judge whether the sampling distribution is close to normal.

■ **Sampling Distribution for the Sample Mean (Continuous Population)**   As illustrated in Activities 2 and 3, you can use this app to simulate the sampling distribution of the sample mean when sampling from a continuous population distribution. The app has several population distributions implemented (based on real population data), but you can also select a uniform, skewed (with a slider that controls the skewness), bell-shaped, or bimodal population distribution. You can even supply data to build your own smooth population distribution. Use the sliders for n or the population mean μ and standard deviation σ (e.g., for bell-shaped population distributions) to visualize how the sampling distribution reacts to changes in these parameters. You can also overlay the normal distribution to see whether the sampling distribution is approximately normal.

■ **Sampling Distribution for the Sample Mean (Discrete Population)**   As illustrated in Activity 3, this app can be used to generate samples from a discrete population distribution, such as the preloaded Amazon Star rating. Other features of the app are similar to the one for continuous populations.

■ **Bootstrap Distribution for One Sample**   As illustrated in Activities 4 and 5, you can use this app to construct, step-by-step, the bootstrap distribution of the mean, median, or standard deviation. It illustrates, by providing a dot plot for the original and bootstrap sample side by side, what a bootstrap sample is. The app comes with several preloaded data sets from the textbook, or you can provide your own data to build a bootstrap distribution for the mean, median, or standard deviation and get important summary statistics from it.

■ **Scatterplots & Correlation** We have used this app in Chapter 3 to construct and explore scatterplots. Under the second tab in this app, titled Bootstrap Distribution, as illustrated in Activity 6, you can construct, step by step, the bootstrap distribution of the correlation coefficient r. By plotting scatterplots of the original and bootstrap sample side by side, you can visualize what a bootstrap sample is in this context. The app comes with several data sets from the textbook pre-loaded, or you can provide your own data to build a bootstrap distribution for the correlation coefficient r and get important summary statistics from it.

R

■ **Bootstrap:** The sample command in R, together with the replace=TRUE option can draw samples with replacement, i.e., bootstrap samples. We illustrate with finding the boot-strap distribution for the median as in Activities 4 and 5, using the cereal sugar data.

```
> sugar <- c(11, 18, 5, 14, 12, 1, 10, 16,
0, 12, 14, 7, 9, 6, 3, 15, 4, 4, 3, 11)
> median(sugar) #observed median
[1] 9.5
> bootsamp1 <- sample(sugar, replace=TRUE) #
a bootstrap sample
> bootsamp1
[1] 9  4 11  4 11  0 12 11  3  7  9  7 15
6  5  6 16 11 16  4
> median(bootsamp1) #median of bootstrap sample
[1] 8
```

```
> bootsamp2 <- sample(sugar, replace=TRUE) #
another bootstrap sample
> median(bootsamp2) #median of bootstrap sample
[1] 6
> bootmedian <- c() #initializing
> for(i in 1:10000) bootmedian[i] <-
median(sample(sugar, replace=TRUE))
#creating 10,000 bootstrap samples
> head(bootmedian) #first 6 bootstrapped medians
[1]  9.5 12.0 11.5  6.5 11.0 10.0
> summary(bootmedian)
Min. 1st Qu. Median Mean 3rd Qu.  Max.
3.00   7.00   9.50 8.96   11.00 14.50
> sd(bootmedian) #bootstrap std. deviation
[1] 2.1797
```

We specified the sugar values and then illustrated how to create a bootstrap sample (bootsamp1, bootsamp2). The for loop generates a bootstrap sample 10,000 times and finds the median for each, saving it to bootsmedian—which we needed to initialize—for each iteration. After the for loop is completed, bootmedian contains the 10,000 medians generated. Summary statistics of the 10,000 generated bootstrap medians are shown via summary and sd. Type > hist(bootmedian) to obtain a histogram of the bootstrap distribution. To obtain the bootstrap distribution for the mean or standard deviation, simply replace the median command with mean or sd in the for loop. For carrying out the bootstrap with R for other statistics, such as the correlation, refer to the book's website for examples.

CHAPTER EXERCISES

Practicing the Basics

7.40 Exam performance An exam consists of 50 multiple-choice questions. Based on how much you studied, for any given question you think you have a probability of $p = 0.70$ of getting the correct answer. Consider the sampling distribution of the sample proportion of the 50 questions on which you get the correct answer.

    a. Find the mean and standard deviation of the sampling distribution of this proportion.

    b. What do you expect for the shape of the sampling distribution? Why?

    c. If truly $p = 0.70$, would it be very surprising if you got correct answers on only 60% of the questions? Justify your answer by using the normal distribution to approximate the probability of a sample proportion of 0.60 or less.

7.41 Blue eyes According to a *Boston Globe* story, only about 1 in 6 Americans has blue eyes, whereas in 1900 about half had blue eyes. (*Source:* Data from *The Boston Globe*, October 17, 2006.)

    a. For a random sample of 100 living Americans, find the mean and standard deviation of the proportion that have blue eyes.

    b. In a course you are taking with 100 students, half of the students have blue eyes. Would this have been a surprising result if the sample were a random sample

of Americans? Answer by finding how many standard deviations that sample result falls from the mean of the sampling distribution of the proportion of 100 students who have blue eyes.

    c. In part b, identify the population distribution, the data distribution, and the sampling distribution of the sample proportion.

7.42 Alzheimer's According to the Alzheimer's Association,[5] as of 2019 Alzheimer's disease affects 1 in 10 Americans over the age of 65. A study is planned of health problems the elderly face. For a random sample of Americans over the age of 65, report the shape, mean, and standard deviation of the sampling distribution of the proportion who suffer from Alzheimer's disease, if the sample size is (a) 200 and (b) 800.

7.43 Basketball three-pointers In college basketball, a shot made from beyond a designated arc radiating about 20 feet from the basket is worth three points instead of the usual two points given for shots made inside that arc. Over his career, University of Florida basketball player Lee Humphrey made 45% of his three-point attempts. In one game in his final season, he made only 3 of 12 three-point shots, leading a TV basketball analyst to announce that Humphrey was in a shooting slump.

    a. Assuming Humphrey has a 45% chance of making any particular three-point shot, find the mean and standard deviation of the sampling distribution of the proportion of three-point shots he will make out of 12 shots.

[5] www.alz.org/alzheimers-dementia/facts-figures

b. How many standard deviations from the mean is this game's result of making 3 of 12 three-point shots?

c. If Humphrey was actually not in a slump but still had a 45% chance of making any particular three-point shot, explain why it would not be especially surprising for him to make only 3 of 12 shots. Thus, this is not really evidence of a shooting slump.

7.44 **Defective chips** A supplier of electronic chips for tablets claims that only 4% of his chips are defective. A manufacturer tests 500 randomly selected chips from a large shipment from the supplier for potential defects. Assuming that the supplier's claim is true

a. find the mean and standard deviation for the distribution of the sample proportion of defective chips in the sample of 500.

b. Is it reasonable to assume a normal shape for the sampling distribution? Explain.

c. The manufacturer will return the entire shipment if it finds more than 5% of the 500 sampled chips to be defective. Find the probability that the shipment will be returned.

7.45 **Returning shipment** Refer to the previous exercise, in which the manufacturer will return the entire shipment if more than 5% defective chips are found in the sample.

a. Find the probability that the shipment will be returned if the manufacturer decides to test only 380 randomly selected chips (instead of 500).

b. Suppose that despite the claim by the supplier, the shipment actually contains 6% defective chips. Find the probability that the shipment will be returned if the manufacturer randomly samples 380 chips from the shipment.

7.46 **Aunt Erma's restaurant** In Aunt Erma's Restaurant, the daily sales follow a probability distribution that has a mean of $\mu = \$900$ and a standard deviation of $\sigma = \$300$. This past week the daily sales for the seven days had a mean of $980 and a standard deviation of $276. Consider these seven days as a random sample from all days.

a. Identify the mean and standard deviation of the population distribution.

b. Identify the mean and standard deviation of the data distribution. What does the standard deviation describe?

c. Identify the mean and the standard deviation of the sampling distribution of the sample mean for samples of seven daily sales. What does this standard deviation describe?

7.47 **Home runs** Based on data from the 2019 Major League Baseball season, $X =$ number of home runs the San Francisco Giants hit in a game has a mean of 1.0 and a standard deviation of 1.0.

a. Do you think X has a normal distribution? Why or why not?

b. Suppose that this year X has the same distribution. Report the shape, mean, and standard deviation of the sampling distribution of the mean number of home runs the team will hit in its 162 games.

c. Based on the answer to part b, find the probability that the mean number of home runs per game in this coming season will exceed 1.50.

7.48 **Physician's assistants** The 2006 AAPA survey of the population of physician's assistants who were working full time reported a mean annual income of $84,396 and standard deviation of $21,975. (*Source:* Data from 2006 AAPA survey [www.aapa.org].)

a. Suppose the AAPA had randomly sampled 100 physician's assistants instead of collecting data for all of them. Describe the mean, standard deviation, and shape of the sampling distribution of the sample mean.

b. Using this sampling distribution, find the z-score for a sample mean of $80,000.

c. Using parts a and b, find the probability that the sample mean would fall within approximately $4,000 of the population mean.

7.49 **Bank machine withdrawals** An executive in an Australian savings bank decides to estimate the mean amount of money withdrawn in bank machine transactions. From past experience, she believes that $50 (Australian) is a reasonable guess for the standard deviation of the distribution of withdrawals. She would like her sample mean to be within $10 of the population mean. Estimate the probability that this happens if she randomly samples 100 withdrawals. (*Hint:* Find the standard deviation of the sample mean. How many standard deviations does $10 equal?)

7.50 **PDI** The scores on the Psychomotor Development Index (PDI), a scale of infant development, have a normal population distribution with mean 100 and standard deviation 15. An infant is selected at random.

a. Find the z-score for a PDI value of 90.

b. A study uses a random sample of 225 infants. Using the sampling distribution of the sample mean PDI, find the z-score corresponding to a sample mean of 90.

c. Explain why a PDI value of 90 is not surprising, but a sample mean PDI score of 90 for 225 infants would be surprising.

7.51 **Number of sex partners** According to recent General Social Surveys, in the United States the population distribution for adults of $X =$ number of sex partners in the past 12 months has a mean of about 1.0 and a standard deviation of about 1.0.

a. Does X have a normal distribution? Explain.

b. For a random sample of 100 adults, describe the sampling distribution of $\bar{x}$ and give its mean and standard deviation. What is the effect of X not having a normal distribution?

7.52 **Possible bootstrap samples** A small random sample on the number of cell phones ever owned was taken from the student population at a large university, with the following result: {3, 2, 0, 1, 1}. Which of the following cannot be a bootstrap resample? Explain. (i) {1, 1, 1, 1, 1}, (ii) {3, 2, 0, 1, 1}, (iii) {2, 0, 1, 3}, (iii) {3, 2, 3, 2, 3}

7.53 End-of-month account balance A bank took a random sample of 300 of its account holders to learn more about the end-of-month balance (for the month of April) carried on accounts. The data (in USD) are preloaded in the *Bootstrap for One Sample* app under the name Bank Account Balance and also available on the book's website.

a. Open the app and use the dot plot and quoted summary statistics of the observed data to write a short statement about the distribution of the end-of-month balances in April.

b. Use the app to generate 5 bootstrap samples and give the mean balance for each resample.

c. Generate 10,000 more bootstrap samples and describe the resulting bootstrap distribution of the sample mean.

d. Can the Central Limit Theorem be used to predict the sampling distribution of the sample mean? Explain.

7.54 Median account balance Refer to the previous exercise on the end-of-month balance for a random sample of 300 bank accounts.

a. Why would we prefer to make inference about the median balance rather than the mean balance of all account holders?

b. Use the *Bootstrap for One Sample* app to find the median for 5 generated bootstrap samples.

c. Generate 10,000 more bootstrap samples and describe the resulting bootstrap distribution of the sample median.

d. Can the Central Limit Theorem be used to predict the sampling distribution of the sample median? Explain.

7.55 Variability of account balances Refer to Exercise 7.53 on the end-of-month balance for a sample of 300 bank accounts. The bank is also interested in the standard deviation of the account balances as a measure of the variability in the end-of-month balances.

a. Can you use the Central Limit Theorem to predict the sampling distribution of the sample standard deviation for such samples of size 300? Explain.

b. Use the *Bootstrap for One Sample* app to find the standard deviation for 5 generated bootstrap samples.

c. Generate 10,000 more bootstrap samples and describe the resulting bootstrap distribution of the sample standard deviation.

d. How far from the sample standard deviation of about $2,480 do you expect the population standard deviation of the end-of-month balances of all accounts to fall?

7.56 Body dissatisfaction Eating disorder symptoms can be divided into cognitive ones (e.g., feelings about one's body, such as body dissatisfaction or fear of weight gain) and behavioral ones (such as restricted food intake, vomiting, or excessive exercising). A study of 229 college freshmen, thought to be representative of freshmen in U.S. colleges and universities, probed for these two types of eating disorders through survey questions. Based on the answers to these questions, students in the study received a score on their cognitive eating disorder and their behavioral eating disorder. One goal of the study was to analyze the relationship between these two variables. The data are available in the *Scatterplots & Correlation* app and on the book's website under the name Eating Disorders.

a. Construct a scatterplot and describe the relationship between the cognitive and behavioral eating disorder scores.

b. Use the app to obtain 5 bootstrap samples and report the correlation coefficient r for each resample.

c. Construct and describe the bootstrap distribution for the correlation coefficient r.

7.57 CLT for the correlation? Refer to Example 6 about the relationship between the energy content and the carbon footprint of commercial ready-made sandwiches. Can we use the Central Limit Theorem to conclude that the sampling distribution of the correlation coefficient is approximately normal? Explain.

Concepts and Investigations

7.58 CLT for custom population Access the *Sampling Distribution for the Sample Mean (Continuous Population)* app and select Build Your Own from the top menu where you select the population distribution. By typing numbers into the text field, you can create your own population distribution. Repeating a number several times will make the population distribution more peaked around that number. Create a population that is very far from bell shaped. Then, use the app to simulate drawing 10,000 samples from this population and obtaining the sampling distribution of the sample mean. Explain how the shape and variability of the simulated sampling distribution changes as n changes from 2 to 5 to 30 to 100. Explain how the Central Limit Theorem describes what you have observed. (Note that the app allows you to download the graphs for the population, data, and simulated sampling distribution.)

7.59 What is a sampling distribution? How would you explain to someone who has never studied statistics what a sampling distribution is? Explain by using the example of polls of 1,000 Canadians for estimating the proportion who think the prime minister is doing a good job.

7.60 What good is a standard deviation? Explain how the standard deviation of the sampling distribution of a sample proportion gives you useful information to help gauge how close a sample proportion falls to the unknown population proportion.

7.61 Purpose of sampling distribution You'd like to estimate the proportion of all students in your school who are fluent in more than one language. You poll a random sample of 50 students and get a sample proportion of 0.12. Explain why the standard deviation of the sampling distribution of the sample proportion gives you useful information to help gauge how close this sample proportion is to the unknown population proportion.

7.62 Sampling distribution for small and large n The owners of Aunt Erma's Restaurant in Boston plan an advertising campaign with the claim that more people prefer the taste of their pizza (which we'll denote by A) than the current leading fast-food chain selling pizza (which we'll denote by D). To support their claim, they plan to sample three people in Boston randomly. Each person is asked to taste a slice of pizza A and a slice of pizza D. Subjects are blindfolded so they cannot see the pizza when they taste it, and the order of giving them the two slices is randomized. They are then asked which pizza tastes better. Use a symbol with three letters to represent the responses for each possible sample. For instance, ADD represents a sample in which the first subject sampled preferred pizza A and the second and third subjects preferred pizza D.

a. List the eight possible samples of size 3, and for each sample report the proportion that preferred pizza A.

b. In the entire Boston population, suppose that exactly half would prefer pizza A and half would prefer pizza D. Then, each of the eight possible samples is equally likely to be observed. Explain why the sampling distribution of the sample proportion who prefer Aunt Erma's pizza, when $n = 3$, is

Sample Proportion	Probability
0	1/8
1/3	3/8
2/3	3/8
1	1/8

c. In theory, you could use the same principle as in part b to find the sampling distribution for any n, but it is tedious to list all elements of the sample space. For instance, for $n = 50$, there are more than 10^{15} elements to list. Despite this, what is the mean, standard deviation, and approximate shape of the *sampling distribution* of the sample proportion when $n = 50$ (still assuming that the population proportion preferring pizza A is 0.5)?

7.63 **Sampling distribution via the binomial** Refer to the previous exercise, in which the proportion of people preferring pizza A is $p = 0.5$ and a sample of size $n = 3$ is taken. The sampling distribution of the sample proportion of people preferring pizza A as shown in part b of that exercise can also be derived using the binomial distribution with $n = 3$ and $p = 0.5$.

a. A sample proportion of 1/3 corresponds to 1 out of 3 randomly sampled persons preferring pizza A. Show that this occurs with probability 3/8. (*Hint:* Use the binomial formula with $p = 0.5$ and $x = 1$ person out of $n = 3$ preferring pizza A.)

b. Find the probabilities for the remaining sample proportions by using the binomial distribution with $x = 0, 2,$ or 3.

c. Find the sampling distribution of the sample proportion when $n = 4$ people (instead of $n = 3$) are sampled and draw its graph.

7.64 **Pizza preference with $p = 0.6$** Refer to the previous two exercises but now suppose the population proportion in Boston preferring pizza A is $p = 0.6$ instead of $p = 0.5$. (Then, the eight possible outcomes (AAA, AAD,…, DDA, DDD) of a sample of size $n = 3$ are *not* equally likely, as in part b of Exercise 7.62)

a. Use the binomial distribution to verify that the sampling distribution of the sample proportion in a sample of size $n = 3$ is given by

Number Preferring A	Proportion Preferring A	Probability
0	0	0.064
1	1/3	0.288
2	2/3	0.432
3	1	0.216

(*Note:* Using the binomial distribution, you can, in principle, find the sampling distribution for the sample proportion for any n and p.)

b. When $n = 100$, what is the mean number of persons that prefer pizza A in a sample of size $n = 100$? (*Hint:* Use the formula for the mean of a binomial distribution.)

c. Part b found the mean number (or expected value) of persons preferring pizza A in a sample of size 100. What then is the expected *proportion* of persons preferring pizza A in a sample of size 100? This is the mean of the sampling distribution of the sample proportion.

7.65 **Simulating pizza preference with $p = 0.5$** Access the *Sampling Distribution of the Sample Proportion* app.

a. For $p = 0.5$ and a sample of size $n = 3$, the graph of the sampling distribution is given below. (This is the graph corresponding to the table in Exercise 7.62, part b.) Compute the mean and standard deviation of the sampling distribution from first principles, i.e., with the formulas for the mean (expected value) and standard deviation for discrete random variables given in Section 6.1.

b. Now, using the app, simulate the sampling distribution for a population proportion when $p = 0.5$ and $n = 3$, using 10,000 simulations. Do the graph and the results from the simulations agree? Compare the shapes, means, and standard deviations from part a with the simulation results displayed by the app. (In the app, under Options, click on Summary Statistics of Samp. Dist.)

7.66 **Simulating pizza preference with $p = 0.6$** Access the *Sampling Distribution of the Sample Proportion* app. When $p = 0.6$ and the sample size $n = 3$, the mean and standard deviation of the sampling distribution (which is given in the table in part a of Exercise 7.64) are equal to 0.6 and 0.283. With the app, simulate the sampling distribution by generating 10,000 samples. Are the mean and standard deviation of the 10,000 simulated sample proportions close to the true mean and standard deviation stated above? (In the app, under Options, click on Summary Statistics of Samp. Dist. to show these statistics for the simulated proportions.)

7.67 **Sampling distribution rolling dice** Access the *Sampling Distribution of the Sample Mean (Discrete Population)* app and select Fair Die as the population distribution. The resulting discrete population distribution with $P(x) = 1/6$ for $x = 1, 2, ..., 6$ has $\mu = 3.5$ and $\sigma = 1.71$.

a. Moving the slider for the sample size to $n = 2$ and pressing the Draw Sample(s) button simulates taking a sample of size 2 from this population, which is the same as observing the outcome of rolling two dice. Press the button a couple of times to observe the possible values for the mean number in two rolls. Then, generate 10,000 samples to simulate the sampling distribution of the sample mean when $n = 2$. Is the distribution approximately normal? Do we expect it to be approximately normal? Explain.

b. Are the reported mean and standard deviation of the simulated sampling distribution close to the theoretical mean and standard deviation for this sampling distribution? Explain.

c. Repeat part a, but now simulate taking samples of size $n = 30$ (e.g., taking the average of the face value of 30 dice rolled). What are the major changes you observe?

Multiple Choice or True/False

7.68 **True or false** As the sample size increases, the standard deviation of the sampling distribution of $\bar{x}$ increases. Explain your answer.

7.69 **Standard deviation** Which of the following is *not* correct? The standard deviation of a statistic describes

a. The standard deviation of the sampling distribution of that statistic.

b. The standard deviation of the observed measurements in the sample.

c. How close that statistic falls to the parameter that it estimates.

d. The variability in the values of the statistic from sample to sample of the same size.

7.70 **Multiple choice: CLT** The Central Limit Theorem implies

a. All variables have approximately bell-shaped data distributions if a random sample contains at least about 30 observations.

b. Population distributions are normal whenever the population size is large.

c. For sufficiently large random samples, the sampling distribution of $\bar{x}$ is approximately normal, regardless of the shape of the population distribution.

d. The sampling distribution of the sample mean looks more like the population distribution as the sample size increases.

7.71 **Sampling distribution of sample proportion** In a class of 150 students, the professor has each person toss a fair coin 50 times and calculate the proportion of times the tosses come up heads. Roughly 95% of students should have proportions between which two numbers?

a. 0.49 and 0.51.

b. 0.05 and 0.95.

c. 0.42 and 0.58.

d. 0.36 and 0.64.

e. 0.25 and 0.75.

Explain your answer.

7.72 **Sampling distribution** The sampling distribution of a sample mean for a random sample size of 100 describes

a. How sample means tend to vary from random sample to random sample of size 100.

b. How observations tend to vary from person to person in a random sample of size 100.

c. How the data distribution looks like the population distribution when the sample size is larger than 30.

d. How the standard deviation varies among samples of size 100.

Advanced Concepts

7.73 **Sample = population** Let $X =$ GPA for students in your school.

a. What would the sampling distribution of the sample mean look like if you sampled *every* student in the school, so the sample size equals the population size? (*Hint:* The sample mean then equals the population mean.)

b. How does the sampling distribution compare to the population distribution if we take a sample of size $n = 1$?

7.74 **Using control charts to assess quality** In many industrial production processes, measurements are made periodically on critical characteristics to ensure that the process is operating properly. Observations vary from item to item being produced, perhaps reflecting variability in material used in the process and/or variability in the way a person operates machinery used in the process. There is usually a target mean for the observations, which represents the long-run mean of the observations when the process is operating properly. There is also a target standard deviation for how observations should vary around that mean if the process is operating properly. A **control chart** is a method for plotting data collected over time to monitor whether the process is operating within the limits of expected variation. A control chart that plots *sample means* over time is called an **$\bar{x}$-chart**. As shown in the following control chart, the horizontal axis is the time scale, and the vertical axis shows possible sample mean values. The horizontal line in the middle of the chart shows the target for the true mean. The upper and lower lines are called the **upper control limit** and **lower control limit,** denoted by **UCL** and **LCL**. These are usually drawn 3 standard deviations above and below the target value. The region between the LCL and UCL contains the values that theory predicts for the sample mean when the process is in control. When a sample mean falls above the UCL or below the LCL, it indicates that something may have gone wrong in the production process.

a. Walter Shewhart invented this method in 1924 at Bell Labs. He suggested using 3 standard deviations in setting

$\bar{x}$-chart

- - - - - - - - - - - - - - - - - - UCL

$\bar{x}$ ——————————————— Target

- - - - - - - - - - - - - - - - - - LCL

Time

the UCL and LCL to achieve a balance between having the chart fail to diagnose a problem and having it indicate a problem when none actually existed. If the process is working properly ("in statistical control") and if n is large enough that $\bar{x}$ has approximately a normal distribution, what is the probability that it indicates a problem when none exists? (That is, what's the probability a sample mean will be at least 3 standard deviations from the target, when that target is the true mean?)

b. What would the probability of falsely indicating a problem be if we used 2 standard deviations instead for the UCL and LCL?

c. When about nine sample means in a row fall on the same side of the target for the mean in a control chart, this is an indication of a potential problem, such as a shift up or a shift down in the true mean relative to the target value. If the process is actually in control and has a normal distribution around that mean, what is the probability that the next nine sample means in a row would (i) all fall above the mean and (ii) all fall above or all fall below the mean? (*Hint:* Use the binomial distribution, treating the successive observations as independent.)

7.75 Too little or too much cola?   Refer to the previous exercise. When a machine for dispensing a cola drink into bottles is in statistical control, the amount dispensed has a mean of 500 ml (milliliters) and a standard deviation of 4 ml.

a. In constructing a control chart to monitor this process with periodic samples of size 4, how would you select the target line and the upper and lower control limits?

b. If the process actually deteriorates and operates with a mean of 491 ml and a standard deviation of 6 ml, what is the probability that the next value plotted on the control chart indicates a problem with the process, falling more than 3 standard deviations from the target? What do you assume in making this calculation?

7.76 Finite populations   The formula $\sigma/\sqrt{n}$ for the standard deviation of $\bar{x}$ actually is an approximation that treats the population size as *infinitely* large relative to the sample size n. The exact formula for a *finite* population size N is

$$\text{Standard deviation} = \sqrt{\frac{N-n}{N-1}}\,\frac{\sigma}{\sqrt{n}}.$$

The term $\sqrt{(N-n)/(N-1)}$ is called the **finite population correction.**

a. When $n = 300$ students are selected from a college student body of size $N = 30{,}000$, show that the standard deviation equals $0.995\,(\sigma/\sqrt{n})$. (When n is small compared to the population size N, the approximate formula works very well.)

b. If $n = N$ (that is, we sample the entire population), show that the standard deviation equals 0. In other words, no sampling error occurs, since $\bar{x} = \mu$ in that case.

Student Activities

7.77 Mean hotel price   The following table (full data are available on the book's website in the file "Inns") provides prices per night for 7 of all 51 available hotel rooms in Panama City Beach, Florida, for a week in March 2015 (spring break). The distribution of prices for these 51 available hotel rooms is characterized by $\mu = \$196$ and $\sigma = \$57.4$.

Hotel	Price
St. Thomas Square	75
American Quality Lodge	92
Hathaway Inn	105
Top Of The Gulf	129
Palm Grove	134
Shores of Panama	139
Sleep Inn	140
...	

a. Each student or the class should construct a graphical display (stem-and-leaf plot, dot plot, or histogram) of the population distribution of the prices e.g., using the *Explore Quantitative Data* app. (Alternatively, access the *Sampling Distribution for the Sample Mean (Continuous Population)* app. Select Build Your Own for the population distribution from the top menu and copy and paste the data from a spreadsheet into the box given in the app. This provides a smoothed curve for the population distribution of hotel prices, with $\mu = 196$ and $\sigma = 58.5$.)

b. Each student should select nine random numbers between 1 and 51, e.g., using the *Random Numbers* app. Using these numbers, each student should sample nine hotels and find the mean price for these hotels. Collect all sample mean prices and construct a graph (using the same graphical display as in part a) of the simulated sampling distribution of the $\bar{x}$-values. Compare it to the distribution in part a. (Alternatively, you can simulate taking random samples of size 9 with the *Sampling Distribution for the Sample Mean (Continuous Population)* app under the setting mentioned in part a.)

c. Find the mean of the $\bar{x}$-values in part b. How does it compare to the value you would expect in a long run of repeated samples of size 9?

d. Find the standard deviation of the $\bar{x}$-values in part b. How does it compare to the value you would expect in a long run of repeated samples of size 9?

7.78 Coin-tossing distributions   For a single toss of a balanced coin, let $x = 1$ for a head and $x = 0$ for a tail.

a. Construct the probability distribution for x and calculate its mean.

b. The coin is flipped 10 times, yielding 6 heads and 4 tails. Construct the data distribution.

c. Each student in the class should flip a coin 10 times and find the proportion of heads. Collect the sample proportion of heads from each student. Summarize the simulated sampling distribution by constructing a plot of all the proportions obtained by the students. Describe the shape and variability of the sampling distribution compared to the distributions in parts a and b.

d. If you performed the experiment in part c a huge number of times, what would you expect to get for the (i) mean and (ii) standard deviation of the sample proportions?

7.79 **Age of coins** Each student should bring 10 coins to class. For each coin, observe its age, the difference between the current year and the year on the coin.

a. Using all the students' observations, the class should construct a histogram of the sample ages. What is its shape?

b. Now each student should find the mean for that student's 10 coins, and the class should plot the means of all the students. What type of distribution is this, and how does it compare to the one in part a? What concepts does this exercise illustrate?

Inferential Statistics

Statistical Inference: Confidence Intervals

Example 1

Analyzing Data from the General Social Survey

Picture the Scenario

For more than 30 years, the National Opinion Research Center at the University of Chicago (www.norc.uchicago.edu) has conducted an opinion survey called the General Social Survey (GSS). The survey randomly samples about 2,000 adult Americans. In a 90-minute in-person interview, the interviewer asks a long list of questions about opinions and behavior for a wide variety of issues. Other nations have similar surveys. For instance, every five years Statistics Canada conducts its own General Social Survey. *Eurobarometer* regularly samples about 1,000 people in each country in the European Union and a host of other polling institutions, such as Gallup (news.gallup.com) or the Pew Research Center (pewresearch.org), feature results from all sorts of polls on their websites.

Analyzing such data helps researchers learn about how people think and behave at a given time and track opinions over time. Activity 1 in Chapter 1 showed how to access the GSS data directly or through the book's website, ArtofStat.com.

Questions to Explore

Based on data from a recent GSS, how can you make an inference about

- The proportion of Americans who are willing to pay higher prices to protect the environment?
- The proportion of Americans who agree that it is better for everyone involved if the man is the achiever outside the home and the woman takes care of the home and family?
- The mean number of hours that Americans watch TV per day?

Thinking Ahead

We will analyze data from the GSS in examples and exercises throughout this chapter. For instance, in Example 3 we'll see how to estimate the proportion of Americans who are willing to pay higher prices to protect the environment.

We'll answer the other two questions in Examples 2 and 5, and in exercises we'll explore opinions about issues such as whether it should or should not be the government's responsibility to reduce income differences between the rich and poor, whether a preschool child is likely to suffer if his or her mother works, and how politically conservative or liberal Americans are.

A sample of about 2,000 U.S. adults (as taken by the GSS) is relatively small. For instance, in the United States, a survey of this size gathers data for less than 1 of every 100,000 adults. How can we possibly make reliable predictions about the entire population with so few people?

Recall

A **statistic** describes a **sample.** Examples are the sample mean $\bar{x}$ and standard deviation s.

A **parameter** describes a **population.** Examples are the population mean μ and standard deviation σ. ◄

We now have the tools to see how this is done. We're ready to learn about a powerful use of statistics: **statistical inference** about population parameters using sample data. Inference methods help us to predict how close a sample statistic falls to the population parameter. We can make decisions and predictions about populations even if we have data for relatively few subjects from that population. The previous chapter illustrated that it's often possible to predict the winner of an election in which millions of people voted, knowing only how a couple of thousand people voted from an exit poll.

For statistical inference methods, you may wonder what the relevance of learning about the role of randomization is in gathering data (Chapter 4), concepts of probability (Chapter 5), and the normal distribution (Chapter 6) and its use as a sampling distribution (Chapter 7). They're important for two primary reasons:

Recall

A **sampling distribution** specifies the possible values a statistic can take and their probabilities. ◄

- Statistical inference methods use probability calculations that assume that the data were gathered with a random sample or a randomized experiment.
- The probability calculations refer to a sampling distribution of a statistic, which is often approximately a normal distribution.

In other words, statistical inference uses sampling distributions of statistics calculated from data gathered using randomization, and those sampling distributions are often approximately normal.

Recall

We use the **proportion** to summarize the *relative frequency* of observations in a category for a categorical variable. The proportion equals the number in the category divided by the sample size. We use the **mean** as one way to summarize the *center* of the observations for a quantitative variable. ◄

There are two types of statistical inference methods—**estimation** of population parameters and **testing hypotheses** about the parameter values. This chapter discusses the first type, estimating population parameters. We'll learn how to estimate population proportions for categorical variables and population means for quantitative variables. For instance, a study dealing with how college students pay for their education might estimate the proportion of college students who work part time and the mean hourly wage for those who work. The most informative estimation method constructs an interval of numbers, called a **confidence interval,** within which the unknown parameter value is believed to fall.

8.1 Point and Interval Estimates of Population Parameters

Population parameters have two types of estimates, a point estimate and an interval estimate.

> **Point Estimate and Interval Estimate**
>
> A **point estimate** is a *single number* that is our best guess for the parameter.
>
> An **interval estimate** is an *interval of numbers* that is quite likely to contain the actual value of the parameter.

For example, one General Social Survey asked, "Do you believe in hell?" From the sample data, the point estimate for the proportion of adult Americans who would respond yes equals 0.73, or 73%. The adjective "point" in *point estimate* refers to using a single number or *point* as the parameter estimate.

An interval estimate, found with the method introduced in the next section, predicts that the proportion of adult Americans who believe in hell falls between 0.71 and 0.75, that is between 71% and 75%. Figure 8.1 illustrates this idea.

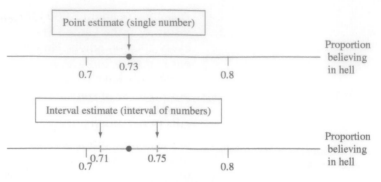

▲ **Figure 8.1** A Point Estimate Predicts a Parameter by a Single Number. An **interval estimate** is an interval of numbers that are believable values for the parameter. **Question** Why is a point estimate alone not sufficiently informative?

A point estimate by itself is not sufficient because it doesn't tell us *how close* the estimate is likely to be to the parameter. An interval estimate is much more useful. It tells us that the point estimate of 0.73 falls within a *margin of error* of 0.02 of the actual population proportion. By incorporating a margin of error, the interval estimate helps us gauge the accuracy of the point estimate.

Point Estimation: Making a Best Guess for a Population Parameter

Once we've collected the data, how do we find a point estimate, representing our best guess for a parameter value? The answer is straightforward—we can use an appropriate sample statistic. For example, for a population mean μ, the sample mean $\bar{x}$ is a point estimate of μ. For a population proportion p, the sample proportion is a point estimate.

Starting here, we will denote the sample proportion by $\hat{p}$, pronounced "*p*-hat." (You have actually seen this symbol before in Chapter 7, when we talked about the sampling distribution of the sample proportion. Look at Figures 7.2 to 7.4, where the orange circle marked the population proportion p and the blue triangle marked the sample proportion $\hat{p}$ computed from a sample drawn from this population.) In statistics, a circumflex ("hat") symbol placed over the symbol for a population parameter represents the point estimate for that parameter. Here, $\hat{p}$ represents the point estimate of the population proportion p. For instance, $\hat{p} = 0.73$ is the point estimate for the proportion p of adults in the U.S. who believe in hell.

Point estimates are the most common form of inference reported by the mass media. For example, the Gallup organization conducted a survey in August 2019 on whether U.S. adults, if given the choice, would prefer to have a job outside the home or stay at home and take care of the home and family. Mass media then disseminates the results of such surveys, for instance by reporting "New survey finds that 66% of adults would prefer a job outside the home." Such a reported percentage is a *point estimate* rather than a parameter because Gallup used a sample of about 1,500 adults living in the U.S. rather than the entire population. For simplicity, we'll usually use the term *estimate* in place of point estimate when there is no risk of confusing it with an interval estimate. Table 8.1 on the next page lists some of the population parameters we have encountered so far, together with their point estimates.

Properties of Point Estimates For any particular parameter, there may be several possible point estimates. Consider, for instance, estimating the parameter μ from a normal distribution, which describes the center. With sample data from a normal distribution, two possible estimates of μ are the sample mean but also

Table 8.1 Examples of Population Parameters and Their Point Estimates

Population Parameter	Point Estimate (Statistic)
Population Proportion p	Sample Proportion $\hat{p}$
Population Mean μ	Sample Mean $\bar{x}$
Population Median	Sample Median
Population Standard Deviation σ	Sample Standard Deviation s
Correlation between two variables in the population	Correlation Coefficient r computed from data
Slope of the linear regression model in the population	Slope b computed from fitting straight line in scatterplot

the sample median because the distribution is symmetric. What makes one point estimate better than another? *A good estimate* of a parameter has two desirable properties:

Property 1: A good estimate has a sampling distribution that is centered at the parameter it tries to estimate. We define *center* in this case as the mean of that sampling distribution. An estimate with this property is said to be **unbiased**. From Section 7.2, we know that under random sampling the mean of the sampling distribution of the sample mean $\bar{x}$ equals the population mean μ. So, the sample mean $\bar{x}$ is an unbiased estimate of μ. Figure 8.2 recalls this result.

Similarly, from Section 7.1, we know that under random sampling the mean of the sampling distribution of the sample proportion $\hat{p}$ equals the population proportion p. So, the sample proportion $\hat{p}$ is an unbiased estimate of the population proportion p.

Property 2: A good estimate has a *small standard deviation* compared to other estimates. This tells us the estimate tends to fall closer than other estimates to the parameter. For example, for estimating the center μ of a normal distribution, both the sample mean and the sample median are unbiased, but the sample mean has a smaller standard deviation (see margin figure and Exercise 8.123). Therefore, the sample mean is the better estimate for μ.

Sampling Distribution

The sampling distribution of the sample mean has the smaller standard deviation.

Recall

From Chapter 7, the standard deviation of the sampling distribution describes the variability in the possible values of the statistic for the given sample size. It also tells us how much the statistic would vary from sample to sample of that size. ◄

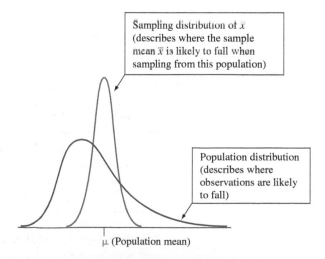

Sampling distribution of $\bar{x}$ (describes where the sample mean $\bar{x}$ is likely to fall when sampling from this population)

Population distribution (describes where observations are likely to fall)

μ (Population mean)

▲ **Figure 8.2 The Sample Mean $\bar{x}$ Is an Unbiased Estimate.** Its sampling distribution is centered at the parameter it estimates—the population mean μ. **Question** When is the sampling distribution bell shaped, as it is in this figure?

Interval Estimation: Constructing an Interval That Is Quite Likely to Contain the Parameter

A recent survey[1] on the starting salary of new college graduates estimated the mean starting salary equal to $55,300. Does $55,300 seem plausible to you? Too high? Too low? Any individual point estimate may or may not be close to the parameter it estimates. For the estimate to be useful, we need to know how close it is likely to fall to the actual parameter value. Is the estimate of $55,300 likely to be within $1,000 of the actual population mean? Within $5,000? Within $10,000? Inference about a parameter should not only provide a point estimate but also indicate its likely precision.

An **interval estimate** indicates precision by giving an interval of numbers around the point estimate. The interval is made up of numbers that are the most believable values for the unknown parameter, based on the data observed. For instance, a survey of new college graduates predicts that the mean starting salary falls somewhere between $52,300 and $58,300, that is, within a *margin of error* of $3,000 of the point estimate of $55,300.

An interval estimate is designed to contain the parameter with some chosen probability, such as 95%. Because interval estimates contain the parameter with a certain degree of confidence, they are referred to as **confidence intervals.**

Confidence Interval

A **confidence interval** is an interval containing the most plausible values for a parameter. It is constructed by a method that combines a **point estimate** with a **margin of error**. The probability that this method produces an interval that contains the parameter is called the **confidence level**, which is a number chosen to be close to 100%, most commonly 95%.

The interval from $52,300 to $58,300 is an example of a confidence interval. It was constructed using a confidence level of 95%. This implies that we have "95% confidence" that the interval contains the parameter. It is a **95% confidence interval.** (Later in this chapter we will discuss why we don't construct 100% confidence intervals.)

What method do we use to construct a confidence interval? The key is the *sampling distribution* of the point estimate. This distribution tells us the probability that the point estimate will fall within any certain distance of the parameter.

Standard Error and Margin of Error

The first step towards constructing a confidence interval is to estimate the standard deviation of the sampling distribution because it typically depends on unknown parameters. For instance, as discussed in Chapter 7, the standard deviation of the sample proportion equals $\sqrt{p(1-p)/n}$, which depends on the unknown population proportion p. To actually compute the standard deviation, we need to replace the unknown population proportion p by its point estimate, the sample proportion $\hat{p}$. Similarly, as we also saw in Chapter 7, the standard deviation of the sample mean equals $\sigma/\sqrt{n}$, which depends on the unknown population standard deviation σ. To compute this standard deviation, we'll have to estimate σ first.

In Practice The Standard Deviation of a Sampling Distribution Needs to Be Estimated

The standard deviation of a sampling distribution typically depends on one (or more) population parameters. The values for these parameters are unknown. To compute the standard deviation, we need to substitute an estimate for the unknown parameters into the formula for the standard deviation.

---

[1]By National Association of Colleges and Employers, www.naceweb.org.

Beginning here, we'll use the term **standard error** to refer to the estimated standard deviation of the sampling distribution for a statistic. For instance, substituting $\hat{p}$ for p in the formula for the standard deviation of the sample proportion gives the standard error $\sqrt{\hat{p}(1-\hat{p})/n}$ for the sample proportion.

Standard Error

The **standard error** is the estimated standard deviation of a sampling distribution.

We will often use the notation *se* as a shorthand for standard error, such as $se = \sqrt{\hat{p}(1-\hat{p})/n}$ for the standard error for a sample proportion.

The second step towards constructing a confidence interval involves the shape of the sampling distribution. If it is approximately normal, then we know from Chapter 6 that 95% of the distribution falls within 2, or, more precisely, 1.96 standard deviations of the mean. For instance, because the sampling distribution of the sample proportion $\hat{p}$ is approximately normal for large n, with probability 95%, the sample proportion $\hat{p}$ falls within 1.96 standard deviations of the population proportion p. The figure in the margin illustrates this fact. Here, the distance of 1.96 standard deviations to either side of the mean p equals $\pm 1.96\sqrt{p(1-p)/n}$, which depends on the unknown population proportion p. To estimate this distance, we substitute $\hat{p}$ for p to obtain $\pm 1.96\sqrt{\hat{p}(1-\hat{p})/n}$, or, for short, $\pm 1.96(se)$, where *se* is the standard error of the sample proportion. This quantity, $\pm 1.96(se)$, is called the **margin of error**. We have been mentioning the margin of error since Chapter 1. It gives an estimate of how close the point estimate is likely to fall to the population parameter.

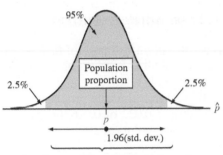

Sampling Distribution of Sample Proportion

95%

Population proportion

2.5%   2.5%

$\hat{p}$

p

1.96(std. dev.)

With 95% probability, $\hat{p}$ falls in this interval.

Margin of Error

The **margin of error** estimates the precision of a point estimate for a given confidence level. It measures how close the point estimate is likely to fall to the population parameter. For a sampling distribution that is approximately normal, the margin of error is a **multiple of the standard error (se)**, such as $\pm 1.96(se)$ when the confidence level is 95%.

Example 2

Standard Error and
Margin of Error ◄

A Wife's Career

Picture the Scenario

One question on the General Social Survey asks about the following statement: "It is much better for everyone involved if the man is the achiever outside the home and the woman takes care of the home and family." In the 2018 GSS, 398 of 1,545 respondents either agreed or strongly agreed with this statement, resulting in a sample proportion of those agreeing of $\hat{p} = 398/1,545 = 0.26$.

Questions to Explore

a. Find the standard error of the sample proportion. What does it tell us?

b. Find the margin of error for this sample proportion when the confidence level is 95%. What does it tell us?

Think It Through

a. The standard error equals the estimated standard deviation of the sampling distribution for the sample proportion. This standard deviation equals $\sqrt{p(1-p)/n}$, where p is the (unknown) proportion of U.S. adults agreeing with that statement. To estimate it, we use the sample proportion $\hat{p} = 0.26$ in place of p to obtain the standard error:

$$se = \sqrt{\hat{p}(1-\hat{p})/n} = \sqrt{0.26(1-0.26)/1{,}545} = 0.011.$$

The se of 0.011 tells us by how much we can expect the sample proportion to vary from sample to sample, when taking samples of such a size from a population. With such a small se of only 0.011, we don't expect the sample proportion to vary a lot when taking samples of size 1,545.

b. For such a large sample size, the sampling distribution of $\hat{p}$ is approximately normal. Then, using a confidence level of 95%, the margin of error for the sample proportion equals

$$\text{margin of error} = \pm 1.96(se) = \pm 1.96(0.011) = \pm 0.022.$$

The margin of error tells us how precise the point estimate of 0.26 is in estimating the true population proportion of all U.S. adults agreeing with that statement. Because the margin of error is relatively small at $\pm$ 0.022, we are quite confident (95% confident) that the true proportion in the population is close to 0.26, i.e., within ± 0.022 of 0.026, or, expressed as a percentage, within ± 2.2 percentage points of 26%.

Insight

Without knowing the margin of error, we have no idea how precise the point estimate of 26% for the population percentage is. It could have been within ± 5, ± 10, or perhaps even within ± 20 percentage points of the true population percentage, in which case it is not worth very much because it is so imprecise.

▶ *Try Exercises 8.4 and 8.8*

Did You Know?

On the 2012 GSS, the point estimate of those agreeing equaled 31%, with a margin of error of also around ± 2 percentage points; in 1977, when this question was first asked, the point estimate was 66%, also with a margin of error of ± 2 percentage points. Is there evidence that the opinion has shifted considerably over time, even between 2012 to 2018? ◀

The Logic Behind Constructing Confidence Intervals

We said that a confidence interval combines a point estimate with a margin of error. More precisely, the point estimate plus or minus the margin of error provides a confidence interval for a population parameter, so a general formula to construct a confidence interval is

$$\text{point estimate } \pm \text{ margin of error.}$$

If the sampling distribution is approximately normal and the confidence level 95%, then the margin of error equals $\pm 1.96(se)$, and the formula for the 95% confidence interval becomes

$$\text{point estimate } \pm 1.96(se).$$

In Words

"point estimate $\pm 1.96(se)$" represents taking the point estimate and adding and subtracting 1.96 times the standard error to obtain the confidence interval.

For instance, the 95% confidence interval for the proportion of U.S. adults agreeing with the statement from Example 2 (where the point estimate was 0.26 and the margin of error was 0.022) is given by 0.26 $\pm$ 0.022, which results in the interval (0.238, 0.282). We interpret this 95% confidence interval as being 95% confident that plausible values for the proportion of U.S. adults agreeing with the statement are between 0.238 and 0.282, or between 23.8% and 28.2%, with a point estimate of 26%.

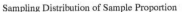

Sampling Distribution of Sample Proportion

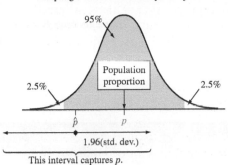

This interval captures p.

What's the logic behind the formula *point estimate* $\pm 1.96(se)$ for a 95% confidence interval? We will illustrate with the sample proportion as a point estimate. Because the sampling distribution of the sample proportion is approximately normal (for large n), there is a 95% chance a sample proportion $\hat{p}$ occurs that is within 1.96 standard deviations of the population proportion. If this is the case, stretching out 1.96 standard deviations to either side of $\hat{p}$ will capture the population proportion p, see the figure in the margin. In other words, the interval

$$\hat{p} \pm 1.96(\text{standard deviation})$$

captures the population proportion with a probability of 95%. Only if a sample proportion $\hat{p}$ occurs that is in the extreme lower or upper tail of the normal distribution, stretching out 1.96 standard deviations to either side of $\hat{p}$ will not be enough and the interval will not capture the population proportion. However, observing such an extreme sample proportion (i.e., one that falls in either of the two tail regions in the margin figure) only happens 5% of the time.

In practice, we don't know the standard deviation, and we can't compute this interval directly. But we can use the standard error to estimate the standard deviation, which leads to the formula $\hat{p} \pm 1.96(se)$ for the 95% confidence interval for the population proportion.

In general, the formula for a confidence interval when the sampling distribution of the point estimate is approximately normal is given by

$$point\ estimate \pm margin\ of\ error.$$

SUMMARY: Confidence Interval

A confidence interval is constructed by taking a point estimate and adding and subtracting a margin of error. The margin of error is based on a multiple of the standard error (*se*) of the point estimate. When the sampling distribution of the point estimate is approximately normal, a 95% confidence interval is given by the formula *point estimate* $\pm 1.96(se)$, where $1.96(se)$ is the margin of error.

The sampling distribution of many important point estimates is approximately normal when the sample size of the random sample is relatively large. Thus, this logic of taking the margin of error for a 95% confidence interval to be 1.96 standard errors applies with large random samples, such as those found in the General Social Survey and many others. The next two sections show more details for finding the margin of error and constructing confidence intervals for population proportions and population means. If the sampling distribution for a point estimate is not bell shaped, the last section in this chapter uses the bootstrap to find confidence intervals for such scenarios.

▶ Activity 1

Download Data from the General Social Survey

We saw in Chapter 1 that it's easy to download data from the GSS. Let's recall how.

- Go to the GSS website sda.berkeley.edu, click on the Archive box near the top, and then select the top link under the General Social Survey (GSS) heading which is the most recent GSS available. (In 2020, this was the Cumulative Datafile from 1972 to 2018.)

- Alternatively, simply follow the GSS link on the book's website, ArtofStat.com.
- The GSS name for the variable in Example 2 (whether the men should be the achiever) is FEFAM. (You can search for these mnemonics by keywords using the Search box, or get a list of available ones from the Standard Codebook.) Type FEFAM as the row variable.
- Next, enter YEAR(2018) in the box called Selection Filter. This ensures you are only seeing results from the 2018 GSS. Alternatively, if you want to see results for all the years this question was asked, enter YEAR into the column box and leave the Selection Filter box empty.

- Select No Weight for the drop-down menu for Weight.
- Press Run Table. This will show that in 2018, 398 of 1,545 respondents either agreed or strongly agreed with the FEFAM statement.

Now, investigate other variables. If you open the Standard Codebook, you will see indexes for other questions asked on the GSS. Look up a subject that interests you and find the GSS code name for a variable. For example, to find the percentage who believe in hell, enter HELL as the code name.

Try Exercise 8.4a ◄

8.1　Practicing the Basics

8.1　Health care　A study dealing with health care issues plans to take a sample survey of 1,500 Americans to estimate the proportion who have health insurance and the mean dollar amount that Americans spent on health care this past year.

　a. Identify two population parameters that this study will estimate.

　b. Identify two statistics (i.e., point estimates) that can be used to estimate these parameters.

8.2　Video on demand　A recent study from Nielsen (available from nielsen.com; search for The Cross-Platform Report) took a sample of U.S. adults to investigate how video on demand and other subscription-based services (such as Netflix, Amazon Prime, and Hulu) change TV viewing behavior. Among others, the study recorded how many adults primarily watch content time-shifted (i.e., not live) and the weekly number of hours adults spend watching content over the Internet.

　a. Mention two population parameters that this survey is trying to estimate.

　b. Mention two corresponding statistics (i.e., point estimates) that will estimate these population parameters.

　c. The sample mean number of hours watched online is an unbiased estimate for what parameter? Explain what unbiased means.

8.3　Projecting winning candidate　News coverage during a recent election projected that a certain candidate would receive 54.8% of all votes cast; the projection had a margin of error of ±3%.

　a. Give a point estimate for the proportion of all votes the candidate will receive.

　b. Give an interval estimate for the proportion of all votes the candidate will receive.

　c. In your own words, state the difference between a point estimate and an interval estimate.

8.4　Believe in hell?　The point estimate of 0.73 for the proportion of U.S. adults who believe in hell that is shown in Figure 8.1 is from an older GSS. Access the GSS website (see Activity 1) or follow the GSS link on the book's website, ArtofStat.com. Enter HELL as the Row Variable, YEAR(2018) as the Selection Filter, select No Weight for Weight, and then press Run Table. This will show that in the 2018 GSS, 814 out of 1,142 respondents to this question answered either "Yes, Definitely" or "Yes, Probably."

　a. Find the point estimate for the proportion of U.S. adults believing in hell in 2018.

　b. Find the standard error for this sample proportion. What does it tell us?

　c. The sampling distribution of the sample proportion is approximately normal for such a large sample. Find the margin of error for this point estimate when the confidence level is 95%. What does it tell us?

8.5　Government spying　In 2014, news reports worldwide alleged that the U.S. government had hacked German chancellor Angela Merkel's cell phone. A Pew Research Center survey of German citizens at about that time asked whether they find it acceptable or unacceptable for the U.S. government to monitor communications from their country's leaders. Results from the survey show that of 1,000 citizens interviewed, 900 found it unacceptable. (*Source:* Pew Research Center, July 2014, "Global Opposition to U.S. Surveillance and Drones, But Limited Harm to America's Image.")

　a. Find the point estimate of the population proportion of German citizens who find spying unacceptable.

　b. The Pew Research Center reports a margin of error at the 95% confidence level of 4.5% for this survey. Explain what this means.

8.6　Game apps　The Google Play app store for smartphones offers hundreds of games to download for free or for a small fee. The ones for which a fee is charged are called paid games. For a random sample of five paid games taken from the Google platform, the following fees were charged: $1.09, $4.99, $1.99, $1.99, $2.99.

　a. Find a point estimate of the mean fee for paid games available on Google's platform.

　b. The margin of error at the 95% confidence level for this point estimate is $1.85. Explain what this means.

8.7　Nutrient effect on growth rate　Researchers are interested in the effect of a certain nutrient on the growth rate of plant seedlings. Using a hydroponics growth procedure that used water containing the nutrient, they planted six tomato plants and recorded the heights of each plant 14 days after germination. Those heights, measured in millimeters, were as follows: 55.5, 60.3, 60.6, 62.1, 65.5, 69.2.

a. Find a point estimate of the population mean height of this variety of seedling 14 days after germination.

b. A method that we'll study in Section 8.3 provides a margin of error of 4.9 mm for a 95% confidence interval for the population mean height. Construct that interval.

c. Use this example to explain why a point estimate alone is usually insufficient for statistical inference.

8.8 **Believe in heaven?**   When the GSS in 2018 asked 1,141 subjects, "Do you believe in heaven?" (coded HEAVEN), 922 replied with yes.

TRY

a. Find a point estimate of the proportion of U.S. adults who believe in heaven.

b. Find the standard error for this point estimate. What does it tell us?

c. Find the margin of error using a 95% confidence level and interpret it.

8.9 **Feel lonely often?**   The GSS has asked, "On how many days in the past seven days have you felt lonely?" (To

GSS see the data, go the the GSS website, see Activity 1, enter LONELY as the row variable, select No Weight for Weight, and select Summary Statistics under Output

Options.) The sample mean number of days the 1,450 respondents felt lonely was 1.5, and the sample standard deviation was 2.21.

a. What is the point estimate for the mean number of days someone feels lonely in the past 7 days among the entire U.S. adult population?

b. The standard error for the sample mean equals 0.06 (we will learn how this is obtained in Section 8.3.). What does this value tell us?

c. The margin of error for this point estimate equals ± 0.12. What does it tell us?

8.10 **CI for loneliness**   Refer to the previous exercise. Use the point estimate and quoted margin of error to construct a 95% confidence interval using the formula point estimate plus or minus margin of error. Is this a confidence interval for a population mean or a population proportion?

8.11 **Newspaper article**   Conduct a search to find an (online) report or article that mentions a margin of error. (Articles about opinion surveys or political elections are likely to mention margins of error, often in the fine print.)

a. Specify the population parameter, the point estimate, and the size of the margin of error.

b. Explain how to interpret the margin of error.

8.2 Confidence Interval for a Population Proportion

Let's now see how to construct a confidence interval for a population proportion. We'll apply the ideas discussed at the end of Section 8.1. When we are interested in a population proportion, the variable we observe is categorical, or more specifically *binary* (two categories), which means that each observation either falls or does not fall in the category of interest. As we have done before (see, for example, Sections 6.3 or 7.1), we'll use the generic terminology "success" and "failure" for these two possible outcomes. From the observed data, we first compute the sample proportion of successes as the point estimate for the proportion of successes in the population. Then, we proceed by finding a 95% confidence interval for this population proportion.

Did You Know?

If a categorical variable has more than two categories, it can still be considered binary by classifying one or more categories as a success and the remaining categories as a failure. ◄

Finding the 95% Confidence Interval for a Population Proportion

One question on the 2018 General Social Survey asked whether it is true that the universe began with a big explosion. Of $n = 338$ respondents, 255 said it is true. The sample proportion of true responses was $\hat{p} = 255/338 = 0.75$, or 75%. How can we construct a confidence interval for the population proportion p who believe it is true?

We construct the confidence interval in two steps, first estimating the standard deviation of the sampling distribution of the sample proportion $\hat{p}$, and then using the normal shape of the sampling distribution. The standard deviation of the sampling distribution equals $\sqrt{p(1-p)/n}$ (see the margin note), which depends on the unknown population proportion p. As discussed in the previous section, the standard error

Recall

$\hat{p}$ denotes the sample proportion, which is a point estimate for the population proportion p. The sampling distribution of $\hat{p}$

■ describes all the possible values of $\hat{p}$ from a sample of size n,

■ is approximately normal for large n,

■ has mean equal to p, the population proportion,

■ has standard deviation equal to

$\sqrt{p(1-p)/n}$. ◄

$$se = \sqrt{\hat{p}(1-\hat{p})/n}$$

estimates this standard deviation by substituting $\hat{p}$ for p in the formula. For the Big Bang question $\hat{p} = 0.75$, and the standard error is equal to $se = \sqrt{0.75(1 - 0.75)/338} = 0.023$. This se of 0.023 estimates by how much the sample proportion for samples of such a size typically vary from sample to sample.

Based on the normal shape of the sampling distribution, for large samples, there is a 95% chance that the sample proportion $\hat{p}$ falls within 1.96 standard errors of the population proportion p. If $\hat{p}$ is within 1.96(se) of p 95% of the time, then, equivalently, p is within 1.96(se) of $\hat{p}$ 95% of the time.[2] Therefore, the interval centered at $\hat{p}$ and stretching out a distance of 1.96(se) to either side has a 95% probability of capturing p.

Recall

We called 1.96(se) the **margin of error**. ◄

In Words

To find the **95% confidence interval,** you take the sample proportion and add and subtract 1.96 standard errors.

A 95% confidence interval for a population proportion p is

$$\hat{p} \pm 1.96(se), \text{ with } se = \sqrt{\frac{\hat{p}(1 - \hat{p})}{n}},$$

where $\hat{p}$ denotes the sample proportion based on n observations.

For the Big Bang question, $1.96(se) = 1.96(0.023) = 0.045$, and stretching out 0.045 to either side of 0.75 gives the 95% confidence interval 0.75 ± 0.045, or $(0.705, 0.795)$. Figure 8.3 shows the sampling distribution of $\hat{p}$. The area shaded in

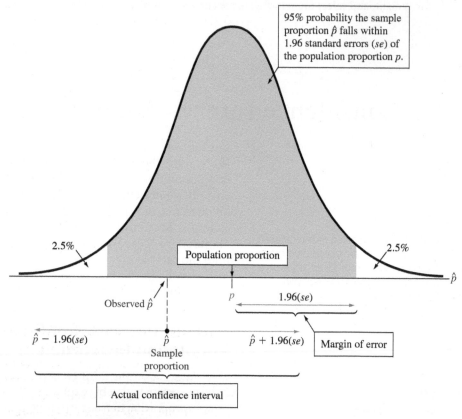

▲ **Figure 8.3** Sampling Distribution of Sample Proportion $\hat{p}$. For large random samples, the sampling distribution is approximately normal and centered at the population proportion p. Then, with 95% probability, $\hat{p}$ falls within 1.96(se) of p. As a consequence, $\hat{p} \pm 1.96(se)$ is a 95% confidence interval for p. **Question** Why is the confidence interval $\hat{p} \pm 1.96(se)$ instead of $p \pm 1.96(se)$?

---

[2]An analogy is throwing darts on a dartboard: If your dart is within a radius of 1 inch from the bull's-eye for 95% of your throws, then, equivalently, the bull's-eye is within a radius of 1 inch from your dart in 95% of the throws.

blue indicates that there's a 95% chance that $\hat{p}$ falls within $1.96(se)$ of the population proportion p and that the interval $\hat{p} \pm 1.96(se)$ has a 95% chance of capturing the population proportion p. The formula for this confidence interval is designed for large samples. We'll be more precise about what "large" means after the following example.

Example 3

> Constructing and Interpreting a Confidence Interval ◄

Paying Higher Prices to Protect the Environment

Picture the Scenario

Many people consider themselves green, meaning that they support (in theory) environmental issues. But how do they act in practice? For instance, Americans' per capita use of energy is roughly double that of Western Europeans. If you live in North America, would you be willing to pay the same price for gas that Europeans do (often about $7 or more per gallon) if the government proposed a significant price hike as an incentive for conservation and for driving more fuel-efficient cars?

Questions to Explore

The last time the GSS asked the question (variable GRNPRICE) whether someone would be willing to pay much higher prices to protect the environment in 2010, 637 of $n = 1{,}361$ respondents were willing to do so.

a. Find a 95% confidence interval for the population proportion of adult Americans willing to do so at the time of that survey.

b. Interpret that interval.

c. Is there evidence that fewer than half of the U.S. population is willing to pay higher prices?

Think It Through

a. The sample proportion that estimates the population proportion p is $\hat{p} = 637/1{,}361 = 0.468$. The standard error of the sample proportion $\hat{p}$ equals

$$se = \sqrt{\hat{p}(1 - \hat{p})/n} = \sqrt{(0.468)(0.532)/1{,}361} = 0.0135.$$

Using this se, a 95% confidence interval for the population proportion is

$$\hat{p} \pm 1.96(se), \text{ which is } 0.468 \pm 1.96(0.0135)$$
$$= 0.468 \pm 0.026, \text{ or } (0.442, 0.494).$$

b. At the 95% confidence level, we estimate that the population proportion of adult Americans willing to pay much higher prices to protect the environment was at least 0.44 but no more than 0.49, that is, between 44% and 49%. Another way you will see this result expressed in scientific journals or the media is: "The proportion of Americans willing to pay higher prices is estimated as 47% (95% CI: 44% − 49%)." Or, using the margin of error: "Survey finds that 47% (ME = ±2.6%) of Americans are willing to pay higher prices to protect the environment."

c. None of the numbers in the confidence interval (0.442, 0.494) for the population proportion fall above 0.50, so we infer that fewer than half the population was willing to pay much higher prices to protect the environment—but not dramatically fewer, as the proportion could be as high as 0.494.

Recall

The se of 0.0135 estimates by how much we would expect the sample proportion to vary in random samples of 1,361 people. Because 0.0135 is small, the sample proportion would not vary a lot, by only about 1.3 percentage points. ◄

The **standard errors** reported in this book and by most software assume **simple random sampling.** The GSS uses a multistage cluster random sample. In practice, the standard error based on the formula for a simple random sample should be adjusted slightly. It's beyond our scope to show the details, but when you request an analysis at the GSS website, you can get the adjusted standard errors by selecting Complex rather than SRS (simple random sample) for the sample design. For this example, it doesn't make a difference.

Insight

As usual, results depend on the question's wording. For instance, when asked whether the government should impose strict laws to make industry do less damage to the environment, a 95% confidence interval for the population proportion responding yes is (0.89, 0.92). (See Exercise 8.15.)

▶ **Try Exercise 8.14**

Figure 8.4 shows a screenshot from the *Inference for a Proportion* app, which provides the confidence interval numerically and graphically. In reporting results from such output, you should use only the first two or three significant digits. Report the confidence interval as (0.44, 0.49) or (0.442, 0.494), rather than (0.4415, 0.4945), using all available digits. Software's extra precision provides accurate calculations in finding *se* and the confidence interval. However, the extra digits are distracting when reported to others and do not tell them anything extra in a practical sense about the population proportion. If you do calculations with a hand calculator, don't round off while doing the calculations or your answer may be affected, but do round off when you report the final answer.

▶ **Figure 8.4** Bar Graph, Descriptive Statistics, and Confidence Interval for the Proportion Willing to Pay Higher Prices. Screenshot from the *Inference for a Proportion* app, providing the sample proportion, the standard error, and the margin of error for a specified confidence level. The confidence interval is given in the last table and in the graph below it. To enter your own data, click on Enter Data.

The interval (0.44, 0.49) is the confidence interval for the population proportion who would be *willing* to pay higher prices. What if instead you are interested in the proportion who would *not be willing* to pay higher prices? For a binary variable, inference about the second category (*not willing* to pay higher prices) follows directly from the one for the first category (*willing* to pay higher prices). Because the population parameter of interest is now $1 - p$, all we have to do is subtract each endpoint of the confidence interval for p from 1.0. So, since $1 - 0.49 = 0.51$ and $1 - 0.44 = 0.56$, the 95% confidence interval for the proportion who wouldn't be willing to pay higher prices is given by (0.51, 0.56). With 95% confidence, we estimate that the population proportion of people who wouldn't be willing to pay higher prices to support the environment falls between 0.51 and 0.56.

Sample Size Requirements for Validity of Confidence Interval for a Proportion

The confidence interval formula $\hat{p} \pm 1.96(se)$ applies only with *large random samples*. This is because the sampling distribution of the sample proportion $\hat{p}$ is then approximately normal and the *se* also tends to be a good estimate of the standard deviation, allowing us to use the z-score of 1.96 from the normal distribution.

In practice, "large" means that *you should have at least 15 successes and at least 15 failures* for the binary outcome.[3] At the end of this section, we'll see how our confidence interval formula can fail when this guideline is not satisfied. There, we'll present a modified interval that you should use when your own data has fewer than 15 successes or 15 failures. This modified interval (and another interval suitable for small sample sizes called the Wilson score confidence interval discussed in Exercise 8.123) are implemented as options in the *Inference for a Proportion* app. You should use them when your sample size is small!

Recall

This guideline mimics one we have mentioned at the end of Section 6.3 for the binomial distribution to be approximately bell shaped. ◄

> **SUMMARY: Sample Size Needed for Large-Sample Confidence Interval for a Proportion**
>
> For the 95% confidence interval $\hat{p} \pm 1.96(se)$ for a proportion p to be valid, you should have at least 15 successes and 15 failures. This can also be expressed as
>
> $$n\hat{p} \geq 15 \text{ and } n(1 - \hat{p}) \geq 15.$$
>
> At the end of this section, we'll learn about a simple adjustment to this confidence interval formula that you should use when this guideline is violated.

The sample size guideline was easily satisfied in Example 3. The binary outcomes had counts 637 willing to pay much higher prices and 724 ($= 1{,}361 - 637$) unwilling, both much larger than 15.

What Does 95% Confidence Mean?

In Example 3, the 95% confidence interval for the population proportion p willing to pay higher prices to protect the environment was (0.44, 0.49). Because we don't know the value of p, we don't know whether our interval (0.44, 0.49) will actually capture the population proportion. If truly $p = 0.45$, then the interval captures it; but if $p = 0.42$, then the interval fails to capture it.

So, what does it then mean to say, "We are 95% confident"? This 95% confidence refers to a long-run probability—the probability whether an interval so constructed captures the population proportion over many random samples (of the given size) taken from the population. If we use this method of constructing the interval over many random samples, then for 95 out of 100 samples we expect to capture the population proportion. For 5 out of 100 samples we expect to not capture the population proportion.

Why do we expect to capture the population proportion 95 out of 100 times? This happens because the sampling distribution of $\hat{p}$ is approximately normal, centered at the population proportion p. Then, in 95 out of 100 random samples, a sample proportion occurs that is within $1.96(se)$ of the population proportion. Line 1 in Figure 8.5 on the next page illustrates such a case. There, a sample proportion occurred such that the interval $\hat{p} \pm 1.96(se)$ captures the population proportion p. On the other hand, Line 2 in Figure 8.5 illustrates a case where a sample proportion occurred for which the interval $\hat{p} \pm 1.96(se)$ does not capture the population proportion p. This only happens 5% of the time because under the normal distribution, such a sample proportion falling in the tails only occurs 5% of the time.

---

[3]Many statistics texts use 5 or 10 as the minimum instead of 15, but research suggests that those sizes are too small (e.g., L. Brown et al., *Statistical Science*, vol. 16, pp. 101–133, 2001).

▶ **Figure 8.5** The Sampling Distribution of the Sample Proportion $\hat{p}$. The lines below the graph show two possible $\hat{p}$ values and the corresponding 95% confidence intervals for the population proportion p. For the interval on Line 1, the inference we draw is correct in the sense that the interval contains p, but for the interval on Line 2, the inference we draw is incorrect. **Question** Can you identify on the figure all the $\hat{p}$ values for which the 95% confidence interval would not contain p? How likely is it to observe these $\hat{p}$ values?

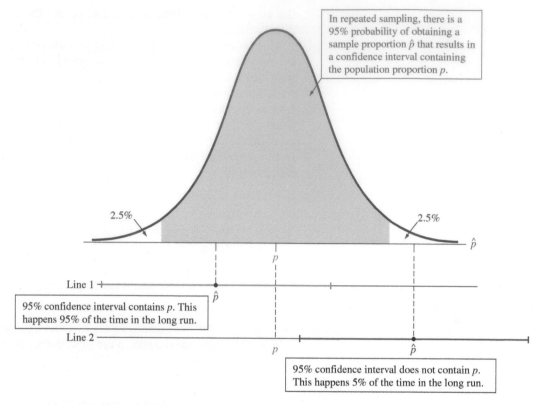

In repeated sampling, there is a 95% probability of obtaining a sample proportion $\hat{p}$ that results in a confidence interval containing the population proportion p.

2.5% 2.5%

Line 1

95% confidence interval contains p. This happens 95% of the time in the long run.

Line 2

95% confidence interval does not contain p. This happens 5% of the time in the long run.

By our choice of the confidence level, we can control the chance that the inference we make is correct. If an error probability of 5% is unacceptably high, we can instead form a 99% confidence interval, which is in error only 1% of the time in the long run. But then we must settle for a wider confidence interval with a larger margin of error and hence less precision.

You might be tempted to interpret a statement such as "With 95% confidence, we estimate that the population proportion p falls between 0.42 and 0.48" as meaning that the *probability* is 0.95 that p falls between 0.42 and 0.48. However, probabilities apply to statistics (such as the sample proportion), not to parameters (such as the population proportion). The estimate $\hat{p}$, not the parameter p, is the random variable having a sampling distribution and probabilities. The 95% confidence refers not to a probability for the population proportion p but rather to a probability that applies to the confidence interval *method* in its relative frequency sense: If we use it over and over for various samples, in the long run we capture the true parameter 95% of the time.

Caution

When interpreting a 95% confidence interval, say that you have 95% confidence that the interval you produced will cover the population parameter. Don't say that there is a 95% probability that the parameter will fall in the interval. ◀

▶ **Activity 2**

Simulate the Performance of Confidence Intervals

Let's get a feel for how to interpret "95% confidence" by using simulation. Similar to Activity 1 in Chapter 7 (where we explored the sampling distribution of the sample proportion), we will simulate drawing a sample of a certain size n from a population with a prespecified population proportion p. From that sample, we compute $\hat{p}$ and use it to compute the 95% confidence interval for p. By repeating this several times, we mimic repeatedly taking a sample of size n from a population with population proportion p and

we can check how often the confidence interval constructed from each sample actually contains the population proportion p. If our theory is correct, this should be about 95% of the time in the long run.

To run and visualize the simulations, we'll use the *Explore Coverage* app. Let's keep the default settings of $p = 0.3$ (a vertical line indicates this location), $n = 50$, and 95% confidence. When you press the Draw Sample(s) button, a random sample of size 50 will be drawn, and the resulting 95% confidence interval is computed and displayed in the graph. The dot in the middle indicates the sample proportion. The interval is shown in green if the interval contains the population proportion and in red otherwise. Keep clicking

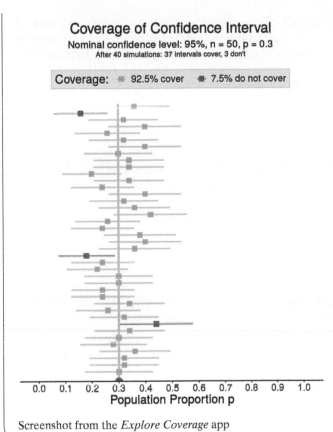

Coverage of Confidence Interval
Nominal confidence level: 95%, n = 50, p = 0.3
After 40 simulations: 37 intervals cover, 3 don't

Coverage: ■ 92.5% cover   ■ 7.5% do not cover

Population Proportion p

Screenshot from the *Explore Coverage* app

the button to add new confidence intervals (each based on a new random sample) to the display. As the graph shows, after 40 generated samples, 37 (which is 92.5%) produced an interval that contained the population proportion $p = 0.3$, while 3 (which is 7.5%) did not contain p. (Your results may vary.)

Use the app to see the effect of changing (i) the confidence level, (ii) the sample size, and (iii) the population proportion. The graph will update as you change each value. For instance, what happens as you change the confidence level from 95% to 99%? Are the intervals getting wider and are more of the intervals containing the population proportion? What about increasing the sample size: Are intervals getting wider or narrower?

To get a feel for what happens in the long run, eventually you should simulate at least 1,000 samples and explore the percentage of intervals that cover the population parameter. Do this for various settings of the true population proportion and sample size.

Try Exercises 8.27 and 8.28.
For the confidence interval
for a mean, try 8.52. ◄

Using a Confidence Level Other Than 95%

So far we've used a confidence level of 95%, which is the most common choice in practice. But some applications may require greater confidence, such as in medical research. For example, when estimating the probability p that a new treatment for a deadly disease works better than the treatment currently used, we may want to be extremely confident about any inference we make. To increase the chance that our inference is correct (that is, having the interval contain the parameter value), we use a larger confidence level, such as 99%.

Recall

From Section 6.2, the z-score for a standard normal distribution with 99% in the middle and 0.5% in each tail equals ±2.58. (Use the *Normal Distribution* app or Table A.) ◄

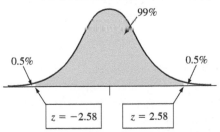

99%

0.5%   0.5%

z = −2.58   z = 2.58

To find the formula for the 99% confidence interval, let's first recall how we found the margin of error of 1.96(*se*) for the 95% confidence interval, in particular the number 1.96. It came from our knowledge that under a normal distribution, 95% of the probability falls within 2, or more precisely, 1.96 standard deviations of the mean (see Section 6.2). What does 1.96 change to when we instead want 99% probability? Then, we need to find the z-score for the normal distribution such that 99% are in the middle and 0.5% are in the tails on either side. As the margin figure illustrates, this z-score equals 2.58. So, 99% of a normal distribution falls within 2.58 standard deviations; and if we wish to construct a 99% confidence interval rather than a 95% confidence interval, we need to use 2.58(*se*) rather than 1.96(*se*) for the margin of error.

Example 4

► 99% Confidence Interval

Influenza Vaccine

Picture the Scenario

According to the Centers for Disease Control and Prevention, the single best way to protect against the flu is to be vaccinated. Traditionally, flu vaccines are manufactured using viruses grown in chicken eggs. A new method allows growing viruses in cell cultures instead. To test the effectiveness of such vaccines, in a recent clinical trial $n = 3,900$ randomly selected healthy subjects aged 18–49 received a cell-derived influenza vaccine by injection. Over a follow-up period of approximately 28 weeks, the subjects were assessed whether they developed influenza, which happened for 26 of the 3,900 subjects.

Questions to Explore

a. Find and interpret a 99% confidence interval for the population proportion developing the flu over the follow-up period. (Here, the population is all 18- to 49-year-old people vaccinated with the cell-derived vaccine.)

b. How does it compare to the 95% confidence interval?

Think It Through

a. The assumptions for the method are satisfied in that the sample was randomly selected, and there were at least 15 successes and 15 failures (26 developing the flu, 3,874 not developing it). The sample proportion developing the flu is $\hat{p} = 26/3,900 = 0.0067$. Its standard error is

$$se = \sqrt{\hat{p}(1 - \hat{p})/n} = \sqrt{0.0067(1 - 0.0067/3,900)} = 0.0013.$$

The 99% confidence interval is

$$\hat{p} \pm 2.58(se) \text{ or } 0.0067 \pm 2.58(0.0013),$$

which is 0.0067 ± 0.0034, or $(0.003, 0.010)$.

With 99% confidence, we estimate that the proportion of people vaccinated but still developing the flu is between 0.3% and 1%, with a point estimate of 0.7%.

b. The 95% confidence interval is $0.0067 \pm 1.96(0.0013)$ which is 0.0067 ± 0.0025, or $(0.004, 0.009)$. This is a bit narrower than the 99% confidence interval, as illustrated in the following figure.

Confidence Interval:

Population Parameter	Lower Bound	Upper Bound	Confidence Level
Proportion: p	0.0033	0.0100	99%

99% Confidence Interval
[0.00331, 0.01002]

0.002 0.003 0.004 0.005 0.006 0.007 0.008 0.009 0.010 0.011 0.012 0.013
p
Population Proportion p

Screenshot from *Inference for a Proportion* app, where we set the slider for the confidence level to 99%.

Sample proportion (middle of confidence interval)

Insight

The inference with a 99% confidence interval is less precise, with margin of error equal to 0.0034 instead of 0.0025. Having a greater margin of error is the sacrifice for gaining greater assurance (99% rather than 95%) of correctly inferring where p falls. A study that uses a higher confidence level will be less likely to make an inference that is incorrect, but it will not be able to narrow in as well on where the true parameter value falls.

▶ **Try Exercise 8.23**

Why settle for anything less than 100% confidence? Why are we constructing 95% (or 99%) and not 100% confidence intervals? For a 100% confidence interval, the probability that the interval contains the parameter must be 100%. Such an interval needs to contain all possible values of the parameter. For a population proportion, this is the interval that goes from 0 to 1. With 100% confidence, we estimate that the population proportion is between 0 and 1 (or 0% and 100%). This is obviously not a very useful conclusion! We really didn't need to collect data (and perhaps spend thousands of dollars) to make such a statement. In practice, we settle for a little less than 100% confidence so we can estimate the parameter much more precisely. As the margin figure illustrates, it is far more informative to have 99% confidence that the population proportion of those developing the flu is between 0.3% and 1% (a very narrow range) than to have 100% confidence that this proportion is between 0% and 100% (a very large range).

In using confidence intervals, *we must compromise between the desired margin of error and the desired confidence of a correct inference.* As one gets better, the other gets worse. This is why you would probably not use a 99.9999% confidence interval. It would usually have too large a margin of error to tell you anything useful about where the parameter falls (its z-score is 4.9). In practice, 95% confidence intervals are the most common.

The general formula for the confidence interval for a population proportion is

sample proportion $\pm$ (z-score from normal distribution) (standard error),

which in symbols is $\hat{p} \pm z(se)$ where z is the z-score. This z-score depends on the desired confidence level. The table in the margin shows the z-scores for the confidence levels typically used in practice. The *Inference for a Proportion* app or any other software can compute the confidence interval for any given level, but 95% is the most common choice.

99% confidence
100% confidence

p

0   1

z-Scores for the Most Common Confidence Levels

Confidence Level	z-Score z	Confidence Interval
90%	1.645	$\hat{p} \pm 1.645(se)$
95%	1.96	$\hat{p} \pm 1.96(se)$
99%	2.58	$\hat{p} \pm 2.58(se)$

SUMMARY: Confidence Interval for a Population Proportion p

A confidence interval for a population proportion p, using the sample proportion $\hat{p}$ and the standard error $se = \sqrt{\hat{p}(1 - \hat{p})/n}$ for sample size n, is

$$\hat{p} \pm z(se), \text{ which is } \hat{p} \pm z\sqrt{\hat{p}(1 - \hat{p})/n}.$$

For 90%, 95%, and 99% confidence intervals, the z-score z equals 1.645, 1.96, and 2.58, respectively. This method assumes:

- Data obtained by randomization (such as a random sample or a randomized experiment).
- A large enough sample size n so that the number of successes and the number of failures, that is, $n\hat{p}$ and $n(1 - \hat{p})$, are both at least 15.

Effect of the Sample Size

We'd expect that estimation is more precise with larger sample sizes. With more data, we know more about the population. The margin of error is $z(se) = z\sqrt{\hat{p}(1 - \hat{p})/n}$, where z is the z-score. This margin decreases as the sample size n increases, for a given value of $\hat{p}$. The larger the value of n, the narrower the interval.

To illustrate, in Example 3, suppose the sample proportion $\hat{p} = 0.468$ of Americans willing to pay much higher prices to protect the environment had resulted from a sample of size $n = 340$, only *one-fourth* the actual sample size of $n = 1{,}361$. Then the standard error would be

$$se = \sqrt{\hat{p}(1 - \hat{p})/n} = \sqrt{0.468(1 - 0.468)/340} = 0.0271,$$

twice as large as the $se = 0.0135$ we got for $n = 3,900$ (up to rounding errors). With the se twice as large, the margin of error would also be twice as large. With 95% confidence, it would double from the $1.96(0.0135) = 0.026$ shown in Example 3 to $1.96(0.0271) = 0.053$, resulting in the interval $\hat{p} \pm 1.96(se)$ or $0.468 \pm 1.96(0.0271)$, which is 0.468 ± 0.053, or $(0.415, 0.521)$. The confidence interval $(0.442, 0.494)$ obtained with the larger n in Example 3 is narrower (and falls entirely below 50%); see the margin figure.

Because the standard error has the square root of n in the denominator, and because $\sqrt{4n} = 2\sqrt{n}$, *quadrupling* the sample size *halves* the standard error. If we want to cut the margin of error in half, we must *quadruple* the sample size. Merely doubling the sample size will not be sufficient for cutting the margin of error in half.

In summary, we've observed the following properties of a confidence interval:

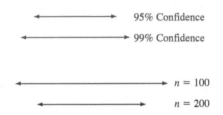

> ### SUMMARY: Effects of Confidence Level and Sample Size on Margin of Error
>
> The **margin of error** for a confidence interval:
>
> - Increases as the confidence level increases.
> - Decreases as the sample size increases.

For instance, a 99% confidence interval is wider than a 95% confidence interval, and a confidence interval with 200 observations is narrower than one with 100 observations (see margin figure). These properties apply to *all* confidence intervals, not just the one for the population proportion.

Choosing the Sample Size

In all the examples so far, the sample size n was given. But how do polling and other organizations actually determine the necessary size of the random sample they are about to collect? Or, suppose you are planning a study for estimating a certain population proportion. One of the first questions you will have to address is how large a random sample you should take for the study. Is a sample size of 50 people sufficient, or do you need to sample 500 or even 5,000?

The answer depends on how precise you want your estimate to be, which is measured by the margin of error. Do you want your estimate to be within ± 10, ± 5, or maybe even within ± 3 or ± 1 percentage points of the true proportion? The smaller you want the margin of error to be, the larger a sample you'll have to take. You'll also have to specify the desired confidence level. Suppose you picked a margin of error of ± 5 percentage points as acceptable for your study. Then, you'll have to decide whether this margin of error should refer to 95% or 99% confidence. In practice, 95% confidence is the most common level chosen.

Did You Know?

When the news media report a **margin of error,** it is typically the margin of error for a 95% confidence interval. ◄

Example 5

Choosing a Sample Size ◄

Exit Poll

Picture the Scenario

A TV network plans to predict the outcome of an election between Levin and Sanchez using an exit poll that randomly samples voters on election day. They want a reasonably accurate estimate of the population proportion that voted for Levin. The final poll a week before election day estimated her to be well ahead, 58% to 42%, so they do not expect the outcome to be close. Since their finances for this project are limited, they don't want to collect a large sample if they don't need it. They decide to use a sample size for which the margin of error is ± 4 percentage points (at a 95% confidence level) rather than their usual margin of error of ± 3 percentage points.

Question to Explore

What is the sample size for which a 95% confidence interval for the population proportion has a margin of error equal to 0.04 (i.e., 4 percentage points)?

Think It Through

The 95% confidence interval for a population proportion p is $\hat{p} \pm 1.96(se)$, where $1.96(se)$ is the margin of error. So, we want $1.96(se)$, which is $1.96\sqrt{\hat{p}(1 - \hat{p})/n}$ to be equal to 0.04. Setting up the equation

$$0.04 = 1.96\sqrt{\hat{p}(1 - \hat{p})/n}$$

and solving the equation for n yields

$$n = (1.96)^2\hat{p}(1 - \hat{p})/(0.04)^2.$$

Now, we face a problem. We're doing this calculation *before* gathering the data, so we don't yet have a sample proportion $\hat{p}$. Since $\hat{p}$ is unknown, we must substitute an educated guess for what we'll get once we gather the sample and analyze the data.

Since the latest poll *before* election day predicted that 58% of the voters preferred Levin, it is sensible to substitute 0.58 for $\hat{p}$ in this equation. Then we find

$$n = (1.96)^2\hat{p}(1 - \hat{p})/(0.04)^2 = (1.96)^2(0.58)(0.42)/(0.04)^2 = 584.9.$$

In summary, a random sample of size about $n = 585$ should give a margin of error of about ± 4 percentage points for a 95% confidence interval for the population proportion.

Insight

Sometimes, we may have no idea what to expect for $\hat{p}$. We may prefer not to guess the value it will take, as we did in this example. We'll next learn what we can do in those situations.

▶ **Try Exercise 8.20**

Selecting a Sample Size Without Guessing a Value for $\hat{p}$

In the previous example, the solution for n was proportional to $\hat{p}(1 - \hat{p})$. The figure in the margin shows how that product depends on the value of $\hat{p}$. The largest possible value for $\hat{p}(1 - \hat{p})$ is 0.25, which occurs when $\hat{p} = 0.50$. You can check by plugging values of $\hat{p}$ into $\hat{p}(1 - \hat{p})$ that this product is near 0.25 unless $\hat{p}$ is quite far from 0.50. For example, $\hat{p}(1 - \hat{p}) = 0.24$ when $\hat{p} = 0.40$ or $\hat{p} = 0.60$.

In the formula for determining n, setting $\hat{p} = 0.50$ out of all the possible values to substitute for $\hat{p}$ gives the largest value for n. This is the safe approach that guarantees we'll have a sample that is large enough. In the election exit poll example, for a margin of error of 0.04, we then get

$$n = (1.96)^2\hat{p}(1 - \hat{p})/(0.04)^2$$
$$= (1.96)^2(0.50)(0.50)/(0.04)^2 = 600.25, \text{ rounded up to } 601.$$

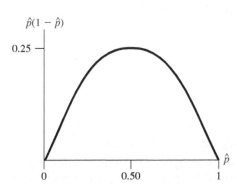

This result compares to $n = 585$ from guessing that $\hat{p} = 0.58$. Using the slightly larger value of $n = 601$ ensures that the margin of error for a 95% confidence interval will not exceed 0.04, no matter what value we get for $\hat{p}$ once we collect the data.

This safe approach is not always sensible, however. Substituting $\hat{p} = 0.50$ gives us an overly large solution for n if $\hat{p}$ actually falls far from 0.50. Suppose that based on other studies we expect $\hat{p}$ to be about 0.10. Then an adequate sample size to achieve a margin of error of 0.04 is

$$n = (1.96)^2 \hat{p}(1 - \hat{p})/(0.04)^2$$

$$= (1.96)^2 (0.10)(0.90)/(0.04)^2 = 216.09, \text{ rounded up to } 217.$$

A sample size of 601 would be much larger and more costly than needed, and a sample size of 217 would have been sufficient.

General Sample Size Formula for Estimating a Population Proportion A general formula exists for determining the sample size, based on computations similar to the ones we carried out in Example 5. Let m denote the desired margin of error such as $m = 0.04$ in Example 5. The general formula also uses the z-score corresponding to the desired confidence level.

Table 8.2 Necessary Sample Size to Achieve Given Margin of Error, when $\hat{p} = 0.5$ or $\hat{p} = 0.2$ (or 0.8).

Desired Margin of Error	$\hat{p} = 0.5$	$\hat{p} = 0.2$ or 0.8
± 15%	43	-
± 10%	97	62
± 5%	385	246
± 4%	601	385
± 3%	1,068	683
± 2%	2,401	1,537
± 1%	9,604	6,147

SUMMARY: Sample Size for Estimating a Population Proportion

The random sample size n for which a confidence interval for a population proportion p has margin of error m (such as $m = 0.04$) is

$$n = \frac{\hat{p}(1 - \hat{p}) z^2}{m^2}.$$

The z-score is based on the confidence level, such as $z = 1.96$ for 95% confidence. You either guess the value you'd get for the sample proportion $\hat{p}$ based on other information or take the safe approach by setting $\hat{p} = 0.5$.

Table 8.2 in the margin shows, for a desired margin of error, the necessary sample size for a 95% confidence interval. Often, though, the desired margin of error is not the only criterion for deciding on the sample size. Cost of sampling and the time it takes to complete it are additional factors that need to be taken into account.

Example 6

Choosing Sample Size ◄

Using an Exit Poll When a Race Is Close

Picture the Scenario

An election is expected to be close. Pollsters planning an exit poll decide that a margin of error of ± 4 percentage points is too large.

Question to Explore

How large should the sample size be for the margin of error of a 95% confidence interval to equal ± 2 percentage points?

Think It Through

Since the election is expected to be close, we expect $\hat{p}$ to be near 0.50. In the formula, we set $\hat{p} = 0.50$ to be safe. We also set the margin of error $m = 0.02$ and use $z = 1.96$ for a 95% confidence interval. The required sample size is

$$ n = \frac{\hat{p}(1 - \hat{p})z^2}{m^2} = \frac{(0.50)(0.50)(1.96)^2}{(0.02)^2} = 2{,}401. $$

Insight

The required sample size of about 2,400 for a margin of error of ± 2 percentage points is *four times* the required sample size of 600 for a margin of error of ± 4 percentage points. This illustrates again that in order to cut the margin of error into half (going from 0.04 to 0.02), the required sample size quadruples, from 600 to 2,400. This is unfortunate, because you can expect the resources (i.e., time and money to conduct the actual survey) to also quadruple (and not just double) if you desire a margin of error only half as large.

▶ *Try Exercise 8.30*

Samples taken by polling organizations typically contain 1,000–2,000 subjects. This is large enough to estimate a population proportion with a margin of error of about ± 2 to ± 3 percentage points. At first glance, it seems astonishing that a sample of this size from a population of perhaps many millions is adequate for predicting outcomes of elections or summarizing opinions on controversial issues. The basis for this inferential power lies in the standard error formulas for the point estimates that occur with random sampling. Precise estimates result no matter how large the population size.[4]

Confidence Interval When the Sample Size Is Small

Sometimes, because of financial or ethical reasons, it's just not possible to take as large of a sample as we'd like. For example, each observation may result from an expensive experimental procedure or may put the health of the sample subjects at risk.

For the confidence interval formula for a proportion, we've seen that we need at least 15 successes and at least 15 failures, so at the very least a total of 30 observations. Why? Otherwise, the Central Limit Theorem no longer applies and the sampling distribution of the sample proportion may be far from normal. An even more serious difficulty is that the standard deviation of the sample proportion depends on the parameter we're trying to estimate. If the estimate $\hat{p}$ is far from the true p, as often happens for small n, then the estimate $se = \sqrt{\hat{p}(1 - \hat{p})/n}$ of the standard deviation of the sample proportion may also be far off. As a result, the confidence interval formula works poorly. The next example shows an extreme case.

---

[4]In fact, the mathematical derivations of these methods treat the population size as infinite. See Exercise 7.76.

Small Sample CI ◀

Example 7

Proportion of Students Who Use Facebook Daily

Picture the Scenario

For a statistics class project, a professor randomly selected and interviewed 20 students at his university to estimate the proportion of students who use Facebook daily. Each of the 20 students interviewed answered yes to using Facebook daily.

Question to Explore

What does a 95% confidence interval reveal about the proportion of students at the university who use Facebook daily?

Think It Through

Let p denote the proportion of students at the university who use Facebook daily. The sample proportion from the interviews was $\hat{p} = 20/20 = 1.0$. When $\hat{p} = 1.0$, then

$$se = \sqrt{\hat{p}(1 - \hat{p})/n} = \sqrt{1.0(0.0)/20} = 0.0.$$

The 95% confidence interval is

$$\hat{p} \pm z(se) = 1.0 \pm 1.96(0.0),$$

which is 1.0 ± 0.0, or $(1.0, 1.0)$. This investigation told the professor that with 95% confidence, the proportion p of students using Facebook daily is estimated to be between 1 and 1, that is, that $p = 1$. He was surprised by this result. It seemed unrealistic to conclude that 100% of students (i.e. *every* student at the university) used Facebook daily.

Insight

Do you trust this inference? Just because everyone in a small sample uses Facebook daily, would you conclude that everyone in the much larger population does so? We doubt it. Perhaps the population proportion p is close to 1, but it is almost surely not exactly equal to 1.

The confidence interval formula $\hat{p} \pm z\sqrt{\hat{p}(1 - \hat{p})/n}$ is valid only if the sample contains at least 15 individuals who use Facebook daily and 15 individuals who don't. The sample did not contain at least 15 individuals who don't, so we have to use a different method. Keep on reading.

▶ *Try Exercise 8.33, parts a–c*

When the sample size is small, such as the $n = 20$ students interviewed in Example 7, we can still use our formula for the confidence interval, but we will need to make adjustments.

Constructing a Small-Sample Confidence Interval for a Proportion p

Suppose a random sample does *not* have at least 15 successes and 15 failures. The confidence interval formula $\hat{p} \pm z\sqrt{\hat{p}(1 - \hat{p})/n}$ still is valid if we use it after adding 2 to the original number of successes and 2 to the original number of failures. This results in adding 4 to the sample size n.

For example, the $n = 20$ students interviewed in Example 7 contained 20 individuals who used Facebook daily and 0 who did not. We can apply the confidence interval formula with $20 + 2 = 22$ individuals who use Facebook daily and $0 + 2 = 2$ who do not. The value of the sample size for the formula is then *n = 24. Now we can use the formula, even though we don't have at least 15 individuals who do not use Facebook daily.* We get

$$\hat{p} = 22/24 = 0.917, se = \sqrt{\hat{p}(1-\hat{p})/n} = \sqrt{(0.917)(0.083)/24} = 0.056.$$

The resulting 95% confidence interval is

$$\hat{p} \pm 1.96(se), \text{ which is } 0.917 \pm 1.96(0.056), \text{ or } (0.807, 1.027).$$

A proportion cannot be greater than 1, so we report the interval as (0.807, 1.0). With 95% confidence, the proportion of individuals at the university who use Facebook daily is estimated to be at least 0.807, or about 81%.

This approach enables us to use a large-sample method even when the sample size is small. This is particularly helpful when the ordinary sample proportion is 0 or 1, which we would not usually expect to be a believable estimate of a population proportion. Why do we add 2 to the counts of the two types? The reason is that the resulting confidence interval is then close to a confidence interval based on a more complex method (described in Exercise 8.123) which works well even for small samples.[5]

Sampling Error versus Other Errors

Finally, a word of caution: In the estimation of parameters, "margin of error" refers to the size of error resulting from having data from a random sample rather than the population—what's called *sampling error*. This is the error that the sampling distribution describes in showing how close the estimate is likely to fall to the parameter. But that's not the only source of potential error. Data may be missing for a lot of the target sample; some observations may be recorded incorrectly by the data collector; and some subjects may not tell the truth. When errors like these occur, the actual confidence level may be much lower than advertised. Be skeptical about a claimed margin of error and confidence level unless you know that the study was well conducted and these other sources of error are negligible.

On the Shoulders of...Ronald A. Fisher

R. A. Fisher was the statistician most responsible for the statistical methods used to analyze data today.

How do you conduct scientific inquiry, whether it be developing methods of experimental design, finding the best way to estimate a parameter, or answering specific questions such as which fertilizer works best?

Compared with other mathematical sciences, statistical science is a mere youth. The most important contributions were made between 1920 and 1940 by the British statistician Ronald A. Fisher (1890–1962). While working at an agricultural research station north of London, Fisher was the first statistician to show convincingly the importance of randomization in designing experiments. He also developed the theory behind point estimation and proposed several new statistical methods.

Fisher was involved in a wide variety of scientific questions, ranging from finding the best ways to plant crops to controversies (in his time) about whether smoking was harmful. He also did fundamental work in genetics and is regarded as a giant in that field as well.

Fisher had strong disagreements with others about the way statistical inference should be conducted. One of his main adversaries was Karl Pearson. Fisher corrected a major error Pearson made in proposing methods for contingency tables, and he criticized Pearson's son's work on developing the theory of confidence intervals in the 1930s. Although Fisher often disparaged the ideas of other statisticians, he reacted strongly if anyone criticized him in return. Writing about Pearson, Fisher once said, "If peevish intolerance of free opinion in others is a sign of senility, it is one which he had developed at an early age."

---

[5]See article by A. Agresti and B. Coull (who proposed this small-sample confidence interval), (1998) *The American Statistician*, vol. 52, p. 119.

8.2 Practicing the Basics

8.12 Putin A Gallup poll of 2,000 Russians taken between April and June 2014 (after the Olympic games in Russia and the annexation of the Crimean peninsula) showed that 83% approved of President Putin's performance. If random sampling were used for this survey, what is the margin of error for this estimate at the 95% confidence level? (In fact, Gallup uses weighted sampling and, based on it, reports a margin of error of 2.7%.) *Source:* gallup .com and search for "Russian Approval."

8.13 Flu shot In a clinical study (the same as mentioned in Example 4), 3,900 subjects were vaccinated with a vaccine manufactured by growing cells in fertilized chicken eggs. Over a period of roughly 28 weeks, 24 of these subjects developed the flu.

APP

   a. Find the point estimate of the population proportion that were vaccinated with the vaccine but still developed the flu.

   b. Find the standard error of this estimate.

   c. Find the margin of error for a 95% confidence interval.

   d. Construct the 95% confidence interval for the population proportion. Interpret the interval.

   e. Can you conclude that fewer than 1% of all people vaccinated with the vaccine will develop the flu? Explain by using results from part d.

8.14 COVID-19 infections When the COVID-19 pandemic broke out in March 2020, one of the important parameters for planning how to respond to the crisis was the proportion of a country's population that was infected with the virus. Because testing for the virus was only available for those who presented with severe symptoms (tests were in short supply), the proportion of those that tested positive for the virus was not a reliable estimate for the general population because many people that contracted the virus never showed any symptoms. In an effort to estimate this proportion, the country of Iceland was one of the first to obtain what could be treated as a representative sample. Between March 13 and March 21, 2020, a genetic lab in Iceland tested 5,571 people, of which only 48 tested positive.

TRY

APP

   a. Estimate the population proportion of infected people in Iceland around the time the testing took place.

   b. Find the margin of error for a 95% confidence interval for this estimate.

   c. Find a 95% confidence interval for that proportion and interpret.

   d. The sample analyzed by the genetic lab included all people who wanted to be tested, i.e., a volunteer sample. State and check the assumptions needed for the interval in part c to be valid.

8.15 Make industry help environment? When the 2016 GSS asked subjects whether it should or should not be the government's responsibility to impose strict laws to make

GSS

APP

industry do less damage to the environment (variable GRNLAWS), 1,223 of 1,353 subjects said yes.

   a. What assumptions are made to construct a 95% confidence interval for the population proportion who would say yes? Do they seem satisfied here?

   b. Construct the 95% confidence interval. Interpret in context. Can you conclude whether a majority or minority of the population would answer yes?

8.16 Favor death penalty In the 2018 GSS, subjects were asked whether they favored or opposed the death penalty for people convicted of murder. Out of 2,193 respondents, 1,385 said they favored the death penalty. These results were entered in the *Inference for a Proportion* app, with output shown below.

APP

   a. Show how to obtain the value reported under Point Estimate.

   b. Show how to obtain the value reported under Standard Error.

   c. Show how to obtain the value reported under Margin of Error.

   d. Show how the 95% confidence interval was obtained, and interpret it.

   e. Explain what it means to have "95% confidence."

   f. Can you conclude that more than 50% of all adult Americans were in favor?

8.17 Oppose death penalty Refer to the previous exercise. Show how you can get a 95% confidence interval for the proportion of American adults who were *opposed* to the death penalty from the confidence interval stated in the previous exercise for the proportion in favor. (*Hint:* The proportion opposed is 1 minus the proportion in favor.)

8.18 Stem cell research A Harris poll of a random sample of 2,113 adults in the United States in October 2010 reported that 72% of those polled believe that stem cell research has merit. (*Source:* theharrispoll.com.) The results, presented using MINITAB software, are

```
X        N        Sample p        95% CI
1521     2113     0.7198          (0.7007, 0.7390)
```

Here, *X* denotes the number who believed that stem cell research has merit.

a. Explain how to interpret "Sample p" and "95% CI" on this printout.

b. What is the 95% margin of error associated with the poll?

8.19 z-score and confidence level Which *z*-score is used in a (a) 90%, (b) 98%, and (c) 99.9% confidence interval for a population proportion?

8.20 Believe in ghosts A researcher at a large university wants to find out what proportion of students at the university believes in ghosts. Because her budget for conducting a survey is limited, she is content estimating the true proportion to within a margin of error of ±10 percentage points.

a. In preparing for this study, the researcher found a 2013 Harris poll (theharrispoll.com), conducted among U.S. adults, that found that 42% believe in ghosts. How large of a sample of students should the researcher aim for if she wants to construct a 95% confidence interval?

b. Suppose the researcher considers the results of the 2013 study outdated. How large a sample should she aim for when not taking any prior information into account?

c. If the researcher wants to use a margin of error of only ±5%, half the initial +5%, how many students does she need to sample in the worst case scenario?

8.21 Stem cell research and religion In Exercise 8.18, it was stated that 72% of the 2,113 adults surveyed in a Harris poll believed that stem cell research has merit. From that same study, 586 of the 1,010 people who identified as Republicans believed that it has merit. Use the *Inference for a Proportion* app to find a 95% confidence interval. Specify the population to which this inference applies and interpret the confidence interval in context.

8.22 Fear of breast cancer A recent survey of 1,000 American women between the ages of 45 and 64 asked them what medical condition they most feared. Of those sampled, 61% said breast cancer, 8% said heart disease, and the rest picked other conditions. By contrast, currently about 3% of female deaths are due to breast cancer, whereas 32% are due to heart disease.[6]

a. Construct a 90% confidence interval for the population proportion of women who most feared breast cancer. Interpret.

b. Indicate the assumptions you must make for the inference in part a to be valid.

8.23 Chicken breast In a 2014 *Consumer Reports* article titled "The High Cost of Cheap Chicken," the magazine reported that out of 316 chicken breasts bought in randomly selected retail stores throughout the United States, 207 contained E. coli bacteria.

a. Find and interpret a 99% confidence interval for the population proportion of chicken breasts in U.S. retail stores that contain E. coli. Can you conclude that this proportion exceeds 50%? Why?

b. Without doing any calculation, explain whether the interval in part a would be wider or narrower than a 95% confidence interval.

8.24 Same-sex marriage A national survey by the Pew Research Center (www.people-press.org), conducted May 1–5, 2013, among 1,504 adults, finds that support for same-sex marriage continues to grow. It states, "For the first time in Pew Research Center polling, just over half (51%) of Americans favor allowing gays and lesbians to marry legally." Based on these data, can we conclude that more than half of Americans support same-sex marriage? Explain.

8.25 Exit poll predictions A national television network takes an exit poll of 1,400 voters after each has cast a vote in a state gubernatorial election. Of them, 660 say they voted for the Democratic candidate and 740 say they voted for the Republican candidate.

a. Treating the sample as a random sample from the population of all voters, would you predict the winner? Base your decision on a 95% confidence interval.

b. Base your decision on a 99% confidence interval. Explain why you need stronger evidence to make a prediction when you want greater confidence.

8.26 Exit poll with smaller sample In the previous exercise, suppose the same proportions resulted from *n* = 140 (instead of 1,400), with counts 66 and 74.

a. Now does a 95% confidence interval allow you to predict the winner? Explain.

b. Explain why the same proportions but with smaller samples provide less information. (*Hint:* What effect does *n* have on the standard error?)

8.27 Simulating coverage Repeat the simulation from Activity 2, but this time simulate 10,000 confidence intervals (in the *Explore Coverage* app, select to simulate 1,000 samples at a time, and then press the Draw Sample(s) button 10 times) when the true population proportion is *p* = 0.5 and the sample size is *n* = 100. Do this for a confidence level of 95% and then 99%. Before running the simulation, what percentage of the 10,000 simulated intervals do you expect to cover the population proportion of 0.5 in each case? What is the actual percent of simulated intervals that cover the population proportion?

8.28 Simulating poor coverage Open the *Explore Coverage* app and set *p* = 0.30, *n* = 10, and leave the confidence level at 95%. Select to draw 100 random samples of size *n* and then click on Draw Sample(s).

a. How many of the intervals you generated with the app fail to contain the true value, *p* = 0.30?

b. How many would you expect not to contain the true value? What does this suggest?

c. To see that this is not a fluke, now select to draw 1,000 instead of 100 samples and see what percentage of 95% confidence intervals contain 0.30. (*Note:* For every interval formed, the number of successes is smaller than 15, so the large-sample formula is not adequate.)

d. Using the *Sampling Distribution for the Sample Proportion* app, generate 10,000 random samples of

---

[6]See B. Lomborg, (2001), *The Skeptical Environmentalist*, Cambridge University Press, p. 222.

size 10 when $p = 0.30$. The app will plot the simulated sampling distribution of the sample proportion values. Is it bell shaped? Use this to help you explain why the large-sample confidence interval performs poorly in this case. (This exercise illustrates that assumptions for statistical methods are important, because the methods may perform poorly if we use them when the assumptions are violated.)

8.29 Binge drinkers A study at the Harvard School of Public Health found that 44% of 10,000 sampled college students were binge drinkers. A student at the University of Minnesota plans to estimate the proportion of college students at that school who are binge drinkers. How large a random sample would she need to estimate it to within 0.05 with 95% confidence, if before conducting the study she uses the Harvard study results as a guideline?

8.30 Abstainers The Harvard study mentioned in the previous exercise estimated that 19% of college students abstain from drinking alcohol. To estimate this proportion in your school, how large a random sample would you need to estimate it to within 0.05 with probability 0.95, if before conducting the study:
a. You are unwilling to guess the proportion value at your school?
b. You use the Harvard study as a guideline?
c. Use the results from parts a and b to explain why strategy (a) is inefficient if you are quite sure you'll get a sample proportion that is far from 0.50.

8.31 How many businesses fail? A study is planned to estimate the proportion of businesses started in the year 2006 that had failed within five years of their start-up. How large a sample size is needed to guarantee estimating this proportion correct to within
a. 0.10 with probability 0.95?
b. 0.05 with probability 0.95?
c. 0.05 with probability 0.99?
d. Compare sample sizes for parts a and b, and b and c, and summarize the effects of decreasing the margin of error and increasing the confidence level.

8.32 Web survey to get large *n* A newspaper wants to gauge public opinion about legalization of marijuana. The sample size formula indicates that it needs a random sample of 875 people to get the desired margin of error. But surveys cost money, and it can only afford to randomly

sample 100 people. Here's a tempting alternative: If it places a question about that issue on its website, it will get more than 1,000 responses within a day at little cost. Is it better off with the random sample of 100 responses or the website volunteer sample of more than 1,000 responses? (*Hint:* Think about the issues discussed in Section 4.2 about proper sampling of populations.)

8.33 Do you like tofu? You randomly sample five students at your school to estimate the proportion of students who like tofu. All five students say they like it.
a. Find the sample proportion who like it.
b. Find the standard error. Does its usual interpretation make sense?
c. Find a 95% confidence interval, using the large-sample formula. Is it sensible to conclude that *all* students at your school like tofu?
d. Why is it not appropriate to use the ordinary large-sample confidence interval in part c? Use a more appropriate approach and interpret the result.

8.34 Alleviate PMS? A pharmaceutical company proposes a new drug treatment for alleviating symptoms of PMS (premenstrual syndrome). In the first stages of a clinical trial, it was successful for 7 out of 10 women.
a. Construct an appropriate 95% confidence interval for the population proportion.
b. Is it plausible that it's successful for only half the population? Explain.

8.35 Google Glass Google started selling Google Glass (a type of wearable technology that projects information onto the eye) in the United States in spring 2014 for $1,500. A national poll reveals that out of 500 people sampled, nobody owned Google Glass.
a. Find the sample proportion who don't own Google Glass and its standard error.
b. Find a 95% confidence interval, using the large-sample formula. Is it sensible to conclude that no one in the United States owns Google Glass?
c. Why is it not appropriate to use the ordinary large-sample confidence interval in part b? Use a more appropriate approach and interpret the result.
d. Is it plausible to say that fewer than 1% of the population own Google Glass? Explain.

8.3 Confidence Interval for a Population Mean

We've learned how to construct a confidence interval for a population proportion—a parameter that summarizes a categorical variable. Next we'll learn how to construct a confidence interval for a **population mean**—a summary parameter for a quantitative variable. We'll analyze GSS data to estimate the mean number of hours per day that Americans watch television. The method resembles that for a proportion. The confidence interval again has the form

$$\text{point estimate} \pm \text{margin of error},$$

and the margin of error again equals a multiple of a standard error. What do you think plays the role of the point estimate and what plays the role of the standard error (*se*) in this formula?

Recall

The sampling distribution of the sample mean $\bar{x}$

- describes all the possible values of $\bar{x}$ in a sample of size n,
- is approximately normal for large n,
- has mean equal to μ, the population mean,
- has standard deviation equal to $\sigma/\sqrt{n}$, where σ is the population standard deviation.

The sample standard deviation $s = \sqrt{\Sigma(x_i - \bar{x})^2/(n-1)}$ and is a point estimate of the population standard deviation σ. ◀

In Words

The standard error of the sample mean $\bar{x}$ is $s/\sqrt{n}$.

How to Construct a Confidence Interval for a Population Mean

The sample mean $\bar{x}$ is the point estimate of the population mean μ. In Section 7.2, we learned that the standard deviation of the sample mean equals $\sigma/\sqrt{n}$, where σ is the population standard deviation. Like the standard deviation of the sample proportion, the standard deviation of the sample mean depends on a parameter whose value is unknown, in this case σ. In practice, we need to estimate σ by the sample standard deviation s to be able to compute a margin of error and a confidence interval. So, the standard error for the sample mean $\bar{x}$ is obtained by replacing σ with s in the formula for the standard deviation to give

$$se = s/\sqrt{n}.$$

For large samples, the logic of obtaining a 95% confidence interval for a population mean μ is the same as the one we used for constructing the confidence interval for a population proportion: Because of the normal distribution of the sample mean $\bar{x}$ around μ, stretching out 1.96(se) to either side of $\bar{x}$ captures the population mean μ 95% of the time. For large samples, the confidence interval is therefore given by $\bar{x} \pm 1.96(se) = \bar{x} \pm 1.96(s/\sqrt{n})$.

Standard Error and Confidence Interval for a Population Mean ◀

| **Example 8** |

Number of Hours Spent Watching Television

Picture the Scenario

How much of a typical person's day is spent in front of the TV? A recent General Social Survey asked respondents, "On the average day, about how many hours do you personally watch television?" The data are available on the book's website and are preloaded in the *Inference for a Mean* app, shown in Figure 8.6. We see that the sample size was $n = 1,555$, the sample mean was $\bar{x} = 2.94$, the sample standard deviation was $s = 2.84$, the standard error of the sample mean was $se = 0.07$, and the 95% confidence interval for the population mean time μ spent watching TV goes from 2.80 to 3.08 hours per day.

▶ **Figure 8.6** Histogram, Box Plot, Descriptive Statistics and Confidence Interval for the Mean Number of Hours of Daily TV Watching. Screenshot from the *Inference for a Mean* app, showing the sample size, sample mean and sample standard deviation and providing the standard error and margin of error of the sample mean. The confidence interval is given in the last table and pictured graphically.

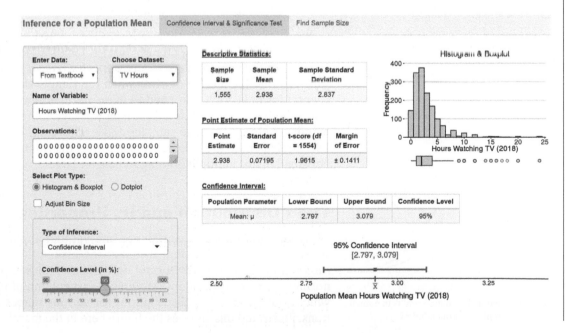

Questions to Explore

a. Describe the distribution of the daily hours of TV watching, addressing shape, center, and variability.

b. How did the app get the standard error? Interpret it.

c. Interpret the 95% confidence interval reported by the app.

Think It Through

a. As the histogram and box plot displayed in the app show, the distribution is skewed to the right, with a mean of 2.9 hours and a standard deviation of 2.8 hours. The lowest possible value of 0 falls only a bit more than 1 standard deviation below the mean. You can get additional descriptive statistics by clicking Show More Descriptive Statistics in the app. From these (see also the box plot), the median number of hours watching daily is 2 and the lower and upper quartiles are 1 and 4, respectively.

b. With sample standard deviation $s = 2.84$ and sample size $n = 1,555$, the standard error of the sample mean is

$$se = s/\sqrt{n} = 2.84/\sqrt{1,555} = 0.072 \text{ hours.}$$

If many studies were conducted about TV watching, with a sample size of $n = 1,555$ for each, the sample mean would not vary much (i.e., only by 0.07 hours) between those studies.

c. A 95% confidence interval for the population mean μ of TV watching in the United States is (2.8, 3.1) hours. With 95% confidence, the mean amount of TV watched by Americans is estimated to be between 2.8 and 3.1 hours a day, with a point estimate of 2.9 hours.

Insight

Because the sample size was relatively large, the estimation is precise (margin of error $= \pm 0.14$ hours) and the confidence interval is very narrow. The larger the sample size, the smaller the standard error and therefore the margin of error.

▶ **Try Exercise 8.36**

We didn't verify how the app found the quoted margin of error of 0.14, but you can check that it is equal to $1.96(se) = 1.96(0.0719)$. However, this formula of $1.96(se)$ for the margin of error only works for large n, such as the $n = 1,555$ in this study. To find the margin of error when the sample size is smaller and develop a general formula, we'll first need to learn about a new distribution. This distribution will give us the multiple by which we have to multiply the se to obtain the margin of error. For large samples and a 95% confidence level, this multiple is 1.96, equivalent to the z-score from a normal distribution with 2.5% in either tail. For small n, this multiple is going to be a bit larger.

The *t* Distribution and Its Properties

We'll now learn about a confidence interval that applies even for small sample sizes. A disadvantage is that it makes the assumption that the *population distribution of the variable is normal*. In that case, the sampling distribution of $\bar{x}$ is normal even for small sample sizes. (The last column of Figure 7.11 on page 351, which showed sampling distributions for various shapes of population distributions, illustrated this, as does the figure here in the margin.) When the population

Sampling distribution for $n = 5$

Population distribution

Normal population distribution results in normal sampling distribution of $\bar{x}$.

distribution is normal, the sampling distribution of $\bar{x}$ is normal for all n, not just large n.

Suppose we knew the standard deviation, $\sigma/\sqrt{n}$, of the sample mean. Then, with the additional assumption that the population is normal, with small n we could use the formula $\bar{x} \pm z(\sigma/\sqrt{n})$, for instance with $z = 1.96$ for 95% confidence. This interval would contain the population mean μ 95% of the time. In practice, we don't know the population standard deviation σ. Substituting the sample standard deviation s for σ to get $se = s/\sqrt{n}$ introduces extra error. This error can be sizeable when n is small. To account for this increased error, we must replace the z-score by a slightly larger score, called a **t-score.** The confidence interval is then a bit wider, with a larger margin of error. *The t-score is like a z-score* but it comes from a bell-shaped distribution that has slightly thicker tails (i.e., shows more variability) than a normal distribution. This distribution is called the **t distribution.**

> **In Practice** The t Distribution Adjusts for Estimating σ
>
> In practice, we estimate the standard deviation of the sample mean using the standard error $se = s/\sqrt{n}$. Then we multiply the standard error se by a t-score from the **t distribution** to get the margin of error for a confidence interval for the population mean.

Recall

From Section 6.2, the **standard normal** distribution has mean 0 and standard deviation 1. ◄

The t distribution resembles the *standard normal* distribution, being bell shaped around a mean of 0. Its standard deviation is a bit larger than 1, the precise value depending on what is called the **degrees of freedom,** denoted by df. For inference about a population mean, the degrees of freedom equal $df = n-1$, i.e., the sample size minus 1. Before presenting this confidence interval for a mean, we list the major properties of the t distribution. Open the t *Distribution* app from the book's website to explore these properties visually.

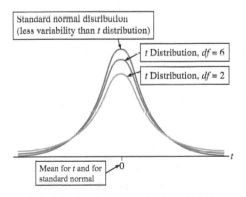

▲ **Figure 8.7** The t Distribution Relative to the Standard Normal Distribution. The t distribution is more spread out than the standard normal but gets closer to it as the degrees of freedom (df) increase. The two are practically identical when $df \geq 30$. **Question** Can you find z-scores (such as 1.96) for a normal distribution on the t table (Table B)?

SUMMARY: Properties of the t Distribution

- The t distribution is bell shaped and symmetric about 0.
- The t distribution has a slightly different shape for each distinct value for the degrees of freedom, df. Probabilities and t-scores computed from the t distribution depend on the value for the degrees of freedom.
- The t distribution has thicker tails and therefore allows for more variability than the standard normal distribution. The larger the df value, however, the closer it gets to the standard normal. Figure 8.7 illustrates this point. When df is about 30 or more, the two distributions are nearly identical.
- A t-score obtained from the t distribution multiplied by the standard error gives the margin of error for a confidence interval for the mean μ.

The t *Distribution* app on the book's website can find t-scores from the t distribution for any given value for the degrees of freedom and any desired probability. Also, the *Inference of a Mean* app computes the appropriate t-score automatically for any given confidence level, so you actually don't need to worry about finding a t-score. However, if you don't have access to technology, Table B in the Appendix (replicated in part as Table 8.3 here) lists t-scores from the t distribution for the right-tail probabilities of 0.100, 0.050, 0.025, 0.010, 0.005, and 0.001, for different values of df. The table labels these by $t_{.100}, t_{.050}, t_{.025}, t_{.010}, t_{.005}$, and $t_{.001}$. For instance, $t_{.025}$ is the t-score with probability 0.025 in the right tail and a two-tail probability of 0.05. It is used in 95% confidence intervals.

Table 8.3 Part of Table B Displaying *t*-Scores

The scores have right-tail probabilities of 0.100, 0.050, 0.025, 0.010, 0.005, and 0.001. When $n = 7$, $df = 6$, and $t_{.025} = 2.447$ is the *t*-score with right-tail probability $= 0.025$ and two-tail probability $= 0.05$. It is used in a 95% confidence interval, $\bar{x} \pm 2.447(se)$.

	Confidence Level					
	80%	90%	95%	98%	99%	99.8%
df	$t_{.100}$	$t_{.050}$	$t_{.025}$	$t_{.010}$	$t_{.005}$	$t_{.001}$
1	3.078	6.314	12.706	31.821	63.657	318.3
...						
6	1.440	1.943	2.447	3.143	3.707	5.208
7	1.415	1.895	2.365	2.998	3.499	4.785

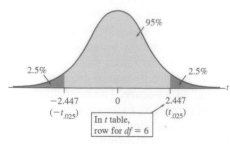

▲ **Figure 8.8** The *t* Distribution with $df = 6$. 95% of the distribution falls between −2.447 and 2.447. These *t*-scores are used with a 95% confidence interval when $n = 7$. **Question** In comparison, what are the values of the *z*-scores that contain the middle 95% of the standard normal distribution?

Screenshot from *t Distribution* app.

To illustrate the use of this *t* table, suppose the sample size is 7. Then the degrees of freedom $df = n - 1 = 6$. Row 6 of the *t* table shows the *t*-scores for $df = 6$. The column labeled $t_{.025}$ contains *t*-scores with right-tail probability equal to 0.025. With $df = 6$, this *t*-score is $t_{.025} = 2.447$. This means that 2.5% of the *t* distribution falls in the right tail above 2.447. By symmetry, 2.5% also falls in the left tail below $-t_{.025} = -2.447$. Figure 8.8 illustrates the *t* distribution and the *t*-score. The screenshot in the margin shows how to use the *t Distrubution* app to find this *t*-score.

We have now found the *t*-score we use for constructing a 95% confidence interval for μ when $n = 7$. The confidence interval is $\bar{x} \pm 2.447(se)$. If you have access to technology, such as the *Inference for a Mean* app, it will compute the *t*-score (and the corresponding confidence interval) automatically for you.

Using the *t* Distribution to Construct a Confidence Interval for a Mean

The confidence interval for a mean has margin of error that equals a *t*-score times the standard error.

SUMMARY: 95% Confidence Interval for a Population Mean

A 95% confidence interval for the population mean μ is

$$\bar{x} \pm t_{.025}(se), \text{ where } se = s/\sqrt{n}.$$

Here, $df = n - 1$ for the *t*-score $t_{.025}$ that has right-tail probability 0.025 (total probability 0.05 in the two tails and 0.95 between $-t_{.025}$ and $t_{.025}$). To use this method, you need:

- Data obtained by randomization (such as a random sample or a randomized experiment).
- An approximately normal population distribution.

Example 9

Using the *t* Distribution for a Confidence Interval for the Mean ◀

Buying on eBay

Picture the Scenario

eBay is a popular Internet company for auctioning just about anything. How much can you save by buying items on eBay compared to their actual retail price? The following data are from a random sample of 11 completed auctions for an unlocked Apple iPhone 5s with 16GB storage in new condition, obtained from eBay in July 2014.

Closing Price (in $): 540, 565, 570, 570, 580, 590, 590, 590, 595, 610, 620

These data are available in the *Inference for a Mean* app, for which a screenshot is shown in Figure 8.9.

▶ **Figure 8.9** Dot and Box Plot, Descriptive Statistics and Confidence Interval for the Mean Closing Price of iPhone Auctions. Screenshot from the *Inference for a Mean* app, showing the sample mean and standard deviation, the standard error, the *t*-score and the margin of error for 95 confidence and, in the last table, the resulting confidence interval. The interval is also shown as a graph.

Questions to Explore

a. Use numerical summaries and graphical displays to check the assumptions for finding a 95% confidence interval for the mean closing price on eBay.

b. Find the 95% confidence interval and interpret it.

Think It Through

a. The dot plot and box plot for the 11 observations shown in the app suggest that the shape of the distribution of prices may be slightly skewed to the left but not too far from symmetric. However, it is hard to tell much with only 11 observations. The mean closing price for these 11 auctions was $584. The lowest price was $540 and is not shown as an outlier on the box plot. The assumptions for using the *t* distribution are that the data come from a random sample and that the distribution of the final auction price is approximately normal. Although these 11 observations can be regarded as a random sample from the population of all possible closing prices for iPhones 5s posted for sale on eBay in the given time period, checking that they roughly follow a normal model is more difficult. With just 11 observations, dot plots, box plots, or histograms are not very informative about the true shape. However, the dot plot does not rule out a bell shape, and the box plot doesn't show an outlier, so we can proceed with the analysis. Later in this section, we discuss this assumption further.

b. Let μ denote the population mean for the closing price of the auction. The point estimate of μ is the sample mean of the 11 observations, which is $\bar{x} = 583.6$. This and the sample standard deviation of $s = 22.15$

are reported in the top table of the app. The standard error of the sample mean is

$$se = s/\sqrt{n} = 22.15/\sqrt{11} = 6.68.$$

Because $n = 11$, the degrees of freedom to use for the t-score are $df = 11 - 1 = 10$. The t-score to use for a 95% confidence interval equals $t_{.025} = 2.228$. The app displays the standard error, this t-score, and the resulting margin of error in the second table. (To display the t-score, check the "Show t-score for Margin of Error" box.) The 95% confidence interval is

$$\bar{x} \pm t_{.025}(se) \text{ or } 583.6 \pm 2.228(6.68),$$

which is 583.6 ± 14.88, or $(569, 599)$ rounded.

With 95% confidence, we estimate that the mean closing price for an unlocked 16GB iPhone 5s posted for sale on eBay is between \$569 to \$599, with a point estimate of \$584.

Insight

The t-score of 2.228 for this confidence interval is larger than a corresponding z-score of 1.96, leading to a larger (i.e., less precise) interval. This is a consequence of having a small sample size and the need to estimate the standard deviation σ with s to compute the standard error.

▶ *Try Exercise 8.42*

Finding a *t* Confidence Interval for Other Confidence Levels

The 95% confidence interval uses $t_{.025}$, the t-score for a right-tail probability of 0.025, since 95% of the probability falls between $-t_{.025}$ and $t_{.025}$. For 99% confidence, the right-tail probability is $0.01/2 = 0.005$, and the appropriate t-score is $t_{.005}$. If you don't use the app, the top margin of Table B shows both the t subscript notation and the confidence level, from which you can find the t-score.

For instance, the eBay auction sample in the preceding example has $n = 11$, so $df = 10$ and from Table B, $t_{.005} = 3.169$. (The *Inference for a Mean* app computes this automatically.) A 99% confidence interval for the mean closing price is

$$\bar{x} \pm t_{.005}(se) = 583.6 \pm 3.169(6.68),$$

which is 583.6 ± 21.17, or $(562, 605)$ rounded.

In the app, you can get this automatically by moving the slider for the confidence level to 99%. As we saw with the confidence interval for a population proportion using a larger confidence level, this 99% confidence interval for a population mean is wider than the 95% confidence interval of $(569, 599)$.

If the Population Is Not Normal, Is the Method Robust?

A basic assumption of the confidence interval using the t distribution is that the population distribution is normal. This is worrisome because many variables have distributions that are far from a bell shape. How problematic is it if we use the t confidence interval even if the population distribution is not normal? For large random samples, it's not problematic at all because of the Central Limit Theorem. The sampling distribution is bell shaped even when the population distribution is not. But what about for small n?

For the confidence interval in Example 9 with $n = 11$ to be valid, we must assume that the probability distribution of closing prices is normal. Does this assumption seem plausible? Because there is an upper limit (no one would pay more than the retail price for a brand new phone), we would expect a distribution that is skewed to the left. A dot plot, histogram, or stem-and-leaf plot gives us some information about the population distribution, but it is not precise when n is small and it tells us little when $n = 11$. Fortunately, the confidence interval using the t distribution is a **robust** method in terms of the normality assumption.

> ### Robust Statistical Method
>
> A statistical method is said to be **robust** with respect to a particular assumption if it performs adequately even when that assumption is modestly violated.

Even if the population distribution is not normal, confidence intervals using t-scores usually work quite well. The actual probability that the 95% confidence interval covers the true population mean is close to 95% and gets closer as n increases.

The most important case when the t confidence interval method does *not* work well is *when the data contain extreme outliers*. Partly this is because of the effect of outliers on summary statistics such as $\bar{x}$ and s. If we had observed an auction in Example 9 that resulted in a very low price of around $400, then this might call into question the validity of the confidence interval procedure. (One approach is to compute the confidence interval with and without the outlier[s] and see whether there are substantial changes.) Another issue with extreme outliers is that the mean itself might not be a representative summary of the center. Section 8.4 will discuss methods (based on the bootstrap, introduced in Section 7.3) for constructing confidence intervals for the mean when the normality assumption is seriously in doubt. There, we'll also discuss methods for finding a confidence interval for the population median, which might be a more meaningful measure for the center of a skewed distribution. Finally, the t distribution does not work with binary data and proportions, for which Section 8.2 presented a separate method for finding a confidence interval.

Recall

Section 2.5 identified an observation as a potential **outlier** if it falls more than $1.5 \times IQR$ below the first quartile or above the third quartile, or if it falls more than 3 standard deviations from the mean. ◄

Caution

The t confidence interval method is not robust to violations of the random sampling assumption. The t method, like all inferential statistical methods, has questionable validity if the method for producing the data did not use randomization. ◄

> ### In Practice Assumptions Are Rarely Perfectly Satisfied
>
> Knowing that a statistical method is **robust** (that is, it still performs adequately) even when a particular assumption is violated is important because in practice assumptions are rarely perfectly satisfied. Confidence intervals for a mean using the **t distribution** are robust against most violations of the normal population assumption. However, you should check the data graphically to identify **outliers** that could affect the validity of the mean or its confidence interval. Also, unless the data production used **randomization**, statistical inference may be inappropriate.

The Standard Normal Distribution Is the t Distribution with *df* = ∞

If you access the t *Distribution* app from the book's website, you can see that as you move the slider for the degrees of freedom from 1 to 40, the t distribution gets closer and closer to the standard normal distribution. After about $df = 30$, you really can't tell the difference any more. Consequently, t-scores computed from the t distribution with larger df are similar to z-scores computed from the standard normal distribution. For instance, the z-score we use for 95% confidence intervals is 1.96. The corresponding t-score is 2.04 when $df = 30$, 2.01 when $df = 50$, and 1.98 when $df = 100$. The larger the df, the closer the t-score gets to the z-score.

For the GSS example about daily hours of watching TV in Example 8, $n = 1,555$, and hence $df = 1,554$. The t-score for the 95% confidence interval (as shown in the *Inference for a Mean* app) equals 1.9615, practically identical to the z-score of 1.96. This is why for large samples, we can use the formula $\bar{x} \pm 1.96(se)$ for the 95% confidence interval for the population mean.

Recall

The reason we use a t-score instead of a z-score in the confidence interval for a mean is that it accounts for the extra error due to estimating σ by s when the sample size is small. ◄

> **In Practice** Use t for Inference About μ Whenever You Estimate
>
> Statistical software and calculators use the t distribution for *all* cases when the sample standard deviation s is used to estimate the population standard deviation σ. The normal population assumption is mainly relevant for small n, but even then the t confidence interval is a robust method, working well unless there are extreme outliers or the data are binary.

Choosing the Sample Size

As with the population proportion, to derive the necessary sample size for estimating a population mean, you set the margin of error equal to its desired value and solve for n. Recall that a 95% confidence interval for the population mean μ is

$$\bar{x} \pm t_{.025}(se),$$

where $se = s/\sqrt{n}$ and s is the sample standard deviation. If you don't know n, you also don't know the degrees of freedom and the t-score. However, we just saw that when $df > 30$, the t-score is very similar to the z-score from a normal distribution, such as 1.96 for 95% confidence, so we'll use this z-score instead of the t-score in the formula for determining the same size. Also, before collecting the data, we wouldn't know the value of the sample standard deviation s, which is used to estimate the population standard deviation σ. To proceed, we typically make an educated guess about the value for σ and use it in place of s. Then, solving the equation $m = z(\sigma/\sqrt{n})$, where m is the desired margin of error, for the sample size n, we have the following result:

In Words

The sample size n needed to estimate the population mean depends on
- how precisely you want to estimate it (by the choice of the margin of error m),
- how sure you want to be (by the confidence level, which determines the z-score), and
- how variable the data will be (by the guess for the population standard deviation σ).

> **SUMMARY: Sample Size for Estimating a Population Mean**
>
> The sample size n of a random sample for which a confidence interval for a population mean μ has margin of error approximately equal to m is
>
> $$n = \frac{\sigma^2 z^2}{m^2}.$$
>
> The z-score is based on the confidence level, such as $z = 1.96$ for 95% confidence. To use this formula, you need to guess the value for the population standard deviation σ.

In practice, you don't know the population standard deviation. You must substitute an educated guess for σ. Sometimes you can guess it using the sample standard deviation from a similar study already conducted, or you can take a *pilot study*, which is a small study taken before the actual study. From the few observations in the pilot study, you can crudely estimate σ. The next example shows another sort of reasoning to form an educated guess.

Finding *n* ◄

Recall

The Empirical Rule in Section 2.4 noted that for bell-shaped distributions, all or nearly all observations fall within 3 standard deviations of the mean. ◄

Example 10

Estimating Mean Education in South Africa

Picture the Scenario

A social scientist studies adult South Africans living in townships on the outskirts of Cape Town, to investigate educational attainment in the black community. Educational attainment is the number of years of education completed. Many of the study's potential subjects were forced to leave Cape Town in 1966 when the government passed a law forbidding blacks to live in the inner cities. Under the apartheid system, black South African children were not required to attend school, so some residents had very little education.

Question to Explore

How large a sample size is needed so that a 95% confidence interval for the mean number of years of attained education has a margin of error equal to 1 year?

Think It Through

No prior information is stated about the standard deviation of educational attainment for the township residents. As a crude approximation, we might guess that the education values will fall within a range of about 18 years, such as between 0 and 18 years. If the distribution is bell shaped, the range from $\mu - 3\sigma$ to $\mu + 3\sigma$ will contain all or nearly all of the possible values. Since the distance from $\mu - 3\sigma$ to $\mu + 3\sigma$ equals 6σ, the range of 18 years would equal about 6σ. Then, solving $18 = 6\sigma$ for σ, $18/6 = 3$ is a crude guess for σ. So we'd expect a standard deviation value of about $\sigma = 3$.

The desired margin of error is $m = 1$ year. Then, the required sample size is

$$n = \frac{\sigma^2 z^2}{m^2} = \frac{3^2(1.96)^2}{1^2} = 34.6.$$

We need to obtain a random sample of at least 35 subjects for a 95% confidence interval for mean educational attainment to have a margin of error of 1 year.

Insight

A more cautious approach would select the *largest* value for the standard deviation that is plausible. This will give the largest sensible guess for how large *n* needs to be. For example, we could reasonably predict that σ will be no greater than 4, since a range of 6 standard deviations then extends over 24 years. Then we get $n = (1.96)^2(4^2)/(1^2) = 62$. If we collect the data and the sample standard deviation is actually less than 4, we will have more data than we need. The margin of error will be even less than 1.0.

► *Try Exercise 8.54*

Other Factors That Affect the Choice of the Sample Size

We've looked at two factors that play a role in determining a study's sample size.

- The first is the desired *precision*, as measured by the *margin of error m*.
- The second is the *confidence level*, which determines the *z*-score in the sample size formulas.

Other factors also play a role.

- A third factor is the *variability* in the data.

Let's look at the formula $n = \sigma^2 z^2 / m^2$ for the sample size for estimating a mean. The greater the value expected for the standard deviation σ, the larger the sample size needed. If subjects have little variation (that is, σ is small), we need fewer data than if they have substantial variation. Suppose a study plans to estimate the mean level of education in several countries. Western European countries have relatively little variation because students are required to attend school until the middle teen years. To estimate the mean to within a margin of error of $m = 1$, we need fewer observations than in South Africa.

■ A fourth factor is *cost*.

Larger samples are more time consuming to collect. They may be more expensive than a study can afford. Cost is often a major constraint. You may need to ask, "Should we go ahead with the smaller sample that we can afford, even though the margin of error will be greater than we would like?"

On the Shoulders of...William S. Gosset

W. S. Gosset: Discovered the *t* distribution allowing statistical methods for working with small sample sizes.

How do you find the best way to brew beer if you have only small samples?

The statistician and chemist William S. Gosset was a brewer in charge of the experimental unit of Guinness Breweries in Dublin, Ireland. The search for a better stout in 1908 led him to the discovery of the *t* distribution. Only small samples

were available from his experiments pertaining to the selection, cultivation, and treatment of barley and hops. The established statistical methods at that time relied on large samples and the normal distribution. Because of company policy forbidding the publication of company work in one's own name, Gosset used the pseudonym "Student" in articles he wrote about his discoveries. The *t* distribution became known as *Student's t* distribution, a name still used today.

8.3 Practicing the Basics

8.36 **Females' ideal number of children** The 2012 General Social Survey asked, "What do you think is the ideal number of children for a family to have?" (Variable NUMKIDS.) The 590 females who gave a numeric response from 0 to 6 had a median of 2, mean of 2.56, and standard deviation of 0.84.

a. What is the point estimate of the population mean?

b. Find the standard error of the sample mean.

c. The 95% confidence interval is (2.49, 2.62). Interpret.

d. Is it plausible that the population mean $\mu = 2$? Explain.

8.37 **Males' ideal number of children** Refer to the previous exercise. For the 530 males in the sample who gave a numeric response from 0 to 6, the mean was 2.51 and the standard deviation was 0.87.

a. Find the point estimate of the population mean and show that its standard error is 0.038.

b. The 95% confidence interval is 2.43 to 2.59. Explain what "95% confidence" means for this interval.

c. Compared to the interval for females, is there much evidence of a difference between the means? Explain.

8.38 Finding *t*-scores   Using the *t Distribution* app (or some other software, or Table B from the back of this book), find the *t*-score that you multiply the standard error with to form the margin of error for a

   a. 95% confidence interval for a mean with 5 observations.

   b. 95% confidence interval for a mean with 15 observations.

   c. 99% confidence interval for a mean with 15 observations.

8.39 Anorexia in teenage girls   A study[7] compared various therapies for teenage girls suffering from anorexia, an eating disorder. For the 17 girls assigned to family therapy, the changes in their weights (in lbs) between the beginning and the end of the study were

11, 11, 6, 9, 14, −3, 0, 7, 22, −5, −4, 13, 13, 9, 4, 6, 11.

A positive value implies a weight gain; a negative, a weight loss over the duration of the study. These values were entered in the *Inference for a Mean* app, resulting in the screenshot shown.

Descriptive Statistics:

Sample Size	Sample Mean	Sample Standard Deviation
17	7.294	7.183

Point Estimate of Population Mean:

Point Estimate	Standard Error	t-score (df = 16)	Margin of Error
7.294	1.742	2.1199	± 3.693

Confidence Interval:

Population Parameter	Lower Bound	Upper Bound	Confidence Level
Mean: μ	3.601	10.99	95%

Dotplot & Boxplot (Weight Change)

   a. Describe the distribution of weight change in this sample.

   b. Verify the standard error of 1.74 lbs shown by the app.

   c. How did the app compute the margin of error of 3.7 lbs?

   d. Show how the app found the 95% confidence interval (3.6, 11.0).

   e. Interpret the confidence interval in context. Explain why it suggests that the true mean weight change is positive.

8.40 Talk time on smartphones   One feature smartphone manufacturers use in advertising is the amount of time one can continuously talk before recharging the battery. Below are 13 values from a random sample of the talktime (in minutes) of smartphones running on lithium-ion batteries. The summary statistics are $\bar{x} = 553$, $s = 227$, Q1 = 420, median = 450, Q3 = 650. Talk time: 320, 360, 760, 580, 1050, 900, 360, 500, 420, 420, 650, 420, 450.

   a. Construct an appropriate graph (dot plot, stem-and-leaf plot, histogram, box plot) to describe the shape of the distribution. What assumptions are needed to construct a 95% confidence interval for μ, the

mean talk time? Point out any assumptions that seem questionable.

   b. Check whether this data set has any potential outliers according to the criterion of (i) 1.5 * IQR below Q1 or above Q3 and (ii) 3 standard deviations from the mean.

   c. Obtain the 95% confidence interval and interpret it in context.

   d. The value of 1,050 minutes is quite a bit larger than the others. Delete this observation, find the new mean and standard deviation, and construct the 95% confidence interval for μ without this observation. How does it compare to the 95% confidence interval using all data?

8.41 Heights of seedlings   Exercise 8.7 reported heights (in mm) of 55.5, 60.3, 60.6, 62.1, 65.5, and 69.2 for six seedlings fourteen days after germination.

   a. Using the *Inference for a Mean* app or other software, verify that the 95% confidence interval for the population mean is (57.3, 67.1).

   b. Name two settings you could change to get a narrower interval than the one in part a.

   c. Construct a 99% confidence interval. Why is it wider than the 95% interval?

   d. On what assumptions is the interval in part a based? Explain how important each assumption is.

8.42 Buy It Now   Example 9 mentioned closing prices for listings of the iPhone 5s on eBay. If you don't feel comfortable bidding (or can't wait until a listing has ended), you can often purchase the item right away at the indicated Buy It Now price. A random sample of Buy It Now prices for an unlocked 16GB iPhone 5s in July 2014 showed the following prices (in $), with dot plot and box plot shown in the figure: 618, 650, 608, 634, 675, 618, 625, 619, 630.

Buy It Now Price

   a. What must we assume to use these data to find a 95% confidence interval for the mean Buy It Now price on eBay? Do these assumptions seem plausible?

   b. The table shows the way many statistical software packages report results. How was the standard error of the mean (SE Mean) obtained?

```
Variable  N  Mean    StDev  SE Mean     95% CI
BuyItNow  9  630.78  20.47  6.82    (615.04 646.52)
```

   c. Interpret the 95% confidence interval in context.

   d. Compared to the confidence interval (569, 599) for prices from auctions obtained in Example 9, is there evidence that the mean price is higher when purchased as Buy It Now? Explain.

   e. Excluding the observation of $675, the confidence interval equals (615, 636). Does this change your answer to part d?

---

[7]Data courtesy of Prof. Brian Everitt, Institute of Psychiatry, London.

8.43 Time spent on e-mail When the GSS asked $n = 1,417$ people in 2018, "About how many hours per week do you spend sending and answering e-mail?" (EMAILHR), the summary statistics were $\bar{x} = 7.1$ and $s = 11.7$. The data are available from the book's website and are preloaded in the *Inference for a Mean* app. A screenshot is shown below.

APP

GSS

a. Interpret the margin of error.

b. Interpret the 95% confidence interval shown in context.

c. The distribution of hours spent is right skewed. Is this a concern for the validity of the confidence interval?

Descriptive Statistics:

Sample Size	Sample Mean	Sample Standard Deviation
1,417	7.109	11.71

Point Estimate of Population Mean:

Point Estimate	Standard Error	Margin of Error
7.109	0.3111	± 0.6103

Confidence Interval:

Population Parameter	Lower Bound	Upper Bound	Confidence Level
Mean: μ	6.499	7.72	95%

95% Confidence Interval
[6.499, 7.72]

Histogram & Boxplot

Population Mean Hours Emailing per Week (2018)

8.44 Grandmas using e-mail For the question about e-mail in the previous exercise, the 15 females in the GSS of age at least 85 had the responses

APP

0, 0, 0, 0, 0, 0, 0, 1, 2, 3, 4, 4, 4, 5, 7.

a. Using the app, software, or a calculator, find the sample mean, the sample standard deviation, and the standard error of the sample mean.

b. Find and interpret a 90% confidence interval for the population mean.

c. Explain why the population distribution may be skewed right. If this is the case, is the interval you obtained in part b still valid? Explain.

8.45 Interpreting confidence interval According to a union agreement, the mean income for all senior-level assembly-line workers in a large company equals $500 per week. A representative of a women's group decides to analyze whether the mean income for female employees matches this norm. For a random sample of nine female employees, using software, she obtains a 95% confidence interval of (371, 509). Explain what is wrong with each of the following interpretations of this interval.

a. We infer that 95% of the women in the population have income between $371 and $509 per week.

b. If random samples of nine women were repeatedly selected, then 95% of the time the sample mean income would be between $371 and $509.

c. We can be 95% confident that $\bar{x}$ is between $371 and $509.

d. If we repeatedly sampled the entire population, then 95% of the time the population mean would be between $371 and $509.

8.46 How often read a newspaper? For the FL Student Survey data file on the book's website, software reports the results for responses on the number of times a week the subject reads a newspaper:

```
Variable   N   Mean  Std Dev  SE Mean      95.0% CI
News       60   4.1    3.0     0.388    (3.307, 4.859)
```

a. Is it plausible that $\mu = 7$, where μ is the population mean for all Florida students? Explain.

b. Suppose that the sample size had been 240, with $\bar{x} = 4.1$ and $s = 3.0$. Find a 95% confidence interval and compare it to the one reported. Describe the effect of sample size on the margin of error.

c. Does it seem plausible that the population distribution of this variable is normal? Why?

d. Explain the implications of the term *robust* regarding the normality assumption made to conduct this analysis.

8.47 Political views The General Social Survey asks respondents to rate their political views on a seven-point scale, where 1 = extremely liberal, 4 = moderate, and 7 = extremely conservative. A researcher analyzing data from the 2012 GSS obtains MINITAB output:

```
Variable    N     Mean    StDev   SE Mean       95% CI
POLVIEWS  1874  4.0624   1.4529   0.0336   (3.9965, 4.1283)
```

a. Show how to construct the confidence interval from the other information provided.

b. Can you conclude that the population mean is lower than the moderate score of 4.0? Explain.

c. Would the confidence interval be wider, or narrower, (i) if you constructed a 99% confidence interval and (ii) if $n = 500$ instead of 1874?

8.48 Length of hospital stays A hospital administrator wants to estimate the mean length of stay for all inpatients using that hospital. Using a random sample of 100 records of patients for the previous year, she reports that "The sample mean was 5.3 days estimated with a margin of error (at the 95% confidence level) of ±1 day." Explain the meaning of this sentence from the report, showing what it suggests about the 95% confidence interval.

8.49 Effect of n Find the margin of error for a 95% confidence interval for estimating the population mean when the sample standard deviation equals 100, with a sample size of (i) 25 and (ii) 100. What is the effect of increasing the sample size? (You can use the *t Distribution* app or Table B from the back of this book to find the appropriate *t*-scores.)

APP

8.50 Effect of confidence level Find the margin of error for estimating the population mean when the sample standard deviation equals 100 for a sample size of 25, using confidence levels (i) 95% and (ii) 99%. What is the effect of the choice of confidence level? (You can use the *t Distribution* app or Table B from the back of this book to find the appropriate *t*-scores.)

APP

8.51 Catalog mail-order sales A company that sells its products through mail-order catalogs wants information about the success of its most recent catalog. The company decides to estimate the mean dollar amount of items ordered from those who received the catalog. For a random sample of 100 customers from their files, only 5 made an order, so 95 of the response values were $0. The overall mean of all 100 orders was $10, with a standard deviation of $10.

a. Is it plausible that the population distribution is normal? Explain and discuss how much this affects the validity of a confidence interval for the mean.

b. Find a 95% confidence interval for the mean dollar order for the population of all customers who received this catalog. Normally, the mean of their sales per catalog is about $15. Can we conclude that it declined with this catalog? Explain.

8.52 Simulating coverage for _t_ intervals Open the _Explore Coverage_ app from the book's website, select the second tab titled Confidence Interval for a Mean, and keep all default settings (skewed population distribution, sample size $n = 30$, confidence level = 95%). Press the Draw Sample(s) button 20 times. Each time you press the button, a random sample of size 30 is taken from the population and the 95% confidence interval is computed from it and displayed in the graph.

a. What percentage of the 20 intervals you generated contained the population mean $\mu = 14.3$?

b. What percentage would you expect to contain the true population mean?

c. To simulate the true coverage rate accurately, we need to simulate more than 20 intervals. In the app, select to draw 1,000 samples from the population. What is the simulated coverage probability for these 1,000 intervals? Why do close to 95% of the intervals contain μ, even though the population distribution is quite skewed?

8.53 Farm size An estimate is needed of the mean acreage of farms in Ontario, Canada. A 95% confidence interval should have a margin of error of 25 acres. A study 10 years ago in this province had a sample standard deviation of 200 acres for farm size.

a. About how large a sample of farms is needed?

b. A sample is selected of the size found in part a. However, the sample has a standard deviation of 300 acres rather than 200. What is the margin of error for a 95% confidence interval for the mean acreage of farms?

8.54 Income of Native Americans How large a sample size do we need to estimate the mean annual income of Native Americans in Onondaga County, New York, correct to within $1,000 with probability 0.99? No information is available to us about the standard deviation of their annual income. We guess that nearly all of the incomes fall between $0 and $120,000 and that this distribution is approximately bell shaped.

8.55 Population variability Explain the reasoning behind the following statement: "In studies about a very diverse population, large samples are often necessary, whereas for more homogeneous populations smaller samples are often adequate." Illustrate for the problem of estimating mean income for all medical doctors in the United States compared to estimating mean income for all entry-level employees at McDonald's restaurants in the United States.

8.4 Bootstrap Confidence Intervals

We've seen how to obtain point and interval estimates of a population proportion and a population mean. Confidence intervals are relatively simple to construct for these parameters. For other parameters, such as the population median or the population correlation, it's not so easy because it's difficult to derive the theoretical sampling distribution or the standard error of a point estimate. In Section 7.3, we learned about the bootstrap as a general method of approximating the sampling distribution for a statistic in the absence of theoretical knowledge. We are now going to use the bootstrap distribution to provide a confidence interval for parameters such as the population median or correlation coefficient. We can also use the bootstrap to construct a confidence interval for a population mean whenever there is doubt about the normality assumption required by the _t_ confidence interval.

We mentioned in Section 7.3 that the bootstrap mimics repeatedly drawing samples from the population, thereby approximating characteristics of the true sampling distribution for a given statistic. As the margin note recalls, this is done by repeatedly sampling, e.g., 10,000 times, with replacement, a sample of size n from the originally observed data. For each such sample (called a bootstrap sample), the statistic of interest is computed.

We now want to use the information provided by these 10,000 bootstrapped values to approximate key characteristics of the sampling distribution of that

Recall

To obtain the bootstrap distribution, we repeatedly

■ generate a bootstrap sample of size n from the original observations (i.e., we draw, with replacement, n observations from the original sample of size n).

■ compute the statistic of interest from the bootstrap sample.

The resulting distribution of the generated statistics can be summarized graphically (i.e., by plotting a histogram) and numerically (i.e., by computing summary statistics). ◀

statistic. For instance, the standard deviation of the 10,000 values can serve as an *estimate* of the true standard deviation of the sampling distribution, i.e., as the standard error (*se*). In cases where we don't have a mathematical formula for the standard deviation of a statistic, this is a straightforward way of estimating it.

In Sections 8.2 and 8.3, we used the *se* to compute the margin of error and a confidence interval for the population proportion or mean. The general formula for the confidence interval, *point estimate* ± *margin of error*, worked because the sampling distribution was bell shaped. However, for statistics such as the median, as we have seen in Section 7.3, the sampling distribution can be highly irregular. For such cases, we need a new way of finding a confidence interval.

The Bootstrap Percentile Method for Constructing a Confidence Interval

The validity of the formula *point estimate* ± 1.96(*se*) to form a 95% confidence interval relies on the normal shape of the sampling distribution. Because of symmetry, stretching out an *equal* distance (e.g., a distance of 1.96(*se*)) to either side of the point estimate is likely to capture the true population parameter. If the sampling distribution is not symmetric, stretching out an equal distance may miss the population parameter more often than desired (i.e., more than 5% of the times for a 95% confidence interval). The first margin figure illustrates this. Because the sampling distribution is right skewed, there is a greater than 5% chance that a sample statistic occurs such that the interval *point estimate* ± 1.96(*se*) does not capture the population parameter.

To compensate, when the sampling distribution is skewed, we let the lower bound of a 95% confidence interval be the 2.5th percentile of the sampling distribution, and the upper bound the 97.5th percentile of the sampling distribution. In other words, the 95% confidence interval consists of the **middle 95% of the sampling distribution**. For skewed sampling distributions, this will result in intervals that are not symmetric about the point estimate, as the second margin figure illustrates. Such intervals are called **percentile confidence intervals** because they use the percentiles of the sampling distribution to form the confidence interval.

With the bootstrap, we can approximate these percentiles using the 10,000 bootstrapped values of the statistic. For instance, to find the 2.5th percentile, the 10,000 bootstrapped values are sorted from smallest to largest and the 250th largest is taken as the 2.5th percentile. Similarly, the 97.5th percentile is the 9,750th largest value among the 10,000 generated ones. Let's first illustrate the percentile method by finding the percentile confidence interval for a familiar case, the one for a population mean.

> Percentile
> Confidence Interval ◄

Example 11

Flight Departure Delays

Picture the Scenario

A travel magazine would like to assess the departure delay of flights taking off from Atlanta International Airport in the month of January. They obtain a random sample of 75 flights from all flights that were delayed by more than 5 minutes, i.e., that departed 5 minutes after their scheduled departure time. (There are many flights that actually depart within or even before 5 minutes of their departure time. These flights are not considered here.) For each sampled flight, the magazine recorded the actual departure delay in minutes, which ranged from 6 minutes to 375 minutes. The data are available on the book's website and preloaded in the *Bootstrap for One Sample* app. The screenshot from this app in Figure 8.10 shows a dot plot of the departure delays that suggests a rather right skewed distribution for such flights. The right skew

▶ **Figure 8.10** Bootstrap Distribution of the Sample Mean Departure Delay. Screenshot taken from the *Bootstrap for One Sample* app, showing data from 75 flights departing from Atlanta International Airport. The dotplot of these data show and extremely right skewed distribution. The blue histogram of 10,000 bootstrapped means from this sample (obtained after pressing Draw Bootstrap Sample(s)) is an approximation for the sampling distribution of the sample mean.

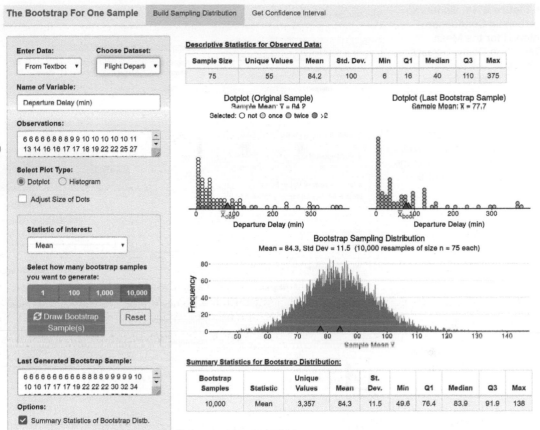

and, in particular, the many large outliers past 300 minutes might cast some doubt on the validity of a confidence interval for the mean constructed via the *t* distribution. The screenshot also shows the histogram of the generated bootstrap distribution for the sample mean, based on 10,000 bootstrap resamples.

Questions to Explore

a. Describe the bootstrap distribution using the given summary statistics.
b. Find the 2.5th and 97.5th percentiles of the 10,000 bootstrapped means. Use them to report and interpret a 95% confidence interval for the mean.

Think It Through

a. The bootstrap distribution of the sample mean is approximately bell shaped, with a mean of 84 minutes and a standard deviation of 11 minutes. The bell shape is a result of the CLT.
b. To find the 2.5th and 97.5th percentiles of these 10,000 generated sample means, we click on the second tab of the *Bootstrap for One Sample* app, titled Get Confidence Interval. A screenshot of this tab is shown in Figure 8.11 on the next page. It shows the bootstrap sampling distribution generated on the first tab, but now marks the 2.5th and 97.5th percentiles corresponding to a 95% confidence interval in red, with values shown in the graph and table for the confidence interval below it. To obtain the 2.5th percentile, the 10,000 generated sample means are sorted from smallest to largest and the 250th largest is taken, which equals 62.8 minutes. You can check this by selecting Show Generated Bootstrap Statistics in the app, which will bring up a table of all 10,000 generated sample means. Click on the header Mean to sort them in increasing order and then scroll down to row number 250. This row will show the 2.5th percentile as 62.8 (see the screenshot in the margin).

Values of Bootstrapped Statistics

	Bootstrap Sample	Mean ↑
248	9,781	62.7
249	5,335	62.8
▶250	8,314	62.8
251	8,477	62.8
252	239	62.9
253	695	62.9

Screenshot from *Bootstrap for One Sample* app.

► **Figure 8.11** Bootstrap Percentile Confidence Interval for the Mean Departure Delay. Screenshot taken from the second tab of the *Bootstrap for One Sample* app after generating 10,000 bootstrap samples. Lower and upper 2.5th percentiles of the bootstrap distribution are shown in red, indicating the endpoints of the 95% bootstrap percentile confidence interval.

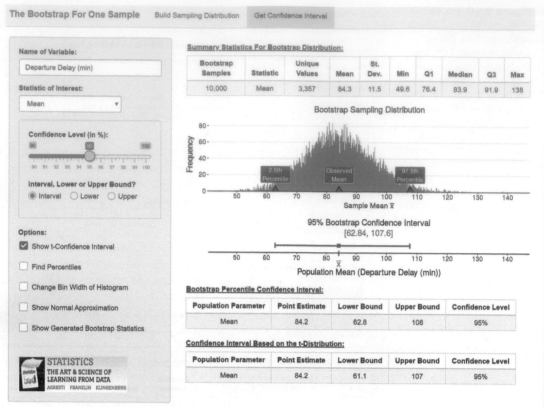

Similarly, the 97.5th percentile is the 9,750th largest among the 10,000 sorted means, and in our simulation equaled 107.6 minutes. (Your results may differ slightly.) With these two percentiles the 95% bootstrap percentile confidence interval is given by (62.8, 107.6), which is the range of the middle 95% of the 10,000 bootstrapped sample means. With 95% confidence, we estimate that the mean departure delay for delayed flights leaving from the airport in January is between 63 and 108 minutes, with a point estimate of 84 minutes.

Insight

The bootstrap percentile interval of (63, 108) minutes (rounded) is nearly identical to the conventional *t*-distribution interval given by (61, 107). (You can get this interval in the app by checking Show t-Confidence Interval, as shown in Figure 8.11.) This is not too surprising, as we already mentioned that the *t* interval is robust to violation of the normality assumption and the sample size of 75 is fairly large.

► **Try Exercise 8.56**

While sampling distributions for sample means are typically approximately normal because of the CLT, sampling distributions for medians are typically not. The next example shows how to use the bootstrap percentile method for finding a 95% confidence interval for the population median.

Example 12

Confidence Interval for a Median ◄

Median Departure Delay

Picture the Scenario

For the departure delay of flights leaving from the Atlanta airport investigated in Example 11, the *median delay* is actually a more informative parameter to estimate than the mean delay, given the right-skewed nature of the population distribution. Note that the sample median delay of 40 minutes is only about half as much as the sample mean delay of 84 minutes. Of all delayed flights in the sample, 50% are actually only delayed by 40 minutes or less.

Question to Explore

Find and interpret a 95% confidence interval for the median departure delay among all delayed flights.

Think It Through

The screenshot from the *Bootstrap for One Sample* app in Figure 8.12 shows the bootstrap distribution of the median departure delay. You can replicate this by opening the app, selecting Flight Departure Delays as the data set, selecting the *median* as the statistic of interest, generating 10,000 bootstrap samples and then switching to the second tab Get Confidence Interval. The app marks the lower and upper 2.5 percentiles of these 10,000 bootstrapped medians on the histogram. These are the endpoints of the bootstrap percentile interval, and they equal 30 minutes (2.5th percentile) and 64 minutes (97.5th percentile), as indicated in the plot of the confidence interval and the table below it. With 95% confidence, we estimate that the median departure delay for delayed flights leaving from the Atlanta airport in January is between 30 minutes and 64 minutes, with a point estimate of 40 minutes.

Summary Statistics For Bootstrap Distribution:

Bootstrap Samples	Statistic	Unique Values	Mean	St. Dev.	Min	Q1	Median	Q3	Max
10,000	Median	28	42	8.77	17	37	40	44	92

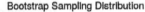

Bootstrap Percentile Confidence Interval:

Population Parameter	Point Estimate	Lower Bound	Upper Bound	Confidence Level
Median	40	30	64	95%

▲ **Figure 8.12** Bootstrap Percentile Confidence Interval for the Median Departure Delay. Screenshot taken from the second tab of the *Bootstrap for One Sample* app, after generating 10,000 bootstrap samples on the first tab. Lower and upper 2.5 percentiles of the bootstrap distribution are shown in red, indicating the endpoints of the 95% bootstrap percentile confidence interval.

Insight

Note how the confidence interval is not symmetric about the sample median of 40 minutes, owing to the particular shape of the sampling distribution of the sample median, which is far from bell shaped.

▶ *Try Exercise 8.57*

Here is a summary for finding bootstrap percentile intervals. The same warnings as given in Section 7.3 apply: When the bootstrap distribution is concentrated on just a few values, obtaining a percentile confidence interval is not sensible.

SUMMARY: Bootstrap Percentile Confidence Interval

The 95% bootstrap percentile confidence interval is given by the range of the **middle 95%** of the bootstrap distribution. The lower bound of the confidence interval is the 2.5th and the upper bound the 97.5th percentile of the generated bootstrap statistics. For other confidence levels, corresponding lower and upper percentiles are used, e.g., the 5th and 95th percentiles for 90% confidence intervals, and the 0.5th and 99.5th percentiles for 99% confidence intervals.

Bootstrap Confidence Interval for the Correlation

With the bootstrap distribution and the percentile method, we now have a general-purpose procedure for obtaining confidence intervals for many important parameters, such as the mean (when there is doubt about the normality assumption), the median, or the standard deviation (see Exercise 8.60). The advantage of the method is that it makes no assumption about the underlying shape of the population distribution because the bootstrap simulates the sampling distribution from the observed data.

The percentile method can also be used to construct confidence intervals for parameters measuring association between two variables in a population, such as the correlation, as demonstrated next.

Example 13

Confidence Interval for the Correlation ◄

Carbon Footprint

Picture the Scenario

Example 6 in Chapter 7 mentioned a data set about ready-made sandwiches, collected to analyze the relationship between their energy content (measured in Calories) and carbon footprint (in CO_2 equivalents), which tries to measure the total environmental impact of producing, transporting, and selling such sandwiches. Figure 7.19 in Chapter 7 showed an approximate linear relationship between these two variables, with a sample correlation coefficient of $r = 0.62$. There, we also showed the bootstrap distribution of the sample correlation coefficient, obtained by generating 10,000 bootstrap samples with the *Scatterplots & Correlation* app under the Bootstrap Distribution tab. Figure 8.13 shows a screenshot from this app after checking the box for Find Confidence Interval & Percentiles.

Questions to Explore

a. How was the bootstrap distribution shown in Figure 8.13 obtained?
b. Find and interpret a 95% confidence interval for the correlation.

Bootstrap Percentile Confidence Interval:

Population Parameter	Point Estimate	Lower Bound	Upper Bound	Confidence Level
Correlation	0.621	0.259	0.837	95%

▲ **Figure 8.13** Bootstrap Percentile Confidence Interval for the Correlation Between Energy Content and Carbon Footprint. Screenshot taken from the Bootstrap tab of the *Scatterplot & Correlation* app, after generating 10,000 bootstrap samples. Lower and upper 2.5 percentiles of the bootstrap distribution are shown in red, indicating the endpoints of the 95% bootstrap percentile confidence interval.

Recall

A bootstrap sample is a sample taken with replacement from the original data. ◄

Think It Through

a. The bootstrap distribution was obtained by repeatedly (10,000 times) taking a bootstrap sample of 24 sandwiches (the original sample size) and computing the correlation coefficient r between the energy content and carbon footprint of those sandwiches included in the bootstrap sample.

b. The 2.5th and 97.5th percentiles of the distribution for the 10,000 resampled correlation coefficients equal 0.26 and 0.84, respectively. They form the lower and upper bound for a 95% confidence interval. With 95% confidence, the population correlation coefficient between the energy content and carbon footprint of ready-made sandwiches is estimated to fall between 0.26 and 0.84, with a point estimate of 0.64. Because of the rather small sample size of 25, the interval is pretty wide, indicating the possibility of just a weak relationship or a pretty strong one.

▶ *Try Exercise 8.61*

With modern computing power, methods such as the bootstrap (and others that will be introduced in Chapters 10 and 11) are now used to conduct inference when it is difficult to find theoretical sampling distributions. Although an app or other specialized software is needed to implement these methods, they have the advantage of relying on fewer assumptions for their validity.

8.4   Practicing the Basics

8.56 Bank account balance   A consulting firm to a large bank took a random sample of 300 customers of the bank to learn about the end-of-month balances carried on their accounts. (They did this for the month of April.) The screenshot from the *Inference for a Mean* app, which has this data preloaded, shows a histogram and box plot of the observations. The mean balance of the 300 sampled accounts equaled $1,823, with a standard deviation of $2,484.

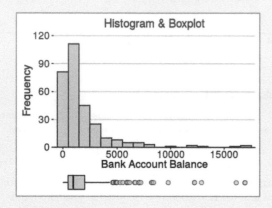

a. Describe the shape of the distribution of account balances from the sample.

b. Find (using the conventional formula from Section 8.3) and interpret a 95% confidence interval for the mean account balance for all of the bank's customers, using the sample of 300 accounts. (This data set is preloaded in the *Inference for a Mean* app.)

c. The normality assumption of account balances made when constructing the confidence interval in part b seems grossly violated because of the extreme right skew and the many outliers, yet the sample size was large. To verify if the interval from part b is valid, open the *Bootstrap for One Sample* app (this data set is preloaded) and generate the bootstrap distribution for the sample mean using 10,000 resamples. Then, switch to the Get Confidence Interval tab and report a 95% bootstrap percentile confidence interval for the mean. Does it differ substantially from the one in part b?

8.57 Median account balance   Refer to the previous exercise. Because of the extreme right skew, the bank would like to obtain a confidence interval for the median account balance for its customers.

a. Is it true that the standard error of the median is $se = s/\sqrt{n} = 1,823/\sqrt{300} = 143$? Why or why not?

b. Find and interpret a 95% confidence interval for the population median.

8.58 Social Security payments   Social Security payments by the federal government provide an important source of income for many Americans. The data set Social Security Payments available on the book's website shows the amount of Social Security received by a random sample of 85 California residents. These data, from the 2017 American Community Survey, show a mean payment of $13,620 and a standard deviation of $7,209.

a. Find the standard error for the sample mean, using the conventional formula from Section 8.3. (The data set is preloaded in the *Inference for a Mean* app.)

b. Find (using the conventional formula from Section 8.3) and interpret a 95% confidence interval for the mean payments to all California residents receiving Social Security payments.

c. Open the *Bootstrap for One Sample* app (the data set is preloaded) and generate the bootstrap distribution for the sample mean using thousands of resamples. Use the generated bootstrap distribution to report a standard error for the sample mean. How does it compare to the standard error in part a?

d. Use the bootstrap percentile method to find a 95% confidence interval for the population mean payment. Why is it close to the confidence interval reported in part b?

8.59 Median Social Security payments   Refer to the previous exercise. Given the right skewed shape of the payment amounts, the median payment received by California residents is an important parameter to estimate. Find and interpret a 95% confidence interval for it, based on the sample of 85 residents.

8.60 Inference on precision   A precision scale is used in the production process of a medical drug for determining the weight of various components necessary to produce the drug. The scale needs to be precise, otherwise the safety and effectiveness of the drug could be compromised. In particular, the standard deviation when repeatedly weighing an amount of 10 mg can be no more than 0.2 mg. In a controlled experiment, the production process of the drug is stopped and a standard weight of exactly 10 mg is put on the precision scale in 5-minute intervals. The readings of the 12 trials are (in mg): 10.03, 9.92, 9.93, 10.05, 10.07, 10.14, 10.03, 10.00, 10.24, 9.84, 9.98, 10.04.

a. Based on these data, find and interpret a 95% confidence interval for the standard deviation of the readings from the scale. (In the *Bootstrap for One Sample* app, select Your Own under Enter Data and then enter the observations into the corresponding box.)

b. To be extra cautious, the quality manager decides to use a 99% confidence level. Find the 99% confidence interval for the standard deviation.

c. Should the quality manager shut down the production process to readjust the scale, or does it meet specifications in terms of its precision?

8.61 Inference for the correlation coefficient   Refer to Exercise 7.38, which mentioned a study of 229 college freshmen investigating the relationship between their self-esteem based on how they think they appear to others (variable Appearance) and their self-esteem based on how they think others approve of them (variable Approval). The data for this study are preloaded in the *Scatterplot & Correlation* app (under Self-Esteem) and are also available on the book's website.

a. Use the Bootstrap Distribution tab of the *Scatterplots & Correlation* app to generate the bootstrap sampling distribution and report a 95% confidence interval for the population correlation coefficient between self-esteem based on approval and appearance among college freshman.

b. Interpret the interval, including mentioning a point estimate.

c. Does the interval include the value of zero, which would indicate no correlation? Is there evidence of a positive correlation? Explain.

8.62 Exercising in the fall semester   A study using a random sample of 106 college freshman investigated how many hours per week they exercised at the beginning and

towards the end of their fall semester. The data (called Weekly Exercise Hours) are preloaded in the *Scatterplots & Correlation* app and available on the book's website. (See Exercise 7.39.)

a. Using the Bootstrap Distribution tab of the app, find and interpret a 95% confidence interval for the population correlation coefficient between the number of exercise hours at the beginning and end of the fall semester.

b. What value for the population correlation coefficient would indicate no relationship between the number of exercise hours at the beginning and end of the fall semester? Check to see if the confidence interval contains this value. What can you conclude in terms of the direction of the relationship?

Chapter Review

SUMMARY OF NOTATION

$\hat{p}$ = sample proportion

se = standard error

m = margin of error

$t_{.025}$ = t-score with right-tail probability 0.025 and two-tail probability 0.05, as used in a 95% confidence interval for the mean

df = degrees of freedom ($= n - 1$ for inference about a mean)

CHAPTER SUMMARY

We've now learned how to **estimate** the population proportion p for categorical variables and the population mean μ for quantitative variables.

- An estimate of the population mean μ is the sample mean $\bar{x}$. An estimate of the population proportion p is the sample proportion $\hat{p}$. A **point estimate** (or **estimate**, for short) is our best guess for the unknown parameter value.

- A **confidence interval** contains the most plausible values for a parameter. Confidence intervals for many parameters have the form

$$\text{point estimate } \pm \text{ margin of error,}$$

in particular: point estimate $\pm$ (z- or t-score) $\times$ (se),

where se is the **standard error of the estimate**. The se, in turn, is the estimated standard deviation of the sampling distribution of the point estimate. For approximately normal sampling distributions and 95% confidence, the **margin of error** is 1.96(se).

- For the confidence interval for a proportion, the **score** is a z-**score** from the normal distribution. For the confidence interval for the mean, the score is a t-**score** from the t **distribution** with degrees of freedom $df = n - 1$. The t-score is similar to a z-score when $df \geq 30$. Table 8.4 summarizes the point and interval estimation methods.

- The z- or t-score depends on the **confidence level**, the probability that the method produces a confidence interval that contains the population parameter value. For instance, the probability that the sample proportion $\hat{p}$ falls within 1.96 standard errors of the true proportion p is 95%, so we use $z = 1.96$ for 95%

confidence. *To achieve greater confidence, we make the sacrifice of a larger margin of error and wider confidence interval.*

- For estimating a **proportion,** the confidence interval formula $\hat{p} \pm (z\text{-score})(se)$ relies on the fact that the sample proportion has a normal sampling distribution for large samples (at least 15 successes and 15 failures). For estimating a proportion with small samples (fewer than 15 successes or fewer than 15 failures), the confidence interval formula $\hat{p} \pm z(se)$ can still be used after adding 2 to the each the success and failure count, and 4 to n and then recomputing $\hat{p}$ and se.

- For estimating a **mean,** the t **distribution** accounts for the extra variability due to using the sample standard deviation s to estimate the population standard deviation in finding a standard error. The t confidence interval formula $\bar{x} \pm (t\text{-score})(se)$ assumes that the population distribution is normal. This ensures that the sampling distribution of $\bar{x}$ is normal. This assumption is mainly important for small n, because when n is large the Central Limit Theorem guarantees that the sampling distribution is normal. However, even for small n, the method is **robust** against departures from the normal assumption as long as there are no extreme outliers.

- When interpreting a confidence interval, use language such as "With 95% confidence, we estimate that the population parameter (e.g., a proportion or mean) is between [insert lower bound] and [insert upper bound]" to make clear that your confidence refers to the performance of the estimation method. In addition, mention the point estimate, as it is your best guess for the value of the parameter. Do not use language such as "There is a 95% probability that the population parameter (e.g., a proportion or mean) falls between [insert lower bound] and [insert upper bound]," and in particular do not say that "there is a 95% probability that the sample proportion (or sample mean) falls between [insert lower bound] and [insert upper bound]."

- Before conducting a study, we can **determine the sample size *n*** necessary to achieve a certain margin of error. Table 8.4 shows the sample size formulas. To use them, we must (1) specify the desired margin of error *m*, (2) specify the confidence level, which determines the *z*-score, and (3) guess the value the data will likely produce for the sample standard deviation *s* (to estimate a population mean) or the sample proportion $\hat{p}$ (to estimate a population

proportion). In the latter case, substituting $\hat{p} = 0.50$ provides the worst-case scenario.

- For estimating parameters other than the population proportion or mean, general purpose formulas for a *se* or a confidence interval are hard to come by without additional assumptions. The **bootstrap** approximates the sampling distribution of point estimates without requiring additional assumptions. The generated bootstrap samples can be used to **approximate** the *se* for such point estimates, and the **middle 95%** of the bootstrapped statistics forms a **bootstrap percentile confidence interval** for the corresponding population parameter. This technique can provide confidence intervals for medians, standard deviations, or correlation coefficients.

Table 8.4 Estimation Methods for Means and Proportions

Parameter	Point Estimate	Standard Error	Confidence Interval	Sample Size for Margin of Error *m*
Proportion *p*	$\hat{p}$	$se = \sqrt{\hat{p}(1 - \hat{p})/n}$	$\hat{p} \pm z(se)$	$n = [\hat{p}(1 - \hat{p})z^2]/m^2$
Mean μ	$\bar{x}$	$se = s/\sqrt{n}$	$\bar{x} \pm t(se)$	$n = (\sigma^2 z^2)/m^2$

Note: The *z*-score or *t*-score depends on the confidence level. The *t*-score has $df = n - 1$.

LEARNING OBJECTIVES

1. State the purpose of a point estimate.

2. Identify the correct point estimates for the population proportion *p*, the population mean μ and the standard deviation σ.

3. Understand the general form *point estimate ± margin of error* for a confidence interval when the sampling distribution is bell shaped. Understand that the margin of error for a 95% confidence interval is 1.96(*se*) when *n* is large.

4. Interpret a confidence interval in context.

5. Interpret a confidence interval as containing plausible values for a parameter at a stated confidence level.

6. Explain the meaning of "confidence level."

7. Explain the balance between level of confidence and the length of the confidence interval.

8. Distinguish between the use of the *z* and *t* distributions for confidence intervals.

9. Understand the assumptions for forming a valid confidence interval and when it is robust.

10. Understand how to determine the sample size needed for a given margin of error.

11. Know how to find a confidence interval for a population proportion when *n* is small and there are not 15 successes or 15 failures ("Agresti/Coull" interval).

12. (Optional) Understand how the bootstrap method is used to find confidence intervals for population parameters such as the median, standard deviation, or correlation coefficient (percentile method).

ANSWERS TO THE CHAPTER FIGURE QUESTIONS

Figure 8.1   A point estimate alone will not tell us how close the estimate is likely to be to the parameter.

Figure 8.2   When the size of the random sample is relatively large, by the Central Limit Theorem.

Figure 8.3   We don't know the value of *p*, the population proportion, to form the interval $p \pm 1.96(se)$. The population proportion *p* is what we're trying to estimate.

Figure 8.5   The $\hat{p}$ values falling in the left and right tail areas of the bell-shaped curve. The probability of falling in these areas is 5%.

Figure 8.7   Using Table B or Table 8.5, $t = 1.96$ when $df = \infty$ with right-tail probability = 0.025.

Figure 8.8 $z = -1.96$ and $z = 1.96$.

STATISTICAL SOFTWARE

Art of Stat Web Apps

- **Inference for a Proportion**   This app carries out inference for a population proportion. It computes the sample proportion, its standard error and margin of error (also displaying the *z*-score) and the confidence interval. A slider controls the desired confidence level. The app shows the confidence interval graphically and provides a bar graph of the proportion of successes and failures. Various data sets from the book are preloaded. You

can provide your own data by typing in the sample size and the number of successes. You can also copy and paste a sequence of individual observations, such as a sequence of 0s and 1s, or any other two characters. The second tab of the app finds the necessary sample size for a desired margin of error.

- **Inference for a Mean**   This app carries out inference for a population mean. It computes the sample mean and sample standard deviation, the standard error and margin of error (also displaying the *t*-score) and the confidence interval for the population mean. A slider controls the desired confidence level. The app shows the confidence interval graphically and provides a dot plot, box plot, or histogram of the data to check assumptions. Various data sets from the book are preloaded. You can provide your own data by typing (or copying and pasting) your observations into a box. You can also provide just the summary statistics (sample size, mean, and standard deviation) if you only have those. The second tab of the app finds the necessary sample size for a desired margin of error.

- **Explore Coverage** This app uses simulation to demonstrate and visualize the concept of the confidence level (i.e., what 95% confidence means) and the coverage of a confidence interval, both for proportions and means. The app allows you to explore the effect on the confidence interval (and coverage) when increasing or decreasing the confidence level, increasing or decreasing the sample size, changing the shape of the population distribution, or changing the population standard deviation.

- **Bootstrap for One Sample** After generating the bootstrap distribution on the first tab, the second tab of this app lets you find the bootstrap percentile confidence interval for parameters such as the mean, median, or standard deviation. It visually provides the bootstrap percentiles on the bootstrap distribution and plots the bootstrap confidence interval. A slider controls the desired confidence level. It offers such features as overlaying a normal distribution (to see if the bootstrap distribution is approximately normal) or looking at all generated bootstrapped values. The app comes preloaded with several data sets from the book, or you can provide your own data.

- **Scatterplots & Correlation** Under the second tab titled Bootstrap Distribution, this app lets you generate the bootstrap distribution and find the percentile confidence interval (check the Find Confidence Interval & Percentiles box) for the correlation coefficient. It plots the bootstrap percentiles on the bootstrap distribution graph and provides a visualization of the bootstrap confidence interval. The app comes preloaded with several data sets from the book, or you can provide your own data.

R

- **Confidence Interval for a Proportion:** In R, using data from Example 3, type

```
> x <- 637
> n <- 1361
> phat <- x/n
```

```
> se <- sqrt(phat * (1- phat)/n)
> zscore <- qnorm(0.975)
> me <- zscore*se
> phat + c(-1,1)*me
```

pressing return after each, to obtain the 95% confidence interval and its components (e.g., to see the margin of error, type me and press return). Alternatively, you can use the `prop.test` function to obtain a confidence interval, with output (edited) shown below:

```
> prop.test(637, 1361, conf.level=0.95,
correct=FALSE)
95 percent confidence interval:
 0.4416559 0.4946004
sample estimates:
        p
0.4680382
```

This is actually the (Wilson) interval from Exercise 8.123, which for large *n* is the same as the one from Section 8.2. For a 99% confidence interval, use `conf.level=0.99`.

- **Confidence Interval for a Mean:** In R, using data from Example 9, type

```
> x <- c(540, 565, 570, 570, 580, 590, 590,
590, 595, 610, 620)
```

to read in the observations, then type

```
> n <- length(x)
> xbar <- mean(x)
> s <- sd(x)
> se <- s/sqrt(n)
> tscore <- qt(0.975, df=n-1)
> me <- tscore*se
> xbar + c(-1,1)*me
```

to obtain the confidence interval. More conveniently, the `t.test` function returns the same, with output (edited):

```
> x <- c(540, 565, 570, 570, 580, 590, 590,
590, 595, 610, 620)
> t.test(x, conf.level=0.95)
95 percent confidence interval:
 568.7583 598.5144
sample estimates:
mean of x
 583.6364
```

For a 99% confidence interval, use `conf.level=0.99`.

CHAPTER EXERCISES

Practicing the Basics

8.63 Unemployment rate In March 2020 (one month before the height of the COVID-19 crisis) the U.S. Census Bureau reported that based on data from the 2019 Current Population Survey, 5.9% of persons with less than a high school diploma are unemployed, while the unemployment rate is 3.9% for those with a high school diploma but no college degree and 2.1% for those with at least a bachelor's degree. Also, 3.6% of all college graduates between the ages of 25 and 64 were unemployed. A larger percentage of men than women were unemployed: 3.7% and 3.5%, respectively.

a. Are these point estimates or interval estimates?

b. Is the information given here sufficient for you to construct confidence intervals for the unemployment rate of persons with at least a bachelor's degree? Why or why not?

8.64 Approval rating for president In July 2014, midway through his second term as president, Gallup estimated Obama's approval rate as 42%. According to gallup.com, "[R]esults are based on telephone interviews with approximately 1,500 national adults; margin of error is ±3 percentage points." How could you explain the meaning of this to someone who has not taken a statistics course? (*Source:* Gallup Daily: U.S. Economic Conditions © 2020 Gallup, Inc.)

8.65 **British monarchy** After the British monarchy celebrated its diamond jubilee in 2012, a July poll conducted by YouGov.com and the *Sunday Times* of 1,667 British residents showed that 86% think the Queen personally has done a good job during her time on the throne, and 73% think that Britain should continue to have a monarchy. If the sample was random, find the 95% margin of error for each of these estimated proportions.

8.66 **Born again** A poll of a random sample of $n = 2,000$ Americans by the Pew Research Center (www.people-press.org) indicated that 36% considered themselves born-again or evangelical Christians. How would you explain to someone who has not studied statistics:

  a. What it means to call this a *point estimate*?

  b. Why this does not mean that *exactly* 36% of *all* Americans consider themselves to be born-again or evangelical Christians?

8.67 **Life after death** The variable POSTLIFE in the 2018 General Social Survey asked, "Do you believe in life after death?" A report based on these data stated that "81% of Americans believe in life after death. The margin of error for this result is plus or minus 1.8%." Explain how you could form a 95% confidence interval using this information and interpret that confidence interval in context.

8.68 **Female belief in life after death** Refer to the previous exercise. For the 1,178 females included in the survey, 1,017 believed in life after death. You want to construct a 95% confidence interval for the proportion of females believing in life after death. Show how to

  a. obtain the standard error.

  b. obtain the margin of error.

  c. obtain the 95% confidence interval. Interpret the confidence interval in context.

8.69 **Vegetarianism** *Time* magazine (July 15, 2002) quoted a poll of 10,000 Americans in which only 4% said they were vegetarians.

  a. What has to be assumed about this sample to construct a confidence interval for the population proportion of vegetarians?

  b. Construct a 99% confidence interval for the population proportion. Explain why the interval is so narrow, even though the confidence level is high.

  c. In interpreting this confidence interval, can you conclude that fewer than 10% of Americans are vegetarians? Explain your reasoning.

8.70 **Alternative therapies** The Department of Public Health at the University of Western Australia conducted a survey in which they randomly sampled general practitioners (GP) in Australia. One question asked whether the GP had ever studied alternative therapy, such as acupuncture, hypnosis, homeopathy, and yoga. Of 282 respondents, 132 said yes. Is the interpretation, "We are 95% confident that the percentage of all GPs in Australia who have ever studied alternative therapy equals 46.8%" correct or incorrect? Explain.

8.71 **Population data** You would like to find the proportion of bills passed by Congress that were vetoed by the president in the last congressional session. After checking congressional records, you see that for the population of all 40 bills passed, 15 were vetoed. Does it make sense to construct a confidence interval using these data? Explain. (*Hint:* Identify the sample and population.)

8.72 **Legalize marijuana?** The General Social Survey has asked respondents, "Do you think the use of marijuana should be made legal or not?" Go to the GSS website, sda.berkeley.edu (or follow the link at the book's website), enter GRASS as the row variable and type YEAR(2018) in the box for the Selection Filter. Select No Weight for Weight and press Run the Table.

  a. Of the respondents, how many said "legal" and how many said "not legal"? Report the sample proportions.

  b. Is there enough evidence to conclude whether a majority or a minority of the population support legalization? Explain your reasoning.

  c. Now remove YEAR(2018) from the Selection Filter and instead enter YEAR as the column variable to obtain the data for each year the question was asked. Describe any trend you see over time in the proportion favoring legalization.

8.73 **Streaming** A Harris Poll of 2,300 U.S. adults surveyed online in April 2014 reports that 43% regularly watch television shows through streaming. (*Source:* "Cable Is King but Streaming Stands Strong When It Comes to Americans' TV Viewing Habits.")

  a. Find a 95% confidence interval and interpret it in context.

  b. Would a 99% confidence interval result in a wider or narrower interval? Explain.

  c. If the survey had found the 43% streaming based on a survey including 5,000 adults (instead of 2,300), would the interval be wider or narrower compared to the one in part a? Explain.

8.74 **Edward Snowden** A report from the Pew Research Center found that disclosures by former National Security Administration (NSA) contractor Edward Snowden about NSA spying have damaged one major element of America's global image: its reputation for protecting individual liberties. One question in the report asked, "Do you think the government of the U.S. respects the personal freedoms of its people?" (*Source:* Pew Research Center, July 2014, "Global Opposition to U.S. Surveillance and Drones, But Limited Harm to America's Image.")

  a. Of 1,000 adults surveyed in the United Kingdom, 65% said yes, resulting in a 99% confidence interval of (0.61, 0.69). **True or false:** The confidence interval means that we can be 99% confident that between 61% and 69% of the population of the United Kingdom believes that the U.S. government respects the personal freedoms of its people.

  b. Of 1,000 adults surveyed in Germany, 58% said yes, resulting in a 99% confidence interval of (0.54, 0.62). **True or false:** The confidence interval means that we can be 99% confident that of 1,000 Germans sampled, between 540 and 620 of them think the U.S. government respects the personal freedom of its people.

8.75 **More NSA spying** Refer to the previous exercise.

    a. Of the 1,001 adults surveyed in Turkey, 49% said yes to the question from the Pew Research Center, resulting in a 95% confidence interval of (0.46, 0.52). **True or false:** We can be 95% confident that less than half of Turkey's population thinks the U.S. government respects the personal freedoms of its people.

    b. In Brazil in 2013 (before the revelations by Ed Snowden), about 76% believed the U.S. government respects personal freedom, but of 1,003 adults surveyed in Brazil in 2014, 51% do so, resulting in a 95% confidence interval of (0.48, 0.54). **True or false:** There is evidence that the opinion of Brazilians on the U.S. government respecting personal freedom has dropped from 2013 levels.

8.76 **Men don't go to the doctor** A survey of 1,084 men age 18 and older in 1998 for the Commonwealth Fund (www.cmwf.org) indicated that more than half did not have a physical exam or a blood cholesterol test in the past year. A medical researcher plans to sample men in her community randomly to see whether similar results occur. How large a random sample would she need to estimate this proportion to within 0.05 with probability 0.95?

8.77 **Driving after drinking** In December 2004, a report based on the National Survey on Drug Use and Health estimated that 20% of all Americans ages 16 to 20 drove under the influence of drugs or alcohol in the previous year (AP, December 30, 2004). A public health unit in Wellington, New Zealand, plans a similar survey for young people of that age in New Zealand. It wants a 95% confidence interval to have a margin of error of 0.04.

    a. Find the necessary sample size if the New Zealand public health unit expects results similar to those in the United States.

    b. Suppose that in determining the sample size, it uses the safe approach that sets $\hat{p} = 0.50$ in the formula for n. Then, how many records need to be sampled? Compare this to the answer in part a. Explain why it is better to make an educated guess about what to expect for $\hat{p}$ when possible.

8.78 **Changing views of United States** The June 2003 report *Views of a Changing World*, conducted by the Pew Global Attitudes Project (www.people-press.org), discussed changes in views of the United States by other countries. In the largest Muslim nation, Indonesia, a poll conducted in May 2003 after the Iraq war began reported that 83% had an unfavorable view of America, compared to 36% a year earlier. The 2003 result was claimed to have a margin of error of 3 percentage points. How can you approximate the sample size the study was based on?

8.79 **Accept a credit card?** A bank wants to estimate the proportion of people who would sign up for a credit card if it sends a particular mailing advertising it. For a trial mailing to a random sample of 100 potential customers,

0 people accept the offer. Can the bank conclude that fewer than 10% of their population of potential customers would take the credit card? Answer by finding an appropriate 95% confidence interval.

8.80 **Kicking accuracy** A football coach decides to estimate the kicking accuracy of a player who wants to join the team. Of 10 extra point attempts, the player makes all 10.

    a. Find an appropriate 95% confidence interval for the probability that the player makes any given extra point attempt.

    b. What's the lowest value that you think is plausible for that probability?

    c. How would you interpret the random sample assumption in this context? Describe a scenario in which it would not be sensible to treat these 10 kicks as a random sample.

8.81 **Airbnb prices** The prices of a random sample of 50 private rooms available for rent in New York City from the platform Airbnb are preloaded in the *Inference for a Mean* app, resulting in the screenshot shown. (The data are also available on the book's website.)

    a. Interpret the 95% confidence interval.

    b. Comment on the shape of the distribution of room prices. Is it normal? If not, is the interval from part a still valid? Explain.

    c. Verify how the app found the standard error.

    d. Verify how the app found the margin of error.

8.82 **Travel to work** As part of the 2000 census, the Census Bureau surveyed 700,000 households to study transportation to work. It reported that 76.3% drove alone to work, 11.2% carpooled, 5.1% took mass transit, 3.2% worked at home, 0.4% bicycled, and 3.8% took other means.

    a. With such a large survey, explain why the margin of error for any of these values is extremely small.

    b. The survey also reported that the mean travel time to work was 24.3 minutes, compared to 22.4 minutes in 1990. Explain why this is not sufficient information to construct a confidence interval for the population mean. What else would you need?

8.83 Finding *t*-scores

a. Show how the *t*-score for a 95% confidence interval changes as the sample size increases from 10 to 20 to 30 to 300 to 3,000.

b. What does the answer in part a suggest about how the *t* distribution compares to the standard normal distribution?

8.84 Fuel efficiency The government website fueleconomy .gov has data on thousands of cars regarding their fuel efficiency. A random sample from this website of SUVs manufactured between 2012 and 2015 gives the following data on the combined (city and highway) miles per gallon (mpg):

26, 23, 21, 23, 19, 29, 15, 26, 19, 26.

a. Construct an appropriate plot (or plots) to check the distributional assumption for computing a *t* interval for the mean mpg for SUVs. Comment briefly.

b. Find and interpret a 95% confidence interval for the mean mpg for SUVs manufactured between 2012 and 2015.

8.85 Psychologists' income In 2003, the American Psychological Association conducted a survey (at research .apa.org) of a random sample of psychologists to estimate mean incomes for psychologists with various academic degrees and levels of experience. Of the 31 psychologists who received a masters degree in 2003, the mean income was $43,834 with a standard deviation of $16,870.

a. Construct a 95% confidence interval for the population mean. Interpret.

b. What assumption about the population distribution of psychologists' incomes does the confidence interval method make?

c. If the assumption about the shape of the population distribution is not valid, does this invalidate the results? Explain.

8.86 More psychologists Refer to the previous exercise. Interpret each item on the following printout that software reports for psychologists with a doctorate but with less than one year of experience.

```
Variable   N   Mean  StDev  SE Mean     95.0% CI
income    190  49411 15440  1120.1   (47204, 51618)
```

8.87 How long lived in town? The General Social Survey has asked subjects, "How long have you lived in the city, town, or community where you live now?" The responses of 1,415 subjects in one survey had a mode of less than 1 year, a median of 16 years, a mean of 20.3, and a standard deviation of 18.2.

a. Do you think that the population distribution is normal? Why or why not?

b. Based on your answer in part a, can you construct a 95% confidence interval for the population mean? If not, explain why not. If so, do so and interpret.

8.88 Happy often? The 1996 GSS asked, "How many days in the past seven days have you felt happy?" (Variable HAPFEEL. This was the only year this question was posed.)

a. Using the GSS variable HAPFEEL, verify that the sample had a mean of 5.27 and a standard deviation of 2.05. What was the sample size?

b. Find the standard error for the sample mean.

c. Stating assumptions, construct and interpret a 95% confidence interval for the population mean. Can you conclude that the population mean is at least 5.0?

8.89 eBay selling prices For eBay auctions of the 16GB Samsung S5 smartphone (unlocked and in new condition), a sample was taken in July 2014 where the Buy It Now prices were (in dollars):

549, 600, 560, 519, 535, 570, 600, 625, 640, 550, 575, 600

a. Explain what a parameter might represent that you could estimate with these data.

b. Find the point estimate of the mean Buy It Now price for such cellphones on eBay.

c. Find the standard deviation of the data and the standard error of the sample mean. Interpret each.

d. Find the 95% confidence interval for the population mean. Interpret the interval in context.

8.90 Income for families in public housing A survey is taken to estimate the mean annual family income for families living in public housing in Chicago. For a random sample of 29 families, the annual incomes (in hundreds of dollars) are as follows:

90 77 100 83 64 78 92 73 122 96 60 85 86 108 70
139 56 94 84 111 93 120 70 92 100 124 59 112 79

a. Construct a plot of the incomes. What do you predict about the shape of the population distribution? Does this affect the possible inferences?

b. Find point estimates of the mean and standard deviation of the family incomes of all families living in public housing in Chicago.

c. Obtain and interpret a 95% confidence interval for the population mean.

8.91 Working mother In response to the statement on a General Social Survey, "A preschool child is likely to suffer if his or her mother works," the response categories (strongly agree, agree, disagree, strongly disagree) had counts (104, 370, 665, 169). Scores $(2, 1, -1, -2)$ were assigned to the four categories to treat the variable as quantitative. Software reported

```
Variable    N    Mean  StDev SE Mean    95.0% CI
Response  1308 -0.325 1.234  0.034   (-0.392,-0.258)
```

a. Explain what this choice of scoring assumes about relative distances between categories of the scale.

b. Based on this scoring, how would you interpret the sample mean of -0.325? Is it plausible that the U.S. adult population is neutral on this issue? Check to see if 0 is contained in the confidence interval. Explain.

c. Explain how you could also make an inference about proportions for these data.

8.92 **Miami spring break** For a trip to Miami, Florida, over spring break 2014, the following data (obtained from travelocity.com) are a random sample of hotel prices per night (in $) for a double room:

> 239 237 245 310 218 175 330 196 178
>
> 245 255 190 330 124 162 190 386 145.

a. Construct a histogram and box plot and comment on the shape of the distribution.

b. Find a 95% confidence interval for the mean price and interpret.

c. Are you concerned that any assumptions about the interval in part b might be violated?

8.93 **Mean property tax** A tax assessor wants to estimate the mean property tax bill for all homeowners in Madison, Wisconsin. A survey 10 years ago got a sample mean and standard deviation of $1,400 and $1,000.

a. How many tax records should the tax assessor randomly sample for a 95% confidence interval for the mean to have a margin of error equal to $100? What assumption does your solution make?

b. In reality, suppose that it would now get a standard deviation equal to $1,500. Using the sample size you derived in part a, without doing any calculation, explain whether the margin of error for a 95% confidence interval would be less than $100, equal to $100, or more than $100.

c. Refer to part b. Would the probability that the sample mean falls within $100 of the population mean be less than 0.95, equal to 0.95, or greater than 0.95? Explain.

8.94 **Median time on homework** A statistics teacher asks a sample of 20 students in the class how much time they have spent on the weekly online homework assignment. Here are the responses the teacher got, in hours:

> 2.3 2.7 2.5 4.1 4.9 6.5 0.6 2.1 4.1 7.1
>
> 10.3 2 2.1 2.6 8.9 3.5 8.6 3.8 4.8 4.1

Treating this sample as representative of the time it takes students to complete weekly online homework assignments by this teacher, find and interpret a 95% confidence interval for the median time students in the teacher's class work on homework.

8.95 **Median sugar content** In a random sample of 20 breakfast cereals, the median sugar content was 9.5 grams per serving. Figure 7.17 in Chapter 7 showed a dot plot of the data and the sampling distribution of the median as approximated by 10,000 bootstrap samples. Replicate this analysis by opening the *Bootstrap for One Sample* app, where this data set is preloaded. Use the app to find a 95% bootstrap percentile confidence interval of the median sugar content in breakfast cereals. Interpret the interval.

8.96 **Variability of account balances** Refer to exercise 8.56 on the account balances for a sample of 300 bank customers. The bank is also interested in the standard deviation of the account balances as a measure of the variability of the balances. Obtain and interpret a 95% confidence interval for the standard deviation of account balances among the bank's customers.

8.97 **Eating disorders** The Eating Disorders data set preloaded in the *Scatterplots & Correlation* app and available on the book's website refers to a study on the relationship between cognitive and behavioral eating disorders. (Refer to Exercise 7.56 in Chapter 7.)

a. Obtain a 95% confidence interval for the population correlation coefficient between these two types of eating disorders.

b. Is there evidence for a (strong) relationship?

Concepts and Investigations

8.98 **Median as point estimate** When the population distribution is normal, the population mean equals the population median. How good is the sample median as a point estimate of this common value? For a random sample, the standard error of the sample median equals $1.25(s/\sqrt{n})$. If the population is normal, explain why the sample mean tends to be a better estimate than the sample median. (*Note:* Both estimates are unbiased.)

8.99 **Religious beliefs** A column by *New York Times* columnist Nicholas Kristof (August 15, 2003) discussed results of polls indicating that religious beliefs in the United States tend to be quite different from those in other Western nations. He quoted recent Gallup and Harris polls of random samples of about 1,000 Americans estimating that 83% believe in the virgin birth of Jesus but only 28% believe in evolution. A friend of yours is skeptical, claiming that it's impossible to predict beliefs of over 200 million adult Americans by interviewing only 1,000 of them. Write a short report using this context to show how you could explain random sampling, the margin of error for a sample proportion, and how the margin of error depends on the sample size.

8.100 **Housework and gender** Using data from the National Survey of Families and Households, a study (from S. South and G. Spitze, *American Sociological Review*, vol. 59, 1994, pp. 327–347) reported the descriptive statistics in the following table for the hours spent on housework. Analyze these data. Summarize results in a short report, including assumptions you made to perform the inferential analyses. (The *Inference for a Mean* app allows entering just these summary statistics to produce confidence intervals.)

Gender	Sample Size	Mean	Std Dev
Men	4,252	18.1	12.9
Women	6,764	32.6	18.2

8.101 **Women's role opinions** When subjects in a recent GSS were asked whether they agreed with the following statements, the (yes, no) counts under various conditions were as follows:

- Women should take care of running their homes and leave running the country up to men: (275, 1,556).

- It is better for everyone involved if the man is the achiever outside the home and the woman takes care of the home and the family: (627, 1,208).

- A preschool child is likely to suffer if his or her mother works: (776, 1,054).

Analyze these data. Prepare a short report stating assumptions, showing results of description and inference, and summarizing conclusions.

8.102 Types of estimates An interval estimate for a mean is more informative than a point estimate, because with an interval estimate you can figure out the point estimate, but with the point estimate alone you have no idea how wide the interval estimate is. Explain why this statement is correct, illustrating using the reported 95% confidence interval of (4.0, 5.6) for the mean number of dates in the previous month based on a sample of women at a particular college.

8.103 Width of a confidence interval Why are confidence intervals wider when we use larger confidence levels but narrower when we use larger sample sizes, other things being equal?

8.104 99.9999% confidence Explain why confidence levels are usually large, such as 95% or 99%, but not extremely large, such as 99.9999%. (*Hint:* What impact does the extremely high confidence level have on the margin of error?)

8.105 Need 15 successes and 15 failures To use the large-sample confidence interval for p, you need at least 15 successes and 15 failures. Show that the smallest value of n for which the method can be used is (a) 30 when $\hat{p} = 0.50$, (b) 50 when $\hat{p} = 0.30$, (c) 150 when $\hat{p} = 0.10$. That is, the overall n must increase as $\hat{p}$ moves toward 0 or 1. (When the true proportion is near 0 or 1, the sampling distribution can be highly skewed unless n is quite large.)

8.106 Outliers and CI For the observations 618, 650, 608, 634, 675, 618, 625, 619, 630 on Buy It Now prices for the 16GB iPhone 5s on eBay considered in Exercise 8.42, a confidence interval for the population mean Buy It Now price on eBay is (615, 647). Suppose the 5th observation was actually 875 instead of 675. What would have been obtained for the 95% confidence interval? Compare to the original interval. How does this warn you about potential effects of outliers when you construct a confidence interval for a mean?

8.107 What affects n? Using the sample size formula $n = [\hat{p}(1 - \hat{p})z^2]/m^2$ for a proportion, explain the effect on n of (a) increasing the confidence level and (b) decreasing the margin of error.

8.108 Margin of error approximately $1/\sqrt{(n)}$ Consider the sample size formula $n = [\hat{p}(1 - \hat{p})z^2]/m^2$ for estimating a proportion. When $\hat{p}$ is close to 0.50, for 95% confidence explain why this formula gives roughly $n = 1/m^2$ or, equivalently, $m = 1/\sqrt{n}$. (*Hint:* Use the fact that $z^2 = 1.96^2$, which is roughly 4.)

8.109 Mean age at marriage A random sample of 50 records yields a 95% confidence interval of 21.5 to 23.0 years for the mean age at first marriage of women in a certain county. Explain what is wrong with each of the following interpretations of this interval.

a. If random samples of 50 records were repeatedly selected, then 95% of the time the sample mean age at first marriage for women would be between 21.5 and 23.0 years.

b. Ninety-five percent of the ages at first marriage for women in the county are between 21.5 and 23.0 years.

c. We can be 95% confident that $\bar{x}$ is between 21.5 and 23.0 years.

d. If we repeatedly sampled the entire population, then 95% of the time the population mean would be between 21.5 and 23.5 years.

8.110 Interpret CI For the previous exercise, provide the proper interpretation.

8.111 College students watching TV Example 1 mentioned a sample from the 2018 GSS where respondents indicated how many hours, on average, they watch TV daily. Among the respondents are a random sample of twenty-eight 18- to 22-year-old college students. The data for these 28 students are preloaded in the *Bootstrap for One Sample* app, under the name Youth Watching TV.

a. Find (using the conventional formula using the t distribution) and interpret a 95% confidence interval for the mean number of hours watching TV. (The app has an option to obtain this interval under the Get Confidence Interval tab. Alternatively, you can copy & paste the 25 observations into the *Inference for a Mean* app by selecting Your Own under Enter Data and obtain the interval there.)

b. To verify whether the interval from part a is valid (what is the concern?), report a 95% bootstrap percentile confidence interval for the mean. Does it differ substantially from the one in part a? Explain.

Multiple Choice or True/False

8.112 CI property Increasing the confidence level causes the margin of error of a confidence interval to **(a)** increase, **(b)** decrease, **(c)** stay the same.

8.113 CI property 2 Other things being equal, increasing n causes the margin of error of a confidence interval to **(a)** increase, **(b)** decrease, **(c)** stay the same.

8.114 Number of close friends Based on responses of 1,467 subjects in a General Social Survey, a 95% confidence interval for the mean number of close friends equals (6.8, 8.0). Which *two* of the following interpretations are correct?

a. We can be 95% confident that $\bar{x}$ is between 6.8 and 8.0.

b. We can be 95% confident that μ is between 6.8 and 8.0.

c. Ninety-five percent of the values of $X =$ number of close friends (for this sample) are between 6.8 and 8.0.

d. If random samples of size 1,467 were repeatedly selected, then 95% of the time $\bar{x}$ would be between 6.8 and 8.0.

e. If random samples of size 1,467 were repeatedly selected, then in the long run 95% of the confidence intervals formed would contain the true value of μ.

8.115 Why z? The reason we use a z-score from a normal distribution in constructing a large-sample confidence interval for a proportion is that:

a. For large random samples the sampling distribution of the sample proportion is approximately normal.

b. The population distribution is normal.

c. For large random samples the data distribution is approximately normal.

d. For any n we use the t distribution to get a confidence interval, and for large n the t distribution looks like the standard normal distribution.

8.116 True or false Suppose a 95% confidence interval for the population proportion of students at your school who regularly drink alcohol is (0.61, 0.67). The inference is that you can be 95% confident that the sample proportion falls between 0.61 and 0.67.

8.117 True or false   The confidence interval for a mean with a random sample of size $n = 2{,}000$ is invalid if the population distribution is bimodal.

8.118 True or false   If you have a volunteer sample instead of a random sample, then a confidence interval for a parameter is still completely reliable as long as the sample size is larger than about 30.

8.119 True or false   Quadrupling the sample size n cuts the margin of error into half, other things being equal.

8.120 Women's satisfaction with appearance   A special issue of *Newsweek* in March 1999 on women and their health reported results of a poll of 757 American women aged 18 or older. When asked, "How satisfied are you with your overall physical appearance?" 30% said very satisfied, 54% said somewhat satisfied, 13% said not too satisfied, and 3% said not at all satisfied. **True or false:** Since all these percentages are based on the same sample size, they all have the same margin of error.

Advanced Concepts

8.121 Opinions over time about the death penalty   For many years, the General Social Survey has asked respondents whether they favor the death penalty for persons convicted of murder. Support has been quite high in the United States, one of few Western nations that currently has the death penalty. The following figure uses the 26 General Social Surveys taken between 1975 and 2012 and plots the 95% confidence intervals for the population

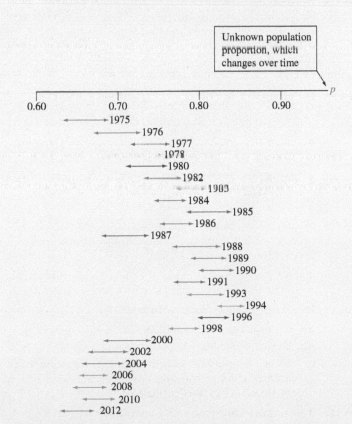

Twenty-six 95% confidence intervals for the population proportions supporting the death penalty.

proportion in the United States who supported the death penalty in each of the 26 years of these surveys.

a.   When we say we have "95% confidence" in the interval for a particular year, what does this mean?

b.   For 95% confidence intervals constructed using data for 26 years, let $X =$ the number of the intervals that contain the true parameter values. Find the probability that $x = 26$, that is, all 26 inferences are correct. (*Hint:* You can use the binomial distribution to answer this.)

c.   Refer to part b. Find the mean of the probability distribution of X.

d.   What could you do differently so it is more likely that all 26 inferences are correct?

8.122 Why called "degrees of freedom"?   You know the sample mean $\bar{x}$ of n observations. Once you know $(n - 1)$ of the observations, show that you can find the remaining one. In other words, for a given value of $\bar{x}$, the values of $(n - 1)$ observations determine the remaining one. In summarizing scores on a quantitative variable, having $(n - 1)$ *degrees of freedom* means that only that many observations are independent. (If you have trouble with this, try to show it for $n = 2$, for instance showing that if you know that $\bar{x} = 80$ and you know that one observation is 90, then you can figure out the other observation. The *df* value also refers to the divisor in $s^2 = \Sigma(x - \bar{x})^2/(n - 1)$.)

8.123 An alternative interval for the population proportion   The large-sample confidence interval for a proportion substitutes $\hat{p}$ for the unknown value of p in the formula for the standard deviation of $\hat{p}$. An alternative method to form a 95% confidence interval determines the endpoints of the interval by finding the values for p that are 1.96 standard deviations from the sample proportion, without a need to estimate the standard deviation. To do this, you solve for p in the equation

$$|\hat{p} - p| = 1.96\sqrt{p(1 - p)/n}.$$

This interval is known as the (Wilson) score confidence interval for a proportion and available in the *Inference for a Proportion* app.

a.   For Example 10 with no students who do not use Facebook daily in a sample of size 20, substitute $\hat{p}$ and n in this equation and show that the equation is satisfied at $p = 0.83887$ and at $p = 1$. So the confidence interval is (0.83887,1), compared to (1, 1) with $\hat{p} \pm 1.96(se)$.

b.   Which confidence interval seems more believable? Why?

Student Activities

8.124 Randomized response   To encourage subjects to make honest responses on sensitive questions, the method of *randomized response* is often used. Let's use your class to estimate the proportion who have had alcohol at a party. Before carrying out this method, the class should discuss what they would guess for the value of the proportion of students in the class who have had alcohol at a party. Come to a class consensus. Now each student should flip a coin in secret. If it is a head, toss the coin once more and report the outcome, head or tails. If the first flip is a tail, report instead the response to whether you have had alcohol, reporting the response *head* if the true response is yes and reporting the response *tail* if the true response is no. Let p denote the true probability of the *yes* response on the sensitive question.

a. Explain why the numbers in the following table are the probabilities of the four possible outcomes.

b. Let $\hat{q}$ denote the sample proportion of subjects who report *head* for the second response. Explain why we can set $\hat{q} = 0.25 + p/2$ and hence use $\hat{p} = 2\hat{q} - 0.5$ to estimate p.

c. Using this approach with your class, estimate the probability of having had alcohol at a party. Is it close to the class guess?

Table for Randomized Response

First Coin	Second Response	
	Head	Tail
Head	0.25	0.25
Tail	$p/2$	$(1 - p)/2$

8.125 **GSS project** The instructor will assign the class a theme to study. Download recent results for variables relating to that theme from the GSS website, sda.berkeley.edu (see Activity 1). Find and interpret confidence intervals for relevant parameters. Prepare a report summarizing results.

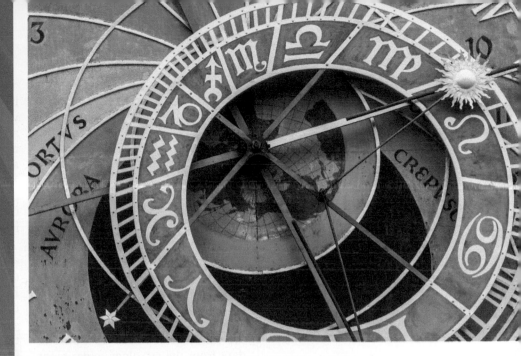

Statistical Inference: Significance Tests About Hypotheses

Example 1

Are Astrology Predictions Better than Guessing?

Picture the Scenario

Astrologers believe that the positions of the planets and the moon at the moment of your birth determine your personality traits. But have you ever seen any scientific evidence that astrology works? One scientific test of astrology used the following experiment: 116 volunteers were asked to give their date and time of birth. From this information, an astrologer prepared each subject's horoscope based on the positions of the planets and the moon at the moment of birth. Each volunteer also filled out a California Personality Index survey. Then the birth data and horoscope for one subject, together with the results of the personality survey for that individual and for two other participants randomly selected from the experimental group, were given to an astrologer. The astrologer was asked to predict which of the three personality charts matched the birth data and horoscope for the subject.[1]

Let p denote the probability of a correct prediction by an astrologer. Suppose an astrologer actually has no special predictive powers, as would be expected by those who view astrology as "quack science." The predictions then merely correspond to random guessing, that is, picking one of the three personality charts at random, in which case $p = 1/3$. However, the participating astrologers claimed that $p > 1/3$. They felt they could predict better than with random guessing.

---

[1] S. Carlson, *Nature*, (1985), vol. 318, pp. 419–425.

Questions to Explore

- How can we use data from such an experiment to summarize the evidence about the claim by the astrologers?

- How can we decide, based on the data, whether the claim is plausible?

Thinking Ahead

In this chapter, we'll learn how to use inferential statistics to answer such questions. We will use an inferential method called a **significance test** to analyze evidence in favor of the astrologers' claim. We'll analyze data from the astrology experiment, referring to a population proportion in Examples 3, 5, and 12. However, you actually already know how to answer the second question: You can compute a confidence interval for p and check if it falls completely above 1/3. If it does, the astrologers' claim is supported. This section will point out connections between confidence intervals and significance tests.

To illustrate a significance test about a population mean, we use data on weight gain in anorexic girls. In an experiment with a cognitive therapy, girls had an average weight gain of 3 pounds. Does this support the claim that the therapy is effective? We will analyze such a claim in Example 8.

The significance test is the second major method for conducting statistical inference about a population. Like a confidence interval for estimating a parameter (the first major method), the significance test uses probability to quantify how plausible a parameter value is while controlling the chance of an incorrect inference. With significance tests, we'll be able to use data to answer questions such as:

- Does a proposed diet truly result in weight loss, on average?
- Is there evidence of discrimination against women in promotion decisions?
- Does one advertising method result in better sales, on average, than another advertising method?

9.1 Steps for Performing a Significance Test

The main goal of many research studies is to check whether the data support certain statements or predictions. These statements are **hypotheses** about a population. They are usually expressed in terms of population parameters for variables measured in the study.

> Hypothesis
>
> In statistics, a **hypothesis** is a statement about a population, usually claiming that a population parameter takes a particular numerical value or falls in a certain range of values.

For instance, the parameter might be a population proportion or a probability. Here's an example of a hypothesis for the astrology experiment in Example 1:

Hypothesis: Using a person's horoscope, the probability p that an astrologer can correctly predict which of three personality charts applies to that person equals 1/3. In other words, astrologers' predictions correspond to random guessing.

A *significance test* (or "test" for short) is a method for using data to summarize the evidence about a hypothesis. For instance, if a high proportion of the astrologers' predictions are correct, the data might provide strong evidence against the hypothesis that $p = 1/3$ and in favor of an alternative hypothesis representing the astrologers' claim that $p > 1/3$.

Before conducting a significance test, we identify the variable measured and the population parameter of interest. For a categorical variable, the parameter is typically a proportion or a probability, and for a quantitative variable the parameter is typically a mean. Section 9.2 shows the details for tests about proportions. Section 9.3 presents tests about means.

The Steps of a Significance Test

A significance test has five steps. In this section, we introduce the general ideas behind these steps.

Step 1: Assumptions

Each significance test makes certain assumptions or has certain conditions under which it applies. Foremost, a test assumes that the data production used randomization. Other assumptions may be about the sample size or about the shape of the population distribution.

Step 2: Hypotheses

Each significance test has two hypotheses about a population parameter: a null hypothesis and an alternative hypothesis.

In Words

H_0: null hypothesis (read as "H zero" or "H naught")
H_a: alternative hypothesis (read as "H a")
In everyday English, "null" is an adjective meaning "of no consequence or effect, amounting to nothing."

Null Hypothesis, Alternative Hypothesis

The **null hypothesis** is a statement that the population parameter equals a particular value.

The **alternative hypothesis** states that the population parameter falls in some alternative range of values.

The value in the null hypothesis usually represents *no effect*. The value in the alternative hypothesis then represents an effect in the positive, in the negative, or in both the positive and negative direction.

The symbol H_0 denotes the **null hypothesis** and the symbol H_a denotes the **alternative hypothesis.**

For the experiment in Example 1, consider the hypothesis, "Based on any person's horoscope, the probability p that an astrologer can correctly predict which of three personality charts applies to that person equals $1/3$." This hypothesis states that there is *no effect* in the sense that an astrologer's predictive power is no better than random guessing. This is a *null hypothesis*. It is symbolized by H_0: $p = 1/3$. If it is true, any difference that we observe between the sample proportion of correct guesses and $1/3$ is due merely to ordinary sampling variability. The *alternative hypothesis* states that there *is* an effect—an astrologer's predictions are *better* than random guessing. It is symbolized by H_a: $p > 1/3$.

A null hypothesis is a statement about a *single* parameter value, such as H_0: $p = 1/3$. An alternative hypothesis is a statement about a *range* of values that are alternatives to the one in H_0, such as H_a: $p > 1/3$ or H_a: $p \neq 1/3$. You formulate the hypotheses for a significance test *before* viewing or analyzing the data.

Null and Alternative Hypotheses ◀

Example 2

Fracking

Picture the Scenario

Through the use of fracking, a drilling method that uses high-pressure water and chemicals to extract oil and natural gas from underground rock formations, the United States has become the largest oil producer in the world. Despite its economic benefits, fracking is becoming more and more controversial due to its potential effects on the environment, and some U.S. states and other countries have already banned it. What does the public think about fracking? Let's investigate whether those who oppose fracking in the United States are in the minority. Let p denote the proportion of people in the United States who oppose fracking.

Questions to Explore

Consider the claim, "In the United States, the proportion of people who oppose fracking is less than 0.50; i.e., they are in the minority."
  a. Is this a null or an alternative hypothesis?
  b. How can we express the hypothesis that the population proportion opposed to fracking may actually be 0.50?

Think It Through

  a. When those opposing fracking are in the minority, $p < 0.50$. This is an *alternative* hypothesis, i.e., $H_a: p < 0.50$. It specifies a range of potential values for the population proportion, all less than 0.50.
  b. The hypothesis stating that the population proportion of those opposing fracking is less than 0.50 is an alternative to the null hypothesis that it may be 0.50. This null hypothesis is formulated as $H_0: p = 0.50$. It specifies a single value for the parameter p. Here, "no effect" means an equal proportion of people are either in opposition to or in support of fracking.

Insight

Fracking has provided a boost to the economy in North Dakota. If we want to investigate whether the mean salary of all workers in North Dakota has increased from its 2000 value of $40,000, the null hypothesis is $H_0: \mu = 40,000$ and the alternative hypothesis is $\mu > 40,000$. Here, the population parameter μ represents the mean salary of all workers.

▶ *Try Exercises 9.1 and 9.2*

In a significance test, the null hypothesis is presumed to be true unless the data give strong evidence against it. The burden of proof falls on the researcher who claims the alternative hypothesis is true. In the astrology study, we assume that $p = 1/3$ (i.e., astrologers are just guessing) unless the data provide strong evidence against it and in favor of the astrologers' claim that $p > 1/3$. In the fracking study, we will assume that an equal proportion (i.e., 0.50) opposes or supports fracking until data provide enough evidence that, in fact, the proportion opposing it is less than 0.50. An analogy may be found in a courtroom trial, in which a jury must decide the guilt or innocence of a defendant. The null hypothesis, corresponding to no effect, is that the defendant is innocent. The alternative hypothesis is that the defendant is guilty. The jury presumes the defendant is innocent (i.e., H_0 is true) unless the prosecutor can provide strong evidence that the defendant is guilty beyond a reasonable doubt. The burden of proof is on the prosecutor to convince the jury that the defendant is guilty.

Step 3: Test Statistic

The population parameter to which the null and alternative hypotheses refer has a point estimate. A **test statistic** describes how far that point estimate falls from the parameter value given in the null hypothesis. Usually this distance is measured by the number of standard errors between the point estimate and the parameter.

For instance, consider the null hypothesis $H_0: p = 1/3$ that, based on a person's horoscope, the probability p that an astrologer can correctly predict which of three personality charts belongs to that person equals $1/3$. For the experiment described in Example 1, 40 of 116 predictions were correct. The estimate of the probability p is the sample proportion, $\hat{p} = 40/116 = 0.345$. The test statistic compares this point estimate to the value in the null hypothesis $(p = 1/3)$, using a z-score that measures the number of standard errors that the estimate falls from the null hypothesis value of $1/3$.

In the analogy with courtroom trials, you can think of the test statistic as the evidence that is provided in a trial.

Step 4: P-value

To summarize the evidence against the null hypothesis (i.e., to decide whether it is weak or strong), we need to assess whether the value of the test statistic is unusual under the null hypothesis. We do this using probability in the following way: We presume that H_0 is true, since the burden of proof is on the alternative, H_a. Then we consider the sorts of values we'd expect to get for the test statistic, according to its sampling distribution. If the test statistic falls well out in a tail of the sampling distribution, it is far from what H_0 predicts. If H_0 were true, such a value would be unusual. To summarize how far out in the tail the test statistic falls, we find the tail probability of the observed value and values even more extreme (meaning, even farther from what H_0 predicts). See Figure 9.1. This tail probability is called the **P-value.**

> ### P-value
>
> The **P-value** is the probability that the test statistic equals the observed value or a value even more extreme. It is calculated by presuming that the null hypothesis H_0 is true.

Sampling distribution of test statistic when H_0 is true

Tail probability = P-value

Expected value of test statistic when H_0 true (= center of sampling distribution)

Observed value of test statistic

More extreme values

▲ **Figure 9.1** Suppose H_0 Were True. The P-value Is the Probability of Observing a Value for the Test Statistic as or even more extreme than the Observed One. This is the shaded area in the tail of the sampling distribution. **Question** Which gives stronger evidence against the null hypothesis, a P-value of 0.20 or of 0.01? Why?

The smaller the P-value, the stronger the evidence is against H_0. In the astrology study, suppose the P-value is small, such as 0.01. This means that if H_0 were true (that an astrologer's predictions correspond to just random guessing), it would be unusual to get values for the test statistic such as the one we observed. This implies that our data are not compatible with the null hypothesis. The small P-value then provides strong evidence against the null hypothesis of random guessing and in support of the astrologers' claim. On the other hand, if the P-value is not near 0, the data are consistent with H_0. For instance, a P-value such as 0.26 or 0.63 indicates that if the astrologers were actually randomly guessing, values such as the one observed for the test statistic would not be unusual and any difference from the hypothesized value of $p = 1/3$ could be attributed to just random variation. We will discuss this reasoning more thoroughly in the next section.

Step 5: Conclusion

The conclusion of a significance test reports the P-value and *interprets* what it says about the question that motivated the test. Sometimes this includes a decision about the validity of the null hypothesis H_0. For instance, based on the P-value, can we reject H_0 and conclude that astrologers' predictions are better than random guessing? As we'll also discuss in the next section, we can reject H_0 in favor of H_a only when the P-value is very small, such as 0.05 or less.

SUMMARY: The Five Steps of a Significance Test

1. **Assumptions**

   First, specify the variable and parameter. The assumptions commonly pertain to the method of data production (randomization), the sample size, and the shape of the population distribution.

2. **Hypotheses**

   State the null hypothesis, H_0 (a single parameter value, usually describing no effect), and the alternative hypothesis, H_a (a set of alternative parameter values) that usually describes some sort of claim.

3. **Test Statistic**

   The test statistic measures the distance between the point estimate of the parameter and its null hypothesis value, usually by the number of standard errors between them.

4. **P-value**

   The P-value is the probability that the test statistic equals the observed value or a value more extreme if we presume H_0 is true. Smaller P-values represent stronger evidence against H_0.

5. **Conclusion**

   Report and interpret the P-value in the context of the study. Based on the P-value, make a decision about H_0 (either reject or do not reject H_0) if a decision is needed.

Significance Tests Are Typically Less Informative than Confidence Intervals

Now that we understand the basic principles behind a significance test, we want to point out that in many cases significance tests are less informative than confidence intervals. Both inferential procedures give us information about an unknown population parameter. However, with a significance test, we only learn that there is evidence (when the P-value is small) that the value of a population parameter falls in the range specified by the alternative hypothesis, i.e., that there is some effect, but we don't learn how large (and hence how important) that effect actually is. A confidence interval, on the other hand, provides a range of plausible values for the population parameter, so we can learn just how large the effect is.

For example, continuing with Example 2 on the opinion of fracking, we will conclude, based on survey data, that there is evidence (we'll find a P-value of 0.032) that the proportion of people opposing fracking is less than 0.5. Such a result is often formulated as the test providing evidence that the population proportion is significantly less than 0.5. However, the 95% confidence interval for the proportion stretches from 0.444 to 0.497. This tells us more than the proportion being "significantly less than 0.5" and suggests that the proportion may be as large as 0.497. In practical terms, this may be considered rather close to 0.5.

We will discuss such issues and other potential misuses of significance testing and the P-value in Section 9.5. You will see that in many of our examples we provide a confidence interval to supplement the conclusions drawn from a significance test. This is not to say that significance tests don't have their place in statistics. Later chapters will discuss important applications of significance tests, so we need to understand their logic and mechanics, as well as the types of errors that can occur when making decisions based on inferential procedures (see Section 9.4).

9.1 Practicing the Basics

9.1 H_0 **or** H_a**?** For parts a and b, is the statement a null hypothesis, or an alternative hypothesis?

    a. In Canada, the proportion of adults who favor legalized gambling equals 0.50.

    b. The proportion of all Canadian college students who are regular smokers is less than 0.24, the value it was 10 years ago.

    c. Introducing notation for a parameter, state the hypotheses in parts a and b in terms of the parameter values.

9.2 H_0 **or** H_a**?** For each of the following, is the statement a null hypothesis or an alternative hypothesis? Why?

    a. The mean annual salary of K-12 teachers in Indiana is higher than $50,000.

    b. The probability of rolling a 6 with a particular die equals 1/6.

    c. The proportion of all start-ups that remain in business for at least five years is less than 0.50.

9.3 **Burden of proof** For a new pesticide, should the Environmental Protection Agency (EPA) bear the burden of proof to show that it is harmful to the environment, or should the producer of the pesticide have to show that it is not harmful to the environment? The pesticide is considered harmful if its toxicity level exceeds a threshold of 100 ppm (parts per million) and not harmful if its toxicity level is at or below 100 ppm. Consider the statements, "The mean toxicity level equals the threshold of 100 ppm," "The mean toxicity level exceeds the threshold of 100 ppm," and "The mean toxicity level is below the threshold of 100 ppm."

    a. Which of these statements should be the null and which the alternative hypothesis when the burden of proof is on the EPA to show that the new pesticide is harmful?

    b. Which of these statements should be the null and which the alternative hypothesis when the burden of proof is on the producer to show that the new pesticide is not harmful?

9.4 **Financial aid** The average financial aid package for students admitted at a Liberal Arts College was $44,000 in 2019. A student organization plans to investigate whether this average has changed for students admitted in 2020. Define the population parameter of interest and state the null and alternative hypotheses for this investigation.

9.5 **Low-carbohydrate diet** A study plans to have a sample of obese adults follow a proposed low-carbohydrate diet for three months and measure the weight change = (weight at start of study − weight at end of study) for each participant. The diet imposes limited eating of starches (such as bread and pasta) and sweets, but otherwise no limit on calorie intake. Consider the hypothesis,

The population mean weight change is larger than zero, where the population refers to all obese adults considering this diet.

    a. Is this a null or an alternative hypothesis? Explain your reasoning.

    b. Define a relevant parameter and express the hypothesis that the diet has no effect in terms of that parameter. Is it a null or an alternative hypothesis?

9.6   Examples of hypotheses   Give an example of a null hypothesis and an alternative hypothesis about a (a) population proportion and (b) population mean, defining the population parameter of interest and stating what it represents in context.

9.7   Proper hypotheses?   Explain what is wrong with each set of null and alternative hypotheses shown. Then, correct each to form a proper set of hypotheses.
   a. $H_0: \hat{p} = 0.50$, $H_a: \hat{p} > 0.50$
   b. $H_0: \mu = 100$, $H_a: \mu = 200$
   c. $H_0: p = 0.30$, $H_a: p > 0.10$
   d. $H_0: \mu > 100$, $H_a: \mu < 100$

9.8   z test statistic   To test $H_0: p = 0.50$ that a population proportion equals 0.50, the test statistic is a z-score that measures the number of standard errors between the sample proportion and the H_0 value of 0.50. If $z = 3.6$, do the data support the null hypothesis, or do they give strong evidence against it? Explain.

9.9   P-value   Indicate whether each of the following P-values gives strong evidence or not especially strong evidence against the null hypothesis.
   a. 0.38
   b. 0.001

9.2 Significance Test About a Proportion

For categorical variables, the parameters of interest are the population proportions in the categories. We'll use the astrology study to illustrate a significance test for population proportions.

Example 3

▶ Hypotheses for a Significance Test

Are Astrologers' Predictions Better than Guessing?

Picture the Scenario

Many people take astrological predictions seriously, but there has never been any scientific evidence that astrology works. One scientific test of astrology used the experiment mentioned in Example 1: For each of 116 adult volunteers, an astrologer prepared a horoscope based on the positions of the planets and the moon at the moment of the person's birth. Each adult subject also filled out a California Personality Index (CPI) survey. For a given adult, the birth data and horoscope were shown to one of the participating astrologers in the experiment, together with the results of the personality survey for that adult and for two other adults randomly selected from the experimental group. The astrologer was asked which personality chart of the three subjects was the correct one for that adult, based on the horoscope.

The 28 participating astrologers were randomly chosen from a list prepared by the National Council for Geocosmic Research (NCGR), an organization dealing with astrology and respected by astrologers worldwide. The NCGR sampling frame consisted of astrologers with some background in psychology who were familiar with the CPI and who were held in high esteem by their astrologer peers. The experiment was double-blind; each subject was identified by a random number, and neither the astrologers nor the experimenter knew which number corresponded to which subject. The chapter of the NCGR that recommended the participating astrologers claimed that the probability of a correct guess on any given trial in the experiment was larger than 1/3, the value for random guessing. (In fact, they felt that it would exceed 1/2.)

Question to Explore

Put this investigation in the context of a significance test by stating the parameter of interest and the null and alternative hypotheses.

Think It Through

The variable specifying the outcome of any given trial in the experiment is categorical and, in fact, binary, with the two outcomes of a correct or incorrect prediction. For each person, let p denote the probability of a correct prediction by the astrologer. We can regard this as the population proportion of correct guesses for the population of people and population of astrologers from which the study participants were sampled. With random guessing, $p = 1/3$ because there are three options to choose from (one correct and two incorrect personality charts). If the astrologers can predict better than random guessing, then $p > 1/3$. The two hypotheses refer to these two scenarios about the probability p. To test the hypothesis of random guessing against the astrologers' claim that $p > 1/3$, we would test $H_0: p = 1/3$ against $H_a: p > 1/3$.

Insight

In the experiment, the astrologers were correct with 40 of their 116 predictions. We'll see how to use these data to test these hypotheses as we work through the five steps of a significance test for a proportion in the next subsection.

▶ *Try Exercises 9.10 and 9.11*

Steps of a Significance Test About a Population Proportion

This section presents a significance test about a population proportion that applies with relatively large samples. Here are the five steps of the test:

Step 1: Assumptions

Recall

Section 7.1 introduced the sampling distribution of a sample proportion. It has mean p and standard deviation

$$\sqrt{p(1-p)/n}$$

and is well approximated by the normal distribution when

$$np \geq 15 \text{ and } n(1-p) \geq 15. \blacktriangleleft$$

- The variable is categorical.
- The data are obtained using randomization (such as a random sample or a randomized experiment).
- The sample size is sufficiently large that the sampling distribution of the sample proportion $\hat{p}$ is approximately normal. The approximate normality happens when the *expected numbers of successes and failures are both at least 15, using the null hypothesis value for p.*

The sample size guideline is the one we used in Chapter 6 for judging when the normal distribution approximates the binomial distribution well. For the astrology experiment with $n = 116$ trials, when H_0 is true that $p = 1/3$, we expect $116(1/3) = 38.7 \approx 39$ correct guesses and $116(2/3) = 77.3 \approx 77$ incorrect guesses. Both of these are above 15, so the sample size guideline is satisfied.

As with other statistical inference methods, if randomization is not used, the validity of the results is questionable. A survey should use random sampling. An experiment should use principles of randomization and blinding with the study subjects, as was done in the astrology study. In that study, the astrologers were randomly selected, but the subjects evaluated were people (mainly students) who volunteered for the study. Consequently, any inference applies to the population of astrologers but only to the particular subjects in the study. If the study could have chosen the subjects randomly from some population as well, then the inference would extend more broadly to *all* people in that population.

Step 2: Hypotheses

The null hypothesis of a test about a proportion has the form

$$H_0: p = p_0,$$

In Words

p_0 is read as "p-zero" (or as "p-naught") and is the hypothesized value of the population proportion under the null hypothesis where p_0 represents a particular proportion value between 0 and 1. In Example 3, the null hypothesis of no effect states that the astrologers' predictions correspond to random guessing. This is $H_0: p = 1/3$. The null hypothesis value p_0 is $1/3$.

The alternative hypothesis refers to alternative parameter values from the number in the null hypothesis. One possible alternative hypothesis has the form

$$H_a: p > p_0.$$

This is used when a test is designed to detect whether p is *larger* than the number in the null hypothesis. In the astrology experiment, the astrologers claimed they could predict *better* than by random guessing. Their claim corresponds to $H_a: p > 1/3$. This is called a **one-sided** alternative hypothesis because it has values falling only on one side of the null hypothesis value. (See margin figure.) We'll use this H_a below. The other possible one-sided alternative hypothesis is $H_a: p < p_0$, such as $H_a: p < 1/3$.

A **two-sided** alternative hypothesis has the form

$$H_a: p \neq p_0.$$

It includes *all* the other possible values, both below and above the value p_0 in H_0. It states that the population proportion *differs* from the number in the null hypothesis. An example is $H_a: p \neq 1/3$, which states that the population proportion equals some number other than $1/3$. (See margin figure.)

In summary, for Example 3 we used $H_0: p = 1/3$ and the one-sided $H_a: p > 1/3$.

Step 3: Test Statistic

The test statistic measures how far the sample proportion $\hat{p}$ falls from the null hypothesis value p_0, relative to what we'd expect if H_0 were true. From the discussion in Chapter 7 we know that the sampling distribution of the sample proportion has mean equal to the population proportion p and standard deviation equal to $\sqrt{p(1-p)/n}$. When H_0 is true, $p = p_0$, so the mean of the sampling distribution is p_0. We can also plug in p_0 for p in the formula for the standard deviation to obtain the standard error $se_0 = \sqrt{p_0(1-p_0)/n}$. (We use the zero subscript on the standard error to reflect using the value p_0 rather than the usual $\hat{p}$ for estimating the standard deviation.) Having found the mean and standard error, the test statistic is the z-score

$$z = \frac{\hat{p} - p_0}{se_0} = \frac{\hat{p} - p_0}{\sqrt{\dfrac{p_0(1-p_0)}{n}}} =$$

$$\frac{\text{Sample proportion} - \text{Value of proportion under } H_0}{\text{Standard error when null hypothesis is true}}.$$

This z-score measures the number of standard errors between the sample proportion $\hat{p}$ and the null hypothesis value p_0. The test statistic is often called the z test statistic.

In testing $H_0: p = 1/3$ for the astrology experiment with $n = 116$ trials, the standard error is $\sqrt{p_0(1-p_0)/n} = \sqrt{(1/3)(2/3)/116} = 0.0438$. The astrologers were correct with 40 of their 116 predictions, a sample proportion of $\hat{p} = 40/116 = 0.345$. The test statistic is

$$z = \frac{\hat{p} - p_0}{se_0} = \frac{\hat{p} - p_0}{\sqrt{\dfrac{p_0(1-p_0)}{n}}} = \frac{0.345 - 1/3}{0.0438} = 0.26.$$

The sample proportion of 0.345 is only 0.26 standard errors above the null hypothesis value of $1/3$.

Step 4: P-value

Does $z = 0.26$ give much evidence against $H_0: p = 1/3$ and in support of $H_a: p > 1/3$? The P-value summarizes the evidence. It describes how unusual the test statistic (and by extension, our observed data) would be if H_0 were true.

One-sided $H_a: p > 1/3$

Two-sided $H_a: p \neq 1/3$

Recall

The standard error estimates the standard deviation of the sampling distribution of $\hat{p}$. Here in the context of a significance test, we are estimating how much $\hat{p}$ would tend to vary from sample to sample of size n if the null hypothesis were true. ◄

Caution

Do not confuse the z test statistic with the z-score (e.g., 1.96 for 95% confidence) used to find the margin of error for a confidence interval for p. ◄

Recall

The numbers shown in formulas are rounded, such as 0.345 for $40/116 = 0.34482758\ldots$, but calculations are done without rounding. ◄

▲ **Figure 9.2** Calculation of P-value, When $z = 0.26$ for Testing H_0: $p = 1/3$ Against H_a: $p > 1/3$. Presuming that H_0 is true, the P-value is the right-tail probability of a test statistic value as or even more extreme than the observed one. **Question** Logically, why are the *right-tail z*-scores considered the *more extreme* values for testing H_0 against H_a: $p > 1/3$?

Recall

The **standard normal** is the normal distribution with mean = 0 and standard deviation = 1. See the end of Section 6.2. ◄

More specifically, the P-value is the probability that the test statistic takes a value like the observed test statistic or an even more extreme one, if actually $p = 1/3$.

Figure 9.2 shows the approximate sampling distribution of the z test statistic when H_0 is true. This is the **standard normal distribution**. For the astrology study, $z = 0.26$. Values even farther out in the right tail, above 0.26, are even more extreme, in that they provide even stronger evidence against H_0.

To find the P-value, we have to find the probability of obtaining a z-score of 0.26 or larger under this standard normal distribution. As Figure 9.2 shows, this probability equals 0.40. The *Normal Distribution* app or, more conveniently, the *Inference for a Proportion* app provides this probability, but you can also get it from Table A. The P-value of 0.40 tells us that if H_0 were true, there is a 40% probability of observing a test statistic at least as large as the observed value of 0.26.

Step 5: Conclusion

We summarize the test by reporting and interpreting the P-value. The P-value of 0.40 is not especially small. It does *not* provide strong evidence against H_0: $p = 1/3$ and in favor of the astrologers' claim that $p > 1/3$. The observed sample proportion (40 correct predictions out of 116) is the kind of sample proportion we'd expect to see if $p = 1/3$ (that is, if astrologers were randomly guessing the personality type). Thus, it is plausible that $p = 1/3$. Based on the data in our sample, we cannot conclude that astrologers have special predictive powers.

Interpreting the P-value

A significance test analyzes the strength of the evidence against the null hypothesis, H_0. We start by presuming that H_0 is true, putting the *burden of proof* on H_a. The approach taken is the indirect one of *proof by contradiction*. To convince ourselves that H_a is true, we must show the data contradict H_0, by showing they'd be unusual if H_0 were true. We analyze whether the data would be unusual if H_0 were true by finding the P-value. If the P-value is small, the data contradict H_0 and support H_a.

In the astrology study, the P-value for H_a: $p > 1/3$ is the right-tail probability of 0.40 from the sampling distribution of the z statistic. We can also see this P-value directly in the sampling distribution for the sample proportion. The P-value of 0.40 is the probability that the sample proportion $\hat{p}$ takes a value that is at least as far above the null hypothesis value of $1/3$ as the observed sample proportion of $\hat{p} = 0.345$. The margin figure illustrates this. Since the P-value is not small, if truly $p = 1/3$, it would not be unusual to observe $\hat{p} = 0.345$ or an even larger sample proportion. Based on the data, it is plausible that the astrologers' predictions merely correspond to random guessing.

Why do we find the P-value (i.e., the probability) in the *right tail*? Because the alternative hypothesis $H_a: p > 1/3$ has values *above* (that is, to the right of) the null hypothesis value of $1/3$. Then, relatively *large* values of $\hat{p}$ support this alternative hypothesis.

Why do smaller P-values indicate stronger evidence against H_0? Because the data would then be more unusual if H_0 were true. For instance, if we got a P-value of 0.01, then we might be more impressed by the astrologers' claims. With such a small P-value, the sample proportion must have fallen more than 2 standard deviations away from the hypothesized null value of $1/3$, out in the right tail of the sampling distribution. This would be considered extreme and unusual, assuming the astrologers were just guessing. The fact that such an extreme sample proportion was observed would call into question (and contradict) the main assumption we made when computing the P-value, namely that H_0 is true, i.e., that $p = 1/3$.

For instance, suppose in the experiment 50 (instead of 40) of the 116 astrologers made correct predictions. Then, the sample proportion is 0.431 and the z-score equals 2.23, indicating a sample proportion falling 2.23 standard deviations above the value of $1/3$, out in the extreme tail of the sampling distribution. As the margin figure illustrates, the corresponding P-value is 0.013, indicating that a sample proportion of 0.431 or an even larger one is rather unlikely to occur when we assume $p = 1/3$. Such a P-value of 0.013 would provide evidence against the assumption that $p = 1/3$ and in support of the astrologers' claim.

Caution

When interpreting the P-value, always include the conditional statement that it is computed assuming that the value specified in the null hypothesis is the true parameter value. ◄

Two-Sided Significance Tests

Sometimes we're interested in investigating whether a proportion falls above or below some point. For instance, can we conclude whether the population proportion who voted for a particular candidate is different from $1/2$ (either above or below)? We then use a *two-sided* alternative hypothesis. This has the form $H_a: p \neq p_0$, such as $H_a: p \neq 1/2$.

For two-sided tests, the values that are more extreme than the observed test statistic value are ones that fall farther in the tail in *either* direction. The P-value is the *two-tail* probability under the standard normal curve because these are the test statistic values that provide even stronger evidence in favor of $H_a: p \neq p_0$ than the observed value. We calculate this by finding the tail probability in a single tail and then doubling it, since the distribution is symmetric. See Figure 9.3.

▲ **Figure 9.3** For the Two-Sided Alternative $H_a: p \neq p_0$, the P-value Is a Two-Tail Probability. **Question** Logically, why are both the left-tail values and the right-tail values the more extreme values for $H_a: p \neq p_0$?

Two-Sided Significance Test ◄

Example 4

Opinion on Fracking

Picture the Scenario

Let's revisit the question on the public opinion about fracking to extract oil and gas discussed in Example 2. We want to find out whether there is evidence that the proportion of people opposing fracking is *different* from 50%. We will use data from a Pew Research survey (www.pewresearch.org) conducted in the United States in November 2014, which used a random sample of $n = 1,353$ people. Of these, 637 were opposed to fracking; the rest either favored it or had no definite opinion.

Question to Explore

How strong is the evidence that the proportion opposing fracking is different from 50%?

Think It Through

Let's follow the five steps of a significance test to organize our response to this question:

1. Assumptions

- The response from each respondent in the survey is categorical, with outcomes "favor," "oppose," or "don't know." You can treat this as a binary response when you consider the two categories "oppose" and "don't oppose."

- The 1,353 people in the survey were selected by random-digit dialing of both landlines and cell phones. The sample can be treated as a random sample representative of the adult population in the United States.

- The sample size requirement to use the large sample test is met. (See next step.)

2. Hypotheses

The hypothesis that the proportion opposing fracking is different from 50% is an *alternative* hypothesis. It is an alternative to the null hypothesis that the proportion is equal to 50%. So, we test the null hypothesis $H_0: p = 0.5$ versus the alternative hypothesis $H_a: p \neq 0.5$, where p represents the proportion of U.S. adults opposed to fracking. The hypothesized null value for the proportion is $p_0 = 0.50$. Because we expect $1,353(0.50) = 676.5$ successes and $1,353(1 - 0.5) = 676.5$ failures under the null, both greater than 15, the sample size criterion from the assumptions is easily fulfilled. Therefore, it is appropriate to use the standard normal distribution as the sampling distribution for the test statistic, i.e., we can use the large-sample z-test.

3. Test Statistic

The sample proportion opposing fracking in the sample of size $n = 1,353$ is $\hat{p} = 637/1,353 = 0.471$. The standard error of $\hat{p}$ when $H_0: p = 0.50$ is true is

$$se_0 = \sqrt{p_0(1 - p_0)/n} = \sqrt{0.50(1 - 0.50)/1,353} = 0.0136.$$

The value of the test statistic is

$$z = \frac{\hat{p} - p_0}{se_0} = \frac{0.471 - 0.50}{0.0136} = -2.15.$$

Recall

H_0 contains a single number, whereas H_a has a range of values. ◄

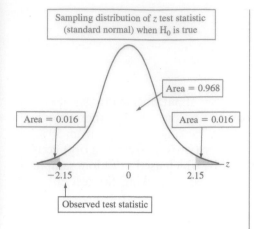

Sampling distribution of z test statistic (standard normal) when H_0 is true

Area = 0.968

Area = 0.016

Area = 0.016

−2.15   0   2.15

z

Observed test statistic

The sample proportion of 0.471 is 2.15 standard deviations below the null hypothesis value of 0.50, so it's rather extreme, assuming the null hypothesis is true.

4. P-value

For testing $H_0: p = 0.50$ against the two-sided alternative $H_a: p \neq 0.50$, the P-value is the *two-tail* probability below $z = -2.15$ and above $z = +2.15$ in the standard normal distribution (see the margin figure). From software (such as the *Normal Distribution* app or the *Inference for a Proportion* app, see Figure 9.4 below) or a normal table (such as Table A), this equals $0.016 + 0.016 = 0.032$.

5. Conclusion

The P-value of 0.032 is pretty small. If the null hypothesis $H_0: p = 0.50$ is true, observing a test statistic (or, equivalently, a sample proportion) such as the one we observed or an even more extreme one is quite unlikely (i.e., occurs with a probability of 0.032, or 3.2%). Based on these data, there is evidence that the proportion of U.S. adults opposing fracking is different from 50%.

Insight

When the P-value in a two-sided test is small, the point estimate tells us the direction in which the parameter appears to differ from the null hypothesis value. Because the sample proportion is 47.1%, there is evidence that the population proportion is less than 50%. How much less? A confidence interval actually gives all the plausible values for p. For these data, the 95% confidence interval for p equals (0.444, 0.497). With 95% confidence, the proportion opposing fracking is estimated to be between 44.4% and 49.7%. The upper bound of 49.7% suggests that the proportion may be very close to 50%, falling just below it by 0.3 percentage points.

In Practice

Statistical software typically reports the P-value for a two-sided test by default. We recommend rounding the P-value to two or three decimal places, to reflect that the normal sampling distribution is only approximate. For example, report the P-value as 0.032 instead of 0.03174. For very small P-values, such as 0.00004, only report that the P-value is less than 0.001.

▶ **Figure 9.4** Test Statistic and Resulting P-value for a Significance Test About a Proportion. Screenshot from the *Inference for a Proportion* app. Under Type of Inference, select Significance Test, and then provide the null value p_0, here 0.5. The app finds the null standard error se_0, the z test statistic and the resulting P-value. It visualizes the P-value in a graph of the standard normal distribution.

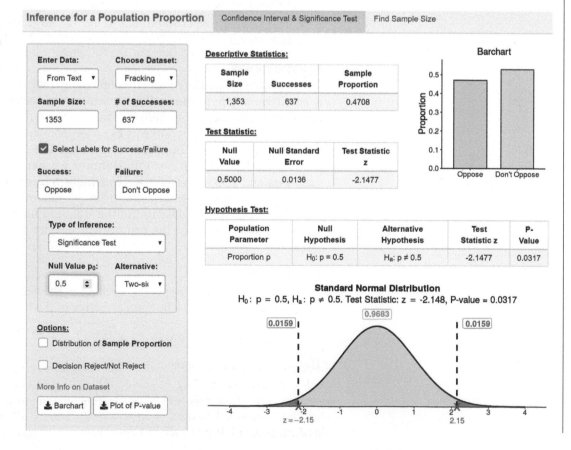

Inference for a Population Proportion   Confidence Interval & Significance Test   Find Sample Size

Enter Data: **Choose Dataset:**

From Text ▾   Fracking ▾

Sample Size: **# of Successes:**

1353   637

☑ Select Labels for Success/Failure

Success: **Failure:**

Oppose   Don't Oppose

Type of Inference:

Significance Test ▾

Null Value p_0:   **Alternative:**

0.5 ⇕   Two-si ▾

Options:

☐ Distribution of **Sample Proportion**

☐ Decision Reject/Not Reject

More Info on Dataset

⬇ Barchart   ⬇ Plot of P-value

Descriptive Statistics:

Sample Size	Successes	Sample Proportion
1,353	637	0.4708

Test Statistic:

Null Value	Null Standard Error	Test Statistic z
0.5000	0.0136	-2.1477

Hypothesis Test:

Population Parameter	Null Hypothesis	Alternative Hypothesis	Test Statistic z	P-Value
Proportion p	$H_0: p = 0.5$	$H_a: p \neq 0.5$	-2.1477	0.0317

Barchart

Proportion: Oppose   Don't Oppose

Standard Normal Distribution

$H_0: p = 0.5$, $H_a: p \neq 0.5$. Test Statistic: $z = -2.148$, P-value = 0.0317

0.0159   0.9683   0.0159

−4 −3 −2 −1 0 1 2 3 4

$z = -2.15$ 2.15

The *Inference for a Proportion* app that we used to find a confidence interval can also be used to obtain and visualize the test statistic and P-value for a significance test about a proportion. Figure 9.4 shows a screenshot of this app, which has the data on fracking preloaded, but you can also enter your own data. To obtain the significance test, select Significance Test under Type of Inference and provide the null value p_0 (here: 0.5) for the proportion. The first table in the screenshot shows the data and resulting sample proportion, and the second table shows the null standard error se_0 and the test statistic z. The third table shows the selected null and alternative hypotheses and, in the last column, the P-value. The app also provides a plot of the standard normal sampling distribution to illustrate the position of the test statistic z and the resulting P-value.

▶ *Try Exercise 9.15*

You may think that because the sample proportion of those opposing fracking in Example 4 was equal to 47.1%, we should have used the one-sided alternative $H_a: p < 0.5$, i.e., that the proportion is less than 50%. This would have violated one of the fundamental principles of significance testing and scientific integrity: You need to decide on your hypotheses before looking at any data you plan to use for the test! Otherwise, your evidence and conclusions may appear much stronger than they actually are.

For instance, with the one-sided alternative $H_a: p < 0.5$, the P-value would be only 0.016, half as much as 0.032. Such a small P-value would signal stronger evidence to reject the null hypothesis $H_0: p = 0.5$ than there actually is when there is uncertainty on which side of 50% the true proportion falls. Because researchers often want to leave open where a population proportion may fall relative to p_0, two-sided tests are commonly used in practice.

Summing up, the P-value is the probability of values as extreme or more extreme than the observed test statistic value, computed under the assumption that the null hypothesis is true. What is "more extreme" and, hence, how the P-value is calculated depends on the alternative hypothesis. For a two-sided alternative, the P-value is the sum of the two tail probabilities, whereas for a one-sided hypothesis, the P-value is the probability in the corresponding tail. The following box summarizes the different scenarios.

SUMMARY: P-values for Different Alternative Hypotheses

Alternative Hypothesis	P-value
$H_a: p > p_0$	Right-tail probability
$H_a: p < p_0$	Left-tail probability
$H_a: p \neq p_0$	Two-tail probability

The Significance Level Tells Us How Strong the Evidence Must Be

Sometimes we need to make a decision about whether the data provide sufficient evidence to reject H_0. Before seeing the data, we decide how small the P-value would need to be to reject H_0. For example, we might decide that we will reject H_0 if the P-value is less than or equal to 0.05. The cutoff point of 0.05 is called the **significance level**. It is shown in Figure 9.5.

▲ **Figure 9.5** **The Decision in a Significance Test.** Reject H_0 if the P-value is less than or equal to a chosen **significance level**, usually 0.05.

Significance Level

The **significance level** is a number such that we reject H_0 if the P-value is less than or equal to that number. In practice, the most common significance level is 0.05.

Table 9.1 summarizes the two possible outcomes for a test decision when the significance level is 0.05. We either reject H_0 or do not reject H_0. If the P-value is larger than 0.05, the data do not contradict H_0 sufficiently for us to reject it. Then, H_0 is still plausible to us. If the P-value is ≤ 0.05, the data provide enough evidence to reject H_0. Recall that H_a had the burden of proof, and in this case we feel that the proof is sufficient.

When we reject H_0, we say the results of the test are **statistically significant**. In particular, for the two-sided alternative $H_a: p \neq p_0$, we say that the true proportion *differs significantly* from the hypothesized value p_0. For the one-sided alternatives, we say that the true proportion is either *significantly lower* (when $H_a: p < p_0$) or significantly higher (when $H_a: p > p_0$).

Table 9.1 Possible Decisions in a Test of Significance with Significance Level of 0.05

P-value	Decision About H_0
≤ 0.05	Reject H_0
> 0.05	Do not reject H_0

Caution

The word *significant* in statistics refers to the P-value of a test being below the significance level, but doesn't necessarily imply a significant result in the everyday meaning of the word (as in important or noteworthy). ◄

Statistical Significance

When the data provide sufficient evidence to reject H_0 and support H_a (i.e., when the P-value is less than the significance level), the results of the test are called **statistically significant**. Then, the value of the true parameter (i.e., a proportion or a mean) is said to be **significantly different** from the hypothesized null value.

As we will emphasize in Section 9.5, statistical significance doesn't necessarily mean that the true parameter value is very far from the hypothesized value, i.e., that the effect differs in a practical sense from what is hypothesized under the null. For instance, the small P-value of 0.032 (which is less than a significance level of 0.05) for testing $H_0: p = 0.5$ vs. $H_a: p \neq 0.5$ in Example 4 leads to the conclusion that the proportion of those opposing fracking is *significantly different* from 0.5, or 50%. Yet, the 95% confidence interval showed us that the true proportion may, in fact, be as large as 49.7%, very close to 50%.

Significance Levels ◄

Example 5

The Astrology Study

Picture the Scenario

Let's continue our analysis of the astrology study from Example 3. The parameter p is the probability that an astrologer picks the correct one of three personality charts, based on the horoscope and birth data provided. We tested $H_0: p = 1/3$ against $H_a: p > 1/3$ and got a P-value of 0.40.

Questions to Explore

What decision would we make for a significance level of (a) 0.05? (b) 0.50?

Think It Through

a. For a significance level of 0.05, the P-value of 0.40 is *not* less than 0.05. So we do not reject H_0. The evidence is not strong enough to conclude that the astrologers' predictions are significantly better than random guessing.

b. For a significance level of 0.50, the P-value of 0.40 *is* less than 0.50. So we reject H_0 in favor of H_a. We conclude that this result provides sufficient evidence to support the astrologers' claim that the probability of correctly identifying a personality chart is larger than 1/3. The results are statistically significant at the 0.50 significance level and the astrologers' predictions are significantly better than random guessing.

Insight

In practice, significance levels are typically close to 0, such as 0.05 or 0.01. The reason for selecting such small numbers is that the significance level is a type of error probability. We'll see in Section 9.4 that when H_0 is true, the significance level is the probability of making an error by rejecting H_0. We used the significance level of 0.50 in part b for illustrative purposes only. Such a significance level would never be used in practice when setting up a significance test.

► *Try Exercise 9.20*

In Practice   Report the P-value

Report the P-value rather than merely indicating whether the results are statistically significant. Learning the actual P-value is more informative than learning only whether the test is "statistically significant at the 0.05 level." The P-values of 0.001 and 0.049 are both statistically significant in this sense, but the first P-value provides much stronger evidence.

In Practice

The decision to reject a hypothesis based on the P-value falling below a certain cutoff should be one out of many criteria considered in an investigative statistical process that culminates in a decision or recommendation. Other important factors are how plausible the assumptions for the test are, the actual size of the effect, the probability and consequences of a wrong decision (see Section 9.4), or whether the experiment, analysis and results can be replicated and confirmed.

Now that we've studied all five steps of a significance test about a proportion, let's use them in a new example, much like those you'll see in the exercises. In this example and in the exercises, it may help you to refer to the following summary box.

SUMMARY: Steps of a Significance Test for a Population Proportion p

1. Assumptions

- Categorical variable, with population proportion p defined in context.
- Randomization, such as a simple random sample or a randomized experiment, for gathering data.
- n large enough to expect at least 15 successes and 15 failures under H_0 (that is $np_0 \geq 15$ and $n(1 - p_0) \geq 15$). This is mainly important for one-sided tests.

2. **Hypotheses**

Null: $H_0: p = p_0$, where p_0 is the hypothesized value.

Alternative: $H_a: p \neq p_0$ (two-sided) or $H_a: p < p_0$ (one-sided) or
$H_a: p > p_0$ (one-sided).

3. **Test Statistic**

$$z = \frac{\hat{p} - p_0}{se_0} \text{ with } se_0 = \sqrt{p_0(1 - p_0)/n}.$$

4. **P-value**

Alternative hypothesis	P-value	
$H_a: p > p_0$	Right-tail probability	
$H_a: p < p_0$	Left-tail probability	
$H_a: p \neq p_0$	Two-tail probability	

5. **Conclusion**

Smaller P-values give stronger evidence against H_0. If a decision is needed, reject H_0 if the P-value is less than or equal to the preselected significance level (such as 0.05). Relate the conclusion to the context of the study.

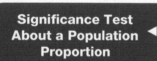

Significance Test About a Population Proportion ◄

Example 6

Cars Stopping for Pedestrians?

Picture the Scenario

In the city of Las Vegas, by law, cars are supposed to stop for pedestrians trying to cross their section of the street. In practice, many drivers do not stop. Is there evidence that fewer than 75% of drivers actually stop? To answer this hypothesis, we are going to use data collected by a team of researchers from the University of Nevada, Las Vegas, who conducted a trial by having a pedestrian wait at the curb of a midblock crosswalk and observe whether the next car approaching would stop.[2] In 76 of a total of 126 such trials, the first car approaching the crosswalk stopped, while in the other 50 trials, the first car approaching did not stop. These data were entered in the *Inference for a Proportion* app, with output shown in Figure 9.6.

Question to Explore

Conduct a significance test and write a conclusion, using a significance level of 5%.

Think It Through

The claim is that fewer than 75% of Las Vegas drivers will stop for pedestrians in the crossroad. The null and alternative hypotheses are $H_0: p = 0.75$ vs. $H_a: p < 0.75$, where p represents the proportion of drivers stopping for

---

[2]C. Coughenour, S. Clark, A. Singh et al., (2017), "*Examining racial bias as a potential factor in pedestrian crashes*." Accident Analysis & Prevention, Vol 98.

▶ **Figure 9.6** Significance Test About a Population Proportion. Screenshot from the *Inference for a Proportion* app. Results of a significance test of H_0: $p = 0.75$ vs. H_a: $p < 0.75$ for the proportion of cars stopping. The app shows the value of the test statistic and the resulting P-value in the last table, together with a graph of the normal distribution marking this P-value.

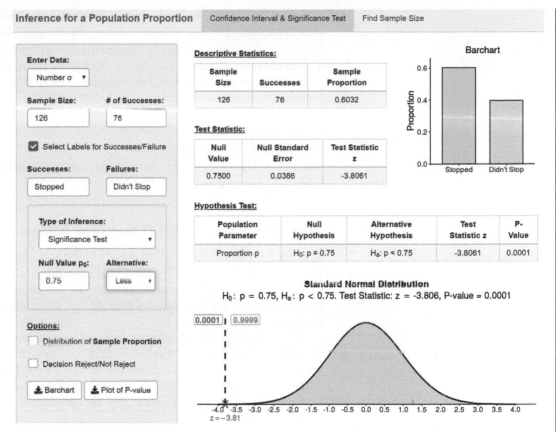

a pedestrian. The assumptions to carry out this test are a categorical response (here: whether driver stops) and data produced by randomization. If the 126 trials can be thought of as a random sample of experiences of pedestrians throughout Las Vegas, then the condition is met and the study results apply to all pedestrians. However, this study considered only two neighborhoods and two types of pedestrians (one white female and one black female) who were repeatedly waiting at the intersection, so conclusions about p are only valid for the experience of such types of pedestrians in these types of neighborhoods. The sample size condition is easily fulfilled, as we expect $126(0.75) = 94.5$ successes and $126(0.25) = 31.5$ failures, both larger than 15.

As the app shows (and you can verify), the test statistic for this null hypothesis equals $z = (0.60 - 0.75)/0.0386 = -3.81$, far out in the left tail of the sampling distribution. The resulting P-value equals 0.0001, computed from the lower left tail of the standard normal distribution (see the graph in the app). The P-value is less than any reasonable significance level (including 0.05), so the data provide sufficient evidence that significantly fewer than 75% of cars stop at crosswalks.

Insight

You can check with the app that the 95% confidence interval equals (0.52, 0.69). The larger question that the researchers tried to answer was whether the proportion of cars stopping differs between a white and a black female trying to cross an intersection. Such comparisons concerning two proportions are the topic of Chapter 10.

▶ **Try Exercise 9.16**

When the app calculates the (null) standard error for the test statistic, it substitutes the null hypothesis value p_0 for the population proportion p in the formula $\sqrt{p(1-p)/n}$ for the standard deviation of the sample proportion. This is correct because we compute the P-value *assuming that* H_0 *is true*, which says that $p = p_0$. However, this practice differs from the way confidence intervals are formed, where the sample proportion $\hat{p}$ is substituted for p (which is unknown) in the standard deviation formula. When we estimate a confidence interval, we do not have a hypothesized value for p, so that method uses the point estimate $\hat{p}$ for p.[3] To differentiate between the two cases, we use $se_0 = \sqrt{p_0(1-p_0)/n}$ for significance tests and $se = \sqrt{\hat{p}(1-\hat{p})/n}$ for confidence intervals.

"Do Not Reject H_0" Does Not Mean "Accept H_0"

A small P-value implies that the observed data would be unusual if H_0 were true. If the P-value is not small, such as 0.40 for the one-sided test in the astrology example, the null hypothesis is plausible. In this case, the conclusion is reported as not to reject H_0 because the data do not contradict H_0, or that there is not enough evidence to reject H_0.

"*Do not reject* H_0" *is not the same as saying* "*accept* H_0." The population proportion has many plausible values besides the number in the null hypothesis. For instance, we did not reject H_0: $p = 1/3$ in the astrology study, where p was the probability of a correct prediction by an astrologer. Thus, p may equal $1/3$, but other values are also plausible. In fact, a 95% confidence interval for p is

$$\hat{p} \pm 1.96\sqrt{\hat{p}(1-\hat{p})/n}, \text{ or } 0.345 \pm 1.96\sqrt{(0.345)(0.655)/116},$$

which equals (0.26, 0.43). Even though insufficient evidence exists to reject H_0, it is improper to accept it and conclude that $p = 1/3$. It is plausible that p is as low as 0.26 or as high as 0.43.

An analogy here is again that of a courtroom trial. The null hypothesis is that the defendant is innocent. The alternative hypothesis is that the defendant is guilty. If the jury acquits the defendant, this does not mean that it *accepts* the defendant's claim of innocence. It merely means that innocence is plausible because guilt has not been established *beyond a reasonable doubt*.

The null hypothesis contains a single possible value for the parameter. Saying "Do not reject H_0" instead of "Accept H_0" emphasizes that that value is merely one of many plausible ones. However, saying "Accept H_a" **is permissible** for the alternative hypothesis when that is the conclusion of the test. When the P-value is sufficiently small (no greater than the significance level), the entire range of plausible values is contained in the values specified in H_a.

Deciding Between a One-Sided or Two-Sided Test

In practice, two-sided tests are more common than one-sided tests. Even if we think we know the direction of an effect, two-sided tests can also detect an effect that falls in the opposite direction. For example, in a medical study, even if we think a drug will perform better than a placebo, using a two-sided alternative allows us to detect whether the drug is actually worse, perhaps because of bad side effects. However, as we saw with the astrology example, in some scenarios a one-sided test is natural.

---

[3]If we instead conduct the test by substituting the sample proportion in the standard deviation of the sample proportion, the standard normal approximation for the sampling distribution of the test statistic z is less precise.

Guidelines in Forming the Alternative Hypothesis

- In deciding between one-sided and two-sided alternative hypotheses in a particular exercise or in practice, *consider the context of the real problem.*

For instance, in the astrology experiment, to test whether someone can guess *better* than with random guessing, we used the values $p > 1/3$ in the alternative hypothesis corresponding to that possibility. An application in which we want to "test whether the population proportion *differs* from 0.50" suggests a two-sided alternative, $H_a: p \neq 0.50$, to allow for p to be larger or smaller than 0.50. "Test whether the population proportion is *larger* than 0.50" suggests the one-sided alternative, $H_a: p > 0.50$.

- In most research articles, significance tests use two-sided P-values.

Partly this reflects an objective approach to research that recognizes that an effect could go in either direction. Using an alternative hypothesis in which an effect can go in either direction is regarded as the most even-handed way to perform the test. In using two-sided P-values, researchers avoid the suspicion that they chose H_a when they saw the direction in which the data occurred. That is not ethical and would be cheating, as we'll discuss in Section 9.5.

- Confidence intervals are two-sided.

The practice of using a two-sided test coincides with the ordinary approach for confidence intervals, which are two-sided, obtained by adding and subtracting a margin of error from the point estimate. There is a way to construct one-sided confidence intervals, for instance, concluding that a population proportion is *at least* equal to 0.70. In practice, though, two-sided confidence intervals are much more common.

> **In Practice** Tests Are Usually Two-Sided
>
> Two-sided tests are more common than one-sided tests. Most examples and exercises in this book reflect the way tests are most often used and employ two-sided alternatives. *In practice, you should use a two-sided test unless you have a well-justified reason for a one-sided test.*

SUMMARY: Three Basic Facts When Specifying Hypotheses

- The null hypothesis has an equal sign (such as $H_0: p = 0.5$), but the alternative hypothesis does not.
- You shouldn't pick H_a based on looking at the data.
- The hypotheses always refer to population parameters, not sample statistics.

The last bullet point implies that you should *never* express a hypothesis by using sample statistic notation, such as $H_0: \hat{p} = 0.5$ (or $H_0: \bar{x} = 40$ in a test about a population mean). There is no need to conduct inference about statistics such as the sample proportion $\hat{p}$ (or the sample mean $\bar{x}$), because you can find their values exactly from the data.

The Binomial Test for Small Samples

The test about a proportion uses normal sampling distributions for the sample proportion $\hat{p}$ and the z test statistic. Therefore, it is a *large-sample* test because the sampling distribution is normal only for large samples. The guideline is that the expected numbers of successes and failures should be at least 15 when H_0 is true; that is, $np_0 \geq 15$ and $n(1 - p_0) \geq 15$.

In practice, the large-sample z test performs well for *two-sided* alternatives even for small samples. When p_0 is below 0.3 or above 0.7 and n is small, the sampling distribution is quite skewed. However, a tail probability that is smaller than the normal probability in one tail is compensated by a tail probability that is larger than the normal probability in the other tail. Because of this, the P-value from the two-sided test using the normal distribution approximates well a P-value from a small-sample test.

> **Recall**
>
> From Section 8.3, a method is **robust** with respect to a particular assumption if it works well even when that assumption is violated. ◄

For one-sided tests, when p_0 differs from 0.5, the large-sample test does not work well when the sample size guideline ($np_0 \geq 15$ and $n(1 - p_0) \geq 15$) is violated. In that case, you should use a small-sample test. This test uses the binomial distribution with parameter value p_0 to find the exact probability of the observed value and all the more extreme values, according to the direction in H_a. Since one-sided tests with small n are not common in practice, we will not study the binomial test here. Exercises 9.125 and 9.126 show how to carry it out.

9.2 Practicing the Basics

9.10 Psychic A person who claims to be psychic says he predicts the outcome of a flip of a fair coin more often right than wrong. If we want to test this claim, we could use the data from an experiment in which he predicts the outcome for n flips of the coin. State the parameter of interest and the hypotheses for a significance test for testing this claim, where the alternative hypothesis reflects the psychic's claim.

9.11 Dogs smelling An experiment used dogs trained in distinguishing healthy patients from patients with bladder cancer by smelling certain compounds in the patient's urine.[4] In each trial of the experiment, one urine sample from a bladder cancer patient was randomly placed among six control urine samples from healthy patients and the dog had to identify the one from the bladder cancer patient. Define the parameter and the null and alternative hypotheses of interest, letting one hypothesis reflect the possibility that dogs actually do better than just randomly guessing which sample is the one from the bladder cancer patient.

9.12 Get P-value from z For a test of H_0: $p = 0.50$, the z test statistic equals 1.04. Using the *Normal Distribution* app, other software, or a table,

a. Find the P-value for H_a: $p > 0.50$.

b. Find the P-value for H_a: $p \neq 0.50$.

c. Find the P-value for H_a: $p < 0.50$. (*Hint:* The P-values for the two possible one-sided tests must sum to 1.)

d. Do any of the P-values in part a, part b, or part c give strong evidence against H_0? Explain.

9.13 Get more P-values from z Refer to the previous exercise. Suppose $z = 2.50$ instead of 1.04.

a. Find the P-value for (i) H_a: $p > 0.50$, (ii) H_a: $p \neq 0.50$, and (iii) H_a: $p < 0.50$.

b. Do any of the P-values in part a provide strong evidence against H_0? Explain.

9.14 Find test statistic and P-value For a test of H_0: $p = 0.50$, the sample proportion is 0.35 based on a sample size of 100.

a. Show that the test statistic is $z = -3.0$.

b. Find the P-value for H_a: $p < 0.50$ using, e.g, the *Normal Distribution* app.

c. Does the P-value in part b give much evidence against H_0? Explain.

9.15 Opinion on fracking a year earlier The question about the opinion on fracking from the November 2014 survey mentioned in Example 4 was also included in an earlier survey in September 2013. Using this earlier survey, let's again focus on those who oppose fracking.

a. Define the parameter of interest and set up hypotheses to test that the proportion opposing fracking is different from 50%.

b. Of the 1,506 respondents in the 2013 survey, 740 indicated that they oppose fracking. Use the *Inference for a Proportion* app or other software to find the test statistic and interpret it.

c. Report and interpret the P-value. Indicate your decision, in the context of this survey, using a 0.05 significance level.

d. Check whether the sample size was large enough to conduct the inference in part c. Indicate what the assumptions are for your inferences to apply to the entire U.S. population.

9.16 Religion important in your life? Americans ages 18 to 29 are considered to be less religious than older Americans. According to recent studies by the Pew Forum on Religion & Public Life, fewer young adults are affiliated with a specific religion than older people today. And, compared with their elders, fewer young people say that religion is very important in their lives. Yet, many young people still believe in traditional religious concepts and practices. Pew Research Center surveys show, for example, that "young adults' beliefs about life after death and the existence of heaven, hell, and miracles closely resemble the beliefs of older people today." According to results of a random sample of 1,679 18- to 29-year-olds, 45% pray daily whereas 55% pray less often.[5] The screenshot from the *Inference for a Proportion* app on the next page shows the results after entering these data. State and interpret the five steps of a significance test in this context, using information shown in the output to provide the particular values for the hypotheses, test statistic, and P-value.

---

[4]Article by C. M. Willis et al., *British Medical Journal*, vol. 329, September 25, 2004.

[5]Accessed from pewforum.org/Age/Religion-Among-the-Millennials.aspx.

Descriptive Statistics:

Sample Size	Successes	Sample Proportion
1,679	756	0.4503

Test Statistic:

Null Value	Null Standard Error	Test Statistic z
0.5000	0.0122	-4.0756

Hypothesis Test:

Population Parameter	Null Hypothesis	Alternative Hypothesis	Test Statistic z	P-Value
Proportion p	H_0: p = 0.5	H_a: p ≠ 0.5	-4.0756	0.0000

9.17 **Another test of astrology**   Examples 1, 3, and 5 referred to a study about astrology. Another part of the study used the following experiment: Professional astrologers prepared horoscopes for 83 adults. Each adult was shown three horoscopes, one of which was the one an astrologer prepared for him or her and the other two were randomly chosen from ones prepared for other subjects in the study. Each adult had to guess which of the three was his or hers. Of the 83 subjects, 28 guessed correctly.

    a. Define the parameter of interest and set up the hypotheses to test that the probability of a correct prediction is 1/3 against the astrologers' claim that it exceeds 1/3.

    b. Show that the sample proportion = 0.337, the standard error of the sample proportion for the test is 0.052, and the test statistic is $z = 0.08$.

APP   **c.** Find the P-value. Would you conclude that people are more likely to select their horoscope than if they were randomly guessing, or are results consistent with random guessing?

9.18 **Dogs and cancer**   A study[6] investigated if dogs could be trained to detect whether a person has lung cancer or breast cancer by smelling the subject's breath. The researchers trained five ordinary household dogs to distinguish, by scent alone, exhaled breath samples of 55 lung and 31 breast cancer patients from those of 83 healthy controls. A dog gave a correct indication of a cancer sample by sitting in front of that sample when it was randomly placed among four control samples. Once trained, the dogs' ability to distinguish cancer patients from controls was tested using breath samples from subjects not previously encountered by the dogs. (The researchers blinded both dog handlers and experimental observers to the identity of breath samples.) Let p denote the probability a dog correctly detects a cancer sample placed among five samples when the other four are controls.

    a. Set up the null hypothesis that the dog's predictions correspond to random guessing.

    b. Set up the alternative hypothesis to test whether the probability of a correct selection *differs* from random guessing.

    c. Set up the alternative hypothesis to test whether the probability of a correct selection is *greater than* with random guessing.

    d. In one test with 83 Stage I lung cancer samples, the dogs correctly identified the cancer sample 81 times. The test statistic for the alternative hypothesis in part c was $z = 17.7$. Is the corresponding P-value larger than 0.1, in between 0.01 and 0.1, or less than 0.01? What about the probability of obtaining a sample proportion of 81 or more successes out of 83 trials when the null hypothesis is true? Is this probability larger than 0.1, in between 0.01 and 0.01, or less than 0.01?

9.19 **Testing a headache remedy**   Studies that compare treatments for chronic medical conditions such as headaches can use the same subjects for each treatment. This type of study is commonly referred to as a crossover design. With a crossover design, each person crosses over from using one treatment to another during the study. One such study considered a drug (a pill called Sumatriptan) for treating migraine headaches in a convenience sample of children.[7] The study observed each of 30 children at two times when he or she had a migraine headache. The child received the drug at one time and a placebo at the other time. The order of treatment was randomized and the study was double-blind. For each child, the response was whether the drug or the placebo provided better pain relief. Let p denote the proportion of children having better pain relief with the drug in the population of children who suffer periodically from migraine headaches. Can you conclude that p is different from 0.5, that is, either more or less than half of the population is getting better pain relief with the drug? Of the 30 children, 22 had more pain relief with the drug and 8 had more pain relief with the placebo.

    a. For testing H_0: $p = 0.50$ against H_a: $p \neq 0.50$, show that the test statistic $z = 2.56$.

APP   **b.** Show that the P-value is 0.01. Interpret.

    c. Check the assumptions needed for this test and discuss the limitations due to using a convenience sample rather than a random sample.

9.20 **Gender bias in selecting managers**   For a large supermarket chain in Florida, a women's group claimed that female employees were passed over for management training in favor of their male colleagues. The company denied this claim, saying it picked the employees from the eligible pool at random to receive this training. Statewide, the large pool of more than 1,000 eligible employees who can be tapped for management training is 40% female and 60% male. Since this program began, 28 of the 40 employees chosen for management training were male and 12 were female.

    a. The company claims that it selected employees for training according to their proportion in the pool of eligible employees. Define a parameter of interest and state this claim as a hypothesis. Explain why this hypothesis is a no-effect hypothesis.

---

[6]M. McCulloch et al., (2006), *Integrative Cancer Therapies*, vol. 5, p. 30.

[7]Data based on those in a study by M. L. Hamalainen et al., (1997), reported in *Neurology*, vol. 48, pp. 1100–1103.

b. State the null and alternative hypotheses for a test to investigate the strength of evidence to support the women's claim of gender bias. (*Hint:* Gender bias means that either males or females are disproportionately selected.)

c. The screenshot shows results from the *Inference for a Proportion* app after entering the data. Explain why the large-sample analysis is justified, and show how the test statistic value was obtained.

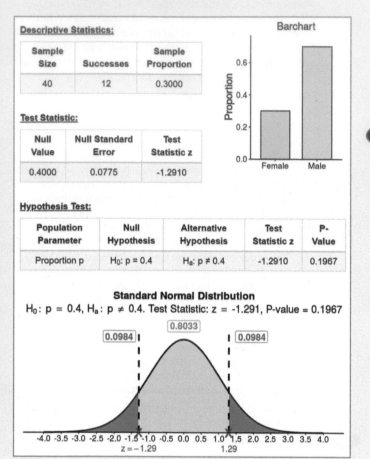

d. To what alternative hypothesis does the P-value given in the app refer? Use it to find the P-value for the significance test you specified in part b and interpret it.

e. What decision would you make for a 0.05 significance level? Interpret.

9.21 Gender discrimination Refer to the previous exercise. The 95% confidence interval for the probability of a woman to be selected for management training equals (0.16, 0.44). Interpret this interval. Is this in accordance with our decision of the significance test from part e of the previous exercise? Explain.

9.22 Garlic to repel ticks A study (*J. Amer. Med. Assoc.*, vol. 284, p. 831, 2000) considered whether daily consumption of 1,200 mg of garlic could reduce tick bites. The study used a crossover design with a sample of Swedish military conscripts, half of whom used placebo first and garlic

second and half the reverse. The authors did not present the data, but the effect they described is consistent with garlic being more effective with 37 subjects and placebo being more effective with 29 subjects. Does this suggest a real difference between garlic and placebo, or are the results consistent with random variation? Answer by:

a. Identifying the relevant variable and parameter. (*Hint:* The variable is categorical with two categories. The parameter is a population proportion for one of the categories.)

b. Stating hypotheses for a large-sample two-sided test and checking that sample size guidelines are satisfied for that test.

c. Finding the test statistic value.

d. Finding and interpreting a P-value and stating the conclusion in context.

9.23 Exit-poll predictions According to an exit poll of the 2010 California gubernatorial election (see Chapter 7), 53.1% of the 3,889 voters sampled reported voting for Brown. Is this enough evidence to predict who won? Test that the population proportion who voted for Brown was 0.50 against the alternative that it differed from 0.50. Answer by:

a. Identifying the variable and parameter of interest and defining notation.

b. Stating hypotheses and checking assumptions for a large-sample test.

c. Reporting the test statistic and P-value, interpreting the latter.

d. Explaining how to make a decision for the significance level of 0.05. Is the proportion voting for Brown significantly different from 50%?

9.24 Which cola? The 49 students in a class at the University of Florida made blinded evaluations of pairs of cola drinks. For the 49 comparisons of Coke and Pepsi, Coke was preferred 29 times. In the population that this sample represents, is this strong evidence that the proportion preferring one of the drinks is different from 50%? Refer to the following screenshot from the *Inference for a Proportion* app.

Hypothesis Test:

Population Parameter	Null Hypothesis	Alternative Hypothesis	Test Statistic z	P-Value
Proportion p	H_0: p = 0.5	H_a: p ≠ 0.5	1.2857	0.1985

a. The sample proportion falls how many standard errors from the value of *p* under the null hypothesis?

b. Explain how to get the P-value. Interpret it.

c. Based on the result in part b, does it make sense to accept H_0? Explain.

d. What does the 95% confidence interval of (0.45, 0.73) for the proportion preferring Coke (which you can get using the same app) tell you that the test does not?

9.25 **How to sell a burger** A fast-food chain wants to compare two ways of promoting a new burger (a turkey burger). One way uses a coupon available in the store. The other way uses a poster display outside the store. Before the promotion, its marketing research group matches 50 pairs of stores. Each pair has two stores with similar sales volume and customer demographics. The store in a pair that uses coupons is randomly chosen, and after a month-long promotion, the increases in sales of the turkey burger are compared for the two stores. The increase was higher for 28 stores using coupons and higher for 22 stores using the poster. Is this strong evidence to support the coupon approach, or could this outcome be explained by chance? Answer by performing all five steps of a two-sided significance test about the population proportion of times the sales would be higher with the coupon promotion.

9.26 **Significantly different?** For the test of $H_0: p = 0.5$ versus $H_a: p \neq 0.5$ in Exercise 9.16, the P-value is less than 0.0001. Such a P-value provides extremely strong evidence that the true proportion is different from 0.5. But how different is it from 0.5? Use the *Inference for a Proportion* app or other software to find a 95% confidence interval for the proportion p of 18- to 29-year-olds who pray daily. Interpret the interval. Is the proportion different from 50% in a practical sense?

9.27 **Evidence in favor of H_0?** The P-value for the two-sided test $H_0: p = 0.4$ vs. $H_a: p \neq 0.4$ in Exercise 9.20 about gender discrimination equals 0.20, where p is the proportion of female managers selected for management training. TRUE or FALSE: This large P-value implies that the true proportion of females tapped for management training is equal to 0.4. Explain your answer.

9.3 Significance Test About a Mean

For quantitative variables, significance tests often refer to the population mean μ. We illustrate the significance test about means with the following example.

Example 7

Significance Test About a Population Mean ◀

The 40-Hour Work Week

Picture the Scenario

Since the Fair Labor Standards Act was passed in 1938, the standard work week in the United States has been 40 hours. In recent years, the standard work week has fallen to less than 40 hours in most of Western Europe and in Australia. But many believe that the work-oriented culture in the United States has resulted in pressure among workers to put in longer hours than the 40-hour standard. In industries such as investment banking, a 40-hour work week is considered slacker behavior and may result in losing a job. Because the mean number of working hours may differ between males and females (perhaps due to females working more part-time jobs), here we will analyze a sample of working hours for males. Exercise 9.32 conducts a similar analysis for a sample of females.

Question to Explore

How could we frame a study of working hours using a significance test that can detect whether the mean work week for the male U.S. working population equals 40 hours or differs from 40 hours? State the null and alternative hypotheses for such a test.

Think It Through

The response variable, length of work week, is quantitative. Hypotheses refer to the mean work week μ for the male U.S. working population, whether it is 40 hours or differs from 40 hours. To use a significance test to analyze the strength of evidence about this question, we'll test

$$H_0: \mu = 40 \text{ against } H_a: \mu \neq 40.$$

Insight

For those who were working in 2012, the General Social Survey asked, "How many hours did you work last week?" For the 583 men included in the survey, the mean was 43.5 hours with a standard deviation of 15.3 hours. (For comparison, for the 583 females included in the survey, the mean was 37.0 hours, with a standard deviation of 15.1 hours.) The next subsection explains the five steps of a significance test about a population mean μ, such as $H_0: \mu = 40$ against $H_a: \mu \neq 40$, where μ is the mean number of hours men work per week. We'll analyze whether the difference between the sample mean work week and the historical standard of 40 hours can be explained by random variability. In Chapter 10, we will learn how to compare males and females directly in terms of the difference in the mean duration of the work week. The data for the example are available on the book's website.

▶ *Try Exercise 9.32, parts a and b*

Steps of a Significance Test About a Population Mean

A significance test about a mean has the same five steps as a test about a proportion: Assumptions, hypotheses, test statistic, P-value, and conclusion. We will mention modifications as they relate to the test for a mean. However, the reasoning is the same as that for the significance test for a proportion.

Five Steps for a Significance Test About a Population Mean

Step 1: Assumptions
The three basic assumptions of a test about a mean are as follows:

- The variable is quantitative.
- The data are obtained using randomization (such as a random sample or a randomized experiment).
- The *population distribution* is approximately normal. This assumption is most crucial when n is small and H_a is one-sided, as discussed later in the section.

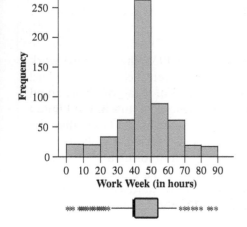

For our study about the length of the work week, the variable is the number of hours worked in the past week, which is quantitative. The GSS used random sampling. The figure in the margin shows a histogram and box plot for the data collected on the males. The histogram reveals a shape that is much more peaked than a normal distribution and a bit skewed to the right. (From the box plot, we see that the median equals the 1st quartile.) There are also many outliers on either side, but none that are dramatically removed from the rest of the observations. All in all, the histogram reveals that the population distribution may be decidedly different from normal but not in a dramatic way. As we will discuss, the sample size is large enough here ($n = 583$) so that meeting the assumption for the normality of the population distribution is not crucial.

Step 2: Hypotheses
The null hypothesis in a test about a population mean has the form

$$H_0: \mu = \mu_0,$$

where μ_0 denotes a particular value for the population mean. The two-sided alternative hypothesis

$$H_a: \mu \neq \mu_0$$

includes values both below and above the number μ_0 specified in H_0. Also possible are the one-sided alternative hypotheses,

$$H_a: \mu > \mu_0 \text{ or } H_a: \mu < \mu_0.$$

For instance, let μ denote the mean work week for the U.S. male working population. If the mean equals the historical standard, then $\mu = 40$. If today's working pressures have forced this above 40, then $\mu > 40$. To test that the population mean equals the historical standard against the alternative that it is greater than that, we would test $H_0: \mu = 40$ against $H_a: \mu > 40$. In practice, the two-sided alternative $H_a: \mu \neq 40$ is more common and lets us take an objective approach that can detect whether the mean is larger or smaller than the historical standard.

Step 3: Test Statistic

The test statistic is the distance between the sample mean $\bar{x}$ and the null hypothesis value μ_0, as measured by the number of standard errors between them. This is measured by

$$\frac{(\bar{x} - \mu_0)}{se} = \frac{\text{sample mean} - \text{null hypothesis mean}}{\text{standard error of sample mean}}.$$

Similar to forming a confidence interval for a mean (see the note in the margin), the standard error is $se = s/\sqrt{n}$. The test statistic is

$$t = \frac{(\bar{x} - \mu_0)}{se} = \frac{(\bar{x} - \mu_0)}{s/\sqrt{n}}.$$

Using the GSS data on the length of the work week, the sample mean for men was $\bar{x} = 43.5$ and the sample standard deviation $s = 15.3$. The standard error $se = s/\sqrt{n} = 15.3/\sqrt{583} = 0.636$. The test statistic equals

$$t = (\bar{x} - \mu_0)/se = (43.5 - 40)/0.636 = 5.54.$$

We use the symbol t rather than z for the test statistic because, as in forming a confidence interval, using s to estimate σ introduces additional error: The t sampling distribution has more variability than the standard normal. When H_0 is true, the t test statistic has approximately the t *distribution*. The t distribution is specified by its degrees of freedom, which equal $n-1$ for inference about a mean. This test statistic is called a *t statistic*.

Figure 9.7 shows the t sampling distribution. The farther $\bar{x}$ falls from the null hypothesis mean μ_0, the farther out in a tail the t test statistic falls, and the stronger the evidence is against H_0.

Recall

From Section 7.2, the standard deviation of the sample mean is $\sigma/\sqrt{n}$, where σ = population standard deviation. In practice, σ is unknown, so from Section 8.3 we estimate the standard deviation by the standard error

$$se = s/\sqrt{n},$$

where s is the sample standard deviation. ◄

Recall

You can review the ***t* distribution** in Section 8.3. ◄

Caution

Do not confuse the t statistic with the t score, which is a certain (e.g., 97.5th) percentile of the t distribution and was used to construct the confidence interval for μ. ◄

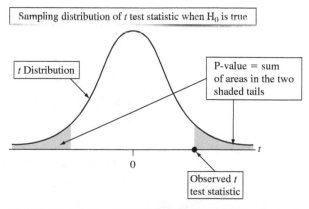

▲ **Figure 9.7** **The *t* Distribution of the *t* Test Statistic.** The t distribution looks like the standard normal but has more variability, i.e., fatter tails. The precise shape depends on the *df*. There is stronger evidence against H_0 when the t test statistic falls farther out in a tail. The P-value for a two-sided H_a is a two-tail probability as indicated in the figure. **Question** Why is it that t-scores farther out in the tails provide stronger evidence against H_0?

Step 4: P-value

The P-value is a single tail or a two-tail probability, depending on whether the alternative hypothesis is one-sided or two-sided.

Alternative Hypothesis	P-value
$H_a: \mu \neq \mu_0$	Two-tail probability from t distribution
$H_a: \mu > \mu_0$	Right-tail probability from t distribution
$H_a: \mu < \mu_0$	Left-tail probability from t distribution

For the length of work week study for men with $H_a: \mu \neq 40$, the P-value is the two-tail probability of a test statistic value farther out in either tail than the observed value of 5.54. This probability is double the single-tail probability.

Figure 9.8 shows a screenshot from the *Inference for a Mean* app, which has the data on the work week preloaded. (You can also provide your own data in a variety of forms.) The first table in the screenshot shows the sample mean and standard deviation, and the second table shows the user-supplied null value μ_0, the standard error of the mean *se* and the *t* test statistic *t*. The third table shows the null and alternative hypotheses, the *t* test statistic again and, in the last column, the P-value. The app also illustrates the P-value in a graph of the *t* distribution.

For this example, the P-value is very small, less than 0.001. It is the two-tailed probability below -5.54 and above 5.54 computed from a *t* distribution with $df = n - 1 = 583 - 1 = 582$. If the null hypothesis that the population mean equals 40 hours is true, the probability of observing a test statistic as or more extreme than the observed one of 5.54 is less than 0.001.

▶ **Figure 9.8** Information for a Significance Test About a Mean. Screenshot from the *Inference for a Mean* app for the work week data. The app shows results from a significance test of $H_0: \mu = 40$ vs. $H_a: \mu \neq 40$ about a population mean μ, including the sample mean and standard deviation, the standard error of the mean, the *t* test statistic and the resulting P-value. The app also shows the *t* sampling distribution, marking the observed test static and the P-value on it.

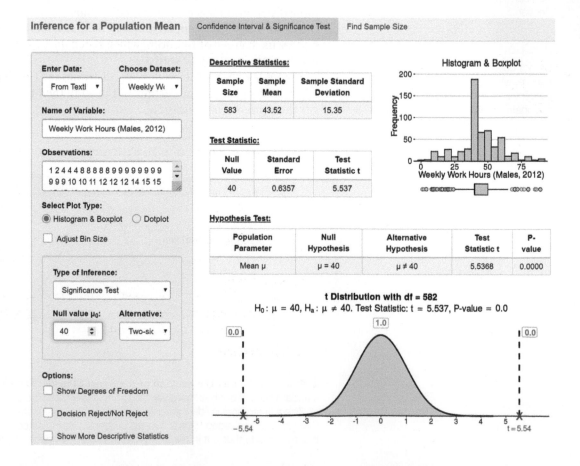

Step 5: Conclusion

The conclusion of a significance test reports the P-value and *interprets* what it says about the question that motivated the test. Sometimes this includes a decision about the validity of H_0. We reject the null hypothesis when the P-value is less than or equal to the preselected significance level. In this study, the P-value of less than 0.001 provides strong evidence against the null hypothesis. If we had preselected a significance level of 0.05, this would be enough evidence to reject H_0: $\mu = 40$ in favor of H_a: $\mu \neq 40$. We conclude that the population mean work week for men is significantly different from 40 hours.

The *Inference for a Mean* app also provides a 95% confidence interval for μ of (42.3, 44.8). This shows the plausible values for the population mean length of the work week for working men. From this interval of values, we can infer that the population mean of 40 is not a plausible value for the mean number of hours in a work week for men, in accordance with the results of the significance test. From the confidence interval, men, on average, work between 2.3 and 4.8 hours more per week than the standard 40 hours.

The *t* Statistic and *z* Statistic Have the Same Form

As you read the examples in this section, notice the parallel between each step of the test for a mean and the test for a proportion. For instance, the *t* test statistic for a mean has the same form as the *z* test statistic for a proportion, namely,

---

Form of Test Statistic

$$z \text{ or } t \text{ test statistic} = \frac{\text{Estimate of parameter} - \text{Value of parameter under } H_0}{\text{Standard error of estimate}}$$

For the test about a mean, the estimate $\bar{x}$ of the population mean μ replaces the estimate $\hat{p}$ of the population proportion p, the H_0 mean μ_0 replaces the H_0 proportion p_0, and the standard error of the sample mean replaces the standard error of the sample proportion.

SUMMARY: Steps of a Significance Test for a Population Mean μ

1. **Assumptions**

   - Quantitative variable, with population mean μ defined in context.
   - Data are obtained using randomization, such as a simple random sample or a randomized experiment.
   - Population distribution is approximately normal (mainly needed for one-sided tests with small n).

2. **Hypotheses**

   Null: H_0: $\mu = \mu_0$, where μ_0 is the hypothesized value (such as H_0: $\mu = 40$).
   Alternative: H_a: $\mu \neq \mu_0$ (two-sided) or H_a: $\mu < \mu_0$ (one-sided) or
   H_a: $\mu > \mu_0$ (one-sided).

3. **Test Statistic**

$$t = \frac{(\bar{x} - \mu_0)}{se}, \text{ where } se = s/\sqrt{n}.$$

4. P-value Use t distribution with $df = n - 1$.

Alternative Hypothesis	P-value
$H_a: \mu \neq \mu_0$	Two-tail probability
$H_a: \mu > \mu_0$	Right-tail probability
$H_a: \mu < \mu_0$	Left-tail probability

5. Conclusion

Smaller P-values give stronger evidence against H_0 and supporting H_a. If using a significance level to make a decision, reject H_0 if P-value is less than or equal to the significance level (such as 0.05). Relate the conclusion to the context of the study.

Performing a One-Sided Test About a Population Mean

One-sided alternative hypotheses apply for a prediction that μ differs from the null hypothesis value in a certain direction. For example, $H_a: \mu > 0$ predicts that the true mean is *larger* than the null hypothesis value of 0. Its P-value is the probability of a t value *larger* than the observed value, that is, in the *right* tail of the t distribution. Likewise, for $H_a: \mu < 0$ the P-value is the *left*-tail probability. In each case, again, $df = n - 1$.

Example 8

One-Sided Significance Test About a Mean ◄

Weight Change in Anorexic Girls

Picture the Scenario

A study compared different psychological therapies for teenage girls suffering from anorexia, an eating disorder that causes them to become dangerously underweight.[8] Each girl's weight was measured before and after a period of therapy. The variable of interest was the weight change, defined as weight at the end of the study minus weight at the beginning of the study. The weight change was positive if the girl gained weight and negative if she lost weight.

In this study, 29 girls received cognitive behavioral therapy. This form of psychotherapy stresses identifying the thinking that causes the undesirable behavior and replacing it with thoughts designed to help improve this behavior. Figure 9.9 shows a screenshot from the *Inference for a Mean* app, which has these data preloaded. You can see the values for the 29 observations in the box titled "Observations," below the variable name. The weight changes for the 29 girls had a sample mean of $\bar{x} = 3.00$ pounds and standard deviation of $s = 7.32$ pounds.

Question to Explore

Conduct a significance test for finding the strength of evidence supporting the effectiveness of the cognitive behavioral therapy, that is, determine whether the therapy results in a positive mean weight change.

---

[8]The data are courtesy of Prof. Brian Everitt, Institute of Psychiatry, London.

▶ **Figure 9.9** One-Sided Significance Test About a Mean. Screenshot from the *Inference for a Mean* app. The app shows all relevant information from a one-sided significance test of H_0: $\mu = 0$ against H_a: $\mu > 0$, based on the weight change in 29 anorexic girls. **Question** Why are large positive, rather than large negative, t test statistic values the ones that support H_a: $\mu > 0$?

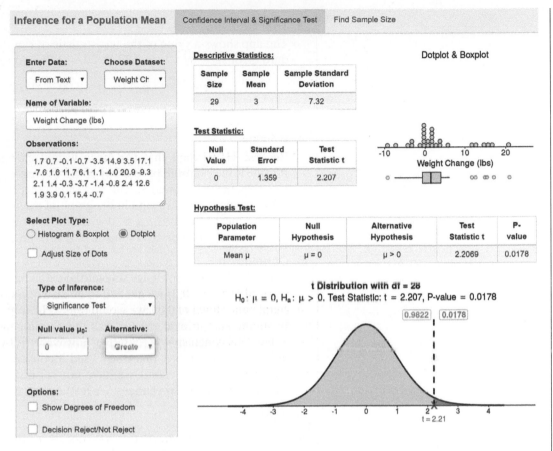

Think It Through

1. Assumptions

The response variable, weight change, is quantitative. A significance test about the population mean weight change assumes that the population distribution of weight change is approximately normal. The dot plot shows a distribution that could be bell-shaped, but the box plot reveals many outliers, especially at the higher end, so the population distribution is more likely right-skewed. However, the sample size of 29 is typically large enough for the sampling distribution of the sample mean to be approximately normal, as long as the population distribution isn't too skewed. In that regard, the assumption about an approximately normal population distribution is less crucial. We will come back to this issue later in the section.

The test also assumes randomization for how the data were obtained. However, this sample of 29 girls was a convenience sample. As a result, inferences drawn from it are tentative. They are more convincing if researchers can argue that the girls in the sample are representative of the population of girls who suffer from anorexia. The study did employ randomization in assigning girls to one of three therapies, only one of which (cognitive behavioral) is considered in this example.

2. Hypotheses

Hypotheses refer to the population mean weight change μ, namely whether it is 0 (the no effect value) or positive. To use a significance test to analyze the strength of evidence about the therapy's effect, we test H_0: $\mu = 0$ against H_a: $\mu > 0$. (In the app, enter 0 for the null value μ_0 and select Greater as the alternative.)

3. Test Statistic

The app shows a value of the test statistic of $t = 2.21$. To check, the standard error $se = s/\sqrt{n} = 7.32/\sqrt{29} = 1.36$ and the test statistic equals

$$t = (\bar{x} - \mu_0)/se = (3.00 - 0)/1.36 = 2.21,$$

with $df = n - 1 = 28$.

4. P-value

Because H_a predicts that the mean weight change is *larger* than 0, the P-value is the right-tail probability *above* the test statistic value of 2.21. This is 0.0178, or 0.018 rounded. The app shows this P-value, both in the table titled "Hypothesis Test" and in the graph of the t-distribution. The P-value of 0.018 means that if H_0: $\mu = 0$ were true, it would be unusual (i.e., only a 1.8% chance) to observe a t statistic of 2.21 or an even larger value.

5. Conclusion

A P-value of 0.018 provides substantial evidence against H_0: $\mu = 0$ and in favor of H_a: $\mu > 0$. If we needed to make a decision and had preselected a significance level of 0.05, we would reject H_0: $\mu = 0$ in favor of H_a: $\mu > 0$. In summary, anorexic girls on this therapy appear to gain weight, on average. This conclusion is tentative, however, for two reasons. First, as with many medical studies, this study used a convenience sample rather than a random sample. Second, we have not yet investigated the shape of the distribution of weight changes. We'll study this issue later in the section.

Insight

We used a one-sided alternative hypothesis in this test to detect a positive effect of the therapy. In practice, the two-sided alternative H_a: $\mu \neq 0$ is more common and lets us take an objective approach that can detect either a positive or a negative effect. For H_a: $\mu \neq 0$, the P-value is the two-tail probability, so the P-value = $2(0.018) = 0.036$. This two-sided test also provides relatively strong evidence against the no effect null hypothesis.

▶ *Try Exercise 9.31*

Null Hypothesis H_0: $\mu \leq \mu_0$

In Example 8, when we reject H_0: $\mu = 0$ in favor of H_a: $\mu > 0$, we can also reject the broader null hypothesis of H_0: $\mu \leq 0$. In other words, once we conclude that $\mu = 0$ is not plausible and there is strong evidence for $\mu > 0$, we automatically know that any $\mu < 0$ is also not plausible. This is why sometimes you see a one-sided significance test hypothesis written as H_0: $\mu \leq 0$ against H_a: $\mu > 0$ (or, equivalently, for proportions H_0: $p \leq p_0$ against H_a: $p > p_0$). However, in computing the test statistic, we use the single number $\mu = 0$ because it presents the most extreme case. If we can reject the null hypothesis in favor of H_a: $\mu > 0$ when $\mu = 0$, we can reject it for any μ less than 0.

Results of Two-Sided Tests and Results of Confidence Intervals Agree

For the anorexia study, we get a P-value of 0.036 when considering the two-sided test H_0: $\mu = 0$ against H_a: $\mu \neq 0$ for the mean weight change with the cognitive behavioral therapy. At a 0.05 significance level, we would reject H_0. A 95% confidence interval for the population mean weight change μ is $\bar{x} \pm t_{.025}(se)$, which is $3.0 \pm 2.048(1.36)$, or $(0.2, 5.8)$ pounds. (In the *Inference for a Mean* app, simply select Confidence Interval instead of Significance Test under Type of Inference to see this.) The confidence interval shows just how different from 0 the population mean weight change is likely to be. It is estimated to fall between 0.2 and 5.8 pounds. We infer that the population mean weight change μ is positive because all the numbers in this interval are greater than 0.

Both the significance test and the confidence interval suggested that μ differs from 0. In fact, conclusions about means using two-sided significance tests are consistent with conclusions using confidence intervals. If the conclusion of a two-sided test is to reject the null hypothesis that $\mu = 0$, then 0 is not in the corresponding confidence interval for μ.

By contrast, suppose that the P-value is larger than 0.05 in a two-sided test of $H_0: \mu = 0$, so we cannot reject H_0 at the 0.05 significance level. Then, a 95% confidence interval for μ will contain 0. Both methods will show that the value of 0 is a plausible one for μ. Figure 9.10 illustrates why decisions from two-sided tests about means are consistent with confidence intervals.

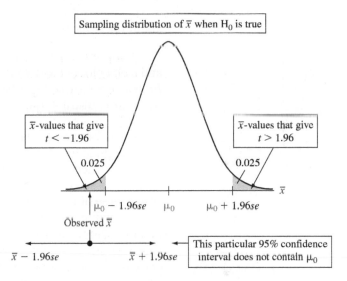

▲ **Figure 9.10 Relation Between Confidence Interval and Significance Test.** With large samples, if the sample mean $\bar{x}$ falls more than 1.96 standard errors from the null value μ_0, then μ_0 does not fall in the 95% confidence interval. Also, the t test statistic in such a case is larger than 1.96 in absolute value and the null hypothesis $H_0: \mu = \mu_0$ is rejected in a test at the 0.05 significance level. **Question** Inference about proportions does not have an *exact* equivalence between confidence intervals and tests. Why? (*Hint:* Are the same standard error values used in the two methods?)

Recall

When introducing the t distribution in Section 8.3, we mentioned that for large n (and hence large df), the t-score $t_{.025}$ is roughly equal to the z score of 1.96. ◄

With large samples, the t-score for a 95% confidence interval is 1.96, so the confidence interval is $\bar{x} \pm 1.96(se)$. If this interval does not contain a particular value μ_0, then the sample mean $\bar{x}$ falls more than 1.96 standard errors from μ_0, which means that the test statistic $t = (\bar{x} - \mu_0)/se$ is larger than 1.96 in absolute value. Consequently, the two-tail P-value is less than 0.05, so we would also reject the hypothesis that $\mu = \mu_0$. Note that this argument is not specific to large samples; we could have used any other t-score $t_{.025}$ for a certain number of df instead of 1.96.

When the Population Does Not Satisfy the Normality Assumption

Recall

From Section 7.2, with random sampling the **sampling distribution of the sample mean is approximately normal** for large n, by the Central Limit Theorem. ◄

For the test about a mean, the third assumption states that the population distribution should be approximately normal. This ensures that the sampling distribution of the sample mean $\bar{x}$ is approximately normal and, after using s to estimate σ, the test statistic has the t distribution. For large samples (roughly about 30 or higher), meeting this assumption is usually not crucial. Then, an approximate normal sampling distribution occurs for $\bar{x}$ regardless of the population distribution. (Remember the Central Limit Theorem? See the Recall box in the margin.)

> **In Practice** Two-Sided Inferences Are Robust
>
> Two-sided inferences using the *t* distribution are *robust* against violations of the normal population assumption. They still usually work well if the actual population distribution is not normal. However, the test may not work well for a one-sided hypothesis with small *n* and a population distribution that is highly skewed.

What do we mean by "may not work well"? For 95% confidence intervals, we said in Chapter 8 that when assumptions are grossly violated, we make incorrect inference (such as the confidence interval not containing the population mean μ) in much more than only 5% of the cases. Similarly, for significance tests, a violation of the assumptions may result in the actual sampling distribution being quite different from the *t* distribution. Then, the actual tail probabilities may be larger or smaller than the reported P-value, potentially leading to wrong conclusions about rejecting the null hypothesis.

Checking for Normality in the Anorexia Study Figure 9.11 shows a histogram and a box plot of the data from the anorexia study, which you can obtain from the *Inference for a Mean* app. With small *n*, such plots are very rough estimates of the population distribution. It can be difficult to determine whether the population distribution is approximately normal. Figure 9.11 and the dot plot in Figure 9.9 suggest some skew to the right, with a small proportion of girls having considerable weight gains.

A two-sided *t* test still works quite well even if the population distribution is skewed. So, we feel comfortable with the two-sided test summarized in the Insight step of Example 8. However, this plot makes us a bit cautious about using a one-sided test for these data. The histogram does suggest a right skew, and the box plot shows several outliers on the higher end. Just like for confidence intervals, you need to be cautious about any conclusions drawn in the presence of extreme outliers. For example, check if the P-value changes substantially when some or all of these outliers are removed. (See Exercise 9.41 on how the P-value changes when removing the largest outlier for the anorexia data.)

Regardless of Robustness, Look at the Data Whether *n* is small or large, you should look at the data to check for severe skew or for outliers that occur primarily in one direction. They could cause the sample mean to be a misleading measure. For the anorexia data, the median weight change is 1.4 pounds, less than the mean of 3.0 because of the skew to the right. Even though the significance test indicated that the population mean weight change was positive, the sample median is another indication that the size of the effect could be small. In fact, the 95% bootstrap percentile confidence interval for the median that we introduced in Section 8.4 equals (−0.3, 2.4) and includes the value of 0, suggesting that the median weight change might be slightly negative, positive, or 0.

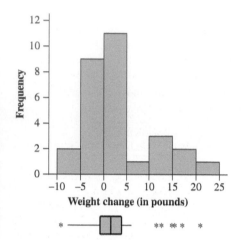

▲ **Figure 9.11** Histogram and Box Plot of Weight Change for Anorexia Sufferers. Question What do these plots suggest about the shape of the population distribution of weight change?

9.3 Practicing the Basics

9.28 **Which *t* has P-value = 0.05?** A *t* test for a mean uses a sample of 15 observations. Using the *t* Distribution app or other software, find the *t* test statistic value that has a P-value of 0.05 when the alternative hypothesis is (a) $H_a: \mu \neq 0$, (b) $H_a: \mu > 0$, and (c) $H_a: \mu < 0$.

9.29 **Practice mechanics of a *t* test** A study has a random sample of 20 subjects. The test statistic for testing $H_0: \mu = 100$ is $t = 2.40$. Using the *t* Distribution app or other software, find the approximate P-value for the alternative, (a) $H_a: \mu \neq 100$, (b) $H_a: \mu > 100$, and (c) $H_a: \mu < 100$.

9.30   Effect of n   Refer to the previous exercise. If the same sample mean and standard deviation had been based on $n = 5$ instead of $n = 20$, the test statistic would have been $t = 1.20$. Would the P-value for H_a: $\mu \neq 100$ be larger, or smaller, than when $t = 2.40$? Why?

9.31   Low carbohydrate diet   In a recent study,[9] 272 moderately obese subjects were randomly assigned to one of three diets: low-fat, restricted-calorie; Mediterranean, restricted-calorie; or low-carbohydrate, nonrestricted-calorie. The prediction was that subjects on a low-carbohydrate diet would lose weight, on the average. After two years, the mean change was -5.5 kg for the 109 subjects in the low-carbohydrate group with a standard deviation of 7.0 kg. The sample size, sample mean, and sample standard deviation (which is all the information needed for the t test) were entered in the *Inference for a Mean* app by selecting the option Summary Statistics under the Enter Data menu. The screenshot from this app below shows results of a significance test for testing H_0: $\mu = 0$ against H_a: $\mu \neq 0$, where μ is the population mean weight change. Note that weight change is determined by calculating after weight — before weight.

Hypothesis Test:

Population Parameter	Null Hypothesis	Alternative Hypothesis	Test Statistic t	P-value
Mean μ	$\mu = 0$	$\mu \neq 0$	-8.2031	0.0000

t Distribution with df = 108

H_0: $\mu = 0$, H_a: $\mu \neq 0$. Test Statistic: t = -8.203, P-value = 0.0

a. Find the standard error for the sample mean
b. Confirm the value shown for the t test statistic.
c. Find and interpret the P-value
d. Write a conclusion for the test when using a significance level of 0.05.
e. Does the 95% confidence interval of $(-6.8, -4.2)$ contradict the conclusion of the hypothesis test? Explain. What information do you get from the confidence interval that you do not get from the significance test?

9.32   Female work week   When the 583 female workers in the 2012 GSS were asked how many hours they worked in the previous week, the mean was 37.0 hours, with a standard deviation of 15.1 hours. Does this suggest that the population mean work week for females is significantly different from 40 hours? Access these data in the *Inference for a Mean* app and use the results to answer some of the following questions:

a. Identify the relevant variable and parameter.
b. State the null and alternative hypotheses.
c. Report and interpret the P-value for the test statistic value.
d. Explain how to make a decision for the significance level of 0.01.

9.33   Facebook friends   Many students brag that they have more than 100 friends on Facebook. For a class project in 2014, a group of students asked a random sample of 13 students at Williams College who used Facebook about their number of friends and got the following data:

55, 130, 210, 75, 80, 205, 20, 130, 150, 50, 270, 110, 110

Is there strong evidence that the mean number of friends for the student population at Williams who use Facebook is larger than 100? Enter the data into the *Inference for a Mean* app (select Your Own under the Enter Data menu) and use the results to answer some of the following questions:

a. Identify the relevant variable and parameter.
b. State the null and alternative hypotheses.
c. Find and interpret the test statistic value.
d. Report and interpret the P-value and state the conclusion in context.

9.34   Lake pollution   An industrial plant claims to discharge no more than 1,000 gallons of wastewater per hour, on the average, into a neighboring lake. An environmental action group decides to monitor the plant in case this limit is being exceeded. Doing so is expensive, and only a small sample is possible. A random sample of four hours is selected over a period of a week. The observations (gallons of wastewater discharged per hour) are

$$2,000, 1,000, 3,000, 2,000.$$

a. Verify (via the *Inference for a Mean* app or otherwise) that $\bar{x} = 2,000$, $s = 816.5$, and the standard error = 408.25.
b. To test H_0: $\mu = 1,000$ vs. H_a: $\mu > 1,000$, show that the test statistic equals 2.45.
c. Verify (via the app or otherwise) that the P-value is less than 0.05, so there is sufficient evidence to reject the null hypothesis at the 0.05 significance level.
d. Explain how your one-sided analysis in part b implicitly tests the broader null hypothesis that $\mu \leq 1,000$.

9.35   Weight change for controls   A disadvantage of the experimental design in Example 8 on weight change in anorexic girls is that girls could change weight merely from participating in a study. In fact, girls were randomly assigned to a therapy or to a control group, so it was possible to compare weight change for the therapy group to the control group. For the 26 girls in the control group, the weight change had $\bar{x} = -0.5$ and $s = 8.0$. Complete all five steps of the test of H_0: $\mu = 0$ against H_a: $\mu \neq 0$ for this group and interpret the P-value. (You can enter the sample information in the *Inference for a Mean* app by selecting Summary Statistics under the Data Entry menu.)

9.36 **Crossover study**   A crossover study of 13 children suffering from asthma (*Clinical and Experimental Allergy*, (1990), vol. 20, pp. 429–432) compared single inhaled doses of formoterol (F) and salbutamol (S). The outcome measured was the child's peak expiratory flow (PEF) 8 hours following treatment. The higher this value, the better. The data (available on the book's website) on PEF follow:

Child	F	S	Diff	Child	F	S	Diff	Child	F	S	Diff
1	310	270	40	6	370	300	70	11	380	350	30
2	385	370	15	7	410	390	20	12	340	260	80
3	400	310	90	8	320	290	30	13	220	90	130
4	310	260	50	9	330	365	−35				
5	410	380	30	10	250	210	40				

Let μ denote the population mean of the difference between the PEF values for the F and S treatments. The 13 observed differences in PEF were entered into the *Inference for a Mean* app, resulting in the screenshot shown.

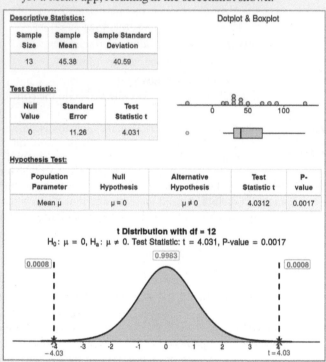

a. Describe the distribution of the observed differences.

b. Carry out the five steps of the significance test for the mean difference between the PEF values using $H_0: \mu = 0$ and $H_a: \mu \neq 0$.

c. Discuss whether the assumptions seem valid for this example. What is the impact of using a convenience sample?

9.37 **Too little or too much wine?**   Wine-pouring vending machines, previously available in Europe and international airports, have become popular in the past few years in the United States. They are even approved to dispense wine in some Walmart stores. The available pouring options are a 5-ounce glass, a 2.5-ounce half-glass, and a 1-ounce taste. When the machine is in statistical control (see Exercise 7.74), the amount dispensed for a full glass is 5.1 ounces. Four observations are taken each day to plot a daily mean over time on a control chart to check for irregularities. The most recent day's observations were 5.05, 5.15, 4.95, and 5.11. Could the difference between the sample mean and the target value be due to random variation, or

can you conclude that the true mean is now different from 5.1? Answer by showing the five steps of a significance test, making a decision using a 0.05 significance level.

9.38 **Selling a burger**   In Exercise 9.25, a fast-food chain compared two ways of promoting a turkey burger. In a separate experiment with 10 pairs of stores, the difference in the month's increased sales between the store that used coupons and the store with the outside poster had a mean of $3,000 and a standard deviation of $4,000. Does this indicate a true difference between mean sales for the two advertising approaches? Answer by using the generic computer software output shown below to test that the population mean difference is 0, carrying out the five steps of a significance test. (You can also enter the summary data into the *Inference for a Mean* app, by selecting Summary Statistics under the Enter Data menu.) Make a decision using a 0.05 significance level.

One-Sample T

```
Test of μ = 0 vs ≠ 0
 N  Mean  StDev  SE Mean   95% CI       T     P
10  3000  4000    1265   (139, 5861)  2.37  0.042
```

9.39 **Assumptions important?**   Refer to the previous exercise.

a. Explain how the result of the 95% confidence interval shown in the output agrees with the test decision using the 0.05 significance level.

b. Suppose you instead wanted to perform a one-sided test because the study predicted that the increase in sales would be higher with coupons. Explain why the normal population assumption might be problematic.

9.40 **Anorexia in teenage girls**   Example 8 described a study about various therapies for teenage girls suffering from anorexia. For each of 17 girls who received the family therapy, the changes in weight were (in pounds)

11, 11, 6, 9, 14, −3, 0, 7, 22, −5, −4, 13, 13, 9, 4, 6, 11.

a. Enter these data into the *Inference for a Mean* app (in the app, select Your Own under the Data Entry menu) or other software to obtain a dot plot or box plot. Use the plot to comment on the distribution of weight changes in the sample.

b. Show that $se = 1.74$ pounds.

c. Give all steps of a significance test about whether the population mean was 0 against an alternative designed to see whether there is any effect.

9.41 **Sensitivity study**   Ideally, results of a statistical analysis should not depend greatly on a single observation. To check this, it's a good idea to conduct a **sensitivity study.** This entails redoing the analysis after deleting an outlier from the data set or changing its value to a more typical value and checking whether results change much. If results change little, this gives us more faith in the conclusions that the statistical analysis reports. For the weight change data for anorexic girls from Example 8 (shown again here and available on the book's website), the greatest reported value of 20.9 pounds was a severe outlier. Suppose this observation was actually 2.9 pounds but was incorrectly recorded. Conduct the two-sided test of that example and summarize how the results differ. Does the ultimate conclusion depend on that single observation? (You can also try removing this outlier and seeing if results change when analyzing the remaining data.)

Weight Changes in Anorexic Girls		
1.7	11.7	−1.4
0.7	6.1	−0.8
−0.1	1.1	2.4
−0.7	−4.0	12.6
−3.5	20.9	1.9
14.9	−9.3	3.9
3.5	2.1	0.1
17.1	1.4	15.4
−7.6	−0.3	−0.7
1.6	−3.7	

9.42   Test and CI   Results of 99% confidence intervals are consistent with results of two-sided tests with which significance level? Explain the connection.

9.4 Decisions and Types of Errors in Significance Tests

In significance tests, the P-value summarizes the evidence about H_0. A P-value such as 0.001 casts strong doubt on H_0 being true because if it were true the observed data would be very unusual.

When we need to decide if the evidence is strong enough to reject H_0, we've seen that the key is whether the P-value falls below a prespecified **significance level.** The significance level is usually denoted by the Greek letter α (alpha). In practice, setting $\alpha = 0.05$ is most common: We reject H_0 if the P-value ≤ 0.05. We do not reject H_0 if the P-value > 0.05. The smaller α is, the stronger the evidence must be to reject H_0. To avoid any *bias* in our decision, we select α *before* looking at the data.

Two Potential Types of Errors in Test Decisions

Because of sampling variability, decisions in significance tests always have some uncertainty. A decision can be in error. For instance, in the anorexia study of Example 8, we got a P-value of 0.018 for testing H_0: $\mu = 0$ of no weight change, on average, against H_a: $\mu > 0$. With significance level $\alpha = 0.05$ we rejected H_0 and concluded that the mean was greater than 0. The data indicated that anorexic girls have a positive mean weight change when undergoing the therapy. If the therapy truly has a positive effect, this is a correct decision. In reality, though, perhaps the therapy has no effect, and the population mean weight change (unknown to us) is actually 0.

We distinguish between two types of wrong decisions in significance testing, called **Type I** and **Type II errors**.

Type I and Type II Errors

When H_0 is true, a **Type I error** occurs when H_0 is rejected.
When H_0 is false, a **Type II error** occurs when H_0 is not rejected.

You can think of a Type I error as a **false positive**. A positive decision is reached by rejecting H_0, yet the decision is false. A Type II error is a **false negative**. A negative decision is reached by not rejecting H_0, yet the decision is false. These are terms borrowed from diagnostic testing where a decision based on a test can also be in error (see Section 5.4 in Chapter 5).

In Example 8, we decided to reject H_0 based on a P-value of 0.018. If the anorexia therapy actually has no effect (that is, if $\mu = 0$), we've made a Type I error. H_0 was actually true, but we rejected it. A consequence of committing this Type I error would be implementing a therapy that actually has no effect on helping with weight gain and thus gives patients false hope.

Consider the experiment about astrology in Example 5. In that study H_0: $p = 1/3$ corresponded to random guessing by the astrologers. We got a P-value of 0.40. With a significance level of $\alpha = 0.05$, we do not reject H_0. If truly $p = 1/3$, this is a correct decision. However, if astrologers actually can predict better than random guessing (so that $p > 1/3$), we've made a Type II error, failing to reject H_0 when it is false. A consequence of committing this Type II error would be calling these astrologers fakes when actually they have predictive powers.

When we make a decision, there are four possible results. These refer to the two possible decisions (rejecting or not rejecting H_0) combined with the two possibilities for whether H_0 is actually true or not. Table 9.2 summarizes these four possibilities. In practice, when we plan to make a decision in a significance test, it's important to know the probability of an incorrect decision.

Table 9.2 The Four Possible Results of a Decision in a Significance Test

Type I and Type II errors are the two possible incorrect decisions. A Type I error (false positive) occurs if we reject H_0 when it is actually true. A Type II error (false negative) occurs if we do not reject H_0 when it is actually false. We make a correct decision if we do not reject H_0 when it is true or if we reject H_0 when it is false.

	Decision	
Reality About H_0	**Do Not Reject H_0**	**Reject H_0**
H_0 true	Correct decision	Type I error
H_0 false	Type II error	Correct decision

An Analogy: Decision Errors in a Legal Trial   The two types of errors can occur with any decision having two options, one of which is incorrect. For instance, consider a decision in a legal trial. The null hypothesis tested is the defendant's claim of innocence. The alternative hypothesis is that the defendant is guilty. The jury rejects H_0 if it decides that the evidence is sufficient to convict. The defendant is then judged guilty. A Type I error, rejecting a true null hypothesis, occurs in convicting a defendant who is actually innocent. Not rejecting H_0 means the defendant is acquitted (judged not guilty). A Type II error, not rejecting H_0 even though it is false, occurs in acquitting a defendant who is actually guilty. See Table 9.3. A potential consequence of a Type I error is sending an innocent person to jail. A potential consequence of a Type II error is setting free a guilty person.

Table 9.3 Possible Results of a Legal Trial

	Legal Decision	
Defendant	**Acquit**	**Convict**
Innocent (H_0)	Correct decision	Type I error
Guilty (H_a)	Type II error	Correct decision

The Probability of a Type I Error

What is the probability of committing a Type I error? We will see that the probability of rejecting H_0 even though it is actually true is equal to the significance level. For instance, when the significance level is $\alpha = 0.05$, the probability of incorrectly rejecting H_0, i.e., committing a Type I error, is 5%. Let's look at a two-sided test about a proportion to see how we got this result.

With a significance level of $\alpha = 0.05$, we reject H_0 if the P-value ≤ 0.05. For two-sided tests about a proportion, the two-tail probability that forms the P-value is ≤ 0.05 whenever the test statistic z is less than -1.96 or larger than $+1.96$, i.e., whenever $|z| \geq 1.96$. The range of test statistic values for which a test rejects H_0 is called the **rejection region**. These are the z test statistic values that occur when the sample proportion falls at least 1.96 standard errors from the null hypothesis value. They are the values we'd least expect to observe if H_0 were true. Figure 9.12 illustrates the rejection regions for a two-sided test.

In Words

The expression $|z| \geq 1.96$ is the same as saying $z < -1.96$ or $z > 1.96$.

▲ **Figure 9.12** The Rejection Region Is the Set of Test Statistic Values That Reject H_0. For a two-sided test about a proportion with significance level 0.05, these are the z test statistic values that exceed 1.96 in absolute value. **Question** If instead we use a one-sided H_a: $p > p_0$, what is the rejection region?

Now, if H_0 is actually true, the sampling distribution of the z test statistic is the standard normal, as drawn in Figure 9.12. The probability of rejecting H_0 is the probability of observing a test statistic that falls in the rejection region. In our case, this would be a test statistic z that is less than -1.96 or larger than 1.96. The probability of observing such a z under the standard normal distribution is exactly 0.05, which is precisely the significance level.

> P(Type I Error) = Significance Level α
>
> Suppose H_0 is true. The probability of rejecting H_0, thereby making a Type I error, equals the chosen significance level α for the test.

In Practice We Don't Know If a Decision Is Correct

In practice, we don't know whether a decision in a significance test is correct, just as we don't know whether a particular confidence interval truly contains an unknown parameter value. However, we can control the *probability* of an incorrect decision for either type of inference.

The good news about this result is that we can control the probability of a Type I error by our choice of the significance level α. The more serious the consequences of a Type I error, the smaller α should be. In practice, $\alpha = 0.05$ is most common, just as a probability of error of 0.05 in interval estimation is most common (that is, 95% confidence intervals). However, this number may be too high when a decision has serious implications. For example, suppose a convicted defendant gets the death penalty. Then, if a defendant is actually innocent, we would hope that the probability of conviction is smaller than 0.05.

Although we don't know if the decision in a particular test is correct, we justify the method in terms of the long-run proportions of Type I and Type II errors. If every time we conduct a test we reject H_0 when the P-value is less than 0.05, in the long run we will make a Type I error in no more than 5% of the cases.

This is similar to how we interpreted 95% confidence for confidence intervals. In the long run, only 5% of the intervals we construct will not contain the true population parameter.

Probability of a Type I Error

Example 9

Type I Errors in Legal Verdicts

Picture the Scenario

In an ideal world, Type I or Type II errors would not occur. In practice, however, whether in significance tests or in applications such as courtroom trials or medical diagnoses, errors do happen. It can be surprising and disappointing how often they occur, as we saw in the diagnostic testing examples of Chapter 5. Likewise, we've all read about defendants who were given the death penalty but were later determined to be innocent, but we don't have reliable information about how often this occurs.

Question to Explore

When we make a decision, why don't we use an extremely small probability of Type I error such as $\alpha = 0.000001$? For instance, why don't we make it almost impossible to convict someone who is really innocent?

Think It Through

When we make α smaller in a significance test, we need a smaller P-value to reject H_0. It then becomes harder to reject H_0. But this means that it will also be harder to reject H_0 even if H_0 is false. The stronger the evidence that is required to convict someone, the more likely it becomes that we will fail to convict defendants who are actually guilty. In other words, the smaller we make the probability of Type I error, the *larger* the probability of Type II error becomes (that is, failing to reject H_0 even though it is false).

If we tolerate only an extremely small chance of a Type I error (such as $\alpha = 0.000001$), then the test may be unlikely to reject the null hypothesis even if it is false—for instance, unlikely to convict someone even if they are guilty. In fact, some of our laws are set up to make Type I errors very unlikely, and as a consequence some truly guilty individuals are not punished for their crimes.

Insight

This reasoning reflects a fundamental relation between the probabilities of the two types of errors for a given sample size n:

As the probability of a Type I error goes down,
the probability of a Type II error goes up.

The two probabilities are inversely related.

▶ *Try Exercises 9.45 and 9.50, part c*

With the probability of a Type I error equal to the chosen significance level, how likely is it to commit a Type II error? We'll discuss how to find the probability of a Type II error in Section 9.6, but it is possible, e.g., with a sufficiently large sample size, to have both a small probability for a Type I error (e.g., 0.05) **and** a small probability for a Type II error (e.g., 0.10 or even 0.01). (The *Errors and Power* app shows visually how this is possible.) In practice, to make a decision in a test, we only need to set the probability of Type I error, which is the significance level α.

These days, most research articles merely report the P-value rather than a decision about whether to reject H_0. From the P-value, readers can see the strength of evidence against H_0 and make their own decisions.

▶ **Activity 1**

Why Is 0.05 Commonly Used as a Significance Level?

One answer to the question above is because of historical reasons. In his influential writings, the statistician R.A. Fisher used 0.05 as a cutoff to warrant further scrutiny of the results. Here is another scenario that may justify using a significance level of 0.05 as a cutoff for the evidence being "sufficient". (However, this doesn't clarify why 0.051 would not be considered sufficient, but shows that values around 0.05 and not, say, 0.125 are used.) Suppose someone tosses a coin you can't confirm ahead of time is fair. Based on a couple of tosses, you need to decide whether you can reject H_0: p = probability of head = 0.50 (fair coin) in favor of H_a: $p \neq 0.50$. Consider the following:

- On the first toss, the coin lands heads. Would you reject H_0 and conclude that the coin is not fair?
- On the second toss, the coin lands heads. Would you now reject H_0 and conclude that the coin is not fair?
- On the third toss, the coin also lands heads. Would you now reject H_0 and conclude that the coin is not fair?
- On the fourth toss, the coin lands heads again. Are you now starting to doubt that H_0 is true and willing to believe that H_a may be true?

- On the fifth toss, the coin lands heads again. Are you now ready to reject H_0 and conclude that the coin cannot be fair?

If you are like many people, by the time you see the fifth straight head, you are willing to predict that the coin is not fair. (By then, you may even visually inspect the coin to make sure it has different sides.) If the null hypothesis that $p = 0.50$ is actually true, the probability of five heads in a row is $(0.50)^5 = 1/32 = 0.03$. For a two-sided test, this result gives a P-value of $2(0.03) = 0.06$, close to 0.05. So, for many people, it takes a P-value near 0.05 before they feel there is enough evidence to reject a null hypothesis. (For comparison, many people would not get too suspicious of the null hypothesis after four straight heads, for which the P-value is 0.125.) This may be one reason the significance level of 0.05 has become common over the years in a wide variety of disciplines that use significance tests.

Exercise 9.129 presents this activity in the context of comparing a drug (for instance, against migraine) to a placebo to test which one is better. You start by assuming they are equally effective (the null hypothesis). One patient after another tries both the drug and the placebo (in random order) and reports which one is better. After the first five patients report better results with the placebo, are you willing to accept that the placebo works better?

Try Exercise 9.129 ◀

9.4   Practicing the Basics

9.43   Drivers in Las Vegas   For the experiment in Example 6, we got a P-value < 0.001 for testing H_0: $p = 0.75$ against H_a: $p < 0.75$, where p was the proportion of Las Vegas drivers stopping for a pedestrian waiting in a crosswalk.

a. For the significance level $\alpha = 0.05$, what decision would you make?

b. If you made an error in part a, what type of error was it? Explain what the error means in context of the experiment.

c. If you repeated this experiment many times, using a significance level of $\alpha = 0.05$ for each test, in the long run, what is the probability of committing a Type I error?

9.44   Error probability   A significance test about a proportion is conducted using a significance level of $\alpha = 0.05$. The test statistic equals 2.58. The P-value is 0.01.

a. For what probability of a Type I error was the test designed?

b. If this test resulted in a decision error, what type of error was it?

9.45   Fracking errors   Example 4, in testing H_0: $p = 0.5$
TRY   against H_a: $p \neq 0.5$, analyzed whether the proportion of adults opposing fracking is different from 0.5. In the words of that example, what would be (a) a Type I error and (b) a Type II error? If you repeatedly took samples of this size and used a significance level of $\alpha = 0.05$ for each test, (c) what is the long-run probability of committing a Type I error?

9.46 Anorexia errors Example 8, under Insight, tested a therapy for anorexia, using hypotheses H_0: $\mu = 0$ and H_a: $\mu \neq 0$ about the population mean weight change μ. In the words of that example, what would be (a) a Type I error and (b) a Type II error? For each part, mention a potential consequence of committing the error.

9.47 Anorexia decision Refer to the previous exercise. When we test H_0: $\mu = 0$ against H_a: $\mu > 0$, we get a P-value of 0.02.

   a. What would the decision be for a significance level of 0.05? Interpret in context.

   b. If the decision in part a is in error, what type of error is it?

   c. Suppose the significance level were instead 0.01. What decision would you make, and if it is in error, what type of error is it? Explain the error in context.

9.48 Errors in the courtroom Consider the test of H_0: The defendant is not guilty against H_a: The defendant is guilty.

   a. Explain, in context, the conclusion of the test if H_0 is rejected.

   b. Describe, in context, a Type I error.

   c. Explain, in context, the conclusion of the test if you fail to reject H_0.

   d. Describe, in context, a Type II error.

9.49 Errors in medicine Consider the test of H_0: The new drug is safe against H_a: the new drug is not safe.

   a. Explain, in context, the conclusion of the test if H_0 is rejected.

   b. Describe, in context, a Type I error.

   c. Explain, in context, the conclusion of the test if you fail to reject H_0.

   d. Describe, in context, a Type II error.

9.50 Decision errors in medical diagnostic testing Consider (TRY) medical diagnostic testing, such as using a mammogram to detect if a woman may have breast cancer. Define the null hypothesis of no effect as the patient does not have the disease. Define rejecting H_0 as concluding that the patient has the disease. See the table for a summary of the possible outcomes:

Medical Diagnostic Testing

Disease	Medical Diagnosis	
	Negative	Positive
No (H_0)	Correct	Type I error
Yes (H_a)	Type II error	Correct

   a. When a radiologist interprets a mammogram, explain why a Type I error is a false positive, predicting that a woman has breast cancer when actually she does not.

   b. A Type II error is a false negative. What does this mean, and what is the consequence of such an error to the woman?

   c. A radiologist wants to decrease the chance of telling a woman that she may have breast cancer when actually she does not. Consequently, a positive test result will be reported only when there is *extremely* strong evidence that breast cancer is present. What is the disadvantage of this approach?

9.51 Detecting prostate cancer Refer to the previous exercise about medical diagnoses. A *New York Times* article (February 17, 1999) about the PSA blood test for detecting prostate cancer stated: "The test fails to detect prostate cancer in 1 in 4 men who have the disease."

   a. For the PSA test, explain what a Type I error is and explain the consequence to a man of this type of error.

   b. For the PSA test, what is a Type II error? What is the consequence to a man of this type of error?

   c. To which type of error does the probability of 1 in 4 refer?

   d. The article also stated that if you receive a positive result, the probability that you do not actually have prostate cancer is 2/3. Explain the difference between this and the conditional probability of a Type I error, given that you do not actually have prostate cancer.

9.52 Which error is worse? Which error, Type I or Type II, would usually be considered more serious for decisions in the following tests? Explain why.

   a. A trial to test a murder defendant's claimed innocence, when conviction results in the death penalty.

   b. A medical diagnostic procedure, such as a mammogram.

9.5 Limitations of Significance Tests

Chapters 8 and 9 have presented the two primary methods of statistical inference—confidence intervals and significance testing. We will use both of these methods throughout the rest of the book. Of the two methods, confidence intervals are often more useful for reasons we'll discuss in this section. Significance tests have more potential for misuse. We'll now summarize the major limitations of significance tests.

Statistical Significance Does Not Imply Practical Relevance

When we conduct a significance test, its main purpose is studying whether the true parameter value is significantly

- above, or below, the value specified in H_0, or, for two-sided tests
- different from the value in H_0.

The P-value of the significance test summarizes the evidence on whether the parameter differs significantly from the value specified in H_0, but we'll see that it alone does not tell us anything meaningful about the practical relevance (or importance) of the finding.

There is an important distinction between *statistical significance* and *practical relevance*. A small P-value, such as 0.001, is considered highly statistically significant, giving strong evidence against H_0. It may not, however, imply an *important* finding in any practical sense. The small P-value means that if H_0 were true, the observed data would be unusual. It does not mean that the true value of the parameter is far from the null hypothesis value in practical terms. In particular, whenever the sample size is large, small P-values can occur even when the point estimate is very close to the parameter value in H_0, as the following example shows.

Statistical Significance Versus Practical Relevance ◄

Example 10

Political Conservatism and Liberalism in America

Picture the Scenario

Where do Americans say they fall on the conservative–liberal political spectrum? The General Social Survey asks, "I'm going to show you a seven-point scale on which the political views that people might hold are arranged from extremely liberal, point 1, to extremely conservative, point 7. Where would you place yourself on this scale?" Table 9.4 shows the scale and the distribution of 2,449 responses for the GSS in 2014.

Table 9.4 Responses of 2,449 Subjects on a Seven-Point Scale of Political Views

Category	Count
1. Extremely Liberal	94
2. Liberal	304
3. Slightly Liberal	263
4. Moderate, Middle of Road	989
5. Slightly Conservative	334
6. Conservative	358
7. Extremely Conservative	107

Data are available from the book's website.

This categorical variable has seven categories that are ordered in terms of degree of liberalism or conservatism. Categorical variables that have *ordered* categories are called **ordinal variables** (see Section 2.1 in Chapter 2). Sometimes we treat an ordinal variable in a quantitative manner by assigning scores to the categories and summarizing the data by the mean. This summarizes whether observations gravitate toward the conservative or the liberal end of the scale. For the category scores of 1 to 7, a mean of 4.0 corresponds to the moderate outcome. A mean below 4 shows a propensity toward liberalism, and a mean above 4 shows a propensity toward conservatism. The 2,449 observations in Table 9.4 have a mean of 4.09 and a standard deviation of 1.43.

Questions to Explore

a. Do these data indicate that the population in 2014 has a propensity toward liberalism or toward conservatism? Answer by conducting a significance test that compares the population mean to the moderate value of 4.0 by testing H_0: $\mu = 4.0$ against H_a: $\mu \neq 4.0$.

b. Does this test show (i) statistical significance? (ii) practical relevance?

Think It Through

a. The standard error of the sample mean is $se = s/\sqrt{n} = 1.43/\sqrt{2{,}449} = 0.0290$. The test statistic for H_0: $\mu = 4.0$ equals

$$t = (\bar{x} - \mu_0)/se = (4.09 - 4.00)/0.0290 = 3.1.$$

Its two-sided P-value is 0.002. There is strong evidence that the population mean differs from 4.0. The data indicates that true mean exceeds 4.0, with the true mean falling on the conservative side of moderate.

b. Although the P-value is very small, on a scale of 1 to 7, the sample mean of 4.09 is very close to the value of 4.0 in H_0. Although the difference of 0.09 between the sample mean of 4.09 and the value of 4.0 specified under the null hypothesis is highly significant statistically, in practical terms this difference is very small. We'd regard a mean of 4.09 as moderate on this 1 to 7 scale. In summary, while the population mean differs significantly (P-value = 0.002) from 4.0, the actual distance from the population mean is practically irrelevant. There is statistical significance, but no practical relevance.

Insight

With large samples, P-values can be small even when the sample estimate falls near the parameter value in H_0. The P-value measures the extent of evidence for H_0, not how far the true parameter value happens to be from H_0. Always inspect the difference between the sample estimate and the null hypothesis value to gauge the practical implications of a test result.

▶ *Try Exercise 9.54*

Significance Tests Are Less Useful Than Confidence Intervals

Although significance tests are useful in some situations, most statisticians believe that this method has been overemphasized in practice.

■ A significance test merely indicates whether the particular parameter value in H_0 (such as $\mu = 0$) is plausible, given the data.

When a P-value is small, the significance test indicates that the hypothesized value is not plausible, but it tells us little about which potential parameter values *are* plausible.

- A confidence interval is more informative because it displays the entire set of plausible values.

A confidence interval shows if H_0 may be badly false by showing if the values in the interval are far from the H_0 value. It helps us to determine whether the difference between the true value and the H_0 value has practical importance.

Let's illustrate with Example 10 and the 1 to 7 scale for political beliefs. A 95% confidence interval for μ is $\bar{x} \pm 1.96(se) = 4.09 \pm 1.96(0.0290)$, or $(4.03, 4.15)$. We can conclude that the difference between the population mean and the moderate score of 4.0 is small. Figure 9.13 illustrates. Although the P-value of 0.002 provided strong evidence against H_0: $\mu = 4.0$, in practical terms the confidence interval shows that H_0 is not wrong by much.

▲ **Figure 9.13 Statistical Significance But No Practical Relevance.** In testing H_0: $\mu = 4.0$, the P-value $= 0.002$, but the confidence interval of $(4.03, 4.15)$ shows that μ is very close to the H_0 value of 4.0. **Question** For H_0: $\mu = 4.0$, does a sample mean of 6.09 and confidence interval of $(6.03, 6.15)$ indicate (a) statistical significance? (b) practical significance?

In contrast, if $\bar{x}$ had been 6.09 (instead of 4.09), the 95% confidence interval would equal $(6.03, 6.15)$. This confidence interval indicates a substantial difference from 4.0, the mean response being near the conservative score rather than near the moderate score.

- Even if the P-value is large, a confidence interval may indicate the potential of a significant effect.

The confidence interval tells us about all plausible values for the parameter. Even if that confidence interval includes the null value (which is the case when the P-value is large), it may indicate other values that are plausible and that may indicate an important effect.

Misinterpretations of Results of Significance Tests

Unfortunately, results of significance tests are often misinterpreted. Here are some important comments about significance tests, some of which we've already discussed:

- **"Do not reject H_0" does not mean "Accept H_0."** If you get a P-value above 0.05 when the significance level is 0.05, you cannot conclude that H_0 is correct. We can never accept a single value, which H_0 contains, such as $p = 0.50$ or $\mu = 0$. A test merely indicates whether a particular parameter value is plausible. A confidence interval shows that there is a *range* of plausible values, not just a single one.

- **Statistical significance does not mean practical relevance.** A small P-value does not tell us if the parameter value differs by much in practical terms from the value in H_0. Even a small and practically unimportant difference between a sample mean or proportion and the null hypothesis value can lead to a statistically significant result if the sample size is large enough. A small P-value alone does not imply that the effect that the alternative hypothesis spells out is practically meaningful. By contrast, a confidence interval allows you to estimate the magnitude or effect size of the parameter. From it, you can better judge whether the effect is practically relevant and important.

Recall

$P(A \mid B)$ denotes the conditional probability of event A, given event B. To find a P-value, we condition on H_0 being true (that is, we presume it is true), rather than find the probability that H_0 is true. ◄

- **The P-value cannot be interpreted as the probability that H_0 is true.** This is a common mistake. The P-value is the conditional probability

P(test statistic takes observed value or beyond in tails | H_0 true),

and **not** the other way around as in

P(H_0 true | observed test statistic value).

We've been calculating probabilities about test statistic values, not about parameters. It makes sense to find the probability that a test statistic takes a value in the tail (i.e., is extreme), but the probability that a population mean $\mu = 0$ does not make sense because probabilities do not apply to parameters (since parameters are fixed numbers and not random variables). The null hypothesis H_0 is either true or not true, and we simply do not know which.[10]

- **It is misleading to report results only if they are "statistically significant."** Some research journals have the policy of publishing results of a study only if the P-value ≤ 0.05. Here's a danger of this policy: If there truly is no effect, but 20 researchers independently conduct studies about it, we would expect about $20(0.05) = 1$ of them to obtain significance at the 0.05 level merely by chance. (When H_0 is true, about 5% of the time we get a P-value below 0.05 anyway.) If that researcher then submits results to a journal but the other 19 researchers do not, the article published will be a Type I error—reporting an effect when there really is not one. The popular media may then also report on this study, causing the general public to hear about an effect that does not actually exist.

  Lately, many disciplines (e.g., psychology, medicine) experience what is called a **reproducibility crisis**, where independent research teams fail to replicate published study results that showed significant effects. The tendency to only publish studies that showed significant results is partly responsible for this crisis.

- **Some tests may be statistically significant just by chance.** You should never scan rows and rows of computer output for results that are statistically significant and report only those. If you run 100 tests, even if all the null hypotheses are true, you would expect to get P-values of 0.05 or less about $100(0.05) = 5$ times. Keep this in mind and be skeptical of reports of significance that might merely reflect ordinary random variability. For instance, suppose an article reports an unusually high rate of a rare type of cancer in your town. It could be due to some cause such as air or water pollution. However, if researchers found this by looking at data for *all* towns and cities nationwide, it could also be due to random variability. Determining which is true may not be easy.

- **True effects may not be as large as initial estimates reported by the media.** Even if a statistically significant result is a true effect, the true effect may be smaller than suggested in the first article about it. For instance, often several researchers perform similar studies, but the results that get attention are the most extreme ones. This sensationalism may come about because the researcher who is the first to publicize the result is the one who got the most impressive sample result, perhaps way out in the tail of the sampling distribution of all the possible results. Then the study's estimate of the effect may be greater than later research shows it to be.

---

[10]It is possible to find probabilities about parameter values by using an approach called *Bayesian statistics,* but this requires extra assumptions and is beyond the scope of this book.

Example 11

Medical "Discoveries"

Picture the Scenario

What can be done with heart attack victims to increase their chance of survival? In the 1990s, trials of a clot-busting drug called anistreplase suggested that it doubled the chance of survival. Likewise, another study estimated that injections of magnesium could double the chance of survival. However, a much larger study of heart attack survival rates among 58,000 patients indicated that this optimism was premature. The actual effectiveness of anistreplase seemed to be barely half that estimated by the original trial, and magnesium injections seemed to have no effect at all.[11] The anistreplase finding is apparently an example of a true effect not being as large as the initial estimate, and the report from the original magnesium study may well have been a Type I error.

Question to Explore

In medical studies, such as clinical trials assessing the effectiveness of various drugs, suppose that a true effect exists only 10% of the time. Suppose also that when an effect truly exists, there's a 50% chance of making a Type II error and failing to detect it. These were the hypothetical percentages used in an article in a medical journal.[12] The authors noted that many medical studies have a high Type II error rate because they are not able to use a large sample size. Assuming these rates, could a substantial percentage of medical "discoveries" actually be Type I errors? Approximate the P(Type I error) for such a scenario by considering a tree diagram of what you would expect to happen with 1,000 medical studies that test various hypotheses.

Think It Through

Figure 9.14 is a tree diagram of what's expected. A true effect exists 10% of the time, or in 100 of the 1,000 studies. We do not get a small enough P-value to detect this true effect 50% of the time, that is, in 50 of these 100 studies. No effect will be reported for the other 50 of the 100 studies that do truly have an effect. Now, for the 900 cases in which there truly is no effect, with the usual significance level of 0.05, we expect 5% of the 900 studies (that is, 45 studies) to reject the null hypothesis incorrectly and predict that there is an effect. So, of the original 1,000 studies, we expect 50 to report an effect that is

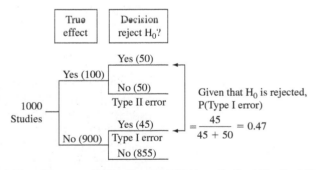

▲ **Figure 9.14 Tree Diagram of Results of 1,000 Hypothetical Medical Studies.** This assumes that a true effect exists 10% of the time and that there's a 50% chance of a Type II error when an effect truly does exist.

---

[11]"The Great Health Hoax," by R. Matthews, in *The Sunday Telegraph*, September 13, 1998.
[12]By J. Sterne, G. Smith, and D. R. Cox, (2001), *BMJ*, vol. 322, pp. 226–231.

truly there, but we also expect 45 to report an effect that does not really exist. If the assumptions are reasonable, then a proportion of $45/(45+50) = 0.47$ of medical studies that report effects (that is, reject H_0) are actually reporting Type I errors. In summary, nearly half the time when an effect is reported, there actually is no effect in the population!

Insight

Be skeptical when you hear reports of new medical advances. The true effect may be weaker than reported, or there may actually be no effect at all.

▶ *Try Exercise 9.58*

The American Statistical Association's Principles on P-values

The misinterpretation and misuse of P-values has prompted the American Statistical Association to publish six remarks about the proper use and interpretation of P-values. These guidelines are a good summary of many of the issues we have discussed in this chapter.[13] (The cited paper expands on each of the six points given below.)

1. P-values can indicate how incompatible the data are with a specified statistical model.

2. P-values do not measure the probability that the studied hypothesis is true or the probability that the data were produced by random chance alone.

3. Scientific conclusions and business or policy decisions should not be based only on whether a P-value passes a specific threshold.

4. Proper inference requires full reporting and transparency.

5. A P-value, or statistical significance, does not measure the size of an effect or the importance of a result.

6. By itself, a P-value does not provide a good measure of evidence regarding a model or hypothesis.

Ethics in Data Analysis

Statistics, like any field, has standards for ethical behavior. The comments just made have implications about proper and improper use of significance tests. For example, when you conduct a study, it's not ethical to perform lots and lots of significance tests but only report results when the P-value is small. (This behavior is called P-value hacking or fishing.) Even when *all* null hypotheses tested are true, just by chance small P-values occasionally occur. You should report *all* the analyses you have conducted. In fact, before you collect the data, you should formulate a research plan that sets out exactly what analyses you will conduct. (For instance, a protocol that has to be approved by authorities is required before the start of a clinical trial to avoid P-value hacking.)

The discussion in Section 9.2 about how to decide between a one-sided and a two-sided test mentioned that it is not ethical to choose a one-sided H_a after seeing the direction in which the data fall. This is because the sampling distribution used in a significance test presumes only that H_0 is true, and it allows sample data in each direction. If we first looked at the data, the valid sampling distribution would be one that is conditioned on the extra information about the direction of the sample data. For example, if the test statistic is positive, the proper sampling distribution would not include negative values. Again, before you collect the data, your research plan should set out the details of the hypotheses you plan to test and the significance level you plan to use.

---

[13]Ronald L. Wasserstein & Nicole A. Lazar (2016), The ASA Statement on p-Values: Context, Process, and Purpose, The American Statistician, 70:2, 129–133.

No Inference for Population Data

Finally, remember that tests and confidence intervals use *sample* data to make inferences about *populations*. If you have data for an entire population, statistical inference is not necessary. For instance, if your college reports that the class of entering freshmen had a mean high school GPA of 3.60, there is no need to perform a test or construct a confidence interval. You already know the mean for the entire population and don't need to estimate it or infer anything about it.

On the Shoulders of...Jerzy Neyman and the Pearsons

Jerzy Neyman, together with Egon Pearson, developed statistical theory for making decisions about hypotheses.

How can you build a framework for making decisions?

The methods of confidence intervals and hypothesis testing were introduced in a series of articles beginning in 1928 by Jerzy Neyman (1894–1981) and Egon Pearson (1895–1980). Neyman emigrated from Poland to England and then to the United States, where he established a statistics department at the University of California at Berkeley. He helped develop the theory of statistical inference, and he applied the theory

to scientific questions in a variety of areas, such as agriculture, astronomy, biology, medicine, and weather modification. For instance, late in his career, Neyman's analysis of data from several randomized experiments showed that cloud-seeding can have a considerable effect on rainfall.

Much of Neyman's theoretical research was done with Egon Pearson, a professor at University College, London. Pearson's father, Karl Pearson, had developed one of the first statistical tests in 1900 to study various hypotheses, including whether the outcomes on a roulette wheel were equally likely. (We'll study his test, the *chi-squared test*, in Chapter 11.) Neyman and the younger Pearson developed the decision-making framework that introduced the two types of errors that we studied in Section 9.4 and the power of a test, which we'll study next.

9.5 Practicing the Basics

9.53 P-value of 0.046 vs 0.057 Two researchers conduct separate studies to test H_0: $p = 0.50$ against H_a: $p \neq 0.50$, each with $n = 400$, for a population proportion p.

a. Researcher A gets 220 observations in the category of interest, and $\hat{p} = 220/400 = 0.550$ and test statistic $z = 2.00$. Show (e.g., using the *Inference for a Proportion* app) that the P-value $= 0.046$ for Researcher A's data.

b. Researcher B gets 219 in the category of interest, and $\hat{p} = 219/400 = 0.5475$ and test statistic $z = 1.90$. Show that the P-value $= 0.057$ for Researcher B's data.

c. Using $\alpha = 0.05$, indicate in each case from part a and part b whether the population proportion p is significantly different from 0.5.

d. From part a, part b, and part c, explain why important information is lost by reporting the result of a test as "P-value ≤ 0.05" versus "P-value > 0.05," or as "reject H_0" versus "do not reject H_0," or as "significantly

different from 0.5" versus "not significantly different from 0.5," instead of reporting the actual P-value.

e. Show (e.g., using the *Inference for a Proportion* app) that the 95% confidence interval for p is (0.501, 0.599) for Researcher A and (0.499, 0.596) for Researcher B. Explain how this shows that, in practical terms, the two studies had very similar results.

9.54 Practical significance A study considers whether the mean score on a college entrance exam for students in 2010 is different from the mean score of 500 for students who took the same exam in 1985. Let μ represent the mean score for all students who took the exam in 2010. For a random sample of 25,000 students who took the exam in 2010, $\bar{x} = 498$ and $s = 100$.

a. Show that the test statistic is $t = -3.16$.

b. Find (e.g., using the *Inference for a Mean* app) the P-value for testing H_0: $\mu = 500$ against H_a: $\mu \neq 500$.

c. Explain why the test result is statistically significant but not practically relevant.

9.55 Effect of *n* Example 10 analyzed political conservatism

and liberalism in the United States. Suppose that the sample mean of 4.09 and sample standard deviation of 1.43 were from a sample size of only 25, rather than 2,449.

a. Find the test statistic.

b. Find (e.g., using the *Inference for a Mean* app) the P-value for testing H_0: $\mu = 4.0$ against H_a: $\mu \neq 4.0$. Interpret.

c. Show that a 95% confidence interval for μ is (3.5, 4.7).

d. Together with the results of Example 10, explain what this illustrates about the effect of sample size on (i) the size of the P-value (for a given mean and standard deviation) and (ii) the width of the confidence interval.

9.56 Fishing for significance A marketing study conducts 60 significance tests about means and proportions for several groups. Of them, 3 tests are statistically significant at the 0.05 level. The study's final report stresses only the tests with significant results, not mentioning the other 57 tests. What is misleading about this?

9.57 Selective reporting In 2004, New York Attorney General Eliot Spitzer filed a lawsuit against GlaxoSmithKline pharmaceutical company, claiming that the company failed to publish results of one of its studies that showed that an antidepressant drug (Paxil) may make adolescents more likely to commit suicide. Partly as a consequence, editors of 11 medical journals agreed to a new policy to make researchers and companies register all clinical trials when they begin, so that negative results cannot later be covered up. The *International Journal of Medical Journal Editors* wrote, "Unfortunately, selective reporting of trials does occur, and it distorts the body of evidence available for

clinical decision-making." Explain why this controversy relates to the argument that it is misleading to report results only if they are "statistically significant." (*Hint:* See the subsection of this chapter on misinterpretations of significance tests.)

9.58 How many medical discoveries are Type I errors? Refer to Example 11. Using a tree diagram, approximate P(Type I error) under the assumption that a true effect exists 20% of the time and that there's a 30% chance of a Type II error.

9.59 Interpret medical research studies

a. An advertisement by Schering Corp. in 1999 for the allergy drug Claritin mentioned that in a clinical trial, the proportion who showed symptoms of nervousness was not significantly greater for patients taking Claritin than for patients taking placebo. Does this mean that the population proportion having nervous symptoms is exactly the same using Claritin and using placebo? How would you explain this to someone who has not studied statistics?

b. An article in the medical journal *BMJ* (by M. Petticrew et al., published November 2002) found no evidence to back the commonly held belief that a positive attitude can lengthen the lives of cancer patients. The authors noted that the studies that had indicated a benefit from some coping strategies tended to be smaller studies with weaker designs. Using this example and the discussion in this section, explain why you need to have some skepticism when you hear that new research suggests that some therapy or drug has an impact in treating a disease.

9.6 The Likelihood of a Type II Error and the Power of a Test

As we learned in Section 9.4, the probability of a Type I error is the prespecified significance level α of the test. Given that H_0 is true, when $\alpha = 0.05$, the probability of rejecting H_0 equals 0.05.

Given that H_0 is false, a Type II error results from *not* rejecting H_0. This probability is not constant but depends on factors such as the actual (but unknown) value of the population parameter, the significance level α, and the sample size n. Let's see how to find the probability of a Type II error in a significance test about a proportion.

Finding the Probability of a Type II Error ◄

Example 12

Part of a Study Design

Picture the Scenario

Examples 1, 3, and 5 discussed an experiment to test astrologers' predictions. For each person's horoscope, an astrologer must predict which of three personality charts is the actual one. Let p denote the probability of a correct prediction. Consider the test of H_0: $p = 1/3$ (astrologers' predictions are like random guessing) against H_a: $p > 1/3$ (better than random guessing), using the 0.05 significance level. Suppose an experiment plans to use $n = 116$ people, as this experiment did.

Questions to Explore

a. For what values of the sample proportion can we reject H_0?

b. The National Council for Geocosmic Research claimed that p would be 0.50 or higher. If truly $p = 0.50$, for what values of the sample proportion would we make a Type II error, failing to reject H_0 even though it's false?

c. If truly $p = 0.50$, what is the probability that a significance test based on this experiment will make a Type II error?

Think It Through

a. For testing H_0: $p = 1/3$ with $n = 116$, the standard error for the test statistic is
$$se_0 = \sqrt{p_0(1-p_0)/n} = \sqrt{(1/3)(2/3)/116} = 0.0438.$$
For H_a: $p > 1/3$, a test statistic of $z = 1.645$ has a P-value (right-tail probability) of 0.05, see the margin figure which shows the standard normal distribution, which is the sampling distribution for z. So, if $z \geq 1.645$, the P-value is ≤ 0.05 and we reject H_0. Plugging in for z, we reject if $(\hat{p} - 1/3)/se_0 > 1.645$, or, reformulating, if
$$\hat{p} \geq 1/3 + 1.645(se_0) = 1/3 + 1.645(0.0438) = 0.405.$$
So we reject H_0 when we get a sample proportion that is 0.405 or larger. Figure 9.15 shows the sampling distribution of $\hat{p}$ and this rejection region.

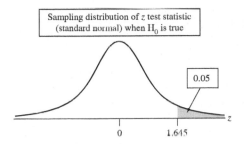

Sampling distribution of z test statistic (standard normal) when H_0 is true

0.05

0   1.645 z

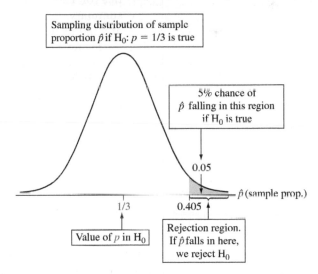

Sampling distribution of sample proportion $\hat{p}$ if H_0: $p = 1/3$ is true

5% chance of $\hat{p}$ falling in this region if H_0 is true

0.05

$\hat{p}$ (sample prop.)

1/3   0.405

Value of p in H_0

Rejection region. If $\hat{p}$ falls in here, we reject H_0

▲ **Figure 9.15 Reject H_0: $p = 1/3$ in Favor of H_a: $p > 1/3$ at the 0.05 Significance Level when the Sample Proportion $\hat{p}$ is Larger Than 0.405.** When the true $p > 1/3$, a Type II error occurs if $\hat{p} < 0.405$, since then the P-value > 0.05 and we do not reject H_0. **Question** With a 0.10 significance level, does the blue area above become smaller or larger? Is the probability of a Type II error smaller or larger compared to a 0.05 significance level?

The distribution is centered at $1/3$ because the test statistic is calculated, and the rejection region is formed presuming that H_0 is correct.

b. When H_0 is false, a Type II error occurs when we fail to reject H_0. From part a and Figure 9.15, we do not reject H_0 if $\hat{p} < 0.405$.

c. If the true value of p is 0.50, then the true sampling distribution of $\hat{p}$ is centered at 0.50 and not at 1/3, as Figure 9.16 (on the next page) shows. The probability of a Type II error is the probability that we obtain a sample proportion $\hat{p} < 0.405$ under this sampling distribution. When $p = 0.5$, the sampling distribution of $\hat{p}$ is approximately normal, with mean 0.5 and standard deviation $\sqrt{0.5(1 - 0.5)/116} = 0.0464$. So, to find the probability of a Type II error when $p = 0.5$, all we need to do is find the area to the left of 0.405 under this normal distribution.

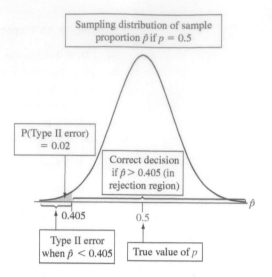

▲ **Figure 9.16** Calculation of P(Type II Error) when True Parameter $p = 0.50$. A Type II error occurs if the sample proportion $\hat{p} < 0.405$. **Question** If the value of p decreases to 0.40, will the probability of Type II error decrease or increase?

Using the *Normal Distribution* app for calculating normal probabilities (or Table A after converting to a z-score), this area equals 0.02. In summary, when $p = 0.50$, the probability of making a Type II error and failing to reject $H_0: p = 1/3$ is only 0.02.

Figure 9.17 shows the two figures together that we used in our reasoning. The normal distribution with mean $1/3$ was used to find the rejection region, based on what we expect for $\hat{p}$ when $H_0: p = 1/3$ is true. The normal distribution with mean 0.50 was used to find the probability that $\hat{p}$ does not fall in the rejection region when $p = 0.50$ (that is, a Type II error occurs).

▲ **Figure 9.17** Sampling Distributions of $\hat{p}$ when $H_0: p = 1/3$ Is True (Left Graph) and when $p = 0.50$ is True (Right Graph). **Question** Why does the shaded area under the left tail of the curve for the case $p = 0.50$ represent P(Type II error) for that value of p?

Insight

If astrologers truly had the predictive power claimed by the National Council for Geocosmic Research, the experiment would have been very likely to detect it, with probability $1 - 0.02 = 0.98$.

You can reproduce the graph in Figure 9.17 and obtain the probability of a Type II error with the *Errors and Power* app. See Activity 2 at the end of this section.

▶ *Try Exercise 9.61*

The probability of a Type II error increases when the true parameter value moves closer to H_0. To verify this, try to find the probability of a Type II error when $p = 0.40$ instead of 0.50. You should get P(Type II error) = 0.54. (Parts a and b of Example 12 are the same and, in part c, the sampling distribution of $\hat{p}$ now has mean 0.4 and standard deviation $\sqrt{0.4(1 - 0.4)/116} = 0.0455$.) If an astrologer can predict better than random guessing but not *much* better, we may not detect it with this experiment. Figure 9.18 plots P(Type II error) for various values of p larger than 1/3. The farther the parameter value falls from the number in H_0, the less likely a Type II error.

▲ **Figure 9.18** Probability of a Type II Error for Testing $H_0: p = 1/3$ Against $H_a: p > 1/3$. This is plotted for the values of p in H_a when the significance level $\alpha = 0.05$. **Question** If the sample size n increases, how do you think this curve would change?

> **SUMMARY: For a Fixed Significance Level α, P(Type II Error) Decreases**
>
> - as the parameter value moves farther into the H_a values and away from the H_0 value.
> - as the sample size increases.

Also, recall from the discussion in Example 9 about legal verdicts that P(Type II error) increases as α decreases. One reason that extremely small values, such as $\alpha = 0.0001$, are not common is that P(Type II error) is then too high. We may be unlikely to reject H_0, even though it is false.

Before conducting a study, researchers should find P(Type II error) for the size of effect they want to be able to detect. If P(Type II error) is high, it may not be worth (or even ethical) conducting the study unless they can use a larger sample size and lower the probability. Graphs such as the one in Figure 9.18 are helpful for this purpose. To draw it, repeat the calculation in Example 12 for different values of p. You can also construct this graph for a different sample size. (In Example 12, we used $n = 116$.) In fact, often several graphs are drawn for several possible sample sizes to see how the probability of a Type II error depends on n.

The Power of a Test

When H_0 is false, you want the probability of rejecting it to be high. The probability of rejecting H_0 when it is false is called the **power** of the test. For a particular value of the parameter from the range of alternative hypothesis values,

$$\text{Power} = 1 - \text{P(Type II error)}.$$

In Example 12, for instance, P(Type II error) = 0.02 when $p = 0.50$. Therefore, the power of the test at $p = 0.50$ is $1 - 0.02 = 0.98$. The higher the power, the better, so a test power of 0.98, or 98% is quite good.

In practice, it is ideal for studies to have high power while using a relatively small significance level such as 0.05 or 0.01. For a fixed α, the power increases in the same cases that P(Type II error) decreases, namely as the sample size increases and as the parameter value moves farther into the H_a values away from the H_0 value.

Did You Know?

Before granting research support, many agencies (such as the National Institutes of Health) expect research scientists to show that for the planned study, reasonable power (usually, at least 0.80) exists at values of the parameter that are considered practically important. ◀

Power of a Test ◄

Example 13

Treating Infertility in Women

Picture the Scenario

The most recent iteration of the National Survey of Family Growth estimated that 2.3 percent, or about 1.4 million, of women aged 15–44 were infertile in the United States. Occlusions (blockages) in fallopian tubes are thought to be one of the major contributors for infertility, which are often treated with surgery. An alternative approach based on manual physical therapy is less invasive. A grant proposal to explore the effectiveness of this therapy plans to recruit women with blocked tubes and measure the rate at which at least one of the two tubes opens after therapy (called the patency rate). Without any intervention, the patency rate is about 10%. To test the effectiveness of the manual therapy, the null hypothesis H_0: $p = 0.1$ is tested against the alternative hypothesis H_a: $p > 0.1$, where p is the probability of at least one unblocked tube after therapy. Under "Statistical Considerations" in the grant proposal, the following sentence can be found regarding the power of the test: "At a 0.05 significance level, the proposed trial will have 82% power when the true patency rate is 25%."

Questions to Explore

a. How should "82% power" be interpreted?

b. In context, what is a Type II error for the proposed trial? What are the consequences of a Type II error?

c. If $p = 0.25$, what is the probability of committing a Type II error?

d. What can be done to lower the probability of a Type II error, i.e., to increase the power of the test?

Think It Through

a. A power of 82% means the probability of correctly rejecting H_0 when it is false is 0.82. If the actual probability of at least one unblocked tube after therapy is 0.25, there is an 82% chance that the significance test performed with the data of the proposed trial will reject H_0.

b. A Type II error occurs if we do not reject H_0 when in fact the probability of at least one unblocked tube after therapy is larger than 0.1. The consequence would be to dismiss a therapy that may actually result in a patency rate that is better than without any intervention.

c. If $p = 0.25$, the value of P(Type II error) is $1 - $ (Power at $p = 0.25$). This is $1 - 0.82 = 0.18$. A Type II error is not that unlikely to occur for the proposed trial.

d. One way to decrease the probability of a Type II error (and hence to increase the power of the test) is to increase the sample size, i.e., to recruit more patients. (Another option would be to increase the significance level, i.e., increase the probability of a Type I error.)

Insight

Those proposing the grant actually felt satisfied with a probability of a Type II error of 0.18. For cost considerations, they didn't want to recruit more patients. Also, preliminary studies showed that the patency rate may actually be larger than 25%, which would result in a smaller Type II error and, hence, greater than 82% power for the test.

► *Try Exercise 9.65*

Explore Type I and Type II Errors and Power with an App

Let's get a feel for the two types of errors possible in hypothesis testing and what affects them. The *Errors and Power* app (screenshot shown below), visualizes these errors (and power) and lets you interactively change various parameters, such as the sample size, to observe how the errors are affected. Let's refer to the example about the astrologers' claim that they can correctly identify a person based on his or her horoscope with a probability greater than 1/3. Set the first slider for the value of the proportion under the null to 0.33, which is the default and, to indicate that we are using a one-sided test, select Greater under Alternative Hypothesis. To visualize and find the Type II error when, in fact, $p = 0.5$, set the slider for the true proportion to 0.5 (which is also the default). To indicate the sample size, set the slider for n to 116. Now select to display the Type I Error or the Type II Error to visualize the probabilities of these two errors in the displayed graph. The subtitle of the graph shows the numerical values for the

probabilities. Use the app to explore interactively how the Type II error changes when

- A larger or smaller sample is taken. Move the corresponding slider for n to explore. What is the probability of a Type II error if only about 50 (rather than 116) astrologers had taken part in the study?
- The true probability of correct identification is actually smaller than 0.5 but still larger than 0.33. Move the slider for p to explore this. What is the Type II error when $p = 0.33$? (Reset the sample size slider for n to 116.)
- A larger or smaller probability of a Type I error (i.e., the significance level) is selected. Move the corresponding slider for α. From Example 12, the probability of a Type II error was 0.02 when $\alpha = 0.05$, $n = 116$ and $p = 0.5$. What is the probability of a Type II error when $\alpha = 0.10$?

Check the box for Power to explore how the power of a test changes as a function of the sample size or the true probability p. The second tab in the app, titled Population Mean, contains similar functionality to explore errors and power for a significance test about a population mean μ.

Try Exercise 9.66 ◀

9.6   Practicing the Basics

9.60 **Find P(Type II error)**   A study is designed to test $H_0: p = 0.50$ against $H_a: p > 0.50$, taking a random sample of size $n = 100$, using significance level 0.05.

- **a.** Show that the rejection region consists of values for which $\hat{p} > 0.582$. (You can verify your answer by checking the Critical Value option in the *Errors and Power* app.)
- **b.** Sketch a single picture that shows (i) the sampling distribution of $\hat{p}$ when H_0 is true and (ii) the sampling

distribution of $\hat{p}$ when $p = 0.60$. Label each sampling distribution with its mean and standard error and highlight the rejection region. (You can download a base plot from the *Errors and Power* app.)

- **c.** Find P(Type II error) when $p = 0.60$.

9.61 **Gender bias in selecting managers**   Exercise 9.20 tested the claim that female employees were passed over for management training in favor of their male colleagues. Statewide, the large pool of more than 1,000 eligible employees who can be tapped for management training is 40% female and 60% male. Let p be the probability of selecting a female for any given selection. For testing H_0: $p = 0.40$ against H_a: $p < 0.40$ based on a random sample of 50 selections, using the 0.05 significance level, verify that:

a. A Type II error occurs if the sample proportion falls less than 1.645 standard errors below the null hypothesis value, which means that $\hat{p} > 0.286$. (You can also verify your answer by checking the Critical Value option in the *Errors and Power* app.)

b. When $p = 0.20$, a Type II error has probability 0.06. (You can verify your answer with the *Errors and Power* app.)

9.62 Balancing Type I and Type II errors Recall that for the
APP same sample size, the smaller the probability of a Type I error, α, the larger the P(Type II error). Let's check this for Example 12. There we found P(Type II error) for testing H_0: $p = 1/3$ (astrologers randomly guessing) against H_a: $p > 1/3$ when actually $p = 0.50$, with $n = 116$. If we use $\alpha = 0.01$, verify that:

a. A Type II error occurs if the sample proportion falls less than 2.326 standard errors above the null hypothesis value, which means $\hat{p} < 0.435$. (You can also verify your answer by checking the Critical Value option in the *Errors and Power* app, but make sure to enter the numerical value 0.333 for p_0.)

b. When $p = 0.50$, a Type II error has probability 0.08. (You can also get this via the *Errors and Power* app. By comparison, Example 12 found P(Type II error) $= 0.02$ when $\alpha = 0.05$, so we see that P(Type II error) increased when P(Type I error) decreased.)

9.63 P(Type II error) large when p close to H_0 For testing
APP H_0: $p = 1/3$ (astrologers randomly guessing) against H_a: $p > 1/3$ with $n = 116$, Example 12 showed that P(Type II error) $= 0.02$ when $p = 0.50$. Now suppose that $p = 0.35$. Recall that P(Type I error) $= 0.05$.

a. Show that P(Type II error) $= 0.89$. (You can obtain the answer via the *Errors and Power* app, but make sure to enter the numerical value 0.333 for p_0.)

b. Explain intuitively why P(Type II error) is large when the parameter value is close to the value in H_0 and decreases as it moves farther from that value.

9.64 Type II error with two-sided H_a In Example 12 for
APP testing H_0: $p = 1/3$ (astrologers randomly guessing) with $n = 116$ when actually $p = 0.50$, suppose we used H_a: $p \neq 1/3$. Then show, via direct computation such as in Example 12 or by simply using the *Errors and Power* app with $p_0 = 0.3333$ that:

a. A Type II error occurs if $0.248 < \hat{p} < 0.419$.

b. The probability is 0.00 that $\hat{p} < 0.248$ and 0.96 that $\hat{p} > 0.419$.

c. P(Type II error) $= 0.04$.

9.65 Power for infertility trial Consider Example 13 about
TRY the power of the test of H_0: $p = 0.1$ against H_a: $p > 0.1$ used to test the effectiveness of a manual therapy in opening blocked tubes, where p is the probability of at least one unblocked tube after therapy. Another statement in that grant proposal read as follows: "However, if the patency rate is only 20%, the power of the test drops to 60%."

a. How should the power of 60% be interpreted?

b. In context, what is a Type II error for this trial?

c. What is the probability of committing a Type II error if $p = 0.2$? (You can verify, or find, the answer with the *Errors and Power* app.)

9.66 Exploring Type II errors Refer to the app from Activity
TRY 2 at the end of this section, now assuming that we are using the two-sided test H_0: $p = 0.33$ against H_a: $p \neq 0.33$.
APP a. Explain the effect of increasing the sample size on the probability of a Type II error when the true $p = 0.50$.

b. Use the app interactively by using the slider for n to find the sample size needed to achieve a power of at least 90% when truly $p = 0.50$.

c. For a fixed sample size, do you think the probability of a Type II error will increase or decrease when the true p is 0.40 instead of 0.50? Check your answer with the app.

d. Does the power increase or decrease when the significance level is 0.10 instead of 0.05? Check your answer with the app.

Chapter Review

SUMMARY OF NOTATION

H_0 = null hypothesis
H_a = alternative hypothesis
p_0 = null hypothesis value of proportion
se_0 = standard error of sample proportion under H_0

μ_0 = null hypothesis value of mean
α = significance level
  = probability of Type I error (usually 0.05; the P-value must be $\leq \alpha$ to reject H_0)

CHAPTER SUMMARY

A significance test helps us judge whether or not a particular value for a parameter is plausible. Each significance test has five steps:

1. **Assumptions** The most important assumption for any significance test is that the data result from a *random sample* or *randomized experiment*. Specific significance tests make other assumptions, such as those summarized below for significance tests about means and proportions.

2. **Null and alternative hypotheses about the parameter** Null hypotheses have the form $H_0: p = p_0$ for a proportion and $H_0: \mu = \mu_0$ for a mean, where p_0 and μ_0 denote particular values, such as $p_0 = 0.4$ and $\mu_0 = 0$. The most common alternative hypothesis is **two-sided**, such as $H_a: p \neq 0.4$. **One-sided** hypotheses such as $H_a: p > 0.4$ and $H_a: p < 0.4$ are also possible.

3. **Test statistic** This measures how far the sample estimate of the parameter falls from the null hypothesis value. The *z* **statistic** for proportions and the *t* **statistic** for means have the form

$$\text{Test statistic} = \frac{\text{Parameter estimate} - \text{Null hypothesis value}}{\text{Standard error}}$$

This measures the number of standard errors that the parameter estimate ($\hat{p}$ or $\bar{x}$) falls from the null hypothesis value (p_0 or μ_0).

4. **P-value** This is a probability summary of the evidence that the data provide about the null hypothesis. It equals the probability that the test statistic takes a value as or even more extreme than the observed one if the hypothesized value in H_0 is true.

   ■ It is calculated by presuming that H_0 is true.

   ■ The test statistic values that are "more extreme" depend on the alternative hypothesis. When H_a is two-sided, the

P-value is a two-tail probability. When H_a is one-sided, the P-value is a one-tail probability.

   ■ When the P-value is small, the observed data would be unusual if H_0 were true. The smaller the P-value, the stronger the evidence against H_0.

5. **Conclusion** A test concludes by interpreting the P-value in the context of the study. Sometimes a decision is needed, using a fixed and prespecified **significance level** α, usually $\alpha = 0.05$. Then we reject H_0 if the P-value $\leq \alpha$. Two types of error can occur:

   ■ A **Type I error** results from rejecting H_0 when it is true. When H_0 is true, the probability of committing a Type I error is equal to the chosen significance level.

   ■ When H_0 is false, a **Type II error** results from failing to reject H_0. The probability of committing a Type II error depends on many factors, such as the sample size and how far from the null the value of the population parameter falls. For a sufficiently large sample size, the probability of committing either type of error can be kept small. The **power** of the test is the probability to reject H_0 correctly.

Limitations of Significance Tests Confidence intervals are more informative than significance tests because they estimate the range of plausible values, instead of just indicating whether a particular value is plausible or not. When possible, provide an estimate of the size of the effect in the conclusions by quoting a confidence interval. However, if a measure for the strength of evidence is needed, the P-value provides one.

P-values can be misinterpreted and misused in a variety of ways, for instance by not understanding the difference between statistical significance and practical relevance or by selective reporting.

SUMMARY: Significance Tests for Population Proportions and Means

	Parameter	
	Proportion	**Mean**
1. Assumptions	Categorical variable Randomization Expected numbers of successes and failures ≥ 15	Quantitative variable Randomization Approximately normal population
2. Hypotheses	$H_0: p = p_0$ $H_a: p \neq p_0$ (two-sided) $H_a: p > p_0$ (one-sided) $H_a: p < p_0$ (one-sided)	$H_0: \mu = \mu_0$ $H_a: \mu \neq \mu_0$ (two-sided) $H_a: \mu > \mu_0$ (one-sided) $H_a: \mu < \mu_0$ (one-sided)
3. Test Statistic	$z = \dfrac{\hat{p} - p_0}{se_0}$ $(se_0 = \sqrt{p_0(1 - p_0)/n})$	$t = \dfrac{\bar{x} - \mu_0}{se}$ $(se = s/\sqrt{n})$
4. P-value	Two-tail ($H_a: p \neq p_0$) or right tail ($H_a: p > p_0$) or left tail ($H_a: p < p_0$) probability from standard normal distribution	Two-tail ($H_a: \mu \neq \mu_0$) or right tail ($H_a: \mu > \mu_0$) or left tail ($H_a: \mu < \mu_0$) probability from t distribution ($df = n - 1$)
5. Conclusion	Interpret P-value in context Reject H_0 if P-value $\leq \alpha$	Interpret P-value in context Reject H_0 if P-value $\leq \alpha$

LEARNING OBJECTIVES

1. Understand the five steps of a significance test for testing about both a population proportion and a population mean.

2. Understand the assumptions underlying each test.

3. Contrast one-sided and two-sided hypothesis tests.

4. Recognize that the test statistic measures the number of standard errors between our statistic (estimate) and the hypothesized parameter, presuming that the null hypothesis is true.

5. Explain and interpret the P-value in the context of the scenario.

6. Understand the distinction between statistical significance and practical relevance.

7. Understand why confidence intervals are often more useful than the decision reached with a significance test.

8. Define Type I and Type II errors and provide potential consequences of each error in the context of the scenario.

9. Understand the notion of a significance level and how it connects to the probability of a Type I and Type II error.

10. Explain which error is more important to minimize, a Type I or Type II error, for a particular scenario.

11. (optional) Understand how the probability of a Type II error depends on the sample size and a particular value in the alternative hypothesis. Understand what the power of a test is.

ANSWERS TO THE CHAPTER FIGURE QUESTIONS

Figure 9.1 A P-value of 0.01 gives stronger evidence against the null hypothesis. This smaller P-value (0.01 compared to 0.20) indicates it would be more unusual to get the observed sample data or a more extreme value if the null hypothesis is true.

Figure 9.2 It is the relatively large values of $\hat{p}$ (with their corresponding right-tail z-scores) that support the alternative hypothesis of $p > 1/3$.

Figure 9.3 Values more extreme than the observed test statistic value can be either relatively smaller or larger to support the alternative hypothesis $p \neq p_0$. These smaller or larger values are ones that fall farther in either the left or right tail.

Figure 9.7 The t-score indicates the number of standard errors $\bar{x}$ falls from the null hypothesis mean. The farther out a t-score falls in the tails, the farther the sample mean falls from the null hypothesis mean, providing stronger evidence against H_0.

Figure 9.9 For $H_a: \mu > 0$, the t test statistics providing stronger evidence against H_0 will be t statistics corresponding to the relatively large $\bar{x}$ values falling to the right of the hypothesized mean of 0. The t test statistics for these values of $\bar{x}$ are positive.

Figure 9.10 The standard error for the significance test is computed using p_0, the hypothesized proportion. The standard error for the confidence interval is computed using $\hat{p}$, the sample proportion. The values p_0 and $\hat{p}$ are not necessarily the same; therefore, there is not an exact equivalence.

Figure 9.11 The plots suggest that the population distribution of weight change is skewed to the right.

Figure 9.12 Using a significance level of 0.05, the rejection region consists of values of $z \geq 1.645$.

Figure 9.13 A sample mean of 6.09 indicates both statistical and practical significance.

Figure 9.15 The blue area becomes larger (i.e., the upper 10% instead of the upper 5%), and we are rejecting for even smaller values of $\hat{p}$. Then, whatever the true value of p, we are more likely to reject the null hypothesis (because the rejection region is larger) and therefore *less likely* to fail to reject the null hypothesis. The Type II error would be *smaller* when using $\alpha = 0.10$ than $\alpha = 0.05$.

Figure 9.16 The probability of a Type II error will increase.

Figure 9.17 A correct decision for the case $p = 0.50$ is to reject $H_0: p = 1/3$. The shaded area under the left tail of the curve for the case $p = 0.50$ represents the probability we would not reject $H_0: p = 1/3$, which is the probability of an incorrect decision for this situation. This shaded area is the probability of committing a Type II error.

Figure 9.18 By increasing the sample size n, the probability of a Type II error decreases. The curve would more quickly approach the horizontal axis, indicating that the Type II error probability more rapidly approaches a probability of 0 as p increases.

STATISTICAL SOFTWARE

Art of Stat Web Apps

■ **Inference for a Proportion** This app carries out inference for a population proportion. When selecting Significance Test under Type of Inference and providing the null hypothesis value p_0, the app displays the null standard error se_0, the z test statistic and the resulting P-value of a significance test. You can choose between a one- or two-sided test. The app displays the standard normal sampling distribution and marks the observed test statistic and the P-value on it. Alternatively, you can also plot the sampling distribution of the sample proportion to help interpret the P-value.

■ **Inference for a Mean** This app carries out inference for a population mean. When selecting Significance Test under Type of Inference and providing the null hypothesis value μ_0, the app displays the t test statistic and the resulting P-value of a significance test. You can choose between a one- or two-sided

test. The app displays the t-distribution and marks the observed test statistic and the P-value on it.

■ **Errors and Power** This app illustrates the types of errors that can occur and finds the probability of a Type II error and the power for a significance test, both for proportions and for means. Various sliders illustrate how the errors are interrelated and how the probability of a Type II error depends on the true parameter value, the sample size, and the chosen significance level.

R

■ **Test for a Proportion:** The `prop.test` function returns results of a significance test about a proportion. Using the data from Example 4,

```
> prop.test(637, 1353, p=0.5, alternative=
'two-sided', correct=FALSE)
```

```
data: 637 out of 1353, null probability 0.5
X-squared = 4.6127, df = 1, p-value = 0.03174
alternative hypothesis: true p is not equal
to 0.5
```

Here, p=0.5 specifies the value for the proportion under the null hypothesis. For the test in Example 3, you would use p=1/3 and also `alternative='greater'` to specify a one-sided test. The output spells out the alternative hypothesis and shows that the P-value is equal to 0.03174 (0.032 rounded), but doesn't show the z test statistic value of -2.15. (Instead, it shows the square of it and labels it X-squared.)

■ **Test for a Mean:** The `t.test` function returns results of a significance test about a mean. Illustrating with the small data set from Exercise 9.33, we get the following output:

```
> x <- c(2000, 1000, 3000, 2000)
> t.test(x, mu=1000, alternative='greater')

        One Sample t-test
data:  x
t = 2.4495, df = 3, p-value = 0.04586
alternative hypothesis: true mean is greater
than 1000
```

Here, mu=1000 specifies the value of the mean under the null hypothesis. The output spells out the alternative hypothesis tested and shows the value of the test statistic ($t = 2.4495$, or 2.45 rounded), the degrees of freedom ($df = 4 - 1 = 3$) and the P-value (0.04586).

CHAPTER EXERCISES

Practicing the Basics

9.67 **H_0 or H_a?** For each of the following hypotheses, explain whether it is a null hypothesis or an alternative hypothesis:

a. For females, the population mean on the political ideology scale is equal to 4.0.

b. For males, the population proportion who support the death penalty is larger than 0.50.

c. The diet has an effect, the population mean change in weight being less than 0.

d. For all Subway stores worldwide, the difference between sales this month and in the corresponding month a year ago has a mean of 0.

9.68 **Write H_0 and H_a** For each of the following scenarios, define the parameter of interest and appropriate null and alternative hypotheses.

a. To motivate more fathers to take a parental leave, the government of Austria extended child care benefits for two more months if the new father stays home for that time. Now, a study wants to investigate whether more new fathers stayed home compared to the 15% of new fathers who stayed home before the incentive was available.

b. To curb CO_2 emissions, the government of Austria subsidized the purchase of green vehicles. Now, a study wants to investigate whether the average CO_2 emissions from cars purchased last year has dropped from the 160 g/km of 5 years ago.

c. The legal retirement age for women in Austria is 60. A study wants to assess whether the actual average retirement age of women is different from 60.

9.69 **ESP** A person who claims to possess extrasensory perception (ESP) says she can guess more often than not the outcome of a flip of a balanced coin. Out of 30 flips, she guesses correctly 18 times. Would you conclude that she truly has ESP? Answer by reporting all five steps of a significance test of the hypothesis that each of her guesses has probability 0.50 of being correct against the alternative that corresponds to her having ESP.

9.70 **Free-throw accuracy** Consider all cases in which a pro basketball player shoots two consecutive free throws and makes exactly one. Which do you think is more common: making the first and missing the second, or missing the first and making the second? One of the best shooters was Larry Bird of the Boston Celtics. During 1980–1982 he made only the first free throw 34 times and made only the second 48 times (A. Tversky and T. Gilovich, (1989), *Chance*, vol. 2, pp. 16–21). Does this suggest that one sequence was truly more likely than the other sequence for Larry Bird? Answer by conducting a significance test (a) defining notation and specifying assumptions and hypotheses, (b) finding the test statistic, and (c) finding the P-value and interpreting it in this context.

9.71 **Brown or Whitman?** California's governor election in 2010 had two major candidates, Brown and Whitman.

a. For a random sample of 650 voters in one exit poll, 360 voted for Brown, 240 for Whitman, and the rest for someone else. Conduct all five steps of a test of H_0: $p = 0.50$ against H_a: $p \neq 0.50$, where p denotes the probability that a randomly selected voter prefers Brown. Would you be willing to predict the outcome of the election? Explain how to make a decision, using a significance level of 0.05. Also, find and then explain why a confidence interval for p is more informative than the result of the significance test.

b. Suppose the sample size had been 50 voters, of whom 28 voted for Brown. Show that the sample proportion is similar to the sample proportion in part a, but the test statistic and P-value are very different. Are you now willing to predict the outcome of the election?

c. Using part a and part b, explain how results of a significance test can depend on the sample size.

9.72 **Protecting the environment?** When the 2010 General Social Survey asked, "Would you be willing to pay much higher taxes in order to protect the environment?" (variable GRNTAXES), 459 out of 1,085 people said they are willing. Let p denote the population proportion who would answer that they are willing. The screenshot from the *Inference for a Proportion* app shows the following results to analyze whether a majority or minority of Americans would be willing:

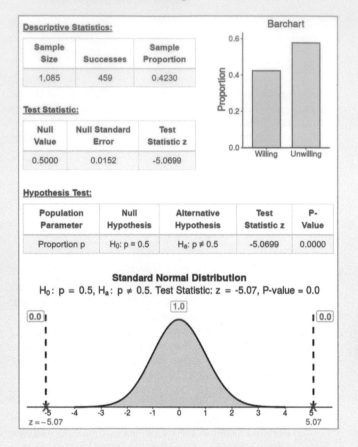

Descriptive Statistics:

Sample Size	Successes	Sample Proportion
1,085	459	0.4230

Test Statistic:

Null Value	Null Standard Error	Test Statistic z
0.5000	0.0152	-5.0699

Hypothesis Test:

Population Parameter	Null Hypothesis	Alternative Hypothesis	Test Statistic z	P-Value
Proportion p	H_0: p = 0.5	H_a: p ≠ 0.5	-5.0699	0.0000

Standard Normal Distribution
H_0: p = 0.5, H_a: p ≠ 0.5. Test Statistic: z = -5.07, P-value = 0.0

z = -5.07   5.07

a. What are the assumptions for the significance test? Do they seem to be satisfied for this application? Explain.

b. Using this screenshot, specify the null and alternative hypotheses that are tested and report the point estimate of *p* and the value of the test statistic. What is the distribution of the test statistic when the null hypothesis is true?

c. Report and interpret the P-value in context.

d. According to the P-value, is it plausible that $p = 0.50$? Explain.

e. Use the app to find a 95% confidence interval for *p*. Explain an advantage of the confidence interval over the significance test.

9.73 Majority supports gay marriage An Associated Press article appearing in the *New York Times* in March 2015 mentioned that "In the late 1980s, support for gay marriage was essentially unheard of in America. Just a quarter century later, it's now favored by a clear majority of Americans." The article supports this conclusion by using data from the 2014 General Social Survey, which asked whether homosexuals should have the right to marry. Of the 1,690 respondents, 955 agreed. Conduct all five steps of a significance test to see whether the proportion among Americans supporting gay marriage in 2014 is different from 0.5. Use a significance level of 0.05.

9.74 Plant inheritance In an experiment on chlorophyll inheritance in maize (corn), of the 1,103 seedlings of self-fertilized green plants, 854 seedlings were green and 249

were yellow. Theory predicts the ratio of green to yellow is 3 to 1. Show all five steps of a test of the hypothesis that 3 to 1 is the true ratio. Interpret the P-value in context.

9.75 Ellsberg paradox You are told that a ball will be randomly drawn from one of two boxes (A and B), both of which contain black balls and red balls, and if a red ball is chosen, you will win $100. You are also told that Box A contains half black balls and half red balls, but you are not told the proportions in Box B. Which box would you pick?

a. Set up notation and specify hypotheses to test whether the population proportion who would pick Box A is 0.50.

b. For a random sample of 40 people, 36 pick Box A. Can you make a conclusion about whether the proportion for one option is higher in the population? Explain all steps of your reasoning. (Logically those who picked Box A would seem to think that Box B has greater chance of a black ball. However, a paradox first discussed by Daniel Ellsberg predicts that if they were now told that they would instead receive $100 if a black ball is chosen, they would overwhelmingly pick Box A again because they prefer definite information over ambiguity.)

9.76 Start a hockey team A fraternity at a university lobbies the administration to start a hockey team. To bolster its case, it reports that of a simple random sample of 100 students, 83% support starting the team. Upon further investigation, their sample has 80 males and 20 females. Should you be skeptical of whether the sample was random if you know that 55% of the student body population was male? Answer this by performing all steps of a two-sided significance test.

9.77 Interest charges on credit card A bank wants to evaluate which credit card would be more attractive to its customers, one with a high interest rate for unpaid balances but no annual cost or one with a low interest rate for unpaid balances but an annual cost of $40. For a random sample of 100 of its 52,000 customers, 38 say they prefer the one that has an annual cost. The data were entered into the *Inference for a Proportion* app which reported a 95% confidence interval of (0.28, 0.48).

a. Interpret the confidence interval.

b. Would the P-value of a hypothesis test H_0: $p = 0.5$ against H_a: $p \neq 0.5$ be less than or larger than 0.05? Explain.

9.78 Jurors and gender A jury list contains the names of all individuals who may be called for jury duty. The proportion of the available jurors on the list who are women is 0.53. Forty people are selected from the list to serve as candidates to serve on the jury.

a. Set up notation and hypotheses and specify assumptions to test whether or not there was gender bias in the selection of the jurors from the list.

b. Five of the 40 selected were women. Find the test statistic.

c. Report the P-value and interpret.

d. Explain how to make a decision using a significance level of 0.01.

9.79   **Type I and Type II errors**   Refer to the previous exercise.

   a. Explain what Type I and Type II errors mean in the context of that exercise.

   b. If you made an error with the decision in part d, is it a Type I or a Type II error?

9.80   **Levine = author?**   The authorship of an old document is in doubt. A historian hypothesizes that the author was a journalist named Jacalyn Levine. Upon a thorough investigation of Levine's known works, it is observed that one unusual feature of her writing was that she consistently began 10% of her sentences with the word "whereas." To test the historian's hypothesis, it is decided to count the number of sentences in the disputed document that begin with the word *whereas*. Out of the 300 sentences in the document, none begin with that word. Let p denote the probability that any one sentence written by the unknown author of the document begins with the word "whereas."

   a. Conduct a test of the hypothesis $H_0: p = 0.10$ against $H_a: p \neq 0.10$. What conclusion can you make, using a significance level of 0.05?

   b. What assumptions are needed for that conclusion to be valid? (F. Mosteller and D. Wallace conducted an investigation similar to this to determine whether Alexander Hamilton or James Madison was the author of 12 of the *Federalist Papers*. See *Inference and Disputed Authorship: The Federalist*, Addison-Wesley, 1964.)

9.81   **Practice steps of test for mean**   For a quantitative variable, you want to test $H_0: \mu = 0$ against $H_a: \mu \neq 0$. The 10 observations are

$$3, 7, 3, 3, 0, 8, 1, 12, 5, 8.$$

   a. Show that (i) $\bar{x} = 5.0$, (ii) $s = 3.71$, (iii) standard error $= 1.17$, (iv) test statistic $= 4.26$, and (v) $df = 9$.

   b. The P-value is 0.002. Make a decision using a significance level of 0.05. Interpret.

   c. If you had instead used $H_a: \mu > 0$, what would the P-value be? Interpret it.

   d. If you had instead used $H_a: \mu < 0$, what would the P-value be? Interpret it. (*Hint:* Recall that the two one-sided P-values should sum to 1.)

9.82   **Lending amount**   The website lendingclub.com is a "trading" platform for personal loans. Borrowers can ask for unsecured personal loans between $1,000 and $40,000, and investors can search and browse the loan listings and select loans that they want to invest in based on the information supplied about the borrower. Historically, the average loan amount funded by investors has been $15,500 in the last couple of years before 2018. To investigate if this has changed in 2018, researchers obtained a random sample of 200 loans funded in 2018. The data from this sample are preloaded in the *Inference for a Mean* app and are also available from the book's website. Use the screenshot from the app to answer the following questions.

   a. Report the test statistic value and show how it was obtained from other values reported in the app. Interpet what it means.

   b. Report and explain what the P-value represents.

   c. Write a conclusion in context.

   d. Does a 95% confidence interval for the population mean include the value 15,500? Explain.

Descriptive Statistics:

Sample Size	Sample Mean	Sample Standard Deviation
200	16,604	9,802

Test Statistic:

Null Value	Standard Error	Test Statistic t
15,500	693.1	1.593

Hypothesis Test:

Population Parameter	Null Hypothesis	Alternative Hypothesis	Test Statistic t	P-value
Mean μ	μ = 15500	μ ≠ 15500	1.5926	0.1128

$H_0: \mu = 15500$, $H_a: \mu \neq 15500$. Test Statistic: $t = 1.593$, P-value $= 0.1128$

t Distribution with df = 199

0.8872   0.0564   0.0564

9.83   **Hours at work in 2018**   The screenshot shows results on female subjects included in the 2018 GSS responding to the question of how many hours they worked in the previous week at all jobs.

Descriptive Statistics:

Sample Size	Sample Mean	Sample Standard Deviation
711	38.15	13.28

Test Statistic:

Null Value	Standard Error	Test Statistic t
40	0.4979	-3.706

Hypothesis Test:

Population Parameter	Null Hypothesis	Alternative Hypothesis	Test Statistic t	P-value
Mean μ	μ = 40	μ ≠ 40	-3.7063	0.0002

t Distribution with df = 710

$H_0: \mu = 40$, $H_a: \mu \neq 40$. Test Statistic: $t = -3.706$, P-value $= 0.0002$

0.9998   0.0001   0.0001

   a. State the hypotheses tested.

   b. Explain how to interpret the values for (i) the standard error, (ii) the t test statistic, and (iii) the P-value.

   c. Write a conclusion of the test in context.

   d. Does a 95% confidence interval for the mean include the value 40? Explain without computing the confidence interval.

9.84 **Females liberal or conservative?**   Example 10 compared
mean political beliefs (on a 1 to 7 point scale) to the
moderate value of 4.0, using GSS data. Test whether the
population mean equals 4.00 for females, for whom
the sample mean was 4.06 and standard deviation was
1.37 for a sample of size 1,345. Carry out the five steps of
a significance test, reporting and interpreting the P-value
in context. (Note: You can enter these summary statistics
in the *Inference for a Mean* app, by selecting Summary
Statistics under the Enter Data menu.)

9.85 **Blood pressure**   When Vincenzo Baranello's blood pressure is in control, his systolic blood pressure reading has
a mean of 130. For the last six times he has monitored his
blood pressure, he has obtained the values

$$140, 150, 155, 155, 160, 140.$$

a. Does this provide strong evidence that his true mean
has changed? Carry out the five steps of the significance test, interpreting the P-value.

b. Review the assumptions that this method makes.
For each assumption, discuss it in context.

9.86 **Increasing blood pressure**   In the previous exercise, suppose you had predicted that if the mean changed, it would
have increased above the control value. State the alternative hypothesis for this prediction and report and interpret
the P-value.

9.87 **Tennis balls in control?**   When it is operating correctly,
a machine for manufacturing tennis balls produces balls
with a mean weight of 57.6 grams. A random sample of
eight balls from the last batch produced has weights

$$57.3, 57.4, 57.2, 57.5, 57.4, 57.1, 57.3, 57.0$$

a. Find the test statistic and P-value for a test of whether
the process is in control against the alternative that
the true mean of the process now differs from 57.6.

b. For a significance level of 0.05, explain what you would
conclude. Express your conclusion so it would be understood by someone who never studied statistics.

c. If your decision in part b is in error, what type of error
have you made?

9.88 **Catalog sales**   A company that sells products through
mail-order catalogs wants to evaluate whether the mean
sales for its most recent catalog were different from the
mean of $15 from past catalogs. For a random sample of
100 customers, the mean sales were $10, with a standard
deviation of $10. Find a P-value to provide the extent of
evidence that the mean differed with this catalog. Interpret.

9.89 **Wage claim false?**   Management claims that the mean income for all senior-level assembly-line workers in a large
company equals $500 per week. An employee decides to
test this claim, believing that it is actually different from
$500. For a random sample of nine employees, the in-
comes are

$$430, 450, 450, 440, 460, 420, 430, 450, 440.$$

Conduct a significance test of whether the population
mean income equals $500 per week. Include all assump-
tions, the hypotheses, test statistic, and P-value and interpret the result in context.

9.90 **CI and test**   Refer to the previous exercise.

a. For which significance levels can you reject H_0?
(i) 0.10, (ii) 0.05, or (iii) 0.01.

b. Based on the answers in part a, for which confidence
levels would the confidence interval contain 500?
(i) 0.90, (ii) 0.95, or (iii) 0.99.

c. Use part a and part b to illustrate the correspondence
between results of significance tests and results of confidence intervals.

d. In the context of this study, what is (i) a Type I error
and (ii) a Type II error?

9.91 **CI and test connection**   The P-value for testing
$H_0: \mu = 100$ against $H_a: \mu \neq 100$ is 0.043.

a. What decision is made using a 0.05 significance level?

b. If the decision in part a is in error, what type of error
is it?

c. Does a 95% confidence interval for μ contain 100?
Explain.

9.92 **Religious beliefs statistically significant?**   A journal article that deals with changes in religious beliefs
over time states, "For these subjects, the difference in
their responses on the scale of religiosity between age
16 and the current survey was statistically significant
(P-value < 0.05)."

a. How would you explain to someone who has never
taken a statistics course what it means for the result to
be "statistically significant" with a P-value < 0.05?

b. Explain why it would have been more informative if
the authors provided the actual P-value rather than
merely indicating that it is below 0.05.

c. Can you conclude that a practically *important* change
in religiosity has occurred between age 16 and the
time of the current survey? Why or why not?

9.93 **How to reduce chance of error?**   In making a decision in
a significance test, a researcher worries about rejecting H_0
when it may actually be true.

a. Explain how the researcher can control the probability of this type of error.

b. Why should the researcher probably not set this probability equal to 0.00001?

9.94 **Legal trial errors**   Consider the analogy discussed in
Section 9.4 between making a decision about a null
hypothesis in a significance test and making a decision
about the innocence or guilt of a defendant in a
criminal trial.

a. Explain the difference between Type I and Type II
errors in the trial setting.

b. In this context, explain intuitively why decreasing the
chance of Type I error increases the chance of Type II
error.

9.95 **P(Type II error) with smaller _n_**   Consider Example 12
about testing $H_0: p = 1/3$ against $H_a: p > 1/3$ for the
astrology study, with $n = 116$. Find P(Type II error) for
testing $H_0: p = 1/3$ against $H_a: p > 1/3$ when actually

$p = 0.50$, if the sample size is 60 instead of 116. Do this by showing that:

a. The standard error is 0.061 when H_0 is true.

b. The rejection region consists of $\hat{p}$ values above 0.433.

c. When $p = 0.50$, the probability that $\hat{p}$ falls below 0.433 is the left-tail probability below -1.03 under a standard normal curve. What is the answer? Why would you expect P(Type II error) to be larger when n is smaller?

(*Hint:* For parts b and c, you can check your answer using the Errors and Power app.)

Concepts and Investigations

9.96 Gender of best friend A GSS question asked the gender of your best friend. Of 1,381 people interviewed, 147 said their best friend had the opposite gender, and 1,234 said their best friend had the same gender. Prepare a short report in which you analyze these data using a confidence interval and a significance test (you can use the *Inference for a Proportion* app to obtain either) where you test whether half of the population has someone from the opposite sex as their best friend. Which do you think is more informative? Why?

9.97 Baseball home team advantage In Major League Baseball's 2010 season, the home team won 1,359 games, and the away team won 1,071 (www.mlb.com).

a. Although these games are not a random sample, explain how you could think of these data as giving you information about some long-run phenomenon.

b. Analyze these data using (i) a significance test and (ii) a confidence interval. Which method is more informative? Why?

9.98 Statistics and scientific objectivity The president of the American Statistical Association stated, "Statistics has become the modern-day enforcer of scientific objectivity. Terms like randomization, blinding, and 0.05 significance wield a no-doubt effective objectivity nightstick." He also discussed how learning what effects *aren't* in the data is as important as learning what effects *are* significant. In this vein, explain how statistics provides an objective framework for testing the claims of what many believe to be quack science, such as astrology and therapeutic touch where practitioners claim to improve medical conditions by using their hands to manipulate the human energy field. (*Source:* Bradley Efron, *Amstat News*, July 2004, p. 3.)

9.99 Two-sided or one-sided? A medical researcher gets a P-value of 0.056 for testing $H_0: \mu = 0$ against $H_a: \mu \neq 0$. Since he believes that the true mean is positive and is worried that his favorite journal will not publish the results because they are not "significant at the 0.05 level," he instead reports in his article the P-value of 0.028 for $H_a: \mu > 0$. Explain what is wrong with

a. Reporting the one-sided P-value after seeing the data.

b. The journal's policy to publish results only if they are statistically significant.

9.100 No significant change and P-value An article in a journal states that "no statistical significant change was found in the mean glucose level of the brain before and after

making a cell phone call for 50 minutes (P-value = 0.63)." In practical terms, how would you explain to someone who has not studied statistics what this means?

9.101 Subgroup lack of significance A crossover study investigated the change in pain scores when using a magnetic device over a placebo for 54 people suffering from low back or knee pain. The study reported a significant result overall, indicating that the magnetic device resulted in significantly less pain. However, when the analysis was done separately for the 27 people with shorter illness duration and the 27 people with longer illness duration, results were not significant. Explain how it might be possible that an analysis could give a P-value below 0.05 using an entire sample but not with subgroups, even if the subgroups have the same effects. (*Hint:* What is the impact of the smaller sample size on the (i) test statistic, (ii) t distribution, and (iii) P-value for each subgroup?)

9.102 Vitamin E and prostate cancer A study in Finland in 1998 suggested that vitamin E pills reduced the risk of prostate cancer in a group of male smokers. This was only one effect in a series of reported successes for vitamin E and other health conditions. A more recent study reported that selenium or vitamin E, used alone or in combination, did not prevent prostate cancer in a population of relatively healthy men (*JAMA*, April 2009). Discuss the factors that can cause different medical studies to come to different conclusions.

9.103 Overestimated effect When medical stories in the mass media report dangers of certain agents (e.g., coffee drinking), later research often suggests that the effects may not exist or are weaker than first believed. Explain how this could happen if some journals tend to publish only statistically significant results.

9.104 Choosing α An alternative hypothesis states that a newly developed drug is better than the one currently used to treat a serious illness. If we reject H_0, the new drug will be prescribed instead of the current one.

a. Why might we prefer to use a smaller significance level than 0.05, such as 0.01?

b. What is a disadvantage of using $\alpha = 0.01$ instead of 0.05?

9.105 Why not accept H_0? Explain why the terminology "do not reject H_0" is preferable to "accept H_0."

9.106 Report P-value It is more informative and potentially less misleading to conclude a test by reporting and interpreting the P-value rather than by merely indicating whether you reject H_0 at the 0.05 significance level. One reason is that a reader can then tell whether the result is significant *at a significance level the reader thinks is acceptable,* which may be different from 0.05. Give another reason.

9.107 Significance Explain the difference between *statistical significance* and *practical relevance.* Make up an example to illustrate your reasoning.

9.108 More doctors recommend An advertisement by Company A says that three of every four doctors recommend pain reliever A over all other brands combined.

a. If the company based this claim on interviewing a random sample of doctors, explain how it could use a significance test to back up the claim.

b. Explain why this claim would be more impressive if it is based on a (i) random sample of 40 doctors than if it is based on a random sample of 4 doctors and (ii) random sample of 40 doctors nationwide than the sample of all 40 doctors who work in a particular hospital.

9.109 Medical diagnosis error Consider the medical diagnosis of breast cancer with mammograms. An AP story (September 19, 2002) said that a woman has about a 50% chance of having a false-positive diagnosis over the course of 10 annual mammography tests. Relate this result to the chance of eventually making a Type I error if you do lots of significance tests.

9.110 Bad P-value interpretations A random sample of size 1,000 has $\bar{x} = 104$. The significance level α is set at 0.05. The P-value for testing $H_0: \mu = 100$ against $H_a: \mu \neq 100$ is 0.057. Explain what is incorrect about each of the following interpretations of this P-value and provide a proper interpretation.

a. The probability that the null hypothesis is correct equals 0.057.

b. The probability that $\bar{x} = 104$ if H_0 is true equals 0.057.

c. If in fact $\mu \neq 100$ so H_0 is false, the probability equals 0.057 that the data would show at least as much evidence against H_0 as the observed data.

d. The probability of a Type I error equals 0.057.

e. We can accept H_0 at the $\alpha = 0.05$ level.

f. We can reject H_0 at the $\alpha = 0.05$ level.

9.111 Interpret P-value One interpretation for the P-value is that it is the smallest value for the significance level α for which we can reject H_0. Illustrate using the P-value of 0.057 from the previous exercise.

9.112 Incorrectly posed hypotheses What is wrong with expressing hypotheses about proportions and means in a form such as $H_0: \hat{p} = 0.50$ and $H_0: \bar{x} = 0$?

Multiple Choice or True/False

9.113 Small P-value The P-value for testing $H_0: \mu = 100$ against $H_a: \mu \neq 100$ is 0.001. This indicates that:

a. There is strong evidence that $\mu = 100$.

b. There is strong evidence that $\mu \neq 100$, since if μ were equal to 100, it would be unusual to obtain data such as those observed.

c. The probability that $\mu = 100$ is 0.001.

d. The probability that $\mu = 100$ is the significance level, usually taken to be 0.05.

9.114 Probability of P-value When H_0 is true in a t test with significance level 0.05, the probability that the P-value falls ≤ 0.05

a. equals 0.05.

b. equals 0.95.

c. equals 0.05 for a one-sided test and 0.10 for a two-sided test.

d. can't be specified because it depends also on P(Type II error).

9.115 Pollution There is concern that an industrial plant of a company is not adhering to environmental laws governing the discharge of wastewater. An environmental action group takes four readings to analyze whether the true mean discharge of wastewater per hour exceeds the company claim of 1,000 gallons. When we make a decision in the one-sided test by using $\alpha = 0.05$:

a. If the company is not exceeding the limit and μ is at most 1,000 there is only a 5% chance that we will conclude that it is exceeding the limit.

b. If the plant is exceeding the limit, there is only a 5% chance that we will conclude that it is not exceeding the limit.

c. The probability that the sample mean equals the observed value is equal to 0.05 if H_0 were true.

d. If we reject H_0, the probability that it is actually true is 0.05.

e. All of the above.

9.116 Interpret P(Type II error) For a test of $H_0: \mu = 0$ against $H_a: \mu > 0$ based on $n = 30$ observations and using $\alpha = 0.05$ significance level, P(Type II error) = 0.36 at $\mu = 4$. Identify the response that is *incorrect*.

a. At $\mu = 5$, P(Type II error) < 0.36.

b. If $\alpha = 0.01$, then at $\mu = 4$, P(Type II error) > 0.36.

c. If $n = 50$, then at $\mu = 4$, P(Type II error) > 0.36.

d. The power of the test is 0.64 at $\mu = 4$.

9.117 True or false: Errors The probability of making a Type I error and the probability of making a Type II error are related through P(Type II error) = 1 − P(Type I error).

9.118 True or false: Rejecting If we reject $H_0: \mu = 0$ in a study about change in weight on a new diet using $\alpha = 0.01$, then we also reject it using $\alpha = 0.05$.

9.119 True or false: P-value and confidence interval A study about the change in weight on a new diet reports P-value = 0.043 for testing $H_0: \mu = 0$ against $H_a: \mu \neq 0$. If the authors had instead reported a 95% confidence interval for μ, then the interval would have contained 0.

9.120 True or false: Confidence interval and P-value A 95% confidence interval for μ = population mean IQ is (96, 110). So, in the test of $H_0: \mu = 100$ against $H_a: \mu \neq 100$, the P-value > 0.05.

9.121 True or false: Significance level For a fixed significance level α, the probability of a Type II error increases when the sample size increases.

9.122 True or false: Type II error When testing $H_0: \mu = 100$ against $H_a: \mu \neq 100$, the probability of a Type II error decreases the further the true population mean μ is from 100.

9.123 True or false: H_0 true? The P-value is the probability that H_0 is true.

9.124 True or false: Power The power of a test = 1 − P(Type II error).

Advanced Concepts

9.125 A binomial headache A null hypothesis states that the population proportion p of headache sufferers who have better pain relief with aspirin than with another pain reliever equals 0.50. For a crossover study with 10 subjects, all 10 have better relief with aspirin. If the null hypothesis were true, by the binomial distribution the probability of this sample result (which is the most extreme) equals $(0.50)^{10} = 0.001$. In fact, this is the small-sample P-value for testing H_0: $p = 0.50$ against H_a: $p > 0.50$. Does this P-value give (a) strong evidence in favor of H_0 or (b) strong evidence against H_0? Explain why.

9.126 P-value for small samples The experiment mentioned in Exercise 9.18, on whether dogs can detect bladder cancer by selecting the correct urine specimen (out of seven), resulted in the following data: In 54 trials, the dog correctly identified the correct specimen (out of 7) 22 times.

a. Explain why the sample size criterion for the hypothesis test H_0: $p = 1/7$ versus H_a: $p > 1/7$ is violated.

b. If H_0: $p = 1/7$ is true, the random variable $X =$ number of correct selections has the binomial distribution with $n = 54$ and $p = 1/7$. Why?

c. For H_a: $p > 1/7$, with $x = 22$, the small sample P-value using the binomial is $P(22) + P(23) + \dots + P(54)$, where $P(x)$ denotes the binomial probability of outcome x with $p = 1/7$. (This equals 0.0000019.) Why would the P-value be this sum rather than just $P(22)$?

9.127 Standard error formulas Suppose you wanted to test H_0: $p = 0.50$, but you had 0 successes in n trials. If you had found the test statistic by using the $se = \sqrt{\hat{p}(1 - \hat{p})/n}$ designed for confidence intervals, show what happens to the test statistic. Explain why $se_0 = \sqrt{p_0(1 - p_0)/n}$ is a more appropriate se for tests.

9.128 Rejecting true H_0? A medical researcher conducts a significance test whenever she analyzes a new data set. Over time, she conducts 100 independent tests.

a. Suppose the null hypothesis is true in every case. What is the distribution of the number of times she rejects the null hypothesis at the 0.05 level?

b. Suppose she rejects the null hypothesis in five of the tests. Is it plausible that the null hypothesis is correct in every case? Explain.

Student Activities

9.129 Pain relief A study compares a new drug for pain relief in patients with chronic migraine against a placebo. Each patient is given both the drug and the placebo (in random order) and reports which one works better. Let p denote the probability that the pain relief is better with the drug. You have to decide whether you can reject H_0: $p = 0.50$ in favor of H_a: $p \neq 0.50$ based on seeing the results of one patient after another. Ahead of time, you have no idea whether the drug or placebo works better, and you assume they are equally effective (i.e., you assume the null hypothesis is true.) Each student should indicate:

a. How many consecutive patients reporting better relief with the drug would be necessary before he or she would feel comfortable rejecting H_0: $p = 0.50$ in favor of H_a: $p \neq 0.50$ and concluding that the drug works better.

b. How many consecutive patients reporting better relief with the placebo would be necessary before he or she would feel comfortable rejecting H_0: $p = 0.50$ in favor of H_a: $p \neq 0.50$ and concluding that the placebo works better.

The instructor will compile a "distribution of significance levels" for the two cases. Are they the same? In principle, should they be?

9.130 Randomized response Refer to Exercise 8.124, "Randomized response," in Chapter 8. Before carrying out the method described there, the class was asked to hypothesize or predict what they believe is the value for the population proportion of students who have had alcohol at a party. Use the class estimate for $\hat{p}$ to carry out the significance test for testing this hypothesized value. Discuss whether to use a one-sided or two-sided alternative hypothesis. Describe how the confidence interval formed in Exercise 8.124 relates to the significance test results.

10

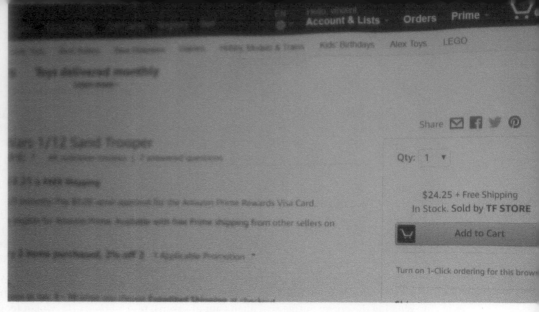

Chapter 9 focused on statistical inference based on a single sample, but often we want to compare parameters such as proportions or means across two different groups. This chapter presents confidence intervals and significance tests for carrying out such inferences, focusing on the difference between two proportions or two means.

Comparing Two Groups

Example 1

Making Sense of Studies Comparing Two Groups

Picture the Scenario

When e-commerce or marketing companies design webpages, there are a lot of things to consider. For instance, Amazon researched extensively which color to use for the Add To Cart button and where to place it on its site. To improve on an existing website, web designers often use so-called A/B tests in which, over a few days, some visitors to the site are routed to the existing design and others to a test site with some new design feature (such as a redesigned button) but otherwise the same functionality. Then, various metrics, such as the proportion of people who signed up for a newsletter or the amount of sales generated from each version of the site, are compared.

Questions to Explore

- How can we use data from such experiments to compare two web designs in terms of number of clicks or amount of sales generated?
- How can we use the information in the data to make an inference about the larger population of all visitors to the website? What are the assumptions we need to make for our inference to be valid?

Thinking Ahead

This chapter shows how to compare two groups on a categorical outcome (e.g., whether a visitor signed up for a newsletter) or on a quantitative outcome (e.g., the dollar amount of products a visitor puts into the shopping cart). To do this, we'll use the inferential statistical methods that the previous two chapters introduced: confidence intervals and significance tests.

For categorical variables, we will compare proportions between two groups. In Examples 2 to 4, we'll look at aspirin and placebo treatments, comparing the proportions of subjects getting cancer under each treatment. Exercise 10.12 presents the results of an A/B test comparing a button that read *Sign Up* to a button that read *Learn More* on the 2008 fundraising website of a then relatively unknown U.S. senator, Barack Obama.

For quantitative variables, we will compare means between two groups. In Examples 6 to 8, we will examine whether including a graph in the product label leads to a higher mean rating of the product's usefulness. In Example 9, we will investigate how the mean reaction time differs between students using a cell phone and those just listening to the radio in a simulated car-driving environment.

In reading this book, you are becoming an educated consumer of information based on statistics, and many stories in popular media and news outlets refer to studies comparing two groups in terms of proportions or means. For instance, in April 2020 people around the world were eagerly awaiting results of a study investigating the 5 and 10-day outcome of treatment with a drug against the new coronavirus for patients with moderate or severe respiratory symptoms. The primary goal of this study was a statistical comparison between these two treatment arms to compare the proportion of patients no longer showing symptoms. This chapter will help you understand such comparisons. By now, you have learned to be skeptical of studies that do not or could not use randomization in the sampling procedure or the experimental design. By the end of this chapter, you'll know about other potential pitfalls. You'll be better able to judge how much credence to give to claims made in such studies. Often, what gets reported are only "statistically significant" results. Occasionally such a report may be a Type I error, claiming an effect that actually does not exist in the population, or predicting an effect that is larger than it truly is in the population.

Bivariate Analyses: A Response Variable and a Binary Explanatory Variable

Consider a study that compares female and male college students on the proportion who say they have participated in binge drinking. Such a study involves two variables. The **response** variable, binge drinking, measures whether a student participated in binge drinking, with outcome categories yes and no. The response variable is the one on which comparisons are made. The **explanatory** variable, gender, measures the sex of each student with outcome categories female and male. The explanatory variable defines the two groups being compared.

An analysis that looks at any type of relationship between two variables is called a **bivariate** analysis. (Analyses with just one variable, such as the ones presented in Chapters 8 and 9, are called **univariate**.) One special case of a bivariate analysis occurs when the explanatory variable is binary (i.e., considers only two possible outcomes, such as female and male). Then, we want to investigate how the outcomes of the response variable differ between the two groups defined by the explanatory variable. In our example, binge drinking is the response variable, and we want to study how it differs by gender.

Dependent and Independent Samples

Most comparisons of groups use **independent samples** from the groups. The observations in one sample are *independent* of those in the other sample. For instance, randomized experiments that randomly allocate subjects to two treatments have independent samples. An example is the A/B experiment mentioned in Example 1 in which visitors to a website are randomly shown one of two versions of that site. The response (i.e., clicking a button) of a visitor directed to the first version of the site is independent of the response of another visitor directed to the second version of the site. Another way independent samples occur is when an observational study separates subjects into groups according to their value for an explanatory variable, such as smoking status. If the overall sample was randomly selected, then the groups (for instance, smokers and nonsmokers) can be treated as independent random samples.

When the two samples involve the same subjects, they are **dependent**. An example is a diet study in which subjects' weights are measured before and after the diet. For a given subject, the observation in the first (before the diet) and second (after the diet) sample are related because they refer to the same

Recall

Chapter 3 defined the **response variable** as the outcome variable on which comparisons are made for different values of the **explanatory variable**. ◄

person. In general, any time the same subject is measured twice (e.g., before and after the diet or in the morning and in the afternoon) produces dependent samples. Data from dependent samples need different statistical methods than data from independent samples. We'll study methods for dependent samples in Section 10.4. Sections 10.1–10.3 show how to analyze independent samples, first for a categorical response variable and then for a quantitative response variable.

10.1 Categorical Response: Comparing Two Proportions

For a *categorical response variable*, we can compare two groups in terms of their population proportions in a particular category. Let p_1 represent the population proportion for the first group and p_2 the population proportion for the second group. One way of comparing the two groups is through the difference of proportions $(p_1 - p_2)$, which we mentioned back in Section 3.1. A point estimate of this difference of the population proportions is the difference of the sample proportions $(\hat{p}_1 - \hat{p}_2)$. In the following, let n_1 and n_2 denote the sample in group 1 and in group 2, respectively.

Comparing Two Proportions ◀

Did You Know?

A meta analysis combines the results of several studies that explore the same underlying effect. ◀

Recall

Section 4.3 discussed the importance of **randomization** in experimental design and introduced **double blinding.** Exercises 4.68–4.70 in that chapter show other data from this study. ◀

Example 2

Aspirin, the Wonder Drug

Picture the Scenario

Most of us think of aspirin as a simple pill that helps relieve pain. In recent years, though, researchers have been on the lookout for new ways that aspirin may be helpful, inspired by a landmark five-year study (Physicians Health Study Research Group, Harvard Medical School) about whether regular aspirin intake reduces deaths from heart disease. Studies have shown that treatment with daily aspirin for five years or longer reduces risk of colorectal cancer. These studies suggest that aspirin might reduce the risk of other cancers as well. A recent meta-analysis combined the results of eight related clinical trials (all randomized and double-blind) with a minimum duration of treatment of four years to determine the effects of aspirin on the risk of cancer death.

Table 10.1 shows the combined study results in a **contingency table**, a form of summarizing categorical data which we introduced in Section 3.1.

Table 10.1 Whether Subject Died of Cancer, for Placebo and Aspirin Treatment Groups

Group	Death from Cancer		Total
	Yes	No	
Placebo	347	11,188	**11,535**
Aspirin	327	13,708	**14,035**
Total	**674**	**24,896**	**25,570**

Of the 25,570 individuals studied, 347 of the 11,535 in the control group died of cancer, whereas 327 of the 14,035 in the aspirin treatment died of cancer within 20 years following the study.

Questions to Explore

a. What is the response variable, and what are the groups to compare?

b. Are the sample of individuals in the placebo and aspirin groups independent samples? Explain.

c. Construct an appropriate graph to visualize the data in the contingency table.

d. What are the two population parameters to compare? Estimate the difference between them using the data in Table 10.1. Interpret that difference.

Think It Through

a. In Table 10.1, the response variable is whether the subjects died of cancer, with categories yes and no. Group 1 consists of the subjects who took placebo and Group 2 consists of the subjects who took aspirin. Placebo and Aspirin are the categories of the explanatory variable measuring which treatment was received.

b. The samples in each of the two groups are independent samples because individuals were randomly assigned to either take placebo or aspirin. The response (death from cancer) of an individual in the placebo group is independent of the response of another individual in the aspirin group.

c. An appropriate graph compares the (conditional) proportions of subjects who died from cancer in the two groups through a bar graph (see Chapter 3, Section 3.1). The figure in the margin shows one based on the data in Table 10.1.

d. The two population parameters to compare refer to the larger (hypothetical) population of subjects taking placebo or aspirin over a prolonged (at least 4 years) period of time. Let p_1 denote the population proportion dying of cancer for those taking placebo, and let p_2 denote the population proportion dying of cancer for those taking aspirin. We can estimate these two population proportions by the sample proportions

$$\hat{p}_1 = 347/11,535 = 0.030$$

for the $n_1 = 11,535$ subjects in the placebo group and

$$\hat{p}_2 = 327/14,035 = 0.023$$

for the $n_2 = 14,035$ subjects in the aspirin group. Since $\hat{p}_1 - \hat{p}_2 = 0.030 - 0.023 = 0.007$, the proportion of those who died of cancer was 0.007 higher for those who took placebo. In percentage terms, the difference was 3.0% − 2.3% = 0.7%, less than 1 percent. For the combined studies, the percentage of cancer deaths was 0.7 percentage points higher in the placebo group than in the aspirin group.

Insight

The sample proportion of subjects who died of cancer was smaller for the aspirin group. But we really want to know whether this result is true also for the larger population. To conduct any inference about the difference of the

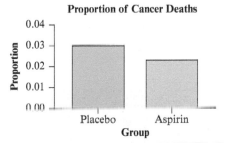

Proportion of Cancer Deaths

Bar Graph Comparing Proportions

Recall

Section 3.1 introduced and showed how to interpret the difference of two (conditional) proportions in a contingency table. ◄

population proportions, we need to learn how much the difference $(\hat{p}_1 - \hat{p}_2)$ of the sample proportions varies from study to study. This is described by the sampling distribution of the difference between the sample proportions and its standard deviation, which we study next.

▶ **Try Exercises 10.2 and 10.3, part a**

Sampling Distribution of the Difference Between Two Sample Proportions

Recall

From Section 7.1, the sampling distribution of $\hat{p}$

- describes the potential values of $\hat{p}$ from a sample of size n,
- is approximately normal for large n,
- has mean equal to p, the population proportion,
- has standard deviation equal to

$\sqrt{p(1-p)/n}$. ◀

Just as a single sample proportion has a sampling distribution that describes its potential values, so does the difference $(\hat{p}_1 - \hat{p}_2)$ between two sample proportions. For large sample sizes n_1 and n_2, recall from Chapter 7 that each of the two sample proportions $\hat{p}_1$ and $\hat{p}_2$ has an approximately normal distribution, centered at p_1 and p_2 and with standard deviations $\sqrt{\dfrac{p_1(1 - p_1)}{n_1}}$ and $\sqrt{\dfrac{p_2(1 - p_2)}{n_2}}$, respectively. Then, the sampling distribution of the **difference** $(\hat{p}_1 - \hat{p}_2)$ of the two sample proportions also has an approximately normal distribution, centered at the population difference $(p_1 - p_2)$ and with a standard deviation shown in the following formula. This sampling distribution describes the distribution of the potential values we could observe for the difference $\hat{p}_1 - \hat{p}_2$ in samples of size n_1 and n_2.

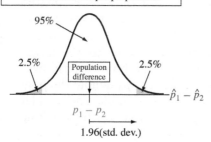

Sampling distribution of the difference between two sample proportions

Sampling Distribution of the Difference of Two Sample Proportions

For two independent random samples of size n_1 and n_2 from two groups with population proportions p_1 and p_2, the sampling distribution of the difference $\hat{p}_1 - \hat{p}_2$ in the sample proportions has

$$\text{mean} = p_1 - p_2 \quad \text{and} \quad \text{standard deviation} = \sqrt{\frac{p_1(1 - p_1)}{n_1} + \frac{p_2(1 - p_2)}{n_2}}.$$

For large sample sizes n_1 and n_2, the sampling distribution of $\hat{p}_1 - \hat{p}_2$ is approximately normal, as illustrated in the margin figure.

Recall

From Section 8.1, the standard error (se) is the estimated standard deviation of a sampling distribution. It measures how close a point estimate falls to the population parameter, here the difference of proportions. ◀

In practice, just as we did for a single proportion back in Section 8.1, we'll have to estimate the standard deviation because it depends on the unknown population proportions. This estimate is called the **standard error** of the difference, which we'll need for constructing a confidence interval. The standard error is obtained by replacing the unknown population proportions p_1 and p_2 in the formula for the standard deviation by the corresponding sample proportions $\hat{p}_1$ and $\hat{p}_2$. It tells us how variable the estimate $(\hat{p}_1 - \hat{p}_2)$ is from one random study of the same size to another and describes how far, in an average sense, the estimated differences from such studies fall from the actual difference $(p_1 - p_2)$ in the population.

The formula for the standard error of $(\hat{p}_1 - \hat{p}_2)$ is

Recall

From Section 8.2, for using a confidence interval to estimate a proportion p, the **standard error** of a sample **proportion** $\hat{p}$ is

$$\sqrt{\frac{\hat{p}(1 - \hat{p})}{n}}. ◀$$

$$se = \sqrt{\frac{\hat{p}_1(1 - \hat{p}_1)}{n_1} + \frac{\hat{p}_2(1 - \hat{p}_2)}{n_2}}.$$

We'll take a closer look at this formula at the end of the section. For now, notice that if you ignore one of the two samples (and half of this formula), you get the usual standard error for a proportion, see the Recall note in the margin.

| Standard Error for the Difference of Two Sample Proportions | **Example 3** |

Cancer Death Rates for Aspirin and Placebo

Picture the Scenario

In Example 2, the sample proportions of subjects who died of cancer were $\hat{p}_1 = 347/11,535 = 0.030$ for placebo (Group 1) and $\hat{p}_2 = 327/14,035 = 0.023$ for aspirin (Group 2). The estimated difference was $\hat{p}_1 - \hat{p}_2 = 0.030 - 0.023 = 0.007$.

Questions to Explore

a. What is the standard error of this estimate?

b. How should we interpret this standard error?

Think It Through

a. Using the standard error formula, we have

$$se = \sqrt{\frac{\hat{p}_1(1 - \hat{p}_1)}{n_1} + \frac{\hat{p}_2(1 - \hat{p}_2)}{n_2}} =$$

$$= \sqrt{\frac{0.030(1 - 0.030)}{11,535} + \frac{0.023(1 - 0.023)}{14,035}} = 0.002.$$

b. Consider all the possible experiments with 11,535 participants in the placebo group and 14,035 participants in the aspirin group, just as in the contingency table shown in Table 10.1. From each experiment, compute the difference $(\hat{p}_1 - \hat{p}_2)$ in the sample proportions between these two groups. This difference will not always equal 0.007, the difference obtained from Table 10.1, but vary from one experiment to the next. The standard error of 0.002 describes how much these differences vary around the actual (unknown) difference in the population.

Insight

From the se formula, we see that se decreases as n_1 and n_2 increase. The standard error is very small for these data because the sample sizes were so large. With such large samples, the $(\hat{p}_1 - \hat{p}_2)$ values would be very similar from study to study. It also implies that $(\hat{p}_1 - \hat{p}_2) = 0.007$ is quite precise as an estimate of the actual difference in the population proportions.

▶ *Try Exercise 10.3, part b*

Confidence Interval for the Difference Between Two Population Proportions

The standard error helps us predict how close an estimate such as 0.007 is likely to be to the population difference $(p_1 - p_2)$. Figure 10.1 on the next page shows the approximate normal sampling distribution of $(\hat{p}_1 - \hat{p}_2)$ and highlights the range within which we expect the sample difference to fall about 95% of the time.

To obtain a confidence interval for $p_1 - p_2$, the same logic as discussed in Section 8.1 applies: We take the estimated difference and add and subtract a margin of error, which is based on the standard error. As in the single proportion case the margin of error is the standard error multiplied by a z-score from the normal distribution. The confidence interval then has the form

$$(\hat{p}_1 - \hat{p}_2) \pm z(se).$$

Recall

Review Section 8.2 for a discussion of the **confidence interval** for a single **proportion**. This has form

$$\hat{p} \pm z(se),$$

with $z = 1.96$ for 95% confidence. ◀

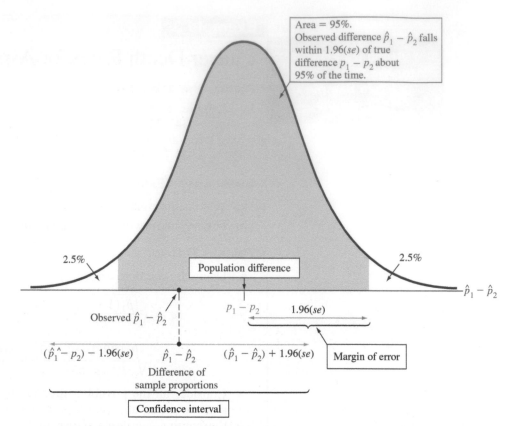

▲ **Figure 10.1 Sampling Distribution of the Difference $(\hat{p}_1 - \hat{p}_2)$ Between Two Sample Proportions.** With large random samples, the sampling distribution is approximately normal, centered at the difference $(p_1 - p_2)$ between the two population proportions. **Questions** For the aspirin and cancer death study (Examples 2 and 3), what are $(\hat{p}_1 - \hat{p}_2)$ and $(p_1 - p_2)$ referring to? What is the mean of this sampling distribution if cancer death rates are identical for aspirin and placebo?

The argument why this interval (with a confidence level of 95% and for large sample sizes) is expected to capture the true difference 95% of the times is the same as the one we used in Chapter 8: Under the normal sampling distribution, stretching out 1.96*(se)* to either side of $(\hat{p}_1 - \hat{p}_2)$ captures the true difference $(p_1 - p_2)$ 95% of the times (and misses it 5% of the times). This happens because under the normal sampling distribution, 95% of the times a difference $(\hat{p}_1 - \hat{p}_2)$ occurs that is within $\pm 1.96(se)$ of the true difference $(p_1 - p_2)$. Figure 10.1 illustrates this fact.

SUMMARY: Confidence Interval for the Difference Between Two Population Proportions

A confidence interval for the difference $(p_1 - p_2)$ between two population proportions is

$$(\hat{p}_1 - \hat{p}_2) \pm z(se), \text{ where } se = \sqrt{\frac{\hat{p}_1(1 - \hat{p}_1)}{n_1} + \frac{\hat{p}_2(1 - \hat{p}_2)}{n_2}}.$$

The z-score depends on the confidence level, such as $z = 1.96$ for 95% confidence. To use this method, you need:

- A categorical response variable observed in each of two groups.
- Independent random samples for the two groups, either from random sampling or a randomized experiment.
- Large enough sample sizes n_1 and n_2 so that, in each sample, there are at least 10 successes and at least 10 failures. The confidence interval for a single proportion required at least 15 successes and 15 failures. Here, the method works well with slightly smaller samples, at least 10 of each type in each group.

Example 4

Confidence Interval for the Difference of Two Proportions ◄

Comparing Cancer Death Rates for Aspirin and Placebo

Picture the Scenario

In the aspirin and cancer study, the estimated difference between placebo and aspirin in the proportions dying of cancer was $\hat{p}_1 - \hat{p}_2 = 0.030 - 0.023 = 0.007$. In Example 3, we found that this estimate has a standard error of 0.002.

Question to Explore

What can we say about the difference in the proportions of cancer deaths for those taking placebo versus those taking aspirin in the population? Construct a 95% confidence interval for $(p_1 - p_2)$ and interpret.

Think It Through

From Table 10.1, shown again in the margin, the four outcome counts (347, 327, 11,188, and 13,708) were at least 10 for each group, so the large-samples confidence interval method is valid because we have at least 10 successes and 10 failures in each group. A 95% confidence interval for $(p_1 - p_2)$ is

$$(\hat{p}_1 - \hat{p}_2) \pm 1.96(se), \text{ or } 0.007 \pm 1.96(0.002),$$

which is 0.007 ± 0.004, or $(0.003, 0.011)$.

Here is how we interpret this 95% confidence interval: With 95% confidence, we estimate that the difference in the population proportion of cancer deaths between those taking placebo and those taking aspirin is between 0.003 and 0.011. Because both endpoints of the interval are positive, we can infer that $(p_1 - p_2)$ is positive, which implies that p_1 is larger than p_2. We can say, with 95% confidence, that the proportion of cancer deaths for those taking placebo is between 0.003 and 0.011 larger than for those taking aspirin. In terms of percentages, we estimate that the percentage of cancer deaths in the population is at least 0.3 and at most 1.1 percentage points higher for those taking placebo compared to those taking aspirin.

The screenshot in Figure 10.2 shows output from the *Compare Two Proportions* app, which computes and visualizes this confidence interval.

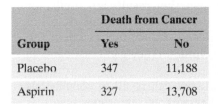

	Death from Cancer	
Group	**Yes**	**No**
Placebo	347	11,188
Aspirin	327	13,708

APP

► **Figure 10.2** Confidence Interval Comparing Two Proportions. Screenshot from the *Compare Two Proportions* app, showing the point estimate for the difference of proportions, its standard error and the margin of error. The third table shows the lower and upper bound of a 95% confidence interval for the difference of proportions, visualized in the graph.

Compare Two Population Proportions   Confidence Interval & Significance Test   Two Dependent Samples

Enter Data: **Dataset:**
From Text ▾   Aspirin & C ▾

Group 1:
Sample Size: **# of Successes:**
11535   347

Group 2:
Sample Size: **# of Successes:**
14035   327

☐ Provide Group Labels

Type of Inference:
Confidence Interval ▾

Confidence Level (in %):
90 |———●———| 100
90 91 92 93 94 95 96 97 98 99 100

Descriptive Statistics:

Group	Sample Size	Successes	Sample Proportion
Placebo	11,535	347	0.03008
Aspirin	14,035	327	0.02330

Estimate of Difference of Proportions:

Point Estimate	Standard Error	Margin of Error
0.00678	0.00204	+/- 0.003993

Confidence Interval:

Population Parameter	Lower Bound	Upper Bound	Confidence Level
Difference $p_1 - p_2$	0.00279	0.0108	95%

95% Confidence Interval
[0.00279, 0.01078]

Barchart

0.002   0.004   0.006   0.008   0.010   0.012   0.014   0.016
$\hat{p}_1 - \hat{p}_2$
Difference of Proportions $p_1 - p_2$

The app has several data sets from the textbook preloaded, but you can also enter your own data.

Insight

All the numbers in the confidence interval fall near 0. This suggests that the population difference $(p_1 - p_2)$ is small. However, this difference, small as it is, may be important in public health terms. For instance, projected over a population of 200 million adults (as in the United States or in Western Europe), a decrease over a 20-year period of 1 percentage point in the proportion of people dying from cancer would mean two million fewer people dying.

This cancer study provided some of the first evidence that aspirin reduces deaths from several common cancers. The benefits were consistent across the different trial populations from the different randomized studies, suggesting that the findings have broader scope of generalization. However, it is important to replicate the study to see whether results are similar or different for populations used in this study and other populations. Also, because there were fewer women than men in the study, findings about the effect of aspirin use and cancers related to women (such as breast cancer) were limited.

This example shows how the use of statistics can result in conclusions that benefit public health. An article[1] about proper and improper scientific methodology stated, "The most important discovery of modern medicine is not vaccines or antibiotics, it is the randomized double-blind study, by means of which we know what works and what doesn't."

▶ *Try Exercise 10.6*

In Practice Interpreting a Confidence Interval

Although the confidence interval refers to proportions, in practice such an interval is typically explained in terms of a percentage point difference. For the aspirin and cancer study, we estimate, with 95% confidence, that the proportion of people dying of cancer is between 0.3 and 1.1 percentage points higher for those taking a placebo instead of aspirin, with a point estimate of a 0.7 percentage point increase.

Recall

For **99% confidence**, we use $z = 2.58$, because 99% of the standard normal distribution falls between -2.58 and 2.58. ◄

Similar to the one-sample case, we can use a higher confidence level, but the interval is then wider. For instance, a 99% confidence interval uses $z = 2.58$ (see margin figure) and equals

$$(\hat{p}_1 - \hat{p}_2) \pm 2.58(se), \text{ or } 0.007 \pm 2.58(0.002),$$
$$\text{which is } 0.007 \pm 0.005, \text{ or } (0.002, 0.012).$$

With 99% confidence, we estimate that the percentage of cancer deaths in the population is between 0.2 and 1.2 percentage points higher for the placebo treatment than for the aspirin treatment. For this example, the confidence interval is slightly wider than the 95% confidence interval of $(0.003, 0.011)$. With very large sample sizes, it is often worth the slight widening to obtain greater confidence.

Interpreting a Confidence Interval That Compares Proportions

Example 4 illustrated how to interpret a confidence interval for $(p_1 - p_2)$ in context. Whether a particular group is called Group 1 or Group 2 is completely arbitrary. If we reverse the labels, each endpoint of the confidence interval reverses sign. For instance, if we instead call aspirin Group 1 and placebo Group 2, then $(\hat{p}_1 - \hat{p}_2) = 0.0023 - 0.0030 = -0.007$. The 95% confidence interval is then $(-0.011, -0.003)$ instead of $(0.003, 0.011)$. Since this confidence interval contains entirely negative numbers, we infer that $(p_1 - p_2)$ is negative; that is, p_1 is smaller than p_2. Since Group 1 is now aspirin, the interval $(-0.011, -0.003)$ predicts that

---

[1] By R. L. Park, *The Chronicle of Higher Education*, January 31, 2003.

▲ Figure 10.3 Three Confidence Intervals for the Difference Between Proportions, $p_1 - p_2$. When the confidence interval for $p_1 - p_2$ contains 0 (the middle interval above), the population proportions may be equal. When it does not contain 0, we can infer which population proportion is larger. **Question** For the two confidence intervals that do not contain 0, how can we tell which population proportion is predicted to be larger?

the percentage of cancer deaths in the population is between 1.1 and 0.3 percentage points lower for aspirin than for placebo. (The negative signs translate to the first percentage being *less* than the second.)

If a confidence interval for the difference between two proportions contains 0, then it is plausible that $(p_1 - p_2) = 0$, that is, $p_1 = p_2$. This suggests that the population proportions might be equal. In such a case, insufficient evidence exists to infer which of p_1 or p_2 is larger. See Figure 10.3.

For instance, Exercise 10.6 summarizes a study comparing population proportions for a placebo group and a treatment group. The study had a much smaller sample size than the aspirin and cancer study, so its standard error was larger. Its 95% confidence interval for $(p_1 - p_2)$ is $(-0.005, 0.034)$. Since the interval contains 0, the population proportions might be very similar, if not identical. This interval infers that the population proportion p_1 for the placebo group may be as much as 0.005 lower or as much as 0.034 higher than the population proportion p_2 for the treatment group. A *negative* value for $(p_1 - p_2)$, such as -0.005, means that p_1 could be *below* p_2, whereas a *positive* value for $(p_1 - p_2)$, such as $+0.034$, means that p_1 could be *above* p_2.

Caution

Although technology will report the endpoints of a confidence interval for a difference of proportions to several decimal places, it is typically sufficient to report and interpret these confidence intervals using at most 3 decimal places for the endpoints. ◄

SUMMARY: Interpreting a Confidence Interval for a Difference of Proportions

- Check whether 0 falls in the confidence interval. If so, it is plausible (but not necessary) that the population proportions are equal.
- If all values in the confidence interval for $(p_1 - p_2)$ are positive, you can infer that $p_1 > p_2$. The interval shows just how much larger p_1 might be. If all values in the confidence interval are negative, you can infer that $p_1 < p_2$. Then, the interval shows just how much lower p_1 might be.
- The magnitude of values in the confidence interval tells you how *large* any true difference is. If all values in the confidence interval are near 0, the true difference may be relatively small in practical terms.

Sampling distribution of $\hat{p}_1 - \hat{p}_2$ when H_0: $p_1 - p_2 = 0$ is true

Significance Tests Comparing Population Proportions

Another way to compare two population proportions p_1 and p_2 is with a significance test. The null hypothesis is H_0: $p_1 = p_2$, stating that the population proportions are the same in each group. In terms of the difference of proportions, this is rewritten as H_0: $p_1 - p_2 = 0$, a *no difference*, or *no effect* null hypothesis.

To form a test statistic, we again need to estimate the standard deviation of the sampling distribution (see figure in the margin) to judge how far the observed difference $(\hat{p}_1 - \hat{p}_2)$ falls from the presumed population difference of 0. Because the null hypothesis presumes that the two proportions p_1 and p_2 are equal, we only have to estimate this one common proportion. Let p denote the common proportion in the two groups. We can estimate p by considering the total number of successes that occurred in the combined data. For example, if Group 1 had 7 successes in $n_1 = 20$ observations and Group 2 had 5 successes in $n_2 = 10$ observations, then $\hat{p} = (7 + 5)/(20 + 10) = 12/30 = 0.40$. Such an estimate seems reasonable because if $p_1 = p_2$, the two groups have identical proportions of successes, and we can combine them. So, to find the estimate of the common proportion $\hat{p}$, find the total number of successes (12) and the total sample size from the two groups combined (30), and take the ratio ($12/30 = 0.4$).

We call $\hat{p}$ the **pooled estimate** of the common proportion because it pools the total number of successes and total number of observations from the two samples. Whenever the sample sizes n_1 and n_2 are roughly equal, it falls about halfway between $\hat{p}_1$ and $\hat{p}_2$. Otherwise, it falls closer to the sample proportion that has the larger sample size.

The test statistic measures the number of standard errors that the point estimate $(\hat{p}_1 - \hat{p}_2)$ of $(p_1 - p_2)$ falls from its null hypothesis value of 0:

$$z = \frac{\text{Estimate} - \text{Null hypothesis value}}{\text{Standard error}} = \frac{(\hat{p}_1 - \hat{p}_2) - 0}{se_0}.$$

The standard error for the test, denoted by se_0, is based on the presumption stated in H_0 that $p_1 = p_2$. If $p_1 = p_2$, we can use the pooled estimate $\hat{p}$ to estimate this common population proportion instead of estimating each separately. This standard error is given by (replacing p_1 and p_2 in the standard deviation formula shown in the margin by $\hat{p}$)

$$se_0 = \sqrt{\frac{\hat{p}(1 - \hat{p})}{n_1} + \frac{\hat{p}(1 - \hat{p})}{n_2}} = \sqrt{\hat{p}(1 - \hat{p})\left(\frac{1}{n_1} + \frac{1}{n_2}\right)}.$$

Similar to the one-sample case, we use the subscript 0 to indicate that this is the standard error when assuming that the null hypothesis is true.

As usual, the P-value for $H_0: p_1 = p_2$ depends on whether the alternative hypothesis is two-sided, $H_a: p_1 \neq p_2$, or one-sided, $H_a: p_1 > p_2$ or $H_a: p_1 < p_2$. When it is two-sided, the P-value is the two-tail probability beyond the observed z test statistic value from the standard normal distribution. This is the probability, presuming H_0 to be true, of obtaining a test statistic as or more extreme than observed in either direction.

Recall

Section 9.2 presented the **significance test** for a single **proportion**. The z test statistic measures the number of standard errors that the sample proportion falls from the value in the null hypothesis. ◄

Recall

From the yellow definition box on page 506, the standard deviation is given by

$$\sqrt{\frac{p_1(1 - p_1)}{n_1} + \frac{p_2(1 - p_2)}{n_2}}. ◄$$

Recall

A **P-value** (introduced in Section 9.1) is the probability that the test statistic equals the observed value or a value even more extreme (in one tail for a one-sided H_a or both tails for a two-sided H_a) presuming that H_0 is true. Smaller P-values provide stronger evidence against H_0. ◄

In Practice Sample Size Guidelines for Significance Tests

Significance tests comparing proportions use the **sample size** guideline from confidence intervals: Each sample should have at least 10 successes and 10 failures. However, *two-sided tests* are robust against violations of this condition. In practice, the two-sided test works well if there are at least **five successes** and **five failures** in each sample.

SUMMARY: Two-Sided Significance Test for Comparing Two Population Proportions

1. **Assumptions**
   - A categorical response variable observed in each of two groups.
   - Independent random samples, either from random sampling or a randomized experiment.
   - n_1 and n_2 are large enough that there are at least five successes and five failures in each group if using a two-sided alternative.

2. **Hypotheses**
   Null $H_0: p_1 = p_2$ (that is, $p_1 - p_2 = 0$).
   Alternative $H_a: p_1 \neq p_2$ (one-sided H_a also possible; see after Example 5).

3. **Test Statistic**
   $$z = \frac{(\hat{p}_1 - \hat{p}_2) - 0}{se_0} \text{ with } se_0 = \sqrt{\hat{p}(1 - \hat{p})\left(\frac{1}{n_1} + \frac{1}{n_2}\right)},$$
   where $\hat{p}$ is the pooled estimate of the common proportion.

4. P-value

P-value = Two-tail probability from standard normal distribution of values as or even more extreme than observed z test statistic, presuming the null hypothesis is true.

5. Conclusion

Smaller P-values give stronger evidence against H_0 and supporting H_a. Interpret the P-value in context. If a decision is needed, reject H_0 if P-value $\leq$ significance level (such as 0.05).

Significance Test Comparing Two Proportions ◀

Proportion Committing Aggressive Acts

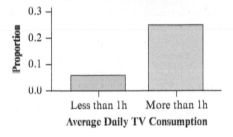

Average Daily TV Consumption

Example 5

TV Watching and Aggressive Behavior

Picture the Scenario

A study[2] considered whether greater levels of television watching by teenagers were associated with a greater likelihood of aggressive behavior. The researchers randomly sampled 707 families in two counties in northern New York state and made follow-up observations over 17 years. Table 10.2 shows results about whether a sampled teenager later conducted any aggressive act against another person, according to a self-report by that person or by a parent. The bar graph in the margin figure summarizes the results.

Table 10.2 TV Watching by Teenagers and Later Aggressive Acts

	Aggressive Act		
TV Watching	**Yes**	**No**	**Total**
Less Than 1 Hour per Day	5	83	**88**
At Least 1 Hour per Day	154	465	**619**

We'll identify Group 1 as those who watched less than 1 hour of TV per day, on average, as teenagers. Group 2 consists of those who averaged at least 1 hour of TV per day, as teenagers. Denote the population proportion committing aggressive acts by p_1 for the lower level of TV watching and by p_2 for the higher level of TV watching.

Questions to Explore

a. Find and interpret the P-value for testing $H_0: p_1 = p_2$ against $H_a: p_1 \neq p_2$.

b. Make a decision about H_0 using the significance level of 0.05.

Think It Through

a. The study used a random sample of teenagers, who were classified into two groups by the level of TV watching (the explanatory variable); therefore, we can treat the sample of teenagers in each group as two independent samples. Each count in Table 10.2 is at least five, so we can use a large-sample test. The sample proportions of aggressive acts were $\hat{p}_1 = 5/88 = 0.057$ for the lower level of TV watching and $\hat{p}_2 = 154/619 = 0.249$ for the higher level, resulting in a difference of $0.057 - 0.249 = -0.192$. Under the null hypothesis presumption that $p_1 = p_2$, the pooled estimate of the common proportion p is $\hat{p} = (5 + 154)/(88 + 619) = 159/707 = 0.225$.

---

[2]By J. G. Johnson et al., (2002, March 29), *Science*, vol. 295, pp. 2468–2471.

The standard error for the test is

$$se_0 = \sqrt{\hat{p}(1 - \hat{p})\left(\frac{1}{n_1} + \frac{1}{n_2}\right)} = \sqrt{(0.225)(0.775)\left(\frac{1}{88} + \frac{1}{619}\right)} = 0.0476.$$

The test statistic for $H_0: p_1 = p_2$ is

$$z = \frac{(\hat{p}_1 - \hat{p}_2) - 0}{se_0} = \frac{(0.057 - 0.249) - 0}{0.0476} = \frac{-0.192}{0.0476} = -4.04.$$

This test statistic indicates that the observed difference of -0.192 falls 4.04 standard errors below the value of 0, the difference expected if the null hypothesis were true. For the two-sided alternative hypothesis, the P-value is the two-tail probability from the standard normal distribution. A z-score of -4.04 is far out in the left tail. As shown in Figure 10.4, the corresponding P-value is small, 0.0001 to be precise. If the two population proportions were the same, the probability of observing such a test statistic or a more extreme one is very small, just 0.0001. Extremely strong evidence exists against the null hypothesis.

b. Since the P-value is less than 0.05, we can reject H_0 and conclude that the population proportions of aggressive acts differ for the two groups. The sample values suggest that the population proportion is higher for the higher level of TV watching.

You can obtain all results (e.g., test statistic, P-value) via the *Compare Two Proportions* app by selecting Significance Test under Type of Inference, as shown in the screenshot in Figure 10.4.

▶ **Figure 10.4** Significance Test Comparing Two Proportions. Screenshot from the *Compare Two Proportions* app, where Significance Test was selected under Type of Inference. The app computes the difference in the sample proportions, the null standard error, the test statistic and the resulting P-value, which is also shown graphically.

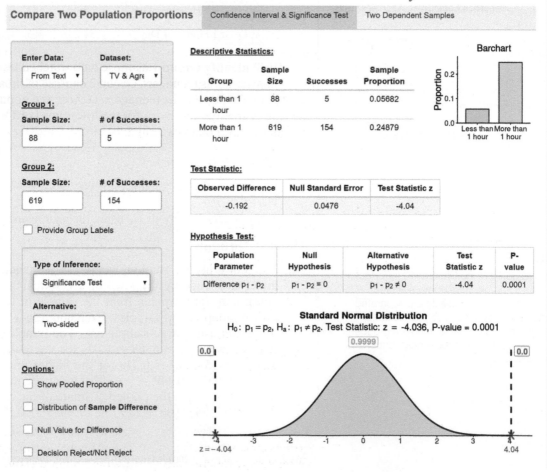

Recall

An **observational** study merely observes the explanatory variable, such as TV watching. An **experimental** study randomly allocates subjects to its levels. Sections 4.1 and 4.4 discussed limitations of observational studies, such as effects that lurking variables may have on the association. ◄

> **Insight**
>
> This was an observational study. In practice, it would be impossible to conduct an experimental study by randomly assigning teenagers to watch little TV or watch much TV over several years. Also, just because a teenager watches more TV does not imply that the teenager watched more violent content, which then leads to more aggressive behavior. We must be cautious of effects of lurking variables when we make conclusions. It is not proper to conclude that watching more TV as a teenager *causes* later aggressive behavior. For instance, perhaps those who watched more TV had lower education levels, and perhaps lower education levels are associated with a greater likelihood of aggressive acts.
>
> ▶ *Try Exercise 10.8*

When the test indicates rejection of H_0 (i.e., when the P-value is less than the significance level), we call the results of the test statistically significant. In the context of comparing two groups, we often speak of a **significant difference.**

> Significant Difference
>
> Two groups are called (statistically) significantly different if a test based on comparing the two population parameters results in a significant result, i.e., a small P-value.

For example, with regard to the proportion committing aggressive acts, the group with teenagers who watched less than 1 hour of TV per day differed significantly (P-value < 0.001) from the group that watched at least one hour of TV. However, the same caution as mentioned in Section 9.5 applies regarding statistical significance versus practical relevance. Just because a difference is statistically significant doesn't mean it's practically relevant. The difference might be small in practical terms. A confidence interval tells us about the size of the effect. For Example 5, the 95% confidence interval for the difference equals $(-0.25, -0.13)$, indicating that the percentage of teenagers committing aggressive acts was at least 13 percentage points lower for those who watched less than one hour of TV per day. This is much more informative than just saying that a (statistically) significant difference was found between the two groups.

Caution

Considering a one-sided alternative would be questionable for this data since one of the counts is less than 10. ◄

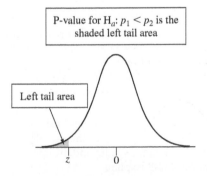

P-value for $H_a: p_1 < p_2$ is the shaded left tail area

Left tail area

A One-Sided Alternative Hypothesis   Example 5 requested a test for the two-sided alternative, $H_a: p_1 \neq p_2$. Two-sided P-values are typically reported in journals. However, suppose the researchers specifically predicted that greater levels of TV watching by teenagers were associated with greater likelihood of committing aggressive acts years later. Then they may have preferred to use the one-sided alternative, $H_a: p_1 < p_2$. This states that the population proportion of aggressive acts is higher at the higher level of TV watching. Equivalently, it is $H_a: (p_1 - p_2) < 0$.

The P-value is then a left-tail probability below the observed test statistic, $z = -4.04$, as illustrated in the margin figure. This P-value is also really small, less than 0.0001. The conclusion is that the proportion of aggressive acts is significantly higher for those who had watched more TV.

The Standard Error for Comparing Two Statistics

Now that we've seen how to compare two proportions, let's learn where the *se* formula comes from. Whenever we estimate a difference between two population parameters, a general rule specifies the standard error.

> ## Standard Error of the Difference Between Two Estimates
>
> For two estimates from independent samples, the standard error is
>
> $$se(\text{estimate 1} - \text{estimate 2}) = \sqrt{[se(\text{estimate 1})]^2 + [se(\text{estimate 2})]^2}.$$

Let's apply the formula for the standard error of the difference between two estimates to the comparison of two proportions. The standard error of a single sample proportion $\hat{p}$ is $se = \sqrt{\hat{p}(1 - \hat{p})/n}$. Then, for two samples, the se of $(\hat{p}_1 - \hat{p}_2)$ is

$$se = \sqrt{[se(\text{estimate 1})]^2 + [se(\text{estimate 2})]^2} = \sqrt{\frac{\hat{p}_1(1 - \hat{p}_1)}{n_1} + \frac{\hat{p}_2(1 - \hat{p}_2)}{n_2}}.$$

We use this se formula to construct a confidence interval for the difference between two population proportions.

Notice that we *add* the (squared) standard errors under the square root sign, rather than subtract. This implies that if we're comparing two proportions, the standard error of the difference is *larger* than the standard error for either sample proportion alone. This implies that there is more uncertainty where the difference of two proportions is going to fall compared to where each individual proportion is going to fall.

Small-Sample Inference for Comparing Proportions

The confidence interval for a difference of proportions specifies that each sample should have at least 10 outcomes of each type. For smaller sample sizes, the method may not work well: The sampling distribution of $(\hat{p}_1 - \hat{p}_2)$ may not be close to normal, and the estimate of the standard error may be poor. We won't cover this case here because most studies you will encounter in practice have sample sizes that are large enough (i.e., as prescribed by an initial power analysis before the study is undertaken, see Section 9.6), but it is briefly discussed in Exercise 10.126. The *Compare Two Proportions* app has this small-sample method implemented. There are also small-sample significance tests for comparing proportions. We will discuss one, called *Fisher's exact test*, in the next chapter. Such tests have their own disadvantages, however, and for two-sided alternatives, the large-sample test usually performs quite well for small samples also.

10.1 Practicing the Basics

10.1 Unemployment rate According to the Bureau of Labor Statistics, the official unemployment rate was 5.8% among Blacks and 3.1% among Whites in February 2020. (This was just one month before the massive increase due to the COVID-19 pandemic.)

a. Identify the response variable and the explanatory variable.

b. Identify the two groups that are the categories of the explanatory variable.

c. The unemployment statistics are based on a sample of individuals. Were the samples of White individuals and Black individuals independent samples or dependent samples? Explain.

10.2 Sampling sleep The 2011 Bedroom Sleep poll of a random sample of 1,500 adults reported that respondents slept an average of 6.5 hours on weekdays and 7.2 hours on weekends, and that 21% of respondents got eight or more hours of sleep on weekdays, whereas 44% got eight or more hours of sleep on weekends (www.sleepfoundation.org).

a. To compare the means or the percentages using inferential methods, should you treat the samples on weekdays and weekends as independent samples or as dependent samples? Explain.

b. When comparing these results to a poll of other people taken in a previous year, should you treat the samples in the two years as independent samples or as dependent samples? Explain.

10.3 Binge drinking The PACE project at the University of Wisconsin in Madison dealt with problems associated with high-risk drinking on college campuses. Based on random samples, the study stated that the percentage of UW students who reported bingeing at least three times within the past two weeks was 42.2% in 1999 ($n = 334$) and 21.2% in 2009 ($n = 843$).

a. Estimate the difference between the proportions in 1999 and 2009 and interpret.

b. Find the standard error for this difference. Interpret it.

c. Define the two relevant population parameters to compare in the context of this exercise.

d. Construct and interpret a 95% confidence interval for the difference of proportions, explaining how your interpretation reflects whether the interval contains 0.

e. State and check the assumptions for the confidence interval in part d to be valid.

10.4 Smoking and lung obstruction A National Center for Health Statistics data brief published in 2015 (Nr. 181) looked at the association between lung obstruction and smoking status in adults 40 to 79 years old. In a random sample of 6,927 adults without any lung obstruction, 54.1% never smoked. In a random sample of 1,146 adults with lung obstruction (such as asthma or COPD), 23.8% never smoked.

a. Find and interpret a point estimate of the difference between the proportion of adults without and with lung obstruction who never smoked.

b. A 99% confidence interval for the true difference is (0.267, 0.339). Interpret.

c. What assumptions must you make for the interval in part b to be valid?

10.5 Do you believe in miracles? Let p_1 and p_2 denote the population proportions of males and females in the United States who answer, yes, definitely when asked whether they believe in miracles. Based on results from the 2008 GSS (variable MIRACLES), 277 males (out of 603 responding) and 461 females (out of 730 responding) indicated "Yes, definitely."

a. Report point estimates of p_1 and p_2.

b. Construct a 95% confidence interval for $(p_1 - p_2)$, specifying the assumptions you make to use this method. Interpret.

c. Based on the interval in part b, explain why the proportion believing in miracles may have been quite a bit larger for females, or it might have been only moderately larger.

10.6 Aspirin and heart attacks in Sweden A Swedish study used 1,360 patients who had suffered a stroke. The study randomly assigned each subject to an aspirin treatment or a placebo treatment and recorded the number of deaths due to heart attack during a follow-up period of about 3 years.[3] The following screenshot from the *Compare Two Proportions* app shows results.

[3]Based on results described in *Lancet*, (1991), vol. 338, pp. 1345–1349.

a. Explain in context what the sample proportions for each group represent.

b. Explain how to interpret the given point estimate for the difference of proportions.

c. Explain how to interpret the confidence interval, indicating the relevance of 0 falling in the interval.

d. If we instead let Group 1 refer to the aspirin treatment and Group 2 to the placebo treatment, explain how the estimate of the difference and the 95% confidence interval would change. Explain how then to interpret the confidence interval.

Descriptive Statistics:

Group	Sample Size	Successes	Sample Proportion
Placebo	684	28	0.04094
Aspirin	676	18	0.02663

Estimate of Difference of Proportions:

Point Estimate	Standard Error	Margin of Error
0.0143	0.00978	+/- 0.01918

Confidence Interval:

Population Parameter	Lower Bound	Upper Bound	Confidence Level
Difference $p_1 - p_2$	-0.00487	0.0335	95%

95% Confidence Interval
[-0.004869, 0.03349]

10.7 Swedish study test Refer to the previous exercise and the following screenshot from the *Compare Two Proportions* app.

Hypothesis Test:

Population Parameter	Null Hypothesis	Alternative Hypothesis	Test Statistic z	P-value
Difference $p_1 - p_2$	$p_1 - p_2 = 0$	$p_1 - p_2 \neq 0$	1.46	0.144

Standard Normal Distribution
H_0: $p_1 = p_2$, H_a: $p_1 \neq p_2$. Test Statistic: $z = 1.459$, P-value = 0.1444

0.8556
0.0722
0.0722

-1.46
$z = 1.46$

a. Explain what the null hypothesis says.

b. Explain how to interpret the P-value for the test.

c. Report the P-value for the one-sided alternative hypothesis that the proportion of patients dying due to heart attack is lower for the aspirin group.

10.8 Significance test for aspirin and cancer deaths study
In the Physicians Health Study (Examples 2–4), consider the null hypothesis that the population proportion of cancer deaths p_1 for placebo is the same as the population proportion p_2 for aspirin. The sample proportions were $\hat{p}_1 = 347/11{,}535 = 0.0301$ and $\hat{p}_2 = 327/14{,}035 = 0.0233$.

a. For testing $H_0: p_1 = p_2$ against $H_a: p_1 \neq p_2$, show that the pooled estimate of the common value p under H_0 is $\hat{p} = 0.026$ and the standard error is 0.002.

b. Show that the test statistic is $z = 3.4$.

c. Find and interpret the P-value in context.

d. For the Swedish study mentioned in the previous two exercises, the difference between the sample proportions for the placebo and aspirin group was larger compared to the Physicians Health study. Yet, the P-value is smaller in the Physicians Health study. Explain how this could be. (*Hint:* How do the sample sizes compare for the two studies? How does this affect the standard error and thus the test statistic and P-value?)

10.9 Police view Example 4 in Chapter 3 mentioned a Pew Research study in which 2,614 of 3,485 randomly sampled Whites and 128 of 384 randomly sampled Blacks indicated that they have a positive view of the job their local police is doing.

a. Go through all five steps of hypothesis testing to test if there is a difference in the proportion of Whites and Blacks with respect to their view on the police.

b. Find a 95% confidence interval for the difference of proportions and interpret. What can you learn from the confidence interval that you cannot learn from the test?

10.10 Comparing marketing commercials Two TV commercials are developed for marketing a new product. A volunteer test sample of 200 people is randomly split into two groups of 100 each. In a controlled setting, Group A watches commercial A and Group B watches commercial B. In Group A, 25 say they would buy the product. In group B, 20 say they would buy the product. The marketing manager who devised this experiment concludes that commercial A is better. Is this conclusion justified? Analyze the data (e.g., using the *Compare Two Proportions* app).

a. Show all steps of your analysis (perhaps including an appropriate graph) and check assumptions.

b. Comment on the manager's conclusion and indicate limitations of the experiment.

10.11 Hormone therapy for menopause The Women's Health Initiative conducted a randomized experiment to see whether hormone therapy was helpful for postmenopausal women. The women were randomly assigned to receive the estrogen plus progestin hormone therapy or a placebo. After five years, 107 of the 8,506 on the hormone therapy developed cancer and 88 of the 8,102 in the placebo group developed cancer. Is this a significant difference?

a. Set up notation and state assumptions and hypotheses.

b. Find the test statistic and P-value (e.g., using the *Compare Two Proportions* app) and interpret.

c. What is your conclusion for a significance level of 0.05? (The study was planned to be eight years long but was stopped after five years because of increased heart and cancer problems for the therapy group. This shows a benefit of doing two-sided tests, because results sometimes have the opposite direction from the expected one.)

10.12 Obama A/B testing To increase Barack Obama's visibility and to raise money for the campaign leading up to the 2008 presidential election, Obama's analytics team conducted an A/B test with his website. In the original version, the button to join the campaign read "Sign Up". In an alternative version, it read "Learn More". Of 77,858 visitors to the original version, 5,851 clicked the button. Of 77,729 visitors to the alternative version, 6,927 clicked the button. Is there evidence that one version was more successful than the other in recruiting campaign members? The following shows computer output from statistical software, but you can also enter the data into the *Compare Two Proportions* app (select Number of Successes under Enter Data).

```
Sample        X          N        Sample p
SignUp      5851       77858      0.075150
LearnMore   6927       77729      0.089117
Difference = p(SignUp) − p(LearnMore)

Estimate for difference: −0.013968
95% CI for difference: (−0.016695, −0.011239)
Test for difference = 0(vs · 0):
Z = −10.03 P-Value = 0.000
```

a. What is an appropriate graph to visualize these data?

b. Show all steps of a significance test, using the computer output or the output from the app. Define any parameters you are using when specifying the hypotheses. Mention whether there is a significant difference at the 0.05 significance level.

c. Interpret the confidence interval shown in the output. Why is this interval more informative than just reporting the P-value?

10.13 Believe in heaven and hell A recent survey asked each participant whether he or she believes in heaven and in hell. Of the 1,314 participants, 1,117 believed in heaven and 959 believed in hell. Can we use the inferential methods (confidence interval, significance test) presented in this section to compare the two proportions? If yes, find and interpret a 95% confidence interval for the difference in the population proportions (e.g., using the *Compare Two Proportions* app). If no, explain why.

10.2 Quantitative Response: Comparing Two Means

We can compare two groups on a *quantitative response variable* by comparing their means. What does the difference between the sample means of the two groups tell us about the difference between the population means? We'll find out in this section.

Comparing Two Groups on a Quantitative Variable ◀

Example 6

A Graph Is Worth a Thousand Words

Picture the Scenario

We learned in previous chapters that graphs provide a powerful way of conveying information. Public relations, media, or marketing companies all use graphs to draw attention to their services or products and ultimately boost sales. Are we giving more credence to a service or product if its description is accompanied by a graph, i.e., looks more scientific? To explore this, in a recent experiment participants were randomly split into two groups. One group just read a short generic text about the effectiveness of a drug. The other group read that same text but now accompanied by a basic bar graph that just mirrored the text and did not provide any new information.[4] After the experiment, participants rated the perceived effectiveness of the drug on a 9-point scale, with 1 representing "not at all effective" and 9 representing "very effective." Figure 10.5 shows side-by-side box plots, and Table 10.3 provides some summary statistics for the ratings in the two groups.

▲ **Figure 10.5** Side-by-Side Box Plots Showing the Distribution of Ratings in the Two Groups. **Question** What other graph would you like to see?

Table 10.3 Summary for Ratings on Perceived Effectiveness of Medication

Group	Ratings		
	Sample Size	**Mean**	**Standard Deviation**
Text and Graph	30	6.83	1.18
Text Only	31	6.13	1.43

Question to Explore

How can we compare the ratings between the group that saw the text and the graph and the group that just saw the text?

Think It Through

One way to compare the two groups compares the mean ratings by looking at their difference. Let Group 1 be the one that read the text and saw the graph and Group 2 be the one that just read the text. The sample mean rating is $\bar{x}_1 = 6.83$ in Group 1 and $\bar{x}_2 = 6.13$ in Group 2 (see Table 10.3), resulting in a difference of $\bar{x}_1 - \bar{x}_2 = 6.83 - 6.13 = 0.7$. In this experiment, the mean

---

[4]A. Tal and B. Wansink, (1994, October), *Public Understanding of Science*. doi: 10.1177/0963662514549688

rating on the perceived effectiveness of the medication is 0.7 points higher in the group that also saw the graph.

Insight

This analysis uses descriptive statistics only. We'll next see how to make inferences about the difference between two population means when the population refers to all people who might read the short description of the medication, one with and one without the graph.

▶ **Try Exercise 10.16, part a**

Recall

From Section 7.2, the sampling distribution of $\bar{x}$

- describes the potential values of $\bar{x}$ in a sample of size n,
- is approximately normal for large n,
- has mean equal to μ, the population mean,
- has standard deviation equal to $\sigma/\sqrt{n}$, where σ is the population standard deviation.

The sample standard deviation $s = \sqrt{\Sigma(x_i - \bar{x})^2/(n-1)}$ and is a point estimate of the population standard deviation σ. ◀

Sampling Distribution of the Difference Between Two Sample Means

How well does the difference $(\bar{x}_1 - \bar{x}_2)$ between two sample means estimate the difference between the corresponding population means $(\mu_1 - \mu_2)$? This is described by the sampling distribution of $(\bar{x}_1 - \bar{x}_2)$ and, in particular, its estimated standard deviation, the standard error. For large sample sizes n_1 and n_2, recall from Chapter 7 that each of the two sample means $\bar{x}_1$ and $\bar{x}_2$ has an approximate normal distribution, centered at μ_1 and μ_2 and with standard deviations $\dfrac{\sigma_1}{\sqrt{n_1}}$ and $\dfrac{\sigma_2}{\sqrt{n_2}}$, respectively. Here, σ_1 is the population standard deviation in the first group, and σ_2 is the population standard deviation in the second group. Then, the **difference** $(\bar{x}_1 - \bar{x}_2)$ in the sample means also has an approximately normal distribution, centered at the difference of the population means $(\mu_1 - \mu_2)$ and with standard deviation given in the following formula.

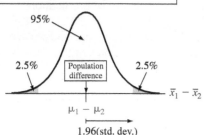

Sampling distribution of the difference between two sample means

Sampling Distribution for the Difference of Two Sample Means

For two independent random samples of size n_1 and n_2 from two groups with population means μ_1 and μ_2 and population standard deviations σ_1 and σ_2, the sampling distribution of the difference in the sample means has

$$\text{mean} = \mu_1 - \mu_2 \quad \text{and} \quad \text{standard deviation} = \sqrt{\frac{\sigma_1^2}{n_1} + \frac{\sigma_2^2}{n_2}}.$$

For large sample sizes n_1 and n_2, the sampling distribution of $\bar{x}_1 - \bar{x}_2$ is approximately normal, as illustrated in the margin figure.

In practice, we will have to estimate the standard deviation because it depends on the unknown population standard deviations. Replacing σ_1 and σ_2 by the sample standard deviations s_1 and s_2, we get the **standard error** of the difference,

$$se = \sqrt{\frac{s_1^2}{n_1} + \frac{s_2^2}{n_2}}.$$

Recall

From the end of Section 10.1, for two estimates from independent samples,

$se(\text{estimate } 1 - \text{estimate } 2) =$

$\sqrt{[se(\text{est. 1})]^2 + [se(\text{est. 2})]^2}$,

the square root of the sum of squared standard errors of the two estimates. ◀

Notice how the expression follows the general rule for the standard error of a difference, shown again in the margin. One adds the squared standard error for each estimate and then takes the square root:

$$se \text{ of } (\bar{x}_1 - \bar{x}_2) = \sqrt{[se(\bar{x}_1)]^2 + [se(\bar{x}_2)]^2} = \sqrt{\frac{s_1^2}{n_1} + \frac{s_2^2}{n_2}}.$$

Standard Error for the Difference of Two Sample Means ◄

Example 7

Text with Graph

Picture the Scenario

In the experiment mentioned in Example 6, the group of $n_1 = 30$ participants that read the text and saw the graph had a sample mean of $x_1 = 6.83$ and a sample standard deviation of $s_1 = 1.18$. For the $n_2 = 31$ participants in the group just reading the text, $\bar{x}_2 = 6.13$ and $s_2 = 1.43$. (See Table 10.3.) We mentioned in Example 6 that the group reading the text and seeing the graph rated the drug, on average, 0.7 points higher than the group just reading the text.

Questions to Explore

What is the standard error of the difference in sample mean ratings? How do you interpret that *se*?

Think It Through

Applying the formula for the *se* of $(\bar{x}_1 - \bar{x}_2)$ for these data,

$$se = \sqrt{\frac{s_1^2}{n_1} + \frac{s_2^2}{n_2}} = \sqrt{\frac{(1.18)^2}{30} + \frac{(1.43)^2}{31}} = 0.335.$$

Sampling distribution of the difference between two sample means

$se = 0.335$

$\bar{x}_1 - \bar{x}_2$

$\mu_1 - \mu_2$
= Population difference
= Mean of sampling distribution

The standard error describes the variability of the sampling distribution of $(\bar{x}_1 - \bar{x}_2)$, as shown in the margin figure. Over many experiments of the same kind, randomly assigning 30 people to the group that reads the text and sees the graph and 31 people to the group that just reads the text, the difference in the sample mean ratings would vary. The standard error of 0.335 measures how far from the mean of the sampling distribution these differences tend to fall. The margin figure illustrates the sampling distribution, which is approximately normal for large samples. It is centered at $\mu_1 - \mu_2$ (the value of which is unknown to us), and its standard deviation is estimated as 0.335.

Insight

This standard error will be used in confidence intervals and in significance tests for comparing means.

► *Try Exercise 10.16, part b*

Confidence Interval for the Difference Between Two Population Means

As usual, a confidence interval takes the point estimate and adds and subtracts a margin of error. For large random samples:

- The sampling distribution of a sample mean is approximately normal, by the Central Limit Theorem.
- The sampling distribution of the difference of two sample means $(\bar{x}_1 - \bar{x}_2)$ is approximately normal as we have just stated.
- For a 95% confidence level, the margin of error is 1.96 times the standard error, so the confidence interval for the difference $(\mu_1 - \mu_2)$ between population means is approximately

$$(\bar{x}_1 - \bar{x}_2) \pm 1.96 \, (se).$$

More precisely, however, the multiple of the *se* is not a *z*-score (such as 1.96) but rather a *t*-score from the *t* distribution. In estimating the standard deviation of

Recall

See Section 8.3 to review the **confidence interval** for a single **mean,** the ***t* distribution** and *t*-scores from it. The 95% confidence interval is

$$\bar{x} \pm t_{.025}(se),$$

where $se = s/\sqrt{n}$. Recall that $df = n - 1$ for inference about a single mean. ◄

the sampling distribution, we replaced the unknown population standard deviations σ_1 and σ_2 by s_1 and s_2. This creates additional uncertainty of how close the sample difference $\bar{x}_1 - \bar{x}_2$ falls to the actual population difference. To counteract, we have to make the confidence interval a bit wider, which we do by using a t-score instead of a z-score.

The degrees of freedom for the t-score depend on the sample standard deviations and the sample sizes. The formula is messy and does not give insight into the method, so we leave it as a footnote.[5] If $s_1 = s_2$ and $n_1 = n_2$, it simplifies to $df = n_1 + n_2 - 2$. This is the sum of the df values for single-sample inference about each group, or $df = (n_1 - 1) + (n_2 - 1) = n_1 + n_2 - 2$. *Generally, df falls somewhere between $n_1 + n_2 - 2$ and the minimum of $(n_1 - 1)$ and $(n_2 - 1)$.*

> ### In Practice Software Finds *df*, the *t*-score, and the Confidence Interval
>
> We use software (such as our app) to find the *df* value, the *t*-score and the confidence interval. When s_1 and s_2 are similar and n_1 and n_2 are close, *df* is close to $n_1 + n_2 - 2$. Without software, you can take *df* to be the smaller of $(n_1 - 1)$ and $(n_2 - 1)$, and this will be safe because the *t*-score will be larger than you actually need.

When either sample size is small (roughly $n_1 < 30$ or $n_2 < 30$), we cannot rely on the Central Limit Theorem for the approximate normality of the sampling distribution of $(\bar{x}_1 - \bar{x}_2)$. In that instance, our method of finding the confidence interval makes the assumption that the population distributions are normal, so $(\bar{x}_1 - \bar{x}_2)$ has a normal sampling distribution regardless of the sample sizes. In practice, this method is *robust*, and it works quite well even if the population distributions are not normal. This statement is subject to the usual caveat: We need to be on the lookout for outliers that might affect the means or their usefulness as a summary measure. If you doubt whether the normality assumption is met for your data, Section 10.3 presents bootstrap methods which do not rely on this assumption.

Recall

From Section 8.3, a method is **robust** with respect to a particular assumption if it works well even when that assumption is violated. ◄

> ### SUMMARY: Confidence Interval for the Difference Between Population Means
>
> For two samples with sizes n_1 and n_2 and standard deviations s_1 and s_2, a 95% confidence interval for the difference $(\mu_1 - \mu_2)$ between the population means is
>
> $$(\bar{x}_1 - \bar{x}_2) \pm t_{.025}(se), \text{ with } se = \sqrt{\frac{s_1^2}{n_1} + \frac{s_2^2}{n_2}}.$$
>
> Software provides $t_{.025}$, the *t*-score with right-tail probability 0.025 (total probability $= 0.95$ between $-t_{.025}$ and $t_{.025}$) and a certain number of degrees of freedom.
> This method assumes:
>
> - A quantitative response variable observed in each of two groups.
> - Independent random samples from the two groups, either from random sampling or a randomized experiment.
> - An approximately normal population distribution for each group. (This is mainly important for small sample sizes, and even then the method is robust to violations of this assumption.)

---

[5]It is $df = \dfrac{\left(\dfrac{s_1^2}{n_1} + \dfrac{s_2^2}{n_2}\right)^2}{\dfrac{1}{n_1 - 1}\left(\dfrac{s_1^2}{n_1}\right)^2 + \dfrac{1}{n_2 - 1}\left(\dfrac{s_2^2}{n_2}\right)^2}$, called the Welch-Satterthwaite formula.

Example 8

**Confidence Interval
for the Difference ◄
of Two Means**

Text with Graph

Picture the Scenario

A 95% confidence interval for the difference between the mean product rating for people who read a short description of the drug accompanied by a graph and people who just read the short description but did not see the graph equals (0.03, 1.38). We obtained this interval using the *Compare Two Means* app, with output shown in Figure 10.6.

▶ **Figure 10.6** Confidence Interval for Comparing Two Means. Screenshot from the *Compare Two Means* app, showing histograms of the data (other plots can be selected, too), the difference in the sample means, its standard error, the *t*-score (and *df*) and the margin of error. The 95% confidence interval is shown in the third table, together with a graph visualizing it.

Questions to Explore

a. Is it reasonable to assume an approximate normal population distribution for product effectiveness ratings in the two groups? How does this affect inference?

b. Show how the confidence interval was obtained and interpret it.

Think It Through

a. The app shows histograms for the ratings in each group, and side-by-side box plots are shown in Figure 10.5. (You can also get these through the app.) The histograms indicate a right skew for the Text and Graph group and a left skew for the Text only group. However, the shape of the histograms doesn't indicate any dramatic deviation from normality. Also, the sample size is large enough for the Central Limit Theorem to apply. In such a case, meeting the assumption of approximate normality for the population distribution of ratings in each group is not crucial. Based on these observations, we can proceed with inference comparing the two means, using the methods developed in this section.

b. Let μ_1 be the mean rating of the population of people who read the text and see the graph. Let μ_2 be the mean rating of the population of people who just read the text. From Example 7, the difference in the sample means is $\bar{x}_1 - \bar{x}_2 = 0.7$, the standard error $se = 0.335$, and the degrees of freedom equals 57.5, leading to a t score of $t_{0.025} = 2.00$. The 95% confidence interval for $\mu_1 - \mu_2$ is

$$(\bar{x}_1 - \bar{x}_2) \pm t_{0.025} \, se, \text{ or } 0.7 \pm 2.00(0.335),$$
$$\text{which equals } 0.7 \pm 0.671, \text{ or } (0.03, 1.38)$$

when rounded two two decimal places. With 95% confidence, we estimate that the difference in the mean ratings between people reading the text and seeing the graph and people just reading the text is between 0.03 points and 1.38 points. Since this interval falls completely above 0, we can infer that people who read the text and see the graph rate the drug's effectiveness, on average, by as little as 0.03 points and as much as 1.38 points higher (on a 9-point scale).

Insight

The lower bound of the confidence interval is close to 0, so the effect on the product rating when including the graph with the text may be small.

▶ *Try Exercise 10.16, parts c and d*

Interpreting a Confidence Interval for a Difference of Means

Besides interpreting the confidence interval comparing two means in context, you can judge the implications using the same criteria as in comparing two proportions:

- *Check whether or not 0 falls in the interval.* When it does, 0 is a plausible value for $(\mu_1 - \mu_2)$, meaning that possibly $\mu_1 = \mu_2$. Figure 10.7 illustrates. For example, suppose the confidence interval for $(\mu_1 - \mu_2)$ equals $(-0.03, 1.38)$. Then, the mean rating for those reading the text and seeing the graph may be as much as 0.03 points *lower* or as much as 1.38 points *higher* compared to those that just read the text. This doesn't rule out that the population mean ratings are the same.

▲ **Figure 10.7 Three Confidence Intervals for the Difference Between Two Means.** When the interval contains 0, it is plausible that the population means may be equal. Otherwise, we can predict which is larger. **Question** Why do positive numbers in the confidence interval for $(\mu_1 - \mu_2)$ suggest that $\mu_1 > \mu_2$?

- *A confidence interval for $(\mu_1 - \mu_2)$ that contains only positive numbers suggests that $(\mu_1 - \mu_2)$ is positive.* We then infer that μ_1 is larger than μ_2. The 95% confidence interval in Example 8 is $(0.03, 1.38)$. Since $(\mu_1 - \mu_2)$ is the difference between the mean ratings, we can infer that the mean rating is higher for those reading the text and seeing the graph.
- *A confidence interval for $(\mu_1 - \mu_2)$ that contains only negative numbers suggests that $(\mu_1 - \mu_2)$ is negative.* We then infer that μ_1 is smaller than μ_2.
- *Which group is labeled 1 and which is labeled 2 is arbitrary.* If you change this, the confidence interval has the same endpoints but with different sign. For instance, $(0.03, 1.38)$ becomes $(-1.38, -0.03)$. We would then conclude that the mean rating for those just reading the text is by at least 0.03 points and at most 1.38 points *lower*. This is the same conclusion as reached in Example 8.

Significance Tests Comparing Population Means

Another way to compare two population means is with a significance test of the null hypothesis H_0: $\mu_1 = \mu_2$ of equal means. The assumptions of the test are the same as for a confidence interval—independent random samples and approximately normal population distributions for each group. When n_1 and n_2 are at least about 30 each, meeting the normality assumption is less crucial because of the Central Limit Theorem. For two-sided alternatives, the test is robust against violations of the normal assumption even when sample sizes are small. However, one-sided t tests are not trustworthy if a sample size is below 30 and the population distribution is highly skewed.

The test uses the usual form for a test statistic,

$$\frac{\text{Estimate of parameter} - \text{Null hypothesis value of parameter}}{\text{Standard error of estimate}}.$$

The parameter of interest is the difference in the population means $(\mu_1 - \mu_2)$, which is estimated by the difference in the sample means $(\bar{x}_1 - \bar{x}_2)$. The null hypothesis H_0: $\mu_1 = \mu_2$ implies that $(\mu_1 - \mu_2) = 0$, so 0 is the null hypothesis value of the parameter. The standard error of $(\bar{x}_1 - \bar{x}_2)$ is the same as the one we used for constructing the confidence interval. With this, the test statistic is

$$t = \frac{(\bar{x}_1 - \bar{x}_2) - 0}{se}, \text{ where } se = \sqrt{\frac{s_1^2}{n_1} + \frac{s_2^2}{n_2}}.$$

When H_0 is true and the assumptions are met, this statistic has a t sampling distribution. Software can compute the df value, which is the same as the one used for constructing a confidence interval, and find the P-value for the test.

The P-value depends on whether the alternative hypothesis is two-sided, H_a: $\mu_1 \neq \mu_2$, or one-sided, H_a: $\mu_1 > \mu_2$ or H_a: $\mu_1 < \mu_2$. For the two-sided alternative, the P-value is the two-tail probability beyond the observed t value. That is, we find the probability of results more extreme in either direction under the presumption that H_0 is true. See the figure in the margin.

This test comparing two means is often referred to as the **two sample t test**. Here is a summary of the test:

Recall

Section 9.3 presented the **significance test** for a single **mean**. The t test statistic measures the number of standard errors that the sample mean falls from the value in the null hypothesis. ◄

t distribution (sampling distribution of t under H_0)

Left tail area   Right tail area

$-t$ 0 t

P-value for H_a: $\mu_1 \neq \mu_2$ is sum of the shaded tail areas

---

SUMMARY: Two-Sided Significance Test for Comparing Two Population Means (Two Sample t Test)

1. **Assumptions**
   - A quantitative response variable observed in each of two groups.
   - Independent random samples, either from random sampling or a randomized experiment.
   - An approximately normal population distribution for each group. (This is mainly important for small sample sizes, and even then the two-sided test is robust to violations of this assumption.)

2. **Hypotheses**
   H_0: $\mu_1 = \mu_2$
   H_a: $\mu_1 \neq \mu_2$ (one-sided H_a: $\mu_1 > \mu_2$ or H_a: $\mu_1 < \mu_2$ also possible)

3. **Test Statistic**
   $$t = \frac{(\bar{x}_1 - \bar{x}_2) - 0}{se} \text{ where } se = \sqrt{\frac{s_1^2}{n_1} + \frac{s_2^2}{n_2}}$$

4. **P-value**
   P-value = Two-tail probability from t distribution of values even more extreme than observed t test statistic, presuming the null hypothesis is true, with df given by software.

5. Conclusion

Smaller P-values give stronger evidence against H_0 and supporting H_a. Interpret the P-value in context and, if a decision is needed, reject H_0 if P-value $\leq$ significance level (such as 0.05).

Example 9

Significance Test Comparing Two Means ◄

Cell Phone Use While Driving Reaction Times

Picture the Scenario

An experiment[6] investigated whether cell phone use impairs drivers' reaction times, using a sample of 64 students from the University of Utah. Students were randomly assigned to a cell phone group or to a control group, 32 to each. On a simulation of driving situations, a target flashed red or green at irregular periods. Participants pressed a brake button as soon as they detected a red light. The control group listened to radio or books on tape while they performed the simulated driving. The cell phone group carried out a phone conversation about a political issue with someone in a separate room.

The experiment measured each subject's mean response time over many trials. Averaged over all trials and subjects, the mean response time was 585 milliseconds (a bit over half a second) for the cell phone group and 533 milliseconds for the control group. Figure 10.8 shows a screenshot of the *Compare Two Means* app, which has these data preloaded and provides a side-by-side box plot of the data.

▶ **Figure 10.8** Significance Test Comparing Two Means. Screenshot from the *Compare Two Means* app, where Significance Test was selected under Type of Inference. The app shows the difference in the sample means, the standard error, the *t* test statistic an the resulting P-value, which is also illustrated in the graph for the *t* distribution. **Question** Does either box plot show any features that could affect the analysis?

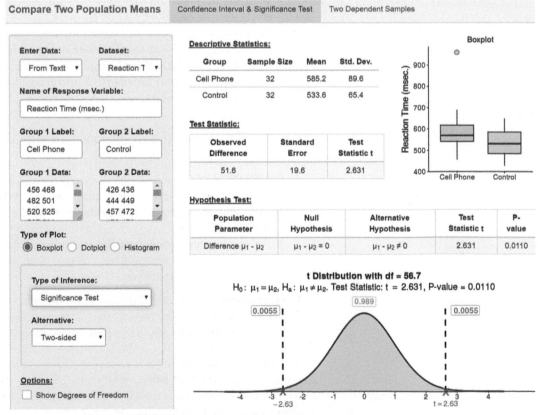

---

[6]Data courtesy of David Strayer, University of Utah. Example based on Experiment 1a in article by D. Strayer and W. Johnston, (2001), *Psych. Science*, vol. 21, pp. 462–466.

Denote the population mean response time by μ_1 for the cell phone group and by μ_2 for the control group.

Questions to Explore

a. Show how the test statistic for testing $H_0: \mu_1 = \mu_2$ against $H_a: \mu_1 \neq \mu_2$ was obtained.

b. Report and interpret the P-value and state the decision you would make about the population using a 0.05 significance level.

c. What do the box plots tell us about the suitability of these analyses? What effect does the outlier for the cell phone group have on the analysis?

Think It Through

a. We estimate the difference $\mu_1 - \mu_2$ by $(\bar{x}_1 - \bar{x}_2) = 585.2 - 533.6 = 51.6$, shown as Observed Difference in the app. The standard error of this estimate is

$$se = \sqrt{\frac{s_1^2}{n_1} + \frac{s_2^2}{n_2}} = \sqrt{\frac{(89.6)^2}{32} + \frac{(65.4)^2}{32}} = 19.6.$$

The test statistic for $H_0: \mu_1 = \mu_2$ equals

$$t = \frac{(\bar{x}_1 - \bar{x}_2)}{se} = \frac{51.6}{19.6} = 2.63.$$

b. The P-value is the two-tail probability from the t distribution (with $df = 56.7$) and equals 0.011, as illustrated in the graph of the t distribution in the app. If H_0 were true, the probability would only be 0.011 of getting a t test statistic this large or larger in either tail. The P-value is less than 0.05, so we can reject H_0. The data provide sufficient evidence to conclude that in the setting of experiments like this, the population mean response time for those using a cell phone while driving differs from the population mean response time for those just listening to the radio. The sample means suggest that the population mean is higher for the cell phone group.

c. The t inferences assume normal population distributions. The box plots do not show any substantial skew, but there is an extreme outlier for the cell phone group. One subject in that group had a very high mean reaction time. Because this observation is so far from the others in that group, it's a good idea to make sure the results of the analysis aren't affected too strongly by that single observation. If we delete the extreme outlier for the cell phone group, its mean and standard deviation decrease substantially. However, as the app reports when we delete the value of 960 in the box for the Group 1 Data, the t test statistic is not much different ($t = 2.52$), and the P-value is still small, 0.014, leading to the same conclusion.

Insight

Even though the difference between the sample means decreased from 51.5 to 39.5 when we deleted the outlier, the standard error for the difference also got smaller (you can check with the app that it equals 15.7) because of the smaller standard deviation for the cell phone group after removing the outlier. That's why the t test statistic did not change much. In practice, you should not delete outliers from a data set without sufficient cause (for example, if it seems the observation was incorrectly recorded). However, it's a good idea to check for *sensitivity* of an analysis to an outlier, as we did here, by repeating the analysis without it. If the results change much, the inference including the outlier is questionable.

▶ *Try Exercise 10.27*

P-value = shaded area = 0.007

Example 9 used a two-sided alternative, which is the way that research results are usually reported in journal articles. But the researchers thought that the mean response time would be *greater* for the cell phone group than for the control. So, for their own purposes, they could find the P-value for the one-sided H_a: $\mu_1 > \mu_2$ (that is, $\mu_1 - \mu_2 > 0$), which predicts a higher mean response time for the cell phone group. For the analysis without the outlier, the P-value is the probability to the *right* of $t = 2.52$. This is half the two-sided P-value, namely $0.014/2 = 0.007$. See the figure in the margin. There is very strong evidence in favor of this alternative.

Connection Between Confidence Intervals and Tests

We learn even more by constructing a confidence interval for $(\mu_1 - \mu_2)$. Let's do this for the data set without the outlier, for which $df = 60.7$ and the difference of sample means of 39.5 had a standard error of 15.7. The t-score with $df = 60.7$ for a 95% confidence interval is $t_{.025} = 2.00$. The confidence interval is (you can easily get the final answer from the app)

$$(\bar{x}_1 - \bar{x}_2) \pm t_{.025}(se), \text{ which is } 39.5 \pm 2.00(15.7), \text{ or } (8.2, 70.8).$$

This result is more informative than the test because it shows the range of plausible values for the difference between the population means. The interval $(8.2, 70.8)$ for $\mu_1 - \mu_2$ is quite wide. It tells us that the population mean reaction times could be similar (differ by only 8 milliseconds), or that the mean reaction time may be as much as 71 milliseconds higher for the cell phone group. This is nearly a tenth of a second, which could be crucial in a practical driving situation.

The confidence interval $(8.2, 70.8)$ does not contain 0. This inference agrees with the significance test that the population mean response times differ. Recall that Section 9.3 showed that the result of a two-sided significance test about a mean is consistent with a confidence interval for that mean. The same is true when comparing two means. If a test rejects H_0: $\mu_1 = \mu_2$, then the confidence interval for $(\mu_1 - \mu_2)$ having the same error probability does not contain 0.

In Example 9 without the outlier, the P-value = 0.014, so we rejected H_0: $\mu_1 = \mu_2$ at the 0.05 significance level. Likewise, the 95% confidence interval for $(\mu_1 - \mu_2)$ of $(8.2, 70.8)$ does not contain 0, the null hypothesis value.

By contrast, when a 95% confidence interval for $(\mu_1 - \mu_2)$ *contains* 0, then 0 is a plausible value for $(\mu_1 - \mu_2)$. In a test of H_0: $\mu_1 = \mu_2$ against H_a: $\mu_1 \neq \mu_2$, the P-value would be larger than 0.05. The test would not reject H_0 at the 0.05 significance level and would conclude that the population means may be equal.

Comparing Means, Assuming Equal Population Standard Deviations

An alternative method to the one described above is sometimes used when, under the null hypothesis, it is reasonable to expect the *variability* as well as the mean to be the same. For example, consider a study comparing a drug to a placebo in terms of lowering blood pressure. If the drug has no effect, then we expect the entire distributions of the response variables (blood pressure) to be the same for the two groups, not just the means. This method requires an extra assumption in addition to the usual ones of independent random samples and approximately normal population distributions. It assumes that the population standard deviations are equal, that is, $\sigma_1 = \sigma_2$ (see Figure 10.9).

This alternative method estimates the common value σ of σ_1 and σ_2 by

$$s = \sqrt{\frac{(n_1 - 1)s_1^2 + (n_2 - 1)s_2^2}{n_1 + n_2 - 2}}.$$

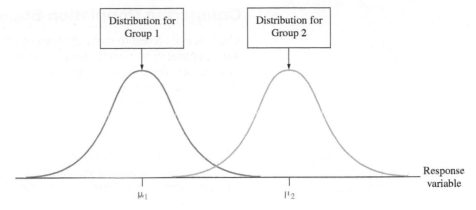

▲ **Figure 10.9** Two Groups with Equal Population Standard Deviations. **Question** What would a histogram of the sample data look like to make you doubt this assumption?

The estimate s, called the **pooled standard deviation**, combines information from the two samples to provide a single estimate of variability and falls somewhere between s_1 and s_2. The degrees of freedom for this method are $df = n_1 + n_2 - 2$, which appears in the denominator of the formula for s.

SUMMARY: Comparing Population Means, Assuming Equal Population Standard Deviations

Using the pooled standard deviation estimate s of $\sigma = \sigma_1 = \sigma_2$, the standard error of $(\bar{x}_1 - \bar{x}_2)$ simplifies to

$$se = \sqrt{\frac{s^2}{n_1} + \frac{s^2}{n_2}} = s\sqrt{\frac{1}{n_1} + \frac{1}{n_2}}.$$

Otherwise, inference formulas look the same as those that do not assume $\sigma_1 = \sigma_2$.

- A 95% confidence interval for $(\mu_1 - \mu_2)$ is $(\bar{x}_1 - \bar{x}_2) \pm t_{.025}(se)$.
- The test statistic for $H_0: \mu_1 = \mu_2$ is $t = (\bar{x}_1 - \bar{x}_2)/se$.

These methods have $df = n_1 + n_2 - 2$. To use them, you assume:

- Independent random samples from the two groups, either from random sampling or a randomized experiment.
- An approximately normal population distribution for each group. (This is mainly important for small sample sizes, and even then the confidence interval and two-sided test are usually robust to violations of this assumption.)
- $\sigma_1 = \sigma_2$ (In practice, this type of inference is not usually relied on if one sample standard deviation is more than double the other one.)

We mention this test here because in Chapters 12 and 13 on linear regression and in Chapter 14 on comparing means across several groups, a similar assumption of equal population standard deviations will be made, using a pooled estimate similar to the one presented here.

Of the two t tests presented here, which one should you use in practice? The t test without the extra assumption is often almost as powerful as the one with the extra assumption, even when $\sigma_1 = \sigma_2$. Here, the **power** of a test refers to the probability of rejecting the null hypothesis when it is false (see Section 9.6). This is the probability of rejecting the null hypothesis of equal population means, when in fact the population means are different. When this probability is similar for the two types of tests, it is often safer to not make the assumption of equal standard deviations. For large sample sizes, the standard error (and degrees of freedom) are similar for both tests, so that in practice both procedures give very similar results. The *Compare Two Means* app can carry out both types of tests, see the Assume Equal Standard Deviation box under Options.

Comparing Population Standard Deviations

There is even a test to compare the population standard deviations to see whether it is reasonable to assume they are equal, with null hypothesis $H_0: \sigma_1 = \sigma_2$. The test statistic for this test is often denoted by F, and the test is called an F-test. It assumes that the population distributions are normal. Unfortunately, this F-test is *not* a robust method.

Recall

For large sample sizes, the normality assumption is less important because the t test is robust against violations of that assumption. ◄

In Practice *F* Test for Comparing Standard Deviations Is Not Robust

The **F test for comparing standard deviations** of two populations performs poorly if the populations are not close to normal. Consequently, statisticians do not recommend it for general use. If the data show evidence of a potentially large difference in standard deviations, with one of the sample standard deviations being at least double the other, it is better to use the two-sample *t*-inference methods that do not have this extra assumption.

10.2 Practicing the Basics

10.14 Alcohol and energy drinks A 2013 article in the journal *Adolescent Health* stated that adding energy drinks to alcohol was associated with an elevated blood alcohol content compared to consuming alcohol without energy drinks in college students.

a. Suppose this conclusion was based on a significance test comparing means. Defining notation in context, identify the groups and the population means and state the null hypothesis for the test.

b. Suppose the study conclusion was based on a P-value of 0.01 obtained for the significance test mentioned in part a. Explain what you could learn from a confidence interval comparing the means that you are not able to learn from this P-value.

10.15 Address global warming You would like to determine what students at your school would be willing to do to help address global warming and the development of alternatively fueled vehicles. To do this, you take a random sample of 100 students. One question you ask them is, "How much would you be willing to add to the price of gasoline (per gallon) to encourage drivers to drive less or to drive more fuel-efficient cars?" You also ask, "Do you believe (yes or no) that global warming is a serious issue?" In your statistical analysis, use inferential methods to compare the mean response for how much should be added to the price of gasoline (the first question) for those who answer yes and for those who answer no to the second question. For this analysis,

a. Identify the response variable and the explanatory variable.

b. Are the two groups being compared independent samples or dependent samples? Why?

c. Identify a confidence interval you could form to compare the groups, specifying the parameters used in the comparison.

10.16 Housework for women and men Do women tend to spend more time on housework than men? If so, how much more? Based on data from the National Survey of Families and Households, one study reported the results in a table for the number of hours spent in housework per week, as shown below. (*Source:* Data from A. Lincoln, *Journal of Marriage and Family,* vol. 70, 2008.) (*Note:* You can enter the information from the table by selecting Summary Statistics under Enter Data in the *Compare Two Means* app. This will compute all necessary statistics for answering parts a–c.)

Gender	Housework Hours		
	Sample Size	Mean	Standard Deviation
Women	476	33.0	21.9
Men	496	19.9	14.6

a. Based on this study, calculate how many more hours, on the average, women spend on housework than men.

b. Find the standard error for the difference in sample means. What factor causes the standard error to be small compared to the sample standard deviations for the two groups?

c. Find the 95% confidence interval comparing the population means for women and men. Interpret the result including the relevance of 0 being within the interval or not. (*Hint:* If you are computing the interval without software, for such large sample sizes, the *t*-score is practically identical to a *z*-score.)

d. State the assumptions upon which the interval in part c is based.

10.17 More confident about housework Refer to part c in the previous exercise.

a. Show that a 99% confidence interval is (10.0, 16.2). Interpret it.

b. Explain why this interval is wider than the 95% confidence interval.

10.18 Time on Facebook A study (R. Junco, 2005, Student class standing, Facebook use, and academic performance, *Journal of Applied Developmental Psychology*) analyzed how many minutes per day students in different class years spend on Facebook. The data for the sample of freshmen and sophomores included in the study are preloaded in the *Compare Two Means* app, with screenshot shown below.

Descriptive Statistics:

Group	Sample Size	Mean	Std. Dev.
Freshmen	439	63.8	71.6
Sophomores	403	70.4	79.0

Estimate of Difference of Means:

Point Estimate	Standard Error	Margin of Error
-6.57	5.21	± 10.23

Confidence Interval:

Population Parameter	Lower Bound	Upper Bound	Confidence Level
Difference $\mu_1 - \mu_2$	-16.80	3.66	95%

95% Confidence Interval
[-16.80, 3.66]

Difference of Means $\mu_1 - \mu_2$

a. Find a point estimate for the difference in the mean number of minutes freshmen and sophomores are on Facebook, and interpret it in context.

b. Interpret the confidence interval in context.

c. Is it plausible that the time spent on Facebook has a normal distribution? Comment. Then, explain the effect of your answer on the validity of the confidence interval.

d. The data for this study came from a survey sent out to students at a large public U.S. university. Explain how this information might affect the validity of the results.

e. Explain how the margin of error was obtained.

10.19 Ideal number of children In 2014, the GSS asked, "What is the ideal number of children for a family to have?" For those giving a numerical response (and treating the response "7 or more" as 7), the following table shows summary statistics. (You can reproduce these data by typing CHLDIDEL(0–7) as the row variable, SEX as the column variable, and YEAR(2014) as the selection filter on the GSS website.) (*Note:* You can enter the information from the table by selecting Summary Statistics under Enter Data in the *Compare Two Means* app. This will compute all necessary statistics for answering parts a and b.)

Ideal Number of Children

Gender	Sample Size	Mean	Standard Deviation
Women	921	2.54	0.89
Men	754	2.50	0.85

a. Find the standard error for the difference in the sample means. If you use the app or other software to find the standard error, verify that what the app or software shows is correct.

b. Find and interpret the 95% confidence interval for the difference between the population means for females and males. (If you are not using software, the sample size for this study is large, resulting in degrees of freedom in excess of 100, so the *t*-score is essentially the same as the *z*-score.)

10.20 Pay by gender The study described in Exercise 10.16 also evaluated personal income by gender. Entering the summary data into the *Compare Two Means* app shows the following results:

Descriptive Statistics:

Group	Sample Size	Mean	Std. Dev.
Men	496	35800	14600
Women	476	23900	21900

Estimate of Difference of Means:

Point Estimate	Standard Error	Margin of Error
11,900	1,199	± 2,353

Confidence Interval:

Population Parameter	Lower Bound	Upper Bound	Confidence Level
Difference $\mu_1 - \mu_2$	9547	14253	95%

95% Confidence Interval
[9547, 14253]

Difference of Means $\mu_1 - \mu_2$

a. Does it seem plausible that income has a normal distribution for each gender? Explain.

b. What effect does the answer to part a have on inference comparing population means? What assumptions are made for the inferences shown?

c. Interpret the 95% confidence interval, indicating the relevance of $0 not falling in the interval.

10.21 Bulimia CI A study of bulimia among college women (J. Kern and T. Hastings, (1995), *Journal of Clinical Psychology*, vol. 51, p. 499) studied the connection between childhood sexual abuse and a measure of family cohesion (the higher the score, the greater the cohesion). The sample mean on the family cohesion scale was 2.0 for 13 sexually abused students ($s = 2.1$) and 4.8 for 17 nonabused students ($s = 3.2$). (You can enter these data as Summary Statistics under Enter Data in the *Compare Two Means* app.)

a. Find the standard error and the margin of error (at the 95% confidence level) for the difference in the sample means.

b. Construct a 95% confidence interval for the difference between the mean family cohesion for sexually abused students and non-abused students. Interpret.

10.22 Chelation useless? Chelation is an alternative therapy for heart disease that uses repeated intravenous administration of a human-made amino acid in combination with oral vitamins and minerals. Practitioners believe it removes calcium deposits from buildup in arteries. However, the evidence for a positive effect is anecdotal or comes from nonrandomized, uncontrolled studies. A double-blind randomized clinical trial comparing chelation to placebo used a treadmill test in which the response was the length of time until a subject experienced ischemia (lack of blood flow and oxygen to the heart muscle).

a. After 27 weeks of treatment, the sample mean time for the chelation group was 652 seconds. A 95% confidence interval for the population mean for chelation minus the population mean for placebo was −53 to 36 seconds. Explain how to interpret the confidence interval.

b. A significance test comparing the means had P-value = 0.69. Specify the hypotheses for this test, which was two-sided.

c. The authors concluded from the test, "There is no evidence to support a beneficial effect of chelation therapy" (*Source:* M. Knudtson et al., (2002), *JAMA*, vol. 287, p. 481, 2002.). Explain how this conclusion agrees with inference based on the values in the confidence interval.

10.23 Nicotine dependence A study on nicotine dependence for teenage smokers obtained a random sample of seventh graders. The response variable was constructed from a questionnaire called the Hooked on Nicotine Checklist (HONC). This is a list of ten questions such as, "Have you ever tried to quit but couldn't?" and "Is it hard to keep from smoking in places where it is banned, like school?" The HONC score is the total number of questions to which a student answered yes, so each student's HONC score falls between 0 and 10. The higher the score, the more hooked that student is on nicotine. One explanatory variable considered in the study was whether a subject reported inhaling when smoking. The following table reports descriptive statistics.

HONC Score			
Group	Students	Mean	Standard Deviation
Inhalers	237	2.9	3.6
Noninhalers	95	0.1	0.5

a. Explain why (i) the overwhelming majority of noninhalers must have had HONC scores of 0 and (ii) on average, those who reported inhaling answered yes to nearly three more questions than those who denied inhaling.

b. Might the HONC scores have been approximately normal for each group? Why or why not?

c. Find the standard error for the estimate $(\bar{x}_1 - \bar{x}_2) = 2.8$. Interpret.

d. The 95% confidence interval for $(\mu_1 - \mu_2)$ is (2.3, 3.3). What can you conclude about the population means for inhalers and noninhalers?

10.24 Inhaling affect HONC? Refer to the previous exercise.

a. Show that the test statistic for H_0: $\mu_1 = \mu_2$ equals $t = 11.7$. If the population means were equal, explain why it would be nearly impossible by random variation to observe this large a test statistic.

b. What decision would you make about H_0, at common significance levels? Can you conclude which group had higher mean nicotine dependence? How?

c. State the assumptions for the inference in this exercise.

10.25 Females or males more nicotine dependent? Refer to Exercise 10.23 about studying nicotine dependence using a random sample of teenagers. Of those seventh graders in the study who had tried tobacco, the mean HONC score was 2.8 ($s = 3.6$) for the 150 females and 1.6 ($s = 2.9$) for the 182 males. (*Note:* You can enter these data by selecting Summary Statistics under Enter Data in the *Compare Two Means* app.)

a. Find a standard error for comparing the sample means. Interpret.

b. Find the test statistic and P-value for H_0: $\mu_1 = \mu_2$ against H_a: $\mu_1 \neq \mu_2$. Interpret and explain what (if any) effect gender has on the mean HONC score.

c. Do you think that the HONC scores were approximately normal for each gender? Why or why not? How does this affect the validity of the analysis in part b?

10.26 Female and male monthly smokers Refer to the previous exercise. A subject was called a monthly smoker if he or she had smoked cigarettes over an extended period of time. The 74 female monthly smokers had a mean HONC score of 5.4 ($s = 3.5$), and the 71 male monthly smokers had a mean HONC score of 3.9 ($s = 3.6$). Repeat parts b and c of the previous exercise.

10.27 Body language In an experiment investigating body language (M. Koppensteiner et al., (2015), *Personality and Individual Differences*, vol. 74), researchers turned short video clips of randomly selected speeches by male and female politicians into animated, gender-neutral stick-figure clips. These clips showed the movements of the upper body parts during the speech. Each clip was rated (on a scale from −100 to 100) by a random sample of students in terms of personality traits. The ratings for one trait, the perceived dominance of a speaker, are preloaded in the *Compare Two Means* app, producing the output shown in the screenshot on the next page.

a. Set up the hypotheses for a significance test to analyze whether the population mean score differs between clips based on a male or female speaker. Define the population parameters in context.

b. Interpret the P-value for the significance test and report the conclusion for a significance level of 0.05.

c. If you were to construct a 95% confidence interval for the difference in population means, would it contain 0? Answer based on the result of part b, without actually finding the interval.

d. Use the box plots to comment on the normality assumption for the test.

e. Explain how the *t* test statistic was obtained from the parts in the output.

Descriptive Statistics:

Group	Sample Size	Mean	Std. Dev.
Male Politicians	30	10.7	26.3
Female Politicians	30	-1.1	27.9

Test Statistic:

Observed Difference	Standard Error	Test Statistic t
11.77	6.999	1.681

Hypothesis Test:

Population Parameter	Null Hypothesis	Alternative Hypothesis	Test Statistic t	P-value
Difference $\mu_1 - \mu_2$	$\mu_1 - \mu_2 = 0$	$\mu_1 - \mu_2 \neq 0$	1.6811	0.0981

t Distribution with df = 57.8

$H_0: \mu_1 = \mu_2$, $H_a: \mu_1 \neq \mu_2$. Test Statistic: $t = 1.681$, P-value = 0.0981

10.28 Student survey   Refer to the FL Student Survey data file on the book's website. Use the number of times reading a newspaper as the response variable and gender as the explanatory variable. The observations are as follows:

Females: 5, 3, 6, 3, 7, 1, 1, 3, 0, 4, 7, 2, 2, 7, 3, 0, 5, 0, 4, 4, 5, 14, 3, 1, 2, 1, 7, 2, 5, 3, 7

Males: 0, 3, 7, 4, 3, 2, 1, 12, 1, 6, 2, 2, 7, 7, 5, 3, 14, 3, 7, 6, 5, 5, 2, 3, 5, 5, 2, 3, 3

Using the *Compare Two Means* app or other software,

a. Construct and interpret an appropriate plot comparing responses by females and males.

b. Find and interpret a 95% confidence interval comparing population means for females and males.

c. Show all five steps of a significance test comparing the population means.

d. State and check the assumptions for part b and part c.

10.29 Study time   A graduate teaching assistant for Introduction to Statistics (STA 2023) at the University of Florida collected data from students in one of her classes to investigate whether study time per week (average number of hours) differed between students in the class who planned to go to graduate school and those who did not. The data were as follows:

Graduate school: 15, 7, 15, 10, 5, 5, 2, 3, 12, 16, 15, 37, 8, 14, 10, 18, 3, 25, 15, 5, 5

No Graduate School: 6, 8, 15, 6, 5, 14, 10, 10, 12, 5

Using the *Compare Two Means* app or other software,

a. Find the sample mean and standard deviation for each group. Interpret.

b. Find the standard error for the difference between the sample means. Interpret.

c. Find a 95% confidence interval comparing the population means. Interpret.

10.30 More on study time   Refer to the data in the previous exercise.

a. Show all steps of a two-sided significance test of the null hypothesis that the population mean is equal for the two groups. Interpret results in context.

b. Based on the explanation given in the previous exercise, do you think that the sample was a random sample or a convenience sample? Why? (In practice, you should not place much faith in inferences using such samples!)

10.31 Time spent on social media   As part of a class exercise, an instructor at a major university asks her students how many hours per week they spend on social media. She wants to investigate whether time spent on social media differs for male and female students at this university. The results for those age 21 or under were:

Males: 5, 7, 9, 10, 12, 12, 12, 13, 13, 15, 15, 20

Females: 5, 7, 7, 8, 10, 10, 11, 12, 12, 14, 14, 14, 16, 18, 20, 20, 20, 22, 23, 25, 40

a. Using an app or other software, find the sample mean and standard deviation for each group. Interpret.

b. Find the standard error for the difference between the sample means.

c. Find and interpret a 90% confidence interval comparing the population means.

10.32 Outliers on social media   In the previous exercise, plot the data. Do you see any outliers that could influence the results? Remove the most extreme observation from each group and redo the analyses. Compare results and summarize the influence of the extreme observations.

10.33 Body dissatisfaction   Female college student participation in athletics has increased dramatically over the past few decades. Sports medicine providers are aware of some unique health concerns of athletic women, including disordered eating. A study (M. Reinking and L. Alexander, (2005), *Journal of Athletic Training,* vol. 40, pp. 47–51) compared disordered-eating symptoms and their causes for collegiate female athletes (in lean and nonlean sports) and nonathletes. The sample mean of the body dissatisfaction assessment score was 13.2 ($s = 8.0$) for 16 lean sport athletes (those sports that place value on leanness, including distance running, swimming, and gymnastics) and 7.3 ($s = 6.0$) for the 68 nonlean sport athletes. Assuming equal population standard deviations,

a. Find the standard error for comparing the means.

b. Construct a 95% confidence interval for the difference between the mean body dissatisfaction for lean sport athletes and nonlean sport athletes. Interpret.

10.34 Body dissatisfaction test   Refer to the previous exercise.

a. Find the P-value for testing whether the population means are equal. Use a two-sided alternative.

b. Summarize assumptions for the analysis in part a. Do you think the normality assumption is justified? If not, what is the consequence of violating it?

10.35 Surgery versus placebo for knee pain   A clinical trial assessed the usefulness of arthroscopic surgery in patients suffering from osteoarthritis in their knees.[7]

---

[7]J. B. Moseley et al., (2002), *New England Journal of Medicine,* vol. 347.

Over a 3-year period, patients were randomly assigned to a placebo group (Group 1) or to a treatment that flushed the joint with fluid but did not use instruments to remove tissue (Group 2). In the placebo procedure, the same incisions were made in the knee as in the treatment group, and the surgeon manipulated the knee as if surgery was being performed, but none was actually done. The patients did not know which treatment they received.

A knee-specific pain scale was created for the study, which ranged from 0 to 100, with higher scores indicating more severe pain. The following computer output (from Minitab) was obtained, assuming equal population standard deviations. (You can also get these results by entering the summary data in the *Compare Two Means* app and checking the Assuming Equal Standard Deviations option.)

a. State and interpret the result of the confidence interval.

b. Is it reasonable to assume equal population standard deviations?

c. State all steps and interpret the result of the significance test.

```
Sample   N      Mean     StDev    SE Mean
1        60     51.6     23.7     3.1
2        61     53.7     23.7     3.0
Difference = μ(1) − μ(2)
Estimate for difference: −2.10
95% CI for difference: (−10.63, 6.43)
T-Test of difference = 0(vs ≠):
T-Value = −0.49 P-Value = 0.627 DF = 119
Both use Pooled StDev = 23.7000
```

10.36 Normal assumption   The methods of this section make the assumption of a normal population distribution. Why do you think this is more relevant for small samples than for large samples? (*Hint:* What shape does the sampling distribution of $\bar{x}_1 - \bar{x}_2$ have for large samples, regardless of the actual shape of the population distributions?)

10.37 Vital capacity   One of the authors of this book has his lung function checked every other year. At each checkup, his lung volume (called the forced vital capacity, or FVC) is measured before and after using an inhaler that contains medication against asthma. The last five checkups provided the following results (in liters):

	Checkup				
	1	2	3	4	5
Before Using Inhaler:	5.08	5.99	5.32	6.03	5.44
After Using Inhaler:	5.36	5.98	5.62	6.26	5.68

Can we use the inferential methods developed in this section to compare the mean FVC before and after using the inhaler? If yes, enter the data in the *Compare Two Means* app and find a 95% confidence interval for the difference in the population means before and after using the inhaler and interpret it. If no, explain why not.

10.3 Comparing Two Groups With Bootstrap or Permutation Resampling

In Section 10.2, we learned about the primary methods for comparing the population means of two groups. These methods work well when the sample sizes are not too small or when the response has an approximate normal distribution. In this section, we focus on cases where the sample size may be small or where the distribution of the response variable is skewed. In the latter case, comparing medians instead of means might be more informative, so we start by presenting a confidence interval for the difference between two medians. Unlike for the difference of sample means, there is no general result describing the sampling distribution of the difference between two sample medians, so we'll rely on the bootstrap approach introduced in Section 7.3 to approximate a sampling distribution via resampling.

Bootstrap Confidence Intervals for Comparing Two Groups

Recall

From Section 7.1, the **sampling distribution** of a statistic describes the distribution of all potential values that could be observed for the statistic when taking a random sample from the population. ◄

As the margin note recalls, the sampling distribution of a statistic describes all the values of the statistic we would observe if we repeatedly draw samples of the same size as the original sample from the population. For instance, in Section 10.2 we learned that the sampling distribution of the difference between two sample means $(\bar{x}_1 - \bar{x}_2)$ is approximately normal for large sample sizes n_1 and n_2. If we repeatedly take samples of size n_1 and n_2 from two groups and compute the difference in sample means, the distribution of all the differences we obtain has an approximate normal shape. The approximate normal shape is a consequence of the Central Limit Theorem, which applies for sample means.

Recall

From Section 7.3, a **bootstrap sample** is a sample drawn *with replacement* from the original sample and of the *same size* as the original sample. Its purpose is to mimic an actual sample drawn from the population. ◄

For sample medians, we are not so lucky to have such a general theorem. However, using a computer we can simulate possible values for a statistic of interest (such as the difference between two medians) when repeatedly drawing samples of the same size from two groups. This is the idea behind the bootstrap, which mimics drawing samples from a population by drawing samples (so-called resamples) from the observed data. The margin note recalls the definition of a bootstrap resample.

When comparing **two groups**, we draw a bootstrap sample from each group, i.e., a bootstrap sample of size n_1 from the observations in Group 1, and a bootstrap sample of size n_2 from the observations in Group 2. Then, we compute the statistic of interest using summary statistics of the two bootstrap samples. For instance, if we are interested in the difference between the group medians, we compute the median for the bootstrap sample in the first group and the median for the bootstrap sample in the second group, and take the difference. This difference represents one possible value for the difference between two medians we could have observed. To approximate the entire sampling distribution of the difference, we repeat this process thousands of times.

Example 10

Bootstrap Distribution of the Difference Between Two Medians ◄

Loan Amounts and Terms

Picture the Scenario

The website lendingclub.com is a peer-to-peer lending website, where personal loans up to $40,000 can be requested. Borrowers can choose between a 3-year term or a 5-year term over which to pay back the loan in monthly installments. Traditionally, 5-year loans are chosen for larger sums, but what is the typical difference between loan amounts on 5-year terms and loan amounts on 3-year terms?

To explore this question, we use a random sample of 3- and 5-year loans funded via the lendingclub.com website. The screenshot from the *Bootstrap for Two Samples* app in Figure 10.10 shows descriptive statistics from the two samples. A plot of the data is shown under the title "Original Sample." The mean loan amounts funded for the two terms are $21,268 and $14,817, for a difference of $6,451, but the distribution is right skewed, so the median amounts are smaller

---

► **Figure 10.10** Bootstrap Distribution of the Difference Between Two Sample Medians. Screenshot from the *Bootstrap for Two Samples* app, using the preloaded loan amounts data. The app shows a plot of the original samples, the bootstrapped samples and, in the histogram on the bottom, the bootstrap distribution.

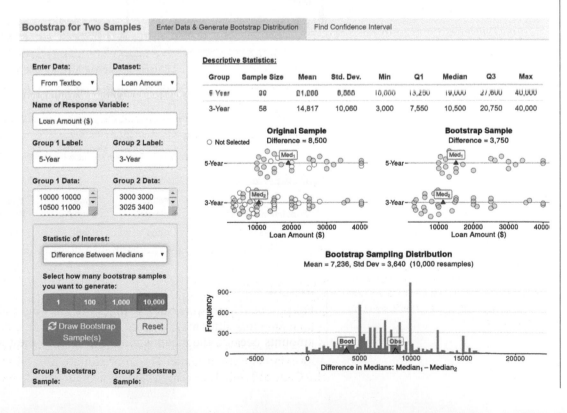

Group	Sample Size	Mean	Std. Dev.	Min	Q1	Median	Q3	Max
5-Year	99	21,268	8,555	10,000	13,250	19,000	27,600	40,000
3-Year	58	14,817	10,060	3,000	7,550	10,500	20,750	40,000

at $19,000 and $10,500, for a difference of $8,500. The median amount on a 5-year loan is estimated to be $8,500 higher compared to a 3-year loan.

Question to Explore

Find a 95% bootstrap percentile confidence interval for the difference in the median loan amounts between a 5-year and a 3-year loan. Interpret the interval.

Think It Through

The plot titled "Bootstrap Sample" in Figure 10.10 shows the results of a bootstrap sample taken from each of the two groups. For this bootstrap sample, the differences in the medians equals $3,750, compared to $8,500 for the original data. Taking 10,000 such bootstrap resamples via the app generates the bootstrap distribution shown in the histogram. This distribution looks rather irregular and is clearly not normal in shape. It shows the distribution of potential differences we could have observed with samples such as the ones we took.

To find the 95% bootstrap percentile confidence interval for the difference in the population medians, we find the 2.5th and 97.5th percentiles of this generated distribution. From the second tab of the app, this interval equals $(500, 15{,}062)$, as shown in Figure 10.10a. With 95% confidence, we estimate that the median loan amount for 5-year loans is between $500 and $15,062 higher than the median loan amount for 3-year loans.

▶ **Figure 10.10a** Bootstrap Percentile Confidence Interval for the Difference of Medians. Screenshot from the second tab "Confidence Interval" from the *Bootstrap for Two Samples* app. The app shows the position of the 2.5th and 97.5th percentile of the bootstrap distribution, which are the lower and upper bounds for the 95% confidence interval. When you replicate this output with the app, your results will vary slightly.

Summary Statistics For Bootstrap Distribution:

Bootstrap Samples	Unique Values	Mean	St. Dev.	Min	Q1	Median	Q3	Max
10,000	398	7,236	3,640	-6,000	5,000	7,000	10,000	20,000

Bootstrap Sampling Distribution

95% Bootstrap Confidence Interval
[500, 15062]

Med$_1$ – Med$_2$
Difference Between Medians (Loan Amount ($))

Bootstrap Percentile Confidence Interval:

Population Parameter	Point Estimate	Lower Bound	Upper Bound	Confidence Level
Difference Between Medians	8,500	500	15,062	95%

Insight

For potential borrowers, but also investors, knowing by how much the median loan amounts differ may be more informative than comparing the mean loan amounts because the mean is more affected by the few but largest possible

Bootstrap Sampling Distribution

95% Bootstrap Confidence Interval
[2251, 10688]

Screenshot from *Bootstrap for Two Samples* app showing a confidence interval for the difference in mean loan amounts.

loan amounts of $40,000, see the plot of the original samples. The 95% bootstrap confidence interval for the difference in means (which you can also get with the app) is equal to (2,251, 10,688), similar to the *t* interval of (2,090, 10,811) we obtain with the methods of Section 10.2. While the difference in the median loan amounts might be as small as $500, the difference in the mean loan amounts is estimated to be at least $2,251, based on the lower bound of the 95% bootstrap percentile interval (see the figure in the margin).

▶ *Try Exercise 10.38*

When the normality assumption of the regular *t* interval from Section 10.2 is questionable, you can also use the *Bootstrap for Two Samples* app to find a percentile confidence interval for the difference between two **means**. This method doesn't need to assume an approximately normal distribution in each group. One assumption that is still crucial, besides having a random sample, is that the two samples are independent. If this is not the case and the samples are dependent, such as the same person appearing in both samples, a different procedure for obtaining a bootstrap sample needs to be used. This will be discussed in Section 10.4. Section 15.2 discusses some alternative inferential methods (called nonparametric methods) for comparing medians that also do not rely on the normality assumption.

Permutation Test for Comparing Two Groups

For large sample sizes, we mentioned that meeting the assumption of normality for the response variable in each group is not crucial in deriving the sampling distribution and P-value for a significance test comparing two means. However, for small sample sizes, we need approximate normality of the population distributions to ensure that the *t* test statistic for testing H_0: $\mu_1 = \mu_2$ has a *t* sampling distribution. If the normality assumption doesn't hold, the P-value and the conclusion based on the *t* test may be invalid. We now present a test that, similar to the bootstrap confidence intervals for the difference of means or medians, doesn't need to assume normality for the population distributions. It is called a permutation test because it derives the sampling distribution of the test statistic under the null hypothesis not by relying on normal population distributions (like the *t* test) but by considering permutations (rearrangements) of the original data.

A permutation test starts from a null hypothesis of **equal population distributions** (see the margin figure showing two identical skewed population distributions).

H_0: population distribution in Group 1 = population distribution in Group 2

Equal Population Distributions for the Two Groups

Group 1

μ_1

Response Variable

Group 2

μ_2

Response Variable

This null hypothesis goes beyond just requiring the population means to be the same and is a stronger statement of "no effect." For instance, if the two groups to be compared refer to two different treatments in a clinical trial, then "no effect" means that the entire population distribution of the response variable is the same under the two considered treatments, not just that their population means are the same. The alternative hypothesis expresses one way in which the two population distributions differ, such as having different population means (H_a: $\mu_1 \neq \mu_2$).

How can we obtain the sampling distribution of a test statistic under the null hypothesis of identical population distributions without assuming normality for them? Recall that the sampling distribution is the distribution of all the possible values a statistic can take on. A permutation test constructs this distribution by considering all possible samples that could have been observed with the given data under the assumption that the null hypothesis is true.

◄ Permutations

Table 10.4 Symptom-Free Days of Allergy Patients on High and Low Doses of an Experimental Drug

Patient	Dose	Days Without Symptoms
1	High	12
2	High	13
3	Low	6
4	Low	6
5	Low	7

Dose: ◯ Low ● High

Symptom-Free Days

Example 11

Comparing Dosages

Picture the Scenario

A new medication for patients suffering from allergies has just passed pre-clinical trials and is now ready to be tested on humans to determine an appropriate dosage. Because this is the first time the drug is evaluated on humans and not much is known about the dose–response profile, the drug is tested on only five allergy patients. Two of the five patients are randomly assigned to receive a high dose of the drug, and the remaining three receive a low dose. The response variable measured is the number of days a patient stays symptom-free. Table 10.4 in the margin and the dot plot below it show the data obtained from this small experiment.

Questions to Explore

a. List all possible ways of assigning two of the five patients to the high-dose group and the remaining three to the low-dose group.

b. For each assignment, find the group means and their differences, using the responses of the patients (days without symptoms) shown in Table 10.4.

Think It Through

a. Each possible assignment divides the five patients into one group of size two and another of size three. You can think of it as writing *High* on two cards and *Low* on the other three cards in a five-card deck, shuffling the deck, and then dealing one card to each patient. Table 10.5 shows all possible ways the cards could have been dealt to the patients. These are all possible ways (there are 10) of assigning two patients to the high-dose group and three to the low-dose group.

Table 10.5 All Ten Possible Ways of Assigning Five Patients Such That Two Are in the High-Dose Group and Three Are in the Low-Dose Group

	Possible Assignments				
Patient	1	2	3	4	5
1	High	High	High	High	Low
2	High	Low	Low	Low	High
3	Low	High	Low	Low	High
4	Low	Low	High	Low	Low
5	Low	Low	Low	High	Low

	Possible Assignments				
Patient	6	7	8	9	10
1	Low	Low	Low	Low	Low
2	High	High	Low	Low	Low
3	Low	Low	High	High	Low
4	High	Low	High	Low	High
5	Low	High	Low	High	High

The first possible assignment listed in Table 10.5 is the original one, with patients 1 and 2 in the high-dose group and patients 3, 4, and 5 in the low-dose group. The second possible assignment has patients 1 and 3 in the high-dose group and patients 2, 4, and 5 in the low-dose group. The third assignment has patients 1 and 4 in the high-dose group and so on. Overall, there are 10 possible assignments of the five patients into two groups of size two and three, respectively.

b. Table 10.6 lists, for each assignment, the means in the high- and low-dose groups. For instance, for the original assignment, the sample mean in the high-dose group was 12.50 and, in the low-dose group, 6.33, for a difference of 6.17. For the second possible assignment, which has patients 1 and 3 in the high-dose group, with responses 12 and 6, the sample mean in the high-dose group is $(12 + 6)/2 = 9$. For patients 2, 4, and 5, which are in the low-dose group under this assignment, the sample mean is $(13 + 6 + 7)/3 = 8.67$, yielding a difference of $9 - 8.67 = 0.33$.

Table 10.6 Group Means and Their Differences for All Possible Assignments

For each assignment, the sample mean of the responses for patients in the high-($\bar{x}_1$) and low-dose ($\bar{x}_2$) groups were computed and their difference taken.

Patient	Response	Possible Assignments				
		1	2	3	4	5
1	12	High	High	High	High	Low
2	13	High	Low	Low	Low	High
3	6	Low	High	Low	Low	High
4	6	Low	Low	High	Low	Low
5	7	Low	Low	Low	High	Low
Mean High: $\bar{x}_1$		12.50	9.00	9.00	9.50	9.50
Mean Low: $\bar{x}_2$		6.33	8.67	8.67	8.33	8.33
Difference: $\bar{x}_1 - \bar{x}_2$		6.17	0.33	0.33	1.17	1.17

Patient	Response	Possible Assignments				
		6	7	8	9	10
1	12	Low	Low	Low	Low	Low
2	13	High	High	Low	Low	Low
3	6	Low	Low	High	High	Low
4	6	High	Low	High	Low	High
5	7	Low	High	Low	High	High
Mean High: $\bar{x}_1$		9.50	10.00	6.00	6.50	6.50
Mean Low: $\bar{x}_2$		8.33	8.00	10.67	10.33	10.33
Difference: $\bar{x}_1 - \bar{x}_2$		1.17	2.00	−4.67	−3.83	−3.83

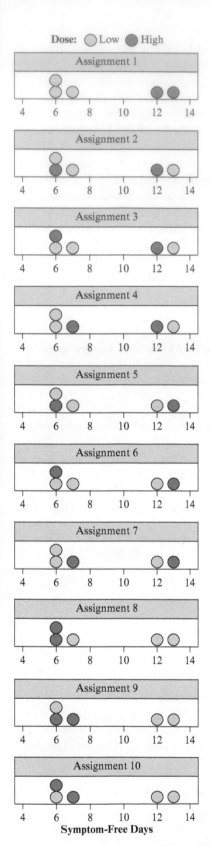

▲ **Figure 10.11** All Possible Permutations
Each dot plot shows the resulting data set under one of the 10 possible assignments.
Question Which dot plot would provide the most evidence that the high dose has more symptom-free days?

The last row in Table 10.6 shows the difference in the sample means for all possible assignments. Figure 10.11 in the margin shows the dot plots we would get under each assignment with the responses from the patients in Table 10.4.

Insight

Each of the 10 possible assignments represents one unique permutation (shuffling) of the five original group labels (High, High, Low, Low, Low). If the population distributions are identical in the two groups (the null hypothesis), each permutation (shuffle) of the group labels results in a data set that could have been observed. A permutation test either considers all or, if there are too many, a large random sample of all such permutations.

▶ **Try Exercise 10.42**

If the population distributions are identical (the null hypothesis), the responses of subjects do not depend on the group they are in. For instance, if the population distribution of the number of symptom-free days is the same in both dose groups, a response of 7 days is equally likely to occur for a patient assigned to the high-dose group as it is for a patient assigned to the low-dose group. In fact, if the null hypothesis of identical population distributions is correct, the responses we observe on all five patients in the experiment are equally likely to occur under *each* of the 10 possible assignments we listed in Table 10.6.

If the responses are equally likely for each of the 10 assignments, so are the differences in the sample means we computed for each assignment in Table 10.6. Because there are 10 of them, each difference occurs with a probability of 1/10 under the null hypothesis of identical population distributions. We have just found the sampling distribution of the difference in the sample means by tabulating all possible differences and their probability of occurrence under the null hypothesis.

Table 10.7 and Figure 10.12 on the next page show the sampling distribution for the difference in the sample means $(\bar{x}_1 - \bar{x}_2)$ for the data in Example 11. Note that some assignments, such as the three assignments 4, 5, and 6, lead to the same difference of 1.17. Then, the probability of observing such a difference is $1/10 + 1/10 + 1/10 = 3/10$.

Table 10.7 Sampling Distribution of $\bar{x}_1 - \bar{x}_2$ Derived By Considering All Possible Permutations (Assignments)

The table shows each possible difference, how often it occurs among the 10 permutations, and the probability of observing this difference under the null hypothesis.

Difference $\bar{x}_1 - \bar{x}_2$	Permutations	Probability
−4.67	1	1/10
−3.83	2	2/10
0.33	2	2/10
1.17	3	3/10
2.00	1	1/10
6.17	1	1/10
Total	**10**	**1**

▲ **Figure 10.12** Graph of Sampling Distribution of $\bar{x}_1 - \bar{x}_2$ Derived By Considering All Possible Permutations. **Question** For large sample sizes, what would be the shape of the sampling distribution of $\bar{x}_1 - \bar{x}_2$?

Permutation P-value

Recall

The P-value is the probability of obtaining a test statistic as or even more extreme than the observed one, assuming the null hypothesis is true. ◄

As in any significance test, we use the sampling distribution to judge how extreme the observed difference of 6.17 is, assuming the null hypothesis of identical population distributions is true. If the alternative hypothesis specifies that the mean number of symptom-free days is larger in the high dose group, i.e., H_a: $\mu_1 > \mu_2$, then all values of the test statistic that are as large or larger than the observed difference of 6.17 are considered more extreme. Of the 10 possible differences, only one, namely the observed one, is extreme. It occurs with a probability of $1/10 = 0.10$. This is the P-value for the permutation test of the null hypothesis of equal population distributions against the alternative H_a: $\mu_1 > \mu_2$. Because the sampling distribution was generated using permutations, this P-value is called a **permutation P-value**. If truly there is no difference in the population distribution of the number of symptom-free days for patients assigned to the high- and low-dose group, we would obtain a difference of 6.17 in the sample means once every 10 times. This is not that unusual. For instance, using a significance level of 0.05, we would fail to reject the null hypothesis.

If we assumed that the population distribution of symptom-free days followed a normal distribution in both dose groups, we could have used a t test to assess whether the mean is larger in the high-dose group. The t statistic for the data in Table 10.4 equals 10.3 ($df = 1.9$), yielding a very small P-value of 0.006, quite different from the permutation P-value. Of course, with small samples such as these, there is no way of checking whether the normality assumption for the population distributions is appropriate, and it is safer to rely on the P-value from the permutation test. On the other hand, note that for these data the smallest possible P-value for the permutation test is 1/10 (the one we actually observed, because the actual data yielded the most extreme difference possible). However, with just a few more observations, the number of possible permutations quickly increases, and it is possible to get much smaller P-values.

Permutation Test for Larger Sample Sizes

In the preceding example with only five patients, we could list all possible permutations of the original data. When the sample size is larger, computing the test statistic (such as the difference in sample means) for all possible permutations can be too computationally demanding because there are simply too many permutations to consider. For instance, for Example 10 comparing loan amounts with 3- or 5-year terms, with 58 and 30 observations in the two groups, there are more than 10^{23} (which is much more than 1 trillion) different permutations. For such cases, one randomly generates a large number (such as 10,000 or 100,000) of permutations. The proportion out of the generated permutations that yield a test statistic as or more extreme than the observed one is then a very accurate approximation of the exact permutation P-value.

For carrying out the permutation test, we need a computer to (i) generate all possible permutations or a very large number of random permutations and (ii) compute the test statistic for each permutation, just as we have done in Example 11 on a much smaller scale. The *Permutation Test* app can run the permutation test and compute the permutation P-value.

▶ **Activity 1**

Exercise 10.92 gives step-by-step instructions on how to use the *Permutation Test* app to build the permutation distribution and find the permutation P-value.

Example 12

Permutation Test for Comparing Two Groups ◀

Do Dogs Prefer Petting to Vocal Praise?

Picture the Scenario

In a study to explore whether dogs prefer petting to vocal praise, researchers set up the following experiment.[8] They randomly divided 14 dogs into two groups of seven dogs each. Each dog in the first group was placed in a room where the dog's owner provided petting and, some distance apart, an assistant (familiarized with the dog for 1 minute before the experiment began) provided vocal praise (e.g., saying in a high tone of voice, "You are such a good doggie! What a sweet dog you are"). For the second group of 7 dogs, the roles were reversed, and the owner of the dog provided vocal praise while the assistant provided petting. The experiment lasted for 5 minutes (= 300 seconds), during which the dog could switch freely between interacting with the owner, the assistant, or neither. The response variable measured was the time the dog interacted with its owner.

Table 10.8 shows the data collected from this experiment, with sample mean $\bar{x}_1 = 232$ seconds in the first group and $\bar{x}_2 = 68$ seconds in the second group.

Group: ○ Petting ○ Vocal Praise

Box- and dot plots of time dogs spent with owners in the two groups (Group1 = Owner provides petting, Group 2 = Owner provides Vocal Praise)

Table 10.8 The Time Dogs Interact with Their Owners

For dogs in Group 1, owners provided petting. For dogs in Group 2, owners provided vocal praise. In each group, values are sorted in ascending order.

Group	Responses	Mean
1	114, 203, 217, 254, 256, 284, 296	232
2	4, 7, 24, 25, 48, 71, 294	68

The figures in the margin show box plots and dot plots, both revealing potentially skewed distributions. All but one dog in the second group spent less time with the owner compared to the dogs in Group 1. This one dog clearly is an outlier in Group 2 but might be typical for some dogs that choose to stay with their owner no matter what kind of interaction is offered. It shows that the distribution might be rather skewed to the right in this group.

Questions to Explore

  a. Why might a *t* test comparing these two groups not be appropriate?

  b. Conduct a permutation test. What are the hypotheses and how can you find the sampling distribution of the difference in sample means?

  c. Obtain the permutation P-value and interpret.

---

[8]E. Feuerbacher and C. Wynne, (2005), *Behavioural Processes*, vol. 110, pp. 47–59.

Two-sample T for Group 1 vs Group 2

Difference = μ(Group 1) − μ(Group 2)

Estimate for difference: 164.4

T-Test of difference = 0(vs >):

T-Value = 3.64 P-Value = 0.0023
DF = 9.8

Software Output for *t* Test.

Note that software doesn't tell you whether the requested analysis is valid, i.e., whether the assumptions hold for the *t* test.

Did you know?

The number 3,432 is equal to the binomial coefficient $\binom{14}{7}$, which we defined in Section 6.3 in Chapter 6 as all possible ways of obtaining exactly $x = 7$ successes in $n = 14$ trials. Here, a trial is whether any of the 14 dogs is assigned to Group 1, with a "success" if it is. ◄

Think It Through

a. The *t* test makes the assumption of a normal distribution for the population distribution of time dogs spent with owners, which is hard to check with just seven observations in each group. From the context and the data observed, this assumption looks implausible. In addition, we are interested in a one-sided alternative hypothesis, and although the *t* test is robust for two-sided hypotheses, it might not be for one-sided hypotheses for small sample sizes. These are reasons we may not trust the result of the *t* test, which reports a P-value of 0.002 for these data, as shown in the margin.

b. A permutation test tests the null hypothesis that the distribution of the time dogs interact with their owners is the same in each group:

H_0: *Distribution of time that dogs spend with owners when owners provide petting = Distribution of time that dogs spend with owners when owners provide vocal praise.*

This null hypothesis in particular implies that the population means are the same. The alternative hypothesis captures some way the two population distributions differ. Here, we are interested in whether the population mean time dogs spend with their owners is larger when the owners provide petting instead of vocal praise, so the alternative hypothesis is H_a: $\mu_1 > \mu_2$. As a test statistic, we choose the difference in the sample means $\bar{x}_1 - \bar{x}_2$, with larger values of this difference providing more support for the alternative hypothesis.

A particular permutation of the original data corresponds to the results we would get for one particular way of dividing the 14 dogs into two groups of seven. Table 10.9 shows one such permutation, for which three dogs previously in Group 1 are now in Group 2, and three dogs from Group 2 are now in Group 1. For this particular permutation, the difference in the sample means is $174 - 125 = 49$, much smaller than the observed difference of $232 - 68 = 164$.

Table 10.9 One Permutation of the Original Dataset

Color shows original group membership (green = Group 1, yellow = Group 2).

Group	Responses	Mean
1	25, 71, 114, 217, 203, 294, 296	174
2	4, 7, 24, 48, 254, 256, 284	125

The screenshot of the *Permutation Test* app in Figure 10.13 shows this particular permutation in the top right graph, titled "Permuted Sample." (The top left graph shows the original data.) Overall, we generated 10,000 random permutations with the app. The blue histogram shows the sampling distribution of $\bar{x}_1 - \bar{x}_2$ based on these 10,000 permutations. The observed difference of 164 is marked with an orange triangle, and the result of the last permutation (for which the difference is 49) is marked by a blue triangle. We immediately see from the histogram that the observed difference is extreme because it is far out in the tail of the sampling distribution. If the null hypothesis is true, observing such a difference or one even larger seems very unlikely.

▶ **Figure 10.13**
Permutation Distribution of the Difference in Means. Screenshot from the *Permutation Test* app. The app shows the result of 10,000 random permutations of the original data on dog behavior to approximate the sampling distribution of $\bar{x}_1 - \bar{x}_2$. **Question** If the assumption of normality were met, the sampling distribution would have what shape?

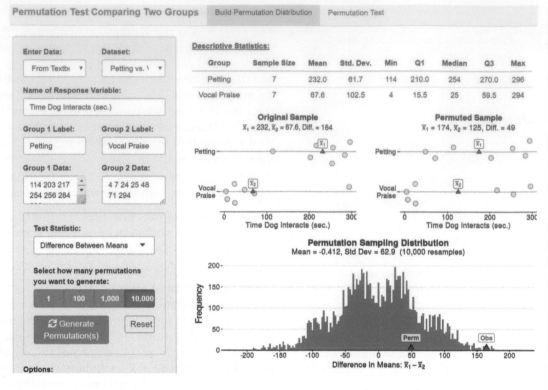

c. To find the permutation P-value, we count how many of the 10,000 permutations yielded a test statistic $\bar{x}_1 - \bar{x}_2$ as large or larger than the observed one of 164. To see this, turn to the second tab of the app, titled "Permutation Test", with the screenshot shown in Figure 10.13a.

Permutation Test:

Number of Permutations	Test Statistic	Observed Value	Number of Permutations with ($\bar{x}_1 - \bar{x}_2$) Larger Than Observed Value	Permutation P-value
10,000	$\bar{x}_1 - \bar{x}_2$	164	33	0.0033

▲ **Figure 10.13a** Permutation P-Value for Testing Whether the Time Dogs Interact with Their Owners is the Same in Both Groups. Screenshot taken from the second tab of the *Permutation Test* app. The app shows how many permutations resulted in a test statistic as or more extreme than the observed one, and the permutation P-value.

From it, we see that 33 permutations yielded a test statistic as large or larger than 164. Therefore, the permutation P-value for our one-sided test equals $33/10,000 = 0.0033$, very small.

In experiments like this, the probability of observing a difference of 164 seconds or larger is only 0.003 if the time dogs interact with their owners is the same in the two groups. This is small, so we have strong evidence to reject the null hypothesis of identical population distributions at any reasonable significance level. We conclude that under the settings of this experiment, the mean time dogs interact with their owners is larger when the owners provide petting than when they provide vocal praise.

Insight

Although the P-value for the permutation test is twice as large as the one from the t test, both are very small, and the same conclusions are reached. However, note that the sampling distribution of $\bar{x}_1 - \bar{x}_2$ as approximated via 10,000 permutations is not normal, so the results of the t test are questionable, which we wouldn't know if we hadn't run the permutation test.

▶ *Try Exercise 10.45*

Another strength of the permutation test besides not requiring normality is that it is not restricted to comparing means. For example, if we want to see whether the *median time* that dogs interact with their owners is larger in the first group (which may be a more reasonable measure of the center of the distribution if it is skewed and there are outliers), all we have to change in Example 12 is the test statistic. Instead of computing the difference of sample means for each permutation, we compute the difference of sample medians. In the app, when we change to the difference of medians as the test statistic, the permutation P-value for the one-sided test equals 0.015, indicating that the median time in the petting group is significantly higher than the median time in the vocal praise group.

SUMMARY: Comparing Two Groups with a Permutation Test

This test derives the sampling distribution by considering all possible (or a large sample of random) permutations of the original data. A permutation is one particular way of dividing the $(n_1 + n_2)$ observations into two groups of size n_1 and n_2, respectively. For each such permutation, the test statistic (e.g., the difference in the sample means) is computed from the resulting dataset.

1. **Assumptions**

   - A quantitative response variable observed in each of two groups.

   - Independent random samples, either from random sampling or a randomized experiment. However, for an experiment, the assumption of a random sample of subjects is not necessary as long as the subjects are assigned to the two groups randomly.

2. **Hypotheses**

   H_0: Identical population distributions for the two groups (this implies equal population means, $\mu_1 = \mu_2$).

   H_a: $\mu_1 \neq \mu_2$. Population means differ between the two groups. One-sided versions are also possible, H_a: $\mu_1 < \mu_2$ or H_a: $\mu_1 > \mu_2$.

   H_a could also be in terms of other population parameters, such as population medians.

> **3. Test Statistic**
>
> The difference $(\bar{x}_1 - \bar{x}_2)$ of the sample means. If the alternative hypothesis is in terms of medians, then the test statistic is the difference in the sample medians.
>
> **4. P-value**
>
> The P-value is the proportion out of all possible permutations with a test statistic as extreme or even more extreme than the observed test statistic. When the number of all possible permutations is too large, a random sample of a large number of permutations (such as 10,000) is considered. Then, the P-value is the proportion out of these 10,000 random permutations that give a test statistic as extreme or even more extreme than the observed one.
>
> **5. Conclusion**
>
> Smaller P-values give stronger evidence against H_0 and supporting H_a. Interpret the P-value in context and, if a decision is needed, reject H_0 if P-value $\leq$ significance level (such as 0.05).

Here, we looked at the permutation test for comparing the distribution of a quantitative response variable between two groups. Section 11.5 discusses a permutation test for comparing the distribution of a categorical response variable between two groups. Section 15.1 discusses an alternative permutation test that uses the ranks of the observations instead of the original observations.

The Ratio of Proportions or Means

So far in this chapter, we have compared two groups through the *difference* between two population parameters. We can also compare two groups using the *ratio* of two population parameters. For instance, Examples 2 through 4 discussed data from a study comparing the proportions of cancer deaths between a group who took placebo and a group that took aspirin. The difference in the sample proportion of $0.030 - 0.023 = 0.007$ seemed small. This effect of aspirin over placebo seems more substantial when viewed as the *ratio* $0.030/0.023 = 1.3$ of the two proportions, which is a statistic commonly reported in medical journals and called the **relative risk**. We first saw how to interpret it in Chapter 3, Section 3.2. The proportion of cancer deaths is estimated to be 30% larger in the placebo group compared to the aspirin group. Inference for the relative risk is discussed in Chapter 11, Section 11.3 (see Example 8).

You can also use the ratio to compare means. For example, the National Center for Health Statistics recently reported that the mean weight for adult American women was 140 pounds in 1962 and 164 pounds in 2002. Since $164/140 = 1.17$, the mean in 2002 was 1.17 times the mean in 1962. This can also be expressed by saying that the mean increased by 17% over this 40-year period.

10.3 Practicing the Basics

10.38 Arrival delay of airlines Arrival delays of incoming flights are problematic because passengers could miss their connecting flights. Are some airlines better than others in terms of getting their passengers to their destination on time? We obtained a random sample of arrival delays for flights from two major airline carriers flying into the Atlanta International Airport, the busiest in the world, to compare the average arrival delay. The samples were taken over the period from June to August 2019, and we only considered flights that were late by 5 minutes or more past their scheduled arrival time. The data are preloaded in the *Bootstrap for Two Samples* app and available on the book's website.

a. Comment on the shape of the distribution of arrival delays and mention why the median arrival delay, rather than the mean arrival delay, might better reflect a typical delay.

b. Find and interpret the difference in the median arrival delay of flights from the two carriers.

c. Obtain and describe the shape of the bootstrap distribution for the difference in the medians.

d. Obtain and interpret a 95% bootstrap percentile confidence interval for the difference in the medians. Consider whether zero falls inside the interval.

e. If you are interested in a confidence interval for the difference in the means, you might be hesitant to use the *t*-interval from Section 10.2 because the population distributions are definitely not normal. Use the bootstrap approach to find a 95% confidence interval for the difference in means. Does it differ from the *t*-interval from Section 10.2? Explain.

10.39 Airbnb Boston vs. Seattle   The dataset Boston Seattle Airbnb on the book's website (and preloaded in the *Bootstrap for Two Samples* app) shows data on room prices on the Airbnb platform for these two cities. The sample size is relatively small, and the distribution of room prices is right skewed.

a. You want to find a confidence interval for the difference in the mean room price charged on Airbnb between these two cities, but you are worried that the assumption of normality underlying the *t* confidence interval are not fulfilled. Create the bootstrap distribution for the difference in means and obtain and interpret a 95% bootstrap percentile confidence interval from it.

b. Because of the right skew, a comparison involving the median room price may be more useful. Obtain and interpret a 95% bootstrap percentile confidence interval for the difference in median prices.

10.40 Median time on Facebook   Exercise 10.18 compared how much time freshmen and sophomores spend on Facebook per day by finding a confidence interval for the difference between the mean number of minutes. (The data are preloaded in the *Bootstrap for Two Samples* app.) The distribution of the number of minutes is extremely right skewed, with a few students reporting 300 minutes (i.e., 5 hours) and more.

a. Check if the confidence interval for the difference in means you found in Exercise 10.18 is valid, even though the distribution of the time on Facebook is far from normal. Do this by finding the confidence interval for the difference in means via the bootstrap and comparing it to the *t*-interval. Explain.

b. It may be more informative to compare the median number of minutes. Find and interpret a 95% confidence interval for the difference in the median time spent on Facebook.

10.41 LendingClub interest rates   The website Lendingclub .com mentioned in Example 10 rates the creditworthiness of borrowers by assigning them to a risk category. The two highest categories are A and B. The assigned-risk category influences the interest rates that borrowers pay

for their loans. How much higher is the median interest rate for loans rated A versus those rated B? Answer by using the data in the *Bootstrap for Two Samples* app (also available on the book's website) and find and interpret a 95% confidence interval for the difference in the median interest rates.

10.42 Permuting therapies   A clinical psychologist wants to choose between two therapies for treating severe cases of mental depression. She selects four patients who are similar in their depressive symptoms and in their overall quality of health. She randomly selects two of the patients to receive Therapy 1 and the other two to receive Therapy 2. She selects small samples for ethical reasons—if her experiment indicates that one therapy is superior, she will use that therapy on all her other depression patients. After 1 month of treatment, the improvement in each patient is measured by the change in a score for measuring severity of mental depression. The higher the score, the better. The improvement scores are

> **Therapy 1:** 30, 60
> **Therapy 2:** 20, 30

a. List all six possible ways these four patients could have been assigned to the two therapies. That is, give all six possible ways of dividing the four patients into two groups of two patients each.

b. Using the observed improvement scores shown in the table, find the sample means in each group and their difference under each possible assignment.

10.43 Sampling distribution via permutations   Refer to the previous exercise comparing improvement scores under two therapies for depression patients.

a. State the null hypothesis of equal population distributions in the context of this experiment.

b. Argue that if the null hypothesis is true, the sampling distribution for the difference in sample means is $P(-20) = 2/6, P(-10) = 1/6, P(10) = 1/6, P(20) = 2/6$.

c. Find the permutation P-value for testing the null hypothesis in part a (which implies the population mean scores are the same) against the alternative that the population mean improvement score is larger under Therapy 1, using the difference in the sample means as a test statistic. Interpret it.

10.44 Two-sided permutation P-value   Refer to the previous exercise and the sampling distribution mentioned there. What is the permutation P-value for the two-sided test with alternative hypothesis that the mean improvement scores are different under Therapies 1 and 2? (*Hint:* As for any regular test, the two-sided P-value is the the sum of the tail probabilities of test statistic values as extreme as the observed one. Extreme differences are those with an absolute value as large as or larger than the absolute value of the observed difference.)

10.45 Time spent on social media revisited Exercise 10.31

considered the following data on the number of hours students spent on social media sites per week:

Males: 5, 7, 9, 10, 12, 12, 12, 13, 13, 15, 15, 20

Females: 5, 7, 7, 8, 10, 10, 11, 12, 12, 14, 14, 14, 16, 18, 20, 20, 20, 22, 23, 25, 40

Enter the observations into the *Permutation Test* app. Let males be Group 1 and females be Group 2. We are interested in testing whether the population mean number of hours spent on social media differs between males and females, using as test statistic the difference in sample means.

a. What are the observed group means and their difference?

b. Press the Generate Random Permutation(s) button once to generate one permutation of the original data. What are the two group means and their difference under this permutation? (The subtitle of the dot plot shows this information.)

c. Did this one permutation lead to a difference that is less extreme, as extreme, or more extreme than the observed difference?

d. Select to generate 10,000 random permutations. How many of them resulted in a test statistic as or more extreme than the observed difference? (Remember, the alternative hypothesis is H_a: $\mu_1 \neq \mu_2$.)

e. Find and interpret the permutation P-value.

10.46 Compare permutation test to *t* test Refer to the previous exercise.

a. Run a *t* test and report the P-value for the two-sided alternative hypothesis.

b. Using a significance level of 0.10, are the decisions based on the *t* test and based on the permutation test comparable? Which one would you trust more?

c. Remove the largest observations (which could be outliers) in each of the two groups, as was done in Exercise 10.32. Does the conclusion of the permutation test change?

10.47 Dominance of politicians For a rating experiment, researchers translated short video clips of randomly selected speeches by 30 male and 30 female politicians

into animated, gender-neutral stick-figures. These animated sequences were rated (on a scale from −100 to 100) by a panel of students on the perceived dominance of the speaker. A higher rating indicates higher dominance. The data are preloaded in the *Permutation Test* app and also available on the book's website. (See also Exercise 10.27.)

a. State the null and alternative hypothesis and run a permutation test to see whether there is a difference in the ratings on dominance between female and male speakers. What is the conclusion when the significance level is 0.05?

b. Run a *t* test. Are results comparable to the ones from the permutation test? Why or why not?

10.48 Sampling distribution of $\bar{x}_1 - \bar{x}_2$ Refer to Example 12, which compared two groups of seven dogs each in terms of their time interacting with their owners. The following graph shows a smoothed version of the sampling distribution of $\bar{x}_1 - \bar{x}_2$ derived from the permutation approach. Superimposed (in blue) is the theoretical sampling distribution of $\bar{x}_1 - \bar{x}_2$ if the sample sizes were large.

a. What would the mean, standard error, and approximate shape of the theoretical sampling distribution of $\bar{x}_1 - \bar{x}_2$ be if the sample sizes were large?

b. Comment on how the permutation sampling distribution of $\bar{x}_1 - \bar{x}_2$ differs from the theoretical, large-sample one.

c. Consider the one-sided alternative H_a: $\mu_1 > \mu_2$. If the actually observed difference in sample means were 100, would the P-values computed from each sampling distribution be the same or different? Explain.

10.4 Analyzing Dependent Samples

With **dependent samples**, each observation in one sample has a matched observation in the other sample. The observations are called **matched pairs**. We've already seen examples of matched-pairs data. In Example 8 of Chapter 9, each of a sample of anorexic girls had her weight measured before and after a treatment for anorexia. The weights before the treatment form one group of observations. The weights after the treatment form the other group. The same girls were in both samples, so the samples are dependent.

By contrast, in Examples 2, 5, and 6 of this chapter, the samples were *independent*. The two groups consisted of different people, and there was no matching of an observation in one sample with an observation from the other sample.

Example 13

Dependent Samples ◀

Cell Phones and Driving

Picture the Scenario

Example 9 in this chapter analyzed whether the use of cell phones impairs reaction times in a driving skills test. The analysis used independent samples—one group used cell phones and a separate control group did not use them. An alternative design uses the same subjects for both groups. Reaction times are measured when subjects performed the driving task without using cell phones and then again while the same subjects used cell phones.

Table 10.10 shows the mean of the reaction times (in milliseconds) for each subject under each condition. Figure 10.14 in the margin shows box plots of the data for the two conditions, which you can also obtain under the "Two Dependent Samples" tab of the *Compare Two Means* app.

Table 10.10 Reaction Times on Driving Skills Before and While Using Cell Phone

The difference score is the reaction time using the cell phone minus the reaction time not using it, such as $636 - 604 = 32$ milliseconds.

Student	Using Cell Phone? No	Yes	Difference	Student	Using Cell Phone? No	Yes	Difference
1	604	636	32	17	525	626	101
2	556	623	67	18	508	501	−7
3	540	615	75	19	529	574	45
4	522	672	150	20	470	468	−2
5	459	601	142	21	512	578	66
6	544	600	56	22	487	560	73
7	513	542	29	23	515	525	10
8	470	554	84	24	499	647	148
9	556	543	−13	25	448	456	8
10	531	520	−11	26	558	688	130
11	599	609	10	27	589	679	90
12	537	559	22	28	814	960	146
13	619	595	−24	29	519	558	39
14	536	565	29	30	462	482	20
15	554	573	19	31	521	527	6
16	467	554	87	32	543	536	−7

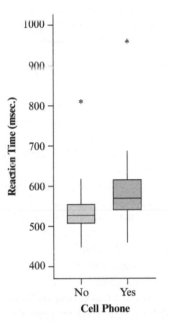

▲ **Figure 10.14** Box Plots of Observations on Reaction Times. **Question** From the data in Table 10.10, what do the outliers for the two distributions have in common?

Questions to Explore

a. Use the box plots to summarize the distribution of the reaction time under the two conditions.

b. To compare the mean response times using statistical inference, should we treat the samples as independent or dependent?

Think It Through

a. The box plots show that the distribution of reaction times is fairly symmetric in each group, save for a very large outlier in each group. In general, reaction times tend to be larger for those using a cell phone.

b. The responses under the No and Yes columns in Table 10.10 were made by the same subject, so they are not independent. A subject who in general is slow to react will have a large reaction time under both experimental conditions. These are matched-pairs data because each control observation (Sample 1) pairs with a cell phone observation (Sample 2). Because this study used the same subjects for each sample, the samples are dependent.

Insight

Table 10.10 shows that subject number 28 had a large reaction time in each case. This one subject was slow to react, regardless of the condition.

▶ *Try Exercise 10.49, part a*

Why would we use dependent instead of independent samples? A major benefit is that sources of potential biases are controlled so we can make a more accurate comparison. By using matched pairs we keep many other factors fixed that otherwise could affect the analysis. Often this results in the benefit of smaller standard errors.

From Figure 10.14, for instance, the sample median was higher when subjects used cell phones. This did not happen because the subjects using cell phones tended to be older than the subjects not using them. Age was not a lurking variable, because each sample had the same subjects. For the design with independent samples (different subjects) for the two conditions in Example 9, the two samples could differ somewhat on characteristics that might affect the results, such as physical fitness or gender or age. With independent samples, studies ideally use randomization to assign subjects to the two groups attempting to minimize the extent to which this happens. With observational studies, however, this is not an option.

Comparing Means with Dependent Samples: Paired Differences

For each matched pair (i.e., for each subject) in Table 10.10, we construct a new variable consisting of the difference (d for difference),

d = reaction time using cell phone − reaction time without cell phone.

For Subject 1, $d = 636 - 604 = 32$. Table 10.10 also shows these 32 differences. The sample mean of these differences, denoted by $\bar{x}_d$, is

$$\bar{x}_d = (32 + 67 + 75 + \cdots -7)/32 = 50.6.$$

The sample mean of the differences necessarily equals the difference between the means for the two samples. In Table 10.10, the mean reaction time without the cell phone is $(604 + 556 + 540 + \cdots + 543)/32 = 534.6$, the mean reaction time using the cell phone is $(636 + 623 + 615 + \cdots + 536)/32 = 585.2$, and the difference between these means is 50.6. This is also the mean of the differences, $\bar{x}_d$.

For Dependent Samples, Mean of Differences = Difference of Means

For dependent samples, the difference $(\bar{x}_1 - \bar{x}_2)$ between the means of the two samples equals the mean $\bar{x}_d$ of the differences for the matched pairs.

In Words

For **dependent** samples, we calculate the **differences** for each matched pair and then use the one-sample methods of Chapters 8 and 9.

Likewise, the difference $(\mu_1 - \mu_2)$ between the population means is identical to the parameter μ_d that is the population mean of the differences. So the sample mean $\bar{x}_d$ of the differences not only estimates μ_d, the population mean difference, but also the difference $(\mu_1 - \mu_2)$. We can base inference about $(\mu_1 - \mu_2)$ on inference about the population mean of the differences. *This simplifies the analysis since it reduces a two-sample (bivariate) problem to a one-sample (univariate) analysis using the differences.* We simply regard the differences as a single sample from the population of differences with population mean μ_d.

Let n denote the number of observations in each sample. This equals the number of differences. The 95% confidence interval for the population mean difference for dependent samples is

$$\bar{x}_d \pm t_{.025}(se) \text{ with } se = s_d/\sqrt{n},$$

Recall

You can review **confidence intervals for a mean** in Section 8.3 and **significance tests for a mean** in Section 9.3. ◄

where $\bar{x}_d$ is the sample mean of the differences and s_d is their standard deviation. You will recognize this formula as the formula for a confidence interval for a population mean, based on a single sample from that population. The t score comes from the t table with $df = n - 1$.

Likewise, to test the hypothesis H_0: $\mu_1 = \mu_2$ of equal population means, we can conduct the single-sample test of H_0: $\mu_d = 0$ with the sample of differences. The test statistic is

$$t = \frac{\bar{x}_d - 0}{se} \text{ with } se = s_d/\sqrt{n}.$$

Caution

Although $\bar{x}_d = \bar{x}_1 - \bar{x}_2$, there is no way of obtaining s_d from the sample standard deviations s_1 and s_2 in the two groups. In particular, s_d is *not* equal to $s_1 - s_2$! You (or the software) have to compute all differences first and then find s_d. ◄

This compares the sample mean of the differences to the null hypothesis value of 0. The standard error is the same as for the confidence interval and you will also recognize this test statistic from the one-sample t test in Section 9.3. The $df = n - 1$. Since this test uses the differences for the pairs of observations, it is called a **paired t test.**

Because these paired-difference inferences are special cases of single-sample inferences about a population mean, they make the same assumptions:

- The sample of differences is a random sample from a population of such differences.
- The differences have a population distribution that is approximately normal. This is mainly important for small samples (less than about 30) and for one-sided inferences.

For example, when checking assumptions for inference with the data in Example 13, we do not need approximate normality of the reaction times in each of the two groups. All we care about is the differences in reaction times, so we only need to check whether the differences follow approximately a normal distribution.

> **Comparing Means for Two Dependent Samples** ◄

Example 14

Cell Phones and Driver Reaction Time

Picture the Scenario

The matched-pairs data in Table 10.10 showed the reaction times for the sampled subjects using and not using cell phones. You could enter the differences between the reaction times in the *Inference for a Mean* app and answer all questions below from its output, but Figure 10.15 shows output from the *Compare Two Means* app, which has a dedicated tab for dependent samples.

Descriptive Statistics:

Group	Sample Size	Mean	Std. Dev.
Cell Phone	32	585.2	89.6
No Cell Phone	32	534.6	66.4
Differences	32	50.6	52.5

Boxplot

Estimate of Difference of Means:

Point Estimate	Standard Error	Margin of Error
50.62	9.28	± 18.92

Distribution of Differences

Confidence Interval:

Population Parameter	Lower Bound	Upper Bound	Confidence Level
Mean Difference μ_d	31.70	69.55	95%

95% Confidence Interval
[31.70, 69.55]

Mean Difference μ_d

▲ **Figure 10.15** Confidence Interval for the Mean Difference Based on Two Dependent Samples. Screenshot from the "Two Dependent Samples" tab of the *Compare Two Means* app. The app shows a plot of the observations in the two samples and one for their differences, and computes the mean difference, the standard error, the margin of error and the confidence interval.

Questions to Explore

a. How can you construct and interpret the confidence interval reported in the screenshot from the *Compare Two Means* app shown in Figure 10.15?

b. Figure 10.15a shows a screenshot from the same app after selecting Significance Test for Type of Inference. Show how the *t* test statistic was computed and write a conclusion for the test.

Think It Through

a. We have to assume that differences in the reaction times of a respondent using and not using a cell phone approximately follow a normal distribution. The histogram for the observed differences from the screenshot in Figure 10.15 shows a right-skewed distribution, but two-sided inference is robust to violations of the normality assumption, and the sample size is fairly large. Also, the box plot of the differences does not reveal any outliers, so using the methods discussed in this section is appropriate.

The sample mean difference is $\bar{x}_d = 50.6$, and the standard deviation of the differences is $s_d = 52.5$. The standard error is

$se = s_d/\sqrt{n} = 52.5/\sqrt{32} = 9.28$ and the margin of error equals 18.9 (obtained by multiplying the se with the t-score of 2.04, which you can request in the app). The confidence interval equals

$$\bar{x}_d \pm t_{.025}(se), \text{ or } 50.6 \pm 2.04(9.28),$$
$$\text{which equals } 50.6 + 18.9, \text{ or } (31.7, 69.5)$$

At the 95% confidence level, we estimate that the population mean when using cell phones is between 32 and 70 milliseconds higher than when not using cell phones. The confidence interval does not contain 0, so we can infer that the population mean reaction time is longer when using a cell phone.

The article about the study did not indicate whether the subjects were randomly selected, so inferential conclusions are tentative.

b. The t test statistic for the significance test of $H_0: \mu_d = 0$ (i.e., equal population means for the two conditions) against $H_a: \mu_d \neq 0$ is

$$t = \bar{x}_d/se = 50.6/9.28 = 5.46.$$

With 32 differences, $df = n - 1 = 31$. Figure 10.15a shows partial output from the second tab of the *Compare Two Means* app, which shows that the P-value for such a large test statistic is less than 0.0001, i.e., tiny. There is extremely strong evidence that the population mean reaction times are different. (As always, we learn just how different they are, on average, from the confidence interval in part a.)

Hypothesis Test:

Population Parameter	Null Hypothesis	Alternative Hypothesis	Test Statistic t	P-value
Mean Difference μ_d	$\mu_d = 0$	$\mu_d \neq 0$	5.456	<0.0001

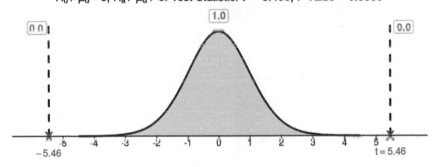

t Distribution with df = 31
$H_0: \mu_d = 0$, $H_a: \mu_d \neq 0$. Test Statistic: $t = 5.456$, P-value = 0.0000

▲ **Figure 10.15a** Results of Hypotheses Test for $H_0: \mu_d = 0$. Screenshot from the "Two Dependent Samples" tab of the *Compare Two Means* app, showing the results of a significance test.

Insight

The study also showed that reaction times were similar with hands-free versus hand-held cell phones. It also showed that the probability of missing a simulated traffic signal doubled when students used cell phones.

A later related study[9] showed that the mean reaction time of students using cell phones was similar to that of older drivers not using cell phones. The study concluded, "The net effect of having younger drivers converse on a cell phone was to make their average reactions equivalent to those of older drivers who were not using a cell phone."

▶ *Try Exercises 10.49 and 10.50*

[9]D. L. Strayer and F. A. Drews, (2004), *Human Factors,* vol. 46, pp. 640–649.

In summary, comparing means for two dependent samples is easy. We merely use methods we've already learned about in Chapters 8 and 9 for single samples.

> **SUMMARY: Comparing Means of Dependent Samples**
>
> To compare means with dependent samples, construct confidence intervals and significance tests using the single sample of differences,
>
> $$d = \text{observation in Sample 1} - \text{observation in Sample 2}.$$
>
> The 95% confidence interval $\bar{x}_d \pm t_{.025}(se)$ and the test statistic $t = (\bar{x}_d - 0)/se$ are the same as for a single sample. The assumptions are also the same: A random sample or a randomized experiment and an approximately normal population distribution of differences.

When the sample of differences looks decidedly non-normal, the bootstrap approach introduced in Section 8.4 can be used to find a confidence interval for the mean difference. Paralleling the procedure for obtaining a bootstrap confidence interval for a single mean, one simply draws many bootstrap samples from the sample of differences to build the sampling distribution and uses the percentile method to obtain a confidence interval.

Comparing Proportions with Dependent Samples

We next present methods for comparing two proportions with dependent samples.

Dependent Proportions

Example 15

Beliefs in Heaven and Hell

Picture the Scenario

A recent General Social Survey asked subjects whether they believed in heaven and whether they believed in hell. For the 1,314 subjects who responded, Table 10.11 shows the data in contingency table form. The rows of Table 10.11 are the response categories for belief in heaven. The columns are the same categories for belief in hell. For the U.S. adult population, let p_1 denote the proportion who believe in heaven and let p_2 denote the proportion who believe in hell.

Table 10.11 Beliefs in Heaven and Hell

Belief in Heaven	Belief in Hell		Total
	Yes	No	
Yes	955	162	**1,117**
No	9	188	**197**
Total	**964**	**350**	**1,314**

Marginal Sample Proportions of Believes in Heaven and Hell

Questions to Explore

a. How can we estimate p_1, p_2, and their difference?

b. Are the samples used to estimate p_1 and p_2 independent or dependent samples?

Think It Through

a. The counts in the two margins of Table 10.11 summarize the responses. Of the 1,314 subjects, 1,117 said they believed in heaven, so $\hat{p}_1 = 1{,}117/1{,}314 = 0.85$. Of the same 1,314 subjects, 964 said they believed in hell, so $\hat{p}_2 = 964/1{,}314 = 0.73$. Since $(\hat{p}_1 - \hat{p}_2) = 0.85 - 0.73 = 0.12$, we estimate that 12% more people believe in heaven than in hell.

b. Each sample of 1,314 responses refers to the same 1,314 subjects. Any given subject's response on belief in heaven can be matched with that subject's response on belief in hell. This falls under the general concept of measuring each subject twice, or matched pairs. So the samples for these two proportions are dependent.

▶ **Try Exercise 10.60, parts a and b**

Confidence Interval Comparing Proportions with Matched-Pairs Data

Recall

From Section 10.1, the sampling distribution of $\hat{p}_1 - \hat{p}_2$ for two *independent* random samples has standard error

$$se = \sqrt{\frac{\hat{p}_1(1 - \hat{p}_1)}{n_1} + \frac{\hat{p}_2(1 - \hat{p}_2)}{n_2}}. \blacktriangleleft$$

To conduct inference about the difference $(p_1 - p_2)$ between the population proportions, we need a point estimate and a standard error. The point estimate is the difference $\hat{p}_1 - \hat{p}_2$ in the marginal sample proportions, 0.12 for the preceding example. To find the standard error of this point estimate, we *cannot* use the result about the sampling distribution of $\hat{p}_1 - \hat{p}_2$ mentioned in Section 10.1. As the margin note recalls, that result only applies for two independent samples, but here we have two dependent samples (matched pairs).

Instead, we need to use a formula that modifies the standard error from the independent sample case to account for the dependency. We will not give the formula here but rely on software (such as the *Compare Two Proportions* app) to compute it. With the point estimate and its standard error, we get the usual confidence interval that applies when the sample size is large: Take the point estimate and add and subtract the margin of error, which is a z-score times the se: $(\hat{p}_1 - \hat{p}_2) \pm z(se)$. Usually, software reports this or a related confidence interval under the heading of McNemar's test.

Example 16

Confidence Interval for $p_1 - p_2$ with Dependent Samples ◀

Beliefs in Heaven and Hell

Picture the Scenario

We continue our analysis of the data on belief in heaven and/or hell. When entering the data into the *Compare Two Proportions* app under the "Two Dependent Samples" tab, we get the output shown in Figure 10.16.

Estimate of Difference in Marginal Proportions:

Point Estimate	Standard Error	Margin of Error
0.116	0.00942	±0.0185

Confidence Interval:

Population Parameter	Lower Bound	Upper Bound	Confidence Level
Difference p_1 - p_2	0.098	0.135	95%

▲ **Figure 10.16** Confidence Interval for the Difference of Proportions Based on Two Dependent Samples. Screenshot from the *Compare Two Proportions* app, second tab.

What do we gain by using two dependent samples instead of two independent samples? Typically, the standard error for the difference is smaller when using two dependent samples. A smaller standard error results in more precise inference, such as shorter confidence intervals and smaller P-values. This implies that a matched-pairs design can reach the desired level of precision (e.g., a certain margin of error) with fewer subjects than a comparable design that uses two independent samples. If observations on subjects are expensive, this can result in substantial savings.

McNemar Test Comparing Proportions with Matched-Pairs Data

For testing H_0: $p_1 - p_2 = 0$ with two dependent samples, there's actually a simple way to calculate a test statistic. If the null hypothesis is true, that is, if an equal proportion believes in heaven and in hell ($p_1 = p_2$), we expect that the number of people believing in heaven ($a + b$, see below) is the same as the number believing in hell ($a + c$, see below). Computing the standard error for the difference in the sample proportions under this assumption results in a simple formula. (See Exercise 10.127.) We can then use the usual way to find a test statistic for H_0, which reduces to (skipping the algebra):

The four cells of a 2×2 contingency table labeled as $a, b, c,$ and d.

$$z = \frac{\text{point estimate} - \text{null value}}{se_0} = \frac{(\hat{p}_1 - \hat{p}_2) - 0}{se_0} = \frac{b - c}{\sqrt{b + c}}.$$

Here, b and c refer to the off-diagonal counts in the 2×2 contingency table, with b the count in the upper right cell and c the count in the lower left cell. Intuitively, if the number of people believing in heaven is the same as the number of people believing in hell, then $a + b = a + c$, which implies that $b = c$. The more b and c are apart (i.e., the larger $b - c$), the more evidence there is for the alternative hypothesis. For the contingency table in Example 15, $b = 162, c = 9$, and $z = (162 - 9)/\sqrt{162 + 9} = 11.7$.

We have called the test statistic z because it has an approximate standard normal distribution when H_0 is true, which we use for computing the P-value. With $z = 11.7$, the two-sided P-value is extremely small (P-value = 0.000, which you can confirm via the "Two Dependent Samples" tab in the *Compare Two Proportions* app). There is very strong evidence that the proportion of U.S. adults believing in heaven differs from (in fact, is larger than) the proportion believing in hell. This conclusion agrees with the confidence interval for $(p_1 - p_2)$ that we found in Example 16. The advantage of the confidence interval is that it indicates *how different* the proportions are likely to be. In percentage terms, we infer that the belief in heaven is about 10 to 13 percentage points higher.

The z test comparing proportions with dependent samples is often called **McNemar's test** in honor of a psychologist (Quinn McNemar) who proposed it in 1947. It is a large-sample test. It applies when the sum, $b + c$, of the two counts used in the test is at least 30 (this sum is $162 + 9 = 171$ for Example 16). For two-sided tests, however, the test is robust and works well even for small samples.

SUMMARY: McNemar Test Comparing Proportions from Two Dependent Samples

Assumption: Random sample of matched pairs.

Hypotheses: H_0: $p_1 = p_2$, H_a can be two-sided or one-sided.

Test Statistic: $z = (b - c)/\sqrt{(b + c)}$, where b and c are the off-diagonal elements in the contingency table, with b the one in the first row and c the one in the second row. The sum of the two off-diagonal counts b and c should be at least 30, but in practice the two-sided test works well even if this is not true.

P-value: For H_a: $p_1 \neq p_2$, two-tail probability of z test statistic values more extreme than observed z, using standard normal distribution.

Example 17

McNemar's Test ◀

Speech Recognition Systems

Picture the Scenario

Research in comparing the quality of different speech recognition systems uses a series of isolated words as a benchmark test, finding for each system the proportion of words for which an error of recognition occurs. Table 10.12 shows data from one of the first articles[10] that showed how to conduct such a test. The article compared speech recognition systems called generalized minimal distortion segmentation (GMDS) and continuous density hidden Markov model (CDHMM). Table 10.12 shows the counts of the four possible sequences to test outcomes for the two systems with a given word, for a test using 2,000 words.

Table 10.12 Results of Test Using 2,000 Words to Compare Two Speech Recognition Systems (GMDS and CDHMM)

	CDHMM		
GMDS	**Correct**	**Incorrect**	**Total**
Correct	1,921	58	**1,979**
Incorrect	16	5	**21**
Total	**1,937**	**63**	**2,000**

Question to Explore

Conduct McNemar's test of the null hypothesis that the probability of a correct outcome is the same for each system.

Think It Through

The article about this test did not indicate how the words were chosen. Inferences are valid if the 2,000 words were a random sample of the possible words on which the systems could have been tested. Let p_1 denote the population proportion of correct results for GMDS and let p_2 denote the population proportion correct for CDHMM. The test statistic for McNemar's test of $H_0: p_1 = p_2$ against $H_a: p_1 \neq p_2$ is

$$z = \frac{58 - 16}{\sqrt{58 + 16}} = 4.88.$$

The two-sided P-value is less than 0.0001, as you can confirm with the *Compare Two Proportions* app. There is extremely strong evidence against the null hypothesis that the correct detection rates are the same for the two systems.

Insight

We learn more by estimating parameters. A confidence interval for $p_1 - p_2$, e.g., as obtained with the *Compare Two Proportions* app, indicates that the GMDS system is better, but the difference in correct detection rates is small. See Exercise 10.59.

▶ **Try Exercise 10.61, part c**

---

[10] From S. Chen and W. Chen, (1995), *IEEE Transactions on Speech and Audio Processing*, vol. 3, pp. 141–145.

10.4 Practicing the Basics

10.49 Does exercise help blood pressure? Several recent studies have suggested that people who suffer from abnormally high blood pressure can benefit from regular exercise. A medical researcher decides to test her belief that walking briskly for at least half an hour a day has the effect of lowering blood pressure. She conducts a small pilot study. If results from it are supportive, she will apply for funding for a larger study. She randomly samples three of her patients who have high blood pressure. She measures their systolic blood pressure initially and then again a month later after they participate in her exercise program. The table shows the results.

Subject	Before	After
1	150	130
2	165	140
3	135	120

a. Explain why the three before observations and the three after observations are dependent samples.

b. Find the sample mean of the before scores, the sample mean of the after scores, and the sample mean of the difference scores $d =$ before − after. How are they related?

c. Find a 95% confidence interval for the difference between the population means of subjects before and after going through such a study. Interpret. (*Hint:* You can enter the three differences in the *Inference for a Mean* app or use the "Two Dependent Samples" tab in the *Compare Two Means* app to find the confidence interval via software.)

10.50 Test for blood pressure Refer to the previous exercise. The output shows some results of using software to analyze the data with a significance test.

```
Paired T for Before—After
              N    Mean    StDev    SE Mean
Before        3   150.0    15.0     8.660
After         3   130.0    10.0     5.774
Difference    3    20.0     5.0     2.887
T-Test of mean difference = 0 (vs ≠ 0):
T-Value = 6.93 P-Value = 0.020
```

a. State the hypotheses to which the reported P-value refers.

b. Explain how to interpret the P-value. Does the exercise program seem beneficial to lowering blood pressure?

c. What are the assumptions on which this analysis is based?

10.51 Social activities for students As part of her class project, a student at the University of Florida randomly sampled 10 fellow students to investigate their most common social activities. For the study, she asked the students to state how many times they had done each of the following activities during the previous year: going to a movie, going to a sporting event, or going to a party. The following table shows the data.

Frequency of Attending Movies, Sports Events, and Parties

Student	Activity		
	Movies	Sports	Parties
1	10	5	25
2	4	0	10
3	12	20	6
4	2	6	52
5	12	2	12
6	7	8	30
7	45	12	52
8	1	25	2
9	25	0	25
10	12	12	4

a. To compare the mean movie attendance and mean sports attendance using statistical inference, should we treat the samples as independent or dependent? Why?

b. The graph in the first screenshot shows a dot plot and box plot of the $n = 10$ differences for movies and sports. Do these show any irregularities that would make statistical inference unreliable?

c. Using the screenshot from the *Compare Two Means* app for these data, show how the 95% confidence interval was obtained from the other information given. Interpret the interval.

d. Show how the test statistic shown on the second screenshot was obtained from information on the first. Report the P-value and interpret in context.

10.52 More social activities Refer to the previous exercise. Open the *Compare Two Means* app and select Party & Sport Attendance as the data set on the second tab.

a. Find and interpret a 95% confidence interval for the difference in the mean number of events attended.

b. State the hypotheses and find the P-value for a significance test comparing mean attendance. Write a conclusion.

c. Explain the connection between the results of the test and the confidence interval.

d. What assumptions are necessary for these inferences to be appropriate?

10.53 Movies versus parties Refer to the previous two exercises. Using the *Compare Two Means* app, compare the responses on movies and parties using (a) all steps of a significance test and (b) a 95% confidence interval. Interpret results in context.

10.54 Freshman 15 a myth? The freshman 15 is the name of a common belief that college students, particularly women, gain an average of 15 pounds during their first year of college. A recent study (*Journal of American Health*, (2009), vol. 58, pp. 223–231) found that female students weighed an average of 133.0 pounds at the start of the school year and an average of 135.1 pounds at the end of the school year. The standard deviation of weights was about 30 pounds at each time. Other reports have been consistent with this finding.

a. Estimate the change in the mean weight.

b. Is this sufficient information to find a confidence interval or conduct a test about the change in the mean? If not, what else do you need to know?

10.55 Checking for freshman 15 Refer to the previous exercise. Suppose that the change in weight scores for the 132 freshmen had a standard deviation of 2.0 pounds.

a. Explain how this standard deviation could be so much less than the standard deviation of 30 for the weight scores at each time.

b. Is 15 pounds a plausible mean weight change in the population of freshmen women? Answer by constructing a 95% confidence interval for the population mean change in weight or conducting a significance test of the hypothesis that the mean weight change in the population equals 15. Interpret.

c. What assumptions are necessary for the inference in part b?

10.56 Internet book prices Anna's project for her introductory statistics course was to compare the prices of textbooks at two Internet bookstores. She first took a random sample of 10 textbooks used that term in courses at her college, based on the list of texts compiled by the college bookstore. The prices of those textbooks at the two Internet sites were

Site A: $115, $79, $43, $140, $99, $30, $80, $99, $119, $69

Site B: $110, $79, $40, $129, $99, $30, $69, $99, $109, $66

a. Are these independent samples or dependent samples? Justify your answer.

b. Find the mean for each sample. Find the mean of the difference scores. Compare and interpret.

c. Construct a 90% confidence interval comparing the population mean prices of all textbooks used that term at her college. Interpret.

10.57 Comparing book prices 2 For the data in the previous exercise, perform a significance test comparing the population mean prices. Show all steps of the test and indicate whether you would conclude that the mean price is lower at one of the two Internet bookstores.

10.58 Lung capacity revisited Refer to Exercise 10.37 about measuring the lung function (called the forced vital capacity, or FVC, measured in liters) before and after using an inhaler. The data are shown again in the following table.

	Checkup				
	1	**2**	**3**	**4**	**5**
Before Using Inhaler:	5.08	5.99	5.32	6.03	5.44
After Using Inhaler:	5.36	5.98	5.62	6.26	5.68

a. By how much, on average, did the FVC improve after using the inhaler?

b. Find a 95% confidence interval for the mean improvement and interpret.

c. Suppose you wrongly analyzed the data as two independent samples. Find the confidence interval for the difference in the population means and show how the conclusions would change substantially.

10.59 Comparing speech recognition systems Table 10.12 in Example 17, repeated here, showed results of an experiment comparing the results of two speech recognition systems, GMDS and CDHMM.

	CDHMM	
GMDS	**Correct**	**Incorrect**
Correct	1,921	58
Incorrect	16	5

a. Estimate the population proportion p_1 of correct results for GMDS and p_2 of correct results for CDHMM.

b. Software (e.g., confer the *Compare Two Proportions* app) reports a 95% interval for $p_1 - p_2$ of (0.013, 0.029). Interpret.

10.60 Treat juveniles as adults? The table that follows refers to a sample of juveniles convicted of a felony in Florida. Matched pairs were formed using criteria such as age and the number of prior offenses to pair two juveniles. For each pair, one subject was handled in the juvenile court and the other was transferred to the adult court. The response of interest was whether the juvenile was rearrested within a year.

a. Are the outcomes for the courts independent samples or dependent samples? Explain.

b. Estimate the population proportions of rearrest for the adult and juvenile courts.

c. Test the hypothesis that the population proportions rearrested were identical for the adult and juvenile court assignments. Use a two-sided alternative, and interpret the P-value.

	Juvenile Court	
Adult Court	**Rearrest**	**No Rearrest**
Rearrest	158	515
No Rearrest	290	1,134

Source: Data provided by Larry Winner.

10.61 Change coffee brand? A study was conducted to see if an advertisement campaign would increase market share for Sanka instant decaffeinated coffee (R. Grover and V. Srinivasan, *J. Marketing Research*, (1987), vol. 24, pp. 139–153). Subjects who use instant decaffeinated coffee were asked which brand they bought last. They were asked this before the campaign and after it. The results are shown in the table, together with two screenshots from the *Compare Two Proportions* app.

a. Estimate the population proportion choosing Sanka for the (i) first purchase and (ii) second purchase. Find the difference and interpret it.

b. Explain how to interpret the 95% confidence interval.

c. The second screenshot (on the next page) shows a P-value. State the hypotheses that this P-value refers to in the context of this exercise and give the conclusion of the test when using a significance level of 0.05.

Two Purchases of Coffee

	Second Purchase	
First Purchase	**Sanka**	**Other Brand**
Sanka	155	49
Other brand	76	261

Estimate of Difference in Marginal Proportions:

Point Estimate	Standard Error	Margin of Error
-0.0499	0.0206	± 0.0403

Confidence Interval:

Population Parameter	Lower Bound	Upper Bound	Confidence Level
Difference $p_1 - p_2$	-0.0902	-0.00962	95%

95% Confidence Interval
[-0.09019, -0.009622]

Difference of Proportions $p_1 - p_2$

Hypothesis Test (McNemar's Test):

Parameter	Null Hypothesis	Alternative Hypothesis	Test Statistic	P-value
Difference $p_1 - p_2$	$p_1 - p_2 = 0$	$p_1 - p_2 \neq 0$	-2.41	0.0157

Standard Normal Distribution

$H_0: p_1 = p_2$, $H_a: p_1 \neq p_2$. Test Statistic: $z = -2.415$, P-value = 0.0157

0.0079   0.9843   0.0079

-4   -3   -2   -1   0   1   2   3   4
$z = -2.41$ 2.41

10.62 President's popularity   Last month a random sample of 1,000 subjects was interviewed and asked whether they thought the president was doing a good job. This month the same subjects were asked this again. The results are: 450 said yes each time, 450 said no each time, 60 said yes on the first survey and no on the second survey, and 40 said no on the first survey and yes on the second survey.

a. Form a contingency table showing these results.

b. Estimate the proportion giving a favorable rating (i) last month and (ii) this month.

c. Find the difference in the proportions and interpret.

d. Find the test statistic and P-value for applying McNemar's test that the population proportion was the same each month. Interpret.

10.63 Heaven and hell   Results of polls about belief in heaven and hell depend strongly on question wording. For instance, a survey conducted by the International Social Science Program at the National Opinion Research Center (NORC) asked Americans whether they "definitely believe in heaven" or "definitely believe in hell." The percentage who answered yes was 63.1% for heaven and 49.6% for hell.

a. Estimate the difference between the population proportions believing in heaven and believing in hell.

b. In this survey, suppose that 65 subjects believed in heaven but not in hell, whereas 35 believed in hell but not in heaven. Report the (i) assumptions, (ii) hypotheses, (iii) test statistic, (iv) P-value, and (v) conclusion for testing that the probability of belief is the same for heaven and for hell.

10.64 Heaven and hell around the world   Refer to the previous exercise. Results in this poll also depended strongly on the country in which the question was asked. For instance, the percentages believing in (heaven, hell) were (52%, 26%) in Ireland, (32%, 19%) in New Zealand, (28%, 22%) in Italy, (25%, 13%) in Great Britain, (21%, 11%) in the Netherlands, and (18%, 9%) in Germany. If for a given country you know the sample size was 1,000, does this give you enough information to compare the two proportions inferentially for that country? Explain.

10.5 Adjusting for the Effects of Other Variables

When a practically significant difference exists between two groups, can we identify a reason for the difference? As Chapters 3 and 4 explained, an association may be due to a *lurking variable* not measured in the study. Example 5 in Section 10.1 indicated that teenagers who watch more TV have a tendency later in life to commit more aggressive acts. Why? Might education be a lurking variable? Perhaps teenagers who watch more TV tend to attain lower educational levels, and perhaps lower education tends to be associated with higher levels of aggression.

To investigate why differences occur between groups, we must measure potential lurking variables and use them in the statistical analysis. For instance, suppose we planned to study TV watching and aggression, and we thought that educational level was a potential lurking variable. Then, in the study we would want to measure educational level.

Let's examine the TV study again. Suppose we did so using categories (did not complete high school, did not attend college, attended college). We could then evaluate TV watching and aggressive behavior separately for subjects in these three educational levels and obtain the results in Table 10.13.

Recall
You can review Section 3.4 to see how **lurking variables** can influence an association. ◄

Table 10.13 Percentage Committing Aggressive Acts, According to Level of Teenage TV Watching, Controlling for Educational Level

For example, for those who attended college who watched TV less than 1 hour per day, 2% committed an aggressive act.

	Educational Level		
TV Watching	**Less than High School**	**High School**	**College**
Less Than 1 Hour per Day	8%	4%	2%
At Least 1 Hour per Day	30%	20%	10%

This analysis uses three variables—level of TV watching, committing of aggressive acts, and educational level. This takes us from a **bivariate** analysis (two variables) to a **multivariate** analysis (more than two variables): Whether the subject has committed aggressive acts is the response variable, the level of TV watching is the explanatory variable, and the educational level is called a **control variable**.

Control Variable

A **control variable** is a variable that is held constant in a multivariate analysis.

Table 10.13 treats educational level as a control variable. Within each of the three education groups, educational level is approximately constant.

Statistical Control

To analyze whether an association can be explained by a third variable, we treat that third variable as a control variable. We conduct the ordinary bivariate analysis, such as comparing two proportions, while holding that control variable constant at fixed values. Then, whatever association occurs cannot be due to effects of the control variable, because in each part of the analysis it is not allowed to vary.

In Table 10.13, at each educational level, the percentage committing an aggressive act is higher for those who watched more TV. If these were the actual results, then the association between TV watching and aggressive acts was not because of education. In each part of Table 10.13, educational level is approximately constant, so changes in aggression as TV watching varies are not due to changes in educational level. To conduct inference, we could use the methods of this chapter to compare the population proportions of aggression at each education level.

Conducting a statistical analysis while holding a control variable constant occurs in scientific laboratory experiments, too. Such experiments hold certain variables constant so they do not affect results. For instance, a chemistry experiment might control temperature by holding it constant throughout the experiment. Otherwise, a sudden increase or decrease in the temperature might cause a reaction that would not happen normally. Unlike experiments, observational studies cannot assign subjects to particular values of variables that we want to control, such as educational level. But we can approximate an experimental control by grouping observations with similar values on the control variable, as just described. This is a **statistical control** rather than an experimental control.

The next example shows that if we control for a variable, the results can look quite different than if we do not take that control variable into account.

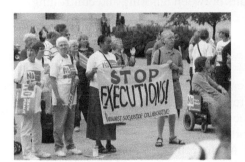

Control Variables ◀

Example 18

Death Penalty and Race

Picture the Scenario

The United States is one of only a few Western nations that still imposes the death penalty. Are those convicted of murder more likely to get the death penalty if they are black than if they are white?

Table 10.14 comes from one of the first studies on racial inequities of the death penalty.[11] The 326 subjects were defendants convicted of homicide in Florida murder trials. The variables are the defendant's race and whether the defendant received the death penalty. The contingency table shows that about 12% of White defendants and about 10% of Black defendants received the death penalty.

Table 10.14 Defendant's Race and Death Penalty Verdict for Homicide Cases in Florida

Defendant's Race	Death Penalty Yes	No	Total	Percentage Yes
White	19	141	**160**	11.9
Black	17	149	**166**	10.2

In this study, the difference between the percentages of White defendants and Black defendants who received the death penalty is small (1.7%), but the percentage was lower for Black defendants.

Is there some explanation for these results? Does a control variable lurk that explains why relatively fewer Black defendants got the death penalty in Florida? Researchers who study the death penalty stress that the *victim's* race is often an important factor. So, let's control for victim's race. We'll construct a table like Table 10.14 *separately* for cases in which the victim was White and for cases in which the victim was Black. Table 10.15 shows this three-variable table.

Table 10.15 shows the effect of a defendant's race on the death penalty verdict while controlling for victim's race, that is, when victim's race is kept constant at White or kept constant at Black. Table 10.15 decomposes Table 10.14 into two contingency tables, one for each victim's race. You can recover Table 10.14 by summing corresponding entries, $19 + 0 = 19, 132 + 9 = 141, 11 + 6 = 17$, and $52 + 97 = 149$.

Table 10.15 Defendant's Race and Death Penalty Verdict, Controlling for Victim's Race

Victim's Race	Defendant's Race	Death Penalty Yes	No	Total	Percentage Yes
White	White	19	132	**151**	12.6
	Black	11	52	**63**	17.5
Black	White	0	9	**9**	0.0
	Black	6	97	**103**	5.8

---

[11]M. Radelet, (1981), *American Sociological Review*, vol. 46, pp. 918–927.

Questions to Explore

a. Summarize the association between a defendant's race and the death penalty verdict in Florida after controlling for victim's race.

b. Describe the difference in the results between ignoring and controlling victim's race.

c. Why does the control for victim's race make such a difference?

Think It Through

a. The top part of Table 10.15 lists cases in which the victim's race was White. Relatively more Black defendants than White defendants got the death penalty in Florida. The difference between the percentages is $17.5 - 12.6 = 4.9$. The bottom part of the table lists cases in which the victim's race was Black. Again, relatively more Black defendants got the death penalty. The difference between the percentages is $5.8 - 0.0 = 5.8$. In summary, controlling for victim's race, more Black defendants than White defendants received the death penalty in Florida.

b. Table 10.14 showed that a *larger* percentage of White defendants than Black defendants got the death penalty. By contrast, controlling for victim's race, Table 10.15 showed that a *smaller* percentage of White defendants than Black defendants got the death penalty. This was true for each victim's race category.

c. In Table 10.15, look at the percentages who got the death penalty. When the victim was White, they are quite a bit larger (12.6 and 17.5) than when the victim was Black (0.0 and 5.8). That is, defendants who killed a White person were more likely to get the death penalty. Now look at the totals for the four combinations of victim's race and defendant's race. The most common cases are White defendants having White victims (151 times) and Black defendants having Black victims (103 times). In summary, White defendants usually had White victims and Black defendants usually had Black victims. Killing a White person was more likely to result in the death penalty than killing a Black person. These two factors operating together produce an overall association that shows (in Table 10.14) that a higher percentage of White defendants than Black defendants got the death penalty.

Insight

Overall, relatively more White defendants in Florida got the death penalty than Black defendants. Controlling for victim's race, however, relatively more Black defendants got the death penalty. The effect changes direction after we control for victim's race. This shows that the association at each level of a control variable can have a different direction than overall when that third variable is ignored instead of controlled. This phenomenon is called **Simpson's paradox**.

In Table 10.15, the death penalty was imposed most often when a Black defendant had a White victim. By contrast, it was never imposed when a White defendant had a Black victim. Similar results have occurred in other studies of the death penalty. See Exercises 10.66 and 3.58.

▶ *Try Exercise 10.66*

Recall

Section 3.4 first introduced **Simpson's paradox.** It is named after a British statistician who wrote an article in 1951 about mathematical conditions under which the association can change direction when you control for a variable. ◀

Recall

From the end of Section 3.4, we say that defendant's race and victim's race are confounded in their effects on the death penalty verdict. ◄

With statistical control imposed for a variable, the results tend to change considerably when that control variable has a strong association both with the response variable and the explanatory variable. In Example 18, for instance, victim's race was the control variable. Victim's race had a noticeable association both with the death penalty response (the death penalty was given more often when the victim was white) and with defendant's race (defendants and victims usually had the same race).

> **In Practice** Control for Variables Associated Both with the Response and Explanatory Variables
>
> In determining which variables to control in observational studies, *researchers choose variables that they expect to have a practically relevant association with both the response variable and the explanatory variable.* A statistical analysis that controls such variables can have quite different results than when those variables are ignored.

Statistical control is also important when the response variable is quantitative. The difference between means for two groups can change substantially after controlling for a third variable. See Exercise 10.68.

► Activity 2

Interpreting Newspaper Articles

This chapter began by stating that many newspaper articles describe research studies that use the statistical methods of this chapter. At this stage of your statistics course, you should be able to read and understand those articles much better than you could before you knew the basis of such terms as margin of error, statistical significance, and randomized clinical trial.

For the next three days, read a daily newspaper or an online news outlet. Make a copy of any article you see that refers to a study that used statistics to help make its conclusions. For one article, prepare a one-page report that answers the following questions:

- What was the purpose of the study?
- Was the study experimental or observational? Can you provide any details about the study design and sampling method?
- Identify explanatory and response variables.
- Can you tell whether the statistical analysis used (1) independent samples or dependent samples and (2) a comparison of proportions or a comparison of means?
- Can you think of any lurking variables that could have affected the results?
- Are there any limitations that would make you skeptical to put much faith in the conclusions of the study?

You might find additional information to answer these questions by browsing the Web or going to the research journal that published the results.

10.5 Practicing the Basics

10.65 Benefits of drinking A *USA Today* story (May 22, 2010) about the medical benefits of moderate drinking of alcohol stated that a major French study links those who drink moderately to a lower risk for cardiovascular disease but challenges the idea that moderate drinking is the cause. "Instead, the researchers say, people who drink moderately tend to have a higher social status, exercise more, suffer less depression and enjoy superior health overall compared to heavy drinkers and lifetime abstainers. A causal relationship between cardiovascular risk and moderate drinking is not at all established." The study looked at the health status and drinking habits of 149,773 French adults.

a. Explain how this story refers to an analysis of three types of variables. Identify those variables.

b. Suppose socioeconomic status is treated as a control variable when we compare moderate drinkers to abstainers in their heart attack rates. Explain how this analysis shows that an effect of an explanatory variable on a response variable can change at different values of a control variable.

10.66 Death penalty in Kentucky A study of the death penalty in Kentucky reported the results shown in the table. (*Source:* Data from T. Keil and G. Vito, *Amer. J. Criminal Justice*, vol. 20, 1995, pp. 17–36.)

a. Find and compare the percentage of White defendants with the percentage of Black defendants who received the death penalty, when the victim was (i) White and (ii) Black.

b. In the analysis in part a, identify the response variable, explanatory variable, and control variable.

c. Construct the summary 2 × 2 table that ignores, rather than controls, victim's race. Compare the overall percentages of White defendants and Black defendants who got the death penalty (ignoring, rather than controlling, victim's race). Compare to part a.

d. Do these data satisfy Simpson's paradox? If not, explain why not. If so, explain what is responsible for Simpson's paradox occurring.

e. Explain, without doing the calculations, how you could inferentially compare the proportions of White and Black defendants who get the death penalty (i) ignoring victim's race and (ii) controlling for victim's race.

Victim's Race	Defendant's Race	Death Penalty Yes	No	Total
White	White	31	360	**391**
	Black	7	50	**57**
Black	White	0	18	**18**
	Black	2	106	**108**

10.67 Basketball paradox The following list summarizes shooting percentage in the 2001–2002 season in the National Basketball Association by Brent Barry and Shaquille O'Neal.

2-point shots
- Brent Barry: 58.8% (237/403)
- Shaquille O'Neal: 58.0% (712/1,228)

3-point shots
- Brent Barry: 42.4% (164/387)
- Shaquille O'Neal: 0% (0/1)

Overall
- Brent Barry: 50.8% (401/790)
- Shaquille O'Neal: 57.9% (712/1,229)

(Data from www.nba.com and article by T. P. Ryan, *Chance,* vol. 16, 2003, p. 16.)

a. Treating the type of shot as a control variable, whether a shot is made as the response variable, and the player as the explanatory variable, explain how these results illustrate Simpson's paradox.

b. Explain how O'Neal could have the higher overall percentage, even though he made a lower percentage of each type of shot.

10.68 Teacher salary, gender, and academic rank The American Association of University Professors (AAUP) reports yearly on faculty salaries for all types of higher education institutions across the United States. The following table lists the mean salary, in thousands of dollars, of full-time instructional faculty on nine-month contracts at four-year public institutions of higher education in 2010, by gender and academic rank. Regard salary as the response variable, gender as the explanatory variable, and academic rank as the control variable.

Mean Salary (Thousands of Dollars) for Men and Women Faculty Members

Gender	Professor	Associate	Assistant	Instructor	Overall
Men	109.2	77.8	66.1	46.0	**84.4**
Women	96.2	72.7	61.8	46.9	**68.8**

a. Find the difference between men and women faculty members on their mean salary (i) overall and (ii) after controlling for academic rank.

b. The overall difference between the mean salary of men and women faculty members was larger than the difference at each academic rank. What could be a reason for this? (Simpson's paradox does not hold here, but the gender effect does weaken when we control for academic rank.)

10.69 Family size in Canada The table shows the mean number of children in Canadian families, classified by whether the family was English speaking or French speaking and by whether the family lived in Quebec or in another province.

Mean Number of Children in Canada

Province	English-Speaking	French-Speaking
Quebec	1.64	1.80
Other	1.97	2.14
Overall	1.95	1.85

a. Overall, compare the mean number of children for English-speaking and French-speaking families.

b. Compare the means, controlling for province (Quebec, Other).

c. How is it possible that for each level of province the mean is higher for French-speaking families, yet overall the mean is higher for English-speaking families? Which paradox does this illustrate?

10.70 Heart disease and age In the United States, the median age of residents is lowest in Utah. At each age level, the death rate from heart disease is higher in Utah than in Colorado. Overall, the death rate from heart disease is lower in Utah than Colorado. Are there any contradictions here, or is this possible? Explain.

10.71 Breast cancer over time The percentage of women who get breast cancer sometime during their lifetime is higher now than in 1900. Suppose that breast cancer incidence tends to increase with age, and suppose that women tend to live longer now than in 1900. Explain why a comparison of breast cancer rates now with the rate in 1900 could show different results if we control for the age of the woman.

Chapter Review

SUMMARY OF NOTATION

A subscript shows which group the parameter or statistic refers to:

p_1, p_2 = population proportion in Group 1 and Group 2

n_1, n_2 = sample size in Group 1 and Group 2

$\hat{p}_1, \hat{p}_2$ = sample proportion in Group 1 and Group 2

μ_1, μ_2 = population mean in Group 1 and Group 2

$\bar{x}_1, \bar{x}_2$ = sample mean in Group 1 and Group 2

σ_1, σ_2 = population standard deviation in Group 1 and Group 2

s_1, s_2 = sample standard deviation in Group 1 and Group 2

μ_d = population mean difference ($= \mu_1 - \mu_2$)

$\bar{x}_d$ = sample mean difference ($= \bar{x}_1 - \bar{x}_2$)

σ_d = population standard deviation of differences

s_d = sample standard deviation of differences

CHAPTER SUMMARY

This chapter introduced inferential methods for comparing two groups.

- For categorical data, we compare the *proportions* of individuals in a particular category. Confidence intervals and significance tests apply to the difference between the population proportions, $(p_1 - p_2)$, for the two groups. The test of $H_0: p_1 = p_2$ analyzes whether the population proportions are equal. If the test has a small P-value, or if the confidence interval for $(p_1 - p_2)$ does not contain 0, we conclude that they differ.

- For quantitative data, we compare the *means* for the two groups. Confidence intervals and significance tests apply to $(\mu_1 - \mu_2)$, the difference in the population means.

Table 10.16 summarizes two-sided estimation and testing methods for large, **independent random samples.** This is the most common case in practice.

Table 10.16 Comparing Two Groups for Large, Independent Random Samples

	Type of Response Variable	
	Categorical	**Quantitative**
Estimation		
1. Parameter	$p_1 - p_2$	$\mu_1 - \mu_2$
2. Point Estimate	$(\hat{p}_1 - \hat{p}_2)$	$(\bar{x}_1 - \bar{x}_2)$
3. Standard Error (se)	$\sqrt{\dfrac{\hat{p}_1(1-\hat{p}_1)}{n_1} + \dfrac{\hat{p}_2(1-\hat{p}_2)}{n_2}}$	$\sqrt{\dfrac{s_1^2}{n_1} + \dfrac{s_2^2}{n_2}}$
4. 95% Confidence Int.	$(\hat{p}_1 - \hat{p}_2) \pm 1.96(se)$	$(\bar{x}_1 - \bar{x}_2) \pm t_{.025}(se)$
Significance Test		
1. Assumptions	Randomization with at least five of each type for each group if using a 2-sided alternative	Randomization from approximately normal population distributions (test robust)
2. Hypotheses	$H_0: p_1 = p_2 \ (p_1 - p_2 = 0)$ $H_a: p_1 \neq p_2$	$H_0: \mu_1 = \mu_2 \ (\mu_1 - \mu_2 = 0)$ $H_a: \mu_1 \neq \mu_2$
3. Test Statistic	$z = (\hat{p}_1 - \hat{p}_2)/se_0$ $se_0 = \sqrt{\hat{p}(1-\hat{p})\left(\dfrac{1}{n_1} + \dfrac{1}{n_2}\right)}$ with $\hat{p}$ = pooled proportion	$t = (\bar{x}_1 - \bar{x}_2)/se$ can also use $se = s\sqrt{\dfrac{1}{n_1} + \dfrac{1}{n_2}}$ with s = pooled standard deviation
4. P-value	Two-tail probability from standard normal distribution	Two-tail probability from t distribution
5. Conclusion	Interpret P-value in context. Reject H_0 if P-value $\leq \alpha$	Interpret P-value in context. Reject H_0 if P-value $\leq \alpha$

Both for differences of proportions and differences of means, confidence intervals have the form

$$\text{Estimate} \pm (z\text{- or }t\text{-score})(\text{standard error}),$$

such as for 95% confidence intervals,

$$(\hat{p}_1 - \hat{p}_2) \pm 1.96(se), \text{ and } (\bar{x}_1 - \bar{x}_2) \pm t_{.025}(se).$$

For significance tests, the test statistic equals the estimated difference divided by the standard error, $z = (\hat{p}_1 - \hat{p}_2)/se_0$ and $t = (\bar{x}_1 - \bar{x}_2)/se$. When the P-value for such a test is small, the two groups are often called **(statistically) significantly different**, indicating that the population parameter (proportion or mean) differs significantly between the two groups. Beware that **statistical significance does not imply practical relevance**. A confidence interval is more informative and estimates the **size of the difference** instead of just concluding whether two groups differ significantly.

When assumptions underlying the t test are in doubt, the relevant sampling distribution can be approximated via **bootstrap** or **permutation resampling**. Confidence intervals for the difference in means or medians can be obtained via the bootstrap percentile method. A permutation test uses thousands of permutations of the original data to determine whether the observed difference is extreme, assuming equal population distributions.

With **dependent samples,** each observation in one sample is matched with an observation in the other sample. This occurs, for instance, when the same subject is measured twice. We compare means by analyzing the mean of the differences between the paired observations. The confidence interval and test procedures apply one-sample methods to the sample of differences. For comparing proportions from two dependent samples (represented in a 2×2 contingency table), specialized methods (McNemar's test) are used.

At this stage, you may feel confused about which method to use for any given exercise. It may help if you use the following checklist. Ask yourself, do you have:

- Means or proportions (a quantitative or categorical response variable)?
- Independent samples or dependent samples?
- Confidence interval or significance test?
- Large n_1 and n_2 or not?

In practice, most applications have large, independent samples, and confidence intervals are more useful than tests. So the following cases are especially important: confidence intervals comparing proportions with large independent samples, and confidence intervals comparing means with large independent samples.

LEARNING OBJECTIVES

1. Identify whether the study design is using independent samples or dependent samples.

2. Construct and interpret a confidence interval for the difference of two population proportions.

3. Construct and interpret a confidence interval for the difference of two population means.

4. Recognize that if zero is contained in the confidence interval for the difference of two population proportions (or means), it is plausible that the two population proportions (or means) are equal.

5. Understand how to conduct a significance test for testing the hypothesis of no difference in two population proportions (or means).

6. Understand and confirm the assumptions underlying the two-sample tests.

7. Understand that statistical significance (i.e., a small P-value) may not imply practical relevance and that a confidence interval is more informative because it estimates the size of the difference.

8. (optional) Understand how to build a sampling distribution for the difference of two means or medians and obtain a confidence interval using the bootstrap.

9. (optional) Understand that the assumption of equal population distributions implies that we can interchange group labels to generate a sampling distribution by permutations and how to obtain a permutation P-value.

10. (optional) Understand when resampling procedures (bootstrap, permutations) are preferred over using t distribution-based inferences.

11. Understand that for comparing means with two dependent samples, inference reduces to the case of using a single sample of differences.

12. Understand how to organize categorical data from two dependent samples in a 2×2 contingency table and conduct inference comparing the two proportions (McNemar's test).

13. Recognize the possible influence of other variables when analyzing the association between an explanatory and a response variable.

ANSWERS TO THE CHAPTER FIGURE QUESTIONS

Figure 10.1 $\hat{p}_1 - \hat{p}_2$ represents the difference between the sample proportions suffering a cancer death with placebo and with aspirin. $p_1 - p_2$ represents the difference between the population proportions. The mean of this sampling distribution is zero if cancer death rates are identical for aspirin and placebo.

Figure 10.3 If the interval contains only negative values, $p_1 - p_2$ is predicted to be negative, so p_1 is predicted to be smaller than p_2. If the interval contains only positive values, p_1 is predicted to be larger than p_2.

Figure 10.5 A histogram of the ratings in each group to get a better idea about the possible shape of the population distribution in each group.

Figure 10.7 Positive numbers in the confidence interval for $(\mu_1 - \mu_2)$ suggest that $\mu_1 - \mu_2 > 0$ and, thus, that $\mu_1 > \mu_2$.

Figure 10.8 The box plot for the cell phone group indicates an extreme outlier. It's important to check that the results of the analysis aren't affected too strongly by that single observation.

Figure 10.9   One histogram will show more variability (a larger spread) than the other.

Figure 10.11   The top one, because it has the two largest observations in the high group and the three smallest observations in the low group, resulting in the largest possible separation (difference) in the sample means.

Figure 10.12   If n_1 and n_2 were large, the sampling distribution of $\bar{x}_1 - \bar{x}_2$ is approximately normal.

Figure 10.13   If the population distributions were normal, the sampling distribution of $(\bar{x}_1 - \bar{x}_2)$ would also be normal.

Figure 10.14   The outliers for the two distributions are both from subject number 28.

STATISTICAL SOFTWARE

Art of Stat Web Apps

- **Compare Two Proportions** This app compares proportions across two groups. You can enter the sample size and success count for each of the two groups, and the app will produce a bar chart and compute and visualize a confidence interval or a significance test for the difference of proportions between the groups. Alternatively, you can provide raw data. The second tab of the app handles confidence intervals and significance tests for two dependent samples (McNemar's test).

- **Compare Two Means** This app compares means across two groups. You can enter the observations from a sample in each of the two groups, and the app will produce a box- or dot plot or a histogram comparing the two groups. Alternatively, you can just provide the summary statistics for the sample from each group (sample size, mean, and standard deviation). The app computes and visualizes a confidence interval or a significance test for the difference of means between the groups. The second tab of the app handles confidence intervals and significance tests for two dependent samples.

- **Bootstrap for Two Samples** This app illustrates and implements the bootstrap for comparing two samples. Step-by-step, you can build the bootstrap distribution for the difference in means or medians (among others) and compute and visualize a bootstrap percentile confidence interval.

- **Permutation Test** This app illustrates and implements the permutation approach for comparing two samples. Step-by-step, you can build the permutation distribution and obtain the permutation P-value for differences in means or medians.

R

- **Comparing two proportions:** The prop.test function returns a confidence interval and results of a significance test for the difference of two proportions. Using data from Example 4,

```
> prop.test(c(347, 327), c(11535, 14035),
correct=FALSE)
X-squared = 11.352, df = 1, p-value = 0.0007536
alternative hypothesis: two.sided
95 percent confidence interval:
 0.002790305 0.010776620
```

returns the 95% confidence interval for $p_1 - p_2$ and the P-value for the two-sided test $H_0: p_1 - p_2 = 0$. (To change the confidence level or type of alternative hypothesis, insert conf.level = 0.99 or alternative = 'greater', respectively; see Chapters 8 and 9.) As mentioned in Chapter 9, the R output doesn't show the z test statistic value directly (here: $z = 3.37$) but rather its square $(3.37)^2 = 11.35$, labeled X-squared. The P-value is not influenced by this. For comparing proportions from two dependent samples, the mcnemar.test function returns results of a significance test, as in

```
> mcnemar.test(matrix(c(1921, 16, 58, 5),
nrow = 2), correct=FALSE)
```

for data from Example 17. (Again, the function returns the square of the test statistic, $(4.88)^2 = 23.8$, but the P-value is not affected by this.)

- **Comparing two means:** The t.test function returns a confidence interval and results of a significance test for the difference of two means, where the user supplies the observations from the samples in the two groups. Using part of the small data set from Exercise 10.31 on the time spent on social media,

```
> males <- c(5, 9, 12, 12, 13, 15, 20)
> females <- c(5, 7, 10, 11, 12, 14, 16, 20,
20, 23, 40)
> t.test(males, females)
t = -1.1404, df = 15.256, p-value = 0.2717
alternative hypothesis: true difference in
means is not equal to 0
95 percent confidence interval:
 -11.167226  3.375018
```

we obtain a 95% confidence interval for $\mu_1 - \mu_2$ and the P-value for the two-sided test $H_0: \mu_1 - \mu_2 = 0$. You cannot use the t.test function when only supplying summary statistics (sample size, mean, and st. dev.). Use the var.equal=TRUE option when you want to use the test assuming equal standard deviations. Use the paired=TRUE option to analyze paired data, as in (using data from Exercise 10.58):

```
> before <- c(5.08, 5.99, 5.32, 6.03, 5.44)
> after <- c(5.36, 5.98, 5.62, 6.26, 5.68)
> t.test(before, after, paired=TRUE)
  Paired t-test
t = -3.7155, df = 4, p-value = 0.02056
95 percent confidence interval:
 -0.36343134  -0.05256866
sample estimates:
mean of the differences
          -0.208
```

CHAPTER EXERCISES

Practicing the Basics

10.72 Pick the method A real estate agency obtains a random sample of 50 houses throughout Sarasota, Florida, from the website zillow.com. Among others, it records the market value of each selected house (both for 2015 and 2020), whether it is east or west of Interstate 75, and whether it is in a designated flood zone. For the following scenarios, pick a statistical method from this chapter that would be appropriate for analyzing the data, indicating whether the samples are independent or dependent, which parameter is relevant, and what inference method you would use:

a. The agency wants to compare the mean market value of houses in Sarasota in 2015 and in 2020 and analyze by how much they differ.

b. The agency wants to compare the proportion of houses in a flood zone east and west of I-75 and analyze whether they differ significantly.

c. The agency wants to estimate by how much the mean market value of houses east and west of I-75 differed in 2020.

10.73 Public versus scientists' opinions on fracking A Pew Research Center survey of 2002 U.S. adults in August 2014 and a survey of 3,748 scientists connected to the American Association for the Advancement of Science (AAAS) in September 2014 both asked the following question: "Do you favor or oppose the increased use of fracking?" In the Pew Research Center survey, fracking was favored by 37%, whereas in the survey of scientists, it was favored by 31%. Both surveys used random samples.

a. Identify the response variable and the explanatory variable.

b. To conduct inference, should we treat the sample of U.S. adults and the sample of scientists from the AAAS as dependent or as independent? Explain.

c. The AAAS survey also asked each of the 3,748 scientists whether they favor or oppose more offshore oil and gas drilling. Thirty-two percent responded that they favor it. To compare this to the percentage who favored fracking, should you treat the samples as dependent or as independent? Why?

10.74 BMI then and now The Centers for Disease Control (www.cdc.gov) periodically administers large randomized surveys to track health of Americans. In a survey of 4,431 adults in 2003/2004, 66% were overweight (body mass index BMI ≥ 25). In the 2011/2012 survey of 5,181 adults, 69% were overweight.

a. Estimate the change in the population proportion who are overweight and interpret.

b. The standard error for estimating this difference equals 0.0096. What is the main factor that causes *se* to be so small?

c. The 95% confidence interval comparing the population proportions in 2011/2012 to the one in 2003/2004 is (0.011, 0.049). Interpret, taking into account whether 0 is in this interval.

10.75 Marijuana and gender In a survey conducted by Wright State University, senior high school students were asked if they had ever used marijuana. The table shows results of typical software output, where X is the count who said yes. Assuming these observations can be treated as a random sample from a population of interest,

a. Interpret the reported estimate and the reported confidence interval. Explain how to interpret the fact that 0 is not in the confidence interval.

b. Explain how the confidence interval would change if males were Group 1 and females were Group 2. Express an interpretation for the interval in that case.

```
Sample          X           N        Sample p
1. Female       445         1120       0.3973
2. Male         515         1156       0.4455
estimate for p(1) − p(2):  −0.0482
95% CI for p(1) − p(2): (−0.0887, −0.0077)
```

10.76 Gender and belief in afterlife The table shows results from the 2014 General Social Survey on gender and whether one believes in an afterlife. (The data are preloaded in the *Compare Two Proportions* app.)

Gender	Belief in Afterlife		Total
	Yes	No	
Female	1,026	207	**1,233**
Male	757	252	**1,009**

a. Denote the population proportion who believe in an afterlife by p_1 for females and by p_2 for males. Estimate p_1, p_2, and $(p_1 - p_2)$.

b. Find the standard error for the estimate of $(p_1 - p_2)$. Interpret.

c. Construct a 95% confidence interval for $(p_1 - p_2)$. Can you conclude which of p_1 and p_2 is larger? Explain.

d. Suppose that, unknown to us, $p_1 = 0.81$ and $p_2 = 0.72$. Does the confidence interval in part c contain the parameter it is designed to estimate? Explain.

10.77 Belief depend on gender? Refer to the previous exercise.

a. Find the standard error of $(\hat{p}_1 - \hat{p}_2)$ for a test of $H_0: p_1 = p_2$.

b. For a two-sided test, find the test statistic and P-value and make a decision using significance level 0.05. Interpret.

c. Suppose that actually $p_1 = 0.81$ and $p_2 = 0.72$. Was the decision in part b in error?

d. State the assumptions on which the methods in this exercise are based.

10.78 Females or males have more close friends? A recent GSS reported that the 486 surveyed females had a mean of 8.3 close friends ($s = 15.6$) and the 354 surveyed males had a mean of 8.9 close friends ($s = 15.5$). (You can enter these data by choosing Summary Statistics under Enter Data in the *Compare Two Means* app.)

a. Estimate the difference between the population means for males and females.

b. The 95% confidence interval for the difference between the population means is 0.6 ± 2.1. Interpret.

c. For each gender, does it seem like the distribution of number of close friends is normal? Why? How does this affect the validity of the confidence interval in part b?

10.79 Heavier horseshoe crabs more likely to mate? A study of a sample of horseshoe crabs on a Florida island (J. Brockmann, *Ethology*, vol. 102, 1996, pp. 1–21) investigated the factors that were associated with whether female crabs had a male crab mate. Basic statistics, including the five-number summary on weight (kg) for the 111 female crabs who had a male crab nearby and for the 62 female crabs who did not have a male crab nearby, are given in the table. Assume that these horseshoe crabs have the properties of a random sample of all such crabs.

Summary Statistics for Weights of Horseshoe Crabs

	n	Mean	Std. Dev.	Min	Q1	Med	Q3	Max
Mate	111	2.6	0.6	1.5	2.2	2.6	3.0	5.2
No Mate	62	2.1	0.4	1.2	1.8	2.1	2.4	3.2

a. Sketch box plots for the weight distributions of the two groups. Interpret by comparing the groups with respect to shape, center, and variability.

b. Estimate the difference between the mean weights of female crabs who have mates and female crabs who do not have mates.

c. Find the standard error for the estimate in part b. (You can use the Summary Statistics option under Enter Data in the *Compare Two Means* app to enter the data.)

d. Construct a 90% confidence interval for the difference between the population mean weights, and interpret.

10.80 College students exercising At the end of the academic year, a sample of college freshmen were asked whether they participated in college athletics and how many hours they typically exercised per week in the last semester. The data are available in the *Compare Two Means* app (from which the following screenshot is taken) and on the book's website.

a. Do you believe that exercise hours has a normal distribution for each group? What effect does this have on inference comparing population means?

b. Explain how to interpret the reported confidence interval. Can you conclude that one population mean is higher? If so, which one? Explain.

c. On what assumptions is this inference based?

Descriptive Statistics:

Group	Sample Size	Mean	Std. Dev.
Athletes	79	12.5	4.99
Not Athletes	84	4.6	3.90

Estimate of Difference of Means:

Point Estimate	Standard Error	Margin of Error
7.911	0.7048	± 1.393

Confidence Interval:

Population Parameter	Lower Bound	Upper Bound	Confidence Level
Difference $\mu_1 - \mu_2$	6.518	9.304	95%

95% Confidence Interval
[6.518, 9.304]

Difference of Means $\mu_1 - \mu_2$

Histograms (Athletes / Not Athletes): Frequency vs Hours Exercising

10.81 Athletes vs. nonathletes Refer to the previous exercise.

a. Specify the hypotheses for a test to see if the mean number of hours exercised differs significantly between college athletes and nonathletes.

b. Show, using the output from the previous exercise, that the test statistic $t = 11.2$. Will this result in a P-value that is larger than 0.10, between 0.10 and 0.05, between 0.05 and 0.01, or less than 0.01? Explain.

c. Write a conclusion to the test, using the 0.05 significance level.

d. Explain the connection between the result of this significance test in part c and the result of the confidence interval in the previous exercise.

e. What can we learn from the confidence interval that we cannot learn from the test?

10.82 Ibuprofen and lifespan Geneticists hypothesized that one reason for a prolonged lifespan observed in yeast cells treated with the common drug ibuprofen stems from inhibiting the uptake of certain amino acids. In an experiment, they compared levels of amino acids in cells treated with ibuprofen to cells from an untreated control group. For the amino acid tryptophan, the six measurements in the treated group had a mean level of 0.0067 with a standard deviation of 0.0038. The six measurements in the control group had a mean level of 0.0080 with a standard deviation of 0.0050.

a. Identify the response variable and explanatory variable. Indicate whether each is quantitative or categorical.

b. Find the standard error of the sample mean in each group and the standard error of the difference in the sample means.

c. A 95% confidence interval for the difference between the mean level of tryptophan in the treated versus the control group is $(-0.007, 0.004)$. Interpret.

10.83 Time spent on Internet In 2018, the General Social Survey asked about the number of hours a week spent on the World Wide Web (variable WWWHR). Some results are as follows (you can replicate these by entering the summary statistics in the *Compare Two Means* app):

Race	n	Mean	StDev	SE Mean
Black	206	16.5	20.1	1.4
White	1,001	13.3	16.1	0.5

Difference = mu(Black) − mu(White)
Estimate for difference: 3.2
95% CI for difference: (0.3, 6.1)
T-Test of difference = 0 (vs ≠):
T-value = 2.15 P-value = 0.0327

a. Identify the response variable and explanatory variable. Indicate whether each variable is quantitative or categorical.

b. Report and interpret the 95% confidence interval shown for the difference between the population means for Whites and Blacks.

c. Report and interpret the steps of the significance test comparing the two population means. Make a decision, using significance level 0.05.

10.84 Sex roles A study of the effect of the gender of the tester on sex-role differentiation scores in Manhattan gave a random sample of preschool children the Occupational Preference Test.[12] Children were asked to give three choices of what they wanted to be when they grew up. Each occupation was rated on a scale from 1 (traditionally feminine) to 5 (traditionally masculine), and a child's score was the mean of the three selections. When the tester was male, the 50 girls had $\bar{x} = 2.9$ and $s = 1.4$, whereas when the tester was female, the 90 girls had $\bar{x} = 3.2$ and $s = 1.2$. Show all steps of a test of the hypothesis that the population mean is the same for female and male testers, against the alternative that they differ. Report the P-value and interpret.

10.85 How often do you feel sad? A recent General Social Survey asked, "How many days in the past seven days have you felt sad?" Accessing the data comparing men and women in the *Compare Two Means* app gave the results shown in the following screenshot.

a. What are μ_1 and μ_2 in the output referring to?

b. Explain how to interpret the P-value and write a conclusion to the test. Do you think that the population means may be equal? Explain.

Descriptive Statistics:

Group	Sample Size	Mean	Std. Dev.
Men	633	1.42	1.83
Women	816	1.81	1.98

Test Statistic:

Observed Difference	Standard Error	Test Statistic t
-0.3967	0.1004	-3.951

Hypothesis Test:

Population Parameter	Null Hypothesis	Alternative Hypothesis	Test Statistic t	P-value
Difference $\mu_1 - \mu_2$	$\mu_1 - \mu_2 = 0$	$\mu_1 - \mu_2 \neq 0$	-3.9512	0.0001

t Distribution with df = 1405.2
$H_0: \mu_1 = \mu_2, H_a: \mu_1 \neq \mu_2$. Test Statistic: t = -3.951, P-value = 0.0001

c. What assumptions are made for these inferences? Do they seem to be violated? What's the effect?

10.86 Parental support and household type A recent study interviewed youths with a battery of questions that provides a summary measure of perceived parental support. This measure had sample means of 46 ($s = 9$) for the single-mother households and 42 ($s = 10$) for the households with both biological parents. One conclusion in the study stated, "The mean parental support was 4 units higher for the single-mother households. If the true means were equal, a difference of at least this size could be expected only 2% of the time. For samples of this size, 95% of the time one would expect this difference to be within 3.4 of the true value." Explain how this conclusion refers to the results of (a) a confidence interval and (b) a significance test.

10.87 Car bumper damage An automobile company compares two types of front bumpers for its new model by driving sample cars into a concrete wall at 20 miles per hour. The response is the amount of damage to the car, as measured by the repair costs, in hundreds of dollars. Due to the costs, the study uses only six cars, obtaining results for three bumpers of each type. The results are in the table. Conduct statistical inference (95% confidence interval or significance test with significance level 0.05) about the difference between the population means, using software if you wish. Can you conclude that the mean is higher for one bumper type?

Bumper A: 11, 15, 13

Bumper B: 1, 3, 4

---

[12]Obtained from Bonnie Seegmiller, a psychologist at Hunter College.

10.88 Teenage anorexia Example 8 in Section 9.3 described a study that used a cognitive behavioral therapy to treat a sample of teenage girls who suffered from anorexia. The study observed the mean weight change after a period of treatment. Studies of that type also usually have a control group that receives no treatment or a standard treatment. Then researchers can analyze how the change in weight compares for the treatment group to the control group. In fact, the anorexia study had a control group that received a standard treatment. Teenage girls in the study were randomly assigned to the cognitive behavioral treatment or to the control group. The data were entered in the *Compare Two Means* app, with output shown in the two screenshots below.

Descriptive Statistics:

Group	Sample Size	Mean	Std. Dev.
Cognitive	29	3.01	7.31
Control	26	-0.45	7.99

Estimate of Difference of Means:

Point Estimate	Standard Error	Margin of Error
3.457	2.073	± 4.161

Confidence Interval:

Population Parameter	Lower Bound	Upper Bound	Confidence Level
Difference $\mu_1 - \mu_2$	-0.7045	7.618	95%

95% Confidence Interval
[-0.7045, 7.618]

Difference of Means $\mu_1 - \mu_2$

Hypothesis Test:

Population Parameter	Null Hypothesis	Alternative Hypothesis	Test Statistic t	P-value
Difference $\mu_1 - \mu_2$	$\mu_1 - \mu_2 = 0$	$\mu_1 - \mu_2 \neq 0$	1.6677	0.1015

t Distribution with df = 51
H_0: $\mu_1 = \mu_2$, H_a: $\mu_1 \neq \mu_2$. Test Statistic: t = 1.668, P-value = 0.1015

0.8985
0.0507   0.0507

-4   -3   -2   -1   0   1   2   3   4
       -1.67   t = 1.67

a. Report and interpret the P-value for testing H_0: $\mu_1 = \mu_2$ against H_a: $\mu_1 \neq \mu_2$.

b. Summarize the assumptions needed for the analysis in part a. Based on the box plots, would you be nervous if you had to perform a one-sided test instead? Why?

c. The reported 95% confidence interval tells us that if the population mean weight change is less for the cognitive behavioral group than for the control group, it is just barely less (less than 1 pound), but if the population mean change is greater, it could be nearly 8 pounds greater. Explain how to get this interpretation from the interval reported.

d. Explain the correspondence between the confidence interval and the decision in the significance test for a 0.05 significance level.

10.89 Bootstrap interval comparing means Refer to Exercise 10.80 about the exercise hours per week for college athletes versus nonathletes. There, we saw that the distribution of exercise hours for nonathletes was right skewed, with outliers at the high end. Use the *Bootstrap for Two Samples* app to

a. Approximate the sampling distribution for the difference between two sample means, using 10,000 bootstrap samples. Does the sampling distribution look approximately normal?

b. Construct a 95% bootstrap percentile confidence interval for the difference in the population means. Interpret the interval and compare to the *t*-interval from Exercise 10.80.

10.90 Bootstrap interval comparing medians Refer to the previous exercise. Because of the right-skewed nature of the distribution of exercise hours per week, it is more informative to compare the median instead of the mean exercise hours for college athletes and nonathletes. Use the *Bootstrap for Two Samples* app to

a. Generate one bootstrap sample from the original data. What is the difference of medians for this one bootstrap sample?

b. Approximate the sampling distribution of the difference in medians using thousands of bootstrap resamples. Obtain and describe the bootstrap distribution.

c. Obtain a 95% bootstrap percentile confidence interval for the difference between medians. What are the lower and upper bounds? Interpret the interval.

10.91 Median dominance Refer to Exercise 10.27, which compared the mean dominance score derived from stick figure renderings of male and female politicians. The box plots displayed in the screenshot for that exercise show skewed distributions for the ratings. While Exercise 10.27 found no significant difference in the mean scores, is there a difference in the median scores? Answer by

a. Approximating and describing the sampling distribution of the difference between two medians using 10,000 bootstrap samples.

b. Finding and interpreting a 95% bootstrap percentile confidence interval for the difference in the median score.

The *Bootstrap for Two Samples* app has these data preloaded.

10.92 Equal pay in sports? The following data refer to a random sample of prize money earned by male and female skiers racing in the 2014/2015 FIS world cup season (in Swiss Franc).

Males: 89,000 179,000 8,820 12,000 10,750 66,000 6,700 3,300 74,000 56,800

Females: 73,000 95,000 32,400 4,000 2,000 57,100 4,500

Enter the observations (separated by spaces) into the *Permutation Test* app. Let male skiers be Group 1 and female skiers be Group 2 and let the test statistic be the difference in sample means. Is there evidence that male skiers earn more, on average, than female skiers?

a. What are the observed group means and their difference? (The subtitle of the dot plot shows this information.)

b. Why would we prefer to run a permutation test over a *t* test?

c. Press the Generate Random Permutation(s) button once to generate one permutation of the original data. What are the two group means and their difference under this permutation?

d. Did this one permutation lead to a difference that is less extreme or more extreme than the observed difference?

e. Click Generate Random Permutation(s) nine more times, for a total of 10 permutations. How many of them resulted in a test statistic at least as extreme as the observed one?

f. Press Reset and then select to generate 10,000 permutations at once. How many of them resulted in a test statistic as or more extreme?

g. Find and interpret the permutation P-value.

h. Press Reset, select Generate All Possible Permutations under Options, and then press Generate Random Permutation(s) again. Do you notice a big difference in the histogram and P-value based on 10,000 randomly sampled permutations and on all possible permutations?

10.93 Anorexia again Refer to Exercise 10.88, comparing mean weight changes in anorexic girls for cognitive behavioral therapy and a control group. The following output from the MINITAB software system shows results of doing analyses while assuming equal population standard deviations. (You can replicate this analysis with the *Compare Two Means* app, selecting the Assume Equal Standard Deviation option.)

MINITAB Output for Comparing Mean Weight Changes

	N	Mean	StDev	SE Mean
cogchange	29	3.01	7.31	1.4
controlchange	26	−0.45	7.99	1.6

Difference = μ(cogchange) − μ(controlchange)
Estimate for difference: 3.46
95% CI for difference:(−0.68, 7.59)
T-Test of difference = 0 (vs ≠):
T-Value = 1.68 P-Value = 0.100 DF = 53
Both use Pooled StDev = 7.6369

a. Interpret the reported confidence interval.

b. Interpret the reported P-value.

c. What would be the P-value for $H_a: \mu_1 > \mu_2$? Interpret it.

d. What assumptions do these inferences make?

10.94 Breast-feeding helps IQ? A Danish study of individuals born at a Copenhagen hospital between 1959 and 1961 reported higher mean IQ scores for adults who were breast-fed for longer lengths of time as babies (E. Mortensen et al., (2002), *JAMA*, vol. 287, pp. 2365–2371). The mean IQ score was 98.1 ($s = 15.9$) for the 272 subjects who had been breast-fed for no longer than a month and 108.2 ($s = 13.1$) for the 104 subjects who had been breast-fed for seven to nine months.

a. Use the *Compare Two Means* app to analyze whether the corresponding population means differ, assuming the population standard deviations are equal. Interpret.

b. Was this an experimental or an observational study? Can you think of a potential lurking variable?

10.95 Australian cell phone use In Western Australia, handheld cell phone use while driving has been banned since 2001, but hands-free devices are legal. A study (published in the *British Medical Journal* in 2005) of 456 drivers in Perth who had been in a crash observed if they were using a cell phone before the crash and if they were using a cell phone during an earlier period when no accident occurred. Thus, each driver served as his or her own control group in the study.

a. In comparing rates of cell phone use before the crash and the earlier accident-free period, should we use methods for independent samples or for dependent samples? Explain.

b. Identify a test you can use to see whether the proportion of drivers using a cell phone differs between the period before the crash and the earlier accident-free period.

10.96 Improving employee evaluations Each of a random sample of 10 customer service representatives from a large department store chain answers a questionnaire about how they respond to various customer complaints. Based on the responses, a summary score measures how positively the employees react to complaints. This is measured both before and after employees undergo an intensive training course designed to improve such scores. A report about the study states, "The mean was significantly higher after taking the training course [$t = 3.40$ ($df = 9$), P-value < 0.05]." Explain how to interpret this to someone who has never studied statistics. What else should have been reported to make this more informative?

10.97 Which tire is better? A tire manufacturer believes that a new tire it is introducing (Brand A) will have longer wear than the comparable tire (Brand B) sold by its main competitor. To get evidence to back up its claim in planned advertising, the manufacturer conducts a study. On each of four cars it uses a tire of Brand A on the left front and a tire of Brand B on the right front. The response is the number of thousands of miles until a tire wears out, according to a tread marking on the tire. The sample mean response is 50 for Brand A and 40 for Brand B.

a. Show a pattern of four pairs of observations with these means for which you think Brand A would be judged better according to statistical inference. You do not need to actually conduct the inference. (*Hint:* What affects the value of the test statistic other than the sample means and n?)

b. How could the design of this study be improved?

10.98 Effect of alcoholic parents A study[13] compared personality characteristics between 49 children of alcoholics and a control group of 49 children of nonalcoholics who were matched on age and gender. On a measure of well-being, the 49 children of alcoholics had a mean of 26.1 ($s = 7.2$) and the 49 subjects in the control group had a mean of 28.8 ($s = 6.4$). The difference scores between the matched subjects from the two groups had a mean of 2.7 ($s = 9.7$).

a. Are the groups to be compared independent samples or dependent samples? Why?

b. Show all steps of a test of equality of the two population means for a two-sided alternative hypothesis. Report the P-value and interpret. (You can enter the summary statistics for the differences in the *Inference for a Mean* app to obtain the P-value.)

c. What assumptions must you make for the inference in part b to be valid?

10.99 CI versus test Consider the results from the previous exercise.

a. Construct a 95% confidence interval to compare the population means.

b. Explain what you learn from the confidence interval that you do not learn from the significance test.

10.100 Breast augmentation and self-esteem A researcher in the College of Nursing, University of Florida, hypothesized that women who undergo breast augmentation surgery would gain an increase in self-esteem. The article about the study[14] indicated that for the 84 subjects who volunteered for the study, the scores on the Rosenberg Self-Esteem Scale were 20.7 before the surgery (std. dev. = 6.3) and 24.9 after the surgery (std. dev = 4.6). The author reported that a paired difference significance test had $t = 9.8$ and a P-value below 0.0001.

a. Were the samples compared dependent samples, or independent samples? Explain.

b. Can you obtain the stated t statistic from the values reported for the means, standard deviation, and sample size? Why or why not?

10.101 Internet use As part of her class project in a statistics course, a student decided to study ways in which her fellow students use the Internet. She randomly sampled 5 of the 165 students in her course and asked them, "In the past week, how many days did you use the Internet to (a) read news stories, (b) communicate with friends using e-mail or text messaging?" The table shows the results. Using an appropriate app or other software, construct a confidence interval or conduct a significance test to analyze these data. Interpret, indicating the population to which the inferences extend.

Pair	News	Communicating
1	2	5
2	3	7
3	0	6
4	5	5
5	1	4

10.102 TV or rock music a worse influence? In a recent General Social Survey, subjects were asked to respond to the following: "Children are exposed to many influences in their daily lives. What kind of influence does each of the following have on children? 1. Programs on network television, 2. rock music." The possible responses were (very negative, negative, neutral, positive, very positive). The responses for 12 of the sampled subjects, using scores ($-2, -1, 0, 1, 2$) for the possible responses are given in the table:

Subject	TV	Rock	Subject	TV	Rock	Subject	TV	Rock
1	0	-1	5	-1	-1	9	-1	-1
2	0	0	6	-2	-2	10	0	1
3	1	-2	7	-1	0	11	1	-1
4	0	1	8	1	-1	12	-1	-2

a. When you compare responses for TV and Rock, are the samples independent or dependent? Why?

b. Use an appropriate app or other software to construct a 95% confidence interval for the population difference in means. Interpret in the context of the variables studied.

c. Use an appropriate app or other software to conduct a significance test of equality of the population means for TV and Rock. Interpret the P-value.

10.103 Influence of TV and movies Refer to the previous exercise. The GSS also asked about the influence of movies. The responses for these 12 subjects were $-1, 1, 0, 2, 0, -2, -1, 0, -1, 1, 1, -1$. The results of using MINITAB to compare the influence of movies and TV are shown on the following page. (You can replicate these results with the second tab of the *Compare Two Means* app.) Explain how to interpret (a) the confidence interval and (b) the significance test results.

[13]D. Baker and L. Stephenson, (1995), *Journal of Clinical Psychology*, vol. 51.
[14]By C. Figueroa-Haas, (2007), *Plastic Surgical Nursing*, vol. 27, p. 16.

```
Paired T for movies - TV
                N     Mean    StDev   SE Mean
Movies          12   -0.083   1.165    0.336
TV              12   -0.250   0.965    0.279
Difference      12    0.167   0.937    0.271
95% CI for mean difference: (-0.429, 0.762)
T-Test of mean difference = 0 (vs ≠ 0):
T-Value = 0.62 P-Value = 0.551
```

10.104 Crossover study The table summarizes results of a crossover study to compare results of low-dose and high-dose analgesics for relief of menstrual bleeding (B. Jones and M. Kenward, *Statistics in Medicine*, vol. 6, 1987, pp. 555–564). (You can enter the data below in the second tab of the *Compare Two Proportions* app to answer parts a and b, or obtain the results by hand calculation and a statistical table.)

a. Find the sample proportion of successes for each dose of the analgesic.

b. Find the P-value for testing that the probability of success is the same with each dose, for a two-sided alternative. Interpret. What assumptions does this inference make?

	High Dose	
Low Dose	**Success**	**Failure**
Success	53	8
Failure	16	9

10.105 Belief in ghosts and in astrology A poll by Louis Harris and Associates of 1,249 Americans indicated that 36% believe in ghosts and 37% believe in astrology.

a. Is it valid to compare the proportions using inferential methods for independent samples? Explain.

b. Do you have enough information to compare the proportions using methods for dependent samples? If yes, do so. If not, explain what else you would need to know.

10.106 Death penalty paradox Exercise 3.58 showed results of another study about the death penalty and race. The data are repeated here.

a. Treating victim's race as the control variable, show that Simpson's paradox occurs.

b. Explain what causes the paradox to happen.

		Death Penalty	
Vic Race	**Def Race**	**Yes**	**No**
W	W	53	414
	B	11	37
B	W	0	16
	B	4	139

10.107 Death rate paradoxes The crude death rate is the number of deaths in a year, per size of the population, multiplied by 1,000.

a. According to the U.S. Census Bureau, in 1995 Mexico had a crude death rate of 4.6 (i.e., 4.6 deaths per 1,000 population) while the United States had a crude death rate of 8.4. Explain how this overall death rate could be higher in the United States even if the United States had a lower death rate than Mexico for people of each specific age.

b. For each age level, the death rate is higher in South Carolina than in Maine. Overall, the death rate is higher in Maine (H. Wainer, (1999), *Chance*, vol. 12, p. 44). Explain how this could be possible.

10.108 Income and gender For a particular Big Ten university, the mean income for male faculty is $8,000 higher than the mean income for female faculty. Explain how this difference could disappear:

a. Controlling for number of years since received highest degree. (*Hint:* What if relatively few female professors were hired until recent years?)

b. Controlling for college of employment.

Concepts and Investigations

10.109 Hepatitis B vaccination adherence In a study of adherence to the hepatitis B vaccination series[15] ninety-six injection drug users were randomized to a monetary incentive group or an outreach group. Of the 48 individuals in the monetary incentive group, 33 were adherent, and of the 48 in the outreach group, 11 were adherent. Using an appropriate app or other software, prepare a short report showing the results of this study graphically and summarizing (including checking assumptions) the use of a confidence interval for inference.

10.110 Review the medical literature Find a recent article of a medical journal that reports results of a statistical analysis (e.g., see Activity 3 on page 579). Describe the statistical analyses that were used in that article. Did the article use (a) descriptive statistics, (b) confidence intervals, and (c) significance tests? If so, explain how these methods were used. Prepare a one-page summary of your findings that you will present to your class.

10.111 Attractiveness and getting dates The results in the table are from a study of physical attractiveness and subjective well-being (E. Diener et al., *Journal of Personality and Social Psychology*, vol. 69, 1995, pp. 120–129). As part of the study, college students in a sample were rated by a panel on their physical attractiveness. The table presents the number of dates in the past three months for students rated in the top or bottom quartile of attractiveness. Analyze these data. Write a short report that summarizes the analyses and makes interpretations.

[15]K. Seal, A. Kral, J. Lorvick, A. McNees, L. Gee, & B. Edlin. (2003). A randomized controlled trial of monetary incentives vs. outreach to enhance adherence to the hepatitis B vaccine series among injection drug users. *Drug and Alcohol Dependence* 71(2):127–131.

Attractiveness	No. Dates, Men			No. Dates, Women		
	Mean	**StdDev**	**n**	**Mean**	**StdDev**	**n**
More	9.7	10.0	35	17.8	14.2	33
Less	9.9	12.6	36	10.4	16.6	27

10.112 Pay discrimination against women? A *Time Magazine* article titled "Wal-Mart's Gender Gap" (July 5, 2004) stated that in 2001 women managers at Wal-Mart earned $14,500 less than their male counterparts.

a. If these data are based on a random sample of managers at Wal-Mart, what more would you need to know about the sample to determine whether this is a "statistically significant" difference?

b. If these data referred to *all* the managers at Wal-Mart and if you can get the information specified in part a, is it relevant to conduct a significance test? Explain.

10.113 Mean of permutation distribution Refer to Example 11, which compared two doses of a medication in terms of the number of symptom-free days, using a permutation approach. Table 10.7 and Figure 10.12 showed the sampling distribution of the difference in sample means between the two doses. If truly the population distribution of the number of symptom-free days is identical for both doses (the null hypothesis), what value would you expect for the center of the sampling distribution of $\bar{x}_1 - \bar{x}_2$? Find the mean of the sampling distribution given in Table 10.7. (*Hint:* Recall the formula for the mean of a discrete probability distribution from Chapter 6.)

10.114 Treating math anxiety Two new programs were recently proposed at the University of Florida for treating students who suffer from math anxiety. Program A provides counseling sessions, one session a week for six weeks. Program B supplements the counseling sessions with short quizzes that are designed to improve student confidence. For ten students suffering from math anxiety, five were randomly assigned to each program. Before and after the program, math anxiety was measured by a questionnaire with 20 questions relating to different aspects of taking a math course that could cause anxiety. The study measured, for each student, the drop in the number of items that caused anxiety. The sample values were

Program A: 0, 4, 4, 6, 6

Program B: 6, 12, 12, 14, 16

Using an appropriate app or other software, analyze these data. Write a report, including appropriate graphs, summarizing the analyses and interpretations.

10.115 Obesity and earnings An AP story (April 9, 2005) with the headline "Study: Attractive People Make More" stated that "A study concerning weight showed that women who were obese earned 17 percent lower wages than women of average weight."

a. Identify the two variables stated to have an association.

b. Identify a control variable that might explain part or all of this association. If you had the original data including data on that control variable, how could you check whether the control variable does explain the association?

Multiple Choice or True/False

10.116 Alcoholism and gender Suppose that a 99% confidence interval for the difference $p_1 - p_2$ between the proportions of men and women in California who are alcoholics equals (0.02, 0.09). Choose the best correct choice.

a. We are 99% confident that the proportion of alcoholics is between 0.02 and 0.09.

b. We are 99% confident that the proportion of men in California who are alcoholics is between 0.02 and 0.09 larger than the proportion of women in California who are.

c. We can conclude that the population proportions may be equal.

d. We are 99% confident that a minority of California residents are alcoholics.

e. Since the confidence interval does not contain 0, it is impossible that $p_1 - p_2$.

10.117 Comparing mean incomes A study compares the population mean annual incomes for Hispanics (μ_1) and for Whites (μ_2) having jobs in construction, using a 95% confidence interval for $\mu_1 - \mu_2$. Choose the best correct choice.

a. If the confidence interval is $(-6,000, -3,000)$, then at this confidence level we conclude that the mean income for Whites is less than for Hispanics.

b. If the confidence interval is $(-3,000, 1,000)$, then the test of $H_0: \mu_1 = \mu_2$ against $H_a: \mu_1 \neq \mu_2$ with significance level 0.05 rejects H_0.

c. If the confidence interval is $(-3,000, 1,000)$, then we can conclude that $\mu_1 = \mu_2$.

d. If the confidence interval is $(-3,000, 1,000)$, then we are 95% confident that the population mean annual income for Hispanics is between 3,000 less and 1,000 more than the population mean annual income for Whites.

10.118 Sample size and significance If the sample proportions in Example 4 comparing cancer death rates for aspirin and placebo had sample sizes of only 1,000 each, rather than about 11,000 each, then the 95% confidence interval for $(p_1 - p_2)$ would be $(-0.007, 0.021)$ rather than $(0.003, 0.011)$. This reflects that

a. When an effect is small, it may take very large samples to have much power for establishing statistical significance.

b. Smaller sample sizes are preferable because there is more of a chance of capturing 0 in a confidence interval.

c. Confidence intervals get wider when sample sizes get larger.

d. The confidence interval based on small sample sizes must be in error because it is impossible for the parameter to take a negative value.

10.119 True or false: Positive values in CI If a 95% confidence interval for $(\mu_1 - \mu_2)$ contains only positive numbers, then we can conclude that both μ_1 and μ_2 are positive.

10.120 True or false: Afford food? A 2013 survey by the Pew Research Center asked whether there have been times in the past year the respondent has been unable to afford food. Of advanced economies, the country with the second highest response was the United States, 24%. Worldwide, the highest response was in Uganda, 70%. Because the same question was asked in both countries, the samples are dependent.

10.121 True or false: Control for clinic Suppose there is a higher percentage of successes with Treatment A than with Treatment B at a clinic in Rochester, and there is a higher percentage of successes with Treatment A than with Treatment B at a clinic in Syracuse. For the overall sample (combining results for the two cities), there must be a higher percentage of successes with Treatment A than with Treatment B.

Advanced Exercises

10.122 Guessing on a test A test consists of 100 true-false questions. Joe did not study, and on each question he randomly guesses the correct response. Jane studied a little and has a 0.60 chance of a correct response for each question.

a. Approximate the probability that Jane's score is nonetheless lower that Joe's. (*Hint:* Use the sampling distribution of the difference of sample proportions.)

b. Intuitively, do you think that the probability answer to part a would decrease or increase if the test had only 50 questions? Explain.

10.123 Standard error of difference From the box formula for the standard error at the end of Section 10.1,

$$se(\text{estimate 1} - \text{estimate 2}) = \sqrt{[se(\text{estimate 1})]^2 + [se(\text{estimate 2})]^2},$$

if you know the *se* for each of two independent estimates, you can find the *se* of their difference. This is useful because often articles report an *se* for each sample mean or proportion, but not the *se* or a confidence interval for their difference. Many medical studies have used a large sample of subjects from Framingham, Massachusetts, who have been followed since 1948. A study (*Annual of Internal Medicine*, (2003), vol. 138, pp. 24–32) estimated the number of years of life lost by being obese and a smoker. For females of age 40, adjusting for other factors, the number of years of life left were estimated to have a mean of 46.3 (*se* = 0.6) for nonsmokers of normal weight and a mean of 33.0 (*se* = 1.8) for smokers who were obese. Construct a 95% confidence interval for the population mean number of years lost. Interpret.

10.124 Gap between rich and poor: $\sqrt{2/n}$ margin

a. For comparisons of groups in which $n_1 = n_2$, with common value denoted by n, use the fact that the largest possible value of $\hat{p}(1 - \hat{p})$ occurs at $\hat{p} = 0.5$ to show that the margin of error for a large-sample 95% confidence interval for $(p_1 - p_2)$ can be no greater than $2\sqrt{0.5/n} = \sqrt{2/n}$.

b. A 2014 survey by the Pew Research Center reported that the percentage of people who think the gap between the rich and the poor is a very big problem in their country is 46% in the United States, 47% in the U.K., 39% in Germany, 74% in Turkey, and 72% in Argentina. Assuming that each country had a random sample of 1,000 people, use the $\sqrt{2/n}$ bound to identify any pairs of countries for which the true percentages might not be different.

10.125 Small-sample CI The small-sample confidence interval for comparing two proportions is a simple adjustment of the large-sample one. Recall that for a small-sample confidence interval for a single proportion, we used the ordinary formula after adding four observations, two of each type (see the end of Section 8.2). In the two-sample case we also add four observations, two of each type, and then use the ordinary formula by adding one observation of each type to each sample.[16] The *Compare Two Proportions* app finds this interval; select "Agresti-Caffo" under Type of Confidence Interval under Options. When the proportions are near 0 or near 1, results are more sensible than with the ordinary formula. Suppose there are no successes in either group, with $n_1 = n_2 = 10$.

a. With the ordinary formula, show that (i) $\hat{p}_1 = \hat{p}_2 = 0$, (ii) *se* = 0, and (iii) the 95% confidence interval for $p_1 - p_2$ is 0 ± 0, or $(0, 0)$. Obviously, it is too optimistic to predict that the true difference is exactly equal to 0. (And we didn't have 5 successes or 5 failures in each group.)

b. Find the 95% confidence interval, using the small-sample method described here. Are the results more plausible?

10.126 Symmetry of permutation distribution Refer to Example 12, which compared two groups of seven dogs each in terms of their time interacting with their owners. Figure 10.13 showed the permutation distribution of 10,000 random permutations, but for these data you can also get the permutation distribution considering all possible permutations. Access the *Permutation Test* app and obtain the permutation distribution using all possible permutations (there is an option for this). When $n_1 = n_2$, as here, explain why the permutation distribution based on all possible permutations is symmetric. (*Hint:* Consider a particular permutation for which you compute the difference in sample means. How does this difference change when all dogs that were in Group 1 are switched to Group 2 and vice versa?)

10.127 Null standard error for matched pairs Under the null hypothesis $H_0: p_1 = p_2$ of equal population proportions, the standard error for the difference in the two sample proportions mentioned toward the end of Section 10.4 reduces to $se_0 = \sqrt{(b + c)/n^2}$, where b and c are the off-diagonal elements and n is the number of subjects.

a. Show that the null standard error se_0 equals 0.010 for the contingency table in Table 10.11.

b. Compute the value of the test statistic
$$z = \frac{\text{estimate} - \text{null value}}{se_0} = \frac{(\hat{p}_1 - \hat{p}_2) - 0}{se_0}$$
and verify that it equals $\frac{b - c}{\sqrt{b + c}}$, the formula of McNemar's test statistic for comparing proportions for two dependent samples.

---

[16]This is a new method. It was first proposed by A. Agresti and B. Caffo in the journal *The American Statistician*, (2000), vol. 54, pp. 280–288.

10.128 Graphing Simpson's paradox The figure illustrates Simpson's paradox for Example 18 on the death penalty. For each defendant's race, the figure plots the percentage receiving the death penalty. Each percentage is labeled by a letter symbol giving the category of the victim's race. Surrounding each observation is a circle of an area representing the number of observations on which that percentage is based. For instance, the W in the largest circle represents a percentage of 12.6 receiving the death penalty for cases with White defendants and White victims. That circle is largest because the number of cases at that combination (151) is largest. When we add results across victim's race to get a summary result ignoring that variable, the largest circles, having the greater number of cases, have greater influence. Thus, the summary percentages for each defendant's race, marked on the figure by an ×, fall closer to the center of the larger circles than to the center of the smaller circles.

Percentage receiving death penalty by defendant's race, controlling victim's race (labels in center of circles) and ignoring victim's race (overall values marked by × for White defendants and Black defendants).

a. Explain why a comparison of a pair of circles having the same letter in the middle indicates that the death penalty was more likely for Black defendants, when we control for victim's race.

b. Explain why a comparison of the × marks shows that overall the death penalty was more likely for White defendants than Black defendants.

c. For White defendants, why is the overall percentage who got the death penalty so close to the percentage for the case with White victims?

Student Activities

10.129 Reading the medical literature Refer to Activity 3, which follows, about reading an article in a medical journal. Your instructor will pick a recent article at the website for the *British Medical Journal.* Prepare a short report in which you summarize the main conclusions of the article and explain how those conclusions depended on statistical analyses. After you have done this, your entire class will discuss this article and the statistical analyses.

▶ **Activity 3**

Interpreting Statistics in a Medical Journal

Medical research makes frequent use of statistical methods shown in this chapter. At *British Medical Journal (BMJ)* bmj.com on the Internet, pull up the April 19, 2003, issue. Browse through the article titled "Behavioural counseling to increase consumption of fruit and vegetables in low income adults: randomized trial" by A. Steptoe et al. You will see a variety of statistical analyses used. See whether you can answer these questions:

■ What was the objective of the study?
■ Was the study experimental or observational? Summarize the design and the subjects used in the study.
■ Identify response and explanatory variables.
■ According to Table 2 in the article, the 135 subjects in the nutrition counseling group had a baseline mean of 3.67 and standard deviation of 2.00 for the number of portions per day they ate of fruits and vegetables. Over the 12 months of the study, the mean increased by 0.99. Report the 95% confidence interval for the change in the mean and interpret. Report the corresponding results for the behavioral counseling group. Were the groups in this analysis independent or dependent samples?

■ Adjusted for confounding variables, the difference between the change in the mean for the behavioral counseling group and the nutrition counseling group was 0.62. Report and interpret the 95% confidence interval for the true difference and report the P-value for testing that the difference was 0. Were the groups in this analysis independent or dependent samples?

■ According to Table 2, at the baseline for the nutrition counseling group, the proportion of subjects who ate at least five portions a day of fruits and vegetables was 0.267, and this increased by 0.287 over the 12 months. Report and interpret the 95% confidence interval for the change in the true proportion. Was this analysis for independent or dependent samples? Was this change in the proportion significantly larger, or smaller, than the change for the behavioral counseling group?

■ What were the primary conclusions of the study?
■ Describe two limitations of the study, as explained in the sections titled "Representativeness of the sample" and "Limitations of the study."

Extended Statistical Methods and Models for Analyzing Categorical and Quantitative Variables

Chapter 3 presented graphs and numerical summaries for categorical data, and Chapter 10 discussed inferential methods for comparing two proportions. This chapter extends these ideas to comparing more than two groups on a categorical response variable with two or more categories. In summary, this chapter provides methods for analyzing data summarized in contingency tables.

Categorical Data Analysis

Example 1

Happiness

Picture the Scenario

What contributes to your overall happiness? Is it love? Your health? Your friendships? The amount of money you make?

To investigate which variables are associated with happiness, we can use data from the General Social Survey (GSS). In each survey, the GSS asks, "Taken all together, would you say that you are very happy, pretty happy, or not too happy?" Table 11.1 uses the 2012 survey (results from 2018 are similar) to cross-tabulate happiness with family income, measured here as the response to the question, "Compared with American families in general, would you say that your family income is below average, average, or above average?"

Questions to Explore

- How can you determine if there is an association between happiness and family income in the population of all adult Americans?

- If there is an association, what is its nature? For example, are people with above-average family income happier than people with below-average family income?

- Can you think of a variable that might have a stronger association with happiness than family income?

Table 11.1 Happiness and Family Income, from 2012 General Social Survey

Income	Happiness			Total
	Not Too Happy	Pretty Happy	Very Happy	
Above Average	29	178	135	**342**
Average	83	494	277	**854**
Below Average	104	314	119	**537**
Total	**216**	**986**	**531**	**1,733**

Thinking Ahead

Both variables in Table 11.1 are categorical. The focus of this chapter is learning how to describe associations between categorical variables to answer questions such as, "Do people with higher family incomes tend to be happier?" and "Are married people happier than unmarried people?" Using our standard tools of statistical inference, we'll analyze Table 11.1 in Examples 3 and 4 and other data on happiness in various exercises.

Association Between Variables

Let's recap where we are at this stage of our study. Chapter 7 introduced the fundamental concept of a *sampling distribution.* Chapter 8 showed how the sampling distribution is the basis of estimation, using *confidence intervals,* and Chapter 9 showed how it is the basis of *significance testing.* Those chapters focused on inference for a single proportion or a single mean.

Chapter 10 introduced methods for comparing two means (when the response was quantitative) or two proportions (when the response was binary). This chapter presents methods for investigating, more generally, the association between two categorical variables. We'll explore what we mean by an association or lack of association in the context of contingency tables such as Table 11.1. The association between two quantitative variables is explored in Chapter 12.

Recall

In the Chapter 3 introduction, we stated that two variables have an **association** if particular values for one variable are more likely to occur with certain values of the other variable—for example, it being very happy is more likely to happen if a person has an above average income. Section 3.1 introduced the analysis of association for categorical variables. ◄

11.1 Independence and Dependence (Association)

First, let's identify the response variable and the explanatory variable. The goal for collecting the data in Table 11.1 was to study how happiness depends on income and not how income depends on happiness. Therefore, we'll treat happiness as the response variable and income as the explanatory variable.

Comparing Percentages

Table 11.1 is easier to digest if we convert the frequencies to percentages for the response categories. Within each category of income, Table 11.2 shows the percentages for the three categories of happiness. For example, of the 342 subjects who reported their family income as above average, 135 identified themselves as very happy. This is a proportion of $135/342 = 0.395$, or 39%. By contrast, 119 out of the 537 below-average income subjects said they were very happy, a percentage of only 22%. The row totals in Table 11.1 are the basis of these percentage calculations. Within each row, apart from rounding errors, the percentages sum to 100%.

Table 11.2 Conditional Percentages for Happiness Categories, Given Each Category of Family Income

The percentages are computed by dividing the counts in Table 11.1 by their row totals and then multiplying by 100. If a particular row doesn't sum to 100%, it is due to rounding errors.

| Income | Happiness | | | |
	Not Too Happy	Pretty Happy	Very Happy	Total
Above Average	8%	52%	39%	**342 (100%)**
Average	10%	58%	32%	**854 (100%)**
Below Average	19%	58%	22%	**537 (100%)**

Recall

Section 3.1 introduced **conditional proportions**, which are proportions for the categories of a categorical response variable that are calculated **conditional** upon (i.e., "given") the value of another variable. ◄

The percentages in a particular row are called **conditional percentages**. They refer to the distribution of happiness, *conditional* on the category for family income. This distribution is called the **conditional distribution** for happiness, given a particular income level. For those who reported above-average family income, the conditional distribution of happiness is the set of percentages (8%, 52%, 39%) for the responses (not too happy, pretty happy, very happy). These percentages are the estimated **conditional probabilities** of happiness, given above-average family income. For instance, given that a subject reported above-average family income, the estimated probability of being very happy is 39%.

Let's compare the happiness percentages for the subjects who reported above-average income to those who reported below-average income. From Table 11.2, subjects with above average income were less likely to be not too happy (8% vs. 19%), less likely to be pretty happy (52% vs. 58%), but more likely to be very happy (38% vs. 22%). Figure 11.1 uses side-by-side bar graphs to portray the three conditional distributions, one for each income category. You can replicate this Figure using the second tab of the *Explore Categorical Data* app.

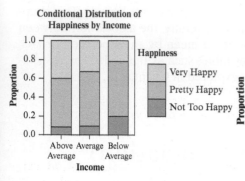

Stacked version of bar plot in Figure 11.1.

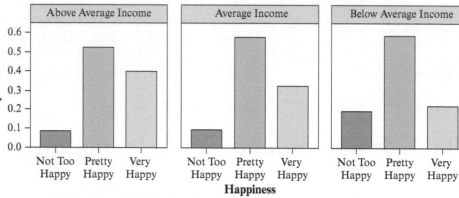

▲ **Figure 11.1** Bar Graph of Conditional Distributions of Happiness, Given Income, from Table 11.2. Each box shows the conditional distribution of happiness for that income category. You can compare how the proportion in a given happiness category (e.g., not too happy) changes across the income categories. **Question** Based on this graph, how would you say that happiness depends on income?

We'll use the following guidelines when constructing tables that show conditional distributions based on a sample:

■ Make the response variable the column variable. The response categories are shown across the top of the table.

■ Compute conditional proportions for the response variable within each row by dividing each cell frequency by the row total. Those proportions multiplied by 100 are the conditional percentages.

■ Include the total sample sizes on which the percentages are based. That way, readers who want to can reconstruct the cell counts.

Independence Versus Dependence (Association)

Table 11.2 showed conditional distributions for a sample. We'll use these sample conditional distributions to make inferences about the corresponding population conditional distributions.

For instance, to investigate how happiness compares for females and males, we'd make inferences about the population conditional distributions of happiness for females and for males. Suppose that those population distributions are as shown in Table 11.3 on the next page. (In fact, the percentages in Table 11.3 are consistent with actual data from the 2012 GSS. See Exercise 11.4.) We see that the percentage classified as not too happy is the same for females and males, 14%. Similarly, the percentage classified as pretty happy (56%) and the percentage classified as very happy (30%) are the same for females and males. The probability that a person randomly selected from the population is classified in a particular happiness category is the same for females and males, i.e., it does not depend on gender. If this is the case, the categorical variables happiness and gender are said to be **independent**.

Table 11.3 Population Conditional Distributions Showing Independence

The conditional distribution of happiness is the same for each gender, namely (14%, 56%, 30%).

	Happiness			
Gender	**Not Too Happy**	**Pretty Happy**	**Very Happy**	**Total**
Female	14%	56%	30%	**100%**
Male	14%	56%	30%	**100%**
Overall	**14%**	**56%**	**30%**	**100%**

Source: Data from CSM, UC Berkeley

In Words

Happiness and gender are **independent** if (as in Table 11.3) the probability of a particular response on happiness is the same for each gender.

Independence and Dependence (Association)

Two categorical variables are **independent** if the population conditional distributions for one variable are identical across all categories of the other variable. The variables are **dependent** (or **associated**) if the conditional distributions are not identical.

For two variables to be independent, the population percentage in any category of one variable is the same for all categories of the other variable, as in Table 11.3. Figure 11.2 portrays this graphically for the conditional distributions in Table 11.3. Note how the graph for females is identical to the one for males.

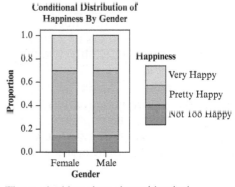

The stacked bar chart shows identical distributions of happiness for females and males, i.e., independence.

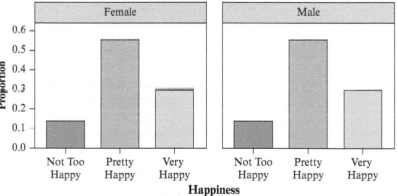

▲ **Figure 11.2** Bar Graph of Population Conditional Distributions Showing Independence. **Question** What feature of the bar graph reflects the independence?

Recall

Section 5.3 in Chapter 5 defined A and B to be **independent events** if

$$P(A \mid B) = P(A).$$

Chapter 10 used **independent samples** to mean that observations in one sample are independent of those in the other sample. ◄

This definition extends independence of **events** to independence of **variables**. Recall that two *events* A and B are independent if P(A) is the same as the conditional probability of A, given B, denoted by P(A | B). When two *variables* are independent, any event about one variable is independent of any event about the other variable. In Table 11.3, let A be an event about happiness and B an event about gender. For example, if A = very happy and B = female, then P(A | B) = 0.30. Notice in Table 11.3 that P(A) is also 0.30, so P(A | B) = P(A).

Example 2

Belief in Life After Death and Race

Picture the Scenario

Table 11.4 cross-tabulates belief in life after death with race, using data from the 2012 GSS. The table also shows sample conditional distributions for life after death, given race, and the overall percentages for the life after death categories. The side-by-side bar graph in the margin shows the distributions graphically.

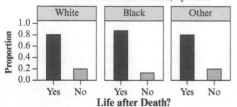

Conditional Distribution of Belief in Life After Death, by Race

Table 11.4 Sample Conditional Distributions for Belief in Life After Death, Given Race.

Race	Postlife		Total
	Yes	**No**	
White	1,043 (79.7%)	266 (20.3%)	**1,309 (100%)**
Black	241 (86.7%)	37 (13.3%)	**278 (100%)**
Other	143 (79.4%)	37 (20.6%)	**180 (100%)**
Overall	**1,427 (80.8%)**	**340 (19.2%)**	**1,767 (100%)**

Source: Data from CSM, UC Berkeley

Question to Explore

Are race and belief in life after death independent or dependent?

Think It Through

The three conditional distributions in Table 11.4 (one in each row) are similar but not exactly identical. So it is tempting to conclude that the variables are dependent. For example, if event A denotes a "yes" for belief in life after death, we estimate $P(A|\text{White}) = 1,043/1,309 = 0.797$, $P(A|\text{Black}) = 0.867$ and $P(A|\text{other}) = 0.794$, similar, but not identical. Overall, we estimate that $P(A) = 1,427/1,767 = 0.808$. However, the definition of independence between variables refers to the *population*. Since Table 11.4 refers to a *sample* rather than a population, it provides evidence but does not definitively tell us whether these variables are independent or dependent.

Even if the variables *were* independent, we would not expect the *sample* conditional distributions to be identical. Because of sampling variability, each sample percentage typically differs somewhat from the true population percentage. We would expect to observe *some* differences between sample conditional distributions such as we see in Table 11.4 even if *no* differences exist in the population.

Insight

If the observations in Table 11.4 were the entire population, the variables would be dependent. But the association would not necessarily be practically important, because the percentages are similar from one category to another of race. The next section presents a significance test of the null hypothesis that the variables are independent against the alternative hypothesis that they are associated.

▶ *Try Exercise 11.2*

11.1 Practicing the Basics

11.1 **Gender gap in politics?** In the United States, is there
a gender gap in political beliefs? That is, do women and
men tend to differ in their political thinking and voting
behavior? The table taken from the 2018 GSS relates gender and political party identification. Subjects indicated
whether they identified more strongly with the Democratic
or Republican party or as Independents. (You can enter
the data below in the second tab of the *Explore Categorical
Variables* app to answer most of the following questions.)

	Political Party Identification			
Gender	Democrat	Independent	Republican	Total
Female	439	525	275	1,239
Male	292	455	252	999

Source: Data from CSM, UC Berkeley

a. Identify the response variable and the explanatory variable.

b. Construct a table that shows the conditional distributions of the response variable. Interpret.

c. Give an example of what the population conditional
distributions would look like if gender and party identification were independent. For the example, try to
choose conditional percentages that are consistent with
the results of the 2018 GSS.

d. Sketch bar graphs to portray the distributions in part b
and in part c.

11.2 **Beliefs of college freshmen** Over many years, a large-
scale poll of college freshmen conducted by the Higher
Education Research Institute at UCLA asks their opinions about a variety of issues. In 2004, although women
were more likely to rate their time management skills as
"above average," they were also twice as likely as men to
indicate that they frequently feel overwhelmed by all they
have to do (36.4% versus 16.3%).

a. If results for the population of college freshmen were
similar to these, would gender and feelings of being
overwhelmed be independent or dependent?

b. Give an example of what the population conditional
distributions would look like if these variables were
independent.

11.3 **Williams College admission** Data from 2013 posted on
the Williams College website shows that of all 3,195 males
applying, 18.2% were admitted, and of all 3,658 females
applying, 16.9% were admitted. Let X denote gender of
applicant and Y denote whether admitted.

a. Which conditional distributions do these percentages
refer to, those of Y at given categories of X, or those of
X at given categories of Y? Set up a table showing the
two conditional distributions.

b. Are X and Y independent or dependent? Explain.
(*Hint:* These percentages refer to the population of all
applicants in 2013.)

11.4 **Happiness and gender** The contingency table shown relates happiness and gender for the 2018 GSS. (You can enter
the counts from the table in the second tab of the *Explore*

Categorical Variables app to answer most of the following
questions.)

	Happiness			
Gender	Not Too Happy	Pretty Happy	Very Happy	Total
Female	180	724	390	**1,294**
Male	156	583	311	**1,050**

Source: Data from CSM, UC Berkeley

a. Identify the response variable and the explanatory variable.

b. Construct a table or graph showing the conditional distributions. Interpret.

c. Give an example of what the population conditional
distributions would look like if gender and happiness
were independent. For the example, try to choose conditional percentages that are consistent with the results
of the 2018 GSS.

11.5 **Marital happiness and income** In the GSS, subjects who
were married were asked about the happiness of their
marriage, the variable coded as HAPMAR.

a. Go to the GSS website sda.berkeley.edu, click on
Archive near the center top, then scroll down to access
the GSS Cumulative Data file, or simply follow the
link to the GSS from the book's website. Construct
a contingency table for 2012 relating family income
(measured as in Table 11.1) to marital happiness:
Enter FINRELA(r:4;3;2) as the row variable (where
4 = "above average," 3 = "average," and 2 = "below
average") and HAPMAR(r:3;2;1) as the column variable (3 = not too, 2 = pretty, and 1 = very happy).
As the selection filter, enter YEAR(2012). Under
Output Options, put a check in the row box (instead of
in the column box) for the Percentaging option and put
a check in the Summary Statistics box further below.
Click on Run the Table.

b. Construct a table or graph that shows the conditional
distributions of marital happiness, given family income.
How would you describe the association?

c. Compare the conditional distributions to those in
Table 11.2. For a given family income, what tends to
be higher, general happiness or marital happiness for
those who are married? Explain.

11.6 **What is independent of happiness?** Which one of the
following variables would you think most likely to be independent of happiness: belief in an afterlife, family income,
quality of health, region of the country in which you live,
satisfaction with job? Explain the basis of your reasoning.

11.7 **Sample evidence about independence** Refer to the previous
exercise. Go to the GSS website and construct a table relating
happiness (HAPPY) to the variable you chose (AFTERLIF,
FINRELA, HEALTH, REGION, or JOBSAT). Enter
YEAR(2018) in the selection filter for all but JOBSAT, for
which you can enter YEAR(2016) to narrow the results to
that year. Inspect the conditional distributions and indicate
whether independence seems plausible, with the sample conditional distributions all being quite similar.

11.2 Testing Categorical Variables for Independence

How can we judge whether two categorical variables are independent or dependent? The definition of independence refers to the *population*. Could any association observed in the *sample* just be due to sampling variation? Or is the observed association unusual if the variables were truly independent?

A significance test can answer these questions. The hypotheses for the test are

H_0: The two variables are independent.

H_a: The two variables are dependent (associated).

The test assumes randomization and a large sample size. The general idea behind the test is to compare the observed cell counts in the contingency table with counts we would expect to see if the null hypothesis of independence were true.

Expected Cell Counts If the Variables Are Independent

If the two categorical variables were independent, what count would we expect to see in a particular cell when we take many random samples of the same size? Such a count is referred to as an **expected cell count** and computed under the presumption that H_0 is true.

Table 11.5 shows the observed cell counts from Table 11.1, with the expected cell counts below them. How did we find the expected cell counts? Recall that when two variables are independent, any event about one variable is independent of any event about the other variable. Consider the events A = not too happy and B = above-average income. Using the row and column totals of the contingency table (Table 11.5 below), we estimate P(A) as 216/1,733 = 12.5% and P(B) as 342/1,733 = 19.7%. The event A and B (not too happy *and* above-average income) corresponds to the first cell in the table, with cell count of 29. Usually, we would estimate the probability of this event as 29/1,733 = 1.7%, but if we presume events A and B to be independent, we can use the probability rule for independent events,

$$P(A \text{ and } B) = P(A) \times P(B),$$

Recall

From Section 5.2, two events A and B are **independent** if

$$P(A \text{ and } B) = P(A) \times P(B). \blacktriangleleft$$

to estimate P(A and B). That is, P(A and B) is estimated as $(216/1{,}733) \times (342/1{,}733) = 2.46\%$. Under independence, we would expect 2.46% of the $n = 1{,}733$ subjects included in the survey to fall in this cell. Because 2.46% of 1,733 subjects equals 42.6 subjects, we call 42.6 the **expected cell count** for that first cell.

Table 11.5 Happiness by Family Income, Showing Observed and Expected Cell Counts

We use the highlighted totals to get the expected count of $42.6 = (216 \times 342)/1{,}733$ in the first cell.

Income	Happiness			
	Not Too Happy	**Pretty Happy**	**Very Happy**	**Total**
Above Average	29	178	135	**342**
	42.6	194.6	104.8	
Average	83	494	277	**854**
	106.4	485.9	261.7	
Below Average	104	314	119	**537**
	66.9	305.5	164.5	
Total	**216 (12.5%)**	**986 (56.9%)**	**531 (30.6%)**	**1,733 (100%)**

To recap, we estimate the expected cell count under independence (i.e., presuming H_0 to be true) by

$$1,733\left(\frac{216}{1,733}\right)\left(\frac{342}{1,733}\right) = \frac{216 \times 342}{1,733} = 42.6.$$

Since the observed cell count of 29 is lower than the expected cell count of 42.6, fewer people had above-average income and were not too happy compared to what we would expect if the two variables were independent.

The equation above illustrates the general rule for finding expected cell counts:

Expected Cell Count

For a particular cell, the **expected cell count** under independence equals

$$\text{Expected cell count} = \frac{(\text{Row total}) \times (\text{Column total})}{\text{Total sample size}}.$$

	Happiness			
Income	**Not Too**	**Pretty**	**Very**	**Total**
Above Average	29	178	135	**342**
Average	83	494	277	**854**
Below Average	104	314	119	**537**
Total	**216**	**986**	**531**	**1,733**

As we have seen, the first cell in Table 11.5 has expected cell count = $(216 \times 342)/1,733 = 42.6$, the product of the row total (342) for that cell by the column total (216) for that cell, divided by the overall sample size (1,733).

Let's see an alternative argument why this rule makes sense. For A = not too happy, we estimated $P(A)$ by $216/1,733 = 0.125$ or 12.5%. If the variables were independent, this probability is the same for any income level. For instance, for B = above-average income, we expect $P(A|B) = P(A)$. Thus, 12.5% of the 342 who report above average income should be classified in the not too happy category. The expected cell count is then $0.125(342) = (216/1,733)(342) = 42.6$, which is the column total of 216 times the row total of 342 divided by the overall sample size of 1,733.

Table 11.5 shows that for the overall sample, the percentages in the three happiness categories are 12.5%, 56.9%, and 30.6%. You can check that when you form the conditional percentages for each row using the expected cell counts, you also get exactly these percentages in each of the three rows. For instance, for the first row, $42.6/342 = 0.125$, $194.6/342 = 0.569$ and $104.8/342 = 0.306$. In fact, the expected cell counts are values that have the same row and column totals as the observed counts, but for which the conditional distributions are identical.

Chi-Squared Test Statistic

The test statistic for the test of independence measures how close the observed cell counts fall to the expected cell counts. Symbolized by X^2, it is called the **chi-squared statistic**, taking the name of its (approximate) sampling distribution. It is the oldest test statistic in use today. Introduced by the British statistician Karl Pearson in 1900, it is sometimes also called Pearson's chi-squared statistic.

In Words

The Greek letter chi is written as χ and pronounced "ki" (k + eye). Later in this section, we'll see that chi-squared (χ^2) is the name of the approximate sampling distribution of the statistic denoted here by X^2. The Roman letter denotes the statistic, and the Greek letter denotes the sampling distribution.

Chi-Squared Statistic

The **chi-squared statistic** is an overall measure of how far the observed cell counts in a contingency table fall from the expected cell counts computed under the presumption of independence. Its formula is

$$X^2 = \Sigma \frac{(\text{observed count} - \text{expected count})^2}{\text{expected count}}.$$

For each cell, square the difference between the observed count and expected count and then divide that square by the expected count. After calculating this term for every cell, sum the terms over all cells to obtain X^2.

If the null hypothesis of independence is true, the observed and expected cell counts should be similar in each cell. Then each part in the sum of the chi-squared statistic is small, leading to an overall X^2 value that is relatively small. If, however, the null hypothesis is false, there are some cells for which the observed and expected cell counts are quite different. For a cell where this happens, the value of $\left[\dfrac{(\text{observed count} - \text{expected count})^2}{\text{expected count}}\right]$ will be large. This and other cells where this happens make a sizable contribution to the overall sum, resulting in a value for X^2 that is relatively large.

Example 3

Chi-Squared Statistic ◄

Happiness and Family Income

Picture the Scenario

Table 11.5 showed the observed and expected cell counts for the data on family income and happiness. You can obtain the expected cell counts via the *Chi-Squared Test* app, which also provides the X^2 statistic, as the screenshot in Figure 11.3 shows.

Questions to Explore

a. State the null and alternative hypotheses for this test in context.

b. Report the X^2 statistic and explain how it was calculated.

▶ **Figure 11.3** Expected Cell Counts and the Chi-Squared Statistic. Screenshot from the *Chi-Squared Test* app. The app provides the X^2 statistic and corresponding P-value for the test of independence. Various options in the app provide expected cell counts (shown here) or the conditional distributions.

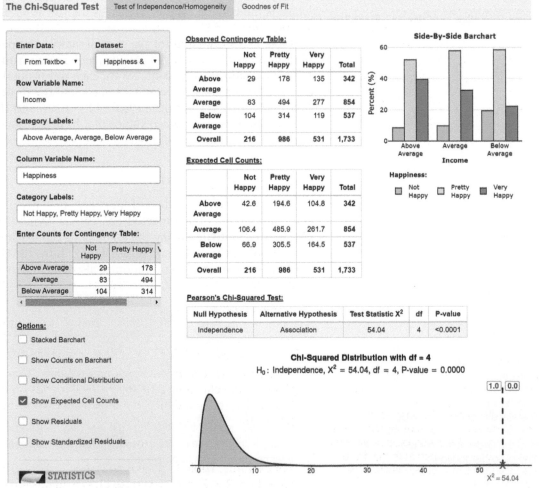

Think It Through

a. The hypotheses for the chi-squared test are

H_0: Happiness and family income are independent.

H_a: Happiness and family income are dependent (associated).

The alternative hypothesis implies that there's an association between happiness and family income.

b. Finding X^2 involves a fair amount of computation, and it's best to let software do the work for us. The app reports a chi-squared statistic of $X^2 = 54.04$. For each cell, it took the difference between the observed and expected cell count, squared that difference, and then divided the result by the expected cell count. Here is the entire computation written out, going over all nine cells of the contingency table:

$$X^2 = \frac{(29 - 42.6)^2}{42.6} + \frac{(178 - 194.6)^2}{194.6} + \frac{(135 - 104.8)^2}{104.8}$$

$$+ \frac{(83 - 106.4)^2}{106.4} + \frac{(494 - 485.9)^2}{485.9} + \frac{(277 - 261.7)^2}{261.7}$$

$$+ \frac{(104 - 66.9)^2}{66.9} + \frac{(314 - 305.5)^2}{305.5} + \frac{(119 - 164.5)^2}{164.5}$$

$$= 4.356 + 1.413 + 8.709 + 5.163 + 0.135 + 0.898$$

$$+ 20.530 + 0.235 + 12.604$$

$$= 54.04.$$

Insight

For a few cells, the difference between the observed and expected counts are large. These cells contribute a large amount towards the overall value of 54.04 of the X^2 statistic. The larger the X^2 value, the greater the evidence against H_0: independence and in support of the alternative hypothesis that happiness and income are associated. But is 54.04 large enough to support the conclusion of an association? We next learn how to interpret the magnitude of the X^2 test statistic, so we know what is a small and what is a large value and how to find the P-value.

▶ *Try Exercise 11.8*

Did You Know?

While our app accepts data in contingency table format, other software may not. For them, first create a data file with nine rows, such as shown below, and then choose an option to create a contingency table and find appropriate statistics. ◀

Income	Happy	Count
above	not	29
above	pretty	178
above	very	135
average	not	83
average	pretty	494
average	very	277
below	not	104
below	pretty	314
below	very	119

Chi-Squared Distribution

To find the P-value for the X^2 test statistic, we use the sampling distribution of the X^2 statistic. This sampling distribution is well approximated by the **chi-squared probability distribution**. Figure 11.4 on the next page shows several chi-squared distributions.

The main properties of the chi-squared distribution are as follows:

■ **Always positive.** The chi-squared distribution falls on the positive part of the real number line. The X^2 test statistic cannot be negative since it sums squared differences divided by positive expected frequencies. The minimum possible value, $X^2 = 0$, occurs if the observed and expected counts are identical for all cells.

■ **Degrees of freedom from row and column.** Similar to the t distribution, the shape of the chi-squared distribution depends on the **degrees of freedom** (df). For testing independence in a table with r rows and c columns (called an $r \times c$ table), the formula for the degrees of freedom is

$$df = (r - 1) \times (c - 1).$$

For example, Table 11.5 has $r = 3$ rows, and $c = 3$ columns, so $df = (3 - 1) \times (3 - 1) = 2 \times 2 = 4$. (Exercise 11.84 explains the reason behind this formula.)

Caution

For the t-distribution, the degrees of freedom depend on the sample size. This is not the case for the chi-squared distribution, where the df are obtained from the number of rows and columns of the contingency table. ◀

▲ **Figure 11.4** The Chi-Squared Distribution. The curve has larger mean and standard deviation as the degrees of freedom increase. **Question** Why can't the chi-squared statistic be negative?

▶ **Activity 1**

The *Chi-Squared Distribution* app lets you explore this distribution interactively, such as using a slider to see how the shape depends on the degrees of freedom. It also allows you to find tail probabilities or percentiles. Use the app to recreate the Chi-squared distributions shown in Figure 11.4. (For the one with $df = 20$, click on the box for adjusting the slider maximum to set it to 20.) When $df = 20$, click on the box to show the normal distribution with the same mean and standard deviation. How does it compare?

- **Mean equals df, standard deviation equals $\sqrt{2df}$.** The mean (or expected value) of the chi-squared distribution equals the df value. The standard deviation of the chi-squared distribution equals $\sqrt{2df}$. Since $df = (r-1)\times(c-1)$, larger numbers of rows and columns produce larger df values. Since larger tables have more terms in the summation for the X^2 statistic, the X^2 values also tend to be larger and vary more in magnitude. Figure 11.4 shows how (i) the center of the chi-squared distribution gets larger for larger df and (ii) the variability of the chi-squared distribution gets larger for larger df.

- **As df increases, distribution approaches bell shape.** The chi-squared distribution is skewed to the right. As df increases, the skew lessens and the chi-squared curve becomes more bell shaped (see the curve for $df = 20$ in Figure 11.4).

- **Large values of X^2 provide evidence against independence.** The larger the value of the X^2 statistic, the greater the evidence against H_0: independence. Thus, the P-value equals the tail probability to the right of the observed X^2 statistic. It measures the probability that the X^2 statistic computed from a contingency table is as large or larger than the observed value if the variables are truly independent. Figure 11.5 depicts the P-value.

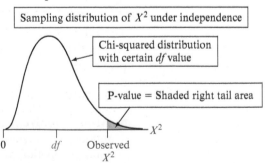

▲ **Figure 11.5** The P-value for the Chi-Squared Test of Independence. This is the right-tail probability, to the right of the observed value of the X^2 test statistic. **Question** Why do we not also use the left tail in finding the P-value?

In practice, we rely on software to find the P-value using the chi-squared distribution. For instance, the screenshot from the *Chi-Squared Test* app in Figure 11.3 shows the appropriate chi-squared distribution with $df = 4$ and marks the P-value on it. If you don't have access to technology, Table C in the back of the book lists values from the chi-squared distribution for various right-tail

Table 11.6 Rows of Table C Displaying Chi-Squared Values

The values have right-tail probabilities between 0.250 and 0.001. For a table with $r = 3$ rows and $c = 3$ columns, $df = (r - 1) \times (c - 1) = 4$, and 9.49 is the chi-squared value with a right-tail probability of 0.05.

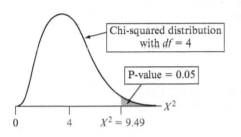

df	.250	.100	.050	.025	.010	.005	.001
1	1.32	2.71	3.84	5.02	6.63	7.88	10.83
2	2.77	4.61	5.99	7.38	9.21	10.60	13.82
3	4.11	6.25	7.81	9.35	11.34	12.84	16.27
4	5.39	7.78	9.49	11.14	13.28	14.86	18.47

Right-Tail Probability

probabilities. Table 11.6 shows an excerpt from Table C for small df values. For example, a 3×3 table has $df = 4$, for which Table 11.6 reports that an X^2 value of 9.49 has P-value $= 0.05$.

Example 4

◀ Chi-Squared Distribution

Happiness and Income

Picture the Scenario

For testing the null hypothesis of independence of happiness and family income, we found in Example 3 a test statistic value of $X^2 = 54.04$.

Questions to Explore

a. What is the P-value for the chi-squared test of independence for these data?

b. State your decision for a significance level of 0.05 and interpret in context.

Think It Through

a. Since the table has $r = 3$ rows and $c = 3$ columns, $df = (r - 1) \times (c - 1) = 4$. The screenshot from the *Chi-Squared Test* app in Figure 11.3 shows the chi-squared distribution with $df = 4$ and marks the observed value of 54.04 as extremely far out in the right tail. Hence, the P-value is very small, such that the app reports the P-value as <0.0001. (From Table C, you can see that the largest X^2 value reported is 18.47, corresponding to a tail area of 0.001.)

b. Since the P-value is below 0.05, we can reject H_0. Based on this sample, we have evidence for an association between happiness and family income in the population.

Insight

The extremely small P-value provides very strong evidence against H_0: independence. If the variables were independent, it would be highly unusual to observe a contingency table with a chi-squared statistic this large or larger.

The small P-value is not surprising when considering the shape of the chi-squared distribution with $df = 4$. Remember that it has mean $= df = 4$ and standard deviation $= \sqrt{2df} = 2.8$. Then, the observed value of 54.04 is many standard deviations to the right of the mean, indicating an extreme value. Note, however, that both the mean and the standard deviation of the chi-squared distribution depend on the df. So, for instance, a X^2 value of 13 is extreme when $df = 4$, but not extreme when $df = 8$.

▶ *Try Exercise 11.11, parts a to e*

The Chi-Squared Test

Presuming H_0 is true, the sampling distribution of the X^2 test statistic gets closer to the chi-squared distribution as the sample size increases. The approximation is good when each expected cell count exceeds about 5. Section 11.5 discusses the sample size issue further and presents an alternative small-sample test.

Let's summarize the steps of the chi-squared test of independence.

> **SUMMARY: The Five Steps of the Chi-Squared Test of Independence**
>
> 1. **Assumptions:**
>   Two categorical variables.
>   Randomization, such as random sampling or a randomized experiment.
>   Expected count ≥ 5 in all cells (otherwise, use small-sample test in Section 11.5).
>
> 2. **Hypotheses:**
> H_0: The two variables are independent.
> H_a: The two variables are dependent (associated).
>
> 3. **Test Statistic:**
> $$X^2 = \sum \frac{(observed\ count - expected\ count)^2}{expected\ count},$$
>   where expected count $= (\text{row total} \times \text{column total})/\text{total sample size}$.
>
> 4. **P-value:** Right-tail probability to the right of observed X^2 value, for the chi-squared distribution with $df = (r - 1) \times (c - 1)$.
>
> 5. **Conclusion:** Report P-value and interpret in context. If a decision is needed, reject H_0 when P-value $\leq$ significance level (such as 0.05).

Caution

As with any hypotheses test, failing to reject the null hypothesis doesn't mean the variables are definitely independent. All that can be said is that independence is still plausible and can't be ruled out. ◄

Did You Know?

The GSS uses a rather complex multistage random sampling design, but its characteristics are similar to simple random sampling. That's why the chi-squared test is routinely used to analyze data from the GSS. ◄

As with other inferential methods, the chi-squared test assumes randomization, such as the simple random sampling that many surveys use. For instance, the results of the chi-squared test in Example 4 are based on the assumption that the 1,733 people included in the survey are a random sample from the population. The chi-squared test is also valid with randomized experiments. In that case, subjects are randomly assigned to different treatments (or groups), and the contingency table summarizes the subjects' responses on a categorical response variable. The next example illustrates this case.

Testing Homogeneity: Comparing Several Groups on a Categorical Response

The chi-squared test **for independence** does not differentiate between a response and explanatory variable. The steps of the test and the results are identical no matter which of the two categorical variables defines the rows or columns of the contingency table. When a response variable *is* identified and the population conditional distributions are identical across the levels of the explanatory variable, they are said to be **homogeneous**. The chi-squared test for this hypothesis is then often referred to as a **test of homogeneity**.

The test of homogeneity uses the same chi-squared test statistic and procedure as the test of independence. The only differences are in the nature of the hypotheses being tested (homogeneity of conditional distributions and independence of two variables, respectively) and the study design employed for collecting data. The independence test is used when each subject provides observations on two categorical variables (e.g., family income and opinion on happiness). A test of homogeneity is used when two or more groups are compared on a single categorical response variable (e.g., comparing a sample of smokers to a sample of nonsmokers in terms of their severity of an asthma diagnosis, such as no symptoms, mild symptoms, or severe symptoms). With two groups, this is the same setup as in Chapter 10 when we compared two proportions, but now the response is not binary but categorical with possibly several categories. Such data arise when a random sample of people from each group (say smokers and nonsmokers) complete the same survey, or they arise from an experiment in which subjects are randomly assigned to different treatment groups and a categorical response is measured.

Example 5

◄ **Testing Homogeneity**

Headache from Receiving a Flu Vaccine

Picture the Scenario

Some vaccines may show side effects such as soreness, fever, or headache. In a recent clinical trial, subjects were randomized to receive either the active ingredient of a flu shot (the active group) or a harmless sugar solution injection (the placebo group). The study was double blind, meaning neither the subject nor the one giving the shot knew what type was administered. For those subjects who reported developing a headache after receiving the injection, Table 11.7 shows the counts for the severity of the headache, rated as mild, moderate, or severe. The first row shows results for subjects in the active group and the second row for subjects in the placebo group. The sample conditional distribution for each group is shown in parentheses.

Table 11.7 Severity of Headache in the Active and Placebo Group
Shown are the counts and conditional distributions (in parentheses) of those reporting a headache after receiving the shot.

Flu Shot	Severity of Headache			Total
	Mild	Moderate	Severe	
Active	486 (79%)	113 (18%)	16 (3%)	615 (100%)
Placebo	355 (81%)	80 (18%)	5 (1%)	440 (100%)
Overall	841 (80%)	193 (18%)	21 (2%)	1,055 (100%)

Questions to Explore

a. State the null and alternative hypotheses of interest.
b. Carry out the chi-squared test and interpret results.

Think It Through

a. The categorical response variable in this study is the severity of headache (with three categories), and the explanatory variable is whether a subject received the active or the placebo shot. The two groups are independent; subjects were randomly assigned to receive either the active or placebo treatment. We want to test whether the distribution of severity of headache is the same in the two groups (homogeneity) or if they differ, leading to the following hypotheses:

H_0: The conditional distribution of severity of headache is the same for patients randomized to the active or placebo group (homogeneity).
H_a: The conditional distributions differ.

b. For the homogeneity test, expected cell counts, the chi-squared statistic X^2, and its P-value are computed in exactly the same way as for the test of independence. The screenshot in Figure 11.6 from the *Chi-Squared Test* app, which has this data set implemented, shows results. All expected cells counts are pretty close to the observed ones, resulting in

$X^2 = 2.86$. Right away, this doesn't seem that large, given that the test has $df = (r-1)(c-1) = (2-1)(3-1) = 2$ and that the corresponding chi-squared distribution, pictured in the screenshot, has mean 2 and standard deviation $\sqrt{2df} = \sqrt{4} = 2$. So, 2.86 is less than one standard deviation away from 2, the value we expect to get under homogeneity. Not surprisingly, the app shows a large P-value of 0.239. We thus fail to reject the hypothesis that the distribution of severity of headache is homogeneous for the two groups. There is no evidence of a difference in the distribution of the severity of headache in the active and placebo groups for those that report a headache after receiving an injection.

Observed Contingency Table:

	Mild	Moderate	Severe	Total
Active	486	113	16	615
Placebo	355	80	5	440
Overall	841	193	21	1,055

Expected Cell Counts:

	Mild	Moderate	Severe	Total
Active	490.3	112.5	12.2	615
Placebo	350.7	80.5	8.8	440
Overall	841	193	21	1,055

Side-By-Side Barchart

Flu Shot

Severity of Headache: ☐ Mild ☐ Moderate ■ Severe

Pearson's Chi-Squared Test:

Null Hypothesis	Alternative Hypothesis	Test Statistic X^2	df	P-value
Independence	Association	2.86	2	0.2393

Chi-Squared Distribution with df = 2

H_0: Independence, $X^2 = 2.86$, df = 2, P-value = 0.2393

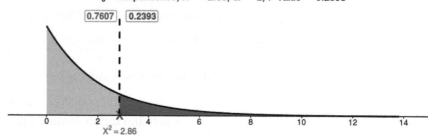

▲ **Figure 11.6 Test of Homogeneity.** Screenshot from the *Chi-Squared Test* app. The app shows results for the test of homogeneity for the distribution of severity of headache between those in the active and placebo groups.

Insight

Whether you use a test of independence or homogeneity depends on the sampling design. If your sample consists of a single sample with two categorical observations on each subject, then you test whether these two variables are independent or associated. When you have a random sample from each of several groups, as in this example, you test for the homogeneity of the categorical response distribution across the groups. Computationally, the chi-squared test statistic and the P-value are identical for the two tests. For simplicity and in practice, both types of tests are often referred to as tests for independence. (For instance, the null hypothesis in the preceding example tests whether severity of headache is *independent* of which treatment group a subject was assigned to.)

▶ *Try Exercise 11.16*

Chi-Squared and the Test Comparing Proportions in 2 × 2 Tables

In practice, contingency tables of size 2×2 are very common. These occur in comparing two groups on a binary response variable, such as males and females on their belief in life after death (yes, no). For convenience, here, as in the discussion of the binomial distribution in Section 6.3, we label the two possible responses by the generic labels *success* and *failure*.

Denote the population proportion of success by p_1 in group 1 and p_2 in group 2, so that the population distribution is $(p_1, 1 - p_1)$ in group 1 and $(p_2, 1 - p_2)$ in group 2. Homogeneity of the population distributions simply implies that $p_1 = p_2$, because, then, also $(1 - p_1) = (1 - p_2)$. Therefore, the test of homogeneity in a 2×2 table is the same as testing whether the success probabilities in the two groups are the same, i.e., whether $p_1 = p_2$.

Section 10.1 presented a z test of $H_0: p_1 = p_2$. The test statistic is the difference between the sample proportions divided by its null standard error; that is,

$$z = (\hat{p}_1 - \hat{p}_2)/se_0$$

where se_0 is the pooled standard error estimated under the presumption that H_0 is true. Using algebra, it can be shown that the chi-squared statistic for 2×2 tables is related to this z statistic by

$$X^2 = z^2.$$

In other words, square the z statistic, and you get the X^2 statistic. Because of this relationship, when the alternative hypothesis is $H_a: p_1 \neq p_2$, the z test has the exact same P-value as the chi-squared test and they reach the exact same conclusion. One advantage of the z test over the chi-squared test is that it also can be used with one-sided alternative hypotheses.

So, for 2×2 tables, we don't really need the chi-squared test because we can use the z test. More importantly, we can find the confidence interval for $p_1 - p_2$ to learn by how much the two conditional proportions differ. However, for larger contingency tables, which occur when we compare more than two groups, or when the categorical response variable has more than two outcomes, the z test doesn't apply. For such scenarios, we need the chi-squared test to study the association in the contingency table.

Limitations of the Chi-Squared Test

The chi-squared test, like other significance tests, provides limited information. If the P-value is very small, strong **evidence** exists against the null hypothesis of independence or homogeneity. We can then infer that the variables are associated, i.e., that the conditional distributions differ. The chi-squared statistic and the P-value tell us nothing, however, about the nature or the strength of the association. We know there is statistical significance, but the test alone does not indicate whether there is a practically relevant difference in the conditional distributions. A large X^2 (i.e., small P-value) means strong evidence for an association but not necessarily a strong association. We'll see how to investigate the strength of an association in the next section.

What about a large P-value? As with any significance test, a large P-value doesn't mean the null hypothesis is true, i.e., that the variables are independent. All we can say is that there is not enough evidence that the two variables are associated. Independence is still a plausible option, but the chi-squared test cannot be used to prove it.

> ### SUMMARY: Misuses of the Chi-Squared Test
>
> The chi-squared test is often misused. Some common misuses are interpreting
>
> - a small P-value as automatically providing evidence for a strong and practically meaningful association.
> - a large P-value as providing evidence for independence.

Recall

Section 10.1 presented a confidence interval and significance test for inference about the difference of two proportions. ◄

Recall

From Section 9.5, a small P-value does not imply an important result in practical terms. Statistical significance is not the same as *practical* relevance. ◄

Other misuses are applying the chi-squared test.

- When some of the expected frequencies are too small (see Section 11.5).
- When separate rows or columns are dependent samples,[1] such as when each row of the table refers to the same subjects.
- To data that do not result from a random sample or randomized experiment.
- To data by classifying quantitative variables into categories. This results in a loss of information. It is usually more appropriate to analyze the data with methods for quantitative variables, like those the next chapter presents.

"Goodness of Fit" Chi-Squared Tests

So far we've used the chi-squared statistic to test the null hypothesis that two categorical variables are independent. The chi-squared statistic can also be used for a hypothesis involving a *single* categorical variable from a *single* sample.

Example 6

▶ Testing "Goodness of Fit"

Mendelian Genetics

Picture the Scenario

In one of his experiments, the geneticist Gregor Mendel crossed pea plants of pure yellow strain with plants of pure green strain. He predicted that a second-generation hybrid seed would have probability 0.75 of being yellow and 0.25 of being green (yellow being the dominant strain). For the 8,023 hybrid seeds produced in the experiment, 6,022 were yellow and 2,001 were green.

Question to Explore

Are these results different enough from Mendel's predictions to give evidence against his theory?

Think It Through

If Mendel's theory is correct, we would expect 75% of the 8,023 seeds produced in the second generation to be yellow and 25% to be green; that is, $8,023(0.75) = 6,017.25$ yellow seeds and $8,023(0.25) = 2,005.75$ green seeds. The table in the margin shows these expected counts alongside the observed ones. To test Mendel's hypothesis, we formulate the null hypothesis as $H_0: P(yellow) = 0.75, P(green) = 0.25$ and the alternative hypothesis as H_a: the probabilities are different from those stated in H_0.

Applying the chi-squared statistic to test Mendel's theory, we obtain

$$X^2 = \sum \frac{(\text{observed count} - \text{expected count})^2}{\text{expected count}} =$$

$$\frac{(6,022 - 6,017.25)^2}{6,017.25} + \frac{(2,001 - 2,005.75)^2}{2,005.75} = 0.015.$$

When using the chi-squared test with a single categorical variable with c categories, the chi-squared distribution has $df = c - 1$. For this example with $c = 2$ categories (green and yellow), $df = 2 - 1 = 1$. The chi-squared statistic value of 0.015 (much lower than its expected value of 1) has

Observed and expected counts for testing Mendel's theory that 75% of the seed will be yellow and 25% green.

Count	Yellow	Green	Total
Observed	6,022	2,001	**8,023**
Expected	6,017.25 (= 8,023 × 0.75)	2,005.75 (= 8,023 × 0.25)	**8,023**

---

[1]With dependent samples, McNemar's test (Section 10.4) is the appropriate test with binary variables, and extensions of it handle categorical variables with more than two categories.

P-value = 0.90. There is no evidence that the data in Mendel's experiment contradicted his hypothesis.

Insight

When testing particular proportion values for a categorical variable, the chi-squared statistic is referred to as a **goodness-of-fit statistic**. The idea behind it is the same as before: to summarize how well the expected counts (computed from the hypothesized proportions) agree with the observed ones. With $c = 2$ categories, the chi-squared statistic equals the square of the z statistic used in Chapter 9 to test a hypothesis about the proportion value for one of the two categories. For example, to test Mendel's hypothesis back then, we would have formulated the null hypothesis as $H_0: p = 0.75$ that the probability p that a second-generation hybrid seed is yellow is 0.75. We find $\hat{p} = 6{,}022/8{,}023 = 0.7506$, $se_0 = \sqrt{p_0(1 - p_0)/n} = \sqrt{0.75(0.25)/8{,}023} = 0.00483$, and

$$z = \frac{\hat{p} - p_0}{se_0} = \frac{0.7506 - 0.75}{0.00483} = 0.124. \text{ Note that } z^2 = 0.015.$$

The P-value using the chi-squared distribution with test statistic X^2 is identical to the two-sided P-value by using the standard normal distribution with test statistic z. An advantage of the X^2 test is that it applies even when there are more than two categories. See Exercise 11.22 for an example.

▶ *Try Exercise 11.22*

A limitation of the goodness-of-fit test is that it does not tell us anything about the ranges of plausible values for the proportion parameters. To do this, we can find confidence intervals for the individual population proportions (Section 8.2). For Mendel's experiment, a 95% confidence interval for the probability of a yellow hybrid seed is

$$0.7506 \pm 1.96(0.0048), \text{ which is } (0.74, 0.76).$$

▶ Activity 2

Analyzing Contingency Tables of GSS Data

It's easy to analyze associations between categorical variables measured by the General Social Survey. Let's see how.

■ Go to the GSS website, sda.berkeley.edu. Click on the Archive box near the top and scroll down to the most current version of the General Social Survey (GSS) Cumulative Datafile, or, alternatively, just follow the link on this book's website.

■ The GSS names for Table 11.1 are HAPPY (for general happiness) and FINRELA (for family income in relative terms). Enter HAPPY in the column space and FINRELA in the row space to construct a table with these as the column and row variables. To obtain the data from the 2018 GSS, type YEAR(2018) in the selection filter box. Select No Weight for the Weight variable, and leave the Control variable empty.

■ Under Output Options, put a check in the row box (instead of in the column box) for the Percentaging option and put a check in the Summary Statistics box further below. Click on Run the Table.

You'll now get a contingency table relating happiness to family income for the 2018 survey. The table shows the cell counts and sample conditional distributions. It treats as the response variable the one you check for the Percentaging option. The output also shows some statistics (such as Chisq-P for the Pearson chi-squared statistic) that we're using in this chapter to analyze contingency tables.

The family income variable has five categories (far below average, below average, average, above average, far above average). Table 11.1 at the very beginning of this chapter only used categories 2, 3 and 4. To create this table, type the family income variable as FINRELA(2, 3, 4) instead of FINRELA. Often, you may want to combine categories, such as categories 1 and 2, into a single category (for below average) and categories 4 and 5 into another single category (for above average). To create this collapsed table, type the family income variable as FINRELA (r: 1-2; 3; 4-5).

Now, create a table relating another variable to happiness. At the page on which you enter the variable names, click Standard Codebook and then Sequential Variable List, and

you will see a range of topics covered by the GSS. Look up a topic that interests you and find the GSS code name for a variable. For the table you create,

- Find the chi-squared statistic and *df* value.
- Report the P-value and interpret the results in context.

11.2   Practicing the Basics

11.8   Life after death and gender   In the 2018 GSS, 703 of 945 males and 1,017 of 1,178 females indicated a belief in life after death. (*Source:* Data from CSM, UC Berkeley.)

a. Construct a 2 × 2 contingency table relating gender of respondent (SEX, categories male and female) as the rows to belief about life after death (POSTLIFE, categories yes and no) as the columns.

b. Find the four expected cell counts when assuming independence. Compare them to the observed cell counts, identifying cells having more observations than expected.

c. For this data, $X^2 = 48.6$. Verify this value by plugging into the formula for X^2 and computing the sum.

11.9   Happiness and gender   For the 2 × 3 table on gender and happiness in Exercise 11.4 (shown below), the *Chi-Squared Test* app (which has these data preloaded) reports that $X^2 = 9.94$ and the P-value = 0.0069.

	Happiness		
Gender	Not	Pretty	Very
Female	439	525	275
Male	292	455	252

a. State the null and alternative hypothesis, in context, to which these results apply.

b. Interpret the P-value in terms of what it says about the magnitude of the X^2 statistic and then write a conclusion to the test.

11.10   What gives P-value = 0.05?   How large does the X^2 statistic need to be in order for the P-value to equal 0.05 when testing independence? Find the answer under each of the following contingency table dimensions. You can use the *Chi-Square Distribution* app to find (and visualize) the answers, or you can use Table C.

a. 2 × 2   **b.** 2 × 3   **c.** 2 × 5   **d.** 5 × 5   **e.** 3 × 9

11.11   Marital happiness and income   The contingency table for relative family income and marital status in 2012 from Exercise 11.5 is as follows:

	Marital Happiness		
Income	Not	Pretty	Very
Above	6	62	139
Average	7	125	283
Below	6	69	115

a. State the null and alternative hypotheses for a test testing whether family income and marital happiness are independent.

b. What is the number of degrees of freedom for the chi-squared test?

c. The chi-squared statistic for the table equals $X^2 = 4.58$. (i) What value do you expect for the chi-squared statistic if the null hypothesis is true? (ii) How many standard deviations is 4.58 from this expected value? (*Hint:* The standard deviation of the chi-squared distribution equals $\sqrt{2df}$). (iii) Is $X^2 = 4.58$ an extreme value? Explain.

d. The P-value for the chi-squared test equals 0.33. Interpret what this P-value says about the magnitude of the X^2 statistic and then write a conclusion to the test using a significance level of 0.05.

e. Verify that the expected cell count in the first cell equals 4.84. Could this be a problem? Explain.

11.12   First and second free throw independent?   In pro basketball games during 1980–1982, when Larry Bird of the Boston Celtics made his first free throw, 251 out of 285 times he made the second one, and when he missed his first free throw, 48 out of 53 times he made the second one.

a. Form a 2 × 2 contingency table that cross-tabulates the outcome of the first free throw (with categories made and missed) and the outcome of the second free throw (made and missed).

b. The chi-squared statistic for this table equals $X^2 = 0.27$, resulting in a P-value of 0.602. Does it seem as if his success on the second shot depends on whether he made the first? Explain how to interpret the result of the chi-squared test. (Here, for the chi-squared test to apply, we assume that each pair of free throws attempted is independent of any other pair during the same or other games. This is reasonable in professional sports.)

11.13   Cigarettes and marijuana   The table on the following page refers to a survey[2] in which senior high school students in Dayton, Ohio, were randomly sampled. It cross-tabulates whether a student had ever smoked cigarettes and whether a student had ever used marijuana. Analyze these data by (a) finding and interpreting conditional distributions with marijuana use as the response variable and (b) reporting all five steps of the chi-squared test of independence. (You can enter the counts from the table in the *Chi-Squared Test* app.)

---

[2]*Source:* Data from Harry Khamis, Wright State University.

	Marijuana	
Cigarettes	**Yes**	**No**
Yes	914	581
No	46	735

11.14 Smoking and alcohol   Refer to the previous exercise.

a. True or false: If we use cigarette use as the column variable and marijuana use as the row variable, then we will get different values for the chi-squared statistic and the P-value.

b. Explain what value you would get for the z statistic and P-value if you conducted a significance test of $H_0: p_1 = p_2$ against $H_a: p_1 \neq p_2$, where p_1 and p_2 are the population proportions of cigarette users and non-cigarette users, respectively, who use marijuana.

11.15 Help the environment   In 2010 the GSS asked whether a subject was willing to accept cuts in the standard of living to help the environment (GRNSOL), with categories (vw = very willing, fw = fairly willing, nwu = neither willing nor unwilling, nvw = not very willing, nw = not at all willing). When this was cross-tabulated with whether the respondent is currently in school or has retired (WORKSTAT), as shown below, $X^2 = 9.56$.

a. What are the hypotheses for the test to which X^2 refers?

b. Report r and c and the df value on which X^2 is based.

c. What value would you expect for the X^2 statistic if, in fact, the distribution on the willingness to help the environment were the same for those in school and those retired?

d. The P-value for the test equals 0.0485. What conclusion would you make, using a significance level of (i) 0.05 and (ii) 0.025? State your conclusion in the context of this study.

	Help the Environment				
Status	**vw**	**fw**	**nwu**	**nvw**	**nw**
In School	14	47	41	43	27
Retired	34	189	177	169	189

11.16 Primary food choice of alligators   For alligators caught in two Florida lakes, the following table shows their primary food choice. The four food categories refer to fish, invertebrates (such as snails, insects, or crayfish), birds and reptiles (such as egrets or turtles), and others, including mammals or plants. Is there evidence that primary food choice differs between the two lakes? (These data are preloaded in the *Chi-Squared Test* app.)

	Primary Food				
Lake	**Fish**	**Invertebrates**	**Birds & Reptiles**	**Others**	**n**
Hancock	30	4	8	13	55
Trafford	13	18	12	10	53

a. Find the conditional sample distribution of primary food choice for alligators caught in lake Hancock, and for alligators caught in lake Trafford.

b. Formulate the hypotheses of interest.

c. Report the X^2 value for this table. Based on the df for the corresponding chi-squared distribution, can this be considered large? Why?

d. Report the P-value for the chi-squared test and write a conclusion of the test in context.

11.17 Aspirin and heart attacks   A Swedish study used 1,360 patients who had suffered a stroke. The study randomly assigned each subject to an aspirin treatment or a placebo treatment. In this study, heart attacks were suffered by 28 of the 684 subjects taking placebo and 18 of the 676 subjects taking aspirin.

a. Report the data in the form of a 2×2 contingency table.

b. Show how to carry out all five steps of the null hypothesis that having a heart attack is not associated with whether one takes placebo or aspirin. (You should get a chi-squared statistic equal to 2.1.) Interpret.

11.18 z test for heart attack study   Refer to the previous exercise. For a 2×2 contingency table, the z test provides the same information as the chi-squared test.

a. Define population proportions p_1 and p_2 and state the hypotheses for that test.

b. Carry out the hypothesis test, by using the *Compare Two Proportions* app. Explain how the result of the chi-squared test in (b) in the previous exercise corresponds to this z test result.

11.19 Severity of fever after flu shot   The study mentioned in Example 5 also looked at the severity of fever (rated as mild, moderate, or severe) for all subjects who developed one after receiving a flu shot. The following table shows counts for subjects randomized to the group that received the active ingredient of the flu shot and the placebo group that received a sugar injection.

	Severity		
Group	**Mild**	**Moderate**	**Severe**
Active	39	12	12
Placebo	19	11	4

a. Researchers want to know whether the distribution of the severity of fever is the same in both groups. Formulate appropriate null and alternative hypotheses.

b. The X^2 value for this table equals 2.49, which you can confirm with the *Chi-Squared Test* app. Based on the df for the chi-squared distribution, argue that this value is not extreme.

c. The P-value for the chi-squared test equals 0.287. Write the conclusion of the test in context.

11.20 What is independent of happiness?   Refer to Exercises 11.6 and 11.7. For the variables that you thought might be independent,

a. At the GSS website or by entering the contingency table in the *Chi-Squared Test* app, conduct all five steps of the chi-squared test.

b. Based on part a, which inference is most appropriate? (i) We accept the hypothesis that the variables are independent; (ii) the variables may be independent; (iii) the variables are associated.

11.21 Testing a genetic theory In an experiment on chlorophyll inheritance in corn, for 1,103 seedlings of self-fertilized heterozygous green plants, 854 seedlings were green and 249 were yellow. Theory predicts that 75% of the seedlings would be green.

a. Specify a null hypothesis for testing the theory.

b. Find the value of the chi-squared goodness-of-fit statistic and report its *df*.

c. Report the P-value and interpret.

11.22 Birthdays by quarters Based on a random sample of 84 students taken at Williams College, the table shows how many had their birthday in the first, second, third, or fourth quarter of the year. Is there evidence that the probabilities of having a birthday in a given quarter are not equal?

Birthday				
Jan-Mar	Apr-Jun	Jul-Sep	Oct-Dec	*n*
19	21	31	13	84

a. Formulate the null and alternative hypotheses.

b. Find the expected values and compute the chi-squared statistic, either by hand or using software.

c. The test will be based on how many degrees of freedom?

d. Find the P-value and write a conclusion in context.

11.23 Checking a roulette wheel Karl Pearson devised the chi-squared goodness-of-fit test partly to analyze data from an experiment to check whether a particular roulette wheel in Monte Carlo was fair, in the sense that each outcome was equally likely in a spin of the wheel. For a European roulette wheel with 37 slots (corresponding to numbers $0, 1, 2, \ldots, 36$), consider the null hypothesis that the wheel is fair.

a. For the null hypothesis, what is the probability for each number?

b. For an experiment with 3,700 spins of the roulette wheel, find the expected number of times each number is selected.

c. In the experiment, the number 0 occurred 110 times. Show the contribution to the X^2 statistic for this number.

d. Comparing the observed and expected counts for all 37 numbers, we get $X^2 = 34.4$. Specify the *df* value and indicate whether there is strong evidence that the roulette wheel is not balanced. (*Hint:* Recall that the *df* value is the mean of the distribution.)

11.3 Determining the Strength of the Association

Three questions are normally addressed in analyzing contingency tables:

- **Is there an association?** The chi-squared test of independence addresses this. When the P-value is small, we infer that the variables are associated.

- **How do the cell counts differ from what independence predicts?** To answer this question, we compare each observed cell count to the corresponding expected cell count. We'll say more about this in Section 11.4.

- **How strong is the association?** Analyzing the *strength* of the association reveals whether the association is an important one or if it is statistically significant but weak and unimportant in practical terms. We now focus on this third question.

Measures of Association

For 2012 GSS data, Table 11.8 shows associations between opinion about the death penalty and two explanatory variables—gender and race. Both sides of Table 11.8 have large chi-squared statistics and small P-values for the test of independence. We can conclude that both gender and race are associated with the death penalty opinion.

The X^2 test statistic is larger for the first table. Does this mean that opinion is more strongly associated with race than with gender? How can we quantify the strength of the association in a contingency table?

Table 11.8 GSS Data Showing Race and Gender as Explanatory Variables
for Opinion About the Death Penalty

Race	Opinion Favor	Oppose	n		Gender	Opinion Favor	Oppose	n
White	70%	30%	1,367		Male	69%	31%	830
Black	48%	52%	268		Female	61%	39%	994
Chi-squared $= 56.4$					Chi-squared $= 12.3$			
$df = 1$, P-value < 0.001					$df = 1$, P-value < 0.001			

Source: Data from CSM, UC Berkeley

Recall

Section 3.1 introduced the difference and ratio of two proportions for measuring the strength of the association between two categorical variables. Section 3.2 discussed the correlation coefficient as a measure of association between two quantitative variables. ◄

Measure of Association

A **measure of association** is a statistic or a parameter that summarizes the strength of the dependence between two variables.

A measure of association takes a range of values from one extreme to another as data range from the weakest to the strongest association. It is useful for comparing associations to determine which is stronger. Later in this section we'll see that although the chi-squared test tells us how strong the evidence is that an association truly exists in the population, it does not describe the strength of that association.

Difference of Proportions

An easily interpretable measure of association is the difference between the proportions making a particular response. The population difference of proportions is 0 whenever the conditional distributions are identical, that is, when the variables are independent. The difference of proportions falls between -1 and $+1$, where 1 and -1 represent the strongest possible association. Whether you get a negative or a positive value merely reflects how the rows are ordered. Section 10.1 showed how to use a sample difference of proportions value to conduct inference (such as a confidence interval) about a population value.

Table 11.9 shows two hypothetical contingency tables relating a subject's income and whether the subject responds to a promotional mailing from a bank offering a special credit card. Case A exhibits the weakest possible association—no association. Both the high-income and the low-income subjects have 60% rejecting the credit card. The difference of proportions is $0.60 - 0.60 = 0$. By contrast, case B exhibits the strongest possible association. All those with high income accept the card, whereas all those with low income decline it. The difference of proportions is $0 - 1.0 = -1$.

Table 11.9 Decision About Accepting a Credit Card Cross-Tabulated by Income

In Case A, the conditional distributions are the same in each row (independence), so the difference of proportions is 0. In Case B, the acceptance decision is completely dependent on income level, and the difference of proportions is -1.

Case A: Income	Accept Credit Card No	Yes	Total	Case B: No	Accept Credit Card Yes	Total
High	240 (60%)	160 (40%)	**400 (100%)**	0 (0%)	400 (100%)	**400 (100%)**
Low	360 (60%)	240 (40%)	**600 (100%)**	600 (100%)	0 (0%)	**600 (100%)**

	Opinion	
Race	**Favor**	**Oppose**
White	70%	30%
Black	48%	52%
Gender		
Male	69%	31%
Female	61%	39%

In practice, we don't expect data to follow either of these extremes, but the stronger the association, the larger the absolute value of the difference of proportions. For Table 11.8, shown again in the margin, the difference of proportions is $0.70 - 0.48 = 0.22$ for Whites and Blacks and $0.69 - 0.61 = 0.08$ for males and females. The difference of 0.22 between Whites and Blacks is much larger than the difference of 0.08 between males and females. The percentage favoring the death penalty is 22 percentage points higher for Whites than for Blacks but only 8 percentage points higher for males than females.

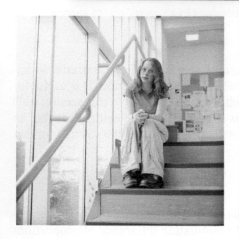

Strength of an Association ◄

Example 7

Student Stress, Depression, and Gender

Picture the Scenario
Every year, the Higher Education Research Institute at UCLA conducts a large-scale survey of college freshmen on a variety of issues. From the survey of more than 165,900 freshmen in 2013 (results available at www.heri.ucla.edu), Table 11.10 compares females and males on the percent who reported feeling frequently stressed (overwhelmed by all they have to do) and the percent who reported feeling frequently depressed during the past year. P-values for chi-squared tests of independence were less than 0.001 for each data set.

Table 11.10 Conditional Distributions of Stress and Depression, by Gender

Gender	Stress Yes	No	Total	Gender	Depression Yes	No	Total
Female	44%	56%	**100%**	Female	11%	89%	**100%**
Male	20%	80%	**100%**	Male	6%	94%	**100%**

Question to Explore
Which response variable, stress or depression, has the stronger sample association with gender?

Think It Through
The difference of proportions between females and males was $0.44 - 0.20 = 0.24$ for feeling stressed and $0.11 - 0.06 = 0.05$ for feeling depressed. Since 0.24 is much larger than 0.05, there is evidence of a greater difference between females and males on their feelings about stress than on depression. In the sample, stress has the stronger association with gender. The proportion feeling stressed was 24 percentage points higher for females, whereas the proportion feeling depressed was only 5 percentage points higher.

Insight
Although the difference of proportions can be as large as 1 or -1, in practice it is rare to find differences near these limits.

In a next step, one would compute confidence intervals for each of these differences in the population, using the methods from Section 10.1. Because of the large sample size (93,824 females and 71,734 males), these are narrow: (0.237, 0.245) for the difference in stress and (0.043, 0.049) for the difference in depression, each at 95% confidence. Because the first one covers much larger values, the association is much stronger for stress.

► **Try Exercise 11.24, part a**

Recall

Section 3.1 introduced the **ratio of two proportions** and showed how to interpret it. ◀

The Ratio of Proportions: Relative Risk

Another measure of association is the ratio of two proportions, p_1/p_2. In medical applications in which the proportion refers to an adverse outcome, it is called the **relative risk**.

Relative Risk ◀

Example 8

Vaccine Efficacy

Picture the Scenario

Example 4 in Chapter 8 mentioned a study in which 3,900 healthy subjects were given a flu shot manufactured with a new method that grows viruses in cell cultures. Twenty-six of the 3,900 subjects still developed the flu. That same study also included a control arm of the same size, in which subjects received a sugar solution. Of these 3,900 subjects, 70 developed the flu. Table 11.11 shows the data, for which $X^2 = 20.4$ ($df = 1$), and the P-value is less than 0.0001.

Table 11.11 Results from a Vaccine Efficacy Study.

	Developed Flu		
Group	Yes	No	Total
Vaccinated	26	3,874	**3,900**
Control	70	3,830	**3,900**

Question to Explore

Find and interpret the relative risk of developing the flu.

Think It Through

The sample proportion developing the flu is $\hat{p}_1 = 26/3,900 = 0.0067$ in the vaccinated group and $\hat{p}_2 = 70/3,900 = 0.0179$ in the control group. The sample relative risk is the ratio $0.0067/0.0179 = 0.374$. The proportion of subjects developing the flu in the vaccinated group is 0.374 times the proportion of subjects developing the flu in the control (unvaccinated) group. So the proportion in the vaccinated group is about a third of the proportion in the control group.

Equivalently, because $0.0179/0.0067 = 1/0.374 = 2.67$, the proportion in the control group is 2.67 times the proportion in the vaccinated group. This reciprocal value is the relative risk when the two rows are interchanged, with the control group in row 1. We see that the proportion developing the flu is 2.67 times higher in the control group compared to the vaccinated group. Commonly, this is interpreted as follows: Unvaccinated subjects are 2.67 times *more likely* to develop the flu, where 2.67 times more likely refers to the relative risk.

Insight

The ordering of rows is arbitrary. Many people find it easier to interpret the relative risk for the ordering for which its value is *above* 1.0. A sample relative risk of 2.67 represents a fairly strong association. To see whether the true relative risk is far from the value of 1.0, which represents independence (i.e., the proportion of developing the flu are the same in each group), we should construct a 95% confidence interval for it. One way to obtain a confidence interval is via the bootstrap (see Section 10.3, which explained the procedure for the difference of means or medians). You can obtain the bootstrap distribution via the *Association Between Two Categorical Variables* app, which takes a bootstrap sample from those in the vaccinated group and another bootstrap sample from those in the control group, finds the resulting 2×2 contingency table, and computes the ratio of proportion from it. Repeating this thousands of times builds the bootstrap sampling distribution. The 2.5th and 97.5th percentile of this distribution are the lower and upper bounds for the confidence interval, which here equals (1.8, 4.4). Other formulas for the confidence interval exist, but they are not covered in this book. From the confidence interval we estimate that the proportion developing the flu is between 1.7 (i.e., 70%) and 4.2 times higher in the control (not vaccinated) group.

▶ *Try Exercises 11.24, part b, and 11.30, part a*

In Example 8, the proportion of interest was close to 0 for each group, but the relative risk was relatively far from 1. When this happens, an association may be practically important even though the difference of proportions is close to 0. (For the data in Example 8, the difference of proportion equals 0.0113, or 1.1 percentage points.) If the chance of getting the flu is only a bit higher in the unvaccinated group, but that chance is nearly three times higher, the association is practically significant. The relative risk is often more informative than the difference of proportions for comparing proportions that are both close to 0.

Properties of the Relative Risk

- The relative risk can equal any nonnegative number.
- When $p_1 = p_2$, the variables are independent, and the relative risk $= 1.0$.
- Values farther from 1.0 (in either direction) represent stronger associations. Two values for the relative risk represent the same strength of association, but in opposite directions, when one value is the reciprocal of the other. See Figure 11.7.

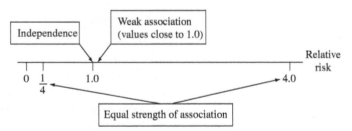

▲ **Figure 11.7** Values of the Relative Risk Farther from 1.0 Represent Stronger Association. **Question** Why do relative risks that take reciprocal values, such as 4 and $\frac{1}{4}$, represent the same strength of association?

A relative risk of 8 is farther from independence and represents a stronger association than a relative risk of 4, and a relative risk of $\frac{1}{8}$ is farther from independence than a relative risk of $\frac{1}{4}$. But a relative risk of 4.0 and a relative risk of $1/4.0 = 0.25$ represent the same strength of association. When the relative risk $p_1/p_2 = 0.25$, then p_1 is 0.25 times p_2. Equivalently, p_2 is $1/0.25 = 4.0$ times p_1. Whether we get 4.0 or 0.25 for the relative risk depends merely on which group we call group 1 and which we call group 2.

Odds and Odds Ratio

A third measure for the association uses the concept of the **odds**. For a generic contingency table such as the one shown in the margin, the odds in a given row are defined as the ratio of the two conditional proportions in that row. This equals $p_1/(1 - p_1)$ in the first row and $p_2/(1 - p_2)$ in the second row. The **odds ratio** is the ratio of these two odds, $\dfrac{p_1/(1 - p_1)}{p_2/(1 - p_2)}$.

Group	Outcome		Total
	Success	**Failure**	
Group 1	p_1	$1 - p_1$	1
Group 2	p_2	$1 - p_2$	1

Conditional Proportions for Table 11.11

Group	Developed Flu		Total
	Yes	No	
Vaccinated	0.0067	0.9933	**1.0**
Control	0.0179	0.9821	**1.0**

Did You Know?

In everyday language, the odds are often synonymous with a probability, but they express different quantities in statistics. For instance, the probability of rolling a 6 with a fair die is 1/6, but the odds of rolling a 6 are 1/5, or 1:5. For every one six rolled, you are expecting 5 numbers that are not 6. What is the "statistically correct" answer to the question "What are the odds of getting heads when flipping a fair coin?" ◄

For the vaccine efficacy study from Example 8, the table in the margin shows the conditional distribution for whether someone developed the flu. For the vaccinated group (row 1), the estimated odds of developing the flu are $\hat{p}_1/(1 - \hat{p}_1) = 0.0067/0.9933 = 0.0067$. For the control group (row 2), the estimated odds equal $\hat{p}_2/(1 - \hat{p}_2) = 0.0179/0.9821 = 0.0182$. How can these numbers be interpreted? The odds compare the proportion of subjects developing the flu to those who don't. For instance, in the control group, the proportion developing the flu is about 0.02 times the proportion not developing the flu. Writing an odds of 0.02 (or 1/50) as 1:50, we get the interpretation that, in the control group, for every one subject developing the flu, 50 did not develop it. In the vaccinated group, the odds of 0.0067, which is 1/150 or 1:150, implies that for every one subject developing the flu, 150 did not.

Clearly, the odds of developing the flu are much lower in the vaccinated group, but how much lower? The odds *ratio* tells you. Because for every subject with the flu there are 150 without it in the vaccinated group, but only about 50 without it in the control group, the odds are about a third lower in the vaccinated group. We get the precise number by computing the sample odds ratio as in

$$\frac{\hat{p}_1/(1 - \hat{p}_1)}{\hat{p}_2/(1 - \hat{p}_2)} = \frac{0.0067}{0.0182} = 0.368.$$ The odds of developing the flu in the vaccinated group are 0.368 times the odds in the control group, so about one-third of it. We could also say that the odds of developing the flu are about two-thirds lower in the vaccinated group.

Similar to the relative risk, when flipping the rows so that the control group is row 1 and the vaccinated group is row 2, we get the reciprocal: The odds of developing the flu in the control group are about $1/(1/3) = 3$ times the odds in the vaccinated group. An odds ratio of 3 (or similarily 1/3) indicates a fairly strong association.

Properties of the Odds Ratio

The odds ratio has several properties in common with the relative risk:

- The odds ratio can equal any nonnegative number.
- Under independence $(p_1 = p_2)$, the odds ratio equals 1.
- Values farther from 1.0 (in either direction) represent stronger associations. Two values for the odds ratio represent the same strength of association, but in opposite directions, when one value is the reciprocal of the other. See Figure 11.8.

▲ **Figure 11.8** Values of the Odds Ratio Farther from 1.0 Represent Stronger Association. An odds ratio of 1 implies independence.

Caution

Do not confuse the odds ratio with the relative risk. Any interpretation involving "times more likely" refers to the relative risk. ◄

Despite these similarities, the odds ratio is **not the same** as the relative risk! One is a ratio of odds, the other a ratio of proportions, and they have different interpretations. For instance, for the study on stress between female and male college freshmen in Table 11.10, you can check that the odds ratio equals 3.14 and the relative risk 2.20. A common mistake is to compute the odds ratio and interpret it like a relative risk, e.g., saying that females are *3.14 times more likely* to experience stress than males. In fact, females are only 2.2 times more likely to experience stress (the relative risk), but the *odds* of experiencing stress are 3.14 times greater.

You may wonder why statisticians bother with computing such a complicated measure that is prone to misinterpretations. There are two main reasons. One is

Smoker	Lung Cancer		Total
	Cases (= Yes)	Controls (= No)	
Yes	688	650	1,338 ◄
No	21	59	70 ◄
Total	**709**	**709**	

Not a random sample

Did you know?

The odds ratio approximately equals the relative risk if the outcome of interest is rare. Because developing lung cancer is rare in general (i.e., for both smokers and nonsmokers), and because the odds ratio was about 3, we can actually conclude from these data that smokers are about 3 times *more likely* to develop lung cancer. ◄

that for case-control studies such as those discussed in Section 4.4, it is impossible to estimate the difference or ratio of proportions because the study design did not employ random sampling. However, because of some special properties the odds ratio can be estimated from such studies and is the only way to measure the association. An example is the case-control study on the association between smoking and lung cancer discussed in Example 8 in Section 4.4 and shown again in the margin.

Because this study did not use a random sample of smokers and nonsmokers, it is incorrect to estimate the proportion of smokers developing lung cancer as $688/1{,}338 = 0.51$, or 51%, and the proportion of nonsmokers developing lung cancer as $21/70 = 0.3$, or 30%. These proportions are clearly too high and they are invalid because they are not based on a random sample of smokers and nonsmokers. If we can't estimate these proportions from the given data, we also can't estimate their difference or ratio. However, one can compute the odds ratio, which is 2.97, indicating a rather strong association between smoking and lung cancer.

There are formulas to find a confidence interval for the odds ratio, but they are not covered in this book. One way to get a confidence interval employs the bootstrap, using ideas similar to the ones discussed for finding a confidence interval the relative risk in Example 9. The *Association Between Two Categorical Variables* app can compute such a bootstrap percentile confidence interval. For the lung cancer data, the 95% bootstrap percentile confidence interval equals (1.8, 5.3). With 95% confidence, we estimate that the odds of lung cancer are between 1.8 and 5.3 times larger for smokers compared to nonsmokers.

The second major reason the odds (and the odds ratio) are so popular is that they naturally appear in regression models for a binary response variable, called **logistic regression**. This will be further discussed in Section 13.6.

Association in $r \times c$ Tables

Income and Happiness from Table 11.1.
The percentages are the conditional distributions of happiness in each row.

Income	Happiness		
	Not Too	Pretty	Very
Above	29 (8%)	178 (52%)	135 (39%)
Average	83 (10%)	494 (58%)	277 (32%)
Below	104 (19%)	314 (58%)	119 (22%)

The difference and ratio of proportions and the odds ratio are all defined for 2×2 tables. How can we measure the association in larger tables? For general $r \times c$ (r = # of rows, c = # of columns) tables, one option is to pick out a particular response category and compare it across two rows. For instance, consider the 3×3 table from Section 11.1 on income and happiness, shown again in the margin. For it, we found a large X^2 statistic, i.e., a significant association, but how strong is it in practical terms and how can we describe it? Let's pick the two rows for above- and below-average income (rows 1 and 3) and compare them on the outcome, Very Happy. Using the ratio of proportions as the measure of association, the proportion reporting being very happy is $0.39/0.22 = 1.77$ times larger (or 77% larger) for those with above- rather than below-average income. For the Not Too Happy outcome, the ratio of proportions is $0.08/0.19 = 0.42$. So the proportion of subjects Not Too Happy is 58% lower for those with above-average income compared to those with below-average income. These numbers (and you can compute those for other comparisons) show an association, but with ratios of proportions around 2 (or 0.5), it is not that strong.

Chi-Squared and Strength of Association

You may be tempted to regard a large value of the X^2 statistic (or a very small P-value) in the test of independence as indicating a strong association. As mentioned before, this is a misuse of the statistic.

In Practice A Large X^2 Statistic Does Not Imply a Strong Association

A large value for X^2 provides strong evidence that the variables are associated. It does not imply, however, that the variables have a strong association. The evidence can be strong, yet the association itself can be weak. The value of the X^2 statistic depends on the sample size. Large X^2 values can occur with weak associations if the sample size is sufficiently large.

For example, Cases A, B, and C in Table 11.12 are hypothetical tables relating gender and whether one attends religious services weekly. The association in each case is weak—the conditional distribution for females (51% yes, 49% no) is nearly identical to the conditional distribution for males (49% yes, 51% no). All three cases show the same weak strength of association: The difference between the proportions of females and males who say yes is $0.51 - 0.49 = 0.02$ in each, and the relative risk of $0.51/0.49 = 1.04$ in each. The measures are close to 0 and 1, respectively, indicating no or very weak association.

Table 11.12 Response on Attending Religious Services Weekly, by Gender

	Case A			Case B			Case C		
	Yes	No	n	Yes	No	n	Yes	No	n
Female	51%	49%	100	51%	49%	200	51%	49%	10,000
Male	49%	51%	100	49%	51%	200	49%	51%	10,000
Chi-squared = 0.08				Chi-squared = 0.16			Chi-squared = 8.0		
P-value = 0.78				P-value = 0.69			P-value = 0.005		

For the sample of size 100 in each group in Case A, $X^2 = 0.08$, which has a P-value of 0.78. Case B has twice as large a sample size in each group, with $X^2 = 0.16$, for which the P-value $= 0.69$. So, when the cell counts double, X^2 doubles. Finally, for the sample size of 10,000 in each group in Case C (100 times as larger as the $n = 100$ in each group from Case A), $X^2 = 8.0$ (100 times as large as $X^2 = 0.08$). Then the P-value $= 0.005$.

This example shows that although the association is the exact same in each case (51% of females says yes, compared to 49% of males), the chi-squared statistic becomes larger with increasing sample size. It is true that the evidence for an association is stronger in Case C, yet that association, although "significant" as measured by the Chi-square test, may be very weak in practical terms. This warning is similar to the one we issued in Chapter 10: Statistical significance (i.e., a small P-value) may not imply a practically relevant difference.

Caution

If the sample size is sufficiently large, a X^2 value large enough to be considered statistically significant can occur even if the association between the two categorical variables is weak. ◄

11.3 Practicing the Basics

11.24 Democrat, race, and gender The two tables show 2012 GSS data on whether someone is identified as Democrat, by race and by gender.

	Democrat				Democrat		
Race	Yes	No	Total	Gender	Yes	No	Total
Black	212	88	**300**	Female	421	660	**1,081**
White	422	1,046	**1,468**	Male	278	601	**879**

a. Find the difference of proportions between Blacks and Whites and between females and males. Interpret each. Which variable has a stronger association with whether someone identifies as Democrat, race or gender? Explain.

b. Find the ratio of proportions between Blacks and Whites and between females and males. Interpret each. Which variable has a stronger association with whether someone identifies as Democrat, race or gender? Explain.

c. Find the odds of identifying as Democrat for Blacks and Whites and interpret each. Then find the odds ratio and interpret.

11.25 Death penalty associations Table 11.8, summarized again here, showed the associations between death penalty opinion and gender or race.

	Opinion			Opinion	
Race	Favor	Oppose	Gender	Favor	Oppose
Black	70%	30%	Female	69%	31%
White	48%	52%	Male	61%	39%

a. True or false: The table with the larger X^2 statistic necessarily has the stronger association. Explain.

b. To make an inference about the strength of association in the population, you can construct confidence intervals around the sample differences of proportions. The 95% confidence intervals are (0.15, 0.28) comparing Whites and Blacks and (0.04, 0.12) comparing males and females. In the *population*, can you make a conclusion about which variable is more strongly associated with the death penalty opinion? Explain.

11.26 Smoking and alcohol The following table refers to a survey of senior high school students in Dayton, Ohio. It cross-tabulates whether a student had ever smoked cigarettes and whether a student had ever drunk alcohol and shows counts and the conditional distributions of alcohol use. (You can enter the counts in the *Association Between Two Categorical Variables* app to compute measures of association.)

Cigarettes	Alcohol Yes	No	Total
Yes	1,449 (97%)	46 (3%)	**1,495 (100%)**
No	500 (64%)	281 (36%)	**781 (100%)**

a. Describe the strength of association by using the difference between users and nonusers of cigarettes in the proportions who have used alcohol. Interpret.

b. Describe the strength of association by using the relative risk of using alcohol, comparing those who have used or not used cigarettes. Interpret.

c. Find the odds of having used alcohol for users and nonusers of cigarettes. Interpret each. Then, describe the strength of association, using the odds ratio.

11.27 Sex of victim and offender   For murders in the United States in 2012, the table cross-tabulates the sex of the victim by the sex of the offender. Find and interpret a measure of association, treating sex of victim as the response variable. (You can enter the counts in the *Association Between Two Categorical Variables* app to compute measures of association.)

Sex of Offender	Sex of Victim Female	Male
Female	124	421
Male	1,609	3,725

Source: Data from www.fbi.gov.

11.28 Smelling and mortality   A recent study (Pinto et al., Olfactory Dysfunction Predicts 5-Year Mortality in Older Adults. PLoS ONE 9(10):e107541, 2014) mentions that anosmic (those with almost no sense of smell) older adults had more than three times the odds of death over a 5-year span compared to normosmic (those with normal smell) individuals. Does this imply that anosmic older adults were more than three times as likely to die over the next 5 years than normosmic ones? Explain.

11.29 Vioxx   In September 2004, the pharmaceutical company Merck withdrew its blockbuster drug rofecoxib (a painkiller, better known under its brand name, Vioxx) from the worldwide market amid concerns about its safety. By that time, millions of people had used the drug. In a 2000 study comparing rofecoxib to a control group (naproxen), it was mentioned that "Myocardial infarctions were less common in the naproxen group than in the rofecoxib group (0.1 percent vs. 0.4 percent; 95 percent confidence interval for the difference, 0.1 to 0.6 percent; relative risk, 0.2; 95 percent confidence interval, 0.1 to 0.7)". (*Source:* Bombadier et al., *New England Journal of Medicine*, vol. 343, 2000, pp. 1520–8.)

a. Find and interpret the difference of proportions between the naproxen and rofecoxib groups.

b. Interpret the stated relative risk.

c. In this study, myocardial infarctions were how much more likely to occur in the rofecoxib group than in the naproxen group?

11.30 Egg and cell derived vaccine   When comparing the cell-derived flu vaccine mentioned in Example 8 to a more traditionally manufactured egg-derived vaccine, the following data were obtained. (You can enter the counts in the *Association Between Two Categorical Variables* app to compute measures of association.)

Group	Developed Flu Yes	No	Total
Cell-Derived	26	3,874	**3,900**
Egg-Derived	24	3,876	**3,900**

a. Find the relative risk of developing the flu and interpret.

b. Find the odds ratio and interpret.

c. Based on either measure, is it likely that the probability of developing the flu is similar in the two groups? Explain.

11.31 Risk of dying for teenagers   According to summarized data from 1999 to 2006 accessed from the Centers of Disease Control and Prevention, the annual probability that a male teenager at age 19 is likely to die is about 0.00135 and 0.00046 for females age 19. (www.cdc.gov)

a. Compare these rates using the difference of proportions, and interpret.

b. Compare these rates using the relative risk, and interpret.

c. Which of the two measures seems more useful when both proportions are very close to 0? Explain.

11.32 Marital happiness   The table shows 2012 GSS data on marital and general happiness for married respondents.

Marital Happiness	General Happiness Not Too Happy	Happy	Very Happy
Not Too Happy	11	11	4
Happy	31	215	34
Very Happy	20	231	337

a. The chi-squared test of independence has $X^2 = 214$. What conclusion would you make using a significance level of 0.05? Interpret.

b. Does this large chi-squared value imply there is a strong association between marital and general happiness? Explain.

c. Find the difference in the proportion of being not too happy between those that are not too happy in their marriage and those that are very happy in their marriage. Interpret that difference.

d. Find and interpret the relative risk of being not too happy, comparing the lowest and highest marital happiness group. Interpret.

11.33 Party ID and gender   The table shows the 2012 GSS data on gender and political party identification from Exercise 11.1. (The row totals are slightly different from the second table in Exercise 11.24 because selecting Independent is ignored.) The chi-squared test of independence has $X^2 = 10.04$ with a P-value of 0.0066, indicating a significant association. Let's describe this association:

	Political Party Identification			
Gender	Democrat	Independent	Republican	Total
Female	421	398	244	1,063
Male	278	367	198	843

Source: Data from CSM, UC Berkeley.

a. Estimate the difference between females and males in the proportion who identify themselves as Republicans. Interpret.

b. Estimate the difference between females and males in the proportion who identify themselves as Democrat. Interpret.

c. Estimate the ratio between females and males in the proportion who identify themselves as Republican. Interpret.

d. Estimate the ratio between females and males in the proportion who identify themselves as Democrat. Interpret.

e. What can you say about the strength of the association between gender and whether identifying as Republican? What about gender and whether identifying as Democrat?

11.34 Chi-squared versus measuring association   For the table on marital happiness in Exercise 11.32, the chi-squared statistic equals 214 ($df = 4$, P-value < 0.0001). Explain the difference between the purposes of the chi-squared test in part a and the descriptive analysis in parts c and d in that exercise, which compares conditional distributions by using measures of association. (*Hint:* Is a chi-squared test a descriptive or inferential analysis?)

11.4 Using Residuals to Reveal the Pattern of Association

The chi-squared test and measures of association such as the difference and ratio of proportions and the odds ratio are fundamental methods for analyzing contingency tables. The P-value for the chi-squared test summarizes the strength of evidence against H_0: independence (or homogeneity). If the P-value is small, then we conclude that somewhere in the contingency table the population cell proportions differ from independence (or homogeneity). The chi-squared test does not indicate, however, for which cells this is the case.

Residual Analysis

Recall

Section 3.3 introduced a **residual** as the difference between an observed response and a predicted response from a regression equation. For categorical variables, a residual compares an observed count to an expected count computed under H_0. ◄

A cell-by-cell comparison of the observed counts with the counts that are expected when H_0 is true reveals the nature of the evidence. The difference between an observed and expected count in a particular cell is called a **residual**.

For example, Table 11.5 (and the screenshot in Figure 11.3) reported observed and expected cell counts for happiness and family income. The first column of this table is summarized in the margin, with the expected cell counts in parentheses. The first cell reports 29 subjects with above-average income who are not too happy. The expected count is 42.6. The residual is $29 - 42.6 = -13.6$. The residual is negative when, as in this cell, fewer subjects are in the cell than expected under independence. The residual is positive when more subjects are in the cell than expected, as in the cell having observed count $= 104$ (below-average income subjects who are not too happy) and residual $104 - 66.9 = 37.1$.

Income	Not Too Happy
Above Average	29 (42.6)
Average	83 (106.4)
Below Average	104 (66.9)

How do we know whether a residual is large enough to indicate strong evidence of a deviation from independence in that cell? To answer this question, we use an adjusted form of the residual that behaves like a z-score. It is called the **standardized residual**.

> **Standardized Residual**
>
> The **standardized residual** for a cell equals
>
> $$(\text{observed count} - \text{expected count})/se.$$
>
> Here, se denotes a standard error for the sampling distribution of (observed count − expected count), when the variables are independent.

A standardized residual reports the number of standard errors that an observed count falls from its expected count. The se describes how much the differences between those two counts tend to vary in repeated random sampling if the variables were independent. Its formula is complex, and we'll not give it here. The *Chi-Squared Test* app or other software can easily find standardized residuals for us.

When H_0: independence is true, the standardized residuals have approximately a standard normal distribution: They fluctuate around a mean of 0, with a standard deviation of 1. There is about a 5% chance that any particular standardized residual exceeds 2 in absolute value, and less than a 1% chance that it exceeds 3 in absolute value. The margin figure illustrates this. A standardized residual larger than 3 in absolute value provides strong evidence against independence in that cell. If independence holds, it is very unlikely (less than a 1% chance) to observe a standardize residual larger than 3 in absolute value just by chance. A value bigger than +3 suggests that the population proportion for that cell is higher than what independence predicts. A value less than −3 indicates that the population proportion for that cell is lower than what independence predicts.

When we inspect many cells in a table, some standardized residuals could be large just by random variation. Values below −3 or above +3, however, are quite convincing evidence of a true effect in that cell.

Shaded area = about 95%

−3 −2 −1 0 1 2 3 z

Standardized Residuals

Standardized Residuals

Example 9

Religiosity and Gender

Picture the Scenario

Table 11.12 showed some artificial data comparing females and males on their religious attendance. Let's look at some actual data on religiosity. Table 11.13, a screenshot from the *Chi-Squared Test* app, shows observed and expected counts as well as residuals and standardized residuals for the association between gender and response to the question, "To what extent do you consider yourself a religious person?" The possible responses were (very religious, moderately religious, slightly religious, not religious at all). The data are from the 2018 GSS. You can compare the conditional percentages for each category using the side-by-side bar graph shown in the app.

Table 11.13 Religiosity by Gender, from the 2018 GSS

Screenshot from the *Chi-Squared Test* app, showing observed and expected counts, the difference between them (the residuals) and the standardized residuals.

Observed Contingency Table:

	very	mod.	slighly	not	Total
Female	145	359	268	275	1,047
Male	227	514	305	235	1,281
Overall	372	873	573	510	2,328

Expected Cell Counts:

	very	mod.	slighly	not	Total
Female	167.3	392.6	257.7	229.4	1,047.0
Male	204.7	480.4	315.3	280.6	1,281.0
Overall	372.0	873.0	573.0	510.0	2,328.0

Side-By-Side Barchart

Religiosity:
very mod. slighly not

Residuals (Observed - Expected):

	very	mod.	slighly	not
Female	-22.3	-33.6	10.3	45.6
Male	22.3	33.6	-10.3	-45.6

Standardized Residuals:

	very	mod.	slighly	not
Female	-2.5	-2.9	1.0	4.6
Male	2.5	2.9	-1.0	-4.6

Questions to Explore

a. How would you interpret the standardized residual of −2.5 for females who are very religious?

b. The X^2 value for this table equals 27.9 ($df = 3$), and the P-value is less than 0.001, providing strong evidence for an association between these two variables. Use the standardize residuals to describe the pattern of this association.

Think It Through

a. The cell for females who are very religious has observed count = 145, expected count = 167.3, and standardized residual = −2.5. The difference between the observed and expected counts is 2.5 standard errors. Because of the relatively large value of the standardized residual, this cell shows a larger discrepancy between the observed and expected counts than what we would expect under independence. There is evidence that the proportion of females who are very religious is lower (because the residual is negative) than what we would expect if gender and religiosity were independent.

b. The largest standardized residuals in absolute value (4.6) occur in the column for "Not Religious." The positive residual for females indicates that the proportion of females who are not religious is much higher than predicted under independence. Conversely, the negative residual for males indicates that the proportion of males who are not religious is much smaller than predicted under independence. Overall, the residuals indicate that females are less likely to be very or moderately religious and more likely to be not religious compared to males. This describes the nature of the association between gender and religiosity.

Insight

To describe the nature of the association even further, you can compare the conditional percentages (not shown in this screenshot, but printed by default in the *Chi-Squared Test* app) numerically. For instance, in the sample, the proportion of males who identified as not religious is 12 percentage points higher than the proportion of females who identified as not religious. If religiosity were independent of gender, we wouldn't expect to see such a large difference.

▶ **Try Exercise 11.35**

In Practice Software Can Find Standardized Residuals

Most software has the option of reporting **standardized residuals.** For instance, we have just seen how the *Chi-Squared Test* app reports them. In MINITAB, they are available under the name "adjusted residuals," and in SPSS, they are called "adjusted standardized residuals." The GSS website also reports standardized residuals under the name Z-statistics, available under Output Options.

11.4 Practicing the Basics

11.35 Standardized residuals for happiness and income The
TRY table displays the observed and expected cell counts and the standardized residuals (in that order, going down a column) for testing independence of happiness and family income, for GSS data.

```
Rows: Income    Columns: Happiness
             not    pretty     very    All
above         29       178      135    342
            42.6     194.6    104.8
          -2.490    -2.021    3.955

average       83       494      277    854
           106.4     485.9    261.7
          -3.410     0.787    1.598

below        104       314      119    537
            66.9     305.5    164.5
           5.830     0.889   -5.131

All          216       986      531   1733
```

a. How would you interpret the standardized residual of −2.49?

b. Interpret the standardized residuals highlighted in green.

c. Interpret the standardized residuals highlighted in red.

11.36 Happiness and religious attendance The table shows MINITAB output for data from the 2008 GSS on happiness and frequency of attending religious services (1 = at most several times a year, 2 = once a month to nearly every week, 3 = every week to several times a week). The first entry in a cell gives the observed cell count; the second entry gives the standardized residual.

```
Rows: religion         Columns:        happiness
Not too happy      Pretty happy     Very happy
1      201                 609              268
       4.057               1.731           -5.107
2       46                 224              132
      -2.566               0.456            1.541
3       66                 265              196
      -2.263              -2.376            4.385
Cell Contents:         Count
                       Adjusted residual
Pearson Chi-Square = 36.445, DF = 4,
P-Value = 0.000
```

a. Based on the chi-squared statistic and P-value, give a conclusion about the association between the variables.

b. The numbers below the counts in the table are standardized residuals. Which cells have strong evidence that in the population there are more subjects than if the variables were independent?

c. Which cells have strong evidence that in the population there are fewer subjects than if the variables were independent?

11.37 Marital happiness and general happiness Exercise 11.32 showed the association between general happiness and marital happiness. The table shown here gives the standardized residuals for those data in parentheses.

a. Explain what a relatively small standardized residual such as −0.9 in the second cell represents.

b. Identify the cells in which you'd infer that the population has more cases than would occur if happiness and marital happiness were independent. Pick one of these cells and explain the association relative to independence.

Marital Happiness	Happiness		
	Not Too Happy	Pretty Happy	Very Happy
Not Too Happy	11 (7.2)	11 (−0.9)	4 (−2.8)
Pretty Happy	31 (3.3)	215 (10.4)	34 (−12.2)
Very Happy	20 (−5.8)	231 (−9.8)	337 (12.9)

11.38 Happiness and marital status The screen shot from the GSS website shows standardized residuals (called Z-statistics) and cell counts for 2012 GSS data on happiness (the column) and marital status (the row). The color coding is based on the magnitude of the Z-statistic (= standardized residual) and is explained in the legend. Summarize the association by indicating which marital statuses have strong evidence of (i) more and (ii) fewer people in the population in the Very Happy category than if the variables were independent.

Frequency Distribution					
		HAPPY			
Cells contain: -Z-statistic -N of cases		1 VERY HAPPY	2 PRETTY HAPPY	3 NOT TOO HAPPY	ROW TOTAL
MARITAL	1: MARRIED	10.3 / 375	-3.8 / 458	-8.1 / 64	--- / 897
	2: WIDOWED	-2.4 / 35	1.2 / 97	1.5 / 29	--- / 161
	3: DIVORCED	-4.2 / 64	1.9 / 191	2.8 / 60	--- / 315
	4: SEPARATED	-2.7 / 10	-1.2 / 32	5.3 / 24	--- / 66
	5: NEVER MARRIED	-5.5 / 109	2.4 / 316	3.8 / 100	--- / 525
	COL TOTAL	--- / 593	--- / 1,094	--- / 277	--- / 1,964

Color coding:	<-2.0	<-1.0	<0.0	>0.0	>1.0	>2.0	Z
N in each cell:	Smaller than expected			Larger than expected			

11.39 Gender gap? The table in Exercise 11.1 on gender and party identification is shown again. The largest standardized residuals in absolute value were +2.98 for females who identified as Democrats and −2.98 for males who identified as Democrats. Interpret.

	Political Party Identification			
Gender	Democrat	Independent	Republican	Total
Female	421	398	244	1,063
Male	278	367	198	843

Source: Data from CSM, UC Berkeley.

11.40 Ideology and political party Go to the GSS website sda.berkeley.edu. Construct the 7 × 8 contingency table relating political ideology (POLVIEWS) and party identification (PARTYID) for the year 2012. (Enter YEAR(2012) in the Selection filter and choose No Weights for the weight variable.) Select Summary Statistics and Z-statistic under Output Options to get the value of the chi-squared statistic and standardized residuals.

a. Summarize the results of carrying out the chi-squared test.

b. What do you learn from the residuals that you did not learn from the chi-squared test?

11.5 Fisher's Exact and Permutation Tests

The chi-squared test of independence, like one- and two-sample z tests for proportions, is a large-sample test. When the expected cell counts are small, any of them less than about 5, the sampling distribution of X^2 may not follow a chi-squared distribution. Then, tests that do not rely on this assumption to find P-values are more appropriate. For 2×2 contingency tables, one such test is **Fisher's exact test** of independence. For larger tables, we present a related **permutation** test. These tests work for any sample size but are particularly useful when the sample size is small. They find the exact sampling distribution of the test statistic rather than using the approximation provided by the chi-squared distribution. This is why such tests are often called exact tests.

Fisher's Exact Test

Fisher's exact test of the null hypothesis that two variables are independent was proposed by the British statistician and geneticist, Sir Ronald Fisher. The test is called *exact* because it uses a sampling distribution that gives exact probability calculations rather than the approximate ones that use the chi-squared distribution.

  The calculations for Fisher's exact test are complex and beyond the scope of this text. However, the principle behind the test is straightforward (see page 616 and Exercise 11.87), and the *Fisher's Exact Test* app or other statistical software provide its P-value. The smaller the P-value, the stronger the evidence that the variables are associated.

Fisher's Exact Test ◄

Example 10

A Tea-Tasting Experiment

Picture the Scenario

In introducing his small-sample test of independence in 1935, Fisher described the following experiment: Fisher enjoyed taking a break in the afternoon for tea. One day, his colleague Dr. Muriel Bristol claimed that when drinking tea she could tell whether the milk or the tea had been added to the cup first (she preferred milk first). To test her claim, Fisher asked her to taste eight cups of tea, four of which had the milk added first and four of which had the tea added first. She was told there were four cups of each type and was asked to indicate which four had the milk added first. The order of presenting the eight cups to her was randomized.

  Table 11.14 shows the result of the experiment. Dr. Bristol identified three of the four cups correctly that had milk poured first.

Table 11.14 Result of Tea-Tasting Experiment
The table cross-tabulates what was actually poured first (milk or tea) by what Dr. Bristol guessed was poured first. She had to indicate which four of the eight cups had the milk poured first. The first row refers to the four cups that had milk poured first, of which Dr. Bristol correctly identified three, and one (incorrectly) as having tea poured first.

Actual	Dr. Bristol's Guess		Total
	Milk	Tea	
Milk	3	1	4
Tea	1	3	4
Total	4	4	8

For those cases when milk was poured first (row 1), denote p_1 as the probability of guessing that milk was added first. For those cases when tea was poured first, denote p_2 as the probability of guessing that milk was added first. If Dr. Bristol has no ability to distinguish what was poured first, then her probability of guessing milk is the same, regardless what was poured first, so $p_1 = p_2$. If she has a higher probability of guessing milk for those cups that actually had milk first, then $p_1 > p_2$. So we shall test H_0: $p_1 = p_2$ (no ability) against H_a: $p_1 > p_2$. This tests the null hypothesis of no association between her guesses and the actual pouring order against the alternative that there is a *positive* association, i.e., that she more often gets it right when indeed milk was added first.

Questions to Explore

a. Show the five possible contingency tables that could have occurred for this experiment. (This is the sample space.)

b. Table 11.15 shows the result of using SPSS software to conduct the chi-squared test (first row) of the null hypothesis that her predictions were independent of the actual order of pouring. Is this test and its P-value appropriate for these data? Why or why not?

Table 11.15 Result of Fisher's Exact Test for Tea-Tasting Experiment

The chi-squared P-value is listed under Asymp. Sig., and the Fisher's exact test P-values are listed under Exact Sig. "Sig" is short for *significance* and "asymp." is short for *asymptotic*.

	Value	df	Asymp. Sig. (2-sided)	Exact Sig. (2-sided)	Exact Sig. (1-sided)
Pearson Chi-Square	2.000	1	.157		
Fisher's Exact Test				.486	.243

4 cells (100.0%) have expected count less than 5.

c. Table 11.15 also shows the result for Fisher's exact test for the two-sided and the one-sided alternative in the second row. The one-sided version of the test pertains to the alternative that she has a higher probability of guessing milk for those cups that actually had milk first (i.e., a positive association). What does this P-value suggest about Dr. Bristol's ability to distinguish what was poured first?

Think It Through

a. The possible sample tables have four observations in each row because there were four cups with milk poured first and four cups with tea poured first. The tables also have four observations in each column because Dr. Bristol was told there were four cups of each type and was asked to identify which four had the milk added first. Of the four cups in which milk was poured first (row 1 of the table), the number she could identify correctly is 4, 3, 2, 1, or 0. These outcomes correspond to the sample tables:

	Guess Poured First									
Poured First	**Milk**	**Tea**	**Milk**	**Tea**	**Milk**	**Tea**	**Milk**	**Tea**	**Milk**	**Tea**
Milk	4	0	3	1	2	2	1	3	0	4
Tea	0	4	1	3	2	2	3	1	4	0

These are the five possible tables with totals of 4 in each row and 4 in each column.

Recall

Expected cell count = (row total × column total) divided by total sample size. ◀

b. The cell counts in Table 11.14 are small. Each cell has expected count $(4 \times 4)/8 = 2$. Since they are less than 5, the chi-squared test may not be appropriate. In fact, the last line of the SPSS output warns us that all four cells have expected counts less than 5. The output reports $X^2 = 2.0$ with P-value $= 0.157$, but software provides results whether or not they are valid, and it's up to us to know when we can use a method.

c. The one-sided P-value reported by SPSS is for the alternative $H_a: p_1 > p_2$. It equals 0.243. This is the probability, presuming H_0 to be true, of the observed table (Table 11.14) and the more extreme table giving even more evidence in favor of $p_1 > p_2$. That more extreme table is the one with counts (4, 0) in the first row and (0, 4) in the second row, corresponding to guessing all four cups correctly. The P-value of 0.243 does not give much evidence against the null hypothesis. This experiment did not establish an association between the actual order of pouring and Dr. Bristol's predictions. In particular, there is not enough evidence to conclude Dr. Bristol can correctly predict what was poured first.

Insight

If Dr. Bristol had predicted all four cups correctly, the one-sided P-value would have been 0.014. We might then believe her claim. With a larger sample, we would not need such extreme results to get a small P-value. For instance, if 12 instead of 8 cups were used, she could afford to guess one incorrectly, and the P-value would still be less than 0.05.

▶ *Try Exercise 11.43*

In Practice To get the P-value, one adds the probability (computed under H_0) of all those tables that are as extreme or even more extreme. For the tea-tasting example, these are the probabilities of 3 or 4 correct guesses.

	Guess		
Actual	**Milk**	**Tea**	**Total**
Milk	3	—	4
Tea	—	—	4
Total	4	4	8

In part a of Example 10, notice that for the given row and column marginal totals of four each, the count in the first cell determines the other three cell counts. For example, for the actual data (Table 11.14), knowing she guessed three of the four cups correctly that had milk poured first determines the other three cells (see the margin). Because the count in the first cell determines the others, that cell count is regarded as the test statistic for Fisher's exact test. The P-value sums the probability of that count and of the other possible counts for that cell that provide even more evidence in support of H_a, assuming the null hypothesis of no association is true.

For the two-sided alternative $H_a: p_1 \neq p_2$, Table 11.15 indicates a P-value of 0.486. This alternative hypothesis investigates whether her predictions are better or worse than with random guessing. The P-value of 0.486 also does not give much evidence against the null hypothesis of no association between her guesses and the actual pouring order.

SUMMARY: Fisher's Exact Test of Independence for 2 × 2 Tables

1. Assumptions:
   Two binary categorical variables.
   Randomization, such as random sampling or a randomized experiment.

2. Hypotheses:
   H_0: The two variables are independent ($H_0: p_1 = p_2$).
   H_a: The two variables are associated.

   (Choose $H_a: p_1 \neq p_2$ or $H_a: p_1 > p_2$ or $H_a: p_1 < p_2$).

3. Test Statistic: First cell count (this determines the others, given the margin totals).

4. P-value: Probability that the first cell count equals the observed value or a value even more extreme than observed in the direction predicted by H_a assuming independence.

5. Conclusion: Report P-value and interpret in context. If a decision is needed, reject H_0 when P-value $\leq$ significance level (such as 0.05).

The main use of Fisher's exact test is for small sample sizes, when the chi-squared test is not valid. However, Fisher's exact test can be used with *any* sample sizes. It also extends to tables of dimension $r \times c$. The computations are complex, and unfortunately most software currently can perform it only for 2×2 tables, but the next section shows how Fisher's exact test is a special case of a permutation test and how this can be used to test independence in general $r \times c$ tables.

Fisher's Exact Test Is a Permutation Test

Suppose the random ordering of the eight cups presented to Dr. Bristol is as shown in the second column of the table in the margin, where M and T stand for milk or tea being poured first, respectively. The third column shows what Dr. Bristol thinks was poured first. We see that three of her guesses of those cups that had milk first are correct (cups 1, 5, and 7) and one is incorrect (cup 2).

Under the null hypothesis of no association, we believe Dr. Bristol is just randomly guessing, i.e., randomly picking a sequence of four Ms and four Ts for column three. Because she is randomly deciding which four have milk first, any sequence of four Ms and four Ts is equally likely to occur. For instance, she could have picked the sequence T M M T T T M M as shown in the last column of the margin table, which would have yielded two incorrect guesses (cups 1 and 3) out of the ones with milk first. Overall, there are 70 different such sequences (or **permutations**) of four Ms and four Ts that could have been picked, all equally likely under the null hypothesis of no association. Using these, we can build the exact sampling distribution under the null hypothesis of no association. Because the test uses permutations of the original observations, it is called a permutation test.

For each of the 70 possible permutations, we form the contingency table as in Table 11.14 and find how many guesses are correct out of the ones when milk was poured first, i.e., we find the count in the first cell. For the random permutation mentioned above, this would be the count of 2 (see the margin table). Table 11.16 shows the possible cell counts for the first cell and how often each one arises among the 70 permutations.

Setup of Tea-Tasting Experiment

The last column shows one random permutation (shuffling) of the original guesses.

Cup	Actual	Guess	Random Permutation
1	M	M	T
2	M	T	M
3	T	T	M
4	T	M	T
5	M	M	T
6	T	T	T
7	M	M	M
8	T	T	M

Contingency Table Based on Random Permutation

Actual	Guess	
	Milk	**Tea**
Milk	2	2
Tea	2	2

Distribution of Test Statistic (First Cell)

Sampling distribution of first cell count. (Screenshot taken from the *Fisher's Exact Test* app.)

Table 11.16 Sampling Distribution of the Number of Correct Guesses of Cups with Milk Poured First

This distribution assumes that the null hypothesis of no association is true. The margin figure shows the distribution graphically.

	Correct Guesses (First Cell Count)					
	0	**1**	**2**	**3**	**4**	**Total**
Number of Permutations	1	16	36	16	1	**70**
Relative Frequency	1.4%	22.9%	51.4%	22.9%	1.4%	**100%**

There is exactly 1 permutation out of the 70 possible with 0 correct guesses (the sequence T T M M T M T M, the exact opposite of the actual pouring sequence), 16 permutations with exactly 1 incorrect guess (one of them the actually observed one from Dr. Bristol), 36 permutations with exactly 2 incorrect guesses (such as the one mentioned), another 16 with exactly 3 incorrect guesses, and exactly 1 permutation in which all 4 guesses are correct (the permutation that equals the actual pouring sequence). We already knew from part a of Example 10 that 0, 1, 2, 3, and 4 are the possible entries for the first cell, but now, by looking at the relative frequencies in Table 11.16, we also know how likely they occur under the null hypothesis of no association. For instance, if we repeated the experiment over and over again, in every 1 out of 70 repetitions (i.e., in 1.4% of all cases), Dr. Bristol would actually correctly identify all four cups with milk added first, simply by chance (i.e., sheer luck) and without having any ability.

Using the exact sampling distribution of the number of correct guesses, we can now judge how likely it is to get 3 or even all 4 (the more extreme outcomes under the alternative $H_a: p_1 > p_2$) correct when one is just guessing. Because $0.229 + 0.014 = 0.243$, there is a 24.3% chance of getting 3 or 4 correct, just by chance. This is precisely the P-value for Fisher's exact test for the one-sided alternative that we obtained in Example 10 and which led to the conclusion indicated there. The P-value is called an exact P-value because it uses the exact, not approximate, sampling distribution derived by considering all possible permutations.

Permutation Test for an Association in General $r \times c$ Tables

The same idea of constructing a sampling distribution by permutations can be extended to general $r \times c$ tables. The only difference to the 2×2 case is that we no longer can use the first cell (the number of correctly identified cups with milk added first) as a test statistic but need a more general measure summarizing the association. We will use one that we have used all along to test for an association, the chi-squared statistic X^2. However, finding the P-value under the chi-squared distribution with $df = (r-1)(c-1)$ may no longer be appropriate because of small cell counts. Instead, we will find its exact sampling distribution considering all possible permutations or, if there are too many, a very large number of randomly generated permutations. This will let us judge whether the observed value of X^2 is large. We used a similar idea when we compared two population means across two groups in Section 10.3. There, we found the permutation distribution of the difference in sample means to judge how extreme the observed difference is under the null hypothesis of equal distributions. Similarly, here we will find the permutation distribution of X^2 to judge how extreme the observed X^2 is under the null hypothesis of independence (i.e., identical conditional distributions). To carry out the permutation test in practice, we will need specialized software, such as the *Permutation Test for Independence* app available on the book's website.

Recall

The larger the value of the chi-squared statistic X^2, the stronger the evidence for an association, but the chi-squared distribution is only appropriate to use as a reference when all expected cell counts are larger than 5. See Section 11.2. ◀

Example 11

Permutation Test ◀

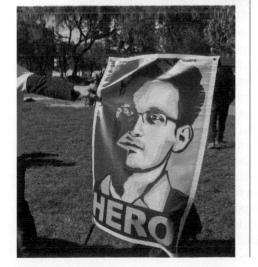

Edward Snowden—Hero or Criminal?

Picture the Scenario

In 2013, Edward Snowden revealed classified material about massive spying activities by the U.S. National Security Agency (NSA), not only on U.S citizens but on citizens worldwide. Although the United States wants to try him in court for breaking several laws, many other countries point out that the activities of the NSA severely violated their privacy laws. In these countries, Snowden is often celebrated as a hero. In a 2014 survey at Williams College, 12 randomly selected U.S. students and 8 randomly selected international students were asked whether Edward Snowden should be considered a hero, a criminal, or neither. Table 11.17 shows the results, for which $X^2 = 6.9$. We want to test whether these data provide evidence that the opinion on Edward Snowden differs between U.S. and international students at Williams College. The null hypothesis is that there is no association, i.e., the conditional distribution of opinion is the same for U.S. and international students.

Table 11.17 Survey Conducted at Williams College on Whether Edward Snowden Should Be Considered a Hero, a Criminal, or Neither
$X^2 = 6.9$ for this table.

| Student Status | Opinion on Edward Snowden | | | Total |
	Hero	Criminal	Neither	
U.S.	1	9	2	12
International	5	2	1	8
Total	6	11	3	20

Questions to Explore

a. Can we use the chi-squared distribution with $df = (2 - 1)(3 - 1) = 2$ to find the P-value for $X^2 = 6.9$?

b. How can we construct the permutation distribution of X^2 under the null hypothesis of no association?

c. How can we judge whether the observed value of 6.9 is extreme and find the permutation P-value?

Think It Through

a. Many counts in Table 11.17 are small, leading to expected values that are smaller than 5. For instance, the expected count is 3.6 in the first cell and 1.2 in the last cell. Using the chi-squared distribution may lead to questionable conclusions because it may not approximate the actual sampling distribution of X^2 well, especially in the upper tail.

b. The first three columns of Table 11.18 in the margin show the raw data from the survey before summarizing it in Table 11.17. (You can check that there are, for instance, 5 international students with response Hero.) Under the null hypothesis of no association, any given response is equally likely to have come from a U.S. student or an international student. For instance, under the null hypothesis, the probability of a student selecting Hero does not depend on whether the student is a U.S. or international student. Then, the status of a student is merely a label that loses its relevance, and we get a data set that is equally likely to occur (under the null hypothesis) when we rearrange (permute) these labels.

This is similar to the tea-tasting experiment, in which, under the null hypothesis of no association, any of the 70 permutations of the four Ms and four Ts was equally likely to occur. Here, any permutation (or shuffling) of the status labels for the 12 U.S. and 8 international students yields a data set that is equally likely to occur.

The last column in Table 11.18 shows one such random permutation. Taken together with the response column, it leads to the cell counts shown in Table 11.19 on the next page. For instance, with the permuted status labels, we now have 4 U.S. students and 2 international students with response Hero.

Table 11.19 has the same row and column margins as the original Table 11.17. (Rearranging the labels as we did in the last column of Table 11.18 didn't change the fact that we have a total of 12 U.S. and 8 international students as well as a total of 6 students responding Hero, 11 responding Criminal, and 2 responding Neither.) However, the cell counts in the body of the table differ from the ones in Table 11.17, leading to a chi-squared statistic of $X^2 = 3.1$. If the null hypothesis is true, this table

Table 11.18 Original Observations for Data Summarized in Table 11.17

The last column shows one random permutation of the original status labels.

Student	Status	Response	Random Permutation
1	Int	Hero	US
2	US	Criminal	Int
3	US	Neither	US
4	US	Criminal	US
5	US	Hero	US
6	US	Criminal	US
7	US	Criminal	Int
8	US	Criminal	US
9	US	Criminal	US
10	Int	Criminal	Int
11	Int	Hero	Int
12	US	Neither	US
13	Int	Hero	US
14	Int	Hero	Int
15	Int	Hero	US
16	US	Criminal	US
17	Int	Criminal	Int
18	Int	Neither	US
19	US	Criminal	Int
20	US	Criminal	Int

Table 11.19 Contingency Table Based on the Permuted Status Labels
$X^2 = 3.1$ for this table.

Student	Opinion on Edward Snowden			Total
	Hero	**Criminal**	**Neither**	
U.S.	4	5	3	12
International	2	6	0	8
Total	**6**	**11**	**3**	**20**

(and hence this value for the chi-squared statistic) is equally likely to be observed as the originally observed table (and its chi-squared value).

A different permutation of the status labels results in yet another table with the same margins but different cell counts. For each such table generated from a permutation, we compute the chi-squared statistic X^2. Note that several permutations can give rise to the same table and hence X^2 statistic. For instance, just switching the last two labels for students 19 and 20 (both U.S. students with response Criminal) results in the same table (and hence X^2 statistic) as the one observed.

Tabulating all the unique values of X^2 that can arise and their frequency of occurrence yields the exact (as opposed to approximate) sampling distribution of X^2 under the null hypothesis of no association. When the cell counts are large, distribution will have the shape of a chi-squared distribution, but for small cell counts, it may look more irregular. The table in the margin shows an excerpt of the permutation distribution, and Figure 11.9, taken from the *Permutation Test for Independence* app, represents it with a histogram. Both are based on 10,000 randomly generated permutations.

Excerpt of sampling distribution of X^2 based on 10,000 random permutations

X^2	# Perms	Freq. (%)	Cumulative Freq. (%)
0.3	1,713	17.3	17.3
...	...	...	...
3.1	554	5.5	84.3
...	...	...	...
6.6	80	0.8	96.8
6.9	154	1.5	98.4
7.4	81	0.8	99.2
...	...	...	...
13.4	1	<0.0	100
	10,000	100%	

Sampling Distribution of X^2

Based on 10,000 random permutations. X^2 of original table: 6.93
315 permutations yield X^2 as large or larger than 6.93: P-value = 0.0315

▲ **Figure 11.9** Permutation Distribution of X^2 Based on Data in Table **11.17.** Screenshot from the *Permutation Test for Independence* app. The orange half circle indicates the observed value of $X^2 = 6.9$. **Question** For tables with larger cell counts than Table 11.19, the shape of the permutation distribution is approximately equal to the shape of which distribution?

c. How extreme is the observed chi-squared statistic of 6.9? Figure 11.9 gives us an idea. The observed value is indicated by the orange half circle, which is in the upper tail of the sampling distribution. To find the permutation P-value, we need to find the proportion of the 10,000 randomly generated permutations that gave a chi-squared statistic as large or larger than the one observed. As the title of the plot in Figure 11.9 indicates, 315 of the 10,000 permutations had an X^2 as large or larger than 6.9, for a proportion of 0.0315. This is the permutation P-value

In Practice When the number of all possible permutations is too large, one takes a large random sample (such as 10,000) of them and computes X^2 for each. The proportion of permutations with X^2 as large or larger than the observed one is then a very good approximation of the exact permutation P-value.

for the chi-squared test. If there were no difference in the opinion of U.S. and international students, observing a test statistic of 6.9 or larger would be unlikely (estimated probability of 0.031). Because the P-value is small, there is evidence that the opinion on Edward Snowden differs between U.S. and international students.

▶ **Try Exercises 11.46 and the Activity in Exercise 11.89**

11.5 Practicing the Basics

11.41 Keeping old dogs mentally sharp In an experiment with beagles ages 7–11, the dogs attempted to learn how to find a treat under a certain black-colored block and then relearn that task with a white-colored block. The control group of dogs received standard care and diet. The diet and exercise group were given dog food fortified with vegetables and citrus pulp and vitamin E and C supplements plus extra exercise and social play. All 12 dogs in the diet and exercise group were able to solve the entire task, but only 2 of the 8 dogs in the control group could do so. (Background material from N. W. Milgram et al., *Neurobiology of Aging,* vol. 26, 2005, pp. 77–90.)

  a. Show how to summarize the results in a contingency table.

  b. Conduct all steps of Fisher's exact test of the hypothesis that whether a dog can solve the task is independent of the treatment group. Use the two-sided alternative hypothesis. Interpret.

  c. Why is it improper to conduct the chi-squared test for these data?

11.42 Tea-tasting results Consider the tea-tasting experiment of Example 11 and Table 11.14. Consider the possible sample table in which all four of her predictions about the cups that had milk poured first are correct. Using software, find the P-value for the one-sided alternative. Interpret the P-value.

11.43 Claritin and nervousness An advertisement by Schering Corporation for the allergy drug Claritin mentioned that in a pediatric randomized clinical trial, symptoms of nervousness were shown by 4 of 188 patients on Claritin and 2 of 262 patients taking placebo. Denote the population proportion who would show such symptoms by p_1 for Claritin and by p_2 for placebo. The computer printout shows results of significance tests for $H_0: p_1 = p_2$.

  a. Report the P-value for the small-sample test with $H_a: p_1 \neq p_2$. Interpret in the context of this study.

  b. Is it appropriate to conduct the chi-squared test for these data? Why or why not?

Analyses of Claritin Data

```
Rows: treatment  Columns: nervousness

              yes      no

Claritin       4      184

Placebo        2      260
Statistic                      P-Value
Fisher's Exact Test (2-Tail)    0.24
Chi-squared = 1.55              0.21
```

11.44 AIDS and condom use Chatterjee et al. (1995, p. 132) described a study about the effect of condoms in reducing the spread of AIDS. This two-year Italian study followed heterosexual couples where one partner was infected with the HIV virus. Of 171 couples who always used condoms, 3 partners became infected with HIV, whereas of 55 couples who did not always use condoms, 8 partners became infected. Test whether the rates are significantly different.

  a. Define p_1 and p_2 in this context and specify the null and two-sided alternative hypotheses.

  b. For these data, software reports

```
Pearson Chi-Square = 14.704, DF = 1,
P-Value = 0.0001
*Note* 1 cell with expected count
less than 5 Fisher's exact test:
P-Value = 0.0007
```

Report the result of the test that you feel is most appropriate for these data. For the test you chose, report the P-value and interpret in the context of this study.

11.45 Quizzes worthwhile? To help students gauge their understanding of basic concepts, short online quizzes with immediate feedback were administered in an introductory statistics (STAT) and an unrelated computer science (CS) course in the first few weeks of the semester. For those students who realized they knew less than they thought after taking the quizzes, did this change their study habits? All 5 students in the STAT course said it did, whereas

6 of the 12 students in the CS course said it did. Is there evidence that students in the STAT course had a larger probability of changing their habits?

a. Write these results as a 2×2 contingency table.

b. The sampling distribution (derived from all possible 6,188 permutations) for the possible counts in the first cell of the contingency table is

Cell Count:	0	1	2	3	4	5	**Total**
#Perms:	6	165	1,100	2,475	1,980	462	**6,188**

Find the proportion of tables that have a cell count as large or larger than the one observed.

c. Find the permutation P-value and write a conclusion for the hypothesis when using a 5% significance level.

d. Check your results by entering the contingency table from part a into the *Fisher's Exact Test* app accessible from the book's website.

11.46 Quizzes enhance learning? Refer to the previous exercise. After the semester, students were asked whether the quizzes were beneficial, with possible answers (i) Yes, I realized that I knew more than I thought,

(ii) Yes, I realized that I knew less than I thought, (iii) No. Results of the survey are shown in the following table. Is there evidence that the distribution of the student responses differ between the two courses?

	Beneficial		
Group	Yes, More	Yes, Less	No
STAT	3	5	18
CS	9	12	20

a. Formulate the null and alternative hypotheses of interest.

b. Suggest a test statistic to use for this test.

c. If all expected cell counts were at least 5, what distribution would the test statistic from part b follow?

d. Of 10,000 random permutations, 2,660 resulted in an X^2 statistic as large or larger than the observed one of 3.2. Approximate the permutation P-value and write a conclusion for the test.

e. Use the *Permutation Test of Independence* app accessible from the book's website to enter the contingency table and replicate the results from part d.

Chapter Review

SUMMARY OF NOTATION

X^2 = chi-squared statistic for testing independence of two categorical variables

$df = (r - 1)(c - 1)$ = degrees of freedom (#rows – 1)(#cols – 1) for X^2 test

residual = observed – expected cell count

$p_1 - p_2$ = difference of proportions

p_1/p_2 = ratio of proportions – relative risk

$p_1/(1 - p_1)$ = odds in group 1

$(p_1/(1 - p_1))/(p_2/(1 - p_2))$ = odds ratio

CHAPTER SUMMARY

This chapter showed how to analyze the association between two categorical variables:

- By *describing the counts* in contingency tables using the **conditional distributions** across the categories of the response variable. If the population conditional distributions are identical, the two variables are **independent**.

- By using the **chi-squared** statistic to **test the null hypothesis of independence**. When comparing two or more groups in terms of a single categorical response variable, the test is also referred to as a test of **homogeneity**.

- By *describing the strength of association with a* **measure of association** such as the **difference of proportions**, the **ratio of proportions** (the **relative risk**) or the **ratio of odds** (the **odds ratio**). Under independence, the population difference of proportions equals 0 and the population relative risk and odds ratio equal 1. The stronger the association, the farther the measures fall on either side from these baseline values.

- By *describing the pattern of association* by comparing observed and expected cell counts using **standardized residuals**. A standardized residual reports the number of standard errors that an observed count falls from an expected count. A value larger than about 3 in absolute value indicates that the cell provides strong evidence of association.

The **expected cell counts** are values we expect to see in the cells when the null hypothesis of independence is true. The **chi-squared test statistic** compares the observed cell counts to the expected cell counts, using

$$X^2 = \sum \frac{(\text{observed count} - \text{expected count})^2}{\text{expected count}}.$$

Under the null hypothesis, the X^2 test statistic has a large sample **chi-squared distribution**. Larger values of X^2 are evidence against independence. The **degrees of freedom** depend on the number of rows r and the number of columns c such that $df = (r - 1) \times (c - 1)$. The P-value is the right-tail probability to the right of the observed value of X^2.

The expected cell counts for the chi-squared test should be at least 5. **Fisher's exact test** does not have a sample size restriction. It is used to test independence in 2×2 tables with samples that are too small for the chi-squared test to apply. Fisher's exact test is a special case of a **permutation test** in general $r \times c$ tables that use the exact rather than the approximate sampling distribution of the X^2 statistic.

The chi-squared statistic can also be used for a hypothesis involving a single categorical variable. For testing a hypothesis that predicts particular population proportion values for each category of the variable, the chi-squared statistic is referred to as a **goodness-of-fit** statistic.

LEARNING OBJECTIVES

1. Understand how to analyze the association between two categorical variables by comparing conditional distributions across the categories of the response variable.

2. Recognize that identical population conditional distributions indicate independence of the two categorical variables.

3. Explain the difference between observed and expected cell counts.

4. Test the null hypothesis of independence, using the chi-squared test statistic.

5. Describe the chi-squared distribution.

6. Interpret what the chi-squared statistic measures and why a larger value provides evidence against the null hypothesis of independence.

7. Understand that the P-value comes from the upper tail of a chi-squared distribution, and interpret the P-value.

8. Understand the limitations of the chi-squared test.

9. Describe the strength of association by using the difference of proportions, the relative risk, or the odds ratio.

10. Describe the pattern of association by using standardized residuals.

11. (Optional) Understand the operations and use of Fisher's exact test and, more generally, permutation tests when the sample size conditions for the chi-squared test are not satisfied.

ANSWERS TO THE CHAPTER FIGURE QUESTIONS

Figure 11.1 The proportion of those not too happy increases with lower income, whereas the proportion of those very happy decreases with lower income. The proportion of those pretty happy is roughly the same in each of the three income categories.

Figure 11.2 The height of the bars is the same for males and females at each level of happiness.

Figure 11.4 The chi-squared statistic can't be negative because it sums squared differences divided by positive expected frequencies.

Figure 11.5 We use only the right tail because larger chi-squared values provide greater evidence against H_0. Chi-squared values in the left tail represent small differences between observed and expected frequencies and do not provide evidence against H_0.

Figure 11.7 Whether we get $\frac{1}{4}$ or 4 for the relative risk depends merely on which group we call group 1 and which we call group 2.

Figure 11.9 For tables with large cell counts, the permutation (= sampling) distribution of X^2 looks like the chi-squared distribution.

STATISTICAL SOFTWARE

Art of Stat Web Apps

- **Chi-Squared Test** This app carries out the chi-squared test by computing the X^2 statistic and its corresponding P-value from the chi-squared distribution, drawing its graph. The app provides conditional proportions, including a side-by-side or stacked bar graph, as well as expected counts and raw and standardized residuals. You can enter your own data in contingency table format or as raw observations. A second tab carries out a chi-squared goodness-of-fit test.

- **Chi-Squared Distribution** This app lets you interactively explore the chi-squared distribution and compute tail probabilities as well as percentiles.

- **Association Between Two Categorical Variables** This app finds the difference of proportions, the ratio of proportions, or the odds ratio, for data in 2×2 contingency tables. It provides a side-by-side bar graph of the conditional proportions. It also allows for finding a bootstrap percentile confidence interval for any of these three measures.

- **Fisher's Exact Test** and **Permutation Test for Independence** These two apps implement the (permutation) test of independence (versus an association) for 2×2 and more generally $r \times c$ contingency tables.

R

- **Chi-squared distribution:** The pchisq function finds (lower-tail) probabilities under the chi-squared distribution, such that $> 1 - $ pchisq(2.86, df = 2) returns the upper tail probability 0.239 from the chi-squared distribution with $df = 2$, which is the P-value from Example 5. qchisq returns percentiles, such as $>$ qchisq(0.95, df = 4) returning 9.49, the value mentioned in Table 11.6.

- **Chi-squared test:** You can get the X^2 statistic, its associated P-value, expected counts, and standardized residuals from the chisq.test function. This function expects a table as input, so if you have raw data, you first need to create a contingency table from them, using the table command. We illustrate with the raw data from Example 5, which you can find on the book's website, under the name "HeadacheRaw.csv." (If you already have the data in contingency table format, you can type it into R as shown in the R code for Chapter 3.)

```
> myfile <- file.choose() #path to file
> headache <- read.csv(myfile) #reads in file
> attach(headache) #can reference names
> mytable <- table(drug, outcome) #get table
> mytable
         outcome
drug      mild moderate severe
  active   486     113     16
  placebo  355      80      5
```

```
> mytest <- chisq.test(mytable)
> mytest
 Pearson's Chi-squared test
data:  mytable
X-squared = 2.8601, df = 2, p-value = 0.2393
```

This shows the X^2 statistic and P-value we obtained in Example 5. You can get the expected cell counts by typing > mytest$expected, and residuals and standardized residuals through > mytest$residuals and > mytest$stdres. To carry out the permutation test with 10,000 random permutations mentioned in Section 11.5, use > chisq.test(mytable, simulate.p.value = TRUE, B = 10000).

CHAPTER EXERCISES

Practicing the Basics

11.47 Female for president? When recent General Social Surveys have asked, "If your party nominated a woman for president, would you vote for her if she were qualified for the job?" about 94% of females and 94% of males answered yes, the rest answered no. (*Source:* Data from CSM, UC Berkeley.)

a. For males and for females, report the conditional distributions on this response variable in a 2 × 2 table, using outcome categories (yes, no).

b. If results for the entire population are similar to these, does it seem possible that gender and opinion about having a woman president are independent? Explain.

11.48 Down syndrome diagnostic test The following table, from Example 8 in Chapter 5, cross-tabulates whether a fetus has Down syndrome by whether the triple blood diagnostic test for Down syndrome is positive (that is, indicates that the fetus has Down syndrome).

a. Tabulate the conditional distributions for the blood test result, given the true Down syndrome status.

b. For the Down cases, what percentage was diagnosed as positive by the diagnostic test? For the unaffected cases, what percentage got a negative test result? Does the diagnostic test appear to be a good one?

c. Construct the conditional distribution on Down syndrome status for those who have a positive test result. (*Hint:* You condition on the first column total and find proportions in that column.) Of those cases, what percentage truly have Down syndrome? Is the result surprising? Explain why this probability is small.

Down Syndrome Status	Blood Test Result		Total
	Positive	**Negative**	
D (Down)	48	6	**54**
D^c (Unaffected)	1,307	3,921	**5,228**
Total	**1,355**	**3,927**	**5,282**

11.49 Down and chi-squared For the data in the previous exercise, show all steps of the chi-squared test of independence. (You can enter the data in the *Chi-Squared Test* app.)

11.50 Herbs and the common cold A recent randomized experiment of a multiherbal formula (Immumax) containing echinacea, garlic, ginseng, zinc, and vitamin C was found to improve cold symptoms in adults over a placebo group. "At the end of the study, eight (39%) of the placebo recipients and 18 (60%) of the Immumax recipients reported that the study medication had helped improve their cold symptoms (chi-squared P-value = 0.01)." (M. Yakoot et al., *International Journal of General Medicine*, vol. 4, 2011, pp. 45–51).

a. Identify the response variable and the explanatory variable and their categories for the 2 × 2 contingency table that provided this particular analysis.

b. How would you explain to someone who has never studied statistics how to interpret the parenthetical part of the quoted sentence?

11.51 Happiness and number of friends The table shows GSS data on happiness and the number of close friends, with expected cell counts given underneath the observed counts.

Number of Close Friends	Happiness			Total
	Not Too Happy	**Pretty Happy**	**Very Happy**	
0–1	34	92	43	**169**
	19.2	95.1	54.7	
2–5	83	418	200	**701**
	79.5	394.6	226.9	
6 or more	47	304	225	**576**
	65.3	324.3	186.4	
Total	**164**	**814**	**468**	**1,446**

a. Suppose the variables were independent. Explain what this means in this context.

b. Explain what is meant by an expected cell count. Show how to get the expected cell count for the first cell, for which the observed count is 34.

c. Compare the expected cell frequencies to the observed counts. Based on this, what is a profile of subjects who tend to be (i) more happy than independence predicts and (ii) less happy than independence predicts.

11.52 Gender gap? Exercise 11.1 showed a 2 × 3 table relating gender and political party identification, shown again here. Conduct all five steps of the chi-squared test. (The *Chi-Squared Test* app has this table preloaded.)

| | Political Party Identification | | | |
Gender	Democrat	Independent	Republican	Total
Female	439	525	275	**1,239**
Male	292	455	252	**999**

Source: Data from CSM, UC Berkeley.

11.53 Job satisfaction and income Data from a GSS were used to cross-tabulate income (<$15 thousand, $15–25 thousand, $25–40 thousand, >$40 thousand) in dollars with job satisfaction (very dissatisfied, little dissatisfied, moderately satisfied, very satisfied) for 96 subjects.

a. For these data, $X^2 = 6.0$. What is its *df* value, and what is its approximate sampling distribution, if H_0 is true?

b. For this test, the P-value is 0.74. Interpret in the context of these variables.

c. What decision would you make with a 0.05 significance level? Can you accept H_0 and conclude that job satisfaction is independent of income?

11.54 Aspirin and heart attacks for women A study in the *New England Journal of Medicine* compared cardiovascular events for treatments of low-dose aspirin or placebo among 39,876 healthy female health care providers for an average duration of about 10 years. Results indicated that women receiving aspirin and those receiving placebo did not differ for rates of a first major cardiovascular event, death from cardiovascular causes, or fatal or nonfatal heart attacks. However, women receiving aspirin had lower rates of stroke than those receiving placebo (*Source:* Data from *New England Journal of Medicine*, vol. 352, 2005, pp. 1293–1304).

| | Cardiovascular Events | | |
Group	Mini-Stroke	Stroke	No Strokes
Placebo	240	259	19,443
Aspirin	185	219	19,530

a. Use the *Chi-Squared Test* app or other software to test independence. Mention (i) assumptions, (ii) hypotheses, (iii) test statistic, (iv) P-value, (v) conclusion in the context of this study.

b. Describe the association by finding and interpreting the relative risk for the stroke category.

11.55 Crossing peas When crossing round (R) and yellow (Y) peas with wrinkled (W) and green (G) peas, one can get any combination of color and appearance, denoted here as RY, RG, WY, and WG, but traits round and yellow are dominant. In particular, Gregor Mendel postulated that these four possible combinations would appear in the ratio 9:3:3:1. From an experiment involving 556 such crossings, 315 were RY, 108 RG, 101 WY, and 32 WG.

a. Construct a table showing these counts.

b. If Mendel's theory about the ratio 9:3:3:2 is correct, how likely is each combination to occur? (*Hint:* Of $9 + 3 + 3 + 1 = 16$ crossings, how many are of type RY?)

c. Find the expected values for the four combinations assuming Mendel's theory is correct.

d. A chi-squared test for testing Mendel's theory will be based on how many degrees of freedom?

e. The chi-squared statistic for these data equals 0.47. Will the P-value for the test be large or small? Why?

11.56 Women's role A recent GSS presented the statement, "Women should take care of running their homes and leave running the country up to men," and 14.8% of the male respondents agreed. Of the female respondents, 15.9% agreed. Of respondents having less than a high school education, 39.0% agreed. Of respondents having at least a high school education, 11.7% agreed.

a. Report the difference between the proportion of males and the proportion of females who agree.

b. Report the difference between the proportion at the low education level and the proportion at the high education level who agree.

c. Which variable, gender or educational level, seems to have the stronger association with opinion? Explain your reasoning.

11.57 Seat belt helps? The following table refers to passengers in autos and light trucks involved in accidents in the state of Maine in a recent year.

a. Use the difference of proportions to describe the strength of association. Interpret.

b. Use the relative risk to describe the strength of association. Interpret.

| | Injury | |
Seat Belt	Yes	No
No	3,865	27,037
Yes	2,409	35,383

Source: Dr. Cristanna Cook, Medical Care Development, Augusta, Maine.

11.58 Serious side effects In 2007, the FDA announced that the popular drug Zelnorm used to treat irritable bowel syndrome was withdrawn from the market, citing concerns about serious side effects. The analysis of several studies revealed that 13 of 11,614 patients receiving the drug had a serious side effect such as heart attack or stroke, compared to just 1 out of 7,031 on placebo. (You can enter the counts in the *Association Between*

Two Categorical Variables app to compute measures of association.)

a. Construct a 2×2 contingency table from these data.

b. Compute the relative risk and interpret.

c. Compute the odds ratio and interpret.

d. In a letter to health care professionals, the drug maker quoted a P-value of 0.024 for the comparison between the probability of a serious side effect in the drug and placebo group. By entering the data into the *Fisher's Exact Test* app (or other software), show that this is the P-value for Fisher's exact test with a two-sided alternative hypothesis. What are the conclusions at a 0.05 significance level?

11.59 Pesticides The following table, on the presence of pesticide residues in samples of organic and conventional food was analyzed in Examples 2 and 3 in Chapter 3. (You can enter the counts in the *Association Between Two Categorical Variables* app to compute measures of association.)

	Pesticides	
Food Type	**Yes**	**No**
Organic	29	98
Conventional	19,485	7,086

a. Compute the relative risk and interpret.

b. Find the reciprocal of your answer to part a and interpret.

c. Compute the odds ratio and interpret.

d. Find the reciprocal of your answer to part c and interpret.

e. What's wrong with this statement: The proportion of conventional food samples with pesticide residues present is more than 9 times higher than the proportion of organic food samples with pesticide residues present.

11.60 Race and party ID The table shows data from an SPSS printout based on 2008 GSS data on race and party ID.

a. Interpret the expected count for the first cell.

b. Interpret the standardized residual of 12.5 for the first cell (SPSS calls it an adjusted residual).

c. How would you summarize to someone who has never studied statistics what you learn from the standardized residuals given in the four corner cells on this printout?

race* party_ID Crosstabulation

			party ID			
			democrat	independent	republican	Total
race	Black	Count	192	75	8	275
		Expected Count	100.0	101.5	73.5	275.0
		Adjusted Residual	12.5	–3.6	–9.7	
	White	Count	459	586	471	1516
		Expected Count	551.0	559.5	405.5	1516.0
		Adjusted Residual	–12.5	3.6	9.7	
Total		Count	651	661	479	1791
		Expected Count	651.0	661.0	479.0	1791.0

Source: Data from CSM, UC Berkeley.

11.61 Happiness and sex A contingency table from the 2012 GSS relating happiness to number of sex partners in the previous year (0, 1, at least 2) had standardized residuals (called Z-statistic here) as shown in the screen shot. Interpret the standardized residuals in the last column.

11.62 Education and religious beliefs When data from a recent GSS were used to form a 3×3 table that cross-tabulates highest degree (1 = less than high school, 2 = high school or junior college, 3 = bachelor or graduate) with religious beliefs (F = fundamentalist, M = moderate, L = liberal), the three largest standardized residuals were: 6.8 for the cell (3, F), 6.3 for the cell (3, L), and 4.5 for the cell (1, F). Summarize how to interpret these three standardized residuals.

11.63 TV and aggression From a study described in Example 5 in the previous chapter, the proportion of males committing aggressive acts was 4 out of 45 for those who watched less than 1 hour of TV a day and 117 out of 315 for those who watched at least 1 hour per day. MINITAB reports the printout shown for conducting Fisher's exact test (two-sided) for these data.

a. State hypotheses for the test, defining the notation.

b. Report the P-value that software reports and interpret in the context of this study.

Data on TV Watching and Aggression
```
Rows: TV  Columns: aggression
               no        yes
high          198        117
low            41          4
Fisher's exact test:
P-Value = 0.0000751
```

11.64 Botox side effects An advertisement for Botox Cosmetic by Allergan, Inc. for treating wrinkles appeared in several magazines. The back page of the ad showed the results of a randomized clinical trial to compare 405 people receiving Botox injections to 130 people receiving placebo in terms of the frequency of various side effects. The side effect of pain in the face was reported by 9 people receiving Botox and 0 people receiving placebo. Use an appropriate app (or other software) to conduct a two-sided test of the hypothesis that the probability of this side effect is the same for each group. Report all steps of the test and interpret results.

11.65 Clarity of diamonds Does the clarity of a diamond depend on its cut? Exercise 3.4 showed data, reproduced below, on the clarity (rated as internally flawless, IF, very very slightly included, VVS, very slightly included, VS, slightly included, SI and included, I) for the two lowest ratings for cut, which are "good" and "fair."

Cut	Clarity					
	IF	VVS	VS	SI	I	Total
Good	2	4	16	55	3	**80**
Fair	1	3	8	30	2	**44**

a. Verify, e.g., with the *Chi-Squared Test* app, that $X^2 = 0.267$ for this table. The (raw) data are available on the book's website as Diamonds.csv.

b. Can you use the chi-squared distribution to find a P-value? Why or why not?

c. Of 10,000 random permutations, 9,908 resulted in an X^2 value as large or larger than the one observed. Find the (approximate) permutation P-value and interpret.

d. Use the *Permutation Test of Independence* app accessible from the book's website to enter the contingency table and replicate the results from part c.

Concepts and Applications

11.66 Benford's Law When looking at a collection of numbers, such as population sizes, the figures on tax returns or the charges on a credit card, one may think that the leading digit of such numbers is equally likely to be any of the numbers from 1 to 9. However, such collection of numbers often show a distribution for the leading digit that is quite different from uniform and is described by Benford's Law. This law stipulates that the probability for the leading digit to be 1 is 30.1%, whereas the probability of the leading digit to be 9 is only 4.6% instead of a uniform $1/9 = 11.1\%$ probability for each. The following table shows the distribution of the leading digit of the last 130 transactions on the credit card of one of the authors. The data are available in the *Chi-Squared Test* app (second tab) and on the book's website.

Leading Digit:	1	2	3	4	5	6	7	8	9	Total
Benford Probabilities (%):	30.1	17.6	12.5	9.7	7.9	6.7	5.8	5.1	4.6	**100**
Observed Counts:	39	24	20	7	6	10	11	6	7	**130**

a. Find the expected counts, assuming the leading digits for the transactions follow Benford's Law.

b. Is there evidence that the distribution of the leading digit does not follow Benford's Law? Write a conclusion based on an appropriate test. If available, use software to read in the raw data and compute the test statistic and P-value.

11.67 Student data Refer to the FL Student Survey data file on the book's website. Using software, create and analyze descriptively and inferentially the contingency table relating religiosity and belief in life after death. Summarize your analyses in a short report.

11.68 Marital happiness decreasing? At the GSS website (see Activity 2), cross-tabulate HAPMAR (row variable) with YEAR (column variable) so you can see how conditional distributions on marital happiness in the GSS have changed since 1973. (Don't forget to select No Weight for the Weight option.) Using conditional distributions and standardized residuals, explain how these results show a very slight trend over time for fewer people to report being very happy. (You can get standardized residuals by checking Z-statistic under Output Options.)

11.69 Another predictor of happiness? Go to the GSS website (see Activity 2) and find a variable that is associated with happiness, other than variables used in this chapter. Use methods from this chapter to describe and make inferences about the association, in a one-page report.

11.70 Pregnancy associated with contraceptive use? Whether a young married woman becomes pregnant in the next year is a categorical variable with categories (yes, no). Another categorical variable to consider is whether she and her partner use contraceptives with categories (yes, no). Would you expect these variables to be independent or associated? Explain.

11.71 Babies and gray hair A young child wonders what causes women to have babies. For each woman who lives on her block, she observes whether her hair is gray and whether she has young children, with the results shown in the table that follows.

a. Construct the 2 × 2 contingency table that cross-tabulates gray hair (yes, no) with "has young children" (yes, no) for these nine women.

b. Treating "has young children" as the response variable, obtain the conditional distributions for those women who have gray hair and for those who do not. Does there seem to be an association?

c. Noticing this association, the child concludes that not having gray hair is what causes women to have children. Use this example to explain why association does not necessarily imply causation.

Woman	Gray Hair	Young Children
Andrea	No	Yes
Mary	Yes	No
Linda	No	Yes
Jane	No	Yes
Maureen	Yes	No
Judy	Yes	No
Margo	No	Yes
Carol	Yes	No
Donna	No	Yes

11.72 When is chi-squared not valid? Give an example of a contingency table for which the chi-squared test of independence should not be used.

11.73 Gun homicide in United States and Britain   According to recent United Nations figures, the annual intentional homicide rate is 4.7 per 100,000 residents in the United States and 1.0 per 100,000 residents in Britain.

   a. Compare the proportion of residents of the two countries killed intentionally using the difference of proportions. Show how the results differ according to whether the United States or Britain is identified as Group 1.

   b. Compare the proportion of residents of the two countries by using the relative risk. Show how the results differ according to whether the United States or Britain is identified as Group 1.

   c. When both proportions are very close to 0, as in this example, which measure do you think is more useful for describing the strength of association? Why?

11.74 Colon cancer and race   The State Center for Health Statistics for the North Carolina Division of Public Health released a report in 2010 that indicates that there are racial disparities in colorectal cancer incidence and mortality rates. The report states, "African Americans are less likely to receive appropriate screenings that reduce the risk of developing or dying from colorectal cancer." During 2002–2006, the rate of incidence for African Americans was 57.3 per 100,000 versus 46.5 per 100,000 for White residents (www.schs.state.nc.us). African Americans were 19% more likely to have been diagnosed with colon cancer. Explain how to get this estimate.

11.75 Statistical versus practical relevance   In any significance test, when the sample size is very large, we have not necessarily established an important result when we reject the null hypothesis (i.e., establish statistical significance). Explain what this means in the context of analyzing contingency tables with a chi-squared test.

Multiple Choice or True/False

11.76 True or false: $X^2 = 0$ The null hypothesis for the test of independence between two categorical variables is $H_0: X^2 = 0$ for the sample chi-squared statistic X^2. (*Hint:* Do hypotheses refer to a sample or the population?)

11.77 True or false: Group 1 becomes Group 2   Interchanging two rows or interchanging two columns in a contingency table has no effect on the value of the X^2 statistic.

11.78 True or false: Relative risk   Interchanging the rows in a 2×2 contingency table has no effect on the value of the relative risk.

11.79 True or false: Relative risk versus odds ratio   Refer to a contingency table that cross-classifies subjects in two rows and two columns (labeled Success and Failure) and for which the odds ratio equals 4. Then, subjects in row 1 are 4 times as likely to have a success as subjects in row 2.

11.80 True or false: Practical relevance   Even when the sample conditional distributions in a contingency table are only slightly different, when the sample size is very large it is possible to have a large X^2 statistic and a very small P-value for testing H_0: independence.

Advanced Concepts

11.81 Normal and chi-squared with $df = 1$ When $df = 1$, the P-value from the chi-squared test of independence is the same as the P-value for the two-sided test comparing two proportions with the z test statistic. This is because of a direct connection between the standard normal distribution and the chi-squared distribution with $df = 1$: Squaring a z-score yields a chi-squared value with $df = 1$, having chi-squared right-tail probability equal to the two-tail normal probability for the z-score.

   a. Illustrate this with $z = 1.96$, the z-score with a two-tail probability of 0.05. Using the *Chi-Squared Distribution* app or a table, show that the square of 1.96 is the chi-squared score for $df = 1$ with a P-value of 0.05.

   b. Show the connection between the normal and chi-squared values with P-value = 0.01.

11.82 Multiple response variables   Each subject in a sample of 100 men and 100 women is asked to indicate which of the following factors (one or more) are responsible for increases in crime committed by teenagers: A—the increasing gap in income between the rich and poor, B—the increase in the percentage of single-parent families, C—insufficient time that parents spend with their children. To analyze whether responses differ by gender of respondent, we cross-classify the responses by gender, as the table shows.

   a. Is it valid to apply the chi-squared test of independence to these data? Explain.

   b. Explain how this table actually provides information needed to cross-classify gender with each of three variables. Construct the contingency table relating gender to opinion about whether factor A is responsible for increases in teenage crime.

Three Factors for Explaining Teenage Crime			
Gender	**A**	**B**	**C**
Men	60	81	75
Women	75	87	86

11.83 Standardized residuals for 2×2 tables   The table that follows shows the standardized residuals in parentheses for GSS data about the statement, "Women should take care of running their homes and leave running the country up to men." The absolute value of the standardized residual is 13.2 in every cell. For chi-squared tests with 2×2 tables, since $df = 1$, only one nonredundant piece of information exists about whether an association exists. If observed count > expected count in one cell, observed count < expected count in the other cell in that row or column. Explain why this is true, using the fact that observed and expected counts have the same row and column totals. (In fact, in 2×2 tables, all four standardized residuals have absolute value equal to the square root of the X^2 test statistic.)

Year	Agree	Disagree
1974	509 (13.2)	924 (−13.2)
1998	280 (−13.2)	1,534 (13.2)

11.84 Degrees of freedom explained For testing independence in a contingency table of size $r \times c$, the degrees of freedom (df) for the chi-squared distribution equal $df = (r - 1) \times (c - 1)$. They have the following interpretation: Given the row and column marginal totals in an $r \times c$ contingency table, the cell counts in a rectangular block of size $(r - 1) \times (c - 1)$ determine all the other cell counts. Consider the following table, which cross-classifies political views by whether the subject would ever vote for a female president, based on the 2010 GSS. For this 3×2 table, suppose we know the counts in the upper left-hand $(3 - 1) \times (2 - 1) = 2 \times 1$ block of the table, as shown.

Political Views	Vote for Female President		
	Yes	No	Total
Extremely Liberal	56		58
Moderate	490		509
Extremely Conservative			61
Total	604	24	628

a. Given the cell counts and the row and column totals, fill in the counts that must appear in the blank cells.

b. Now, suppose instead of the preceding table, you are shown the following table, this time only revealing a 2×1 block in the lower-right part. Find the counts in the remaining cells.

Political Views	Vote for Female President		
	Yes	No	Total
Extremely Liberal			58
Moderate		19	509
Extremely Conservative		3	61
Total	604	24	628

This example serves to show that once the marginal totals are fixed in a contingency table, a block of only $(r - 1) \times (c - 1)$ cell counts is free to vary. Once these are given (as in part a or b), the remaining cell counts follow automatically. The value for the degrees of freedom is exactly the number of cells in this block, or $df = (r - 1) \times (c - 1)$.

11.85 What is *df*? The contingency table that follows has $df = 4$. Show that you can reconstruct the entire table by filling in the remaining cell counts based on the 4 cell counts shown.

	A	B	C	D	E	Total
	24	21	12	10	—	100
	—	—	—	—	—	100
Total	40	40	40	40	40	200

11.86 Variability of chi-squared For the chi-squared distribution, the mean equals df and the standard deviation equals $\sqrt{2(df)}$.

a. Explain why, as a rough approximation, for a large df value, 95% of the chi-squared distribution falls within $df \pm 2\sqrt{2(df)}$.

b. With $df = 8$, show that $df \pm 2\sqrt{2(df)}$ gives the interval $(0, 16)$ for *approximately* containing 95% of the distribution. Using the chi-squared table, show that *exactly* 95% of the distribution actually falls between 0 and 15.5.

11.87 Explaining Fisher's exact test A pool of six candidates for three managerial positions includes three females and three males. Denote the three females by F1, F2, F3 and the three males by M1, M2, M3. The result of choosing three individuals for the managerial positions is (F2, M1, M3).

a. Identify the 20 possible samples that could have been selected. Explain why the contingency table relating gender to whether chosen for the observed sample is

Gender	Chosen for Position	
	Yes	No
Male	2	1
Female	1	2

b. For each of the 20 samples, find the corresponding contingency table as in part a. Show that of these 20 tables, 1 has a cell count of 0, 9 have a cell count of 1, another 9 have a cell count of 2, and 1 has a cell count of 3 in the first cell. Hence, show that 10 of the 20 tables have a cell count in the first cell as large or larger than the observed table from part a. (Note that, if the managers were randomly selected, each of the 20 tables is equally likely to be observed. Then, the probability is $10/20 = 0.5$ of observing a table that shows equal or even stronger evidence that males are selected more often, and 0.5 is the P-value for Fisher's exact test with $H_a: p_1 > p_2$, where p_1 is the proportion of males and p_2 the proportion of females chosen for the position.)

11.88 Likelihood-ratio chi-squared For testing independence, most software reports Pearson's Chi-Squared statistic and another chi-squared statistic, called **likelihood-ratio chi-squared.** It equals

$$G^2 = 2\sum \left[\text{observed count} \times \log\left(\frac{\text{observed count}}{\text{expected count}} \right) \right].$$

It has similar properties as the X^2 statistic, such as $df = (r - 1) \times (c - 1)$.

a. Show that $G^2 = X^2 = 0$ when each observed count = expected count.

b. Explain why in practice you would not expect to get *exactly* $G^2 = X^2 = 0$, even if the variables are truly independent.

Student Activities

11.89 Voting with 16 A recent survey of Austrian high school students asked whether it makes sense for 16-year-olds to be allowed to vote in the next parliamentary election. The following table shows results.

	Voting with 16			
Grade	Definitely	Probably	Probably Not	Definitely Not
Sophomores	9	12	5	3
Juniors	16	9	3	6
Seniors	20	5	2	0

a. Verify, using an app, that $X^2 = 14.1$ for this table.

b. Can you use the chi-squared distribution to find a P-value for testing whether an association exists between the grade level and the opinion on voting with 16? Why or why not?

c. Enter the data in the *Permutation Test for Independence* app. Press the Generate Random Permutation(s) button once to generate one random permutation of the data. Did this permutation lead to a chi-squared test statistic smaller, equal, or larger than the observed value?

d. Press the button 9 more times. How many of the 10 permutations you generated resulted in a X^2 value as large or large than the observed? (The subtitle of the plot shows this information.)

e. Generate 10,000 permutations and find the permutation P-value. Interpret it.

11.90 Conduct a research study using the GSS Go to the GSS codebook at the GSS website (see Activity 2). Your instructor will assign a categorical response variable. Conduct a research study in which you find at least two other categorical variables that have both a statistically significant and a practically significant association with that response variable, using data for the most recent year in which the response variable was surveyed. Analyze each association, using the methods of this chapter. Write a two-page report, describing your analyses and summarizing the results of your research study. Be prepared to discuss your results in a class discussion, because the class will discuss which variables seemed to be especially relevant.

BIBLIOGRAPHY

Agresti, A. (2007). *An Introduction to Categorical Data Analysis*, 2nd edition. Hoboken, New Jersey: Wiley.

Chatterjee, S., Handcock, M. S., and Simonoff, J. S. (1995). A Case Book for *A First Course in Statistics and Data Analysis*. Hoboken, New Jersey: Wiley.

CHAPTER 12

Chapter 11 analyzed the association between two categorical variables. This chapter discusses methods for describing and conducting inference about the relationship between two *quantitative* variables. We'll learn more about the correlation and regression methods that we discussed in Chapter 3. Using the inferential tools we acquired since then, we can find a confidence interval for the slope or for a prediction to reflect the margin of error in such estimates.

Regression Analysis

Example 1

Estimate a Person's Strength

Picture the Scenario

How can you measure a person's strength? One way is to find the *maximum* number of pounds that the individual can bench press. However, this technique can be risky for people who are unfamiliar with proper lifting techniques or who are inexperienced in using a bench press. Is there a variable that is easier to measure yet is a good predictor of the maximum bench press?

There have been many studies about strength using males but relatively few using females. One exception was a recent study of 57 female athletes in a Georgia high school. Several variables were measured, including ones that are easier and safer to assess than maximum bench press but are thought to correlate highly with it. One such variable is the number of times that a female athlete can lift a bench press set at only 60 pounds (a relatively low weight) before she becomes too fatigued to lift it again. The data are in the High School Female Athletes data file on the book's website. Let x = number of 60-pound bench presses performed (before fatigue)

and let y = maximum bench press (in lbs.).

Questions to Explore

■ How well can we predict an athlete's maximum bench press from knowing the number of 60-pound bench presses that she can perform?

■ What can we say about the relationship between these variables in the population?

Thinking Ahead

The bench press variables are quantitative. This chapter presents methods for analyzing the relationship between two quantitative variables. Like the methods presented in the previous chapter for categorical variables, these methods enable us to answer questions such as:

■ Could the variables x and y realistically be independent (in the population), or can we conclude that there is a relationship between them?

■ If the variables are related, how strong is the relationship?

■ How does the outcome for the response variable depend on the value of the explanatory variable, and which observations are unusual?

To address these questions, we will use what is known as a **regression analysis.** (We will even explain where this name comes from.) Several examples in this chapter will illustrate the use of regression analysis with data from the female strength study. A regression analysis that includes a single explanatory variable to study its linear relationship with a response variable is called a simple linear regression.

Recall

From Section 3.3, a **regression line** is a straight line that predicts the value of a response variable y from the value of an explanatory variable x. From Section 3.2, the **correlation coefficient** r is a summary measure of the relationship that falls between −1 and +1. ◀

Chapter 3 introduced regression analysis. Here we'll review and learn more about using a **regression line** to predict the response variable y and the **correlation coefficient** to describe the strength of the relationship. We'll study how to make inferences about the regression line for a population and how the variability of data points around the regression line helps us predict how far from the line a value of y is likely to fall. Finally, we'll discuss an alternative regression analysis that is useful when two quantitative variables have a curved rather than a straight-line relationship.

12.1 The Linear Regression Model

In Words

y = response variable
Graph on vertical (y) axis.

x = explanatory variable
Graph on horizontal (x) axis.
Regression uses x to predict y.

As in most statistical analyses, the first step of a regression analysis is to identify the **response and explanatory variables**. In Example 1 we want to know how well we can predict an athlete's maximum bench press, so that's the response variable. The predictor, the number of 60-pound bench presses that an athlete can manage, is the explanatory variable. As in Chapter 3, we use y to denote the response variable and x to denote the explanatory variable. The goal of this section is to introduce a framework that models the mean of the response variable y in terms of the explanatory variable x. Such a model is called a **regression model**.

The Scatterplot: Evaluating Whether a Straight-Line Trend Exists

Is there a relationship between the number of 60-pound bench presses and the maximum bench press? The first step in answering this question and building a model is to look at the data. Recall that a **scatterplot** shows, for each observation, a point representing its value on the two variables. The points are shown relative to the x (horizontal) and y (vertical) axes. The scatterplot shows whether there is roughly a straight-line trend, in which case the relationship between x and y is said to be approximately **linear**.

Example 2

Scatterplot ◀

Athlete	x	y
1	10	80
2	12	85
3	20	85
4	5	65

The Strength Study

Picture the Scenario

Let's look at the High School Female Athletes data file on the book's website. For each of the 57 female athletes in the study, the response variable y is the maximum weight that the athlete bench pressed (in 5-pound increments). The explanatory variable x is the number of times she could bench press 60 pounds. The first four entries of the data file (where x refers to BP60 and y to maxBP) are shown in the table in the margin. The sample mean of the *x* variable is 11.0 (standard deviation = 7.1), and the sample mean of the *y* variable is 79.9 pounds (standard deviation = 13.3 pounds).

Question to Explore

Using the entire data file for the 57 athletes, construct a scatterplot and interpret it.

Think It Through

With any statistical software, you can construct a scatterplot after identifying in the data file the variables that play the role of *x* and *y*. For the column names in the Bench Press data file, *x* = BP60 and *y* = maxBP. Figure 12.1 shows the scatterplot that the *Linear Regression* app produces, which has this data set preloaded. It shows that female athletes with higher numbers of 60-pound bench presses also tended to have higher values for the maximum bench press. The data points follow roughly an increasing linear trend. The figure in the margin shows the same screenshot, but with a smooth trend line superimposed.

Scatterplot
Data on 57 Female High School Athletes

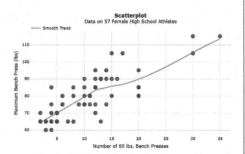

Screenshot of scatterplot from the *Linear Regression* app, showing a smooth trend line.

▲ **Figure 12.1** Scatterplot for *y* = Maximum Bench Press and *x* = Number of 60-Pound Bench Presses. Screenshot from the *Linear Regression* app. *Note:* If you count the number of dots, you will see that there are actually fewer than 57, the number of athletes. This is because some athletes had identical (*x,y*)-values and their dots are plotted on top of each other. They are represented by a slightly darker shade of red. **Question** How can you tell from this plot that (a) two athletes had a maximum bench press of only 60 pounds, and (b) 5-pound increments were used in determining maximum bench press—60, 65, 70, and so on?

Insight

The three data points at the upper right represent subjects who could do a large number of 60-pound bench presses. Their maximum bench presses were also high.

▶ *Try Exercise 12.9, part a*

Describing the Relationship in the Scatterplot by the Correlation Coefficient

In Chapter 3, we learned that if the scatterplot shows an approximate linear relationship, we can describe the strength of this relationship by computing the correlation coefficient *r*.

Did You Know?

r is often referred to as **Pearson's correlation coefficient**, after the British scientist Karl Pearson who also developed the chi-squared test from Chapter 11. ◄

SUMMARY: Properties of the Correlation Coefficient *r*

- The correlation coefficient *r* falls between -1 and $+1$ ($-1 \leq r \leq +1$). The relationship is positive if $r > 0$, negative if $r < 0$.
- The larger the absolute value of *r*, the stronger the linear relationship ($r = \pm 1$ when data points fall exactly on a straight line.)
- The value of *r* does not depend on the variables' units and is not affected by linear transformations of the response or explanatory variable.
- *r* does not depend on which variable is the response and which the explanatory variable.

For example, because the scatterplot in Example 2 showed an approximate linear relationship, it is reasonable to compute the correlation coefficient between the two variables number of 60-pound bench presses and maximum possible bench press to measure how strongly they are related. Using output from the *Linear Regression* app, $r = 0.80$, indicating a strong and positive linear relationship.

The Regression Line Equation Uses *x* to Predict *y*

When the scatterplot shows a linear trend, a straight line fitted through the data points describes that trend. As in Chapter 3, we use the notation

$$\hat{y} = a + bx$$

for this line, called the **regression line**. The symbol $\hat{y}$ represents the *predicted value* of the response variable *y*. In the formula, *a* is the **y-intercept** and *b* is the **slope**. The regression line allows us to further describe the nature of the linear relationship in a way that goes beyond just stating the strength of the relationship using the correlation coefficient *r*.

In Words

$\hat{y}$ ("y-hat") denotes the predicted value you get for the response variable *y* by plugging a value into the equation for the explanatory variable *x*.

Regression Line ◄

Example 3

Regression Line Predicting Maximum Bench Press

Picture the Scenario

Let's continue our analysis of the Bench Press data.

Questions to Explore

a. Using software, find the regression line for $y =$ maximum bench press and $x =$ number of 60-pound bench presses.

b. Interpret the slope by comparing the predicted maximum bench press for subjects at the highest and lowest levels of *x* in the sample (35 and 2).

Think It Through

a. Let's denote the maximum bench press variable by maxBP and the number of 60-pound bench presses by BP60. Using software, we pick the regression option with maxBP as the response variable and BP60

Scatterplot
Data on 57 Female High School Athletes
— Regression Line: $\hat{y} = 63.5 + 1.49x$

Linear Regression Equation:

Parameter	Estimate
Intercept	63.54
Slope (BP60)	1.491

Screenshot from *Linear Regression* app, showing scatterplot with superimposed regression line (in blue, with regression equation shown in the top left corner) and estimates for intercept and slope.

as the explanatory variable. Table 12.1 shows output statistical software such as MINITAB produces. We'll interpret some of this, such as standard errors and t statistics, later in the chapter. The margin figure shows output from the *Linear Regression* app.

Table 12.1 MINITAB Printout for Regression Analysis of y = Maximum Bench Press (maxBP) and x = Number of 60-Pound Bench Presses (BP60)

```
The regression equation is maxBP = 63.54 + 1.491 BP60

Coefficients

Term          Coef        SE Coef      T-Value      P-Value

Constant      63.54       1.96         32.48        0.000

BP60          1.491       0.150        9.96         0.000
```

The output tells us that $\hat{y}$ = predicted maximum bench press (maxBP) relates to x = number of 60-pound bench presses (BP60) by

$$\text{maxBP} = 63.5 + 1.49\ \text{BP60},\quad \text{that is, } \hat{y} = 63.5 + 1.49x.$$

The y-intercept is 63.5 and the slope is 1.49. These are also shown in the column labeled "Coef," an abbreviation for *coefficient*. The slope appears opposite the variable name for which it is the coefficient, "BP60." The term "Constant" refers to the y-intercept. The line $\hat{y} = 63.5 + 1.49x$ is what you see superimposed over the scatterplot in the margin figure.

b. The slope of 1.49 tells us that the predicted maximum bench press $\hat{y}$ increases by an average of 1.49 pounds for every additional 60-pound bench press an athlete can do. The impact on $\hat{y}$ of a 33-unit change in x, from the sample minimum of $x = 2$ to the maximum of $x = 35$, is $33(1.49) = 49.2$ pounds. An athlete who can do thirty-five 60-pound bench presses has a predicted maximum bench press nearly 50 pounds higher than an athlete who can do only two 60-pound bench presses. Those predicted values are $\hat{y} = 63.5 + 1.49(2) = 66.5$ pounds at $x = 2$ and $\hat{y} = 63.5 + 1.49(35) = 115.7$ pounds at $x = 35$.

Insight

The slope of 1.49 is positive: As x increases, the predicted value $\hat{y}$ increases. The relationship is *positive*. When the relationship is *negative*, the predicted value $\hat{y}$ *decreases* as x increases. When the slope = 0, the regression line is horizontal.

▶ *Try Exercise 12.1*

Recall

The direction of the relationship (positive or negative) refers to the sign of the slope and whether the line slopes upward or downward. ◀

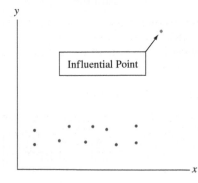

One reason for plotting the data before you do a regression analysis is to check for outliers. The regression line can be pulled toward an outlier and away from the general trend of points. We observed in Section 3.4 that an observation can be **influential** in affecting the regression line when two things happen (see margin figure):

■ Its x value is low or high compared to the rest of the data.

■ It does not fall in the straight-line pattern that the rest of the data have.

In Figure 12.1, three subjects had quite large values of x. However, their values of y fit in with the trend exhibited by the other data, so those points are not influential with respect to changing the equation of the regression line. However, as we will discuss later, the correlation may strengthen.

Finding the Correlation Coefficient and the Prediction Equation

In Practice Check the Model Graphically; Use Software for Computations

Check whether it is sensible to do a regression analysis by looking at a scatterplot. If you see an approximately linear relationship, you can let technology such as the *Linear Regression* app do the computational work of finding the correlation coefficient, slope, and y-intercept.

Software uses the sample data to find the prediction equation $\hat{y} = a + bx$ and the correlation coefficient r. Sections 3.2 and 3.3 in Chapter 3 gave the formulas. We saw there that $r > 0$ and $b > 0$ when most observations are in the quadrants where x and y are both above their means or both below their means. See Figure 12.2. By contrast, $r < 0$ and $b < 0$ when subjects who are above the mean on one variable tend to be below the mean on the other variable.

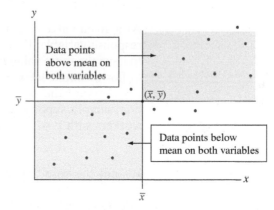

▲ **Figure 12.2** The Correlation Coefficient r and the Slope b Are Positive When Most Data Points Are Above the Mean on Both Variables or Below the Mean on Both. These are the areas shaded in this figure. **Question** Where do most data points usually fall when the slope and correlation coefficient are negative?

Recall

From Section 3.3,

$$b = r\left(\frac{s_y}{s_x}\right),$$

$$a = \bar{y} - b\bar{x}. \blacktriangleleft$$

The formulas for the slope b and the y-intercept a (shown again in the margin) use the correlation coefficient r and the sample means $\bar{x}$ and $\bar{y}$ of the x values and the y values and the sample standard deviations s_x and s_y. The slope b is proportional to the correlation coefficient r, and we'll discuss their connection in Section 12.3. The formula $a = \bar{y} - b\bar{x}$ for the y-intercept can be rewritten as $\bar{y} = a + b\bar{x}$. This shows that if we substitute $x = \bar{x}$ into the regression equation $\hat{y} = a + bx$, then the predicted outcome is $\hat{y} = a + b\bar{x} = \bar{y}$. In words, *a subject who is average on x is predicted to be average on y.*

Residuals Are Prediction Errors for the Least Squares Line

The regression equation is often called a **prediction equation** because substituting a particular value of x into the equation provides a prediction for y at that value of x. For instance, the third athlete in the data file could do $x = 20$ bench presses of 60 pounds. Her predicted maximum bench press is

$$\hat{y} = 63.5 + 1.49x = 63.5 + 1.49(20) = 93.3 \text{ pounds.}$$

Recall

From Section 3.3, the residual is the difference between the actual and predicted value of the response variable. ◀

The difference $y - \hat{y}$ between an observed outcome y and its predicted value $\hat{y}$ is the *prediction error*, called a **residual**. The third athlete in the data file had a maximum bench press of $y = 85$ pounds. Since her $\hat{y} = 93.3$ pounds, the prediction error is $y - \hat{y} = 85 - 93.3 = -8.3$ pounds.

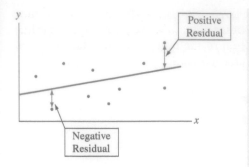

The Regression Model Describes How the Mean of *y* Depends on *x*

At a given value of x, the equation $\hat{y} = a + bx$ predicts a single value $\hat{y}$ of the response variable. However, we should not expect all subjects at that value of x to have the same value of y. Variability occurs in their y values.

For example, let x = number of years of education and y = annual income in dollars for the adult residents in the workforce of your hometown. For a random sample, suppose you find a regression line of $\hat{y} = -20,000 + 4,000x$. Those workers with $x = 12$ years of education have predicted annual income

$$\hat{y} = -20,000 + 4,000(12) = 28,000.$$

It's not the case that every worker with 12 years of education would have an annual income of $28,000. Income is not completely dependent upon education. One person may have an income of $35,000, another $15,000, and so forth. Instead, you can think of $\hat{y} = 28,000$ as estimating the **mean annual income** for all workers with $x = 12$ years of education.

In fact, there's a mean for the annual income at each separate education value. For those residents with 13 years of education, the estimated mean annual income is $-20,000 + 4,000(13) = 32,000$. The slope is 4,000, so the estimated mean goes up by $4,000 (from $28,000 to $32,000) for this one-year increase in education (from 12 to 13 years).

A similar equation describes the relationship between x and the means of y in the population. This **population regression equation** is denoted by

$$\mu_y = \alpha + \beta x.$$

Recall

Parameters describe the population. They are often denoted by Greek symbols. Here, α is *alpha*, β is *beta*, and μ_y is *mu-sub-y*. ◄

Here, α is a population y-intercept and β is a population slope. These are parameters, so in practice their values are unknown. The parameter μ_y denotes the population mean of y for all the subjects at a particular value of x. It takes a different value at each separate x value. To obtain estimates for the parameters in the population regression equation, we use the prediction equation fitted to the observed data. We use a to estimate α, b to estimate β and $a + bx$ to estimate μ_y. We'll see how to use these estimates to conduct inference (such as obtaining a confidence interval for the slope β) about the unknown parameters in Sections 12.2 and 12.4.

A straight line is the simplest way to describe the relationship between two quantitative variables. In practice, most relationships are not *exactly* linear. The equation $\mu_y = \alpha + \beta x$ merely *approximates* the actual relationship between x and the population means of y. It is a **regression model**.

Regression Model

A **regression model** is a simple approximation for how variables relate in a population.

Figure 12.3 shows how a regression model can approximate the true relationship between x and the mean of y. The true relationship is unlikely to be exactly a straight line. That's not a problem as long as a straight line provides a reasonably good approximation, as we expect of a model.

▲ **Figure 12.3** The Regression Model $\mu_y = \alpha + \beta x$ for the Means of y Is a Simple Approximation for the True Relationship Between x and the Mean of y. Question Can you sketch a true relationship for which this model is a very *poor* approximation?

If the true relationship is far from a straight line, this regression model may be a poor one. Figure 12.4 illustrates. In that case, the figure shows a U-shaped relationship. It requires a parabolic curve rather than a straight line to describe it well. To check the straight-line assumption, you should always construct a scatterplot.

How could you get into trouble by using a straight-line regression model even when the true relationship is U-shaped? First, predictions about y would be poor. Second, inference about the relationship could be misleading. The variables are related, since the mean of y changes as x does. The slope (and correlation coefficient) might not detect this, however, since the prediction line would be close to horizontal (slope close to 0, r close to 0), even though a substantial relationship exists.

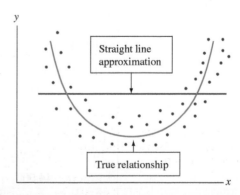

▲ **Figure 12.4** The Straight-Line Regression Model Provides a Poor Approximation When the Actual Relationship Is Highly Nonlinear. Question What type of mathematical function might you consider using for a regression model in this case?

The Regression Model Also Allows Variability About the Line

At each fixed value of x, variability occurs in the y values around their mean μ_y. For instance, at education $= 12$ years, annual income varies around the mean annual income for all workers with 12 years of education. The probability distribution of y values at a fixed value of x is a **conditional distribution**. At each value of x, there is a conditional distribution of y values. The standard deviation of this conditional distribution (denoted by σ) tells us how much the response variable varies around the mean μ_y at the given x value. In practice, σ is unknown. It is another population parameter that is part of the regression model specification and which we'll need to estimate from the data.

In Words

A **regression model** uses a formula (usually a straight line) to approximate how the expected value (the mean) for y changes at different values of x. It also describes the variability of observations on y around the line.

SUMMARY: Regression Model

A **regression model** describes how the population mean μ_y of each conditional distribution for the response variable depends on the value x of the explanatory variable. A **linear regression model** uses the line $\mu_y = \alpha + \beta x$ to connect the means. The model also has a parameter σ that describes variability of observations around the mean of y at each x value.

Example 4

Regression Model and Variability of y at Given x ◄

Income and Education

Picture the Scenario

As described previously, suppose the regression line $\mu_y = -20{,}000 + 4{,}000x$ models the relationship for the population of working adults in your hometown between $x =$ number of years of education and the mean of $y =$ annual income. This model tells us that, on average, income goes up as education increases. But how much variability is there in the income, for a given number of years of education? Suppose that the conditional distribution of annual income at each value of x is modeled by a normal distribution, with standard deviation $\sigma = 13{,}000$.

Question to Explore

Use this regression model to describe the mean income and the variability around the mean income for workers with (i) 12 and (ii) 16 years of education.

Think It Through

This regression model states that for workers with x years of education, their annual incomes have a normal distribution with a mean of $\mu_y = -20{,}000 + 4{,}000x$ and a standard deviation of $\sigma = 13{,}000$. For those having a high school education ($x = 12$), the mean annual income is $\mu_y = -20{,}000 + 4{,}000(12) = 28{,}000$ and the standard deviation is 13,000. Those with a college education ($x = 16$) have a mean annual income of $\mu_y = -20{,}000 + 4{,}000(16) = 44{,}000$ and a standard deviation of 13,000.

Since the conditional distributions are modeled as normal, the model predicts that about 95% of all incomes for a given number of years of education fall within 2 standard deviations of the mean. For instance, for those with 16 years of education, $\mu_y = 44{,}000$ and $\sigma = 13{,}000$. Since

$$44{,}000 - 2(13{,}000) = 18{,}000 \text{ and } 44{,}000 + 2(13{,}000) = 70{,}000$$

the model predicts that 95% of their annual incomes fall between \$18,000 and \$70,000. This is a rather wide interval, due to the relatively large value of σ.

Insight

Figure 12.5 portrays this regression model. It plots the regression equation (in red) and the conditional distributions of y = income at x = 12 years and at x = 16 years of education (in blue). Observe how the blue distribution curve at x = 16 stretches roughly from 18,000 to 70,000 on the y-axis. The value of σ determines the shape of the normal curves. In practice, σ is unknown, but we'll see how to estimate it later in the chapter.

▲ **Figure 12.5** The Population Regression Model $\mu_y = -20,000 + 4,000x$, with $\sigma = 13,000$, Relating the Means of y = Annual Income to x = Years of Education. **Question** What do the bell-shaped curves around the line at x = 12 and at x = 16 represent?

▶ *Try Exercise 12.4*

In Figure 12.5, each conditional distribution is normal, and each has the same standard deviation, $\sigma = 13,000$. But a regression model merely approximates reality. In practice, the means of the conditional distributions would not perfectly follow a straight line. Those conditional distributions would not be exactly normal. The standard deviation would not be exactly the same for each conditional distribution. For instance, the conditional distributions might be somewhat skewed to the right, and incomes might vary more for college graduates than for high school graduates.

In Practice A Regression Model Is a Simple *Approximation* of Reality

A **regression model** never holds exactly in practice. It is merely a simple approximation of reality. But even though it does not describe reality exactly, a regression model is useful if the true relationship is close to what the model predicts.

12.1   Practicing the Basics

12.1 Car mileage and weight   The Car Weight and Mileage data file on the book's website (also preloaded in the *Linear Regression* app) shows the weight (in pounds) and mileage (miles per gallon) of 25 different model autos.

a. Identify the natural response variable and explanatory variable.

b. Using software output such as the one from the *Linear Regression* app shown in the following table, state the prediction equation and report the y-intercept and slope.

Parameter	Estimate	Standard Error	t Statistic	P-value
Intercept	45.64536	2.602758	17.54	<0.0001
Slope (Weight)	−0.00522	0.000627	−8.33	<0.0001

   c. Interpret the slope in terms of a 1,000-pound increase in the vehicle weight.

   d. Does the y-intercept have any contextual meaning for these data? (*Hint:* The weight values range between 2,460 and 6,400 pounds.)

12.2 Predicting car mileage Refer to the previous exercise.

   a. Find the predicted mileage for the Toyota Corolla, which weighs 2,590 pounds.

   b. Find the residual for the Toyota Corolla, which has observed mileage of 38.

   c. Sketch a graphical representation of the residual in part b.

12.3 Predicting maximum bench strength in males For the Male Athlete Strength data file on the book's website, the prediction equation relating y = maximum bench press (maxBP) in kilograms to x = repetitions to fatigue bench press (repBP) is $\hat{y} = 117.5 + 5.86x$.

   a. Find the predicted maxBP for a male athlete with a repBP of 35, which was one of the highest repBP values.

   b. Find the predicted maxBP for a male athlete with a repBP of 0, which was the lowest repBP value.

   c. Interpret the y-intercept. Use the slope to describe how predicted maxBP changes as repBP increases from 0 to 35.

12.4 Income higher with age Suppose the regression line $\mu_y = -10,000 + 1,000x$ models the relationship for the population of working adults in Canada between x = age and the mean of y = annual income (in Canadian dollars). The conditional distribution of y at each value of x is modeled as normal, with $\sigma = 5,000$. Use this regression model to describe the mean and the variability around the mean for the conditional distribution at age (a) 20 years and (b) 50 years.

12.5 Mu, not y For a population regression equation, why is it more sensible to write $\mu_y = \alpha + \beta x$ instead of $y = \alpha + \beta x$? Explain with reference to the variables x = height and y = weight for the population of girls in elementary schools in your hometown.

12.6 Parties and dating Let y = number of parties attended in the past month and x = number of dates in the past month, measured for all single students at your school. Explain the mean and variability aspects of the regression model $\mu_y = \alpha + \beta x$ in the context of these variables. In your answer, explain why (a) it is more sensible to use a straight line to model the *means* of the conditional distributions rather than individual observations and (b) the model needs to allow variation around the mean.

12.7 Study time and college GPA Exercise 3.40 in Chapter 3 showed data collected at the end of an introductory statistics course to investigate the relationship between x = study time per week (average number of hours) and

y = college GPA. The table here shows the data for the eight males in the class on these variables and on the number of class lectures for the course that the student reported skipping during the term.

Student	Study Time	GPA	Skipped
1	14	2.8	9
2	25	3.6	0
3	15	3.4	2
4	5	3.0	5
5	10	3.1	3
6	12	3.3	2
7	5	2.7	12
8	21	3.8	1

   a. In the *Linear Regression* app, select Your Own under Enter Data, and then enter the Study Time and GPA variable values into the app. (Alternatively, create a data file and use it with your software.) Create a scatterplot and use it to describe the relationship between GPA and study time.

   b. Find the prediction equation and interpret the slope.

   c. Find the predicted GPA for a student who studies 25 hours per week.

   d. Find and interpret the residual for Student 2, who reported x = 25.

12.8 GPA and skipping class Refer to the previous exercise. Now let x = number of classes skipped and y = college GPA.

   a. Construct a scatterplot. Does the relationship seem to be positive or negative?

   b. Find the prediction equation and interpret the y-intercept and slope.

   c. Find the predicted GPA and residual for Student 1.

12.9 Cell phone specs Refer to the cell phone data set available on the book's website and preloaded in the *Linear Regression* app, which shows various specs of a random sample of cell phones. Engineers would like to analyze how the weight (measured in grams) of a phone depends on the size of the battery, the heaviest component of a cell phone. Here, the size is measured by the capacity of the battery, which is the amount of energy it can supply on a full charge (measured in milliampere hours, mAh).

   a. Identify the response and explanatory variables and then construct and interpret the scatterplot. Mention any outliers you see.

   b. What effect will the outlier have on the fitted regression equation? Will its residual be positive or negative, and will it be small or large in absolute value?

   c. Remove the outlier (in the app, check the option for Click to Remove Points and then click on the outlier to remove it) and find the prediction equation. Predict the weight of a cell phone when the battery capacity is (i) 1,000 mAh and (ii) 1,500 mAh.

   d. Interpret the slope in context.

12.10 Exercise and watching TV   For the Georgia Student Survey file on the book's website (preloaded in the *Linear Regression* app), let y = exercise and x = watch TV (minutes per day). (In the app, select these via the drop-down menu for the x and y variable.)

   a. Use the *Linear Regression* app or other software to construct a scatterplot. Identify an outlier that could have an impact on the fit of the regression model. What would you expect its effect to be on the slope?

   b. Fit the model with and without that observation. Summarize its impact. (In the app, check Click to Remove Points and then click on the outlier to remove it.)

12.2 Inference About Model Parameters and the Relationship

Section 12.1 showed how a linear regression model specifies the relationship between two quantitative variables, when the means of y at various values of x follow approximately a straight line. For the population that the sample refers to, we have learned that this relationship is given by $\mu_y = \alpha + \beta x$. Statistical inference is concerned with constructing confidence intervals and testing hypotheses about these parameters so that we can draw conclusions that apply to the larger population that is studied. For instance, we would like to use the data on the 57 female athletes analyzed in the previous section to learn (and predict) more broadly how various strength measures are related in the broader population of all high-school female athletes.

Assumptions for Regression Analysis

We have already mentioned that we must inspect the scatterplot first to see whether there is an approximate linear trend before we can use a linear regression model. More formally, we need to assume that the model we use accurately represents the true relationship in the population.

> **SUMMARY: Basic Assumption for Using a Linear Regression Model**
>
> The population means of y at different values of x have a straight-line relationship with x, that is, $\mu_y = \alpha + \beta x$.

If this assumption is met, fitting the proposed linear regression model is valid. If it is violated, the model we use misrepresents the actual relationship between the response and the explanatory variable in the population. Any descriptions (such as interpreting the slope), conclusions, and inferences drawn from the model will be invalid. The foremost tool to check this assumption is the scatterplot. Section 13.4 will discuss additional plots using the residuals to check this assumption.

If the model we propose is valid and we want to use it not only for describing the relationship observed in the data but more generally to draw inferences about the underlying population, we need two more assumptions.

> **SUMMARY: Extra Assumptions When Using Linear Regression Model for Statistical Inference**
>
> ■ The data were gathered using **randomization**, such as random sampling from a population or a randomized experiment.
>
> ■ The population values of y at each value of x follow a **normal distribution**, with the same standard deviation (σ) at each x value.

The randomness assumption applies for any statistical inference. For inferences to be valid, the sample must be representative of the population.

As in the case of inference about a mean, the assumption about normality is what leads to t test statistics having t distributions. This assumption is never exactly satisfied in practice. However, the closer reality resembles this ideal, the more appropriate are the confidence interval and test procedures for the regression model. Meeting this assumption is less crucial than meeting the other two, especially when the sample size is large. In that case, an extended Central Limit Theorem implies that estimates from regression models (such as the estimated slope b) have bell-shaped sampling distributions, no matter what shape the population distribution of y has at each value of x.

Testing Independence Between Quantitative Variables

Suppose that the slope β of the regression line $\mu_y = \alpha + \beta x$ equals 0, as Figure 12.6 shows. Then, the population mean of y is identical at each x value and the two quantitative variables are statistically independent: The outcome for y does not depend on the value of x. In other words, it does not help us to know the value of x when predicting the value of y.

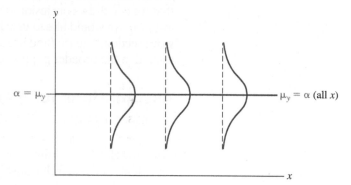

▲ **Figure 12.6** Quantitative Variables x and y Are Statistically Independent When the True Slope $\beta = 0$. Each normal curve shown here represents the variability in y values at a particular value of x. When $\beta = 0$, the normal distribution of y is the same at each value of x. **Question** How can you express the null hypothesis of independence between x and y in terms of a parameter from the regression model?

The null hypothesis that x and y are statistically independent is H_0: $\beta = 0$. Its significance test has the same purpose as the chi-squared test of independence for categorical variables (Chapter 11). It investigates how much evidence there is that the variables truly are linearly related. The smaller the P-value, the greater the evidence.

Usually, the alternative hypothesis for the test of independence is two-sided, H_a: $\beta \neq 0$. Also possible is a one-sided alternative, H_a: $\beta > 0$ or H_a: $\beta < 0$, when you predict the direction of the relationship to be either positive or negative. The test statistic in each case equals

Sampling distribution of the estimated slope b

$$t = \frac{b - 0}{se},$$

where b is the estimated slope computed from the sample and se denotes its standard error. The *Linear Regression* app or other software supplies the slope b, the se, the t test statistic, and its P-value. The formula for se is rather complex, and we won't need it here (it's in Exercise 12.104). The form of the test statistic is the usual one for a t or z test. We take the observed slope b, subtract the hypothesized value for it under the null hypothesis (0), and divide by the standard error of the sampling distribution of b. The t test statistic tells us how far (i.e., how many standard errors) the observed slope falls from the null value of 0.

The symbol t is used for this test statistic because, under the assumptions stated, it has a t sampling distribution. The P-value for H_a: $\beta \neq 0$ is the two-tail probability from the t distribution. The degrees of freedom are $df = n - 2$. The app or other software provides the P-value.

> ### Summary: Steps of Two-Sided Significance Test About a Population Slope β
>
> 1. **Assumptions:** (1) Relationship in population satisfies regression model $\mu_y = \alpha + \beta x$, (2) data gathered using randomization, (3) population y values at each x value have normal distribution, with same standard deviation at each x value.
> 2. **Hypotheses:** H_0: $\beta = 0$, H_a: $\beta \neq 0$.
> 3. **Test Statistic:** $t = (b - 0)/se$, where software supplies sample slope b and its se.
> 4. **P-value:** Two-tail probability of observing t test statistic as or even more extreme than observed one, assuming $\beta = 0$. Computed using software from t distribution with $df = n - 2$.
> 5. **Conclusions:** Interpret P-value in context. If a decision is needed, reject H_0 if P-value $\leq$ significance level (such as 0.05).

Recall

Sections 8.3 and 9.3 used $df = n - 1$ for inference using the t distribution, so why is $df = n - 2$ here? We'll see that in regression, $df = n - number\ of\ parameters$ in the equation for the mean, μ_y.

The equation $\mu_y = \alpha + \beta x$ has two parameters (α and β), so $df = n - 2$. ◄

Example 5

Inference About the Slope ◄

60-Pound Strength and Bench Presses

Picture the Scenario

One purpose of the strength study introduced in Example 1 was to analyze whether x = number of times an athlete can lift a 60-pound bench press helps us predict y = maximum number of pounds the athlete can bench press. Table 12.2 shows the regression analysis for the 57 female athletes, with x denoted by BP60 and y denoted by maxBP. The margin shows a screenshot from the *Linear Regression* app showing the same information.

Table 12.2 MINITAB Printout for Regression Analysis of y = Maximum Bench Press (maxBP) and x = Number of 60-Pound Bench Presses (BP60)

Scatterplot
Data on 57 Female High School Athletes
— Regression Line: $\hat{y} = 63.5 + 1.49x$

Linear Regression Equation:

Parameter	Estimate	Standard Error	t Statistic	P-value
Intercept	63.54	1.956	32.48	<0.0001
Slope (BP60)	1.491	0.1497	9.96	<0.0001

Screenshot from *Linear Regression* app, showing the estimated intercept and slope, together with their standard errors, t test statistics and P-values.

```
The regression equation is maxBP = 63.54 + 1.491 BP60

Coefficients

Term          Coef        SE Coef      T-Value      P-Value

Constant      63.54        1.96        32.48        0.000

BP60           1.491       0.150        9.96        0.000
```

Questions to Explore

a. Conduct a two-sided significance test of the null hypothesis of independence.

b. Report the P-value for the alternative hypothesis of a positive relationship which is a sensible hypothesis for these variables. Interpret the results in context.

Think It Through

a. From Table 12.2, the prediction equation is $\hat{y} = 63.5 + 1.49x$. Here are the steps of a significance test of the null hypothesis of independence.

   1. Assumptions: The scatterplot shown in the output of the *Linear Regression* app revealed a linear trend, with scatter of points having similar variability (or spread) at different x values. The straight-line regression model $\mu_y = \alpha + \beta x$ seems appropriate. The 57 female athletes were *all* the female athletes at a particular high school. This was a convenience sample rather than a random sample of the population of female high school athletes. Although the goal was to make inferences about that population, inferences are tentative because the sample was not random.

2. **Hypotheses:** The null hypothesis that the variables are independent is H_0: $\beta = 0$. The two-sided alternative hypothesis of dependence is H_a: $\beta \neq 0$.

3. **Test Statistic:** For the estimated slope $b = 1.49$, Table 12.2 reports a standard error of $se = 0.150$. This is listed under "SE Coef," in the row of the table for the term BP60 and also shown in the *Linear Regression* app. For testing H_0: $\beta = 0$, the *t* test statistic is

$$t = (b - 0)/se = 1.49/0.150 = 9.96.$$

This is extremely large. The sample slope falls nearly 10 standard errors above the null hypothesis value. The *t* test statistic appears in Table 12.2 under the column labeled "T-Value," and is also shown as "t Statistic" in the *Linear Regression* app. The sample size equals $n = 57$, so $df = n - 2 = 55$.

Sampling distribution of *t* test statistic under H_0: $\beta = 0$

t distribution with $df = 55$

−9.96   0   9.96   *t*

observed *t*

4. **P-value:** The P-value listed in Table 12.2 right next to the *t* statistic of 9.96 is 0.000, rounded to three decimal places. In the *Linear Regression* app, it is shown as <0.0001. The app or other software report the P-value for the two-sided alternative, H_a: $\beta \neq 0$. It is the two-tailed probability of "more extreme values" above 9.96 and below −9.96. See the margin figure.

5. **Conclusion:** If the population slope β were equal to 0 (i.e., the null hypothesis is true), it would be extremely unusual to get a sample slope as far from 0 as $b = 1.49$. The P-value gives very strong evidence against H_0. We conclude that a linear relationship exists between the number of 60-pound bench presses and maximum bench press.

b. The one-sided alternative H_a: $\beta > 0$ predicts a positive linear relationship. For it, the P-value is halved because it is then the right-tail probability of $t > 9.96$. This also equals 0.000, to three decimal places. On average, we infer that maximum bench press increases (because the slope is significantly larger than 0) as the number of 60-pound bench presses increases.

Insight

In practice, studies must often rely on convenience samples. Results may be biased if the study subjects differ in an important way from those in the population of interest. Here, inference is reliable only to the extent that the sample is representative of the population of female high school athletes. This is a common problem with studies of this type, in which it would be difficult to arrange for a random sample of subjects but a sample is conveniently available locally. We can place more faith in the inference if similar results occur in other studies.

The printout in Table 12.2 and the screenshot from the *Linear Regression* app also provide a standard error and *t* statistic for testing that the population *y*-intercept α equals 0. This information is usually not of interest. Rarely is there any reason to test the hypothesis that the *y*-intercept α equals 0.

▶ *Try Exercise 12.12, part a*

You probably did not expect maximum bench press and number of 60-pound bench presses to be independent. The test confirms that they are positively related. As usual, a confidence interval for the slope is more informative. It will tell us more about the actual size of the effect.

A Confidence Interval Tells Us How Precisely We Can Estimate the Slope

A small P-value in the significance test of H_0: $\beta = 0$ suggests that the population regression line has a nonzero slope. To learn just how far the slope β for the population regression model falls from 0, we construct a confidence interval. A 95% confidence interval for β has the typical form of adding and subtracting a margin of error (a multiple of the *se*) from the point estimate:

$$b \pm t_{.025}(se).$$

Recall

For **95% confidence,** the error probability is 0.05, and the *t*-score with half this probability in the right tail is denoted $t_{.025}$ in the *t* table. ◄

The *t*-score $t_{.025}$ can be found by software, using the *t-Distribution* app, or in a *t* table (such as Table B) with $df = n - 2$. (Don't confuse it with the *t* statistic shown for the significance test, which is something different!) More conveniently, the *Linear Regression* app computes this confidence interval directly when checking the Confidence Interval for Slope box. The inference provided by the confidence interval is valid under the same assumptions as the significance test.

Example 6

◄ **A 95% Confidence Interval for the Slope**

Estimating the Slope for Predicting Maximum Bench Press

Picture the Scenario

For the female athlete strength study, the sample regression equation is $\hat{y} = 63.5 + 1.49x$. From Table 12.2, the estimated slope $b = 1.49$ has standard error $se = 0.150$.

Questions to Explore

a. Construct a 95% confidence interval for the population slope β.
b. What are the plausible values for the increase in maximum bench press, on average, for each additional 60-pound bench press that a female athlete can do?

Think It Through

a. For a 95% confidence interval, the $t_{.025}$ value for $df = n - 2 = 55$ is $t_{.025} = 2.00$. The confidence interval is

$$b \pm t_{.025}(se) = 1.49 \pm 2.00(0.150),$$

$$\text{which is } 1.49 \pm 0.30$$

$$\text{or } (1.2, 1.8).$$

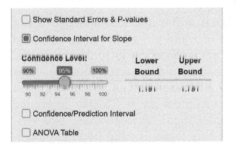

Screenhot from *Linear Regression* app, showing a 95% confidence interval for the slope.

The *Linear Regression* app provides this interval directly, as shown in the screenshot in the margin.

b. With 95% confidence, we estimate that the population slope β falls between 1.2 and 1.8. On average, the maximum bench press increases by between 1.2 and 1.8 pounds for each additional bench press (of 60 lbs) that an athlete can do.

Insight

Confidence intervals and two-sided significance tests about slopes are consistent: When a two-sided test has P-value below 0.05, providing evidence against $\beta = 0$, the 95% confidence interval for β does not contain 0.

► *Try Exercise 12.12, part b*

A confidence interval for β may not have a useful interpretation if a one-unit increase in x is relatively small (or large) in practical terms. In that case, we can estimate the effect for an increase in x that is a more relevant portion of the actual range of x values. For instance, for every 10 unit change in x, we predict the mean of y to change by 10β. To find the confidence interval for 10β, multiply the endpoints of the confidence interval for β by 10.

In the strength study, the number of bench presses varied between 2 and 35, with a standard deviation of 7.1. A change of 1 is very small. Let's estimate the effect of a 10-unit increase in x. Since the 95% confidence interval for β is (1.2, 1.8), the 95% confidence interval for 10β has endpoints $10(1.2) = 12$ and $10(1.8) = 18$. We infer that, on average, the maximum bench press increases by at least 12 pounds and at most 18 pounds, for every 10 additional bench presses that an athlete can complete.

SUMMARY: Confidence Interval for β

Assumptions: (1) Relationship in population satisfies regression model $\mu_y = \alpha + \beta x$, (2) data gathered using randomization, (3) population y values at each x value have normal distribution, with same standard deviation at each x value.

A 95% confidence interval for the slope β in the population regression model $\mu_y = \alpha + \beta x$ is

$$b \pm t_{.025}(se).$$

Software provides the estimated slope b, its standard error se, and the t-score with right tail probability 0.025, if not the entire interval itself.

Inferences Also Apply to the Correlation Coefficient

When the slope $\beta = 0$ for the population regression model $\mu_y = \alpha + \beta x$, the value of x is irrelevant in determining μ_y. In that case, the conditional distribution of y at a particular x value does not depend on x, i.e., it is the same for all values of x. Then, the two variables x and y are independent, and their correlation coefficient in the population is zero. (Compare Figure 12.5, where the mean of y and, hence, the distribution of y depends on x, with Figure 12.6, which shows identical distributions at each x value, i.e., independence.)

Because of this connection, the test of H_0: $\beta = 0$ is also automatically a test of H_0: the population correlation coefficient of x and y is zero. We do not need to come up with a new test statistic and sampling distribution to determine the P-value for this latter test; we just use the results from the test about the slope. For example, the sample correlation coefficient between the number of 60-pound bench presses and the maximum possible bench press is $r = 0.80$. To determine whether in the population the correlation coefficient between these two variables is different from zero, we test the null hypothesis H_0: the population correlation coefficient between number of 60-pound bench presses and maximum bench press is zero (i.e., independence) against the two-sided alternative hypothesis H_a: the population correlation coefficient is different from zero (a linear relationship).

The P-value for this test equals 0.000, which is the P-value we obtained when testing H_0: $\beta = 0$. We have sufficient evidence (P-value < 0.001) to reject the null hypothesis and conclude that the correlation coefficient between the number of 60-pound bench presses and maximum possible bench press is different from zero, i.e., a significant linear relationship exists. Because $r = 0.80$, we can conclude that the linear relationship is, in fact, positive and relatively strong. The assumptions under which this test is valid are the same as those for the significance test of whether $\beta = 0$. (Section 8.4 discussed a confidence interval for the correlation.)

12.11 *t*-score?   A regression analysis is conducted with 25 observations,

a. What is the *df* value for inference about the slope β?

b. Which two *t* test statistic values would give a P-value of 0.05 for testing $H_0: \beta = 0$ against $H_a: \beta \neq 0$?

c. What is the value of the *t*-score that you multiply the standard error by to find the margin of error for a 95% confidence interval for β?

12.12 Predicting house prices   For the House Selling Prices FL data file on the book's website (and preloaded in the *Linear Regression* app), results of a regression analysis are shown for 100 homes relating y = selling price (in dollars) to x = the size of the house (in square feet).

Parameter	Estimate	Standard Error	t Statistic	P-value
Intercept	9,161	10,760	0.85	0.3966
Slope (Size)	77	6.63	11.6	<0.0001

a. Using this output (which you can replicate with the *Linear Regression* app), go through all steps of a significance test of independence (testing whether the population slope equals 0) by (i) mentioning the necessary assumptions for inferences to be valid, (ii) stating the hypotheses, (iii) giving the value of the test statistic, (iv) stating the P-value, and (v) writing a conclusion.

b. Show that a 95% confidence interval for the population slope is (64, 90). (*Hint:* The *t*-score with $df = 98$ equals 1.984 or use the app.)

c. A builder had claimed that the selling price increases $100, on average, for every extra square foot. Based on part b, what would you conclude about this claim?

12.13 Confidence interval for slope   Refer to the previous exercise, which mentioned a confidence interval of (64, 90) for the slope. The 100 houses included in the data set had sizes ranging from 370 square feet to 4,050 square feet.

a. Interpret what the confidence interval implies for a one-unit increase in the size of the house.

b. Repeat part a, now using a more meaningful increase of 100 square feet in the size of a house.

12.14 House prices in bad part of town   Refer to the previous exercise. Of the 100 homes, 25 were in a part of town considered less desirable. For a regression analysis using y = selling price and x = size of house for these 25 homes:

a. You plan to test $H_0: \beta = 0$ against $H_a: \beta > 0$. Explain what H_0 means and why a data analyst might choose a one-sided H_a for this test.

b. For this one-sided alternative hypothesis, how large would the *t* test statistic need to be to get a P-value equal to (i) 0.05 and (ii) 0.01?

12.15 Strength through leg press   The high school female athlete strength study also considered prediction of y = maximum leg press (maxLP) using x = number of 200-pound leg presses (LP200). You can choose these variables for the x- and y-variables in the *Linear Regression* app, which has these data preloaded and leads to the following output:

Parameter	Estimate	Standard Error	t Statistic	P-value
Intercept	234	13.1	17.9	<0.0001
Slope (LP200)	5.27	0.547	9.64	<0.0001

a. Show all steps of a two-sided significance test of the hypothesis of independence.

b. Use the quoted *se* to find and then interpret a 95% confidence interval for the true slope. (*Hint:* $t_{0.025} = 2.00$.) What do you learn from the interval that you cannot learn from the significance test in part a?

12.16 More boys are bad?   A study of 375 women who lived in pre-industrial Finland (by S. Helle et al., *Science*, vol. 296, p. 1085, 2002), using Finnish church records from 1640 to 1870, found that there was roughly a linear relationship between y = life length (in years) and x = number of sons the woman had, with a slope estimate of -0.65 ($se = 0.29$).

a. Interpret the sign of the slope. Is the effect of having more boys good or bad?

b. Show all steps of the test of the hypothesis that life length is independent of number of sons for the two-sided alternative hypothesis. Interpret the P-value. (You can use the *t Distribution* app to find the P-value.)

c. Construct a 95% confidence interval for the true slope. Interpret. Is it plausible that the effect is relatively weak, with true slope near 0? (You can use the *t Distribution* app to find the appropriate *t*-score.)

12.17 More girls are good?   Repeat the previous exercise using x = number of daughters the woman had, for which the slope estimate was 0.44 ($se = 0.29$). (You can use the *t Distribution* app to find the P-value and the *t*-score.)

12.18 CI and two-sided tests correspond   Refer to the previous two exercises. Using significance level 0.05, what decision would you make? Explain how that decision is in agreement with whether 0 falls in the confidence interval. Do this for the data for both the boys and the girls.

12.19 Advertising and sales   For four randomly selected months, the owner of Café Gardens restaurant recorded y = monthly total sales receipts and x = amount spent that month on advertising, both in thousands of dollars. The observations are as shown in the table. The correlation coefficient equals $r = 0.857$.

Advertising	Sales
0	4
1	7
2	8
5	9

a. Find the mean and standard deviation for each variable. (You can enter the data in the *Linear Regression* app by selecting Your Own under Enter Data. Check the box for Summary Statistics under Options to obtain basic summary statistics for x and y.)

b. Using the formulas for the slope and the y-intercept or just using the app, find the regression line.

c. The *se* of the slope estimate is 0.364. Test the null hypothesis that these variables are independent, using a significance level of 0.05.

12.20 GPA and study time—revisited Refer to the relationship you investigated in Exercise 12.7 between study time and college GPA. Using the *Linear Regression* app or other software with the data file you constructed, conduct a significance test of the hypothesis of independence for the one-sided alternative of a positive population slope. Report the hypotheses, appropriate assumptions, sample slope, its standard error, the test statistic, and the P-value and interpret.

12.21 GPA and skipping class—revisited Refer to the relationship you investigated in Exercise 12.8 between skipping class and college GPA. Using the *Linear Regression* app or other software with the data file you constructed, construct a 90% confidence interval for the slope in the population. Interpret.

12.22 Battery capacity Refer to the cell phone data set from Exercise 12.9 about various specs of cell phones, which is preloaded in the *Linear Regression* app. Treat the weight of the phone as the response and the capacity of the battery as the explanatory variable. Remove the outlier (phone no. 70). (In the app, check the option for Click to Remove Points. Then, click on the outlier to remove it.)

a. Is there evidence for a linear relationship between these two variables? Show all steps of a relevant significance test with significance level 0.05 and interpret.

b. Confirm, using the output of the *Linear Regression* app or other software, that the 95% confidence interval for the population slope equals (0.028, 0.060). Interpret the interval and explain the correspondence with the result of the significance test in part a.

12.3 Describing the Strength of the Relationship

In the linear regression model, the slope indicates whether the relationship is positive or negative and describes the trend. The slope does not, however, describe the *strength* of the relationship. As always, a small P-value in a significance test for testing whether the slope (or correlation coefficient) equals 0 only implies that a relationship exists; it does not give any information about how strong that relationship is. For instance, the P-value for testing H_0: $\beta = 0$ (or, equivalently, H_0: population correlation coefficient = 0) can be less than 0.001, indicating strong evidence for a correlation, yet in practical terms that correlation can be very small and practically meaningless, for instance if $r = 0.1$. In this section, we will discuss ways of using the correlation coefficient and its squared value to interpret the strength of the relationship.

The Correlation Coefficient Is a Standardized Slope

Why do we need the correlation coefficient? Why can't we use the slope to describe the strength of the relationship? The reason is that the slope's numerical value depends on the units of measurement. Example 3 found a slope of 1.49 pounds in predicting y = maximum bench press using x = number of 60-pound bench presses. Suppose we instead measure y in kilograms (kg). Since 1 kg = 2.2 pounds, a slope of 1.49 pounds is equivalent to a slope of $1.49/2.2 = 0.68$ kilograms. In grams, the slope would be 680. Whether a slope is a small number or a large number merely depends on the units of measurement!

The correlation coefficient r is a *standardized* version of the slope. Unlike the slope b, r does not depend on units of measurement. It takes the same value regardless of whether maximum bench press is measured in pounds, kilograms, or grams. Since the correlation coefficient r and the slope b are related by $b = r(s_y/s_x)$, we can write

Recall

From Section 3.3,

$$b = r\left(\frac{s_y}{s_x}\right),$$

$$a = \bar{y} - b\bar{x}. \blacktriangleleft$$

$$r = b\left(\frac{s_x}{s_y}\right).$$

You can see from this formula that the correlation coefficient equals the slope when $s_x = s_y$. In practice, the two standard deviations will never be identical. However, remember that the correlation coefficient does not depend on the units of measurements, which means we can compute it with the z-scores for x and y (i.e., the standardized variables) and still get the same value. (If you remember from Chapter 3, that's actually what we did when we discussed the formula for r, which we expressed in terms of z-scores.) By construction, z-scores have standard

Recall

From Section 2.5, the z-score for an observation y, e.g.,

$$z_y = (y - \bar{y})/s_y$$

measures how many standard deviations the observation falls from the mean of all y values. Section 2.6 showed that z-scores have mean 0 and standard deviation 1. ◄

deviation equal to 1. Let z_x and z_y denote the z-scores of x and y, respectively. Then, $s_{z_x} = s_{z_y} = 1$, and the slope estimated from the regression model using the z-scores instead of the original variables equals the correlation coefficient r.

This leads to an important interpretation for r as a standardized slope: Technically, for every one-unit change in the z-score of x, we predict the z-score of y to change by r units. Remember, however, that a z-score just expresses how many standard deviations an observation falls from its mean, so the technical interpretation implies more practically that if x changes by one standard deviation, we predict y to change by r standard deviations.

Predicted Change in y When x Changes by One Standard Deviation ◄

Example 7

Predicting Strength

Picture the Scenario

For the female athlete strength study (Examples 1–3), with x = number of 60-pound bench presses and y = maximum bench press, we had:

    x: mean = 11.0, standard deviation = 7.1

    y: mean = 79.9, standard deviation = 13.3 (both in pounds)

    regression equation: $\hat{y} = 63.5 + 1.49x$.

Questions to Explore

a. Find the correlation coefficient r between these two variables.

b. Show that r does not change value if you measure y in kilograms.

c. Predict the change in maximum bench press when the number of 60-pound presses increases *by one standard deviation*.

Think It Through

a. The slope of the regression equation is b = 1.49. Since $s_x = 7.1$ and $s_y = 13.3$,

$$r = b\left(\frac{s_x}{s_y}\right) = 1.49\left(\frac{7.1}{13.3}\right) = 0.80.$$

The variables have a strong, positive linear relationship.

b. If y had been measured in kilograms, the y values would have been divided by 2.2, since 1 kg = 2.2 pounds. For instance, Subject 1 had y = 80 pounds, which is 80/2.2 = 36.4 kg. Likewise, the standard deviation s_y of 13.3 in pounds would have been divided by 2.2 to get 13.3/2.2 = 6.05 in kg. The slope of 1.49 expressing the change in pounds for a unit change in x would have been divided by 2.2, giving 0.68, since a change of 1.49 pounds = a change of 0.68 kg. Then

$$r = b(s_x/s_y) = 0.68(7.1/6.05) = 0.80.$$

The correlation coefficient is the same (0.80) whether we measure y in pounds or in kilograms. (Alternatively, we could have argued that the correlation coefficient is computed from the z-scores of x and y, and since the z-scores for y are the same when y is measured in pounds or in kilograms, the correlation coefficient is the same.)

c. As mentioned just before Example 7, when x changes by *one standard deviation*, we predict y to change by r standard deviation. So, for a one-standard deviation change in the number of bench presses, we predict the maximum possible bench press to change by 0.80 standard deviations.

Insight

Now if we change units from kilograms to grams, s_y changes from 6.05 to 6,050 and b changes from 0.68 to 680, but again $r = 0.80$ because r does not depend on the units. Similarly, the predicted change in y will always be 0.80 standard deviations of y, regardless of the units we use for y.

▶ *Try Exercise 12.26*

Regression Toward the Mean

We now want to show that at any particular x value, the predicted value of y is relatively closer to its mean on the y-axis than x is to its mean on the x-axis. As we have just argued when discussing that the correlation coefficient r is a standardized slope:

If x changes by one standard deviation, $\hat{y}$ changes by r standard deviations.

Suppose $r = 0.5$ and consider the x-value changing from an initial value of $\bar{x}$ to a new value of $\bar{x} + s_x$, i.e., an increase of exactly 1 standard deviation on the x-axis. Then the predicted value of y changes from its initial value of $\bar{y}$ to $\bar{y} + 0.5s_y$, which is only 0.5 standard deviations above the mean on the y-axis. So, for a one-standard deviation increase in x, the predicted value for y increases by only 0.5 standard deviations. See Figure 12.7, which also recalls that for subjects at the mean $\bar{x}$ of x, their predicted value of y is $\bar{y}$.

▲ **Figure 12.7** The Predicted Value of y Is Closer to Its Mean $\bar{y}$ Than x Is to Its Mean $\bar{x}$ (in Number of Standard Deviations). When x is 1 standard deviaton above $\bar{x}$, the predicted y value is r standard deviations above $\bar{y}$ In the figure, $r = 0.5$. **Question** When x is 2 standard deviations above $\bar{x}$, how many standard deviations does the predicted y value fall above $\bar{y}$ (if $r = 0.5$)?

Example 8

Regression Toward the Mean ◀

Tall Parents and Tall Children

Picture the Scenario

British scientist Francis Galton discovered the basic ideas of regression and correlation in the 1880s. He observed that very tall parents tended to have tall children, but on average not quite so tall. For instance, for all fathers with height 7 feet, their sons averaged 6 feet 5 inches when fully grown—taller than average but not extremely tall. Likewise, for fathers with height 5 feet, perhaps their sons averaged 5 feet 5 inches—shorter than average, but not extremely short.

In his research, Galton accounted for gender height differences by multiplying each female height by 1.08, so heights of mothers and daughters had about the same mean as heights of fathers and sons. Then, for each son or daughter, he summarized their father's and mother's heights by parents' height = (father's height + mother's height)/2, the mean of their heights.

Question to Explore

Galton found a correlation coefficient of 0.5 between x = parents' height and y = child's height. How does his observation about very tall or very short parents with children who are not so very tall or so very short relate to the property about the correlation coefficient that a predicted value of y is relatively closer to its mean than x is to its mean?

Think It Through

From the property of r with $r = 0.5$, when x = parents' height is a certain number of standard deviations from its mean, then y = child's predicted height is *half* as many standard deviations from its mean. For example, if the parents' height is 2 standard deviations above the mean, the child is predicted to be 1 standard deviation above the mean (half as far, in relative terms, when $r = 0.5$). At $x = \bar{x} + 3s_x$, we predict $\hat{y} = \bar{y} + 1.5s_y$. In each case, on average a child's height is above the mean but only half as far above the mean as his or her parent's height is above the parent's mean.

Insight

The correlation coefficient r is no greater than 1 in absolute value. So, a y value is predicted to be fewer standard deviations from its mean than x is from its mean.

▶ *Try Exercise 12.35*

In Words

In English, "regression" means going back, or returning. Here, the predicted value of y is going back toward the mean.

In summary, the predicted y is relatively closer to its mean than x is to its mean. Because of this, there is said to be **regression toward the mean**. This is the origin of the name that Francis Galton chose for regression analysis.

For all cases in which parents' height is *extremely* tall, say 3 standard deviations above the mean (essentially at the upper limit of observed heights), it's no surprise that their children would tend to be shorter. For all cases in which parents' height is extremely short, say 3 standard deviations below the mean, it's no surprise that their children would tend to be taller. In both these cases, we'd expect regression toward the mean. What's interesting and perhaps surprising is that regression of y toward the mean happens not only at the very extreme values of x.

Example 9

Regression Toward the Mean in Medical Studies ◀

The Placebo Effect

Picture the Scenario

A clinical trial admits subjects suffering from high blood cholesterol (over 225 mg/dl). The subjects are randomly assigned to take either a placebo or a drug being tested for reducing cholesterol levels. After the three-month study, the mean cholesterol level for subjects taking the drug drops from 270 to 230. However, the researchers are surprised to see that the mean cholesterol level for the placebo group also drops, from 270 to 250.

Question to Explore

Explain how this placebo effect could merely reflect regression toward the mean.

Think It Through

For a group of people, a person's cholesterol reading at one time would likely be positively correlated with their reading three months later. So, for all people who are not taking the drug, a subject with relatively high cholesterol at one time would also tend to have relatively high cholesterol three months later. By regression toward the mean, however, subjects who are relatively high at one time will, on average, be lower at a later time. So, if a study gives placebo to people with relatively high cholesterol (that is, in the right-hand tail of the blood cholesterol distribution), on average we expect their values three months later to be lower.

Insight

Regression toward the mean is pervasive. In sports, excellent performance tends to be followed by good, but less outstanding, performance. A football team that wins all its games in the first half of its schedule will probably not win all its games in the second half. A baseball player who hits 0.400 in the first month will probably not be hitting that high at the end of the season.

By contrast, the good news about regression toward the mean is that very poor performance tends to be followed by improved performance. If you got the worst score in your statistics class on the first exam, you probably did not do so poorly on the second exam (but you were probably still below the mean).

▶ *Try Exercise 12.32*

The Squared Correlation Coefficient (r^2) Describes Predictive Power

If you know how many times a person can bench press 60 pounds, can you predict well their maximum bench press? Another way to describe the strength of the relationship refers to how close predictions for y tend to be to observed y values. The variables are strongly related if you can predict y much better by substituting x values into the prediction equation $\hat{y} = a + bx$ than by merely using the sample mean $\bar{y}$, ignoring x and its relationship with y.

For a given person, the prediction error is the difference between the observed and predicted values of y.

- The error using the regression line to make a prediction is $y - \hat{y}$.
- The error using $\bar{y}$ to make a prediction is $y - \bar{y}$.

For each potential predictor ($\hat{y}$ and $\bar{y}$), some errors are positive, some errors are negative, some errors may be zero, and the sum of the errors for the sample equals 0. You can summarize the sizes of the errors by the sum of their squared values,

$$\text{Error summary} = \Sigma(\text{observed } y \text{ value} - \text{predicted } y \text{ value})^2.$$

When we predict y using $\bar{y}$ (that is, ignoring x), the error summary equals

$$\Sigma(y - \bar{y})^2.$$

Recall

$\Sigma(y - \bar{y})^2$ is the numerator of the variance of the y values. $\Sigma(y - \hat{y})^2$ is what's minimized in finding the least squares estimates for the regression equation. ◀

This is called the **total sum of squares**. When we predict y using $\hat{y}$ (that is, using x with the regression equation), the error summary equals

$$\Sigma(y - \hat{y})^2.$$

This is called the **residual sum of squares** because it sums the squared residuals.

When a strong linear relationship exists, the regression equation predictions ($\hat{y}$) tend to be much better than $\bar{y}$. Then, $\Sigma(y - \hat{y})^2$ is much less than $\Sigma(y - \bar{y})^2$. The difference between the two error summaries depends on the units of measure: It's different, for instance, with weight measured in kilograms than in pounds. We can eliminate this dependence on units by converting the difference to a proportion, by dividing by $\Sigma(y - \bar{y})^2$. This gives the summary measure

$$r^2 = \frac{\Sigma(y - \bar{y})^2 - \Sigma(y - \hat{y})^2}{\Sigma(y - \bar{y})^2}.$$

This measure, often called the coefficient of determination, falls between 0 and 1 and is interpreted as the **proportional reduction in error.** If $r^2 = 0.40$, for instance, the error using $\hat{y}$ to predict y is 40% smaller than the error when using $\bar{y}$ to predict y. We use the notation r^2 for this measure because, in fact, it can be shown that this measure equals the square of the correlation coefficient r.

In Practice Get r^2 by Squaring the Correlation Coefficient

If you know the correlation coefficient r, it is simple to calculate r^2 by squaring the correlation coefficient. The formula shown previously for r^2 is useful for interpretation of r^2, but it's not needed for calculation.

Example 10

The Squared
Correlation
Coefficient r^2 ◄

The Strength Study

Picture the Scenario

For the female athlete strength study, Example 7 showed that $x =$ number of 60-pound bench presses, and $y =$ maximum bench press had a correlation coefficient of 0.80.

Question to Explore

Find and interpret r^2.

Think It Through

Since the correlation coefficient $r = 0.80$, $r^2 = (0.80)^2 = 0.64$, or 64%. For predicting maximum bench press, the regression equation has 64% less error than $\bar{y}$ has. "Error" here refers to the summary given by the sum of squared prediction errors. The overall prediction error when using the regression equation with number of 60-pound bench presses to predict the maximum bench press is 64% smaller compared to using the sample mean maximum bench press for predictions.

Insight

Since $r^2 = 0.64$ is quite far from 0, we can predict y much better using the regression equation than using $\bar{y}$. In this sense, the relationship is quite strong.

▶ *Try Exercise 12.27, part b*

Model Summary:

Statistic	Value
Correlation Coefficient r	0.802
Coefficient of Determination r^2	64.3%
Residual Standard Deviation	8.003

Screenshot from *Linear Regression* app, showing summary statistics such as r and r^2.

The *Linear Regression* app (see the screenshot in the margin, where r^2 is labeled as the coefficient of determination) and all other software report r^2 as part of the standard output. Software for regression also routinely provides tables of sums of squares. Table 12.3 is an example. The heading SS stands for "sum of squares." From Table 12.3, or the screenshot from the *Linear Regression* app next to it,

Table 12.3 Annotated MINITAB Table Showing Sums of Squares and r^2 for Strength Study

Under the heading for Source, "Total" refers to $\Sigma(y - \bar{y})^2$ and "Error" refers to $\Sigma(y - \hat{y})^2$. The "Regression" sum of squares equals their difference, which is the numerator of r^2.

Source	SS		
		←	SS stands for "sum of squares"
Regression	6351.8	←	This is 9,874.6 − 3,522.8, the numerator of r^2
Error	3522.8	←	$\Sigma(y - \hat{y})^2$
Total	9874.6	←	$\Sigma(y - \bar{y})^2$
R-Sq = 64.3%		←	This is r^2, in percentage terms

ANOVA Table:

Source	Df	Sum Sq
Regression	1	6,351.8
Residuals	55	3,522.8
Total	56	9,874.6

Screenshot from *Linear Regression* app, showing sums of squares in the ANOVA table.

the residual sum of squared errors is $\Sigma(y - \hat{y})^2 = 3,522.8$, and the total sum of squares is $\Sigma(y - \bar{y})^2 = 9,874.6$. Thus,

$$r^2 = \frac{\Sigma(y - \bar{y})^2 - \Sigma(y - \hat{y})^2}{\Sigma(y - \bar{y})^2} = \frac{9,874.6 - 3,522.8}{9,874.6} = 0.643.$$

In practice, it is unnecessary to perform this computation, since the *Linear Regression* app and other software reports both r and r^2.

A table that reports the sums of squares used in regression analysis is called an **analysis of variance table**, or **ANOVA table** for short. We'll discuss the ANOVA table further in Section 12.4.

Properties of r^2

The r^2 measure, like the correlation coefficient r, measures the strength of the *linear* relationship. We emphasize *linear* because r^2 compares predictive power of the *straight-line* regression equation to $\bar{y}$.

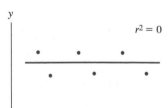

> **SUMMARY: Properties of r^2**
>
> - Since $-1 \le r \le 1$, r^2 falls between 0 and 1.
> - $r^2 = 1$ when $\Sigma(y - \hat{y})^2 = 0$, which happens only when all the data points fall exactly on the regression line. There is then no prediction error using x to predict y (that is, $y = \hat{y}$ for each observation). This corresponds to $r = \pm 1$. (See top scatterplot in margin figure.)
> - $r^2 = 0$ when $\Sigma(y - \hat{y})^2 = \Sigma(y - \bar{y})^2$. This happens when the slope $b = 0$, in which case each $\hat{y} = \bar{y}$. The regression line and $\bar{y}$ then give the same predictions. (See bottom scatterplot in margin figure.)
> - The closer r^2 is to 1, the stronger the linear relationship and the more effective the regression equation $\hat{y} = a + bx$ is in predicting y.

Next to the interpretation of r^2 as the proportional reduction in the prediction error, it has a second interpretation as the **percentage of the variability** in the response variable y that can be explained by its linear relationship with the explanatory variable x. For instance, the r^2 value of 0.64 from Example 10 indicates that 64% of the variability observed in maximum bench press can be explained by its linear relationship with the number of 60-pound bench presses. (We will show the reasoning behind this interpretation by using a graph in Section 12.4.)

Did You Know

Software that fits regression models provides the estimated intercept and slope, their standard errors and their P-values. The r^2 measure is also part of the default output. You need to know how to interpret these values, but not how to compute them by hand. ◄

SUMMARY: Correlation Coefficient r and Its Square r^2

Both the correlation coefficient r and its square r^2 describe the strength of the linear relationship. They have different interpretations. The correlation coefficient falls between -1 and $+1$. It represents by how many standard deviations y is predicted to change when x changes by one standard deviation. Thereby, it governs the extent of "regression toward the mean." The r^2 measure falls between 0 and 1 (or 0% and 100% when reported as a percentage). It summarizes the reduction in the prediction error when using the regression equation rather than $\bar{y}$ to predict y. It is also used to indicate what percent of the variability in y can be explained by x.

Factors Affecting the Correlation Coefficient

Section 3.4 showed that certain regression outliers can unduly influence the slope and the correlation coefficient. A single observation can have a large influence if its x value is unusually large or unusually small and if it falls quite far from the trend of the rest of the data.

Besides being influenced by outliers, the size of the correlation coefficient r (and r^2) depends strongly on two other factors.

- First, if the subjects are grouped for the observations, such as when the data refer to county summaries instead of individual people, the correlation coefficient r tends to increase in magnitude.

Suppose you want to find the correlation coefficient between number of years of education completed and annual income. You could measure these variables for a sample of individuals. Or you could use summary education and income measures such as means or medians for counties (or states or provinces). The scatterplot in Figure 12.8 shows that at the individual level, the correlation could be much weaker. Lots of variability in income exists for individuals, but not much variability in income (mean or median) exists for counties. The summary values for counties fall closer to a straight line.

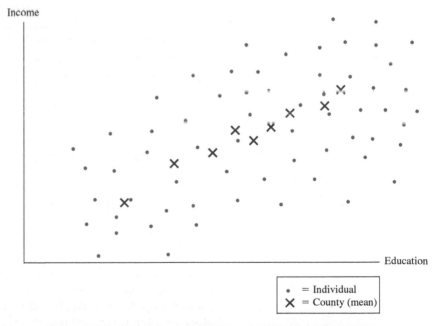

▲ **Figure 12.8** The Effect of Grouping of Subjects on the Correlation. There is a stronger linear trend for the countywide data than for the data on individuals. **Question** Why would you expect much more variability for income of individuals than for mean income of counties?

Did You Know?

The **ecological fallacy** is a danger even with single variables. If the mean income in your town is $50,000, you'd be wrong to assume that each worker makes $50,000. Perhaps half are professionals making $90,000 and half are service workers making $10,000. ◄

Weaker correlation over a narrow *x*-range

Because correlations can change dramatically when data are grouped, it is misleading to take results for groupings such as counties and extend them to individuals. If income and education are strongly correlated when we measure the summary means for each county, this does not imply they will be strongly correlated for measurements on individuals. Making predictions about individuals based on the summary results for groups is known as the **ecological fallacy** and should be avoided.

■ Second, the size of the correlation coefficient *r* depends on the range of *x* values sampled: *r* tends to be smaller when we sample only a restricted range of *x* values than when we use the entire range. (See margin figure.)

By contrast, the prediction equation remains valid when we observe a restricted range of *x* values. The slope is usually not much affected by the range of *x* values, and we simply limit our predictions to that range. The correlation coefficient makes most sense, however, when *x* takes its full range of values. Otherwise, it can be misleading.

Factors Affecting the Correlation ◄

Example 11

High School GPA Predicting College GPA

Picture the Scenario

Consider the correlation between high school GPA and later performance in college measured by college GPA.

Question to Explore

For which group would these variables have a larger correlation coefficient: A sample of students who graduate from Harvard University this year, or a sample of students who graduate from college somewhere in the United States this year?

Think It Through

The magnitude of the correlation coefficient depends on the variability in high school GPA. For Harvard students, the high school GPAs will concentrate narrowly at the upper end of the scale. So, the correlation would probably be weak and the correlation coefficient *r* close to 0. By contrast, for the sample of students who finish college, high school GPA values would range from very low to very high. We would likely see a much larger correlation coefficient for them.

Insight

What reason explains this property of the correlation coefficient? Recall the formula, $r = b(s_x/s_y)$. When we use a much wider range of *x* values, s_x increases a lot. So, if the slope does not change much and if the variability of the *y* values is not much larger with the expanded sample, *r* will tend to increase because it is proportional in value to s_x.

▶ *Try Exercise 12.38*

▶ On the Shoulders of ... Francis Galton

Heights and peas—what do they have in common?

—Francis Galton (1822–1911)

Francis Galton

Francis Galton, like his cousin Charles Darwin, was interested in genetics. In his work on inheritance, he collected data on parents' and children's heights. He found that, on average, the heights of children were not as extreme as those of the parents and tended toward the mean height. There was regression toward the mean. This refers to this average, not to every

observation. It does not imply that over the course of many generations, heights will all vary less from the mean height.

Galton also conducted experiments examining the weight of sweet peas. The mean weight of offspring peas was closer than the weight of the parent group to the mean for all peas. Again, Galton observed regression toward the mean.

Galton discovered a way to summarize linear relationships numerically. He named this numerical summary the "coefficient of correlation." In 1896, the British statistician Karl Pearson (who proposed the chi-squared test for contingency tables in 1900) derived the current method for estimating the correlation using sample data, now called the Pearson correlation coefficient r.

12.3 Practicing the Basics

12.23 Dollars and thousands of dollars   If a slope is 1.50 when x = income in thousands of dollars, then what is the slope when x = income in dollars? (*Hint:* A \$1 change has only 1/1,000 of the impact of a \$1,000 change.)

12.24 When can you compare slopes?   Although the slope does not measure the strength of the linear relationship, it *is* useful for comparing effects for two variables that have the *same* units. For the Internet Use data file of 32 nations on the book's website, let x = GDP (thousands of dollars per capita). For predicting y = percentage of adults using the Internet, the prediction equation is $\hat{y} = 34.8 + 1.02x$. For predicting y = percentage of adults using Facebook, the prediction equation is $\hat{y} = 23.0 + 0.46x$.

a. Explain how to interpret the two slopes.

b. For these nations, explain why a one-unit increase in GDP has a slightly greater impact on the percentage using the Internet than on the percentage using Facebook.

12.25 Sketch scatterplot   Sketch a scatterplot, identifying quadrants relative to the sample means as in Figure 12.2, for which (a) the slope and correlation coefficient would be negative and (b) the slope and correlation coefficient would be approximately zero.

12.26 Sit-ups and the 40-yard dash   Is there a relationship between x = how many sit-ups you can do and y = how fast you can run 40 yards (in seconds)? The output of a regression analysis based on the female athlete strength study is shown here. You can replicate this output using the *Linear Regression* app, which has this data set preloaded.

a. Find the predicted time in the 40-yard dash for a subject who can do (i) 10 sit-ups and (ii) 40 sit-ups. (The minimum and maximum in the study were 10 and 39.) Relate the difference in predicted times to the slope.

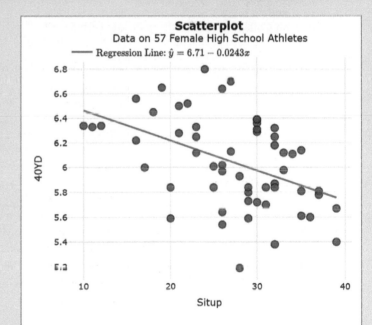

Scatterplot
Data on 57 Female High School Athletes
Regression Line: $\hat{y} = 6.71 - 0.0243x$

Linear Regression Equation:

Parameter	Estimate	Standard Error	t Statistic	P-value
Intercept	6.707	0.1779	37.7	<0.0001
Slope (Situp)	-0.02435	0.006349	-3.83	0.0003

Model Summary:

Statistic	Value
Correlation Coefficient r	-0.459
Coefficient of Determination r^2	21.1%
Residual Standard Deviation	0.3272

b. Predict by how many standard deviations the time of the 40-yard dash decreases for a one standard deviation increase in the number of sit-ups the athlete can do.

c. The number of sit-ups had mean 27.175 and standard deviation 6.887. The time in the 40-yard dash had mean 6.045 and standard deviation 0.365. Show how the correlation coefficient r relates to the slope and verify the value shown in the screenshot.

d. The time difference for the 40-yard run between two athletes that are one standard deviation apart in the number of sit-ups they can do is predicted to be how much? First, answer in terms of standard deviations of the time for the 40-yard dash. Then, using the standard deviation given in part c, answer in absolute terms (i.e., in seconds).

12.27 Body fat For the Male Athlete Strength data file on the book's website, the correlation coefficient r between weight (pounds) and percent body fat (BF%) equals 0.883.

a. Interpret the sign and the strength of the correlation coefficient.

b. Find and interpret r^2.

c. If weight were measured instead with metric units, would any results differ in parts a and b? Explain.

12.28 Verbal and math SAT All students who attend Lake Wobegon College must take the math and verbal SAT exams. Both exams have a mean of 500 and a standard deviation of 100. The regression equation relating y = math SAT score and x = verbal SAT score is $\hat{y} = 250 + 0.5x$.

a. Find the predicted math SAT score for a student who has the mean verbal SAT score of 500. (*Note*: At the x value equal to $\bar{x}$, the predicted value of y equals $\bar{y}$.)

b. Show how to find the correlation coefficient. Interpret its value as a standardized slope. (*Hint:* Both standard deviations are equal.)

c. Find r^2 and interpret its value.

12.29 SAT regression toward mean Refer to the previous exercise.

a. Predict the math SAT score for a student who has a verbal SAT = 800.

b. The correlation coefficient r is 0.5. Interpret the prediction in part a in terms of regression toward the mean.

12.30 GPA and TV watching For the Georgia Student Survey data file on the book's website (and preloaded in the *Linear Regression* app), the correlation coefficient r between daily time spent watching TV and college GPA is −0.35.

a. Interpret r and r^2. Use the interpretation of r^2 that (i) refers to the prediction error and (ii) the percent of variability explained.

b. One student is 2 standard deviations above the mean on time watching TV. (i) Would you expect that student to be above or below the mean on college GPA? Explain (ii) How many standard deviations would you expect that student to be away from the mean on college GPA? Use your answer to explain "regression toward the mean."

12.31 GPA and study time Refer to the relationship you investigated in Exercise 12.7 between study time and college GPA. Using the *Linear Regression* app or other software with the data file you constructed for that exercise,

a. Find and interpret the correlation coefficient.

b. Find and interpret r^2. Use the interpretation of r^2 that (i) refers to the prediction error and (ii) the percent of variability explained.

12.32 Placebo helps cholesterol? A clinical trial admits subjects suffering from high cholesterol, who are then randomly assigned to take a drug or a placebo for a 12-week study. For the population, without taking any drug, the correlation coefficient r between the cholesterol readings at times 12 weeks apart is 0.70. The mean cholesterol reading at any given time is 200, with the same standard deviation at each time. Consider all the subjects with a cholesterol level of 300 at the start of the study, who take placebo.

a. What would you predict for their mean cholesterol level at the end of the study?

b. Does this suggest that placebo is effective for treating high cholesterol? Explain.

12.33 Does tutoring help? For a class of 100 students, the teacher enrolls the 10 students who performed poorest on the midterm exam in a special tutoring program. Both the midterm and final have a class mean of 70 with standard deviation 10, and the correlation coefficient r is 0.50 between the two exam scores. The mean for the specially tutored students increases from 50 on the midterm to 60 on the final. Can we conclude that the tutoring program was successful? Explain, identifying the response and explanatory variables and the role of regression toward the mean.

12.34 What's wrong with your stock fund? Last year you looked at all the financial firms that had stock growth funds. You picked the growth fund that had the best performance last year (ranking at the 99th percentile on performance) and invested all your money in it this year. This year, with its new investments, it ranked only at the 65th percentile on performance. Your friend suggests that its stock picker became complacent or was burned out. Can you give another explanation?

12.35 Golf regression In the first round of a golf tournament, five players tied for the lowest round, at 65. The mean score of all players was 75. If the mean score of all players is also 75 in the second round, what does regression toward the mean suggest about how well we can expect the five leaders to do, on the average, in the second round? (*Hint:* Suppose the standard deviation is also the same in each round.)

12.36 Car weight and mileage The Car Weight and Mileage data file on the book's website and preloaded in the *Linear Regression* app shows the weight and the mileage per gallon of gas of 25 cars of various models. The regression of mileage on weight has $r^2 = 0.75$. Explain how to interpret this in terms of how well you can predict a car's mileage if you know its weight.

12.37 Food and drink sales The owner of Bertha's Restaurant is interested in whether a relationship exists between the amount spent on food and the amount spent on drinks for the restaurant's customers. She decides to measure each variable for every customer in the next month. Each day she also summarizes the mean amount spent on food and the mean amount spent on drinks. Which correlation coefficient between amounts spent on food and drink do you think would be higher, the one computed for the 2,500 customers in the next month, or the one computed using the means for the 30 days of the month? Why? Sketch a sample scatterplot showing what you expect for each case as part of your answer.

12.38 Yale and UConn   For which sample from the student body do you think the correlation coefficient between high school GPA and college GPA would be higher: Yale University or the University of Connecticut? Explain why.

TRY

12.39 Violent crime and single-parent families   Use the *Linear Regression* app or other software to analyze the U.S. Statewide Crime data file on the book's website on y = violent crime rate and x = percentage of single parent families. The app has this data set preloaded.

APP

a. Construct a scatterplot. What does it show?

b. One point is quite far removed from the others, having a much higher value on both variables than the rest of the sample, but it fits in well with the linear trend exhibited by the rest of the points. Show that the

correlation coefficient r changes from 0.77 to 0.59 when you delete this observation. (In the app, check the box for Click to Remove Points and then click on the point to remove it.) Why does it drop so dramatically?

12.40 Correlations for the strong and for the weak   Refer to the High School Female Athlete and Male Athlete Strength data files on the book's website. (If using the *Linear Regression* app, select Enter Own under Enter Data for part b. You cannot use the preloaded dataset because you cannot delete observations in the app, which you are required to do for part b. But under Enter Own, you can copy and paste any x and y values from a spreadsheet into the app.)

APP

a. Find the correlation coefficient r between number of 60-pound bench presses before fatigue and bench press maximum for females and between bench presses before fatigue ("repBP") and bench press maximum for males. Interpret.

b. Find the correlation coefficient r using only the x values (i) below the median of 10 for females and below the median of 17 for males and (ii) above the median of 10 for females and above the median of 17 for males. Compare to the correlation coefficient in part a. Why are they so different?

12.4 How the Data Vary Around the Regression Line

We've used regression to describe and make inferences about the relationship between two quantitative variables. Now, we'll see what we can learn from the variability of the data around the regression line. We'll see that a type of residual helps us detect unusual observations. We'll also see that the sizes of the residuals affect how well we can predict y or the mean of y at any given value of x.

Standardized Residuals

The magnitude of the residuals depends on the units of measurement for y. If we measure the bench press in kilograms instead of pounds, we'll get different residuals. A *standardized* version of the residual does not depend on the units. It equals the residual divided by a standard error that describes the sampling variability of the residuals. This ratio is called a **standardized residual**,

Recall

A **residual** is a prediction error, the difference $y - \hat{y}$ between an observed outcome y and its predicted value $\hat{y}$. For contingency tables, Section 11.4 constructed a **standardized residual** by dividing the difference between a cell count and its expected count by a standard error. In regression, an observation y takes the place of the cell count, and the predicted value $\hat{y}$ takes the place of the expected cell count. ◄

$$\text{Standardized residual} = \frac{y - \hat{y}}{se \text{ of } (y - \hat{y})}.$$

The *se* formula is complex, but we can rely on the *Linear Regression* app or other software to find and plot standardized residuals.

A standardized residual behaves like a z-score. It indicates how many standard errors a residual falls from the overall mean of all residuals, which is 0. If the relationship is truly linear and if the standardized residuals have approximately a bell-shaped distribution, absolute values larger than about 3 should be quite rare. Often, observations with standardized residuals larger than 3 in absolute value represent outliers—observations that are far from what the model predicts.

Standardized Residual ◀

Example 12

Detecting an Underachieving College Student

Picture the Scenario

Two of the variables in the Georgia Student Survey data file on the book's website are college GPA and high school GPA (variables CGPA and HSGPA). These were measured for a sample of 59 students at the University of Georgia. Identifying y = CGPA and x = HSGPA, we find $\hat{y} = 1.19 + 0.64x$.

Question to Explore

The screenshot from the second tab of the *Linear Regression* app in Table 12.4 shows a table that has the standardized residuals in the last column. The app also produces a scatterplot of the standardized residuals plotted against HSGPA. In the app, we highlighted the standardized residual for student 59 by hovering over that point. (You can also click on the column name "Standardized Residual" in the table to sort the residuals from largest to smallest.) Using this output, interpret the results for observation (=student) 59.

Table 12.4 Standardized Residuals in Regression Model for Student GPA
Screenshot from the second tab of the *Linear Regression* app.

Dataset, with new columns for fitted values and residuals added at the end:

	Student	HSGPA	CGPA	Fitted Value	Residual	Standardized Residual
53	53	3.9	3.2	3.6739	-0.4739	-1.511
54	54	3.9	3.6	3.6739	-0.0739	-0.2357
55	55	4	3.75	3.7376	0.0124	0.0396
56	56	3.97	3.77	3.7185	0.0515	0.1645
57	57	4	3.83	3.7376	0.0924	0.2955
58	58	4	3.7	3.7376	-0.0376	-0.1203
59	59	3.6	2.5	3.4828	-0.9828	-3.1439

Think It Through

Observation 59 is a student who had high school GPA $x = 3.60$, college GPA $y = 2.50$, predicted college GPA $\hat{y} = 3.48$, and residual = $y - \hat{y} = -0.98$. The reported standardized residual of -3.14 indicates that the residual is 3.14 standard errors below 0. This student's actual college GPA is far below what the regression line predicts.

Insight

Based on the student's high school GPA and predicted college GPA, this student with an actual college GPA of 2.50 seems to be an underachiever in college.

▶ *Try Exercise 12.41*

When a standardized residual is larger than about 3 in absolute value, check out if the observation is unusual in some way. Why does it fall away from the linear trend that the other points follow? Does it have too much influence on the results? As we've observed, a severe regression outlier can substantially affect the fit, especially when the value of the explanatory variable is relatively high or low and when the overall sample size is not very large.

Keep in mind that some large standardized residuals may occur just because of ordinary random variability. As you can confirm with the app, there are three observations with standardized residual larger than 2 in absolute value. Even if the model is perfect we'd expect about 5% of the standardized residuals to have absolute value above 2 just by chance. So it's not at all surprising to find 3 such values out of 59 observations. This does not suggest that the model fits poorly.

Recall

About 5% of a normal distribution is more than 2 standard deviations from the mean. ◀

Checking the Response Distribution With a Histogram of Residuals

To detect unusual observations, it's helpful to construct a scatterplot of the (standardized) residuals versus the explanatory variable as we have shown in Table 12.4 and to construct a histogram of the residuals. A histogram helps us check the inference assumption that the conditional distribution of y is normal. If this assumption is true, the histogram of the residuals should look approximately bell-shaped. To check this, we construct a histogram of the residuals or the standardized residuals.

Using Residuals to Check Our Model Assumptions ◀

Example 13

College GPA

Picture the Scenario

For the regression model of Example 12 predicting college GPA from high school GPA, Figure 12.9 on the next page shows a screenshot from the *Linear Regression* app, displaying a histogram and box plot of the standardized residuals.

Question to Explore

What does Figure 12.9 tell us?

Think It Through

The standardized residuals show some skew to the left. It may be that for a fixed value of high school GPA, college GPA tends to be skewed to the left, with some students doing much more poorly than the regression model would predict. The large negative standardized residual of -3.14 in Example 12, and another negative standardized residual identified as outliers in the box plot, may merely reflect skew in the distribution of college GPA.

Insight

The sample size was 59. When n is not especially large, a graph like Figure 12.9 is an imprecise estimate of a corresponding graph for the population. Although this graph shows some evidence of skew, much of this evidence is based on only two observations. This is not strong evidence that the conditional distribution is far from normal. In viewing such graphs, we need to be careful not to let a few observations influence our judgment too much. We're mainly looking for dramatic departures from the assumptions.

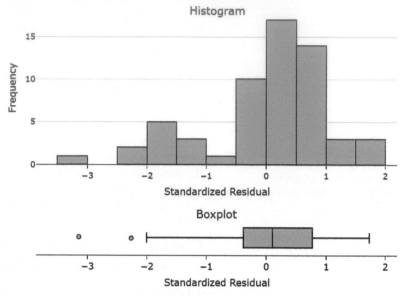

▲ **Figure 12.9** Histogram and Box Plot of Standardized Residuals for Regression Model Predicting College GPA. Screenshot from the Fitted Values & Residual Analysis tab of the *Linear Regression* app.

▶ *Try Exercise 12.43*

If the distribution of the residuals is not normal, two-sided inferences about the slope parameter still work quite well. The *t* inferences are *robust*. The normality assumption is not as important as the assumption that the regression equation approximates well the true relationship between the explanatory variable and the mean of *y*. If the model assumes a linear effect but the effect is actually U-shaped, for instance, descriptive and inferential statistics will be seriously faulty.

We'll study residuals in more detail in the next chapter. We'll learn there how to plot them to check other model assumptions.

The Residual Standard Deviation

Recall that the sample prediction equation $\hat{y} = a + bx$ estimates a population regression equation, $\mu_y = \alpha + \beta x$. For statistical inference, the regression model also assumes that the conditional distribution of *y* at a fixed value of *x* is normal, with the same standard deviation at each *x*. This standard deviation, denoted by σ, refers to the variability of *y* values for all subjects with the same value of *x*. This is a parameter that also can be estimated from the data.

The estimate of σ uses $\Sigma(y - \hat{y})^2$, the *residual sum of squares*, which summarizes sample variability about the regression line. The estimate, called the **residual standard deviation,** is

$$s = \sqrt{\frac{\Sigma(y - \hat{y})^2}{n - 2}}.$$

The $n - 2$ term in the denominator is the *df* value of the *t* distribution used for inference about β in the previous section.

Recall

From Section 12.1, σ **describes the variability** of *y* values from the mean of *y* at each fixed *x* value, that is, the variability of a **conditional distribution** of *y* values. (See figure below.) ◄

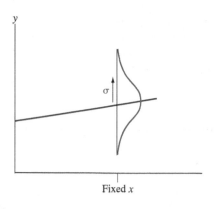

Residual Standard Deviation

Model Summary:

Statistic	Value
Correlation Coefficient r	0.802
Coefficient of Determination r^2	64.3%
Residual Standard Deviation	8.003

Screenshot from *Linear Regression* app, showing residual standard deviation.

```
Coefficients
Term      Coef  SE Coef  T-Value  P-Value
Constant  63.54  1.96     32.48    0.000
BP60      1.49   0.15     9.96     0.000
Model Summary
S          R-sq
8.00319    64.32%
```

MINITAB output of regression analysis

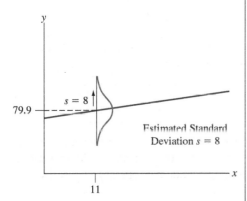

Recall

$$s_y = \sqrt{\frac{\Sum(y - \bar{y})^2}{n - 1}} \blacktriangleleft$$

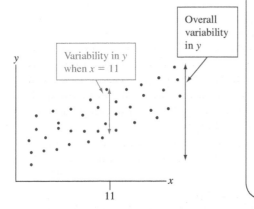

Example 14

Variability of the Athletes' Strengths

Picture the Scenario

Let's return to the analysis of y = maximum bench press and x = number of 60-pound bench presses for 57 female high school athletes. The prediction equation is $\hat{y} = 63.5 + 1.49x$. We'll see later in Table 12.6 that the residual sum of squares equals 3,522.8.

Questions to Explore

a. Find the residual standard deviation of y.

b. Interpret the value you obtain in context when $x = 11$ (the mean of the x-values).

Think It Through

a. Since $n = 57, df = n - 2 = 55$. The residual standard deviation of the y values is

$$s = \sqrt{\frac{\Sigma(y - \hat{y})^2}{n - 2}} = \sqrt{\frac{3{,}522.8}{55}} = \sqrt{64.1} = 8.0.$$

The residual standard deviation s is part of the standard software output, such as in the *Linear Regression* app (see the first screenshot in the margin) or in the MINITAB output under the heading Model Summary (denoted by S; see the second screenshot in the margin).

b. At any fixed value x of number of bench presses, the model estimates that the maximum bench press values vary around a mean of $\hat{y} = 63.5 + 1.49x$ with a standard deviation of 8.0. See the figure in the margin.

At $x = 11$, the predicted maximum bench press is $\hat{y} = 63.5 + 1.49(11) = 79.9$. For female high school athletes who can do eleven bench presses, we estimate that the maximum bench press values have a mean of 79.9 pounds and a standard deviation of 8.0 pounds.

Insight

Why does the residual standard deviation ($s = 8.0$) differ from the standard deviation ($s_y = 13.3$) of the 57 y values in the sample? The reason is that s_y refers to the variability of *all* the y values, not just those at a fixed x value. That is, $s_y = 13.3$ describes the variability around the overall mean of $\bar{y} = 80$ for *all* 57 high school female athletes, whereas $s = 8.0$ describes the variability at a fixed x value such as $x = 11$. See the margin figure.

When the correlation is strong, at a fixed value of x we see less variability than the overall sample has. For instance, at the fixed value $x = 11$, we estimate the variability in maximum bench press values by $s = 8.0$, whereas overall we estimate the variability in maximum bench press values by $s_y = 13.3$.

▶ *Try Exercise 12.47, part a*

r^2: Percentage of Overall Variability

The last figure in the margin sheds light on the interpretation of r^2 as the percentage of the overall variability observed in the response variable y that can be explained by the linear relationship with x. Here, variability refers to the sum of squares. $\Sigma(y - \bar{y})^2$ is a summary measure (a sum of squares) of the overall variability in the response variable (represented by the red arrow in the margin figure). $\Sigma(y - \hat{y})^2$ is a summary measure (a sum of squares) of the variability in the residuals (represented by the green arrow in the margin figure). The ratio $\Sigma(y - \hat{y})^2/\Sigma(y - \bar{y})^2$ expresses the proportion of the overall variability that is left unexplained after fitting the linear regression model. For instance, this proportion would be 0 if all points would fall on a straight line. Then, none of the variability in y is left unexplained and all (100%) of it can be explained by the (perfect) linear relationship with x.

In practice, the ratio is larger than 0 because there is some variation around the line and therefore some variability of y is left unexplained. To get the proportion of the variability that *can be explained* by the linear regression model, we subtract this ratio from 1, as in $1 - \dfrac{\Sigma(y - \hat{y})^2}{\Sigma(y - \bar{y})^2}$. This is exactly the formula for r^2, just written slightly differently. So, r^2 gives the proportion of the overall variability in y that can be attributed to the linear regression model, i.e., that can be explained by the change in x.

Variability explained by x

Residual Variability (unexplained)

Overall variability

Confidence and Prediction Intervals

Consider all female high school athletes who can manage $x = 11$ bench presses before fatigue. Based on the results for the sample, which do you think you can estimate more precisely: The maximum bench press for a randomly chosen one of them or the mean of the maximum bench press values for all of them? We'll see that the estimate is the same in each case, but the margins of error are quite different for the two situations.

For the straight-line regression model, we estimate μ_y, the population mean of y at a given value of x, by $\hat{y} = a + bx$. How good is this estimate? We can use its *se* to construct a 95% **confidence interval for μ_y.** This interval is

$$\hat{y} \pm t_{.025}(se \text{ of } \hat{y}).$$

Again, the *t*-score has $df = n - 2$. The standard error formula is complex (we'll show a simple approximation later), and in practice we rely on software.

The estimate $\hat{y} = a + bx$ for the mean of y at a fixed value of x is also a prediction for the outcome on y for a particular subject at that value. With most regression software, you can form an interval within which an outcome y itself is likely to fall. This interval is called a **prediction interval for y.**

What's the difference between the prediction interval for y and the confidence interval for μ_y? The prediction interval for y is an inference about where individual observations fall, whereas the confidence interval for μ_y is an inference about where a population mean falls. Use a prediction interval for y if you want to predict where a single observation on y will fall. Use a confidence interval for μ_y if you want to estimate the mean of y for everyone having a particular x value. These inferences make the same assumptions as the regression inferences of Section 12.2.

Screenshot from *Linear Regression* app, showing 95% confidence and prediction intervals.

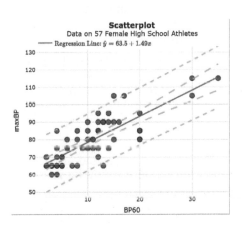

Screenshot from *Linear Regression* app, showing the confidence interval for the mean response (long-dashed line) and the prediction interval for individual responses (short-dashed lines) over the entire range of x-values.

Example 15

Confidence and Prediction Intervals ◀

Maximum Bench Press and Its Mean

Picture the Scenario

We've seen that the equation $\hat{y} = 63.5 + 1.49x$ predicts $y =$ maximum bench press using $x =$ number of 60-pound bench presses. For $x = 11$, Table 12.5 shows how MINITAB reports a confidence interval (CI) for the population mean of y and a prediction interval (PI) for a single y value. The predicted value, $\hat{y}$, is reported under the heading "Fit." The screenshot from the *Linear Regression* app in the margin also shows these two types of intervals. In addition, the app plots the limits of the confidence interval and the prediction interval across the entire range of the x-variable. (See the figure in the margin.)

Table 12.5 MINITAB Output for Confidence Interval (CI) and Prediction Interval (PI) on Maximum Bench Press for Athletes Who Do Eleven 60-Pound Bench Presses Before Fatigue

Variable	Setting		
BP60	11		
Fit	SE Fit	95% CI	95% PI
79.9384	1.06005	(77.8140, 82.0628)	(63.7596, 96.1173)

Questions to Explore

a. Using $\hat{y}$ and its *se* reported in Table 12.5, find and interpret a 95% *confidence interval* for the population mean of the maximum bench press values for all female high school athletes who can do $x = 11$ bench presses.

b. Report and interpret a 95% *prediction interval* for a single new observation on maximum bench press for a randomly chosen female high school athlete with $x = 11$.

Think It Through

a. At $x = 11$, the predicted maximum bench press is $\hat{y} = 63.5 + 1.49(11) = 79.94$ pounds. Table 12.5 reports a standard error for this estimate, $se = 1.06$, under the heading "SE Fit." With $n = 57$ we've seen that $df = n - 2 = 55$ and the t-score is $t_{.025} = 2.00$. So, the 95% confidence interval for the population mean of maximum bench press values at $x = 11$ is

$$\hat{y} \pm t_{.025}(se \text{ of } \hat{y}),$$

which is $79.94 \pm 2.00(1.06)$, or 79.94 ± 2.12, which is $(77.8, 82.1)$.

This is labeled "95% CI" on the MINITAB printout and shown as "Confidence Interval" in the *Linear Regression* app. For all female high school athletes who can do eleven 60-pound bench presses, we estimate (with 95% confidence) that the mean of their maximum bench press values is between about 78 and 82 pounds.

b. MINITAB reports the 95% prediction interval (63.8, 96.1) under the heading "95% PI," shown as "Prediction Interval" in the *Linear Regression* app.

This predicts where the maximum bench press y will fall for a randomly chosen female high school athlete having $x = 11$. Equivalently, this refers to where 95% of the corresponding population values fall. For all female high school athletes who can do eleven 60-pound bench presses, we predict that 95% of them have maximum bench press between about 64 and 96 pounds. Look at the scatterplot in the margin of the previous page. Locate $x = 11$. Of all possible observations at that x value, we predict that 95% of them will fall between about 64 and 96.

Insight

The 95% prediction interval (63.8, 96.1) predicts the maximum bench press y for a randomly chosen female high school athlete having $x = 11$. The 95% confidence interval (77.8, 82.1) estimates the mean of such y values for all female high school athletes having $x = 11$. The prediction interval for a single observation y is much wider than the confidence interval for the mean of y. In other words, you can estimate a population mean more precisely than you can predict a single observation, which seems intuitive.

▶ *Try Exercise 12.45*

The margins of error for these intervals use the residual standard deviation s. For an approximately normal conditional distribution for y, about 95% of the observations fall within about 2 standard deviations of the true mean μ_y at a particular value of x. For large n, $\hat{y}$ is close to μ_y, especially near the mean of the x values. Also, for large n the residual standard deviation s estimates the standard deviation σ well. So we could predict that about 95% of the y values would fall within $\hat{y} \pm 2s$. In fact, this is roughly what software does to form a prediction interval when n is large and x is at or near the mean. The margin of error is approximately a t-score times s for predicting an individual observation and a t-score times $s/\sqrt{n}$ for estimating a mean.

SUMMARY: Prediction Interval for y and Confidence Interval for μ_y at Fixed Value of x

For large samples with an x value equal to or close to the mean of x:

- The 95% **prediction interval** for y is approximately $\hat{y} \pm 2s$.
- The 95% **confidence interval** for μ_y is approximately

$$\hat{y} \pm 2(s/\sqrt{n}),$$

where s is the residual standard deviation. Software uses *exact* formulas. We show these *approximate* formulas here merely to give an idea how these intervals are obtained. *In practice, use software.*

For instance, for female student athletes, about 95% of the observations fall within about $2s = 2(8.0) = 16$ of the true mean at a particular value of x. At $x = 11$, which is the mean of x for the sample, $\hat{y} = 79.94 \approx 80$. So we predict that about 95% of the maximum bench press values would fall within $\hat{y} \pm 2s$, which is 80 ± 16, or between 64 and 96. This is the 95% PI result in Table 12.5. This formula is only an approximate one (because of using $\hat{y}$ as an approximation for μ_y and 2 as an approximation for the t-score), and you should rely on software for more precise results.

Use these confidence intervals and prediction intervals with caution. For these intervals to be valid, the true relationship must be close to linear, with about the same variability of y values at each fixed x value. You can get a rough visual check from the scatterplot. The variability of points around the regression line should be similar for the various possible x values. If it isn't, don't use these confidence and prediction intervals.

Because the model assumptions never hold exactly in practice, these inferences are sometimes inaccurate. For instance, suppose the variability in y values is smaller at small values of x and larger at large values of x. The prediction interval will have similar widths in each case. See Figure 12.10, which shows curves for the lower and upper endpoints of prediction intervals at all the possible x values. At a fixed x value, there should be a 95% chance a data point falls between the curves. In Case A, prediction intervals are justified. In Case B, they are not. At a large value of x in Case B, a 95% prediction interval for y actually has a much smaller than 95% chance (perhaps even less than 50%) of containing a value of y.

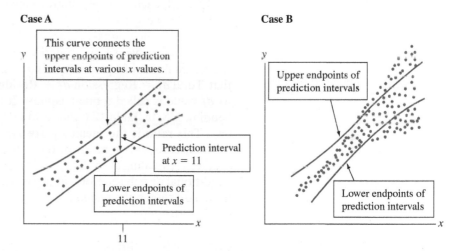

▲ **Figure 12.10** When a Regression Model Assumption Is Badly Violated, Prediction Intervals May Perform Poorly. The curves plot how the endpoints of a 95% prediction interval change as x changes. For Case A, inferences are valid. For Case B, a 95% prediction interval has actual probability of containing y above 0.95 for small x and below 0.95 for large x. **Question** How can you tell from the figure that Case B will lead to inaccurate inferences?

The Analysis of Variance (ANOVA) Table Summarizes Variability

Software reports the sums of squares (SS) used in estimating standard deviations and variances (their squares) in an **analysis of variance (ANOVA) table**. Table 12.6 shows the ANOVA table that MINITAB software reports for the strength study. In the *Linear Regression* app, check the box for ANOVA Table to obtain this table.

ANOVA Table:

Source	Df	Sum Sq	Mean Sq	F value	P-value
Regression	1	6,351.8	6,351.8	99.2	<0.0001
Residuals	55	3,522.8	64.1		
Total	56	9,874.6			

Screenshot from *Linear Regression* app, showing ANOVA table.

Table 12.6 Analysis of Variance (ANOVA) Table for the Strength Study

```
Analysis of Variance

Source        DF          SS          MS         F          P

Regression     1        6351.8      6351.8     99.17      0.000

Error         55        3522.8       64.1

Total         56        9874.6
```

In the ANOVA table, the *total sum of squares* is $\Sigma(y - \bar{y})^2$. It summarizes the total variability of the y values and the overall error when using $\bar{y}$ to predict y. The ANOVA table breaks the total SS into two parts. One part is the *residual sum of squares,* $\Sigma(y - \hat{y})^2$. It represents the overall error when using the regression line to predict y. MINITAB labels this row Error, but other labels in common use are "Residuals" or "Residual Error." The other sum of squares is called the *regression sum of squares.* Its formula is

$$\text{regression SS} = \Sigma(\hat{y} - \bar{y})^2, \text{ and it equals } \Sigma(y - \bar{y})^2 - \Sigma(y - \hat{y})^2.$$

It summarizes how much less error there is in predicting y using the regression line compared to using $\bar{y}$. Recall that this difference is the numerator of r^2.

These three types of sums of squares are connected by the basic **ANOVA identity**

$$\text{Total SS} = \text{Regression SS} + \text{Residual SS}.$$

In Table 12.6, regression SS + residual SS = 6,351.8 + 3,522.8 = 9,874.6, the total SS.

By itself, each sum of squares cannot be interpreted, but viewed relative to each other, we get statements about the reduction in the prediction error (e.g., through r^2, which equals Regression SS/Total SS). Each sum of squares in the ANOVA table has an associated degrees of freedom value. For instance, df for the residual sum of squares equals $n - 2 = 57 - 2 = 55$. For the df, it also holds that Total df = Regression df + Residual df. The ratio of a sum of squares to its df value is called a **mean square**. It is listed in the ANOVA table under the heading MS. In Table 12.6 the ratio of $\Sigma(y - \hat{y})^2 = 3,522.8$ to its $df = 55$ gives 64.1. This ratio is the **mean square error,** often abbreviated as **MS error** or as **MSE.** It is roughly a mean of the squared errors in using the regression line to predict y. Equaling $s^2 = \Sigma(y - \hat{y})^2/(n - 2)$, it estimates the variance σ^2 of the conditional distribution of y at a given x value. In practice, it's easier to interpret its square root, s, the residual standard deviation of y.

Recall

We also used s to estimate the standard deviation σ of the conditional distribution of the y values at a given x value. ◀

Mean Square Error

The **mean square error** is the residual sum of squares divided by its df value, where $df = n - 2$. Its square root s is the residual standard deviation and can be interpreted as a typical size of a residual (i.e., the typical prediction error).

The ANOVA *F* Statistic Also Tests for a Relationship

The ANOVA table contains values labeled F and P. The F value is the ratio of the mean squares,

$$F = \frac{\text{Mean square for regression}}{\text{Mean square error}}.$$

This is an alternative test statistic for testing H_0: $\beta = 0$ against H_a: $\beta \neq 0$. In fact, it can be shown that F *is the square of the t statistic* for this null hypothesis. Using the sampling distribution of F values, which we'll discuss in the next chapter, we get exactly the same P-value as with the t test for the two-sided alternative hypothesis.

In Table 12.6, the F statistic equals the ratio of MS values, 6,351.8/64.1 = 99.17. Table 12.2, which listed the parameter estimates and their standard errors, showed the t test:

Term	Coef	SE Coef	T-Value	P-Value
Constant	63.54	1.96	32.48	0.000
BP60	1.491	0.150	9.96	0.000

The F statistic of 99.17 here is the square of the t statistic value $t = 9.96$. The P-value, labeled as P on Table 12.6, is 0.000 to three decimal places, necessarily the same as the P-value for the two-sided t test.

Why do we need the F statistic if it does the same thing as a t statistic? In the next chapter, which generalizes regression to handle multiple explanatory variables, we'll see that the main use of an F statistic is for testing effects of several explanatory variables at once. The t test can only be used to test the effect of a single explanatory variable, one at a time.

12.4 Practicing the Basics

12.41 Poor predicted strengths The MINITAB output shows the three largest standardized residuals for the female athlete strength study. (You can also get these through the *Linear Regression* app, which has this data preloaded.)

TRY
APP

Large Standardized Residuals for Strength Study:

Obs	maxBP (lbs)	Fit	Resid	Std Resid
10	105.00	85.90	19.10	2.41
25	105.00	88.88	16.12	2.04
37	65.00	82.92	-17.92	-2.26

a. Explain how to interpret all the entries in the row of the output for athlete 10, who had $x = BP60 = 15$.

b. Out of 57 observations, is it surprising that 3 observations would have standardized residuals with absolute value above 2.0? Explain.

12.42 Loves TV and exercise For the Georgia Student Survey file on the book's website, let $y =$ time exercising and $x =$ time watching TV. One student reported watching TV an average of 180 minutes a day and exercising 60 minutes a day. This person's residual was 48.8 and the standardized residual was 6.41. (You can confirm this with the *Linear Regression* app, which has this data set preloaded.)

APP

a. Interpret the residual, and use it to find the predicted value of exercise.

b. Interpret the standardized residual.

12.43 Bench press residuals The screenshot from the *Linear Regression* app shows a histogram and box plot of the standardized residuals for the regression of maximum

TRY
APP

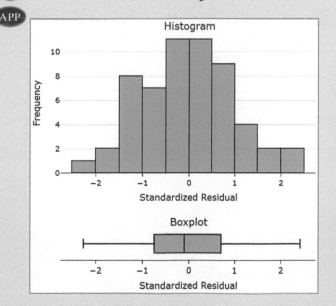

bench press on number of 60-pound bench presses for the high school female athletes.

a. Which distribution do these graphs provide information about?

b. What would you conclude based on these graphs?

12.44 Predicting house prices The House Selling Prices FL data file on the book's website has several predictors of house selling prices. The table here shows the ANOVA table for a regression analysis of $y =$ the selling price (in thousands of dollars) and $x =$ the size of house (in thousands of square feet). The prediction equation is $\hat{y} = 9.2 + 77x$. (You can replicate this output with the *Linear Regression* app, which has this data set preloaded.)

APP

ANOVA Table for Selling Price and Size of House:

Source	DF	SS	MS	F	P
Regression	1	182220	182220	135.07	0.000
Error	98	132213	1349		
Total	99	314433			

a. What was the sample size? (*Hint:* You can figure it out from the residual *df.*)

b. The sample mean house size was 1.53 thousand square feet. What was the sample mean selling price? (*Hint:* What does $\hat{y}$ equal when $x = \bar{x}$?)

c. Estimate the standard deviation of the selling prices for homes that have $x = 1.53$. Interpret.

d. Report an approximate prediction interval within which you would expect about 95% of the selling prices to fall for homes of size $x = 1.53$.

12.45 Predicting clothes purchases For a random sample of children from a school district in South Carolina, a regression analysis is conducted of $y =$ amount spent on clothes in the past year (dollars) and $x =$ year in school. MINITAB reports the tabulated results for observations at $x = 12$.

TRY

Variable	Setting			
year	12			

Fit	SE Fit	95% CI	95% PI
448.0	10.6	(427, 469)	(101, 795)

a. Interpret the value listed under "Fit."

b. Interpret the interval listed under "95% CI."

c. Interpret the interval listed under "95% PI."

12.46 CI versus PI Using the context of the previous exercise, explain the difference between the purpose of a 95% prediction interval (PI) for an observation and a 95% confidence interval (CI) for the mean of y at a given value of x. Why would you expect the PI to be wider than the CI?

12.47 ANOVA table for leg press Exercise 12.15 referred to an analysis of leg strength for 57 female athletes, with y = maximum leg press and x = number of 200-pound leg presses until fatigue, for which $\hat{y} = 233.89 + 5.27x$. The table shows ANOVA results from SPSS for the regression analysis. (You can replicate this output with the *Linear Regression* app, which has this data set preloaded.)

ANOVA

Source	Sum of Squares	df	Mean Square	F	Sig.
Regression	121082.4	1	121082.4	92.875	.000[a]
Residual	71704.4	55	1303.7		
Total	192786.8	56			

a. Show that the residual standard deviation is 36.1. Interpret it.
b. For this sample, $\bar{x} = 22.2$. For female athletes with $x = 22$, what would you estimate the variability to be of their maximum leg press values? If the y values are approximately normal, find an interval within which about 95% of them would fall.

12.48 Predicting leg press Refer to the previous exercise. MINITAB reports the tabulated results for observations at $x = 25$. (You can replicate the confidence and prediction intervals shown in the output via the *Linear Regression* app, which has this data set preloaded.)

```
Variable    Setting

LegPress      25

Fit         SE Fit      95% CI          95% PI
365.7        5.02   (355.6, 375.7)  (292.6, 438.7)
```

a. Show how MINITAB got the "Fit" of 365.7.
b. Using the predicted value and *se* value, explain how MINITAB got the interval listed under "95% CI." Interpret this interval.
c. Interpret the interval listed under "95% PI."

12.49 Variability and F Refer to the previous two exercises.
a. In the ANOVA table, show how the Total SS breaks into two parts and explain what each part represents.
b. From the ANOVA table, explain why the overall sample standard deviation of y values is $s_y = \sqrt{192,787/56} = 58.7$. Explain the difference between the interpretation of this standard deviation and the residual standard deviation s of 36.1.

c. Exercise 12.15 reported a t statistic of 9.64 for testing independence of these variables. Report the F test statistic from the table here and explain how it relates to that t statistic.

12.50 Assumption violated For prediction intervals, an important inference assumption is a constant standard deviation σ of y values at different x values. In practice, the standard deviation often tends to be larger when μ_y is larger.
a. Sketch a hypothetical scatterplot for which this happens, using observations on x = family income and y = amount donated to charity.
b. Explain why a 95% prediction interval would not work well at very small or at very large x values.

12.51 Understanding an ANOVA table For a random sample of U.S. counties, the ANOVA table shown refers to hypothetical data on x = percentage of the population aged over 50 and y = per capita expenditure (dollars) on education.
a. Fill in the blanks in the table.
b. For what hypotheses can the F test statistic be used?

Source	DF	SS	MS	F
Regression	1	200000	____	____
Error	31	700000	____	
Total	32	900000		

12.52 Predicting cell phone weight Refer to the cell phone specs data file on the book's website, which is also preloaded in the *Linear Regression* app. Regress y = weight on x = capacity of battery, excluding the outlier (phone no. 70). (In the app, check the option for Click to Remove Points, then click on the outlier to remove it.)
a. Stating the necessary assumptions, find a 95% confidence interval for the mean weight of cell phones with a battery capacity of 1500mAh. Interpret the interval.
b. Find a 95% prediction interval for the weight of a cell phone with a battery capacity of 1500mAh. Interpret.
c. Explain the difference between the purposes of the intervals in part a and part b.

12.53 Cell phone ANOVA Report the ANOVA table for the previous exercise. (Click the ANOVA Table option in the *Linear Regression* app.)
a. Verify that total SS = residual SS + regression SS. Explain what each of the three sums of squares represent.
b. Find the estimated residual standard deviation of y. Interpret it.
c. Find the sample standard deviation sy of y values. Explain the difference between the interpretation of this standard deviation and the residual standard deviation in part b.

12.5 Exponential Regression: A Model for Nonlinearity

The straight line is by far the most common equation for a regression model. Sometimes, however, a scatterplot indicates substantial curvature in a relationship. In such cases, equations that provide curvature are more appropriate.

Occasionally a scatterplot has a parabolic appearance: As x increases, y tends to go up and then it goes back down (as shown in the margin figure), or the reverse. Then the regression model can use an equation giving the shape of a parabola. Other times, y tends to continually increase or to continually decrease, but the trend shows curvature. Let's see a mechanism for how this can happen.

Example 16

Exponential Growth ◀

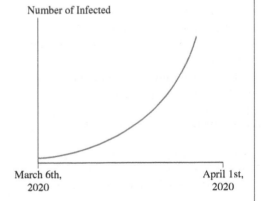

The COVID-19 Pandemic

Picture the Scenario

The number of people infected with a virus grows rapidly in an pandemic, especially in places where people live in close proximity to each other. For example, on March 6th, 2020, New York City had a total of only 5 confirmed cases of people infected with the novel coronavirus.

Questions to Explore

a. In the early stage of the COVID-19 pandemic, it was estimated that the number of infected people might grow at a rate of 40% per day in New York City. Under this assumption, find the number of infected people in New York City after (i) 1 day (i.e., on March 7th), (ii) 2 days (i.e., on March 8th), and (iii) 26 days (i.e., on April 1st).

b. Give a formula for the number of infected people in terms of x = number of days since March 6th, 2020.

Think It Through

a. With a 40% growth rate, the number of infected people one day after March 6th is $5 \times 1.40 = 7$. That is, an increase in the number of infected people by 40% a day corresponds to multiplying the number of infected people from the previous day by 1.40. The number of infected people after 2 days is another 40% higher than this, or

$$7 \times 1.40 = (5 \times 1.40) \times 1.40 = 5 \times (1.40)^2 = 9.8 \text{ persons.}$$

After 26 days, the number of infected people is $5 \times 1.40 \times 1.40 \times 1.40 \times \ldots \times 1.40 = 5 \times (1.40)^{26} = 31{,}499$ persons.

b. Can you see the pattern? For each additional day, we multiply by another factor of 1.40. After x days, the number of infected people is $5 \times (1.40)^x$ persons.

Insight

The population size formula, 5×1.40^x, is called **exponential growth**. When plotted, the response (i.e., the number of infected people) goes up much faster than a straight line. See the margin figure. Also, the amount of change in y per unit change in x increases as x increases and is not constant as in linear growth. The actual reported number of infected people in NYC on April 1st was equal to 47,440, more than predicted by this model. However, on April 7th, there were 76,876 reported cases of COVID-19, while the exponential growth model with a 40% daily increase predicts $5 \times (1.40)^{33} = 332{,}043$ cases. Clearly, the rate of increase slowed down, due to measures such as social distancing and stay-at-home orders.

▶ *Try Exercise 12.54*

Number of Infected

March 6th, 2020   April 1st, 2020

A statistical analysis that uses a regression function with x in the *exponent* is called **exponential regression**.

> ### SUMMARY: Exponential Regression Model
> An **exponential regression model** has the formula
> $$\mu_y = \alpha\beta^x$$
> for the mean μ_y of y at a given value of x, where α and β are parameters.

The formula 5×1.40^x for the number of infected people in Example 16 has the form $\alpha\beta^x$, with $\alpha = 5$, $\beta = 1.40$, and $x = $ number of days since March 6th. Exponential regression can model quantities that tend to increase (or decrease) by progressively large amounts over time.

In the exponential regression equation, the explanatory variable x appears as the exponent of a parameter. Unlike linear regression, the mean μ_y and the effect parameter β can take only positive values. As x increases, the mean μ_y continually increases when $\beta > 1$. It continually decreases when $0 < \beta < 1$. Figure 12.11 shows the shape for these two cases. We provide interpretations for the model parameters later in this section.

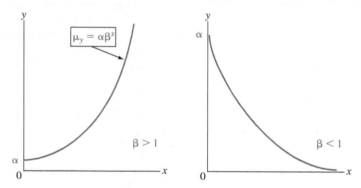

▲ **Figure 12.11** The Exponential Regression Curve for $\mu_y = \alpha\beta^x$. **Question** Why does μ_y decrease if $\beta = 0.5$, even though $\beta > 0$?

For exponential regression, the logarithm of the mean is a linear function of x. When the exponential regression model holds, a plot of the log of the y values versus x should show an approximate straight-line relation with x. Don't worry if you have forgotten logarithms. You will not need to use logarithms to understand how to fit the model. Software can do it. It's more important to know when it is appropriate and to be able to interpret the model fit.

Example 17

Exponential Regression ◄

Moore's Law

Picture the Scenario

In 1965, Gordon Moore, who a couple of years later would go on to co-found the chip company Intel, had been asked by the journal *Electronics* to predict what would happen in the microchip industry over the next 10 years. In a

Logarithm of number of components on a microchip over time. (*Source:* G. Moore, 1965, "Cramming More Components onto Integrated Circuits," *Electronics,* pp. 114–117.)

graph (see margin figure, where the y axis is on the logarithmic scale), Moore showed that the number of components that could be packed on a microchip roughly doubled each year, and he predicted that this trend would continue. He speculated that by 1975, it was possible to squeeze as many as 65,000 components economically on a single chip. (In 1965, only 64 components fitted on a chip.) Based on the graph from Moore, we constructed Table 12.7, which shows the number of components on a chip for several years, beginning with the first microchip in 1959.

The first graph in Figure 12.12 plots the number of components on a microchip over the years, based on the data in Table 12.7. The number of components increases over time, and the amount of increase from one year to the next seems itself to increase over time. Moore's graph plotted the log values (base 2) of the number of components (shown in the third column of Table 12.7) over time. They appear to follow a linear trend. In fact, the correlation coefficient r between the log of the number of components and the year is 0.997, indicating an extremely strong linear relationship. This suggests that the increase in the number of components was approximately exponential over those years.

Table 12.7 Number of Components Per Square Inch on Microchips Produced Between 1959 and 1965

Year	Years Since 1959 (x)	Number of Components (y)	Logarithm of Number ($\log_2(y)$)	Predicted Number ($\hat{y}$)
1959	0	1	0.00	1
1962	3	7	2.85	8
1963	4	19	4.25	16
1964	5	29	4.85	32
1965	6	64	6.00	63

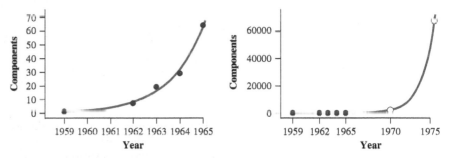

▲ **Figure 12.12** Plot of Number of Components on a Microchip Over the Years. The first graph shows the data from Table 12.7 for the years 1959 to 1965 and overlays the prediction curve from an exponential regression model. The second graph shows the same data but now displays what would happen if the exponential trend would continue for 10 years after 1965, to 1975. The circles for 1970 and 1975 shown in the plot are predictions beyond the observed range of the data.

Questions to Explore

Let x denote the years since the invention of the microchip in 1959 ($x = 0$ for 1959, $x = 3$ for 1962, $x = 4$ for 1964, etc.) and let y be the number of components on a chip x years after the invention of the first chip. Using software to fit the exponential regression model for the mean of y, we obtain

$$\hat{y} = 0.973 \times 2.006^x.$$

What does this equation predict for the number of components on a chip in the year 1965 (i.e., $x = 6$), the year Moore published the graph? And what is the predicted number of components in 1975, $x = 16$ years after the invention of the first chip and the year for which Moore predicted 65,000 components?

Think It Through

By plugging $x = 6$ into the preceding prediction equation, we obtain $\hat{y} = 0.973 \times 2.006^6 = 63.4$. This is pretty close to the observed number of 64 for that year (1965). Ten years later, in 1975 and $x = 16$ years after the invention of the first chip, we obtain $\hat{y} = 0.973 \times 2.006^{16} = 66{,}897$ as a prediction for the mean number of components that would fit on a microchip. Table 12.7 also shows the predicted numbers for each of the other years, and the right graph in Figure 12.12 shows how the trend would look if it were to continue into the year 1975.

Insight

Ten years after Moore's prediction, in 1975, a new chip that had almost 65,000 components was indeed introduced to the market. In subsequent years, the rate of packing ever more components on a chip slowed down a little, although it was still exponential. In an interview in March 2015 (celebrating the 50th anniversary of Moore's law, which now is used to describe trends in the entire computer industry), Moore once again made a prediction—the likely demise of Moore's law within the next decade or so. He indicated that technological advancement would inevitably slow down from the rate of progress we have seen in the 1990s through 2010s.[1] For the applicability of Moore's law to microchips used between 1994 and 2015, see Exercise 12.56.

▶ *Try Exercise 12.56*

Interpreting Exponential Regression Models

From what we've just seen in the example, here's how to interpret the parameters in the exponential regression model, $\mu_y = \alpha\beta^x$. The parameter α represents the mean of y when $x = 0$ because $\beta^0 = 1$. The parameter β represents the *multiplicative* effect on the mean of y for a one-unit increase in x. The mean of y at $x = 1$ equals the mean of y at $x = 0$ multiplied by β. For instance, for the equation $\hat{y} = 0.973 \times 2.006^x$ that uses the estimated β of 2.006, the predicted number of components is 0.973 (or roughly 1) in 1959, for which $x = 0$. One year later, the predicted number is $0.973(2.006) = 1.95$ (or roughly 2), larger by a factor of roughly 2. Another year later, the predicted number of components is $0.973(2.006)^2 = 1.95(2.006) = 3.9$ and increases by a factor of roughly 2 from the previous year's number of 1.95.

By contrast, the parameter β in the straight-line model $\mu_y = \alpha + \beta x$ represents an *additive* effect on the mean of y for a one-unit increase in x. The mean of y at $x = 1$ equals the mean of y at $x = 0$ plus β. The straight-line (i.e., the linear regression) model fitted to Moore's data is $\hat{y} = -8.9 + 9.1x$. (See the green line in the margin figure.) This model predicts that the number of components on a chip increases by 9.1 every year (as opposed to doubling every year as the exponential regression model suggests). The model may not be appropriate for these data, although this is difficult to judge with so few observations (and the

Exponential model (blue line) and linear model (green line) fit for Moore's data.

[1]IEEE Spectrum. Interview with Rachel Courtland. Special Report: 50 Years of Moore's Law, 2015. The entire interview is accessible at http://spectrum.ieee.org/computing/hardware/gordon-moore-the-man-whose-name-means-progress

insufficient knowledge of the industry in 1965). For example, the model predicts a negative number for the year 1959 and gives an inaccurate prediction for the year 1965: Plugging in $x = 6$, it predicts $\hat{y} = -8.9 + 9.1(6) = 46$ components, when the actual value was 65. (The standardized residual for this observation is 4.0.) Compare this to the prediction of 64 from the exponential regression model.

For the straight-line model, μ_y changes by the same amount (9.1) for each one-unit increase in x, whereas for the exponential model, μ_y changes by the same *factor* (or percentage) for each one-unit increase. For instance, by using the estimate of 2 for β in the exponential model for Moore's data, we predict that with every passing year since the invention of the microchip, the number of components the chip can hold increases by a factor of 2; that is, it doubles. (This corresponds to an increase of 100%.)

12.5 Practicing the Basics

12.54 Savings grow exponentially   You invest $100 in a savings account with interest compounded annually at 10%.

TRY

   a. How much money does the account have after one year?

   b. How much money does the account have after five years?

   c. How much money does the account have after x years?

   d. How many years does it take until your savings more than double in size?

12.55 Growth by year versus decade   You want your savings to double in a decade.

   a. Explain why 7.2% interest a year would do this. (*Hint:* What does $(1.072)^{10}$ equal?)

   b. You might think that 10% interest a year would give 100% interest (that is, double your savings) over a decade. Explain why interest of 10% a year would actually cause your savings to multiply by 2.59 over a decade.

12.56 Moore's law today   The following data show the number of components (per square inch, in millions) being packed on a Pentium-type chip, for years 1994 to 2015. Let x be the number of years since 1994 (e.g., $x = 0$ for 1994, $x = 3$ for 1997, ..., $x = 21$ for 2015) and let y be the number of components on a chip. The prediction equation when fitting an exponential regression model to these data equals $\hat{y} = 151.61 \times 1.191^x$.

TRY

Chip	Year	Count	Chip	Year	Count
Pentium	1994	14	PentiumE	2008	1794
PentiumII	1997	24	PentiumG	2010	3043
PentiumIII	1999	48	PentiumG	2011	2482
Pentium4	2000	125	PentiumG	2013	5645
PentiumD	2005	720	PentiumG	2015	5103
PentiumE	2007	971			

   a. What is the predicted number of components per square inch in 2015?

   b. By how much does the predicted number of components increase per year over the time range that these data cover?

   c. The correlation coefficient r between the logarithm of the count and x equals 0.985, and the scatterplot with the log counts shows a linear trend. What does this suggest about whether the exponential regression model is appropriate for these data?

12.57 U.S. population growth   The table shows the approximate U.S. population size (in millions) at 10-year intervals beginning in 1900. Let x denote the number of decades since 1900. That is, 1900 is $x = 0$, 1910 is $x = 1$, and so forth. The exponential regression model fitted to $y = $ population size and x gives $\hat{y} = 81.14 \times 1.1339^x$.

U.S. Population Sizes (In Millions) From 1900 to 2010					
Year	**Size**	**Year**	**Size**	**Year**	**Size**
1900	76.2	1940	132.1	1980	226.5
1910	92.2	1950	150.7	1990	248.7
1920	106.0	1960	179.3	2000	281.4
1930	122.8	1970	203.3	2010	308.7

Source: U.S. Census Bureau.

   a. Show that the predicted population sizes are 81.14 million in 1900 and 323.3 million in 2010.

   b. Explain how to interpret the value 1.1339 in the prediction equation.

   c. The correlation coefficient r equals 0.98 between the log of the population size and the year number. What does this suggest about whether the exponential regression model is appropriate for these data?

12.58 Future shock   Refer to the previous exercise, for which predicted population growth was 14.18% per decade.

Suppose the growth rate is now 15% per decade. Explain why the population size will (a) double after five decades, (b) quadruple after 100 years (10 decades), and (c) be 16 times its original size after 200 years. (The exponentially increasing function has the property that its doubling time is constant. This is a fast increase, even though the annual rate of growth seems small.)

12.59 Coronavirus cases in NYC   The data set CoronaCasesNYC shows the number of confirmed infections with the coronavirus COVID-19 in NYC, from March 5th to March 15th. Based on these data, the prediction equation for an exponential regression model equals $\hat{y} = 5.53(1.51)^x$, where x is the number of days since March 6th.

a. Interpret 5.53 and 1.51 in this equation.

b. Find the predicted number of infected cases for (i) March 7th, (ii) March 10th, and (iii) March 20th.

c. How many days does it take for the number of infected people to double? (*Hint:* What is x such that $(1.51)^x = 2$? If you don't know logarithms, simply try a couple of reasonable values for x with your calculator to approximate the answer.)

12.60 Leaf litter decay   Ecologists believe that organic material decays over time according to an *exponential decay* model. This is the case $0 < \beta < 1$ in the exponential regression model, for which μ_y decreases over time. The rate of decay is determined by a number of factors, including composition of material, temperature, and humidity. In an experiment carried out by researchers at the University of Georgia Ecology Institute, leaf litter was allowed to sit for a 20-week period in a bag in a moderately forested area.

Initially, the total weight of the organic mass in the bag was 75.0 kg. Each week, the remaining amount (y) was measured. The table shows the weight y by x = number of weeks of time that have passed.

x	y	x	y	x	y	x	y	x	y	x	y
0	75.0	1	60.9	2	51.8	3	45.2	4	34.7	5	34.6
6	26.2	7	20.4	8	14.0	9	12.3	11	8.2	15	3.1
20	1.4										

a. Construct a scatterplot. Why is a straight-line model inappropriate?

b. Show that the ordinary regression model gives the fit $\hat{y} = 54.98 - 3.59x$. Find the predicted weight after $x = 20$ weeks. Does this prediction make sense? Explain.

c. Plot the log of y against x. Does a straight-line model now seem appropriate?

d. The exponential regression model has prediction equation $\hat{y} = 80.6(0.813)^x$. Find the predicted weight (i) initially and (ii) after 20 weeks.

e. Interpret the coefficient 0.813 in the prediction equation.

12.61 More leaf litter   Refer to the previous exercise.

a. The correlation coefficient r equals -0.890 between x and y and -0.997 between x and $\log(y)$. What does this tell you about which model is more appropriate?

b. The half-life is the time for the weight remaining to be one-half of the original weight. Use the equation $\hat{y} = 80.6(0.813)^x$ to predict the half-life of this organic material. (*Hint:* By trial and error, find the value of x for which $(0.813)^x$ is about 1/2.)

Chapter Review

SUMMARY OF NOTATION

μ_y = population mean of conditional distribution of y at given value of x

$\mu_y = \alpha + \beta x$ = population straight-line regression equation, or regression model; (α and β are the population intercept and slope)

$\hat{y} = a + bx$ = prediction equation computed from the sample; it estimates the population regression equation; (a and b are the estimated intercept and slope)

σ = population standard deviation of conditional distribution of y at given value of x

s = residual standard deviation; estimates σ.

r^2 = percent reduction in prediction error = percent of variability in y that can be explained by x; square of correlation coefficient r

$\Sigma (y - \hat{y})^2$ = residual sum of squares, which summarizes how well $\hat{y}$ predicts y. This is used to compute the mean square error, s and r^2.

$\Sigma (y - \bar{y})^2$ = total sum of squares, which summarizes how well $\bar{y}$ predicts y. This is used in finding r^2.

$\mu_y = \alpha\beta^x$ = exponential regression model; mean = α when $x = 0$ and the mean multiplies by β for each one-unit increase in x.

CHAPTER SUMMARY

In this chapter we have learned how to analyze a *linear relationship between two quantitative variables*. A regression analysis investigates the relationship between a quantitative explanatory variable x and a quantitative response variable y. The **linear regression model** describes how the mean of y depends on the explanatory variable x.

■ At each value of x, a conditional distribution of y values summarizes how y varies at that value. We denote the population mean of the conditional distribution of y by μ_y. The **simple linear regression model** $\mu_y = \alpha + \beta x$, with y-intercept α and slope β, uses a straight line to approximate the relationship between x and the mean μ_y of the conditional distribution of y at the different possible values of x. The **prediction equation** $\hat{y} = a + bx$ predicts the regression model using data from a sample and estimates the mean of y at the fixed value of x.

■ The **correlation coefficient** r describes the strength of the linear relationship. It has the same sign as the slope b but falls between -1 and $+1$. It can be interpreted a a standardized slope, telling us by how many standard deviations y is predicted to change when x changes by one standard deviation, signaling the amount of *regression toward the mean*. The squared correlation coefficient, r^2, describes the proportional reduction in the sum of squared errors using the prediction equation $\hat{y} = a + bx$ to predict y compared to using the sample mean $\bar{y}$ to predict y. It also tells us what **percent of the variability** in the response variable can be explained by the change in the explanatory variable.

■ Inference: A significance test of $\mathbf{H_0}$: $\boldsymbol{\beta = 0}$ for the population slope β tests **statistical independence** of x and y. It has test statistic

$$t = (b - 0)/se,$$

for the sample slope b and its standard error.

Interval estimation is also useful for:

■ A confidence interval for β.

■ A confidence interval for μ_y, the mean of y at a given value of x.

■ A **prediction interval** for a value of y at a given value of x.

These inferences all use the t distribution with $df = n - 2$. Their basic assumptions are:

1. The population mean of y has a straight-line relationship with x.

2. The data were gathered using randomization.

3. The distribution of y at each value of x is normal, with the same standard deviation at each x value.

■ An **ANOVA table** displays sums of squares, their df values, and an **F statistic** (which equals the square of the t statistic) that also tests H_0: $\beta = 0$. In this table, the **residual sum of squares** $\Sigma (y - \hat{y})^2$ is a sum of the squared **residuals** (prediction errors) $y - \hat{y}$. The residual SS divided by its df value of $n - 2$ is the **mean square error**. Its square root is the **residual standard deviation** s, which estimates the parameter σ. This parameter σ describes the variability of the conditional distribution of y at each fixed x. A residual divided by its se is a **standardized residual**, which measures the number of standard errors that a residual falls from 0. It helps us identify unusual observations.

■ The **exponential regression** model $\mu_y = \alpha \beta^x$ has an increasing or a decreasing curved shape. For it, a one-unit increase in x has a *multiplicative* effect of β on the mean rather than an *additive* effect as in the linear regression model $\mu_y = \alpha + \beta x$.

LEARNING OBJECTIVES

1. Understand what is meant by a regression model.

2. Interpret the meaning of a and b in the regression model.

3. Explain the difference between the population regression model and the prediction equation.

4. State and check the assumptions for regression inference.

5. Test the hypothesis of statistical independence of x and y.

6. Compute and interpret a confidence interval for the slope.

7. Recognize the relationship between the correlation coefficient r and the slope b.

8. Interpret an r^2 value.

9. Understand the difference between a confidence interval for the mean of y and a prediction interval for a single y and know how to interpret each.

10. Understand the role of residuals in regression analysis.

11. (Optional) Understand and use the ANOVA table to determine if a linear relationship is statistically significant.

12. (Optional) Recognize when an exponential regression analysis is appropriate and understand how to interpret an exponential regression model obtained using technology.

ANSWERS TO THE CHAPTER FIGURE QUESTIONS

Figure 12.1 (a) There are two dots at the value of 60 pounds on the vertical axis (representing maximum bench press); (b) all dots in the scatterplot are in rows corresponding to the values 60, 65, 70, etc., on the vertical axis.

Figure 12.2 This happens when most observations are in the quadrants where data points are above the mean on one variable and below the mean on the other variable, which are the upper-left and lower-right quadrants.

Figure 12.3 Answers will vary. One possible sketch is Figure 12.4.

Figure 12.4 A mathematical function that has a parabolic shape.

Figure 12.5 The bell-shaped curves represent the conditional distributions of income at $x = 12$ years and $x = 16$ years. Each conditional distribution is assumed to be normal and to have the same standard deviation, $\sigma = \$13,000$.

Figure 12.6 H_0: $\beta = 0$.

Figure 12.7 One standard deviation.

Figure 12.8 The variability of the sampling distribution of a sample mean is much less than the variability of the distribution of individual observations.

Figure 12.10 The curves that represent the lower and upper endpoints of the prediction interval are too wide for the *x* values on the lower end

(the 95% prediction interval for *y* has a greater than 95% chance of containing a value of *y*) and too narrow for the *x* values on the upper end (a 95% prediction interval for *y* has a much smaller than 95% chance of containing a value of *y*).

Figure 12.11 When *x* increases by 1, the mean μ_y is multiplied by β. When $0 < \beta < 1$, multiplying by β causes the mean to decrease.

STATISTICAL SOFTWARE

Art of Stat Web Apps

- **Linear Regression** This app provides all statistical output associated with fitting a simple linear regression model, together with an interactive scatterplot. The app comes with several data sets preloaded, but you can upload your own .csv file (with a header row) or type in (or copy/paste from an existing spreadsheet) values for a response and explanatory variable. Default outputs are the estimates for the intercept and slope, the correlation coefficient r, r^2, and the residual standard deviation s. Several options allow for finding predicted values, displaying residuals on the plot, displaying the standard error, *t*-statistic, and P-value (for the test of H_0: $\beta = 0$), showing a confidence interval for the slope, computing a confidence interval for the mean or a prediction interval for an individual observation at a given *x*-value and obtaining the ANOVA table. The second tab of the app is dedicated to analyzing residuals, providing a table that shows the fitted values and raw and standardized residuals. An interactive graph plots the residuals in a scatterplot against the explanatory variable (or the fitted values) and another graph provides a histogram and a box plot of the residuals.

- **Exponential Regression:** This app fits and visualizes the exponential regression model discussed in Section 13.5.

R

- **Linear Regression:** The lm function fits linear regression models and was introduced in the R code for Chapter 3. We illustrate by loading the female athlete data set into R and fitting a linear regression model to replicate the output of Table 12.1:

```
> myfile <- file.choose() #path to file
> athletes <- read.csv(myfile) #reads in file
> head(athletes,3) #check column names
  Athlete BP60 maxBP LP200 maxLP
1       1   10    80    15   295
2       2   12    85    35   330
3       3   20    85    23   410
> myfit <- lm(maxBP ~ BP60, data=athletes)
#fits regression model
> summary(myfit) #replicates Table 12.1
Coefficients:
            Estimate Std. Error t value Pr(>|t|)
(Intercept) 63.5369     1.9565   32.475  < 2e-16
BP60         1.4911     0.1497    9.958  6.48e-14
  Residual standard error: 8.003 on 55 degrees
    of freedom
  Multiple R-squared: 0.6432,
  Adjusted R-squared: 0.6368
  F-statistic: 99.17 on 1 and 55 DF,
  p-value: 6.481e-14
```

We recognize the columns of Table 12.1: Estimate, standard error, *t* statistic and P-value, labeled Pr(>|t|) in R. Because both P-values are extremely small, R prints them in scientific notation, e.g., 6.48e-14 for the slope, which stands for 6.48×10^{-14}. We also recognize the residual standard deviation 8.003 (R calls it the residual standard error), the r^2 statistic 0.6432, and the F-statistic 99.17 and P-value 6.481e-14 from Table 12.6.

To obtain the predicted mean of the response at given *x*-value of 11 and to obtain the confidence interval for the mean, use the predict function:

```
> predict(myfit, newdata=data.frame(BP60=11),
interval='confidence', se.fit=TRUE)
$fit
      fit      lwr      upr
1 79.93844 77.81405 82.06283

$se.fit
[1] 1.060051
```

This shows the predicted value 79.9, the confidence interval's lower bound 77.8 and upper bound 82.1, and the *se* of 1.06 for the construction of the confidence interval. Compare this to Table 12.5. The prediction interval is

```
> predict(myfit, newdata=data.frame(BP60=11),
interval='prediction')
      fit      lwr      upr
1 79.93844 63.75961 96.11727
```

which is also the one shown in Table 12.5 or the screenshot from the *Linear Regression* app.

You can obtain fitted values, residuals, and residual plots through:

```
> myfitted <- fitted(myfit) #fitted values for
observations in dataset
> myres <- residuals(myfit) #raw residuals
> mystdres <- rstandard(myfit) #standardized
residuals
> head(mystdres,4)
         1          2          3          4
 0.1957575  0.4501844 -1.0692080 -0.7602345
> hist(mystdres) #histogram of std. residuals
> boxplot(mystdres) #box plot of std. residuals
```

Finally, the ANOVA table in Table 12.6 is requested through:

```
> anova(myfit).
Analysis of Variance Table
Response: maxBP
           of Sum sq  Mean sq F value    Pr(>F)
BP60        1  6351.8  6351.8  99.161  6.481e-14
Residuals  55  3522.8    64.1
```

CHAPTER EXERCISES

Practicing the Basics

12.62 Parties and sports Let y = number of parties attended in the past month and x = number of sports events watched in the past month, measured for all students at your school. Explain the mean and variability about the mean aspects of the regression model $\mu_y = \alpha + \beta x$ in the context of these variables. In your answer, explain why (a) it is more sensible to let $\alpha + \beta x$ represent the *means* of the conditional distributions rather than individual observations, (b) the model allows variation around the mean with its σ parameter.

12.63 Verbal–math correlation A report summarizing scores for students on a verbal aptitude test x and a mathematics aptitude test y states that $\bar{x} = 480$, $\bar{y} = 500$, $s_x = 80$, $s_y = 120$, and $r = 0.60$.

   a. Find the slope of the regression line, based on its connection with the correlation coefficient.

   b. Find the y-intercept of the regression line (*Hint:* Use its formula in Section 12.1) and state the prediction equation.

   c. Find the prediction equation for predicting verbal test result using math test result.

12.64 Stem cells In the article, "Variation in cancer risk among tissues can be explained by the number of stem cell divisions" (Tomasetti and Vogelstein, *Science*, vol. 47, 2015), the authors stated: "A linear correlation equal to 0.804 suggests that 65% of the differences in cancer risk among different tissues can be explained by the total number of stem cell divisions in those tissues."

   a. How did they get 65%?

   b. By how many percentage points does the overall prediction error (as measured by the sum of squares) decrease when using the prediction equation from a linear regression model to predict cancer risk rather than using the sample mean of the observed risks to predict it?

12.65 Short people Do very short parents tend to have children who are even shorter, or short but not as short as they are? Explain, identifying the response and explanatory variables and the role of regression toward the mean.

12.66 Income and education in Florida The FL Crime data file on the book's website contains data for all counties in Florida on y = median annual income (thousands of dollars) for residents of the county and x = percentage of residents with at least a high school education. The table shows some summary statistics and results of a regression analysis.

Income and Education for Florida Counties

Variable	Mean	Std Dev	Predictor	Parameter Estimate
INCOME	24.51	4.69	INTERCEPT	−4.60
EDUC	69.49	8.86	EDUC	0.42

   a. Find the correlation coefficient r. Interpret (i) the sign and (ii) the magnitude.

   b. Find the predicted median income for a county that is 1 standard deviation above the mean on x and use it to explain the concept of regression toward the mean.

12.67 Bedroom residuals The screenshot below shows output from the *Linear Regression* app for the House Selling Prices FL data set, modeling y = selling price (in dollars) in terms of x = number of bedrooms.

   a. One home with three bedrooms sold for $338,000. Find the residual and interpret.

   b. The home in part a had a standardized residual of 4.02. Interpret.

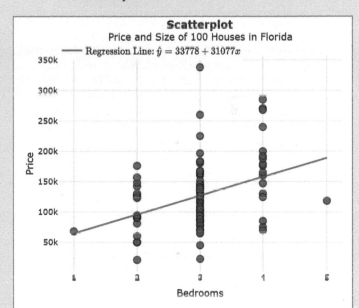

Scatterplot
Price and Size of 100 Houses in Florida
— Regression Line: $\hat{y} = 33778 + 31077x$

Linear Regression Equation:

Parameter	Estimate	Standard Error	t Statistic	P-value
Intercept	33,778	24,637	1.37	0.1735
Slope (Bedrooms)	31,077	8,049	3.86	0.0002

Model Summary:

Statistic	Value
Correlation Coefficient r	0.363
Coefficient of Determination r^2	13.2%
Residual Standard Deviation	52,772

12.68 Bedrooms affect price? Refer to the previous exercise.

   a. Explain what the regression parameter β means in this context.

   b. Construct and interpret a 95% confidence interval for β. (You can get this from the *Linear Regression* app, or use the fact that the t-score equals 1.98.)

c. Use the result of part b to form a 95% confidence interval for the difference in the mean selling prices for homes with $x = 4$ bedrooms and with $x = 2$ bedrooms. (*Hint:* How does this difference in means relate to the slope?)

12.69 Types of variability Refer to the previous two exercises.

a. Explain the difference between the residual standard deviation of 52,771 and the standard deviation of 56,357 reported for the selling prices.

b. Since they're not much different, explain why this means that number of bedrooms is not strongly related with selling price. Support this by reporting and interpreting the value of r^2.

12.70 Exercise and college GPA For the Georgia Student Survey file on the book's website and preloaded in the *Linear Regression* app, let $y =$ exercise and $x =$ college GPA.

a. Construct a scatterplot. Identify an outlier that could influence the regression line. What would you expect its effect to be on the slope and the correlation coefficient?

b. Fit the model. Find the standardized residual for the outlier. Interpret.

c. Fit the model without the outlying observation. (In the app, check the box for Click to Remove Points and then click on the outlier to remove it.) Summarize its impact.

12.71 Bench press predicting leg press For the study of high school female athletes, when we use $x =$ maximum bench press (maxBP) to predict $y =$ maximum leg press (maxLP), we get the results that follow. (You can replicate these results with the *Linear Regression* app, which has these data preloaded.) The sample mean of maxBP was 80.

```
Regression Equation

maxLP (lbs) = 174.0 + 2.216 maxBP (lbs)

Term        Coef    SE Coef   T-Value   P-Value
Constant    174.0   41.7      4.17      0.000
maxBP (lbs) 2.216   0.515     4.30      0.000

Variable     Setting
maxBP (lbs)     80

 Fit    SE Fit    95% CI             95% PI
351.25 6.7847 (337.65, 364.84) (247.70, 454.79)
```

a. Interpret the confidence interval listed under "95% CI."

b. Interpret the interval listed under "95% PI." What's the difference between the purpose of the 95% PI and the 95% CI?

12.72 Leg press ANOVA The analysis in the previous exercise has the ANOVA table shown.

```
Analysis of Variance

Source      DF    SS      MS      F       P
Regression  1     48483   48483   18.48   0.000
Error       55    144304  2624
Total       56    192787
```

a. For those female athletes who had maximum bench press equal to the sample mean of 80 pounds, what is the estimated standard deviation of their maximum leg press values?

b. Assuming that maximum leg press has a normal distribution, show how to find an approximate 95% prediction interval for the y values at $x = 80$.

12.73 Savings grow You invest $1,000 in an account having interest such that your principal doubles every 10 years.

a. How much money would you have after 50 years?

b. If you were still alive in 100 years, show that you'd be a millionaire.

c. Give the equation that relates $y =$ principal to $x =$ number of decades for which your money has been invested.

12.74 Florida population The population size of Florida (in thousands) since 1830 has followed approximately the exponential regression $\hat{y} = 46(1.036)^x$. Here, $x =$ year $- 1,830$ (so, $x = 0$ for 1,830 and $x = 170$ for the year 2000).

a. What has been the approximate rate of growth per year?

b. Find the predicted population size in (i) 1830 and (ii) 2000.

c. Find the predicted population size in 2100. Do you think that this same formula will continue to hold between 2000 and 2100? Why?

12.75 World population growth The table shows the world population size (in billions) since 1900.

World Population Sizes (in billions)			
Year	Population	Year	Population
1900	1.65	1975	4.07
1910	1.75	1980	4.43
1920	1.86	1985	4.83
1930	2.07	1990	5.26
1940	2.30	1995	5.67
1950	2.52	2000	6.07
1960	3.02	2005	6.47
1970	3.69	2010	6.85

Source: U.S. Census Bureau.

a. Let x denote the number of years since 1900. The exponential regression model fitted to $y =$ population size and x gives $\hat{y} = 1.424 \times 1.014^x$. Show that the predicted population sizes are 1.42 billion in 1900 and 6.57 billion in 2010.

b. Explain why the fit of the model corresponds to a rate of growth of 1.4% per year.

c. For this model fit, explain why the predicted population size (i) doubles after 50 years and (ii) quadruples after 100 years.

d. The correlation coefficient r equals 0.961 between the population size and the year number, and it equals 0.991 between the log of the population size and the year number. What does this suggest about whether the straight-line regression model or the exponential regression model is more appropriate for these data?

12.76 Match the scatterplot   Match each of the following scatterplots to the description of its regression and correlation coefficient. The plots are the same except for a single point. Justify your answer for each scatterplot. (*Hint:* Think about the possible effect of an outlier in the *x*-direction and an outlier in the *y*-direction relative to the regression line for the rest of the data.)

a. $r = -0.46 \, \hat{y} = 142 - 15.6x$

b. $r = -0.86 \, \hat{y} = 182 - 25.8x$

c. $r = -0.74 \, \hat{y} = 165 - 21.8x$

Concepts and Investigations

12.77 Softball data   The Softball data file on the book's web site contains the records of a University of Georgia coed intramural softball team for 277 games over a 20-year period. (The players changed, but the team continued.) The variables include, for each game, the team's number of runs scored (RUNS), number of hits (HIT), number of errors (ERR), and the difference (DIFF) between the number of runs scored by the team and by the other team. Let DIFF be the response variable. Note that DIFF > 0 means the team won and DIFF < 0 means the team lost.

a. Construct a box plot of DIFF, e.g., using the *Explore Quantitative Data* app. What do the three outlying observations represent?

b. Find the prediction equation relating DIFF to RUNS. Show that the team is predicted to win when RUNS = 8 or more.

c. The pairwise correlations between RUNS, HIT, ERR, and DIFF are given in the following table. Interpret what these show.

	Run	Hits	Errors
Hits	0.819		
Errors	−0.259	−0.154	
Diff	0.818	0.657	−0.501

d. Conduct statistical inference about the slope of the relationship between DIFF and RUNS.

12.78 Runs and hits   Refer to the previous exercise. Conduct a regression analysis of y = RUNS and x = HIT. Does a straight-line regression model seem appropriate? Prepare a report

a. Using graphical ways of portraying the individual variables and their relationship.

b. Interpreting descriptive statistics for the individual variables and their relationship.

c. Viewing standardized residuals to find games with unusual results.

d. Conducting statistical inference about the slope of the relationship.

12.79 GPA and TV watching   Using software with the FL Student Survey data file on the book's website, conduct regression analyses relating y = high school GPA and x = hours of TV watching. Prepare a two-page report, showing descriptive and inferential methods for analyzing the relationship.

12.80 Female athletes' speed   For the High School Female Athletes data set on the book's website and preloaded in the *Linear Regression* app, conduct a regression analysis using the time for the 40-yard dash as the response variable and weight as the explanatory variable. Prepare a two-page report, indicating why you conducted each analysis and interpreting the results.

12.81 Football point spreads   For a football game in the National Football League, let y = difference between number of points scored by the home team and the away team (so, $y > 0$ if the home team wins). Let x be the predicted difference according to the Las Vegas betting spread. For the 768 NFL games played between 2003 and 2006, MINITAB results of a regression analysis follow.[2]

a. Explain why you would expect the true y-intercept to be 0 and the true slope to be 1 if there is no bias in the Las Vegas predictions.

b. Based on the results shown in the table, is there much evidence that the sample fit differs from the model $\mu_y = \alpha + \beta x$ with $\alpha = 0$ and $\beta = 1$? Explain.

```
Term        Coef    SE Coef   T-Value   P-Value

Constant   -0.4022  0.5233    -0.77     0.442

LasVegas    1.0251  0.0824    12.44     0.000

R - Sq = 16.8%
```

---

[2]Source: Data from P. Everson, (2007), *Chance*, vol. 20, pp. 49–56.

12.82 Iraq war and reading newspapers   A study by the Readership Institute[3] at Northwestern University used survey data to analyze how newspaper reader behavior was influenced by the Iraq war. The response variable was a Reader Behavior Score (RBS), a combined measure summarizing newspaper use frequency, time spent with the newspaper, and how much was read. Comparing RBS scores pre-war and during the war, the study noted that there was a significant increase in reading by light readers (mean RBS changing from 2.05 to 2.32) but a significant decrease in reading by heavy readers (mean RBS changing from 5.87 to 5.66). Identify x = pre-war RBS and y = during-war RBS and explain how this finding could merely reflect regression toward the mean.

12.83 Sports and regression   One of your relatives is a big sports fan but has never taken a statistics course. Explain how you could describe the concept of regression toward the mean in terms of a sports application, without using technical jargon.

12.84 Regression toward the mean paradox   Does regression toward the mean imply that, over many generations, there are fewer and fewer very short people and very tall people? Explain your reasoning. (*Hint:* What happens if you look backward in time in doing the regressions?)

12.85 Height and weight   Suppose the correlation coefficient between height and weight is 0.50 for a sample of males in elementary school and 0.50 for a sample of males in middle school. If we combine the samples, explain why the correlation coefficient will probably be larger than 0.50.

12.86 Income and education   Explain why the correlation coefficient between x = number of years of education and y = annual income is likely to be smaller if we use a random sample of adults who have a Ph.D. than if we use a random sample of all adults.

12.87 Dollars and pounds   Annual income, in dollars, was the response variable in a regression analysis. For a British version of a written report about the analysis, all responses were converted to British pounds sterling (£1 equaled $2.00 when this was done).

a. How, if at all, does the slope of the prediction equation change?

b. How, if at all, does the correlation coefficient change?

c. How, if at all, does the t statistic change for testing the effect of an explanatory variable?

12.88 All models are wrong   The statistician George Box, who had an illustrious academic career at the University of Wisconsin, is often quoted as saying, "All models are wrong, but some models are useful." Why do you think that, in practice,

a. All models are wrong?

b. Some models are *not* useful?

12.89 *df* for *t* tests in regression   In regression modeling, for t tests about regression parameters, $df = n -$ number of parameters in equation for the mean.

a. Explain why $df = n - 2$ for the model $\mu_y = \alpha + \beta x$.

b. Chapter 8 discussed how to estimate a single mean μ. Treating this as the parameter in a simpler regression model, $\mu_y = \mu$, with a single parameter, explain why $df = n - 1$ for inference about a single mean.

12.90 Assumptions   What assumptions are needed to use the linear regression model to (a) obtain a meaningful fit that represents the true relationship well and (b) to make *inferences* about the relationship. For part b, which assumption is least critical?

12.91 Assumptions fail?   Refer to the previous exercise. In view of these assumptions, indicate why such a model would or would not be good in the following situations:

a. x = year (from 1900 to 2005), y = percentage unemployed workers in the United States. (*Hint:* Does y continually tend to increase or decrease?)

b. x = age of subject, y = subject's annual medical expenses. (*Hint:* Suppose expenses tend to be relatively high for the newborn and for the elderly.)

c. x = per capita income, y = life expectancy, for nations. (*Hint:* The increasing trend eventually levels off.)

12.92 Lots of standard deviations   Explain carefully the interpretations of the standard deviations (a) s_y, (b) s_x, (c) residual standard deviation s, and (d) *se* of slope estimate b.

12.93 Decrease in home values   A Freddie Mac quarterly statement (May 2010) reported that U.S. home sales for one of the central regions (including Illinois, Indiana, Ohio, and Wisconsin) have shown that home values decreased by 3.4% in the last previous year. What if someone interprets this information by saying, "The decrease in home sales is of concern. The decreased rate of 3.4% amounts to a decrease of 17% over five years and 34% over ten years."

a. Explain what is incorrect about this statement.

b. If, in fact, the current median house price for this region is $175,000 and in each of the next 10 years the house values decrease in price by 3.4% relative to the previous year, then what is the estimated house value after a decade? What percentage decrease occurs for the decade?

12.94 Population growth   Exercise 12.57 about U.S. population growth showed a predicted growth rate of 13% per decade.

a. Show that this is equivalent to a 1.23% predicted growth *per year*.

b. Explain why the predicted U.S. population size (in millions) x years after 1900 is $81.137(1.0123)x$

---

[3]www.readership.org/consumers/data/FINAL_war_study.pdf.

Multiple Choice or True/False

12.95 Interpret r One can interpret $r = 0.30$ or the corresponding $r^2 = 0.09$ as follows:

a. A 30% reduction in error occurs in using x to predict y.

b. A 9% reduction in error occurs in using x to predict y compared to using y to predict y.

c. 9% of the time $\hat{y} = y$.

d. y changes 0.3 unit for every one-unit increase in x.

e. x changes 0.3 standard deviations when y changes 1 standard deviation.

12.96 Correlation coefficient appropriate? The correlation coefficient is appropriate for describing relationships between two quantitative variables:

a. Even when different people measure the variables using different units (e.g., kilograms and pounds).

b. When the relationship is highly nonlinear.

c. When the slope of the regression equation is 0 using nearly all the data, but a couple of outliers are extremely high on y at the high end of the x-scale.

d. When the sample has a much narrower range of x values than does the population.

e. When the response variable and explanatory variable are both categorical.

12.97 Slope and correlation coefficient The slope of the least squares regression equation and the correlation coefficient are similar in the sense that:

a. They both must fall between -1 and $+1$.

b. They both describe the strength of the linear relationship.

c. Their squares both have proportional reduction in error interpretations.

d. They have the same t statistic value for testing H_0: Independence.

e. They both are unaffected by severe outliers.

12.98 Regress x on y The regression of y on x has a prediction equation of $\hat{y} = -2.0 + 5.0x$ and a correlation coefficient of 0.3. Then, the regression of x on y

a. also has a correlation coefficient of 0.3.

b. could have a negative slope.

c. has $r^2 = \sqrt{0.3}$.

d. equals $1/(-2.0 + 5.0y)$.

12.99 Income and height University of Rochester economist Steven Landsburg surveyed economic studies in England and the United States that showed a positive correlation coefficient between height and income. The article stated that in the United States each one-inch increase in height was worth about $1,500 extra earnings a year, on the average (*Toronto Globe and Mail*, 4/1/2002). The regression equation that links $y =$ annual earnings (in thousands of dollars) to $x =$ height (in inches)

a. has y-intercept $= \$1,500$.

b. has slope 1.5.

c. has slope 1/1500.

d. has slope 1,500.

e. has correlation coefficient 0.150.

12.100 True or false: Interpreting linear regression The variables $y =$ annual income (thousands of dollars), $x_1 =$ number of years of education, and $x_2 =$ number of years experience in job are measured for all the employees having city-funded jobs in Knoxville, Tennessee. Suppose that the following regression equations and correlation coefficients apply:

i. $\hat{y} = 10 + 1.0x_1, \quad r = 0.30$.

ii. $\hat{y} = 14 + 0.4x_2, \quad r = 0.60$.

The correlation coefficient is -0.40 between x_1 and x_2. Which of the following statements are true and which are false?

a. The strongest linear relationship is between y and x_2.

b. A standard deviation increase in education corresponds to a predicted increase of 0.3 standard deviations in income.

c. There is a 30% reduction in error in using education, instead of $\bar{y}$, to predict y.

d. When x_1 is the predictor of y, the sum of squared residuals is larger than when x_2 is the predictor of y.

e. If $s = 8$ for the model using x_1 to predict y, then it is not unusual to observe an income of $100,000 for an employee who has 10 years of education.

Advanced Concepts

12.101 Golf club velocity and distance A study about the effect of the swing on putting in golf (by C. M. Craig et al., *Nature*, vol. 405, 2000, pp. 295–296) showed a very strong linear relationship between $y =$ putting distance and the square of $x =$ club's impact velocity (r^2 is in the range 0.985 to 0.999).

a. For the model $\mu_y = \alpha + \beta x^2$, explain why it is sensible to set $\alpha = 0$.

b. If the appropriate model is $\mu_y = \beta x^2$, explain why if you double the velocity of the swing, you can expect to quadruple the putting distance.

12.102 Why is there regression toward the mean? Refer to the relationship $r = (s_x/s_y)b$ between the slope and correlation coefficient, which is equivalently $s_x b = r s_y$.

a. Explain why an increase in x of s_x units relates to a change in the predicted value of y of $s_x b$ units. (For instance, if $s_x = 10$, it corresponds to a change in $\hat{y}$ of $10b$.)

b. Based on part a, explain why an increase of one standard deviation in x corresponds to a change of only r standard deviations in the predicted y-variable.

12.103 r^2 and variances Suppose $r^2 = 0.30$. Since $\Sigma(y - \bar{y})^2$ is used in estimating the overall variability of the y values and $\Sigma(y - \hat{y})^2$ is used in estimating the residual variability at any fixed value of x, explain why approximately the estimated variance of the conditional distribution of y for a given x is 30% smaller than the estimated variance of the marginal distribution of y.

12.104 Standard error of slope The formula for the standard error of the sample slope b is $se = s/\sqrt{\Sigma(x - \bar{x})^2}$, where s is the residual standard deviation.

  a. Show that the smaller the value of s, the more precisely b estimates β.

  b. Explain why a small s occurs when the data points show little variability about the prediction equation.

  c. Explain why the standard error of b decreases as the sample size increases and when the x values display more variability.

12.105 Regression with an error term[4] An alternative to the population regression formula $\mu_y = \alpha + \beta x$ expresses each y value, rather than the mean of the y values, in terms of x. This approach models an observation on y as

$$y = \text{mean} + \text{error} = \alpha + \beta x + \epsilon,$$

where the mean $\mu_y = \alpha + \beta x$ and the error $= \epsilon$.

The **error term** denoted by ϵ (the Greek letter epsilon) represents the deviation of the observation from the mean, that is, $\epsilon = \text{error} = y - \text{mean}$.

  a. If an observation has $\epsilon > 0$, explain why the observation falls above the mean.

  b. What does ϵ equal when the observation falls exactly at the mean? The ϵ term represents the error that results from using the mean value $(\alpha + \beta x)$ of y at a certain value of x for the prediction of the individual observation on y.

  c. For the sample data and their prediction equation $\hat{y} = a + bx$, explain why an analogous equation to the population equation $y = \alpha + \beta x + \epsilon$ is

$y = a + bx + e$, where e is the residual, $e = y - \hat{y}$. (The residual e estimates ϵ. We can interpret e as a sample residual and ϵ as a **population residual**.)

  d. Explain why it does not make sense to use the simpler model, $y = \alpha + \beta x$, which does not have the error term.

12.106 Rule of 72 You invest \$1,000 at 6% compound interest a year. How long does it take until your investment is worth \$2,000?

  a. Based on what you know about exponential regression, explain why the answer is the value of x for which $1{,}000(1.06)^x = 2{,}000$.

  b. Using the property of logarithms that $\log(a^x) = x\log(a)$, show that the answer x satisfies $x[\log(1.06)] = \log(2)$, or $x = \log(2)/\log(1.06) = 12$.

  c. The rule of 72 says that if you divide 72 by the interest rate, you will find approximately how long it takes your money to double. According to this rule, about how long (in years) does it take your money to double at an interest rate of (i) 1% and (ii) 18%?

Student Activities

12.107 Analyze your data Refer to the data file you created in Exercise 1.50 at the end of Chapter 1. For variables chosen by your instructor, conduct a regression and correlation analysis. Report both descriptive and inferential statistical analyses, interpreting and summarizing your findings and prepare to discuss the results in class.

 APP

▶ Activity 1

SAT French Exam and Years of Study

In 2003, high school students taking the SAT French II language exam after two to four years of study scored, on average, 35 points higher for each additional year of study (*Source:* www.collegeboard.com/). The scores of students with two years of study averaged 505. For each number of years of study, the standard deviation was approximately 100. Let y = French II exam score and x = number of years of study beyond two years (so x = 0, 1, or 2 for 2, 3, and 4 years of study).

1. Explain why the regression equation $\mu_y = \alpha + \beta x$ is $\mu_y = 505 + 35x$.

2. Suppose y has a normal conditional distribution. Using software, randomly select a student who has two years of

French study, a student who has three years, and a student who has four years, by simulating from the appropriate normal distributions. Record each exam score.

3. Perform Step 2 at least 100 times. Store your results in a data file. You now have 100 values of y at each value of x.

4. Construct parallel dot plots and/or box plots for the sample conditional distributions. Compare the mean of the simulated distribution at each x to the actual mean, based on $\mu_y = 505 + 35x$. Is the variability similar for the three sample conditional distributions?

5. Fit a regression line, $\hat{y} = a + bx$, to the simulated values. How does this line compare to the actual regression line, $\mu_y = 505 + 35x$?

    The simulated results in Step 4 and Step 5 are not *exactly* equal to those for the model because they use a sample, whereas $\mu_y = 505 + 35x$ refers to a population.

---

[4] This formula is less useful than the one for the mean because it does not apply to regression models when y is not assumed to be normal, such as logistic regression for binary data.

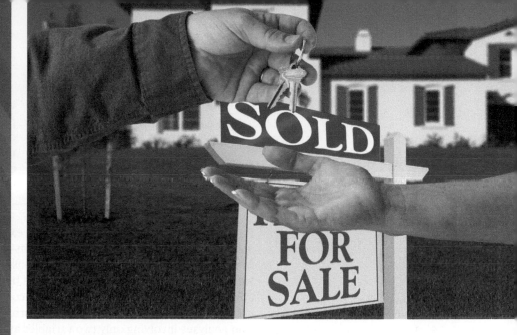

Chapter 12 used a linear regression model with a single explanatory variable to analyze the relationship and make predictions. In this chapter, we learn how we can extend this model to include several explanatory variables.

Multiple Regression

Example 1

Predicting the Selling Price of a House

Picture the Scenario

You are saving to buy a home, and you wonder how much it will cost. The House Selling Prices OR data file on the book's website has observations on 200 recent home sales in Corvallis, Oregon. Table 13.1 shows data for two homes.

Variables listed are the selling price (in dollars), house size (in square feet), number of bedrooms, number of bathrooms, the lot size (in square feet), the year built, and whether the house has a garage. Table 13.2 reports the mean and

standard deviation of these variables for all 200 home sales. Note that in the descriptive summaries, the variable 'Year Built' is used to determine the variable 'Age'.

Questions to Explore

In your community, if you know the values of such variables,

- How can you predict a home's selling price?

- How can you describe the relationship between selling price and the other variables?

- How can you make inferences about the population of all houses in the community, based on the information in the sample?

Table 13.1 Selling Prices and Related Factors for a Sample of Home Sales

House	Selling Price	House Size (sq. ft)	Number of Bedrooms	Number of Bathrooms	Lot Size (sq. ft)	Year Built	Garage (Y/N)
1	$232,500	1,679	3	1.5	10,019	1976	Y
2	$158,000	1,292	1	1	217,800	1958	N

Table 13.2 Descriptive Statistics for Sales of 200 Homes

	Selling Price	House Size (sq. ft)	Number of Bedrooms	Number of Bathrooms	Lot Size (sq. ft)	Age
Mean	$267,466	2,551	3.08	2.03	23,217	34.75
Standard deviation	$115,808	1,238	1.10	0.77	47,637	24.44

Thinking Ahead

You can find a regression equation to predict selling price by treating one of the other variables as the explanatory variable. However, since there are *several* explanatory variables, you might make better predictions by using *all* of them at once. That's the idea behind **multiple regression**. It uses *more than one* explanatory variable to predict a response variable.

A further benefit of including several explanatory variables in the regression model—besides more accurate predictions—is that it allows us to assess the effect of one explanatory variable on the response while adjusting for other explanatory variables. Such adjustments are important because the effect of an explanatory variable can change considerably after one accounts for potential lurking variables. A multiple regression analysis provides information not available from simple regression analyses involving only two variables at a time.

Section 13.1 presents the basics of multiple regression. Section 13.2 extends the concepts of correlation and r^2 for describing the strength of the relationship and the accuracy of the model to multiple predictors (explanatory variables). Section 13.3 presents inference methods, and Section 13.4 shows how to check the model. Section 13.5 extends the model further to incorporate categorical explanatory variables. The final section presents a regression model for a categorical response variable.

Recall

Review the concept of *lurking variables* in Section 3.4. ◄

Recall

This chapter builds strongly on the content in Chapter 12 on **regression** and **correlation** methods. You may want to review Sections 12.1 through 12.3 as you read through this chapter. ◄

13.1 Using Several Variables to Predict a Response

Chapter 12 modeled the mean μ_y of a quantitative response variable y using a quantitative explanatory variable x through the straight-line equation $\mu_y = \alpha + \beta x$. We refer to this model with a *single* predictor as a **simple regression model** because it contains only one explanatory variable that is linearly related to the mean of y.

Now, suppose there are two explanatory variables, denoted by x_1 and x_2. The simple regression model generalizes to the **multiple regression** model

$$\mu_y = \alpha + \beta_1 x_1 + \beta_2 x_2.$$

In this equation, α, β_1, and β_2 are parameters. When we substitute values for x_1 and x_2, the equation specifies the population mean of y for all subjects with those values of x_1 and x_2. When there are additional explanatory variables, each contributes another βx term.

In Words

As in the simple regression model, we use the Greek letter β (beta) for parameters describing effects of explanatory variables, with β_1 and β_2 read as "beta one" and "beta two."

Multiple Regression Model

The **multiple regression model** relates the mean μ_y of a quantitative response variable y to a set of explanatory variables $x_1, x_2, \ldots$. For three explanatory variables, for example, the multiple regression equation is

$$\mu_y = \alpha + \beta_1 x_1 + \beta_2 x_2 + \beta_3 x_3,$$

and the sample prediction equation is

$$\hat{y} = a + b_1 x_1 + b_2 x_2 + b_3 x_3.$$

As with simple regression, we'll rely on software to provide the parameter estimates for the multiple regression equation for a given data set. The way software computes the prediction equation is the same as before: It uses the method of **least squares** to find the best prediction equation, where best refers to the one with the smallest possible sum of the squared residuals.

Example 2

Multiple Regression ◀

Predicting Selling Price Using House Size and Number of Bedrooms

Picture the Scenario

For the house selling price data described in Example 1, MINITAB reports the results for a multiple regression analysis in Table 13.3, with selling price as the response variable and with house size and number of bedrooms as explanatory variables. (You can replicate the results of this output with the *Multiple Linear Regression* app.)

Table 13.3 Regression of Selling Price on House Size and Bedrooms

```
Regression Equation

Price = 60102 + 62.98 House Size + 15170 Bedrooms

Coefficients
```

Term	Coef	SE Coef	T-Value	P-Value
Constant	60102	18623	3.23	0.001
House Size	63.0	4.75	13.25	0.000
Bedrooms	15170	5330	2.85	0.005

Questions to Explore

a. State the prediction equation.

b. The first home listed in Table 13.1 has house size = 1,679 square feet, three bedrooms, and selling price $232,500. Find its predicted selling price and the residual (prediction error). Interpret the residual.

Think It Through

a. The response variable is y = selling price. Let x_1 = house size and x_2 = the number of bedrooms. From Table 13.3, the prediction equation is

$$\hat{y} = 60,102 + 63.0x_1 + 15,170x_2,$$

where $\hat{y}$ is the predicted price.

b. For $x_1 = 1,679$ and $x_2 = 3$, the predicted selling price is

$$\hat{y} = 60,102 + 63.0(1,679) + 15,170(3) = 211,389, \text{ that is, } \$211,389.$$

The residual is the prediction error,
$$y - \hat{y} = \$232,500 - \$211,389 = \$21,111.$$

This result tells us that the actual selling price was $21,111 higher than predicted.

Insight

The coefficients of house size and number of bedrooms are positive. As these variables increase, the predicted selling price increases, as we would expect.

▶ *Try Exercise 13.1*

In Practice The Number of Explanatory Variables You Can Use Depends on the Amount of Data

In practice, you should not use many explanatory variables in a multiple regression model unless you have lots of data. A rough guideline is that *the sample size n should be at least 10 times the number of explanatory variables.* For example, to use two explanatory variables, you should have at least $n = 20$ observations. (When the number of explanatory variables is very large, more recently developed guidelines and statistical methodologies apply, which are beyond the scope of this book.)

Plotting Relationships

Always look at the data before conducting a multiple regression analysis. Most software (including the *Multiple Linear Regression* app) has the option of constructing scatterplots on a single graph for each pair of variables. This type of plot is called a **scatterplot matrix**.

Figure 13.1 shows a MINITAB scatterplot matrix for selling price, house size, and number of bedrooms. It shows each pair of variables twice. For a given pair, in one plot a variable is on the *y*-axis and in another it is on the *x*-axis. For instance, selling price of house is on the *y*-axis for the plots in the first row, whereas it is on the *x*-axis for the plots in the first column. Since selling price is the response variable for this example, the plots in the first row (where selling price is on the *y*-axis) are the ones of primary interest. These graphs show positive linear relationships between selling price and both house size and number of bedrooms. Because a scatterplot matrix shows each pair of variables twice, you only need to look at the plots above the diagonal.

▲ **Figure 13.1** Scatterplot Matrix for Selling Price, House Size, and Number of Bedrooms. The middle plot in the top row has house size on the *x*-axis and selling price on the *y*-axis. The first plot in the second row reverses this, with selling price on the *x*-axis and house size on the *y*-axis. **Question** Why are the plots of main interest the ones in the top row?

Each scatterplot portrays only *two* variables. It's a two-dimensional picture. A multiple regression equation, which has *several* variables, is more difficult to portray graphically. Note also that the scatterplot involving the variable Number of Bedrooms as an explanatory variable has an appearance of columns of points. This is due to the highly discrete nature of this quantitative variable.

Interpretation of Multiple Regression Coefficients

The simplest way to interpret a multiple regression equation is to look at it in *two dimensions* as a function of a *single* explanatory variable. We can do this by fixing values for the other explanatory variable(s). For instance, let's fix x_1 = house size at the value 2,000 square feet. Then the prediction equation simplifies to one with x_2 = number of bedrooms alone as the predictor,

$$\hat{y} = 60,102 + 63.0(2,000) + 15,170x_2 = 186,102 + 15,170x_2.$$

For 2,000-square-foot houses, the predicted selling price relates to the number of bedrooms by $\hat{y} = 186,102 + 15,170x_2$. Since the slope coefficient of x_2 is 15,170, the predicted selling price increases by \$15,170 for every additional bedroom.

Likewise, we could fix the number of bedrooms and then describe how the predicted selling price depends on the house size. Let's consider houses with number of bedrooms $x_2 = 3$. The prediction equation becomes

$$\hat{y} = 60,102 + 63.0x_1 + 15,170(3) = 105,612 + 63.0x_1.$$

For houses with three bedrooms, the predicted selling price increases by \$63 for every additional square foot in house size, or \$6,300 for every 100 square foot in size increase.

Can we say an increase of one bedroom has a larger impact on the selling price (\$15,170) than an increase of a square foot in house size (\$63 per square foot)? No, we cannot compare these slopes for these explanatory variables because their units of measurement are not the same. Slopes can't be compared when the units differ. We could compare house size and lot size directly if they had the same units of square feet.

Summarizing the Effect While Controlling for a Variable

The multiple regression model states that *each* explanatory variable has a straight-line relationship with the mean of y, given fixed values of the other explanatory variables. Specifically, *the model assumes that the slope for a particular explanatory variable is identical for all fixed values of the other explanatory variables.* For instance, the coefficient of x_1 in the prediction equation $\hat{y} = 60,102 + 63.0x_1 + 15,170x_2$ is 63.0 regardless of whether we plug in $x_2 = 1$, $x_2 = 2$, or $x_2 = 3$ for the number of bedrooms. When you fix x_2 at each of these three levels, you can check that:

x_2	$\hat{y} = 60,102 + 63.0x_1 + 15,170x_2$
1	$\hat{y} = 75,272 + 63.0x_1$
2	$\hat{y} = 90,442 + 63.0x_1$
3	$\hat{y} = 105,612 + 63.0x_1$

The slope of house size (x_1) is 63.0 for each equation. Setting x_2 at a variety of values yields a collection of parallel lines, each having slope 63.0. See Figure 13.2.

When we fix the value of x_2 we are holding it constant: We are *controlling* for x_2. That's the major difference between the interpretation of slopes in multiple and simple regression:

- In multiple regression, a slope describes the effect of an explanatory variable while *controlling* effects of the other explanatory variables in the model.
- Simple regression has only a single explanatory variable. The slope in a simple regression model describes the effect of that variable while *ignoring* all other possible explanatory variables.

Recall

Section 10.5 showed that in multivariate analyses, we can **control** a variable statistically by keeping its value constant while we study the relationship between other variables. ◀

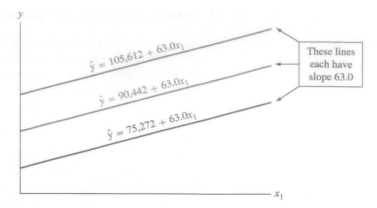

▲ **Figure 13.2** The Relationship Between $\hat{y}$ and x_1 for the Multiple Regression Equation $\hat{y} = 60{,}102 + 63.0x_1 + 15{,}170x_2$. This shows how the equation simplifies when number of bedrooms $x_2 = 1$ (red line), $x_2 = 2$ (blue line), or $x_2 = 3$ (green line). **Question** The lines jump upward (to higher $\hat{y}$-values) as x_2 increases. How would you interpret this fact?

For example, the prediction equation for the simple regression between y = selling price and x_1 = house size is $\hat{y} = 97{,}997 + 66.4x_1$. In this equation, the number of bedrooms and other possible predictors are ignored, not controlled. The prediction equation describes the relationship for *all* the house sales in the data set regardless of how many bedrooms they have. On the other hand, the equation $\hat{y} = 90{,}442 + 63.0x_1$ we obtained above by substituting $x_2 = 2$ into the multiple regression equation applies only for houses that have two bedrooms. In this case, number of bedrooms is controlled. This is why the slopes are different, 66.4 for simple regression and 63.0 for multiple regression.

One of the main uses of multiple regression is to identify potential lurking variables and control for them by including them as explanatory variables in the model. Doing so can have a major impact on a variable's effect. When we control a variable, we keep that variable from influencing the relationships among the other variables in the study. As we've seen before, the direction of the effect can change after we control for a variable. Exercise 13.5 illustrates this for multiple regression modeling.

13.1 Practicing the Basics

13.1 Predicting weight For a study of female college athletes, the prediction equation relating y = total body weight (in pounds) to x_1 = height (in inches) and x_2 = percent body fat is $\hat{y} = -121 + 3.50x_1 + 1.35x_2$.

TRY

a. Find the predicted total body weight for a female athlete at the mean values of 66 and 18 for x_1 and x_2.

b. An athlete with $x_1 = 66$ and $x_2 = 18$ has actual weight $y = 115$ pounds. Find the residual and interpret it.

13.2 Does study help GPA? For the Georgia Student Survey file on the book's website (and available in the *Multiple Linear Regression* app), the prediction equation relating y = college GPA to x_1 = high school GPA and x_2 = study time (hours per day), is $\hat{y} = 1.13 + 0.643x_1 + 0.0078x_2$.

APP

a. Find the predicted college GPA of a student who has a high school GPA of 3.5 and who studies three hours a day.

b. For students with fixed study time, what is the change in predicted college GPA when high school GPA increases from 3.0 to 4.0?

13.3 Predicting college GPA For all students at Walden University, the prediction equation for y = college GPA (range 0–4.0) with x_1 = high school GPA (range 0–4.0) and x_2 = college board score (range 200–800) is $\hat{y} = 0.20 + 0.50x_1 + 0.002x_2$.

a. Find the predicted college GPA for students having (i) high school GPA = 4.0 and college board score = 800 and (ii) $x_1 = 2.0$ and $x_2 = 200$.

b. For those students with $x_2 = 500$, show that $\hat{y} = 1.20 + 0.50x_1$.

c. For those students with $x_2 = 600$, show that $\hat{y} = 1.40 + 0.50x_1$.

d. Consider two students with the same high school GPA, where the first has college board score 500 and the other 600. Which one has the higher predicted college GPA?

13.4 Interpreting slopes on GPA Refer to the previous exercise.

a. Explain why setting x_2 at a variety of values yields a collection of parallel lines relating $\hat{y}$ to x_1. What is the value of the slope for those parallel lines?

b. Since the slope 0.50 for x_1 is larger than the slope 0.002 for x_2, does this imply that x_1 has a larger effect than x_2 on y in this sample? Explain.

13.5 **Does more education cause more crime?**   The FL Crime data file on the book's website has data for the 67 counties in Florida on

y = crime rate: Annual number of crimes in county
per 1000 population

x_1 = education: Percentage of adults in county with at
least a high school education

x_2 = urbanization: Percentage in county living in an
urban environment.

The figure shows a scatterplot matrix. MINITAB multiple regression results are also displayed. (You can also obtain this output with the *Multiple Linear Regression* app.)

Scatterplot matrix for crime rate, education, and urbanization.

Multiple Regression for y = Crime Rate, x_1 = Education, and x_2 = Urbanization.

Term	Coef	SE Coef	T-Value	P-Value
Constant	59.1	28.4	2.08	0.041
education	−0.583	0.472	−1.23	0.221
urbanization	0.683	0.123	5.54	0.000

a. Find the predicted crime rate for a county that has 0% in an urban environment and (i) 70% high school graduation rate and (ii) 80% high school graduation rate.

b. Use results from part a to explain how education affects the crime rate, controlling for urbanization, interpreting the slope coefficient −0.58 of education.

c. Using the prediction equation, show that the equation relating crime rate and education when urbanization is fixed at (i) 0, (ii) 50, and (iii) 100, is as follows:

x_2	$\hat{y} = 59.1 - 0.58x_1 + 0.68x_2$
0	$\hat{y} = 59.1 - 0.58x_1$
50	$\hat{y} = 93.2 - 0.58x_1$
100	$\hat{y} = 127.4 - 0.58x_1$

Sketch a plot with these lines and use it to interpret the effect of education on crime rate, controlling for urbanization.

d. The scatterplot matrix shows that education has a *positive* relationship with crime rate, but the multiple regression equation shows that the relationship is *negative* when we keep x_2 = urbanization fixed. Consider the hypothetical figure that follows. Sketch lines that represent (i) the prediction equation from a simple regression model using only education and ignoring the information on urbanization and (ii) the prediction equation from the multiple regression model for counties having urbanization = 50. Use these lines to explain the difference in the interpretation of the slope for education in simple and multiple regression models with regard to ignoring or controlling for urbanization. (*Note:* The reversal in the relationship between crime rate and education is an example of **Simpson's paradox**; see Example 15 in Sec. 3.4 and the discussion after it).

Hypothetical scatterplot for crime rate and education, labeling by urbanization.

13.6 **Crime rate and income**   Refer to the previous exercise. MINITAB reports the following results for the multiple regression of y = crime rate on x_1 = median income (in thousands of dollars) and x_2 = urbanization. (You can also obtain this output with the *Multiple Linear Regression* app.)

Results of Regression Analysis

Term	Coef	SE Coef	T-Value	P-Value
Constant	40.0	16.4	2.44	0.017
income	−0.791	0.805	−0.98	0.330
urbanization	0.642	0.111	5.78	0.000

a. Report the prediction equations relating crime rate to income at urbanization levels of (i) 0 and (ii) 100. Interpret.

b. For the simple regression model relating y = crime rate to x = income, MINITAB reports

```
crime = -11.6 + 2.61 income
```

Interpret the effect of income, according to the sign of its slope. How does this effect differ from the effect of income in the multiple regression equation?

c. Use the estimated slope for income in the simple and multiple regression model to explain the difference in the interpretation of the slope when (i) ignoring urbanization (ii) controlling urbanization. (*Note:* The reversal in the relationship between income and education is an example of **Simpson's paradox**.)

13.7 **The economics of golf**   The earnings of a PGA Tour golfer are determined by performance in tournaments. A study analyzed tour data to determine the financial return for certain skills of professional golfers. The sample consisted of 393 golfers competing in one or both of the 2002 and 2008 seasons. The most significant factors that contribute to earnings were the percent of attempts a player was able to hit the green in regulation (GIR), the number of times that a golfer made par or better after hitting a bunker divided by the number of bunkers that were hit (SS), the average of putts after reaching the green (AvePutt), and the number of PGA events entered (Events). The resulting coefficients from multiple regression to predict yearly earnings (in $) are:

Predictor	Coefficient
Constant	26,417,000
GIR	168,300
SS	33,859
AvePutt	−19,784,000
Events	−44,725

Source: Some data from K. Rinehart, *Major Themes in Economics*, 2009.

a. State the prediction equation for a PGA Tour golfer's yearly earnings.

b. Explain how to interpret the coefficient for AvePutt.

c. Find the predicted earnings for a golfer who had a GIR score of 60, SS score of 50, AvePutt of 1.5 and participated in 20 events.

13.8 Comparable number of bedrooms and house size effects In Example 2, the prediction equation between y = selling price and x_1 = house size and x_2 = number of bedrooms was $\hat{y} = 60{,}102 + 63.0x_1 + 15{,}170x_2$.

a. For fixed number of bedrooms, how much is the house selling price predicted to increase for each square foot increase in house size? Why?

b. For a fixed house size of 2,000 square feet, how does the predicted selling price change for two, three, and four bedrooms?

13.9 Controlling can have no effect Suppose that the correlation coefficient between x_1 and x_2 equals 0. Then, for multiple regression with those predictors, it can be shown that the slope for x_1 is the same as in simple linear regression when x_1 is the only predictor. Explain why you would expect this to be true. (*Hint:* If you don't control x_2, would you expect it to have an impact on how x_1 affects y, if x_1 and x_2 are not correlated?)

13.10 House selling prices Using the *Multiple Linear Regression* app or other software with the House Selling Prices OR data file (also available on the book's website), analyze y = selling price, x_1 = house size, and x_2 = lot size.

a. Construct box plots for each variable and a scatterplot matrix or scatter plots between y and each of x_1 and x_2. Interpret.

b. Find the multiple regression prediction equation.

c. If house size remains constant, what, if any, is the effect of an increase in lot size? Why do you think this is?

13.11 Used cars The following data (preloaded in the *Multiple Linear Regression* app and available from the book's website) are from a random sample of campus newspaper ads on used cars for sale. Consider the age and horsepower (HP) of a car to predict its selling price. (The variable Type stands for whether the car is from the United States, coded as 1, or a foreign car, coded as 0. This variable will be considered in exercises 13.41 and 13.48.)

a. Construct a scatterplot matrix (or separate scatterplots) to investigate the relationship among price, age, and horsepower and interpret.

b. Find the multiple regression prediction equation for the selling price in terms of age and horsepower of a car. What is the predicted price for a car that has a horsepower of 80 and (i) is 8 years old and (ii) 10 years old, rounded to the nearest hundred?

c. Based on this multiple regression, can you predict the price difference between a car with 60 HP and a car with 80 HP without knowing the ages of the two cars? Explain.

Car	Price	Age	HP	Type	Car	Price	Age	HP	Type
1	8700	9	55	1	11	5050	10	44	1
2	11200	7	75	1	12	14800	7	75	0
3	9000	9	69	0	13	1800	12	55	1
4	10300	10	76	0	14	7200	10	82	1
5	10500	8	76	0	15	8600	9	73	1
6	5250	12	49	1	16	13000	9	130	0
7	12000	5	120	0	17	11790	8	95	0
8	2500	11	79	1	18	12350	7	124	0
9	8300	8	90	0	19	6100	10	74	1
10	9300	8	38	0					

13.2 Extending the Correlation Coefficient and R^2 for Multiple Regression

The correlation coefficient r and its square r^2 describe the strength of the relationship and the accuracy of the prediction equation in a simple linear regression analysis. These measures can also summarize the strength of the relationship between y and a whole set of explanatory variables that predict y in a multiple regression model.

Correlation matrix of selling price (y), house size (x_1), number of bedrooms, (x_2) and age (x_3)

	y	x_1	x_2	x_3
y	—	0.71	0.32	−0.17
x_1	0.71	—	0.26	−0.09
x_2	0.32	0.26	—	−0.19
x_3	−0.17	−0.09	−0.19	—

Correlation Matrix

After plotting the scatterplot matrix and checking whether the relationships are roughly linear, software can compute a **correlation matrix**. This is a square table, arranged in a fashion similar to the scatterplot matrix. It lists the variables in the rows and again in the columns and shows the correlation coefficient r between each pair. The table in the margin shows the correlation matrix for the three variables of selling price (y), house size (x_1), and number of bedrooms (x_2) for which Figure 13.1 displayed the scatterplot matrix. In addition, it includes a fourth variable, the age of the house (x_3). Remember that the correlation coefficient does not distinguish between response and explanatory variable and that the correlation coefficient between x and y is the same as the correlation coefficient between y and x. This is why you see identical values above and below the diagonal. It is a good idea to look at the scatterplot matrix and the corresponding correlation matrix before fitting a multiple regression model to get a feel for the strengths of the relationships among the variables considered.

From the correlation matrix, we see that house size has a moderately strong correlation ($r = 0.71$) with selling price. As the size increases, the price tends to increase. The strength of the linear relationship between price and number of bedrooms is much weaker, with $r = 0.32$. The correlation coefficient between price and age of the house is negative ($r = -0.17$), indicating that older houses tend to cost less. However, the relationship is very weak, and a scatterplot reveals no visible trend. Also, note that the correlation between the house size and the number of bedrooms is, perhaps surprisingly, relatively weak ($r = 0.26$).

Multiple Correlation Coefficient

To summarize how well a multiple regression model predicts y, we analyze how well the observed y values correlate with the predicted $\hat{y}$ values. As a set, the explanatory variables are strongly related with y if the correlation between the y and $\hat{y}$ values is strong. Treating $\hat{y}$ as a variable gives us a way of summarizing several explanatory variables by *one* variable, for which we can use its ordinary correlation with the y values. The correlation coefficient computed between the observed y values and the predicted $\hat{y}$ values from the multiple regression model is called the **multiple correlation coefficient**.

In Words

The **correlation coefficient r** describes the relationship between the response variable y and a single explanatory variable x. The **multiple correlation coefficient** describes the relationship between y and a set of explanatory variables in a multiple regression model. It is denoted by R (uppercase).

Multiple Correlation Coefficient R

For a multiple regression model, the **multiple correlation coefficient** is the correlation coefficient between the observed y values and the predicted $\hat{y}$ values. It is denoted by R.

For each subject in the dataset, the regression equation provides a predicted value $\hat{y}$. So, each subject has a y value and a $\hat{y}$ value. For the two houses listed in Table 13.1, Table 13.4 shows the actual selling price y and the predicted selling price $\hat{y}$ from the equation $\hat{y} = 60,102 + 63.0x_1 + 15,170x_2$ with house size and number of bedrooms as predictors. The correlation coefficient computed between all 200 pairs of y and $\hat{y}$ values is the multiple correlation coefficient, R. Software tells us that this equals 0.72. The scatterplot in the margin displays these pairs of y and $\hat{y}$ values.

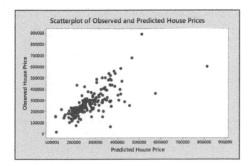

Table 13.4 Selling Prices and Their Predicted Values

These values refer to the two home sales listed in Table 13.1. The predictors are x_1 = house size and x_2 = number of bedrooms.

House	Selling Price	Predicted Selling Price
1	232,500	$\hat{y} = 60,102 + 63.0(1,679) + 15,170(3) = 211,389$
2	158,000	$\hat{y} = 60,102 + 63.0(1,292) + 15,170(1) = 156,668$

Recall

For the first home sale listed in Table 13.1, $y = 232,500$, $x_1 = 1679$, and $x_2 = 3$. ◄

The larger the multiple correlation coefficient, the better the predictions of y by the set of explanatory variables. For the housing data, $R = 0.72$ indicates a moderately strong relationship.

The predicted values $\hat{y}$ cannot correlate negatively with y. Otherwise, the predictions would be worse than merely using $\bar{y}$ to predict y. Therefore, R *falls between 0 and 1*. In this way, the multiple correlation coefficient R differs from the correlation coefficient r between y and a single variable x, which falls between -1 and $+1$.

R^2

Recall

Sections 3.3 and 12.3 introduced r^2 (*r*-**squared**) as measuring the proportional reduction in prediction error from using $\hat{y}$ to predict y compared to using $\bar{y}$ to predict y. It falls between 0 and 1, with larger values representing a stronger relationship. ◄

For predicting y, the statistic R^2 describes the relative improvement from using the prediction equation instead of using the sample mean $\bar{y}$. The error in using the prediction equation to predict y is summarized by the *residual sum of squares*, $\Sigma(y - \hat{y})^2$. The error in using $\bar{y}$ to predict y is summarized by the *total sum of squares*, $\Sigma(y - \bar{y})^2$. The *proportional reduction in error* is

$$R^2 = \frac{\Sigma(y - \bar{y})^2 - \Sigma(y - \hat{y})^2}{\Sigma(y - \bar{y})^2}.$$

The better the predictions are using the regression equation, the larger R^2 is. The measure r^2 we discussed in Section 12.3 is the special case of R^2 applied to regression with one explanatory variable. As the notation suggests, for multiple regression, R^2 is the square of the multiple correlation coefficient R. Regression software reports R^2 (some as a decimal, others as a percentage), and you can take the positive square root of it to get the multiple correlation coefficient, R.

Example 3

Multiple Correlation Coefficient and R^2 ◄

Predicting House Selling Prices

Picture the Scenario

For the 200 observations on y = selling price in thousands of dollars, using x_1 = house size in thousands of square feet and x_2 = number of bedrooms, Table 13.5 shows part of the ANOVA (analysis of variance) table that MINITAB reports for the multiple regression model which you can also replicate with the *Multiple Linear Regression* app.

Table 13.5 ANOVA Table and R^2 for Predicting House Selling Price (in thousands of dollars) Using House Size (in thousands of square feet) and Number of Bedrooms

```
R-Sq = 52.4%

Analysis of Variance
```

Source	DF	SS
Regression	2	1399524
Error	197	1269345
Total	199	2668870

Questions to Explore

a. Show how to use the sums of squares in the ANOVA table to find R^2 for this multiple regression model. Interpret.

b. Find and interpret the multiple correlation coefficient R.

Think It Through

a. From the sum of squares (SS) column, the total sum of squares is $\Sigma(y - \bar{y})^2 = 2{,}668{,}870$. The residual sum of squares from using the multiple regression equation to predict y is $\Sigma(y - \hat{y})^2 = 1{,}269{,}345$. The value of R^2 is

$$R^2 = \frac{\Sigma(y - \bar{y})^2 - \Sigma(y - \hat{y})^2}{\Sigma(y - \bar{y})^2} = \frac{2{,}668{,}870 - 1{,}269{,}345}{2{,}668{,}870} = 0.524.$$

Using house size and number of bedrooms together to predict selling price reduces the prediction error by 52%, relative to using $\bar{y}$ alone to predict selling price. The R^2 statistic appears (in percentage form) in Table 13.5 under the heading "R-sq."

b. The multiple correlation coefficient between selling price and the two explanatory variables is $R = \sqrt{R^2} = \sqrt{0.524} = 0.72$. This equals the correlation coefficient for the 200 homes between the observed selling prices y and the predicted selling prices $\hat{y}$ from multiple regression that we mentioned before. There's a moderately strong relationship between the observed and the predicted selling prices. In summary, house size and number of bedrooms are very helpful in predicting selling prices.

Insight

From the correlation matrix, we saw that the correlation coefficient between price and size of a house is $r = 0.71$. In that case, the r^2 measure for the simple regression model with just size as a predictor equals $r^2 = (0.71)^2 = 0.50$. The multiple regression model has $R^2 = 0.52$, only a marginally larger value. We appear to be just as well off with the simple model using house size alone as the predictor as using the multiple model. An advantage of using the simple model is easier interpretation of the coefficients.

▶ *Try Exercise 13.12*

Properties of R^2

The example showed that R^2 for the multiple regression model was larger than r^2 for a simple model using only one of the explanatory variables. In fact, *a key property of R^2 is that it cannot decrease when predictors are added to a model.*

The difference $\Sigma(y - \bar{y})^2 - \Sigma(y - \hat{y})^2$ that forms the numerator of R^2 (see the definition of R^2) also appears as a separate row in the ANOVA table. It is called the *regression sum of squares*. A simpler formula for it is

$$\text{Regression SS} = \Sigma(\hat{y} - \bar{y})^2.$$

If each $\hat{y} = \bar{y}$, then the regression equation predicts no better than $\bar{y}$. Then the regression SS $= 0$, and $R^2 = 0$.

The numerical values of the sums of squares reported in Table 13.5 result when y is measured in *thousands* of dollars (for instance, the y-value for the first house is 232.5 rather than 232,500, and $\hat{y}$ is 211.4 rather than 211,389). We truncated the numbers for convenience because the sums of squares would otherwise be enormous with each one having six more zeros on the end! It makes no difference to the result. Another property of R and R^2 is that, like the correlation coefficient r, *their values don't depend on the units of measurement.*

In summary, the properties of R^2 are similar to those of r^2 for the simple linear regression model. Here's a list of the main properties:

Recall

From Section 12.3, the correlation coefficient r and the squared correlation coefficient r^2 (the coefficient of determination) do not depend on the units of measurements. ◄

SUMMARY: Properties of R^2

- R^2 falls between 0 and 1 or, when expressed as a percentage, between 0% and 100%. The larger the value, the better the explanatory variables collectively predict y.
- $R^2 = 1$, or 100% only when all residuals are 0, that is, when all regression predictions are perfect (each $y = \hat{y}$), so residual $SS = \Sigma(y - \hat{y})^2 = 0$.
- $R^2 = 0$, or 0% when each $\hat{y} = \bar{y}$. In that case, the estimated slopes all equal 0, and the correlation coefficient between y and each explanatory variable equals 0.
- R^2 gets larger, or at worst stays the same, whenever an additional explanatory variable is added to the multiple regression model.
- The value of R^2 does not depend on the units of measurement.

Values of r^2 between selling price and various explanatory variables in a simple linear regression model

Explanatory Variable	r^2
House Size	0.50
Bedrooms	0.10
Lot Size	0.05
Baths	0.33
Garage	0.01
Age	0.03

Table 13.6 shows how R^2 increases as we add explanatory variables to a multiple regression model to predict y = house selling price. As we saw from the correlation matrix, the single predictor in the data set that is most strongly related with y is the house size ($r^2 = 0.50$). See the margin table. When we add number of bedrooms as a second predictor, R^2 goes up from 0.50 to 0.52. As other predictors are added, R^2 continues to go up, but not by much, except when adding number of bathrooms, for which there is a more noticeable jump in R^2. Predictive power is not much worse with only house size as a predictor than with all six predictors in the regression model.

Table 13.6 R^2 Value for Multiple Regression Models for y = House Selling Price

Explanatory Variables in Model	R^2
House Size	0.50
House Size, Number of Bedrooms	0.52
House Size, Number of Bedrooms, Lot Size	0.52
House Size, Number of Bedrooms, Lot Size, Number of Bathrooms	0.60
House Size, Number of Bedrooms, Lot Size, Number of Bathrooms, Garage	0.61
House Size, Number of Bedrooms, Lot Size, Number of Bathrooms, Garage, Age	0.61

Although R^2 goes up by only small amounts when we add other variables after house size is already in the model, this does not mean that the other predictors are only weakly correlated with selling price. Because the predictors are themselves highly correlated, once one or two of them are in the model, the remaining ones don't help much in adding to the predictive power. For instance, lot size is highly positively correlated with number of bedrooms and with the size of the house. So, once the size of the house and the number of bedrooms are included as predictors in the model, there's not much benefit to including lot size as an additional predictor.

In Practice R^2 Often Does Not Increase Much After a Few Predictors Are in the Model

When there are many explanatory variables but the correlations among them are strong, once you have included a few of them in the model, R^2 usually doesn't increase much more when you add additional ones. This does not mean that the additional variables are uncorrelated with the response variable but merely that they don't add much new information for predicting y, given the values of the predictors already in the model.

Recall

In Sections 3.3 and 12.3 for the simple linear regression model, we interpreted r^2 as the proportion (or, when given as a percentage, as the percentage) of the variability in the response variable y that can be explained by the change in x. ◄

R^2 as the Percent of Variability Explained

Similar to the simple regression model, we can also interpret R^2 as the percentage of the variability in the response variable y that can be explained by the regression model. The total sum of squares $\Sigma(y - \bar{y})^2$ measures the variability of y over the entire range of all predictor values, and the residual sum of squares $\Sigma(y - \hat{y})^2$ measures the variability of y at a fixed setting for all predictors (see the discussion in the next section). Their ratio $\dfrac{\Sigma(y - \hat{y})^2}{\Sigma(y - \bar{y})^2}$ is the proportion of the overall variability that occurs locally at a fixed setting for all predictors. For instance, from Table 13.5, this ratio equals $\dfrac{1{,}269{,}345}{2{,}668{,}870} = 0.476$, indicating that 47.6% of the overall variability we observe in house prices is due to the variability that occurs locally at any particular setting for the number of bedrooms and size of the house.

This is the variability that *cannot* be explained or accounted for by these predictors because they are fixed. So, for the house price data, about 48% of the variability in the selling price of a house cannot be explained by the number of bedrooms or its size. However, the other 52% of the overall variability in selling prices *can* be explained by the varying number of bedrooms and sizes of houses. This "explained variability" is R^2, expressed as a percentage. Rewriting the formula for R^2 from the previous pages just a bit, we see that $R^2 = 1 - \dfrac{\Sigma(y - \hat{y})^2}{\Sigma(y - \bar{y})^2} = 1 - 0.476 = 0.524$.

With this interpretation of R^2 we can see that 52.4% of the overall variability in selling prices can be explained by differences in number of bedrooms and house sizes. The remaining 47.6% of the variability must be due to other sources that we didn't or couldn't measure, such as the quality of the school district.

13.2 Practicing the Basics

13.12 Predicting sports attendance Keeneland Racetrack in Lexington, Kentucky, has been a social gathering place since 1935. Every spring and fall thousands of people come to the racetrack to socialize, gamble, and enjoy the horse races that have become so popular in Kentucky. A study investigated the different factors that affect the attendance at Keeneland. To many people, the social aspect of Keeneland is just as important as watching the races, if not more. The study investigates which factors significantly contribute to attendance by Keeneland visitors. (*Source:* Data from Gatton School of Business and Economics publication, Gatton College, 2009.)

ANOVA Table for y = Attendance at Keeneland

Source	DF	SS	MS	F-Value	P-Value
Regression	6	2360879925	393479988	21.71	0.00
Error	110	1993805006	18125500		
Total	116	4354684931			

   a. Show how R^2 is calculated from the SS values and report its value.

   b. Interpret the R^2 value. Does the multiple regression equation help us predict the attendance much better than we could without knowing that equation?

   c. Find the multiple correlation coefficient. Interpret.

13.13 Predicting weight Let's use multiple regression to predict total body weight (TBW, in pounds) using data from a study of female college athletes. Possible predictors are HGT = height (in inches), %BF = percent body fat, and age. The display shows the correlation matrix for these variables, which you can replicate with the *Multiple Linear Regression* app.

	TBW	HGT	%BF	AGE
TBW	–	0.74	0.39	−0.19
HGT	0.74	–	0.10	−0.12
%BF	0.39	0.10	–	0.02
AGE	−0.19	−0.12	0.02	–

   a. Which explanatory variable gives by itself the best predictions of weight? Explain.

   b. With height as the sole predictor, $\hat{y} = -106 + 3.65$ (HGT) and $r^2 = 0.55$. If you add %BF as a predictor, you know that R^2 will be at least 0.55. Explain why.

   c. When you add % body fat to the model, $\hat{y} = -121 + 3.50(\text{HGT}) + 1.35(\%\text{BF})$ and $R^2 = 0.66$. When you add age to the model, $\hat{y} = -97.7 + 3.43(\text{HGT}) + 1.36(\%\text{BF}) - 0.960(\text{AGE})$ and $R^2 = 0.67$. Once you know height and % body fat, does age seem to help you in predicting weight? Explain, based on comparing the R^2 values.

13.14 When does controlling have little effect? Refer to the previous exercise. Height has a similar estimated slope for each of the three models. Why do you think that controlling for % body fat and then age does not change the effect of height much? (*Hint:* How strongly is height correlated with the other two variables?)

13.15 Price of used cars For the 19 used cars listed in the Used Cars data file preloaded in the *Multiple Linear Regression* app and available on the book's website (see also Exercise 13.11), modeling the mean of y = used car price in terms of x_1 = age results in $r^2 = 0.66$. Adding x_2 = horsepower (HP) to the model yields the results in the following display.

```
Regression Equation
Price = 19349 - 1406 Age + 25.5 HP
Coefficients
Term          Coef    SE Coef   T-Value   P-Value
Constant      19349    4053      4.77      0.000
Age           -1406     320     -4.40      0.000
HP             25.5     22.3      1.14      0.270


Model Summary
    S       R-sq
2084.69    68.69%
Analysis of Variance
Source      DF      SS          MS       F-value  P-value
Regression   2   152567500   76283750    17.55    0.000
Error       16    69534753    4345922
Total       18   222102253
```

a. Report R^2 and show how it is determined by SS values in the ANOVA table.

b. Interpret its value as a proportional reduction in prediction error.

c. Interpret its value as the percentage of the variability in the response variable that can be explained.

13.16 Price, age, and horsepower In the previous exercise, $r^2 = 0.66$ when age is the predictor and $R^2 = 0.69$ when both age and HP are predictors. Why do you think that

the predictions of price don't improve much when HP is added to the model? (The correlation coefficient between HP and price is $r = 0.56$, and the correlation coefficient between HP and age is $r = -0.51$.)

13.17 Softball data For the Softball data set on the book's website and available in the *Multiple Linear Regression* app, for each game, the variables are a team's number of runs scored (RUNS), number of hits (HIT), number of errors (ERR), and the difference (DIFF) between the number of runs scored by that team and by the other team, which is the response variable. MINITAB reports

$$\text{Difference} = -4.03 + 0.0260 \text{ Hits} + 1.04 \text{ Run} - 1.22 \text{ Errors.}$$

a. If you know the team's number of runs and number of errors in a game, explain why it does not help much to know how many hits the team has.

b. Explain why the result in part a is also suggested by knowing that $R^2 = 0.7594$ for this model, whereas $R^2 = 0.7593$ when only runs and errors are the explanatory variables in the model.

13.18 Slopes, correlations, and units Example 2 modeled y = house selling price in terms of x_1 = house size and x_2 = number of bedrooms. The prediction equation is $\hat{y} = 60,102 + 63.0x_1 + 15,170x_2$, with $R = 0.72$.

a. Interpret the value of the multiple correlation coefficient.

b. Suppose house selling prices are changed from dollars to *thousands* of dollars. If each price in Table 13.1 is divided by 1,000, explain why the prediction equation changes to $\hat{y} = 60.102 + 0.063x_1 + 15.170x_2$.

c. In part b, does the multiple correlation coefficient change to 0.00072? Justify your answer.

13.19 Predicting college GPA Using software (such as the *Multiple Linear Regression* app) with the Georgia Student Survey data file from the book's website, find and interpret the multiple correlation coefficient and R^2 for the relationship between y = college GPA, x_1 = high school GPA, and x_2 = study time. Use both interpretations of R^2 as the reduction in prediction error and the percentage of the variability explained.

13.3 Inferences Using Multiple Regression

We've seen that multiple regression uses more than one explanatory variable to predict a response variable y. With it, we can study an explanatory variable's effect on y while controlling other variables that could affect the results. Now, let's turn our attention to using multiple regression to make inferences about the population.

Inferences require the same assumptions as in simple regression:

■ The regression equation between the mean of the response variable and the explanatory variables holds for the considered population.

■ The data were gathered using randomization.

■ The response variable y has a normal distribution at each combination of values of the explanatory variables, with the same standard deviation.

The first assumption implies that there is a straight-line relationship between the mean of y and each explanatory variable for given values for the other predictors. This straight line has the same slope, no matter what values are considered for these other predictors. (See Figure 13.2 for an illustration with two explanatory variables.) We will see how to check this assumption in Section 13.4. There, we will also discuss how to check the third assumption about normality of the response variable and a constant standard deviation. How to estimate this standard deviation is discussed next.

Estimating Variability Around the Regression Equation

As in the simple linear regression model, the parameter σ describes the variability of the response variable at a fixed setting of predictor variables. Its sample estimate is called the **residual standard deviation** and is given by

$$s = \sqrt{\frac{\text{Residual SS}}{df}} = \sqrt{\frac{\Sigma(y - \hat{y})^2}{n - (\text{number of parameters in regression equation})}}.$$

Recall

In Section 12.1, the parameter σ described the standard deviation of the response y at a given value of x. Figure 12.5 illustrated this. The estimate of σ was called the residual standard deviation (see Section 12.4). ◄

This residual standard deviation describes the variability of y at given predictor settings and equals the typical size of the residuals. Its degrees of freedom are $df =$ sample size n – number of parameters in the regression equation. Software reports s and its square, called the **mean square error**.

Example 4

Estimating Residual Standard Deviation ◄

Female Athletes' Weight

Picture the Scenario

The College Athletes data set on the book's website comes from a study of 64 University of Georgia female athletes who participated in Division I sports. The study measured several physical characteristics, including total body weight in pounds (TBW), height in inches (HGT), the percent of body fat (%BF), and age. Table 13.7 shows the ANOVA table for the regression of weight on height, % body fat, and age.

Table 13.7 ANOVA Table for Multiple Regression Analysis of Athlete Weights

```
Analysis of Variance

Source          DF      SS        MS      F-Value    P-Value

Regression       3    12407.9    4136.0    40.48      0.000

Error           60     6131.0     102.2

Total           63    18539.0

S = 10.1086    R-Sq = 66.9%
```

Question to Explore

For female athletes at particular values of height, percent of body fat, and age, estimate the standard deviation of their weights.

Think It Through

Recall

Recall that the prediction equation was $\hat{y} = -97.7 + 3.43x_1 + 1.36x_2 - 0.96x_3$, so there were four parameters in the regression model. ◄

The SS column tells us that the residual sum of squares is 6,131.0. There were $n = 64$ observations and 4 parameters in the regression model, so the DF column reports $df = n - 4 = 60$ opposite the residual SS. The mean square error is

$$s^2 = (\text{residual SS})/df = 6{,}131.0/60 = 102.2.$$

It appears in the mean square (MS) column, in the row labeled "Error." The residual standard deviation is $s = \sqrt{102.2} = 10.1$, identified as S. For athletes with certain fixed values of height, percent body fat, and age, the weights vary with a standard deviation of about 10 pounds.

Insight

If the conditional distributions of weight are approximately bell shaped, about 95% of the weight values fall within about $2s = 20$ pounds of the true mean, as determined by the regression equation. More precisely, software can report *prediction intervals* within which a response outcome has a certain chance of falling. For instance, at $x_1 = 66$, $x_2 = 18$, and $x_3 = 20$, which are close to the sample means for height, body fat, and age, software reports $\hat{y} = 133.9$ and a 95% prediction interval of 133.9 ± 20.4.

▶ *Try Exercise 13.22*

Recall

For simple regression, Example 15 in Section 12.4 discussed confidence intervals for the mean and prediction intervals for *y* at a particular setting of *x*. These intervals can be formed with multiple regression as well. ◀

For the sample of athletes, weight has a standard deviation of 17 pounds, describing the variability around the mean weight of 133 pounds (see Table 13.9 on page 706). How is it that the *residual* standard deviation could be only 10 pounds? The residual standard deviation is smaller because it refers to variability at *fixed* values of the predictors. (Recall the margin figure next to Example 15 in Chapter 12.) Weight varies less at given values of the predictors than it does overall. If we could predict weight perfectly knowing height, percent body fat, and age, the residual standard deviation would be 0.

The ANOVA table also reports another mean square, called a *mean square for regression*, or *regression mean square* for short. We'll next see how to use the mean squares to conduct a significance test about all the slope parameters together.

The Collective Effect of Explanatory Variables

Do the explanatory variables collectively have a statistically significant effect on the response variable *y*? With three predictors in a model, we can check this by testing

$$H_0: \beta_1 = \beta_2 = \beta_3 = 0.$$

This hypothesis states that the mean of *y* does not depend on *any* of the predictors in the model. That is, *y is statistically independent of all the explanatory variables.* The alternative hypothesis is

$$H_a: \text{At least one } \beta \text{ parameter is different from 0.}$$

This states that *at least one* explanatory variable is related with *y*.

The null hypothesis that all the slope parameters equal 0 is equivalent to the hypothesis that the population values of the multiple correlation coefficient and R^2 equal 0. The equivalence occurs because the population values of R and R^2 equal 0 only in those situations in which all the β parameters equal 0.

The test statistic for H_0 is denoted by F. It equals the ratio of the mean squares from the ANOVA table,

$$F = \frac{\text{Mean square for regression}}{\text{Mean square error}}.$$

Caution

The opposite (alternative) of all betas being equal to zero is that **at least** one of them is different from zero and not that **all** of them are different from zero. ◀

When H_0 is true, the expected value of the F test statistic is approximately 1. When H_0 is false, F tends to be larger than 1. The larger the F test statistic, the stronger the evidence against H_0. The P-value is the right-tail probability from the sampling distribution of the F test statistic.

From the ANOVA table in Table 13.7 (shown again in the margin) for the regression model predicting weight, the mean square for regression $= 4{,}136.0$ and the mean square error $= 102.2$. Then the test statistic

$$F = 4{,}136.0/102.2 = 40.5.$$

Before conclusions can be made about this test, we must first understand the F distribution better.

ANOVA Table from Table 13.7

Source	DF	SS	MS	F	P
Reg.	3	12407.9	4136.0	40.5	0.000
Error	60	6131.0	102.2		
Total	63	18539.0			

The F Distribution and Its Properties

The sampling distribution of the F test statistic is called the **F distribution.** The symbol for the F statistic and its distribution honors the eminent British statistician R. A. Fisher, who derived the F distribution in 1922. Like the chi-squared distribution, the F distribution can assume only nonnegative values and is skewed to the right. See Figure 13.3. The mean is approximately 1.

Sampling distribution of the F statistic under H_0

Shaded tail area = P-value

0   1.0   Observed F F

▲ **Figure 13.3** The F Distribution and the P-Value for F Tests. **Question** Why does the P-value use the right tail but not the left tail?

The precise shape of the F distribution is determined by two degrees of freedom terms, denoted by df_1 and df_2. These are the df values in the ANOVA table for the two mean squares whose ratio equals F. The first one is

$$df_1 = \text{number of explanatory variables in the model.}$$

The second,

$$df_2 = n - \text{number of parameters in regression equation,}$$

is the df for the residual sum of squares. Sometimes df_1 is called the **numerator df** because it is listed in the ANOVA table next to the mean square for regression, which goes in the numerator of the F test statistic. Likewise, df_2 is called the **denominator df**, because it is listed in the ANOVA table next to the mean square error, which goes in the denominator of the F test statistic.

The *F Distribution* app lets you explore the F distribution interactively and you can use it to easily find upper tail probabilities for given numerator and denominator degrees of freedom. The margin figure shows a screenshot. If you don't have access to technology, Table D in the Appendix lists the F values that have P-value $= 0.05$, for various df_1 and df_2 values. Table 13.8 shows a small excerpt. For instance, when $df_1 = 3$ and $df_2 = 40$, $F = 2.84$ has P-value $= 0.05$. When $F > 2.84$, the test statistic is farther out in the tail and the P-value < 0.05. (See the margin figure here and the one next to Table 13.8.) **In practice**, you will neither need the *F Distribution* app nor Table D to obtain a P-value. All software packages that carry out multiple regression will report the P-value for the observed F-statistic next to it. The F value for our example is extremely large ($F = 40.5$). See Table 13.7. With this large value of F, the ANOVA table reports P-value $= 0.000$.

The F Distribution

Table 13.8 An Excerpt of Table D Displaying *F* Values

These are the values that have right-tail probability equal to 0.05. For given df_1 and df_2, they will help you determine whether an *F*-statistic value is extreme at the 0.05 significance level. For example, when $df_1 = 3$ and $df_2 = 40$, any value larger than 2.84 can be considered extreme.

Shaded tail area = 0.05

df_2	df_1				
	1	2	3	4	5
30	4.17	3.32	2.92	2.69	2.69
40	4.10	3.23	2.84	2.61	2.45
60	4.00	3.15	2.76	2.52	2.37

SUMMARY: *F* Test That All the Multiple Regression β Parameters Are Equal to 0

1. **Assumptions:**

   ■ Multiple regression model holds for population mean. This implies that there is a linear relationship between the mean of *y* and each explanatory variable, holding the others constant. The slope of this line is the same, no matter what the values for these other predictors.

   ■ Data gathered using randomization.

   ■ Normal distribution for *y* with same standard deviation at each combination of predictors.

2. **Hypotheses:**

   H_0: $\beta_1 = \beta_2 = \ldots = 0$ (all the β parameters in the model = 0).
   H_a: At least one β parameter differs from 0.

3. **Test Statistic:** $F = $ (mean square for regression)/(mean square error).

4. **P-value:** Right-tail probability above observed *F* test statistic value from *F* distribution with

   $df_1 = $ number of explanatory variables ($=$ number of β parameters),
   $df_2 = n - $ (number of parameters in regression equation).

5. **Conclusion:** The smaller the P-value, the stronger the evidence that at least one explanatory variable has an effect on *y*. If a decision is needed, reject H_0 if P-value ≤ significance level, such as 0.05. Interpret in context.

Example 5

Overall *F* Test for Predictors ◄

Athletes' Weight

Picture the Scenario

For the 64 female college athletes, the ANOVA table for the multiple regression predicting $y = $ weight using $x_1 = $ height, $x_2 = $ percent body fat, and $x_3 = $ age shows:

Source	DF	SS	MS	F-Value	P-Value
Regression	3	12407.9	4136.0	40.48	0.000
Error	60	6131.0	102.2		

Questions to Explore

a. State and interpret the null hypothesis tested in this table.

b. Report the observed test statistic and P-value. Interpret the P-value and make a decision for a 0.05 significance level.

Think It Through

a. Since there are three explanatory variables, the null hypothesis is H_0: $\beta_1 = \beta_2 = \beta_3 = 0$. It states that weight is independent of height, percent body fat, and age.

b. From the ANOVA table, the observed F test statistic value is 40.48, resulting in a P-value of 0.000. If H_0 were true, it would be extremely unusual to get such a large F test statistic. We can reject H_0 at the 0.05 significance level. In summary, we conclude that at least one predictor has an effect on weight.

Insight

The F test tells us that *at least one* explanatory variable has an effect. The following section discusses how to follow up from the F test to investigate which explanatory variables have a statistically significant effect on predicting y.

▶ *Try Exercise 13.26*

Inferences About Individual Regression Parameters

Recall

Section 12.2 showed that the *t* **test** statistic for H_0: $\beta = 0$ in the simple model is

$$t = \frac{\text{sample slope} - 0}{\text{std. error of sample slope}}$$

$$= (b - 0)/se,$$

with $df = n - 2$. ◀

For the simple linear regression model, $\mu_y = \alpha + \beta x$, we have used a t test for the null hypothesis H_0: $\beta = 0$ that x and y are statistically independent. Likewise, a t test applies to any slope parameter in multiple regression. Let's consider a particular parameter, say β_1 in the model $\mu_y = \alpha + \beta_1 x_1 + \beta_2 x_2 + \beta_3 x_3$.

If $\beta_1 = 0$, the mean μ_y of y is identical for all values of x_1, at fixed values for the other explanatory variables. So, H_0: $\beta_1 = 0$ states that *y and x_1 are statistically independent, controlling for the other variables.* This implies that once the other explanatory variables are in the model, it doesn't help to have x_1 in the model. The alternative hypothesis usually is two sided, H_a: $\beta_1 \neq 0$, but one-sided alternative hypotheses are also possible.

The test statistic for H_0: $\beta_1 = 0$ is

$$t = (b_1 - 0)/se,$$

where se is the standard error of the slope estimate b_1 of β_1. Software (such as the *Multiple Linear Regression* app) provides b_1, the se value, the t test statistic, and the P-value. If H_0 is true and the inference assumptions hold, the t test statistic has the t distribution. The degrees of freedom are

$$df = n - \text{number of parameters in the regression equation.}$$

The degrees of freedom are also equal to those used to calculate the residual standard deviation. The simple model $\mu_y = \alpha + \beta x$ has two parameters (α and β), so $df = n - 2$, as Section 12.2 used. The model with two predictors, $\mu_y = \alpha + \beta_1 x_1 + \beta_2 x_2$, has three parameters, so $df = n - 3$. Likewise, with three predictors, $df = n - 4$, and so on.

SUMMARY: Significance Test About a Multiple Regression Parameter (such as β_1)

1. Assumptions:

- Multiple regression model holds for population mean. This implies that there is a linear relationship between the mean of y and each explanatory variable, holding the others constant. The slope of this line is the same, no matter what the values for these other predictors.
- Data gathered using randomization.
- Normal distribution for y with same standard deviation at each combination of predictors.

2. **Hypotheses:**
   H_0: $\beta_1 = 0$.
   H_a: $\beta_1 \neq 0$.

   When H_0 is true, y is independent of x_1, controlling for the other predictors.

3. **Test Statistic:** $t = (b_1 - 0)/se$. Software supplies the slope estimate b_1, its se, and the value of t.

4. **P-value:** Two-tail probability from t distribution of values larger than observed t test statistic (in absolute value). The t distribution has

   $$df = n - \text{number of parameters in regression equation}$$

   (such as $df = n - 3$ when $\mu_y = \alpha + \beta_1 x_1 + \beta_2 x_2$, which has three parameters).

5. **Conclusion:** Interpret P-value in context; compare to significance level if decision needed.

Hypothesis Test for Multiple Regression Parameter β ◄

Example 6

What Helps Predict a Female Athlete's Weight?

Picture the Scenario

The College Athletes data set (Examples 4 and 5) measured several physical characteristics, including total body weight in pounds (TBW), height in inches (HGT), the percent of body fat (%BF), and age. Table 13.9 shows summary statistics for these variables.

Table 13.9 Summary Statistics for Study of Female College Athletes
Variables are TBW = total body weight, HGT = height, %BF = percent body fat, and AGE.

Variable	Mean	StDev	Minimum	Q1	Median	Q3	Maximum
TBW	133.0	17.2	96.0	119.2	131.5	143.8	185.0
HGT	65.6	3.5	56.0	63.0	65.0	68.2	75.0
%BF	18.4	4.1	11.2	15.2	18.5	21.5	27.6
AGE	20.0	1.98	17.0	18.0	20.0	22.0	23.0

Table 13.10 shows results of fitting a multiple regression model for predicting weight using the other variables. The predictive power is good, with $R^2 = 0.669$.

Table 13.10 Multiple Regression Analysis for Predicting Weight
Predictors are HGT = height, %BF = body fat, and age of subject.

Term	Coef	SE Coef	T-Value	P-Value
Constant	−97.7	28.8	−3.39	0.001
HGT	3.428	0.368	9.32	0.000
%BF	1.364	0.313	4.36	0.000
AGE	−0.960	0.648	−1.48	0.144

R-Sq = 66.9%

Questions to Explore

a. Interpret the effect of age on weight in the multiple regression equation.

b. In the population, does age help you to predict weight if you already know height and percent body fat? Show all steps of a significance test and interpret.

Think It Through

a. Let $\hat{y}$ = predicted weight, x_1 = height, x_2 = %body fat, and x_3 = age. Then

$$\hat{y} = -97.7 + 3.43x_1 + 1.36x_2 - 0.96x_3.$$

The slope coefficient of age is -0.96. The sample effect of age on weight is negative, which may seem surprising, but in practical terms it is small: For athletes having fixed values of x_1 and x_2, the predicted weight decreases by only 0.96 pounds for a one-year increase in age, and the ages vary only from 17 to 23.

b. If $\beta_3 = 0$, then x_3 = age has *no* effect on weight in the population of female college athletes, controlling for height and body fat. The hypothesis that age does *not* help us better predict weight, if we already know height and body fat, is H_0: $\beta_3 = 0$. Here are the steps:

1. **Assumptions:** The 64 female athletes were a convenience sample, not a random sample. Any inferences we make are conditional on this sample being representative of the larger population of female athletes. We'll discuss the other assumptions and learn how to check them in Section 13.4.

2. **Hypotheses:** The null hypothesis is H_0: $\beta_3 = 0$. Since there's no prior prediction about whether the effect of age is positive or negative (for fixed values of x_1 and x_2), we use the two-sided H_a: $\beta_3 \neq 0$.

3. **Test Statistic:** Table 13.10 reports a slope estimate of -0.960 for age and a standard error of $se = 0.648$. It also reports the t test statistic of

$$t = (b_3 - 0)/se = -0.960/0.648 = -1.48.$$

   Since the sample size equals $n = 64$ and the regression equation has four parameters, the degrees of freedom are $df = n - 4 = 60$.

4. **P-value:** Table 13.10 reports the P-value = 0.14. This is the two-tailed probability of a t statistic below -1.48 or above 1.48 if H_0 were true.

5. **Conclusion:** The P-value of 0.14 does not give much evidence against the null hypothesis that $\beta_3 = 0$. At common significance levels, such as 0.05, we cannot reject H_0. Age does not contribute significantly in predicting weight if we already know height and percentage of body fat. These conclusions are tentative because the sample of 64 female athletes was selected using a convenience sample rather than a random sample.

Insight

By contrast, Table 13.10 shows that $t = 9.3$ for testing the effect of height (H_0: $\beta_1 = 0$) and $t = 4.4$ for testing the effect of %BF (H_0: $\beta_2 = 0$). Both P-values are 0.000. It *does* help to have each of these variables in the model, given the other two.

▶ *Try Exercise 13.20*

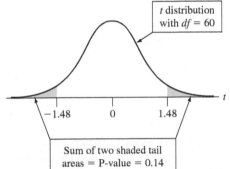

t distribution with *df* = 60

-1.48 0 1.48 t

Sum of two shaded tail areas = P-value = 0.14

As usual, a test merely tells us whether the null hypothesis is plausible. In Example 6 we saw that β_3 may equal 0, but what are its other plausible values? A confidence interval answers this question.

> ### Confidence Interval for a Multiple Regression β Parameter
>
> A 95% confidence interval for a slope parameter β in multiple regression equals
>
> $$\text{Estimated slope} \pm t_{.025}(se).$$
>
> The t-score has $df = n -$ number of parameters in regression equation, as in the t test. The assumptions are also the same as for the t test.

Confidence Interval for β ◄

Example 7

What's Plausible for the Effect of Age on Weight?

Picture the Scenario

For the college athletes data, consider the multiple regression analysis of y = weight and predictors x_1 = height, x_2 = %body fat, and x_3 = age.

Question to Explore

Find and interpret a 95% confidence interval for β_3, the effect of age while controlling for height and percent of body fat.

Recall

From Table 13.10,

Term	Coef	SE Coef
Constant	−97.7	28.8
HGT	3.428	0.368
%BF	1.364	0.313
AGE	−0.960	0.648

◄

Think It Through

From the previous example, $df = 60$. For $df = 60, t_{.025} = 2.00$. From Table 13.10 (shown partly in the margin), the estimate of β_3 is -0.96, with $se = 0.648$. The 95% confidence interval equals

$$b_3 \pm t_{.025}(se) = -0.96 \pm 2.00(0.648),$$

$$\text{or} -0.96 \pm 1.30, \text{roughly } (-2.3, 0.3).$$

For given height and percent body fat, we predict that the mean weight of female athletes changes between a decrease of 2.3 lbs to an increase of 0.3 lbs for a one-year increase in age.

Insight

The confidence interval contains 0. Age may have *no* effect on weight, once we control for height and percent body fat. This is in agreement with not rejecting H_0: $\beta_3 = 0$ in favor of H_a: $\beta_3 \neq 0$ at the $\alpha = 0.05$ level in the significance test.

▶ *Try Exercise 13.21*

Model Building

Unless the sample size is small and the correlation is weak between y and each explanatory variable, the F test usually has a small P-value. If the explanatory variables are chosen sensibly, at least one should have *some* predictive power. When the P-value is small, we can conclude merely that *at least* one explanatory variable affects y. The more narrowly focused t inferences about individual slopes judge *which* effects are nonzero and estimate their sizes.

After finding the highly significant *F* test result of Example 5, we would study the individual effects, as we did in Examples 6 and 7. When we look at an individual *t* inference, suppose we find that the plausible values for a parameter are all relatively near 0. This was the case for the effect of age on weight (controlling for the other variables) as shown by the confidence interval in Example 7. Then, to simplify the model, you can remove that predictor, refitting the model with the other predictors. When we do this for y = weight, x_1 = height, and x_2 = percent body fat, we get

$$\hat{y} = -121.0 + 3.50x_1 + 1.35x_2.$$

For the simpler model, $R^2 = 0.66$. This is nearly as large as the value of $R^2 = 0.67$ with age also in the model. The predictions of weight are essentially as good without age in the model.

When you have several potential explanatory variables for a multiple regression model, how do you decide which ones to include? As just mentioned, the lack of statistical and practical significance is one criterion for deleting a term from the model. Many other possible criteria can also be considered. Most regression software has automatic procedures that successively add or delete predictor variables from models according to criteria such as statistical significance. Three of the most common procedures are **backward elimination, forward selection,** and **stepwise regression.** It is possible that all three procedures result in identical models; however, this is not always the case. In a situation where you must choose between models it is best to look at R^2 values and sensibility of model. These procedures must be used with great caution. There is no guarantee that the final model chosen is sensible. Model selection requires quite a bit of statistical sophistication, and for applications with many potential explanatory variables we recommend that you seek guidance from a statistician.

Recall

The multiple regression equation using all three predictors was

$\hat{y} = -97.7 + 3.43x_1 + 1.36x_2 - 0.96x_3.$

The effects of height and percent body fat are similar in the equation without x_3 = age. ◄

Caution

Procedures for regression model selection must be used with care. Consultation with a trained statistician is recommended. ◄

13.3   Practicing the Basics

13.20 Predicting GPA   For the 59 observations in the Georgia Student Survey data file on the book's website, the result of regressing college GPA on high school GPA and study time follows. (You can replicate these results with the *Multiple Linear Regression* app.)

```
Regression Equation
CGPA = 1.126 + 0.643 HSGPA + 0.0078 Studytime
Coefficients
Term        Coef     SE Coef   T-Value   P-Value
Constant    1.126    0.569     1.98      0.053
HSGPA       0.643    0.146     4.41      0.000
Studytime   0.0078   0.0161    0.48      0.633
Model Summary
      S        R-sq
 0.318824    25.82%
```

a. Explain in nontechnical terms what it means if the population slope coefficient for high school GPA equals 0.

b. Show all steps for testing the hypothesis that this slope equals 0.

13.21 Study time help GPA?   Refer to the previous exercise.

a. Report and interpret the P-value for testing the hypothesis that the population slope coefficient for study time equals 0.

b. Find a 95% confidence interval for the true slope for study time. Explain how the result is in accord with the result of the test in part a.

c. Does the result in part a imply that in the corresponding population, study time has no relationship with college GPA? Explain. (*Hint:* What is the impact of also having HSGPA in the model?)

13.22 Variability in college GPA Refer to the previous two exercises.

TRY

APP

a. Report the residual standard deviation. What does this describe?

b. Interpret the residual standard deviation by predicting where approximately 95% of the Georgia college GPAs fall when high school GPA = 3.80 and study time = 5.0 hours per day, which are the sample means.

13.23 Does leg press help predict body strength? Chapter

APP

12 analyzed strength data for 57 female high school athletes. Upper body strength was summarized by the maximum number of pounds the athlete could bench press (denoted maxBP). This was predicted well by the number of times she could do a 60-pound bench press (denoted BP60). Can we predict maxBP even better if we also know how many times an athlete can perform a 200-pound leg press? The table (which you can obtain via the *Multiple Linear Regression* app) shows results after adding this second predictor (denoted LP200) to the model.

Term	Coef	SE Coef	T-Value	P-Value
Constant	60.60	2.87	21.10	0.000
BP60	1.332	0.188	7.10	0.000
LP200	0.211	0.152	1.39	0.171

Analysis of Variance

Source	DF	Adj SS	Adj MS	F-Value	P-Value
Regression	2	6473.3	3236.65	51.39	0.000
Error	54	3401.3	62.99		
Total	56	9874.6			

a. Does LP200 have a significant effect on maxBP if BP60 is also in the model? Show all steps of a significance test to answer this.

b. Show that the 95% confidence interval for the slope for LP200 equals 0.21 ± 0.30, roughly (−0.1, 0.5). Based on this interval, does LP200 seem to have a strong impact, or a weak impact, on predicting maxBP if BP60 is also in the model?

c. Given that LP200 is in the model, provide evidence from a significance test that shows why it *does* help to add BP60 to the model.

13.24 Leg press uncorrelated with strength? The P-value of 0.17 in part a of the previous exercise suggests that LP200 plausibly had no effect on maxBP once BP60 is in the model. Yet when LP200 is the sole predictor of BP, the correlation coefficient is 0.58 and the significance test for its effect has a P-value of 0.000, suggesting very strong evidence of an effect. Explain why this is not a contradiction.

13.25 Interpret strength variability Refer to the previous two exercises. The sample standard deviation of maxBP was 13.3. The residual standard deviation of maxBP when BP60 and LP200 are predictors in a multiple regression model is 7.9.

a. Explain the difference between the interpretations of these two standard deviations.

b. If the conditional distributions of maxBP are approximately bell shaped, explain why most maximum bench press values fall within about 16 pounds of the regression equation when the predictors BP60 and LP200 are near their sample mean values.

c. At BP60 = 11 and LP200 = 22, which are close to the sample mean values, software reports $\hat{y} = 80$ and a 95% prediction interval of 80 ± 16, or (64, 96). Is this interval an inference about where the population maxBP values fall or where the population *mean* of the maxBP values fall (for subjects having BP60 = 11 and LP200 = 22)? Explain.

d. Refer to part c. Would it be unusual for a female athlete with these predictor values to be able to bench press more than 100 pounds? Why?

13.26 Any predictive power? Refer to the previous three

TRY

APP

exercises.

a. State and interpret the null hypothesis tested with the F statistic in the ANOVA table given in Exercise 13.23.

b. Report the observed F test statistic and its P-value. Interpret the P-value, and make a decision for a 0.05 significance level. Explain in nontechnical terms what the result of the test means.

13.27 Predicting pizza revenue Aunt Erma's Pizza restaurant keeps monthly records of total revenue, amount spent on TV advertising, and amount spent on newspaper advertising.

a. Specify notation and formulate a multiple regression equation for predicting the monthly revenue. Explain how to interpret the parameters in the equation.

b. State the null hypothesis that you would test if you want to analyze whether TV advertising is helpful, for a given amount of newspaper advertising.

c. State the null hypothesis that you would test if you want to analyze whether *at least one* of the sources of advertising has some effect on monthly revenue.

13.28 Regression for mental health A study in Alachua County, Florida, investigated an index of mental health impairment, which had $\bar{y} = 27.3$ and $s = 5.5$. Two explanatory variables were x_1 = life events score (mean = 44.4, $s = 22.6$) and x_2 = SES (socioeconomic status, mean = 56.6, $s = 25.3$). Life events is a composite measure of the number and severity of major life events, such as death in the family, that the subject experienced within the past three years. SES is a composite index based on occupation, income, and education. The table shows data for 6 subjects. The complete data[1] for a random sample of 40 adults in the county is in the Mental Health data file on the book's website. Some regression results are also shown on the next page.

a. Find the 95% confidence interval for β_1.

b. Explain why the interval in part a means that an increase of 100 units in life events corresponds to anywhere from a 4- to 17-unit increase in mean mental impairment, controlling for SES. (This lack of precision reflects the small sample size.)

y = **Mental Impairment,** x_1 = **Life Events Index,** and x_2 = **Socioeconomic Status**

y	x_1	x_2	y	x_1	x_2	y	x_1	x_2
17	46	84	26	50	40	30	44	53
19	39	97	26	48	52	31	35	38

[1]Based on a larger survey reported in a Ph.D. thesis by C. E. Holzer III at University of Florida.

Coefficients

Term	Coef	SE Coef	T-Value	P-Value
Constant	28.23	2.17	12.98	0.000
life	0.1033	0.0325	3.18	0.003
ses	−0.0975	0.0291	−3.35	0.002

Model Summary

S	R sq
4.55644	33.92%

Analysis of Variance

Source	DF	SS	MS	F-Value	P-Value
Regression	2	394.2	197.12	9.49	0.000
Error	37	768.2	20.76		
Total	39	1162.4			

13.29 Mental health again   Refer to the previous exercise.

   a. Report the test statistic and P-value for testing $H_0: \beta_1 = \beta_2 = 0$

   b. State the alternative hypothesis that is supported by the result in part a.

   c. Does the result in part a imply that necessarily *both* life events and SES are needed in the model? Explain.

13.30 More predictors for selling price   The MINITAB results (which you can replicate with the *Multiple Linear Regression* app) are shown for predicting selling price using x_1 = size of home, x_2 = number of bedrooms, and x_3 = age.

Regression Equation

Price = 80489 + 62.65 House Size + 13543
Bedrooms − 418 Age

Coefficients

Term	Coef	SE Coef	T-Value	P-Value
Constant	80489	21810	3.69	0.000
House Size	62.65	4.73	13.24	0.000
Bedrooms	13543	5380	2.52	0.013
Age	−418	236	−1.77	0.078

   a. State the null hypothesis for an *F* test, in the context of these variables.

   b. The *F* statistic equals 74.23, with P-value = 0.000. Interpret.

   c. Explain in nontechnical terms what you learn from the results of the *t* tests reported in the table for the three explanatory variables.

13.31 House prices   Use the *Multiple Linear Regression* app or other software to carry out further analyses with the multiple regression model when y − selling price of home in thousands (HP_in_thousands), x_1 = size of home, and x_2 = number of bedrooms, considered in Section 13.1. The data file House Selling Prices OR is also on the book's website.

   a. Report the *F* statistic and state the hypotheses to which it refers. Report its P-value and interpret. Why is it not surprising to get a small P-value for this test?

   b. Report and interpret the *t* statistic and P-value for testing $H_0: \beta_2 = 0$ against $H_a: \beta_2 > 0$.

   c. Construct a 95% confidence interval for β_2 and interpret. This inference is more informative than the test in part b. Explain why.

13.4 Checking a Regression Model Using Residual Plots

Recall that the three assumptions for inference with a multiple regression model are that (1) the regression equation approximates the true relationship between the predictors and the mean of y (that is, straight line relationships between the mean of y and each explanatory variable, at fixed values of the other explanatory variables), (2) the data were gathered randomly, and (3) y has a normal distribution with the same standard deviation at each combination of predictors. Now, let's see how to check the assumptions about the regression equation and the distribution of y.

For simple linear regression, the 2-dimensional scatterplot provides a simple visual check of whether the straight-line model is appropriate. For multiple regression, a plot of all the variables at once would require many dimensions. So instead, we study how the predicted values $\hat{y}$ from the multiple regression model compare to the observed values y. This is done using the residuals, $y − \hat{y}$.

Checking Shape and Detecting Unusual Observations

Consider first the assumption that the conditional distribution of y is normal at a fixed set of values for the explanatory variables. If this is true, the residuals, which measure the deviations from the mean of y as predicted by the regression

Recall

As discussed in Section 12.4, software such as the *Linear Regression* app can plot a histogram of the residuals or the *standardized residuals*, which are the residuals divided by their standard errors. ◄

equation, should have approximately a bell-shaped histogram. When standardized, nearly all of them should fall between about −3 and +3. A standardized residual below −3 or above +3 indicates a potential regression outlier.

When some observations have large standardized residuals, you should think about whether there is an explanation. Often this merely reflects skew in the conditional distribution of *y*, with a long tail in one direction. Other times the observations differ from the others on a variable that was not included in the model. Once that variable is added, those observations cease to be so unusual. For instance, suppose the data file from the weight study of Examples 4–7 also contained observations for a few males. Then we might have observed a few *y* values considerably above the others and with very large positive standardized residuals. These residuals would probably diminish considerably once the model also included gender as a predictor.

Histogram of Standardized Residuals ◄

Example 8

House Selling Price

Picture the Scenario

For the House Selling Price OR data set (Examples 1–3), Figure 13.4 is a MINITAB histogram of the standardized residuals for the multiple regression model predicting selling price by the house size and the number of bedrooms. (You can also get this plot from the Fitted Values & Residual Analysis tab of the *Multiple Linear Regression* app.)

▲ **Figure 13.4** Histogram of Standardized Residuals for Multiple Regression Model Predicting Selling Price. **Question** Give an example of a shape for this histogram that would indicate that a few observations are highly unusual.

Question to Explore

What does Figure 13.4 tell you? Interpret.

Think It Through

The distribution of the standardized residuals looks roughly bell shaped, and almost all of them fall between −3 and 3. This indicates that the normal assumption for the distribution of the price of the house at given predictor settings is reasonable.

Insight

When *n* is small, don't make the mistake of reading too much into such plots. We're mainly looking for dramatic departures from normality and highly unusual observations that stand apart from the others.

▶ *Try Exercise 13.32*

Two-sided inferences about slope parameters are *robust*. The normality assumption is not as crucial as the assumption that the regression equation approximates the true relationship between the predictors and the mean of *y*. We consider this assumption and the assumption that the standard deviation of *y* is constant next.

Plotting Residuals Against Each Explanatory Variable

Plots of the residuals against each explanatory variable help us check for potential problems with the regression model. We discuss this in terms of x_1, but you should view a plot for each predictor. Ideally, the residuals should fluctuate randomly about the horizontal line at 0, as in Figure 13.5a. There should be no obvious change in trend or change in variation as the values of x_1 increase.

By contrast, a pattern of the residuals as in Figure 13.5b suggests that *y* is actually *nonlinearly* related to x_1. It suggests that *y* tends to be *below* $\hat{y}$ for very small and very large x_1 values (giving negative residuals) and *above* $\hat{y}$ for medium-sized x_1 values (giving positive residuals).

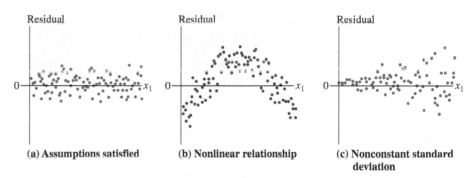

(a) Assumptions satisfied   (b) Nonlinear relationship   (c) Nonconstant standard deviation

▲ **Figure 13.5** Possible Patterns for Residuals, Plotted Against an Explanatory Variable. **Question** Why does the pattern in (b) suggest that the effect of x_1 is not linear?

Another common occurrence is that the variability in the residuals increases as x_1 increases, as seen in Figure 13.5c. A pattern like this indicates that the standard deviation of *y* is not constant—the response variable displays more variability at larger values of x_1 (see the margin figure). Two-sided inferences about slope parameters still perform well. However, ordinary prediction intervals are invalid. The width of such intervals is similar at relatively high and relatively low x_1 values, but in reality, observations on *y* are displaying more variability at high x_1 values than at low x_1 values.

Figure 13.5a suggests that *y* is linearly related to x_1. It also suggests that the variability in *y* stays constant across the entire range of x_1 values and doesn't increase or decrease as x_1 changes. Therefore, Assumption 1 and part of Assumption 3 are met.

Scatterplot of data with nonconstant variance

> **In Practice** Use Caution in Interpreting Residual Patterns
>
> Residual patterns are often not as neat as the ones in Figure 13.5. Be careful not to let a single outlier or ordinary sampling variability overly influence your reading of a pattern from the plot.

Example 9

Plotting Residuals ◀

House Selling Price

Picture the Scenario

For the House Selling Price OR data set, Figure 13.6 is a residual plot for the multiple regression model relating selling price to house size and to number of bedrooms. It plots the standardized residuals against house size.

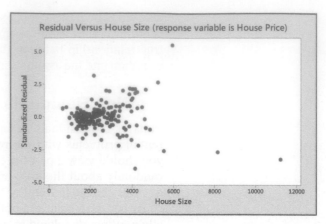

▲ **Figure 13.6** Standardized Residuals of Selling Price Plotted Against House Size, for Model With House Size and Number of Bedrooms as Predictors. **Questions** How does this plot suggest that selling price has more variability at higher house size values, for given number of bedrooms? You don't see number of bedrooms on the plot, so how do its values affect the analysis?

Question to Explore

Does this plot suggest any irregularities with the model?

Think It Through

The residual plot does not show any clear trend, so the assumption about a linear relationship between price and size of a house (for given number of bedrooms) seems reasonable. However, as house size increases, the variability of the standardized residuals seems to increase. This suggests more variability in selling prices when house size is larger, for a given number of bedrooms. We must be cautious, though, because the few points with large negative residuals for the largest houses and the one point with a large positive residual may catch our eyes more than the others. Generally, it's not a good idea to allow a few points to overly influence your judgment about the shape of a residual pattern, but here the variability of the residuals around a size of 4,000 square feet seems to be a bit larger than at, say, 2,000 square feet. A larger data set would provide more evidence about this.

Insight

Nonconstant variability does not invalidate the use of multiple regression. It would, however, make us cautious about using prediction intervals. We would expect predictions about selling price to have smaller prediction errors when house size is small than when house size is large. In addition, further inspecting the observation with the standardized residual larger than 5 may reveal some special characteristics of the corresponding house.

▶ *Try Exercise 13.33*

We have seen several examples illustrating the components of multiple regression analysis. A summary of the entire process of multiple regression follows.

SUMMARY: The Process of Multiple Regression

Steps should include:

1. Identify response and potential explanatory variables.
2. Create a multiple regression model; perform appropriate tests (F and t) to see if and which explanatory variables have a statistically significant effect in predicting y.
3. Plot y versus $\hat{y}$ for resulting models and find R and R^2 values.

4. Check assumptions (residual plot, randomization, histogram of standardized residuals).
5. Choose appropriate model.
6. Create confidence intervals for slope.
7. Make predictions at specified levels of explanatory variables.
8. Create confidence intervals for the mean or prediction intervals for individual observations at specific settings of the explanatory variables.

13.4 Practicing the Basics

13.32 Body weight residuals   Examples 4–7 used multiple regression to predict total body weight of college athletes in terms of height, percent body fat, and age. The following figure (which you can replicate via the *Multiple Linear Regression* app) shows a histogram of the standardized residuals resulting from fitting this model.

a. About which distribution do these give you information— the overall distribution of weight or the conditional distribution of weight at fixed values of the predictors?

b. What does the histogram suggest about the likely shape of this distribution? Why?

13.33 Strength residuals   In Chapter 12, we analyzed strength data for a sample of female high school athletes. The following figure is a residual plot (which you can replicate via the *Multiple Linear Regression* app) for the multiple regression model relating the maximum number of pounds the athlete could bench press (maxBP) to the number of 60-pound bench presses (BP60) and the number of 200-pound leg presses (LP200). It plots the standardized residuals against the values of LP200.

a. You don't see BP60 on the plot, so how do its values affect the analysis?

b. Explain how the plot might suggest less variability at the lower values of LP200.

c. Suppose you remove the three points with standardized residuals around −2. Then is the evidence about variability in part b so clear? What does this suggest about cautions in looking at residual plots?

13.34 More residuals for strength   Refer to the previous exercise. The following figure is a residual plot for the model relating maximum bench press to LP200 and BP60. It plots the standardized residuals against the values of BP60. Does this plot suggest any irregularities with the model? Explain.

13.35 Nonlinear effects of age   Suppose you fit a straight-line regression model to $y =$ amount of time sleeping per day and $x =$ age of subject. Values of y in the sample tend to be quite large for young children and for elderly people, and they tend to be lower for other people. Sketch what you would expect to observe for (a) the scatterplot of x and y and (b) a plot of the residuals against the values of age.

13.36 Driving accidents   Suppose you fit a straight-line regression model to $x =$ age of subjects and $y =$ driving accident rate. Sketch what you would expect to observe for (a) the scatterplot of x and y and (b) a plot of the residuals against the values of age.

13.37 Why inspect residuals?   When we use multiple regression, what's the purpose of doing a residual analysis? Why can't we just construct a single plot of the data for all the variables at once to tell whether the model is reasonable?

13.38 College athletes The College Athletes data set on the book's website (and available in the *Multiple Linear Regression* app) comes from a study of University of Georgia female athletes. Using the column names from the data set, the response variable 1RM = maximum bench press has explanatory variables LBM = lean body mass (which is weight times 1 minus the proportion of body fat) and REPS70 = number of repetitions before fatigue with a 70-pound bench press. Let's look at all the steps of a regression analysis for these data. (Note that computer output is shown at the end of the exercise.)

Scatterplot matrix for Exercise 13.38, part a.

Residual plot for Exercise 13.38, part g.

Residual plot for Exercise 13.38, part h.

a. The first figure shows a scatterplot matrix. Which two plots in the figure describe the relationship with 1RM as a response variable? Describe those relationships.

b. Results of a multiple regression analysis are shown. Write down the prediction equation and interpret the coefficient of REPS70.

c. Report R^2 and interpret its value in the context of these variables.

d. Based on the value of R^2, report and interpret the multiple correlation coefficient.

e. Interpret results of the F test that 1RM is independent of these two predictors. Show how to obtain the F statistic from the mean squares in the ANOVA table.

f. Once REPS70 is in the model, does it help to have LBM as a second predictor? Answer by showing all steps of a significance test for a regression parameter.

g. Examine the histogram shown of the residuals for the multiple regression model. What does this describe, and what does it suggest?

h. Examine the plot shown of the residuals plotted against values of REPS70. What does this describe, and what does it suggest?

i. From the plot in part h, can you identify a subject whose 1RM value was considerably lower than expected based on the predictor values? Identify by indicating the approximate values of REPS70 and the standardized residual for that subject.

```
Regression Equation
1RM = 55.01 + 0.1668 LBM + 1.658 REPS70
Coefficients
Term         Coef     SE Coef   T-Value   P-Value
Constant     55.01    7.74      7.11      0.000
LBM          0.1668   0.0752    2.22      0.030
REPS70       1.658    0.109     15.21     0.000
Model Summary
      S        R-sq
7.11957      83.17%

Analysis of Variance
Source        DF      SS       MS     F-Value  P-Value
Regression     2    15283    7641.5   150.75   0.000
Error         61     3092     50.7
Total         63    18375
```

13.39 House prices Use the *Multiple Linear Regression* app or other software with the House Selling Prices OR data file on the book's website to do residual analyses with the multiple regression model for y = house selling price (in thousands), x_1 = lot size, and x_2 = number of bathrooms.

a. Find a histogram of the standardized residuals. What assumption does this check? What do you conclude from the plot?

b. Plot the standardized residuals against the lot size. What does this check? What do you conclude from the plot?

13.40 Selling prices level off In the previous exercise, suppose house selling price tends to increase with a straight-line trend for small to medium size lots, but then levels off as lot size gets large, for a fixed value of number of bathrooms. Sketch the pattern you'd expect to get if you plotted the residuals against lot size. What assumption of the multiple regression model is violated?

13.5 Regression and Categorical Predictors

So far, we've studied regression models for quantitative variables. Next, we'll learn how to include a *categorical explanatory* variable. The final section shows how to perform regression for a *categorical response* variable.

Indicator Variables

Regression models specify categories of a categorical explanatory variable using artificial variables called **indicator variables.** The indicator variable for a particular category is binary. It equals 1 if the observation falls into that category, and it equals 0 otherwise.

In the house selling prices (Oregon) data set, the condition of the house is a categorical variable. It was measured with categories (good, not good). The indicator variable x for condition is

$$x = 1 \text{ if house in good condition}$$
$$x = 0 \text{ otherwise.}$$

This indicator variable indicates whether a home is in good condition. Let's see how an indicator variable works in a regression equation. To start, suppose condition is the only predictor of selling price. The simple regression model is then $\mu_y = \alpha + \beta x$, with x as just defined. Substituting the possible values 1 and 0 for x,

$$\mu_y = \alpha + \beta(1) = \alpha + \beta, \text{ if a house is in good condition } (x = 1)$$
$$\mu_y = \alpha + \beta(0) = \alpha, \qquad \text{ if a house is not in good condition } (x = 0).$$

The difference between the mean selling price for houses in good condition and houses in not good condition is

$$(\mu_y \text{ when } x = 1) - (\mu_y \text{ when } x = 0) = (\alpha + \beta) - \alpha = \beta.$$

The coefficient β of the indicator variable x is the difference between the mean selling prices for houses in good condition and for houses in not good condition.

Example 10

Indicator Variables ◀

Including House Condition in Multiple Regression for Selling Price

Picture the Scenario

Let's now fit a multiple regression model for $y =$ selling price of house using $x_1 =$ house size and $x_2 =$ condition of the house. Table 13.11 shows MINITAB output when fitting the model $\mu_y = \alpha + \beta_1 x_1 + \beta_2 x_2$.

Table 13.11 Regression Analysis of $y =$ Selling Price Using $x_1 =$ House Size and $x_2 =$ Indicator Variable for Condition (Good, Not Good)

```
The regression equation is

Price = 96271 + 66.5 House Size + 12927 Condition

Term                Coef        SE Coef      T-Value      P-Value

Constant           96271        13465          7.15        0.000

House Size        66.463         4.682         14.20        0.000

Condition          12927        17197          0.75        0.453

S = 81787.4 R-Sq = 50.6%
```

Questions to Explore

a. Find and plot the lines showing how the predicted selling price varies as a function of house size for houses in good condition and for houses in not good condition.

b. Interpret the coefficient of the indicator variable for condition.

Think It Through

a. Table 13.11 reports the prediction equation,

$$\hat{y} = 96{,}271 + 66.5x_1 + 12{,}927x_2.$$

For houses not in good condition, $x_2 = 0$. The prediction equation for y = selling price using x_1 = house size then simplifies to

$$\hat{y} = 96{,}271 + 66.5x_1 + 12{,}927(0) = 96{,}271 + 66.5x_1.$$

For houses in good condition, $x_2 = 1$. The prediction equation then simplifies to

$$\hat{y} = 96{,}271 + 66.5x_1 + 12{,}927(1) = 109{,}198 + 66.5x_1.$$

Both lines have the same slope, 66.5. For houses in either condition, the predicted selling price increases by \$66.5 for each square-foot increase in house size. Figure 13.7 plots the two prediction equations. The quantitative explanatory variable, house size, is on the x-axis. The figure portrays a separate line for each category of condition (good, not good).

▲ **Figure 13.7** Plot of Equation Relating $\hat{y}$ = Predicted Selling Price to x_1 = House Size, According to x_2 = Condition (1 = Good, 0 = Not Good). Question Why are the lines parallel?

b. At a fixed value of x_1 = house size, the difference between the predicted selling prices for houses in good ($x_2 = 1$) versus not good ($x_2 = 0$) condition is

$$(109{,}198 + 66.5x_1) - (96{,}271 + 66.5x_1) = 12{,}927.$$

This is precisely the coefficient of the indicator variable x_2 shown in Table 13.11. For any fixed value of house size, we predict that the selling price is \$12,927 higher for houses that are in good condition compared to those that are in not good condition.

Insight

Since the two lines have the same slope, they are parallel. The line for houses in good condition is above the other line because its y-intercept is larger. This means that for any fixed value of house size, the predicted selling price is higher for houses in good condition. The P-value of 0.453 for the test

H_0: $\beta_2 = 0$ for the coefficient of the indicator variable suggests that this difference is not statistically significant and that the mean house price, for a given house size, may be the same between a house in good condition and one in not good condition.

▶ **Try Exercise 13.41**

A categorical variable having more than two categories uses an additional indicator variable for each category. For instance, assume that we measured condition with the three categories "good," "fair," and "poor" instead of just using the two categories "good" and "not good." Then, instead of just including one indicator variable x_2 in the multiple regression model as in Example 10, we need to include (in addition to x_1 for house size) two indicator variables x_2 and x_3, such that:

$$x_2 = 1 \text{ for houses in good condition, and } x_2 = 0 \text{ otherwise.}$$
$$x_3 = 1 \text{ for houses in fair condition, and } x_3 = 0 \text{ otherwise.}$$

If $x_2 - x_3 = 0$, the house is neither in good condition nor in fair condition, so it must be in poor condition. Therefore, we don't need a third indicator variable for coding houses in poor condition because this is already determined by the settings of the first two indicator variables. That is, we can tell whether a house is in poor condition merely from seeing the values of x_2 and x_3. Generally, *a categorical explanatory variable in a regression model uses one fewer indicator variable than the number of categories.* For instance, with the two categories (good, not good) condition, we needed only a single indicator variable, whereas for the three categories (good, fair, poor) condition, we needed two indicator variables.

Why can't we specify the three categories merely by setting up a variable x that equals 1 for homes in good condition, 0 for homes in fair condition, and say, -1 for poor condition? Because this would treat condition as *quantitative* rather than *categorical*. It would treat condition as if different categories corresponded to different *amounts* of the variable. But the variable measures *which* condition, not *how much* condition. Treating it as quantitative is inappropriate in many cases.

Interactions Between Explanatory Variables

In Example 10, the regression equation simplified to two straight lines:

$$\hat{y} = 109{,}198 + 66.5x_1 \text{ for houses in good condition,}$$
$$\hat{y} = 96{,}271 + 66.5x_1 \text{ for houses in not good condition.}$$

Both equations have the same slope. The model forces the effect of $x_1 =$ house size on selling price to be the same for both conditions. For houses in either condition, the predicted selling price increases by \$66.5 for every additional square foot in size.

More generally, in a multiple regression model, *the slope of the relationship between the population mean of y and each explanatory variable is identical for all values of the other explanatory variables.* Such models are sometimes too simple. The effect of an explanatory variable may change considerably as the value of another explanatory variable in the model changes. The multiple regression models we've considered so far assume this does not happen. When it does happen, there is **interaction.**

Interaction

For two explanatory variables, **interaction** exists when the slope of the linear relationship between μ_y and one explanatory variable changes as the other explanatory variable changes.

Suppose the *actual* population relationship between x_1 = house size and the mean selling price is

$$\mu_y = 100{,}000 + 50x_1 \text{ for houses in good condition,}$$

and

$$\mu_y = 80{,}000 + 35x_1 \text{ for houses in not good condition.}$$

The slope of the regression line between the mean selling price μ_y and the size of the house x^1 changes (from 50 to 35) when x^2 changes from 1 to 0, that is, from considering houses in good condition to houses in not good condition. There is then interaction between house size and condition in their effects on selling price. The mean price increases by \$50 for every one square foot increase in size for houses in good condition but only by \$35 for houses in not good condition. Figure 13.8 illustrates the different slopes.

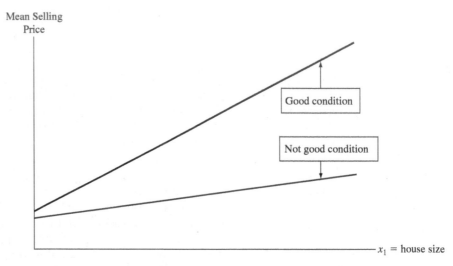

▲ **Figure 13.8** An Example of Interaction. There's a larger slope between selling price and house size for houses in good condition than in not good condition.

How can you allow for interaction when you do a regression analysis? With two explanatory variables, one quantitative and one categorical (as in Example 10), you can fit a separate line with a different slope for each category of the categorical variable.

Example 11

Comparing Winning High Jumps for Men and Women

Picture the Scenario

Men have competed in the high jump in the Olympics since 1896 and women since 1928. Figure 13.9 shows how the winning high jump in the Olympics has changed over time for men and women. The High Jump data file on the book's website contains the winning heights for each year up to 2016. A multiple regression analysis of y = winning height (in meters) as a function of x_1 = number of years since 1928 (when women first participated in the high jump) and x_2 = gender (1 = men, 0 = women) gives $\hat{y} = 1.63 + 0.0054x_1 + 0.35x_2$.

Questions to Explore

a. Interpret the coefficient of year and the coefficient of gender in the equation.

b. To allow interaction, we can fit equations separately to the data for men and the data for women. We then get $\hat{y} = 1.98 + 0.0053x_1$ for men and $\hat{y} = 1.62 + 0.0057x_1$ for women. Describe the interaction by comparing slopes.

c. Describe the interaction allowed in part b by comparing predicted winning high jumps for men and women in 1928 and in 2016.

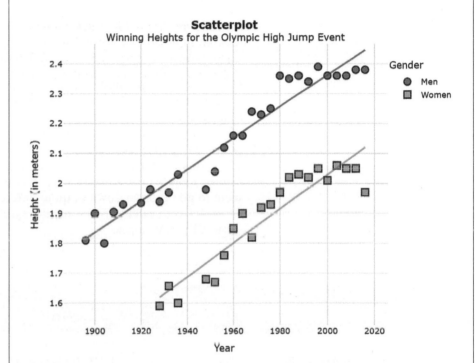

Recall

These data were first analyzed in Example 12 in Chapter 3. ◄

▲ **Figure 13.9** Scatterplot for the Winning High Jumps (in Meters) in the Olympic Games from 1896-2016. Screenshot from the *Multivariate Relationships* app.

Think It Through

a. For the prediction equation $\hat{y} = 1.63 + 0.0054x_1 + 0.35x_2$, the coefficient of year is 0.0054. For each gender, the predicted winning height increases by 0.0054 meters per year. This seems small, but over fifty years, it projects to an increase of 0.0054(50) = 0.27 meters, about 11 inches. The model does not allow interaction because it assumes that the slope of 0.0054 is the same for each gender. The coefficient of gender is 0.35. In any given year, the predicted winning height for men is 0.35 meters higher than for women. Because this model does not allow for an interaction, the predicted height difference between men and women is the same in each year.

b. The slope of 0.0057 for women is higher than the slope of 0.0053 for men. So the predicted winning height increases a bit more for women than for men over this time period.

c. In 1928, $x_1 = 0$, and the predicted winning height was $\hat{y} = 1.98 + 0.0053(0) = 1.98$ for men and $\hat{y} = 1.62 + 0.0057(0) = 1.62$ for women, a difference of 0.36 meters. In 2016, $x_1 = 2016 - 1928 = 88$ and the predicted winning height was $1.98 + 0.0053(88) = 2.45$ for men and $1.62 + 0.0057(88) = 2.12$ for women, a difference of 0.33 meters. The predicted difference between the winning height of men and women decreased just a little bit between 1928 and 2016.

Insight

When we allow interaction, the estimated slope is just a bit higher for women than for men. This is what caused the difference in predicted winning heights to be less in 2016 than in 1928. However, the slopes are almost identical, as shown by the fitted regression lines for each gender superimposed in Figure 13.9. The observed degree of interaction is very weak and the regression model with a common slope (of 0.0054) fits equally well.

▶ **Try Exercises 13.47 and 13.48**

How do we know whether the interaction shown by the sample is sufficiently large to indicate that there is interaction in the population? There is a significance test for checking this, but it is beyond the scope of this book. In practice, it's usually adequate to investigate interaction informally by using graphics. For example, suppose there are two predictors, one quantitative and one categorical. Then you can plot y against the quantitative predictor, identifying the data points by the category of the categorical variable, as we did in Example 11. Do the points seem to go up or go down at quite different rates, taking into account sampling error? If so, it's safer to fit a separate regression line for each category, which then allows different slopes.

13.5 Practicing the Basics

13.41 U.S. and foreign used cars Refer to the used car data file from Exercise 13.11, which is preloaded in the *Multivariate Relationships* app. The prediction equation relating y = selling price of used car (in $) as a function of x_1 = age of car and x_2 = type of car (1 = US, 0 = Foreign) is $\hat{y} = 20{,}493 - 1{,}185x_1 - 2{,}379x_2$, which you can verify with the *Multiple Linear Regression* app.

   a. Using this equation, find the prediction equation relating selling price and age, separately for U.S. and foreign cars. (In the app, you can do this by selecting Type(Grouping) as the grouping variable.)

   b. Predict by how much the price changes for a one year increase in the age of the car. Does this apply for both types of cars? Explain.

   c. Find the predicted price of a (i) U.S. and (ii) foreign car that is eight years old. Show how the difference between them relates to a parameter estimate for the model.

13.42 Mountain bike prices The Mountain Bike data file on the book's website shows selling prices for mountains bikes. When y = mountain bike price ($) is regressed on x_1 = weight of bike (lbs) and x_2 = the type of suspension (0 = full, 1 = front end), $\hat{y} = 2{,}741.62 - 53.752x_1 - 643.595x_2$.

   a. Interpret the estimated effect of the weight of the bike.

   b. Interpret the estimated effect of the type of suspension on the mountain bike.

13.43 Predict using house size and condition For the House Selling Prices OR data set available in the *Multiple Linear Regression* app, when we regress y = selling price (in thousands) on x_1 = house size and x_2 = condition (1 = Good, 0 = Not Good), we get the results shown.

Term	Coef	SE Coef	T-Value	P-Value
Constant	96.27	13.46	7.15	0.000
House Size	0.066463	0.004682	14.20	0.000
Condition	12.93	17.20	0.75	0.453

S = 81.7874 R-Sq = 50.6%

   a. Report the regression equation. Find and interpret the separate lines relating predicted selling price to house size for good condition homes and for homes in not good condition.

   b. Sketch how selling price varies as a function of house size for homes in good condition and for homes in not good condition.

   c. Estimate the difference between the mean selling price of homes in good and in not good condition, controlling for house size.

13.44 Quality and productivity The table shows data from 27 automotive plants on y = number of assembly defects per 100 cars and x = time (in hours) to assemble each vehicle. The data are in the Quality and Productivity file on the book's website.

Number of Defects in Assembling 100 Cars and Time to Assemble Each Vehicle

Plant	Defects	Time	Plant	Defects	Time	Plant	Defects	Time
1	39	27	10	89	17	19	69	54
2	38	23	11	48	20	20	79	18
3	42	15	12	38	26	21	29	31
4	50	17	13	68	21	22	84	28
5	55	12	14	67	26	23	87	44
6	56	16	15	69	30	24	98	23
7	57	18	16	69	32	25	100	25
8	56	26	17	70	31	26	140	21
9	61	20	18	68	37	27	170	28

Source: Data from S. Chatterjee, M. Handcock, and J. Simonoff, *A Casebook for a First Course in Statistics and Data Analysis* (Wiley, 1995); based on graph in *The Machine That Changed the World*, by J. Womack, D. Jones, and D. Roos (Macmillan, 1990).

a. The prediction equation is $\hat{y} = 61.3 + 0.35x$. Find the predicted number of defects for a car having assembly time (i) 12 hours (the minimum) and (ii) 54 hours (the maximum).

b. The first 11 plants were Japanese facilities and the rest were not. Let x_1 = time to assemble vehicle and x_2 = whether facility is Japanese $(1 = \text{yes}, 0 = \text{no})$. The fit of the multiple regression model is $\hat{y} = 105.0 - 0.78x_1 - 36.0x_2$. Interpret the coefficients that estimate the effect of x_1 and the effect of x_2.

c. Explain why part a and part b indicate that Simpson's paradox has occurred.

d. Explain *how* Simpson's paradox occurred. To do this, construct a scatterplot between y and x_1 in which points are identified by whether the facility is Japanese. Note that the Japanese facilities tended to have low values for both x_1 and x_2.

13.45 Predicting hamburger sales   A chain restaurant that specializes in selling hamburgers wants to analyze how y = sales for a customer (the total amount spent by a customer on food and drinks, in dollars) depends on the location of the restaurant, which is classified as inner city, suburbia, or at an interstate exit.

a. Construct indicator variables x_1 for inner city and x_2 for suburbia so you can include location in a regression equation for predicting the sales.

b. For part a, suppose $\hat{y} = 5.8 - 0.7x_1 + 1.2x_2$. Find the difference between the estimated mean sales in suburbia and at interstate exits.

13.46 Houses, size, and garage   Use the House Selling Prices OR data file on the book's website and available in the *Multiple Linear Regression* app to regress selling price in thousands on house size and whether the house has a garage.

a. Report the prediction equation. Find and interpret the equations predicting selling price using house size for homes with and without a garage.

b. How do you interpret the coefficient of the indicator variable for whether the home has a garage?

13.47 House size and garage interact?   Refer to the previous exercise.

a. Explain what the no interaction assumption means for this model.

b. Sketch a hypothetical scatter diagram, showing points identified by garage or no garage, suggesting that there is actually a substantial degree of interaction.

13.48 Equal slopes for car prices?   Refer to Exercise 13.41, with $\hat{y}$ = predicted selling price of used car and x_1 = age of car. When equations are fitted *separately* for U.S. and foreign cars, we get $\hat{y} = 23{,}417 - 1{,}715x_1$ for U.S. cars and $\hat{y} = 15{,}536 - 557x_1$ for foreign cars.

a. In allowing the lines to have different slopes, we allow for an _____ between age and type of car in their effects on the price. (Fill in the correct word.)

b. Predict by how much the price changes for a one-year increase in the age of the car. Do you need to do this separately for each type of car? Explain.

c. Based on the separate prediction equations, find the predicted price of a (i) U.S. and (ii) foreign car that is eight years old.

13.49 Comparing sales   You own a gift shop that has a campus location and a shopping mall location. You want to compare the regressions of y = daily total sales on x = number of people who enter the shop, for total sales listed by day at the campus location and at the mall location. Explain how you can do this using regression modeling

a. With a single model, having an indicator variable for location, that assumes the slopes are the same for each location.

b. With separate models for each location, permitting the slopes to be different.

13.6 Modeling a Categorical Response: Logistic Regression

The regression models studied so far are designed for a quantitative response variable y. When y is categorical, a different regression model applies, called **logistic regression.** Logistic regression can model the probability of:

■ A voter's choice in an election (Democrat or Republican), with explanatory variables of annual income, political ideology, religious affiliation, and race.

- Whether a credit card holder pays his or her bill on time (yes or no), with explanatory variables of family income and the number of months in the past year that the customer paid the bill on time.

We'll study logistic regression in this section for the special case of a **binary** response variable y.

The Logistic Regression Model

Recall

From Section 5.1 for a (binary) random variable y with two possible outcomes 0 (for failure) and 1 (for success), occurring with probability $1 - p$ and p, the mean is given by $\mu_y = 0(1 - p) + 1(p) = p$. So p, the probability of success, is the mean of the binary random variable. ◄

Just like linear regression models the mean of a quantitative response variable, logistic regression models the mean of a binary response variable, whose two possible outcomes we generically label *success* and *failure*. When we assign the numerical values 1 (for success) and 0 (for failure), the mean μ_y of the binary response variable is equal to p, the probability of observing a success. The margin note recalls this fact. The logistic regression model then specifies how the probability p depends on explanatory variables.

For a single explanatory variable, x, Figure 13.10 shows the straight-line regression model

$$p = \alpha + \beta x.$$

This model has the disadvantage that p can be larger than 1 (or smaller than 0) for sufficiently large (small) x values. However, the probability p must fall between 0 and 1. Although the straight-line model may be valid over a restricted range of x-values, it is usually inadequate when there are multiple explanatory variables.

Figure 13.10 also shows a more realistic model. It has a curved, S-shape instead of a straight-line trend. The regression equation that describes this S-shaped curve is known as the **logistic regression equation.**

▲ **Figure 13.10** Two Possible Regression Models for a Success Probability p of a Binary Response Variable. A straight line is usually less appropriate than an S-shaped curve. **Question** Why is the straight-line regression model for a binary response variable often inadequate?

Logistic Regression

A regression equation for an S-shaped curve for the probability of success p is

$$p = \frac{e^{\alpha + \beta x}}{1 + e^{\alpha + \beta x}}.$$

This equation for p is called the **logistic regression** equation. Logistic regression is used when the response variable has only two possible outcomes (it's binary.)

Here, e raised to a power represents the *exponential function* evaluated at that number. The model has two parameters, α and β. Since the numerator of the formula for p is smaller than the denominator, the model forces p to fall between 0 and 1. With a regression model having this S-shape, the probability p falls between 0 and 1 for all possible x values.

Like the slope of a straight line, the parameter β in this model refers to whether the probability of success increases or decreases as x increases. When $\beta > 0$, the probability p increases as x increases. When $\beta < 0$, the probability p decreases as

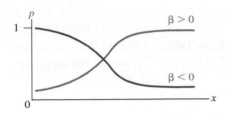

x increases. See the margin figure. If $\beta = 0$, p does not change as x changes, so the curve flattens to a horizontal straight line. The steepness of the curve increases as the absolute value of β increases. However, unlike in the straight-line model, β is *not* a slope and therefore cannot be interpreted as the change in the probability of success per one-unit change in x. For this S-shaped curve, the rate at which the curve climbs or descends *changes* over the range of x values.

Software such as the *Logistic Regression* app can estimate the parameters α and β in the logistic regression model and find estimated probabilities $\hat{p}$ based on the model fit.

Example 12

Logistic Regression Model ◄

Travel Credit Cards

Picture the Scenario

An Italian study with 100 randomly selected Italian adults considered factors associated with whether a person has at least one travel credit card. Table 13.12 shows results for the first 15 people on this response variable and on the person's annual income, in thousands of euros.[2] The complete data set is in the Credit Card and Income data file on the book's website. Let x = annual income and let y = whether the person has a travel credit card (1 = yes, 0 = no).

Table 13.12 Annual Income (in thousands of euros) and Whether Person Has a Travel Credit Card

The response y equals 1 if a person has a travel credit card and equals 0 otherwise. The complete data set is on the book's website.

Adult	Income	y	Adult	Income	y	Adult	Income	y
1	12	0	6	14	1	11	15	0
2	13	0	7	14	0	12	15	1
3	14	1	8	14	0	13	15	0
4	14	0	9	14	0	14	15	0
5	14	0	10	14	0	15	15	0

Source: Data from R. Piccarreta, Bocconi University, Milan (personal communication).

Questions to Explore

Table 13.13 shows what software provides for conducting a logistic regression analysis.

Table 13.13 Results of Logistic Regression for Italian Credit Card Data

Term	Coef	SE Coef	Z-Value	P-Value
Constant	−3.5180	0.71034	−4.95	0.000
income	0.1054	0.02616	4.03	0.000

a. State the prediction equation for the probability of owning a travel credit card and explain whether annual income has a positive or a negative effect.

b. Find the estimated probability of having a travel credit card at the lowest and highest annual income levels in the sample, which were $x = 12$ and $x = 65$ (in thousands of euros).

---

[2]The data were originally recorded in Italian lira but have been changed to euros and adjusted for inflation.

Think It Through

a. Substituting the α and β estimates from Table 13.13 into the logistic regression model formula, $p = e^{\alpha+\beta x}/(1 + e^{\alpha+\beta x})$, we get the equation for the estimated probability $\hat{p}$ of having a travel credit card,

$$\hat{p} = \frac{e^{-3.52+0.105x}}{1 + e^{-3.52+0.105x}}.$$

Because the estimate 0.105 of β (the coefficient of x) is positive, this sample suggests that annual income has a positive effect: The estimated probability of having a travel credit card is higher at higher levels of annual income. The margin figure shows a plot of the estimated probability.

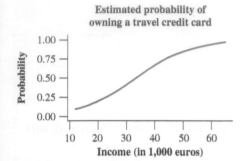

Estimated probability of owning a travel credit card

b. For subjects with income $x = 12$ thousand euros, the estimated probability of having a travel credit card equals

$$\hat{p} = \frac{e^{-3.52+0.105(12)}}{1 + e^{-3.52+0.105(12)}} = \frac{e^{-2.26}}{1 + e^{-2.26}} = \frac{0.104}{1.104} = 0.09.$$

For $x = 65$, the highest income level in this sample, you can check that the estimated probability equals 0.97.

Insight

There is a strong effect. The estimated probability of having a travel credit card changes from 0.09 to 0.97 (i.e., from about 10% to almost 100%) as annual income changes over the observed range.

Using software, we could also fit the straight-line regression model. Its prediction equation is $\hat{p} = -0.159 + 0.0188x$. However, its $\hat{p}$ predictions are quite different at the low end and at the high end of the annual income scale. At $x = 65$, for instance, it provides the prediction $\hat{p} = 1.06$. This is an invalid prediction because we know that a probability must fall between 0 and 1.

▶ **Try Exercise 13.51**

Ways to Interpret the Logistic Regression Model

The sign of β in the logistic regression model tells us whether the probability p increases or decreases as x increases. Besides looking at the graph for the estimated probability, how else can we interpret the model parameters and their estimates? Here, we'll describe four ways:

1. To describe the effect of x, you can compare estimates of p at two values of x. One possibility is to compare $\hat{p}$ found at the minimum and maximum values of x, as we did in Example 12. There we saw that the estimated probability changed from 0.09 to 0.97, a considerable change. An alternative is instead to use values of x to evaluate this probability that are not as affected by outliers, such as the first and third quartiles.

2. It's good to know the value of x at which $p = 0.50$, that is, that value of x for which each outcome is equally likely. This depends on the logistic regression parameters α and β. It can be shown that for $x = -\alpha/\beta$ the probability of success $p = 0.50$. (Exercise 13.93).

3. The simplest way to use the logistic regression parameter β to interpret the *steepness* of the curve uses a straight-line approximation. Because the logistic regression formula is a curve rather than a straight line, β itself is no longer the ordinary slope. At the x-value where $p = 0.50$, the line drawn tangent to the logistic regression curve has slope $\beta/4$. See Figure 13.11. The value $\beta/4$ represents the approximate change in the probability p for a one-unit increase in x, when x is close to the value at which $p = 0.50$. Tangent lines at other points have weaker slopes (Exercise 13.92), close to 0 when p is near 0 or 1.

▲ **Figure 13.11** When the Probability $p = 0.50$, for a One-Unit Change in x, p Changes by About $\beta/4$. Here, β is the coefficient of x from the logistic regression model.

4. Using algebra, an equivalent way of writing the logistic regression model is as

$$\text{odds of success} = p/(1 - p) = e^{\alpha + \beta x}.$$

The term on the left-hand side, the odds of success $p/(1 - p)$, was discussed in Section 11.3 of Chapter 11. The model implies that these odds of success increase by a factor of e^{β} for every one-unit increase in x.

Example 13

Interpreting a Logistic Regression Model ◀

Effect of Income on Credit Card Use

Picture the Scenario

For the Italian travel credit card study, Example 12 found that the equation

$$\hat{p} = \frac{e^{-3.52 + 0.105x}}{1 + e^{-3.52 + 0.105x}}$$

estimates the probability p of having such a credit card as a function of annual income x.

Questions to Explore

Interpret this equation by **(a)** finding the income value at which the estimated probability of having a credit card equals 0.50, **(b)** finding the approximate rate of change in the probability at that income value, and **(c)** by interpreting the effect of income on the odds of owning a travel card.

Think It Through

a. The estimate of α is -3.52 and the estimate of β is 0.105. Substituting the estimates into the expression $-\alpha/\beta$ for the value of x at $p = 0.50$, we get $x = (3.52)/(0.105) = 33.5$. The estimated probability of having a travel credit card equals 0.50 when annual income equals €33,500.

b. A line drawn tangent to the logistic regression curve at the point where $p = 0.50$ has slope equal to $\beta/4$. The estimate of this slope is $0.105/4 = 0.026$. For each increase of €1,000 in annual income near the income value of €33,500, the estimated probability of having a travel credit card increases by approximately 0.026, or 2.6 percentage points.

c. First, let's find the estimated odds of having a travel credit card when the annual income is €40,000. Using the equation in point 4 for the odds of success, because $e^{\;3.52 + 0.105(40)} = 1.97$, or roughly 2, the estimated odds are 2, or 2:1. For every two persons with that income owning a card, there is one who doesn't. How much are the odds increasing when income increases by €1,000? The estimated odds at an income of 41,000 are 2.19, which you can confirm when plugging in $x = 41$ into the equation for the odds in part 4. This is an increase of 11% from the odds of 1.97. You will get the same result (i.e., an increase of 11% in the odds when income increases by €1,000), regardless at which income you start. For each increase of €1,000, the *odds* of having a travel card increase by a factor of 1.11, i.e., by 11%.

Insight

It is often easier to explain the logistic regression model in terms of the approximate effects on the probability of success (parts a and b) instead the odds of success (part c). A graph such as the one shown in the margin next to Example 12 that plots the estimated probabilities over the range of the observed x values is very helpful. From it, we see that the estimated probability of having a travel card is 50% when income is €33,500, and how this probability changes from the smallest value of 9% at the lowest income to 97% at the highest income.

▶ *Try Exercise 13.55*

Table 13.13 Results of Logistic Regression

Term	Coef	SE	Z-Value	P-Value
Constant	-3.518	0.710	-4.95	0.000
income	0.105	0.0262	4.03	0.000

Inference for Logistic Regression

Software also reports a z test statistic for the hypothesis H_0: $\beta = 0$. When $\beta = 0$, the probability of possessing a travel credit card is the same at all income levels. Then, the logistic curve in Figure 13.11 is a straight, horizontal line, indicating a constant probability of success p. The test statistic equals the ratio of the estimate b of β divided by its standard error. Sections 8.2 and 9.2 showed that inference about proportions uses z test statistics rather than t test statistics. From Table 13.13 (shown again in the margin), the z test statistic equals

$$z = (b - 0)/se = (0.105 - 0)/0.0262 = 4.0.$$

This has a P-value of 0.000 for H_a: $\beta \neq 0$. Since the sample slope is positive, for the population of adult Italians, there is strong evidence of a positive relationship between annual income and having a travel credit card.

The result of this test is no surprise. We would expect people with higher annual incomes to be more likely to have travel credit cards. Some software, such as the *Logistic Regression* app can construct a confidence interval for the probability p at various x levels. A 95% confidence interval for the probability of having a credit card equals (0.04, 0.20) at the lowest sample income level of €12,000 and (0.78, 0.996) at the highest sample income level of €65,000.

Multiple Logistic Regression

Just as ordinary regression extends to handle several explanatory variables, so does logistic regression. Also, logistic regression can include categorical explanatory variables using indicator variables.

Example 14

Multiple Logistic Regression ◄

Estimating Proportion of Students Who Have Used Marijuana

Picture the Scenario

Table 13.14 is a three-variable contingency table from a Wright State University survey asking senior high school students near Dayton, Ohio, whether they had ever used alcohol, cigarettes, or marijuana. We'll treat marijuana use as the response variable and cigarette use and alcohol use as explanatory variables.

Table 13.14 Alcohol, Cigarette, and Marijuana Use for High School Seniors

Alcohol Use	Cigarette Use	Marijuana Use — Yes	Marijuana Use — No
Yes	Yes	911	538
	No	44	456
No	Yes	3	43
	No	2	279

Source: Data from Professor Harry Khamis, Wright State University (personal communication).

Questions to Explore

Let y indicate marijuana use, coded $1 = $ yes, $0 = $ no. Let x_1 be an indicator variable for alcohol use ($1 = $ yes, $0 = $ no), and let x_2 be an indicator variable for cigarette use ($1 = $ yes, $0 = $ no). Table 13.15 shows MINITAB output for a logistic regression model.

Table 13.15 MINITAB Output for Estimating the Probability of Marijuana Use Based on Alcohol Use and Cigarette Use

Term	Coef	SE Coef	Z-Value	P-Value
Constant	-5.30904	0.475190	-11.17	0.000
alcohol	2.98601	0.464671	6.43	0.000
cigarettes	2.84780	0.163039	17.38	0.000

a. Report the prediction equation and interpret.
b. Find the estimated probability $\hat{p}$ of having used marijuana (i) for students who have not used alcohol or cigarettes and (ii) for students who have used both alcohol and cigarettes.

Think It Through

a. From Table 13.15, the logistic regression prediction equation is

$$\hat{p} = \frac{e^{-5.31 + 2.99x_1 + 2.85x_2}}{1 + e^{-5.31 + 2.99x_1 + 2.85x_2}}.$$

The coefficient of alcohol use (x_1) is positive (2.99). The indicator variable x_1 equals 1 for those who've used alcohol. Thus, the alcohol users have a higher estimated probability of using marijuana, controlling for whether they used cigarettes. Likewise, the coefficient of cigarette use (x_2) is positive (2.85), so the cigarette users have a higher estimated probability of using marijuana, controlling for whether they used alcohol. Table 13.15 tells us that for each predictor, the test statistic is large. In other words, the estimated effect is a large number of standard errors from 0. The P-values are both 0.000, so there is strong evidence that the corresponding population effects are positive also.

b. For those who have not used alcohol or cigarettes, $x_1 = x_2 = 0$. For them, the estimated probability of marijuana use is

$$\hat{p} = \frac{e^{-5.31 + 2.99(0) + 2.85(0)}}{1 + e^{-5.31 + 2.99(0) + 2.85(0)}} = \frac{e^{-5.31}}{1 + e^{-5.31}} = \frac{0.0049}{1.0049} = 0.005.$$

For those who have used alcohol and cigarettes, $x_1 = x_2 = 1$. For them, the estimated probability of marijuana use is

$$\hat{p} = \frac{e^{-5.31 + 2.99(1) + 2.85(1)}}{1 + e^{-5.31 + 2.99(1) + 2.85(1)}} = 0.629.$$

In summary, the probability that students have tried marijuana seems highly related to whether they've used alcohol and cigarettes.

Insight

Likewise, you can find the estimated probability of using marijuana for those who have used alcohol but not cigarettes (let $x_1 = 1$ and $x_2 = 0$) and for those who have not used alcohol but have used cigarettes. Table 13.16 summarizes results. We see that marijuana use is unlikely unless a student has used both alcohol and cigarettes.

Table 13.16 Estimated Probability of Marijuana Use, by Alcohol Use and Cigarette Use, Based on Logistic Regression Model

The sample proportions of marijuana use are shown in parentheses for the four cases.

Alcohol Use	Cigarette Use	
	Yes	**No**
Yes	0.629 (0.629)	0.089 (0.088)
No	0.079 (0.065)	0.005 (0.007)

► *Try Exercises 13.57 and 13.58*

Checking the Logistic Regression Model

Alcohol	Cigarette	Marijuana Yes	Marijuana No
Yes	Yes	911	538
	No	44	456
No	Yes	3	43
	No	2	279

How can you check whether a logistic regression model fits the data well? When the explanatory variables are categorical, you can find the sample proportions for the outcome of interest. Table 13.16 also shows these for the marijuana use example. For instance, for those who had used alcohol and cigarettes, from Table 13.14 (shown again in the margin) the sample proportion who had used marijuana is $911/(911 + 538) = 0.629$. Table 13.16 shows that the sample proportions are close to the estimated proportions generated by the model. The model seems to fit well.

Table 13.16 may suggest the question, why bother to fit the model? Why not merely inspect a table of sample proportions? One important reason is that the model enables us to conduct inferences about the effects of explanatory variables easily while controlling for other variables. For instance, if we want to test the effect of alcohol use on marijuana use, controlling for cigarette use, we can test $H_0: \beta_1 = 0$ in the model with alcohol use and cigarette use as predictors.

13.6 Practicing the Basics

13.50 Income and credit cards Example 12 used logistic regression to estimate the probability of having a travel credit card when $x =$ annual income (in thousands of euros). At the mean income of €25,000, show that the estimated probability of having a travel credit card equals 0.29.

13.51 Hall of Fame induction Baseball's highest honor is election to the Hall of Fame. The history of the election process, however, has been filled with controversy and accusations of favoritism. Most recently, there is also the discussion about players who used performance enhancement drugs. The Hall of Fame has failed to define what the criteria for entry should be. Several statistical models have attempted to describe the probability of a player being offered entry into the Hall of Fame. How does hitting 400 or 500 home runs affect a player's chances of being enshrined? What about having a .300 average or 1500 RBI? One factor, the number of home runs, is examined by using logistic regression as the probability of being elected:

$$P(\text{HOF}) = \frac{e^{-6.7+0.0175\text{HR}}}{1 + e^{-6.7+0.0175 \text{ HR}}}.$$

a. Compare the probability of election for two players who are 10 home runs apart—say, 369 home runs versus 359 home runs.

b. Compare the probability of election for a player with 475 home runs versus the probability for a player with 465 home runs. (These happen to be the figures for Willie Stargell and Dave Winfield.)

13.52 Horseshoe crabs A study of horseshoe crabs by zoologist Dr. Jane Brockmann at the University of Florida used logistic regression to predict the probability that a female crab had a male partner nesting nearby. One explanatory variable was $x =$ weight of the female crab (in kilograms). The results were

```
Term        Coef
Constant    -3.695
Weight       1.815
```

The quartiles for weight were Q1 = 2.00, Q2 = 2.35, and Q3 = 2.85.

a. Find the estimated probability of a male partner at Q1 and at Q3.

b. Interpret the effect of weight by estimating how much the probability increases over the middle half of the sampled weights, between Q1 and Q3.

13.53 More crabs Refer to the previous exercise. For what weight values do you estimate that a female crab has probability (a) 0.50, (b) greater than 0.50, and (c) less than 0.50, of having a male partner nesting nearby?

13.54 Voting and income A logistic regression model describes how the probability of voting for the Republican candidate in a presidential election depends on x, the voter's total family income (in thousands of dollars) in the previous year. The prediction equation for a particular sample is

$$\hat{p} = \frac{e^{-1.00+0.02x}}{1 + e^{-1.00+0.02x}}.$$

Find the estimated probability of voting for the Republican candidate when (a) income = $10,000, (b) income = $100,000. Describe how the probability seems to depend on income.

13.55 Equally popular candidates Refer to the previous exercise.

a. At which income level is the estimated probability of voting for the Republican candidate equal to 0.50?

b. Over what region of income values is the estimated probability of voting for the Republican candidate (i) greater than 0.50 and (ii) less than 0.50?

c. At the income level for which $\hat{p} = 0.50$, give a linear approximation for the change in the probability for each $1,000 increase in income.

13.56 Many predictors of voting Refer to the previous two exercises. When the explanatory variables are $x_1 =$ family income, $x_2 =$ number of years of education, and $x_3 =$ gender (1 = male, 0 = female), suppose a logistic regression reports

```
Term          Coef    SE Coef
Constant     -2.40     0.12
income        0.02     0.01
education     0.08     0.05
gender        0.20     0.06
```

For this sample, x_1 ranges from 6 to 157 with a standard deviation of 25, and x_2 ranges from 7 to 20 with a standard deviation of 3.

a. Interpret the effects by using the sign of the coefficient for each predictor.

b. Illustrate the gender effect by finding and comparing the estimated probability of voting Republican for (i) a man with 16 years of education and income $40,000 and (ii) a woman with 16 years of education and income $40,000.

13.57 Graduation, gender, and race   The U.S. Bureau of the Census lists college graduation numbers by race and gender. The table shows the data for graduating 25-year-olds.

College Graduation

Group	Sample Size	Graduates
White Females	31,249	10,781
White Males	39,583	10,727
Black Females	13,194	2,309
Black Males	17,707	2,054

Source: J. J. McArdle and F. Hamagami, *J. Amer. Statist. Assoc.*, vol. 89 (1994), pp. 1107–1123. Data from U.S. Bureau of the Census, American Community Survey 2005–2007.

a. Identify the response variable.

b. Express the data in the form of a three-variable contingency table that cross-classifies whether graduated (yes, no), race, and gender.

c. When we use indicator variables for race (1 = White, 0 = Black) and for gender (1 = Female, 0 = Male), the coefficients of those predictors in the logistic regression model are 0.975 for race and 0.375 for gender. Based on these estimates, which race and gender combination has the highest estimated probability of graduation? Why?

13.58 Death penalty and race   The three-dimensional contingency table shown is from a study of the effects of racial characteristics on whether individuals convicted of homicide receive the death penalty. The subjects classified were defendants in indictments involving cases with multiple murders in Florida between 1976 and 1987.

Death Penalty Verdict by Defendant's Race and Victims' Race

Defendant's Race	Victims' Race	Death Penalty Yes	Death Penalty No	Percent Yes
White	White	53	414	11.3
	Black	0	16	0.0
Black	White	11	37	22.9
	Black	4	139	2.8

Source: Data from M. L. Radelet and G. L. Pierce, *Florida Law Rev.*, vol. 43, 1991, pp. 1–34.

a. Based on the percentages shown, controlling for victims' race, for which defendant's race was the death penalty more likely?

b. Let y = death penalty verdict (1 = yes, 0 = no), let d be an indicator variable for defendant's race (1 = White, 0 = Black), and let v be an indicator variable for victims' race (1 = White, 0 = Black). The logistic regression prediction equation is

$$\hat{p} = \frac{e^{-3.596 - 0.868d + 2.404v}}{1 + e^{-3.596 - 0.868d + 2.404v}}.$$

According to this equation, for which of the four groups is the death penalty most likely? Explain your answer.

13.59 Death penalty probabilities   Refer to the previous exercise.

a. Based on the prediction equation, when the defendant is Black and the victims were White, show that the estimated death penalty probability is 0.233.

b. The model-estimated probabilities are 0.011 when the defendant is White and victims were Black, 0.113 when the defendant and the victims were White, and 0.027 when the defendant and the victims were Black. Construct a table cross-classifying defendant's race by victims' race and show the estimated probability of the death penalty for each cell. Use this to interpret the effect of defendant's race.

c. Collapse the contingency table over victims' race, and show that (ignoring victims' race) White defendants were more likely than Black defendants to get the death penalty. Comparing this with what happens when you control for victims' race, explain how Simpson's paradox occurs.

Chapter Review

SUMMARY OF NOTATION

$\mu_y = \alpha + \beta_1 x_1 + \beta_2 x_2 + \beta_3 x_3$ = multiple regression model, expressing the mean of y in terms of explanatory variables

$\hat{y} = a + b_1 x_1 + b_2 x_2 + b_3 x_3$ = prediction equation obtained from fitting model to data

$x_1, x_2, \ldots$ = explanatory variables in multiple regression model

R = multiple correlation coefficient = correlation coefficient between observed y and predicted y values

R^2 = proportional reduction in prediction error, for multiple regression = percentage of the variability explained

F = test statistic for testing that all β parameters in regression model are equal to zero

$e^{\alpha + \beta x}$ = exponential function used in numerator and denominator of logistic regression equation, which models the probability of success p for a binary response variable by

$$p = e^{\alpha + \beta x} / (1 + e^{\alpha + \beta x}).$$

CHAPTER SUMMARY

This chapter generalized regression to include more than one explanatory variable in the model. The **multiple regression model** relates the mean μ_y of a response variable y to several explanatory variables, for instance,

$$\mu_y = \alpha + \beta_1 x_1 + \beta_2 x_2$$

for two predictors. Advantages over simple linear regression include better predictions of y and being able to study the effect of an explanatory variable on y while *controlling* (keeping fixed) values of other explanatory variables in the model.

- The **regression parameters** (the betas) are slopes that represent effects of the explanatory variables while controlling for the other variables in the model. For instance, β_1 represents the change in the mean of y for a one-unit increase in x_1, at fixed values of the other explanatory variables.

- The **multiple correlation coefficient** R and its square (R^2) describe the predictability of the response variable y by the set of explanatory variables. The multiple correlation coefficient R equals the correlation coefficient between the observed and predicted y values. Its square, R^2, is the proportional reduction in error from predicting y using the prediction equation instead of using $\bar{y}$ (and ignoring all explanatory variables). Both R and R^2 fall between 0 and 1, with larger values representing stronger relationships. R^2 also tells us what percent of the variability in the response variable y can be explained by

the regression model, and how much of that variability is left unexplained by the predictors.

- An **F statistic** tests $H_0: \beta_1 = \beta_2 = \ldots = 0$, which states that y is independent of all the explanatory variables in the model. The F test statistic equals a ratio of mean squares. A small P-value suggests that at least one explanatory variable affects the response.

- Individual t **tests** and **confidence intervals** for each β parameter analyze separate population effects of each explanatory variable, controlling for the other variables in the model.

- Categorical explanatory variables can be included in a regression model using **indicator variables.** With two categories, the indicator variable equals 1 when the observation is in the first category and 0 when it is in the second. (Some software define this the other way around.) For a categorical variable with three categories, two indicator variables are needed.

- For binary response variables, the **logistic regression model** describes how the probability of a particular category depends on the values of explanatory variables. An S-shaped curve describes how the probability changes as the value of a quantitative explanatory variable increases.

Table 13.17 summarizes the basic properties and inference methods for multiple regression and those that Chapter 12 introduced for simple linear regression, with quantitative variables.

Table 13.17 Summary of Simple and Multiple Regression

	Simple Regression	Multiple Regression	
Model Formula	$\mu_y = \alpha + \beta x$	$\mu_y = \alpha + \beta_1 x_1 + \beta_2 x_2 + \ldots$	
		Simultaneous Effect	Separate Effects
Parameters describing relationship	$\beta = $ slope, $r = $ correlation coefficient $(-1 \le r \le 1)$, r^2 is proportional reduction in error or percent of variability explained	$R = $ multiple correlation coefficient $(0 \le R \le 1)$, R^2 is proportional reduction in error or percent of variability explained	$\beta_1, \beta_2, \ldots$ are slopes for each predictor at fixed values of others
Hypotheses of no effect	$H_0: \beta = 0$	$H_0: \beta_1 = \beta_2 = \ldots = 0$	$H_0: \beta_1 = 0, H_0: \beta_2 = 0, \ldots$
Test Statistic	$t = (b - 0)/se$	$F = \dfrac{\text{MS Regression}}{\text{MS Error}}$	$t = (\beta_1 - 0)/se,$ $t = (\beta_2 - 0)/se, \ldots$
Degrees of Freedom	$df = n - 2$	$df_1 = $ # predictors, $df_2 = n - $ # regression parameters.	$df = n - $ # regression parameters.

LEARNING OUTCOMES

1. Write and understand the multiple regression model for two or more predictors.

2. Identify advantages of multiple regression over simple linear regression.

3. Interpret the estimated regression coefficients.

4. Recognize that interpretation of the regression coefficients can only be made holding the other explanatory variables constant.

5. Interpret the multiple correlation coefficient R and R^2 in terms of the predictability of the response variable y by the set of explanatory variables and the percent of the variability explained.

6. Write the hypotheses for stating that y is independent of all the explanatory variables in the multiple regression model.

7. Use the F statistic and its associated P-value to make an appropriate conclusion about the multiple regression model.

8. Use t tests and confidence intervals to make conclusions about the effect of each explanatory variable in the multiple regression model on the response variable.

9. Set up, employ, and interpret indicator variables for categorical predictors in multiple regression.

10. Use the logistic regression model for binary response variables, find the estimated probability of success and explain how it changes when the explanatory variable changes.

ANSWERS TO THE CHAPTER FIGURE QUESTIONS

Figure 13.1 Selling price is the response variable, and the graphs that show it as the response variable are in the first row.

Figure 13.2 The coefficient (15,170) of x_2 = number of bedrooms is positive, so increasing it has the effect of increasing the predicted selling price (for fixed house size).

Figure 13.3 We use only the right tail because larger F values provide greater evidence against H_0.

Figure 13.4 A histogram that shows a few observations that have extremely large or extremely small standardized residuals, well removed from the others.

Figure 13.5 The pattern suggests that y tends to be below $\hat{y}$ for very small and large x_1-values and above $\hat{y}$ for medium-sized x_1-values. The effect of x_1 appears to be better modeled by a mathematical function that has a parabolic shape.

Figure 13.6 As house size increases, the variability of the standardized residuals appears to increase, suggesting more variability in selling prices when house size is larger, for a given number of bedrooms. The number of bedrooms affects the analysis because it has an effect on the predicted values for the model, on which the residuals are based.

Figure 13.7 Each line has the same slope. The effect of house size on the predicted selling price is the same for houses in good shape and not so good shape.

Figure 13.10 A straight line implies that p falls below 0 or above 1 for sufficiently small or large x-values. This is a problem because a proportion must always fall between 0 and 1.

STATISTICAL SOFTWARE

Art of Stat Web Apps

- **F Distribution** This app lets you interactively explore the shape of the F distribution and compute tail probabilities and percentiles, which are visualized on the graph.

- **Multiple Linear Regression** This app, similar to the *Linear Regression* app, provides all statistical output associated with fitting a multiple regression model. The app has several datasets preloaded, but you can upload your own .csv file (with a header row). The app allows obtaining a scatterplot and correlation matrix. Standard output are the estimates for the intercept and the slope parameters for all selected predictors, the multiple correlation coefficient R, R^2, the residual standard deviation s, and the overall F test for testing whether all regression parameters are equal to 0. Options allow finding the predicted value for a user-defined set of predictor values (set to their mean, by default); displaying standard errors, t statistics and P-values for the beta parameters or finding their confidence intervals their confidence intervals; and obtaining the ANOVA table. The app can also find confidence and prediction intervals for the mean or an individual observation, but this is not covered in the book. The second tab of the app is dedicated to residual analysis, giving a table that shows the fitted values and raw and standardized residuals as well as a scatterplot of residuals against user-selected predictors (or the fitted values) and a histogram with a box plot.

- **Logistic Regression** This app fits the logistic regression model with a single quantitative explanatory variable. It provides the estimates, standard errors and P-values for the parameters in the model, provides a graph of the fitted probability of success and computes predicted probabilities and their confidence intervals.

R

- **F Distribution:** The pf function finds (lower-tail) probabilities under the F distribution, such that > 1 pf(40.48, df1=3, df2=60) returns the upper tail probability 0.000 from the F distribution that is reported as the P-value in Example 5. qf returns percentiles, such as > qf(0.95, df1=3, df2=40) returning 2.84, as shown in Table 13.8.

- **Multiple Regression:** The lm function also fits multiple regression models. It was introduced in the R code for Chapter 3 and expanded on in the R code for Chapter 12. To illustrate multiple regression with two quantitative predictors, we load the Oregon house selling price data set and replicate Table 13.3 about the parameter estimates and their standard errors. (Below, some original output that R produces has been removed to focus on the essentials. We also created simple variable names in the Oregon .csv file for ease of presentation.)

```
> myfile <- file.choose() #path to file
> oregon <- read.csv(myfile) #reads in file
> head(oregon,3) #show the first three rows and column names
    Price Size Acres Lotsize Bedrooms Bathrooms
1 232500 1679  0.23 10018.8        3       1.5
2 470000 4494  0.52 22651.2        5       4.0
3 150000 2542  0.11  4791.6        4       0.0
> myfit <- lm(Price ~ Size + Bedrooms, data=oregon) #fits multiple regression model
> summary(myfit) #provides estimates, standard errors, P-values and R2, compare to Table 13.3
Coefficients:
              Estimate  Std. Error  t value  Pr(>|t|)
(Intercept) 60102.140   18622.905    3.227   0.00146
Size           62.983       4.753   13.250   < 2e-16
Bedrooms    15170.411    5329.806    2.846   0.00489

Residual standard error: 80270 on 197 degrees of freedom
Multiple R-squared:  0.5244, Adjusted R-squared:  0.5196
F-statistic: 108.6 on 2 and 197 DF,  p-value: < 2.2e-16
```

We recognize the elements of Table 13.3 (parameter estimates, standard errors, t statistics and P-values, labeled `Pr(>|t|)`) in the output. We also recognize R^2 as `0.5244` (compare to Table 13.5), the residual standard deviation `80270` (R calls it the `Residual standard error`), and the F statistic `108.6` for the overall test with corresponding P-value `2.2e-16`, which is essentially 0. We can obtain 95% confidence intervals for each slope parameter through

```
> confint(myfit)
                 2.5 %        97.5 %
Size          53.60892      72.35647
Bedrooms    4659.61107   25681.20995
```

We get the predicted price of the first home (see Example 2) and a confidence interval for it via

```
> predict(myfit, newdata=data.frame(Size=1679, Bedrooms=3), interval='confidence')
      fit        lwr        upr
1  211361.3   197605.3    225117.3
```

You can obtain all fitted values, residuals, and residual plots (histogram and standardized residuals plotted against house size, see Examples 8 and 9) through:

```
> myfitted <- fitted(myfit)  #fitted values for all observations
> myres <- residuals(myfit) #raw residuals
> mystdres <- rstandard(myfit) #standardized residuals
> hist(mystdres) #histogram of std. residuals
> plot(mystdres ~ oregon$Size) #scatterplot of std. residuals vs size
```

- **Categorical Predictors:** To illustrate multiple regression with one categorical predictor, we consider the condition of the house, together with its size. (In our data set, condition had the two categories "Good" and "Bad," and we keep it that way to illustrate how R creates indicator variables automatically. However, in the .csv file, you can replace "Good" with 1 and "Bad" with 0 to create the indicator variables yourself.)

```
> oregon[c(1,2,11), c(1,2,9)] #show rows 1, 2 and 11 and columns 1, 2 and 9 of the oregon data
     Price Size Condition
1   232500 1679      Good
2   470000 4494      Good
11  357500 3189       Bad
> myfit1 <- lm(Price ~ Size + Condition, data=oregon)
> summary(myfit1)
Coefficients:
                Estimate Std. Error t value Pr(>|t|)
(Intercept)   109197.911  19951.982   5.473 1.34e-07
Size              66.463      4.682  14.196  < 2e-16
ConditionGood -12926.940  17196.712  -0.752    0.453
```

This replicates the output from Table 13.11. By default, for categorical variables with two categories, R creates indicator variables following this rule: The category that comes alphabetically first (here: "Bad") is set to 0, the other (here: "Good") is set to 1.

- **Scatterplot and Correlation Matrix:** To obtain the scatterplot matrix, type `> pairs(oregon[, c(1,2,5)])`, where `c(1,2,5)` specifies the column numbers of the variables in the data set you want to plot (e.g., Bedroom is the 5th column in the `oregon` data set). This reproduces Figure 13.1. The correlation matrix is obtained in a similar fashion, using `> cor(oregon[, c(1,2,5)])`. This reproduces the correlation matrix shown in the margin at the beginning of Section 13.2.

CHAPTER EXERCISES

Practicing the Basics

13.60 House prices This chapter has considered many aspects of regression analysis. Let's consider several of them at once by using software with the House Selling Prices OR data file on the book's website (and available in the *Multiple Linear Regression* app) to conduct a multiple regression analysis of y = selling price of home in thousands (HP_in_thousands), x_1 = size of home, x_2 = number of bedrooms, x_3 = number of bathrooms.

a. Construct a scatterplot matrix. Identify the plots that pertain to selling price as a response variable. Interpret and explain how the highly discrete nature of x_2 and x_3 affects the plots.

b. Fit the model. Write down the prediction equation and interpret the coefficient of size of home by its effect when x_2 and x_3 are fixed.

c. Show how to calculate R^2 from SS values in the ANOVA table. Interpret its value in the context of these variables.

d. Find and interpret the multiple correlation coefficient.

e. Show all steps of the F test that selling price is independent of these predictors. Explain how to obtain the F statistic from the mean squares in the ANOVA table.

f. Report the t statistic for testing H_0: $\beta_2 = 0$. Report the P-value for H_a: $\beta_2 < 0$ and interpret. Why do you think this effect is not significant? Does this imply that the number of bedrooms is not related with selling price?

g. Construct and examine the histogram of the residuals for the multiple regression model. What does this describe, and what does it suggest?

h. Construct and examine the plot of the residuals plotted against size of home. What does this describe, and what does it suggest?

13.61 Predicting body strength   In Chapter 12, we analyzed strength data for a sample of female high school athletes. When we predict the maximum number of pounds the athlete can bench press using the number of times she can do a 60-pound bench press (BP60), we get $r^2 = 0.643$. When we add the number of times an athlete can perform a 200-pound leg press (LP200) to the model, we get $\hat{y} = 60.6 + 1.33(\text{BP60}) + 0.21(\text{LP200})$ and $R^2 = 0.656$.

a. Find the predicted value and residual for an athlete who has maxBP = 85, BP60 = 10, and LP200 = 20.

b. Find the prediction equation for athletes who have LP200 = 20, and explain how to interpret the slope for BP60.

c. Note that $R^2 = 0.656$ for the multiple regression model is not much larger than $r^2 = 0.643$ for the simple model with LP200 as the only explanatory variable. What does this suggest?

13.62 Softball data   Refer to the Softball data set on the book's website and available in the *Multiple Linear Regression* app. Regress the difference (DIFF) between the number of runs scored by that team and by the other team on the number of hits (HIT) and the number of errors (ERR).

a. Report the prediction equation, and interpret the slopes.

b. From part a, approximately how many hits does the team need so that the predicted value of DIFF is positive (corresponding to a predicted win) if they can play error-free ball (ERR = 0)?

13.63 Violent crime   A MINITAB printout is provided from fitting the multiple regression model to U.S. crime data for the 50 states (excluding Washington, D.C.)

on y = violent crime rate, x_1 = poverty rate, and x_2 = percent living in urban areas.

a. Predict the violent crime rate for Massachusetts, which has violent crime rate = 476, poverty rate = 10.2%, and urbanization = 92.1%. Find the residual and interpret.

b. Interpret the effects of the predictors by showing the prediction equation relating y and x_1 for states with (i) $x_2 = 0$ and (ii) $x_2 = 100$. Interpret.

Regression of Violent Crime Rate on Poverty Rate and Urbanization:

Term	Coef	SE Coef	T-Value	P-Value
Constant	−270.7	121.1	−2.23	0.030
poverty	28.334	7.249	3.91	0.000
urbanization	5.416	1.035	5.23	0.000

13.64 Effect of poverty on crime   Refer to the previous exercise. Now we add x_3 = percentage of single-parent families to the model. The SPSS table below shows results. Without x_3 in the model, poverty has slope 28.33, and when x_3 is added, poverty has slope 14.95. Explain the differences in the interpretations of these two slopes.

Violent Crime Predicted by Poverty Rate, Urbanization, and Single-Parent Family

		Coefficients[a]			
		Unstandardized Coefficients			
Model		B	Std. Error	t	Sig.
1	(Constant)	−631.700	149.604	−4.222	.000
	poverty	14.953	7.540	1.983	.053
	urbanization	4.406	.973	4.528	.000
	singleparent	25.362	7.220	3.513	.001

[a] Dependent Variable: violent crime rate.

13.65 Modeling fertility   For the World Data for Fertility and Literacy data file on the book's website, a MINITAB printout follows that shows fitting a multiple regression model for y = fertility, x_1 = adult literacy rate (both sexes), x_2 = combined educational enrollment (both sexes). Report the value of each of the following:

a. r between y and x_1.

b. R^2.

c. Total sum of squares.

d. Residual sum of squares.

e. Standard deviation of y.

f. Residual standard deviation of y.

g. Test statistic value for H_0: $\beta_1 = 0$.

h. P-value for H_0: $\beta_1 = \beta_2 = 0$.

Analysis of Fertility, Literacy, and Combined Educational Enrollment

Variable	N	Mean	SE Mean	StDev	Median
Adolescent fertility	142	60.42	3.73	44.50	49.55
Adult literacy rate (both sexes)	142	80.80	1.64	19.56	88.40
Combined educ enrol (both sexes)	142	68.59	1.32	15.79	71.20

```
Term                    Coef    SE Coef  T-Value  P-Value
Constant               187.95    12.92    14.55    0.000
Adult literacy rate    -1.2590   0.2416   -5.21    0.000
(both sexes)
Combined educ          -0.3762   0.2994   -1.26    0.211
enrollment(both sexes)
S = 33.4554 R-Sq = 44.3%

Analysis of Variance
Source        DF      SS       MS     F-Value  P-Value
Regression     2    123582    61791   55.21    0.000
Error        139    155577    1119
Total        141    279160
Correlations:
```

	y	x_1	x_2
y	–	-0.661	-0.578
x_1	-0.661	–	0.803
x_2	-0.578	0.803	–

13.66 Significant fertility prediction? Refer to the previous exercise.

a. Show how to construct the F statistic for testing H_0: $\beta_1 = \beta_2 = 0$ from the reported mean squares, report its P-value, and interpret.

b. If these are the only nations of interest to us for this study, rather than a random sample of such nations, is this significance test relevant? Explain.

13.67 GDP, CO₂, and internet Consider predicting the per capita GDP (gross domestic product, in thousands of dollars), of a country, using x_1 = carbon dioxide emissions per capita (in metric tons) and x_2 = percent of country population not using the Internet. Based on data for several countries, the following computer output was obtained:

```
Coefficients:
             Estimate  Std. Error    t    Pr(>|t|)
Intercept     39892      4474       8.9   0.0000
CO2             798       254       3.1   0.0119
NoInternet     -399        51      -7.8   0.0000
```

a. Find the equation relating predicted GDP to the explanatory variables listed.

b. Interpret the coefficients in the equation for each of the explanatory variables.

13.68 Education and gender in modeling income Consider the relationship between $\hat{y}$ = annual income (in thousands of dollars) and x_1 = number of years of education by x_2 = gender. Many studies in the United States have found that the slope for a regression equation relating y to x_1 is larger for men than for women. Suppose that in the population, the regression equations are $\mu_y = -10 + 4x_1$ for men and $\mu_y = -5 + 2x_1$ for women. Explain why these equations imply that there is *interaction* between education and gender in their effects on income.

13.69 Horseshoe crabs and width A study of horseshoe crabs found a logistic regression equation for predicting the probability that a female crab had a male partner nesting nearby by using x = width of the carapace shell of the female crab (in centimeters). The results were

```
Term         Coef
Constant    -12.351
Width         0.497
```

a. For width, Q1 = 24.9 and Q3 = 27.7. Find the estimated probability of a male partner at Q1 and at Q3. Interpret the effect of width by estimating the increase in the probability over the middle half of the sampled widths.

b. At which carapace shell width level is the estimated probability of a male partner (i) equal to 0.50, (ii) greater than 0.50, and (iii) less than 0.50?

13.70 AIDS and AZT In a study (reported in the *New York Times*, February 15, 1991) on the effects of AZT in slowing the development of AIDS symptoms, 338 veterans whose immune systems were beginning to falter after infection with the AIDS virus were randomly assigned either to receive AZT immediately or to wait until their T cells showed severe immune weakness. The study classified the veterans' race, whether they received AZT immediately, and whether they developed AIDS symptoms during the three-year study. Let x_1 denote whether they used AZT (1 = yes, 0 = no) and let x_2 denote race (1 = White, 0 = Black). A logistic regression analysis for the probability of developing AIDS symptoms gave the prediction equation

$$\hat{p} = \frac{e^{-1.074 - 0.720x_1 + 0.056x_2}}{1 + e^{-1.074 - 0.720x_1 + 0.056x_2}}.$$

a. Interpret the sign of the effect of AZT.

b. Show how to interpret the AZT effect for a particular race by comparing the estimated probability of AIDS symptoms for Black veterans with and without immediate AZT use.

c. The *se* value was 0.279 for the AZT use effect. Does AZT use have a significant effect at the 0.05 significance level? Show all steps of a test to justify your answer.

13.71 Factors affecting first home purchase The table summarizes results of a logistic regression model for predictions about first home purchase by young married households. The response variable is whether the subject owns a home (1 = yes, 0 = no). The explanatory variables are husband's income, wife's income (each in ten-thousands of dollars), the number of years the respondent has been married, the number of children aged 0–17 in the household, and an indicator variable that equals 1 if the subject's parents owned a home in the last year the subject lived in the parental home.

a. Explain why, other things being fixed, the probability of home ownership increases with husband's earnings, wife's earnings, the number of children, and parents' home ownership.

b. From the table, explain why the number of years married seems to show little evidence of an effect, given the other variables in the model.

Results of Logistic Regression for Probability of Home Ownership

Variable	Estimate	Std. Error
Husband earnings	0.569	0.088
Wife earnings	0.306	0.140
No. years married	−0.039	0.042
No. children	0.220	0.101
Parents' home ownership	0.387	0.176

Source: Data from J. Henretta, "Family Transitions, Housing Market Context, and First Home Purchase," *Social Forces,* vol. 66, 1987, pp. 520–536.

Concepts and Investigations

13.72 Student data   Refer to the FL Student Survey data file on the book's website. Using software, conduct a regression analysis using y = college GPA and predictors high school GPA and sports (number of weekly hours of physical exercise). Prepare a report, summarizing your graphical analyses, simple regression models and interpretations, multiple regression models and interpretations, inferences, checks of effects of outliers, and overall summary of the relationships.

13.73 Why regression?   In 100–200 words, explain to someone who has never studied statistics the purpose of multiple regression and when you would use it to analyze a data set or investigate an issue. Give an example of at least one application of multiple regression. Describe how multiple regression can be useful in analyzing complex relationships.

13.74 Unemployment and GDP   Refer to Exercise 13.67. When unemployment rate of a country is added as an additional predictor to the model already containing CO_2 and percentage of population not using the Internet, we get the following output.

```
Coefficients:
             Estimate  Std. Error    t   Pr(>|t|)
(Intercept)    38923       7259      5.4   0.0007
CO2              813        282      2.9   0.0204
NoInternet      -395         58     -6.9   0.0001
Unemployed       107        606      0.2   0.8645
```

a. Interpret the sign of the coefficient for unemployment. Is this the direction of the effect you would expect?

b. Is the coefficient for unemployment significantly different from zero? Explain. Does this automatically mean unemployment is unrelated to GDP? (*Hint:* Does the effect of employment depend on other variables in the model?)

c. What measure would you use to investigate whether unemployment helps in predicting GDP?

d. R^2 increases from 94.26% to 94.28% when adding unemployment to the model with CO_2 and NoInternet. Explain what this means.

13.75 Scores for religion You want to include religious affiliation as a predictor in a regression model, using the categories Protestant, Catholic, Jewish, Other. You set up a variable x_1 that equals 1 for Protestants, 2 for Catholics, 3 for Jewish, and 4 for Other, using the model $\mu_y = \alpha + \beta x_1$. Explain why this is inappropriate.

13.76 Lurking variable   Give an example of three variables for which you expect $\beta \neq 0$ in the model $\mu_y = \alpha + \beta x_1$ but $\beta_1 = 0$ in the model $\mu_y = \alpha + \beta_1 x_1 + \beta_2 x_2$. (*Hint:* The effect of x_1 could be completely due to a lurking variable, x_2.)

13.77 Properties of R^2   Using its definition in terms of SS values, explain why $R^2 = 1$ only when all the residuals are 0, and $R^2 = 0$ when each $\hat{y} = \bar{y}$. Explain what this means in practical terms.

13.78 Why an F test?   When a model has a very large number of predictors, even when none of them truly have an effect in the population, one or two may look significant in t tests merely by random variation. Explain why performing the F test first can safeguard against getting such false information from t tests.

13.79 Multicollinearity   For the high school female athletes data file available from the book's website and in the *Multiple Linear Regression* app, regress the maximum bench press on weight and percent body fat.

a. Show that the F test is statistically significant at the 0.05 significance level.

b. Show that the P-values are both larger than 0.35 for testing the individual effects with t tests. (It seems like a contradiction when the F test tells us that at least one predictor has an effect but the t tests indicate that neither predictor has a significant effect. This can happen when the predictor variables are highly correlated, so a predictor has little impact when the other predictors are in the model. Such a condition is referred to as **multicollinearity.** In this example, the correlation coefficient is 0.871 between weight and percent body fat.)

13.80 Logistic versus linear   For binary response variables, one reason that logistic regression is usually preferred over straight-line regression is that a fixed change in x often has a smaller impact on a probability p when p is near 0 or near 1 than when p is near the middle of its range. Let y refer to the decision to rent or to buy a home, with $p =$ the probability of buying, and let $x =$ weekly family income. In which case do you think an increase of $100 in x has greater effect: when $x = 50,000$ (for which p is near 1), when $x = 0$ (for which p is near 0), or when $x = 500$? Explain how your answer relates to the choice of a linear versus logistic regression model.

Multiple Choice or True/False

13.81 Interpret parameter   If $\hat{y} = 2 + 3x_1 + 5x_2 - 8x_3$, then controlling for x_2 and x_3, the change in the estimated mean of y when x_1 is increased from 10 to 20

a. equals 30.

b. equals 0.3.

c. Cannot be given—depends on specific values of x_2 and x_3.

d. Must be the same as when we ignore x_2 and x_3.

13.82 Interpret indicator In the model $\mu_y = \alpha + \beta_1 x_1 + \beta_2 x_2$, suppose that x_2 is an indicator variable for gender, equaling 1 for females and 0 for males.

a. We set $x_2 = 0$ if we want a predicted mean without knowing gender.

b. The slope effect of x_1 is β_1 for males and β_2 for females.

c. β_2 is the difference between the population mean of y for females and for males.

d. β_2 is the difference between the population mean of y for females and males, for all those subjects having x_1 fixed, such as $x_1 = 10$.

13.83 Regression effects Multiple regression is used to model y = annual income using x_1 = number of years of education and x_2 = number of years employed in current job.

a. It is possible that the coefficient of x_2 is positive in a simple regression but negative in multiple regression.

b. It is possible that the correlation coefficient between y and x_1 is 0.30 and the multiple correlation coefficient between y and x_1 and x_2 is 0.26.

c. If the F statistic for H_0: $\beta_1 = \beta_2 = 0$ has a P-value = 0.001, then we can conclude that *both* predictors have an effect on annual income.

d. If $\beta_2 = 0$, then annual income is independent of x_2 in simple regression.

13.84 True or false: R and R^2 For each of the following statements, indicate whether it is true or false. If false, explain why it is false.

a. The multiple correlation coefficient is always the same as the ordinary correlation coefficient computed between the values of the response variable and the values $\hat{y}$ predicted by the regression model.

b. The multiple correlation coefficient is like the ordinary correlation coefficient in that it falls between -1 and 1.

c. R^2 describes how well you can predict y using x_1 when you control for the other variables in the multiple regression model.

d. It's impossible for R^2 to go down when you add explanatory variables to a regression model.

13.85 True or false: Regression For each of the following statements, indicate whether it is true or false. If false, explain why it is false. In regression analysis:

a. The estimated coefficient of x_1 can be positive in the simple model but negative in a multiple regression model.

b. When a model is refitted after y = income is changed from dollars to euros, R^2 will not change.

c. If $r^2 = 0.6$ between y and x_1 and if $r^2 = 0.6$ between y and x_2, then for the multiple regression model with both predictors, $R^2 = 1.2$.

d. The multiple correlation coefficient between y and $\hat{y}$ can equal -0.40.

13.86 True or false: Slopes For data on y = college GPA, x_1 = high school GPA, and x_2 = average of

mathematics and verbal entrance exam score, we get $\hat{y} = 2.70 + 0.45x_1$ for simple regression and $\hat{y} = 0.3 + 0.40x_1 + 0.003x_2$ for multiple regression. For each of the following statements, indicate whether it is true or false. Give a reason for your answer.

a. The correlation coefficient between y and x_1 is positive.

b. A one-unit increase in x_1 corresponds to a change of 0.45 in the predicted value of y, controlling for x_2.

c. Controlling for x_1, a 100-unit increase in x_2 corresponds to a predicted increase of 0.30 in college GPA.

Advanced Concepts

13.87 Adjusted R^2 When we use R^2 for a random sample to estimate a population R^2, it's slightly biased. It tends to be a bit too large, especially when n is small. Some software also reports

$$\text{Adjusted } R^2 = R^2 - \{p/[n - (p + 1)]\}(1 - R^2),$$

where p = number of predictor variables in the model. This is slightly smaller than R^2 and is less biased. Suppose $R^2 = 0.500$ for a model with $p = 2$ predictors. Calculate adjusted R^2 for the following sample sizes: 10, 100, 1000. Show that the difference between adjusted R^2 and R^2 diminishes as n increases.

13.88 R can't go down The least squares prediction equation provides predicted values $\hat{y}$ with the strongest possible correlation coefficient with y out of all possible prediction equations of that form. Based on this property, explain why the multiple correlation coefficient R cannot decrease when you add a variable to a multiple regression model. (*Hint:* The prediction equation for the simpler model is a special case of a prediction equation for the full model that has coefficient 0 for the added variable.)

13.89 Indicator for comparing two groups Chapter 10 presented methods for comparing means for two groups. Explain how it's possible to perform a significance test of equality of two population means as a special case of a regression analysis. (*Hint:* The regression model then has a single explanatory variable—an indicator variable for the two groups being compared. What does $\mu_1 = \mu_2$ correspond to in terms of a value of a parameter in this regression model?)

13.90 Simpson's paradox Let y = death rate and x = average age of residents, measured for each county in Louisiana and in Florida. Draw a hypothetical scatterplot, identifying points for each state, such that the mean death rate is higher in Florida than in Louisiana when x is ignored, but lower when it is controlled. (*Hint:* When you fit a line for each state, the line should be higher for Louisiana, but the y-values for Florida should have an overall higher mean.)

13.91 Polynomial (quadratic) regression A regression formula that gives a quadratic shape instead of a straight line for the relationship between two variables is

$$\mu_y = \alpha + \beta_1 x + \beta_2 x^2.$$

a. Explain why this is a multiple regression model, with x playing the role of x_1 and x^2 (the square of x) playing the role of x_2.

b. For x between 0 and 5, sketch the prediction equation (i) $\hat{y} = 10 + 2x + 0.5x^2$ and (ii) $\hat{y} = 10 + 2x - 0.5x^2$. This shows how the shape of the quadratic regression equation changes, depending on whether the coefficient for x^2 is positive or negative.

13.92 Logistic slope At the x value where the probability of success is some value p, the line drawn tangent to the logistic regression curve has slope $\beta p(1 - p)$.

a. Explain why the slope is $\beta/4$ when $p = 0.5$.

b. Show that the slope is weaker at other p values by evaluating this at $p = 0.1, 0.3, 0.7,$ and 0.9. What does the slope approach as p gets closer and closer to 0 or 1? Sketch a curve to illustrate.

13.93 When is $p = 0.50$? When $\alpha + \beta x = 0$, so that $x = -\alpha/\beta$, show that the logistic regression equation $p = e^{\alpha + \beta x}/(1 + e^{\alpha + \beta x})$ gives $p = 0.50$.

Student Activities

13.94 Class data Refer to the data file your class created in Exercise 1.50 at the end of Chapter 1. For variables chosen by your instructor, fit a multiple regression model and conduct descriptive and inferential statistical analyses. Interpret and summarize your findings and prepare to discuss these in class.

CHAPTER

14

In Chapter 10, we learned how to compare two groups on a quantitative response variable by comparing their means, using a *t* test. In this chapter, we extend these ideas to compare means across several groups and show how to follow up a significance test with pairwise comparisons. We will also explore ways in which two explanatory variables can interact in their effect on the mean of a response variable.

14.1 One-Way ANOVA: Comparing Several Means

14.2 Estimating Differences in Groups for a Single Factor

14.3 Two-Way ANOVA: Exploring Two Factors and Their Interaction

Comparing Groups: Analysis of Variance Methods

Example 1

Investigating Customer Satisfaction

Picture the Scenario

In recent years, many companies have increased the attention paid to measuring and analyzing customer satisfaction. Here are examples of two recent studies of customer satisfaction:

- A company that makes personal computers has provided a toll-free telephone number for owners of their PCs to call and seek technical support. For years the company had two service centers for these calls: San Jose, California, and Toronto, Canada. Recently the company outsourced many of the customer service jobs to a new center in Bangalore, India, because employee salaries are much lower there. The company wanted to compare customer satisfaction at the three centers.

- An airline has a toll-free telephone number that potential customers can call to make flight reservations. Usually the call volume is heavy and callers are placed on hold until an agent is free to answer. Researchers working for

the airline recently conducted a randomized experiment to analyze whether callers would remain on hold longer if they heard (a) an advertisement about the airline and its current promotions, (b) recorded Muzak ("elevator music"), or (c) recorded classical music. Currently, recordings are five minutes long and then repeated; the researchers also wanted to find out whether it would make a difference if recordings were instead ten minutes long before repeating.

Questions to Explore

In the second study, the company's CEO had some familiarity with statistical methods, based on a course he took in college. He asked the researchers:

- In this experiment, are the sample mean times that callers stayed on hold before hanging up significantly different for the three recording types?

- What conclusions can you make if you take into account both the type of recording and whether it was repeated every five minutes or every ten minutes?

Thinking Ahead

Chapter 10 showed how to compare two means. In practice, there may be *several* means to compare, such as in the first and second examples. This chapter shows how to use statistical inference to compare several means.

We'll see how to determine whether a set of sample means is significantly different and how to estimate the differences among corresponding population means. To illustrate, we'll analyze data from the second study in Examples 2–4 and 7.

The methods introduced in this chapter apply when a quantitative response variable has a categorical explanatory variable. The categories of the explanatory variable identify the groups to be compared in terms of their means on the response variable. For example, the first study in Example 1 compared mean customer satisfaction for three groups—customers who call the service centers at the three locations. The response variable is customer satisfaction (on a scale of 0 to 10), and the explanatory variable is the service center location.

The inferential method for comparing means of several groups is called **analysis of variance**, denoted **ANOVA**. Section 14.1 explains that the name "analysis of variance" refers to the significance test's focus on two types of variability in the data. Section 14.2 shows how to construct confidence intervals comparing the means. It also shows that ANOVA methods are special cases of a multiple regression analysis.

Categorical explanatory variables in multiple regression and in ANOVA are often referred to as **factors**. ANOVA with a single factor, such as service center location, is called **one-way ANOVA**. Section 14.3 introduces ANOVA for two factors, called **two-way ANOVA**. The second study in Example 1 requires the use of two-way ANOVA to analyze how the mean telephone holding time (the response variable) varies across categories of recording type (factor 1) and categories defined by the length of time before repeating the recording (factor 2).

14.1 One-Way ANOVA: Comparing Several Means

The analysis of variance method compares means of *several* groups. Let g denote the number of groups. Each group refers to a corresponding population of subjects. The means of the response variable for the g populations are denoted by $\mu_1, \mu_2, \ldots, \mu_g$.

Hypotheses and Assumptions for the ANOVA Test Comparing Means

The analysis of variance is a significance test of the null hypothesis of equal population means,

$$H_0: \mu_1 = \mu_2 = \cdots = \mu_g.$$

An example is $H_0: \mu_1 = \mu_2 = \mu_3$ for testing population mean satisfaction at $g = 3$ service center locations. The null hypothesis says that the population mean satisfaction scores are the same at all three service centers. The alternative hypothesis is

$$H_a: \text{at least two of the population means are different.}$$

If H_0 is false, perhaps all the population means differ, but perhaps merely one mean differs from the others. The test analyzes whether the differences observed among the *sample* means could have reasonably occurred by chance, if the null hypothesis of equal *population* means were true.

The assumptions for the ANOVA test comparing population means are as follows:

- The population distributions of the response variable for the g groups are normal, with the same standard deviation for each group.
- Randomization (depends on data collection method): In a survey sample, independent random samples are selected from each of the g populations. For an experiment, subjects are randomly assigned to the g groups.

Under the first assumption, when the population means are equal, the population distribution of the response variable is the same for each group. If that is the case, the population distribution does not depend on the group to which a subject belongs.

Recall

For $g = 2$ groups, the assumptions for the ANOVA test are the same as those used towards the end of Section 10.2 for the t test assuming equal standard deviations to compare two population means. ◄

ANOVA Hypotheses ◄

Example 2

Tolerance of Being on Hold?

Picture the Scenario

Let's refer back to the second scenario in Example 1. An airline has a toll-free telephone number for reservations. Often the call volume is heavy, and callers are placed on hold until a reservation agent is free to answer. The airline hopes a caller remains on hold until the call is answered, so as not to lose a potential customer.

The airline recently conducted a randomized experiment to analyze whether callers would remain on hold longer, on average, if they heard (a) an advertisement about the airline and its current promotions, (b) Muzak, or (c) classical music (Vivaldi's *Four Seasons*). The company randomly selected one out of every 1,000 calls in a particular week. For each call, they randomly selected one of the three recordings to play and then measured the number of minutes that the caller remained on hold before hanging up (these calls were purposely not answered). The total sample size was 15. The company kept the study small, hoping it could make conclusions without alienating too many potential customers! Table 14.1 shows the data. It also shows the mean and standard deviation for each recording type.

Table 14.1 Telephone Holding Times by Type of Recorded Message

Each observation is the number of minutes a caller remained on hold before hanging up, rounded to the nearest minute.

Recording	Holding Time Observations	Sample Size	Mean	Standard Deviation
Advertisement	5, 1, 11, 2, 8	5	5.4	4.2
Muzak	0, 1, 4, 6, 3	5	2.8	2.4
Classical	13, 9, 8, 15, 7	5	10.4	3.4

Questions to Explore

a. What is the factor in this experiment and what are the hypotheses for the ANOVA test?

b. Figure 14.1 displays the sample means. Since these means are quite different, is there sufficient evidence to conclude that the population means differ?

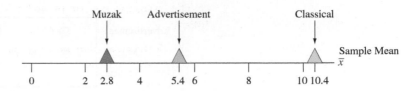

▲ **Figure 14.1** Sample Means of Telephone Holding Times for Callers Who Hear One of Three Recordings. *Question* Since the sample means are quite different, can we conclude that the population means differ?

Think It Through

a. The factor (= explanatory variable) is the type of recording (advertisement, Muzak, or classical music) that was played for a randomly selected caller. Let μ_1, μ_2, and μ_3 denote the mean holding time for the population of callers that were played an advertisement, Muzak, or classical music, respectively. ANOVA tests whether these three population means are equal. The null hypothesis is $H_0: \mu_1 = \mu_2 = \mu_3$. The alternative hypothesis is that at least two of the population means are different.

b. The sample means are quite different. But even if the population means are equal, we expect the sample means to differ because of sampling variability. So these differences alone are not sufficient evidence to enable us to reject H_0.

Insight

The strength of evidence against H_0 will also depend on the sample sizes and the variability of the observations. We'll next study how to test H_0.

▶ *Try Exercise 14.1, parts a and b*

Variability Between Groups and Within Groups

The ANOVA method is used to compare population *means*. So, why is it called analysis of *variance*? The reason is that the test statistic uses evidence about two types of variability. Rather than presenting a formula now for this test statistic, which is rather complex, we'll discuss the reasoning behind it, which is quite simple.

Table 14.1 listed data for three groups. Figure 14.2a on the next page shows dot plots of these data. Suppose the data were different, as shown in Figure 14.2b. The data in Figure 14.2b have the same means as the data in Figure 14.2a but have smaller standard deviations within each group. Which case do you think gives stronger evidence against $H_0: \mu_1 = \mu_2 = \mu_3$?

What's the difference between the data in these two cases? The variability *between* the three group means is the same in each case because the group means are identical. However, the variability *within* each of the three groups is much smaller in Figure 14.2b than in Figure 14.2a. The sample standard deviation is about 1.0 for each group in Figure 14.2b whereas it is between 2.4 and 4.2 for the groups in Figure 14.2a. We'll see that the evidence against $H_0: \mu_1 = \mu_2 = \mu_3$ is stronger when the variability *within* each group is smaller. Figure 14.2b shows less variability within each group than Figure 14.2a. Therefore, it gives stronger evidence against H_0. The evidence against H_0 is also stronger when the variability *between* group means increases (that is, when the group means are farther apart) and as the sample sizes increase. These considerations lead to the ANOVA test statistic that compares variability between and within groups.

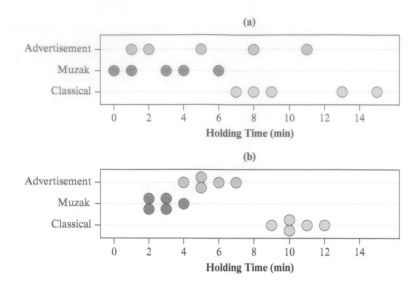

▲ **Figure 14.2** Dot Plots Based on (a) Data in Table 14.1 and (b) Hypothetical Data With the Same Means but Less Variability Within Groups. **Question** Do the data in Figure 14.2b give stronger or weaker evidence against H_0: $\mu_1 = \mu_2 = \mu_3$ than the data in Figure 14.2a. Why?

ANOVA *F* Test Statistic

The **analysis of variance (ANOVA) *F* test statistic** compares the variability between groups to the variability within groups through the ratio

$$F = \frac{\text{Between-groups variability}}{\text{Within-groups variability}}.$$

The larger the variability *between* groups relative to the variability *within* groups, the larger the *F* test statistic tends to be. For instance, $F = 6.4$ for the data in Figure 14.2a, whereas $F = 67.8$ for the data in Figure 14.2b. The between-groups variability is the same in each figure, but Figure 14.2b has much less within-groups variability and thus a larger test statistic value. Later in the section, we'll see that the two types of variability described in the *F* test statistic are measured by estimates of *variances*.

The Test Statistic for Comparing Means Has the *F* Distribution

When H_0 is true, the *F* test statistic has the *F* sampling distribution. The formula for the *F* test statistic is such that when H_0 is true, the *F* distribution has a mean of approximately 1. When H_0 is false, the *F* test statistic tends to be larger than 1, more so as the sample sizes increase. The larger the *F* test statistic value, the stronger the evidence against H_0.

Recall that we used the *F* distribution in the *F* test that the slope parameters of a multiple regression model are all zero (Section 13.3). As in that test, the P-value here is the probability (presuming that H_0 is true) that we obtain an *F* test statistic that is as large or larger than the observed *F* value. That is, it is the right-hand tail probability, as shown in the margin figure, representing values even more extreme than the one observed. The larger the observed *F* test statistic, the smaller the P-value.

In Section 13.3, we learned that the *F* distribution has two *df* values. For ANOVA with *g* groups and total sample size for all groups combined of $N = n_1 + n_2 + \cdots + n_g$,

$$df_1 = g - 1 \text{ and } df_2 = N - g.$$

You can obtain right-tail probabilities (as well as percentiles) for the F distribution from the *F Distribution* app. However, when you carry out the ANOVA analysis, we have a special app called *ANOVA (One Way)*. This app, as well as other software, computes the P-value for the F test statistic automatically. (In addition, the *ANOVA (One Way)* app illustrates the P-value with a plot of the F distribution.) In case you don't have access to technology, Table D in the Appendix reports F values having P-value of 0.05 for various df_1 and df_2 values. The following summarizes the steps of an ANOVA F test.

Recall

The **F distribution** was introduced in Section 13.3. It's used for tests about several parameters (rather than a single parameter or a difference between two parameters, for which we can use a t test). ◄

> **SUMMARY: Steps of ANOVA F Test for Comparing Population Means of Several Groups**
>
> 1. **Assumptions:** Independent random samples (either from random sampling or a randomized experiment), normal population distributions with equal standard deviations.
>
> 2. **Hypotheses:** $H_0: \mu_1 = \mu_2 = \cdots = \mu_g$ (Equal population means for g groups).
> H_a: at least two of the population means are different.
>
> 3. **Test Statistic:** $F = \dfrac{\text{Between-groups variability}}{\text{Within-groups variability}}$.
>
> F sampling distribution has $df_1 = g-1$, $df_2 = N - g =$ total sample size $-$ number of groups.
>
> 4. **P-value:** Right-tail probability above observed F value.
>
> 5. **Conclusion:** Interpret in context. If decision needed, reject H_0 if P-value $\leq$ significance level (such as 0.05).

Example 3

One-Way ANOVA ◄

Telephone Holding Times

Picture the Scenario

Examples 1 and 2 discussed a study of the length of time that 15 callers to an airline's toll-free telephone number remain on hold before hanging up. The study compared three recordings: an advertisement about the airline, Muzak, and classical music. Let μ_1, μ_2, and μ_3 denote the population mean telephone holding times for the three recordings.

Questions to Explore

a. For testing $H_0: \mu_1 = \mu_2 = \mu_3$ based on this experiment, what value of the F test statistic would have a P-value of 0.05?

b. For the data in Table 14.1, we'll see that the *ANOVA (One Way)* app as well as other software reports $F = 6.4$. Based on the answer to part a, will the P-value be larger, or smaller, than 0.05?

c. Can you reject H_0, using a significance level of 0.05? What can you conclude from this?

Think It Through

a. With $g = 3$ groups and a total sample size of $N = 15$ (5 in each group), the test statistic has

$$df_1 = g - 1 = 2 \text{ and } df_2 = N - g = 15 - 3 = 12.$$

From Table D (see the excerpt in the margin) with these df values, an F test statistic value of 3.89 results in a P-value of 0.05.

F values corresponding to a P-value of 0.05

df_2	df_1 1	2	3
6	5.99	5.14	4.76
12	4.75	3.89	3.49
18	4.41	3.55	3.16
24	4.26	3.40	3.01
30	4.17	3.32	2.92
120	3.92	3.07	2.68

F distribution with $df_1 = 2$, $df_2 = 12$

Shaded right tail area = 0.05

b. Since the F test statistic of 6.4 is farther out in the tail than 3.89 (see figure in margin), the right-tail probability above 6.4 is less than 0.05. So, the P-value is less than 0.05.

c. Since the P-value < 0.05, there is sufficient evidence to reject H_0: $\mu_1 = \mu_2 = \mu_3$. We conclude that the population mean time that customers are willing to remain on hold differs for at least two of the three types of recordings.

Insight

We'll see that software reports a P-value = 0.013. This is quite strong evidence against H_0. If H_0 were true, there'd be only about a 1% chance of getting an F test statistic value as large or larger than the observed F value of 6.4.

▶ *Try Exercise 14.2, parts a–c*

The Variance Estimates and the ANOVA Table

Now let's take a closer look at the F test statistic. Denote the group sample means by $\bar{y}_1, \bar{y}_2, \ldots, \bar{y}_g$. (We use y rather than x because the quantitative variable is the response variable when used in a corresponding regression analysis.) We'll see that the F test statistic depends on these sample means, the sample standard deviations $s_1, s_2, \ldots, s_g$ for the g groups, and the sample sizes.

One assumption for the ANOVA F test is that each population has the same standard deviation. Let σ denote the standard deviation for each of the g population distributions. The F test statistic for H_0: $\mu_1 = \mu_2 = \cdots = \mu_g$ is the ratio of two estimates of σ^2, the population *variance* for each group. Since we won't perform computations by hand, we'll show formulas merely to give a better sense of what the F test statistic represents. The formulas are simplest when the group sample sizes are equal (as in Example 3), the case we'll show.

The estimate of σ^2 in the *denominator* of the F test statistic uses the variability *within* each group. The sample standard deviations $s_1, s_2, \ldots, s_g$ summarize the variation of the observations within the groups around their means.

Recall

With $g = 2$, s^2 is the square of the pooled standard deviation we used for the t test towards the end of Section 10.2. ◀

- With equal sample sizes, the **within-groups estimate** of the variance σ^2 is the average of the g sample variances for the g groups,

$$\text{Within-groups variance estimate } s^2 = \frac{s_1^2 + s_2^2 + \cdots + s_g^2}{g}.$$

When the sample sizes are not equal, the within-groups estimate is a *weighted average* of the sample variances, with greater weight given to samples with larger sample sizes. In either case, this estimate is unbiased: Its sampling distribution has σ^2 as its mean, regardless of whether H_0 is true.

The estimate of σ^2 in the *numerator* of the F test statistic uses the variability *between* each sample mean and the overall sample mean $\bar{y}$ for all the data.

Did You Know?

Without n in the formula, the between-groups estimate is the sample variance of the g sample means. That sample variance of $\{\bar{y}_1, \bar{y}_2, \ldots, \bar{y}_g\}$ estimates the variance of the sampling distribution of each sample mean, which is σ^2/n. Multiplying by n then gives an estimate of σ^2 itself. See Exercise 14.67. ◀

- With equal sample sizes, n in each group, the **between-groups estimate** of the variance σ^2 is

$$\begin{matrix}\text{Between-groups} \\ \text{variance estimate}\end{matrix} = \frac{n[(\bar{y}_1 - \bar{y})^2 + (\bar{y}_2 - \bar{y})^2 + \cdots + (\bar{y}_g - \bar{y})^2]}{g - 1}.$$

If H_0 is true, this estimate is also unbiased. We expect this estimate to take a similar value as the within-groups estimate, apart from sampling error. If H_0 is false, however, the population means differ and the sample means tend to differ more greatly. Then, the between-groups estimate tends to overestimate σ^2.

The F test statistic is the ratio of these two estimates of the population variance,

$$F = \frac{\text{Between-groups estimate of } \sigma^2}{\text{Within-groups estimate of } \sigma^2}.$$

Computer software displays the two estimates in an ANOVA table similar to tables displayed in regression. Table 14.2 shows the basic format, illustrating the test in Example 3:

■ The MS column contains the two estimates, which are called *mean squares*.

■ The ratio of the two mean squares is the F test statistic, $F = 74.6/11.6 = 6.4$.

This F test statistic has P-value $= 0.013$, also shown in Table 14.2.

The mean square in the group row of the ANOVA table is based on variability *between* the groups. It is the *between-groups* estimate of the population variance σ^2. This is 74.6 in Table 14.2, listed under MS. The mean square error is the *within-groups* estimate s^2 of σ^2. This is 11.6 in Table 14.2. The "Error" label for this MS refers to the fact that it summarizes the error from not being able to predict subjects' responses exactly if we know only the group to which they belong.

Table 14.2 ANOVA Table for F Test Using Data From Table 14.1

	Source	DF	SS	MS	F	P
Between groups	Group	2	149.2	74.6	6.43	0.013
	Error	12	139.2	11.6		
Within groups	Total	14	288.4			

F test statistic = ratio of the MS values

Each mean square equals a sum of squares (in the SS column) divided by a degrees of freedom value (in the DF column). The *df* values for Group and Error in Table 14.2 are the *df* values for the F distribution, $df_1 = g - 1 = 3 - 1 = 2$ and $df_2 = N - g = 15 - 3 = 12$.

The sum of the between-groups sum of squares and the within-groups (Error) sum of squares is the **total sum of squares**. This is the sum of squares of the combined sample of N observations around the overall sample mean. The analysis of variance partitions the total sum of squares into two independent parts, the between-groups SS and the within-groups SS. It can be shown that the total sum of squares equals

$$\text{Total SS} = \Sigma(y - \bar{y})^2 = \text{between-groups SS} + \text{within-groups SS}.$$

In Table 14.2, for example,

$$\text{Total SS} = 288.4 = 149.2 + 139.2.$$

The total SS divided by $N - 1$ (the *df* for the total SS) is the sample variance when the data for the g groups are combined and treated as a single sample.

Assumptions and the Effects of Violating Them

The assumptions for the ANOVA F test comparing population means are:

(1) The population distributions of the response variable for the g groups are normal,

(2) Those distributions have the same standard deviation σ, and

(3) The data resulted from randomization.

Figure 14.3 portrays the population distribution assumptions.

The assumptions that the population distributions are normal with identical standard deviations seem stringent. They are never satisfied exactly in practice. Moderate violations of the normality assumption are not serious. The F sampling distribution still provides a reasonably good approximation to the actual sampling distribution of the F test statistic. This becomes even more the case as the

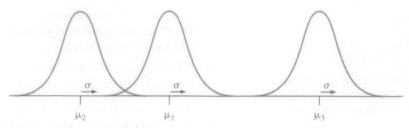

▲ **Figure 14.3** The Assumptions About the Population Distributions: Normal With Equal Standard Deviations. **Question** In practice, what types of evidence would suggest that these assumptions are badly violated?

sample sizes increase, because the sampling distribution then has weaker dependence on the form of the population distributions.

Moderate violations of the equal population standard deviation assumption are also not serious. When the sample sizes are identical for the groups, the F test still works well even with severe violations of this assumption. When the sample sizes are not equal, the F test works quite well as long as the largest group standard deviation is no more than about twice the smallest group standard deviation.

You can construct box plots or dot plots for the sample data distributions to check for extreme violations of normality. (The *ANOVA (One Way)* app provides both plots by default.) Misleading results may occur with the F test if the distributions are highly skewed and the sample size N is small, or if there are relatively large differences among the standard deviations (the largest sample standard deviation being more than double the smallest one) and the sample sizes are unequal. When the distributions are highly skewed, the mean may not even be a relevant summary measure.[1]

In Practice Robustness of ANOVA F test

Since the ANOVA F test is robust to moderate breakdowns in the population normality and equal standard deviation assumptions, in practice it is used unless (1) graphical methods show extreme skew for the response variable or (2) the largest group standard deviation is more than about double the smallest group standard deviation and the sample sizes are unequal.

Example 4

ANOVA Assumptions ◄

Telephone Holding Time Study

Picture the Scenario

Let's check the assumptions for the F test on telephone holding times (Example 3).

Question to Explore

Is it appropriate to apply ANOVA to the data in Table 14.1 to compare mean telephone holding times for three recording types?

Think It Through

Subjects were selected randomly for the experiment and assigned randomly to the three recording types. From Table 14.1 (summarized in the margin), the largest sample standard deviation of 4.2 is less than twice the smallest standard deviation of 2.4. (In any case, the sample sizes are equal, so this assumption is not crucial.) The sample sizes in Table 14.1 are small, so it is difficult to make judgments about shapes of population distributions. However,

Recall

Table 14.1 showed the following:

Recording	Sample Size	Mean	Std. Dev.
Advert.	5	5.4	4.2
Muzak	5	2.8	2.4
Classical	5	10.4	3.4

◄

---

[1]Chapter 15 discusses methods that apply when these assumptions are badly violated.

Type of Message

the dot plots in Figure 14.2a did not show evidence of severe nonnormality, and the side-by-side box plots in the margin show no outliers. Thus, ANOVA is suitable for these data.

Insight

As in other statistical inferences, the method used to gather the data is the most crucial factor. Inferences have greater validity when the data are from an experimental study that randomly assigned subjects to groups or from a sample survey that used random sampling.

▶ **Try Exercise 14.11, part c**

Recall

See the beginning of Chapter 10 to review the distinction between **independent samples** and **dependent samples**. ◀

The ANOVA methods in this chapter are designed for *independent* samples. Recall that for independent samples, the subjects in one sample are distinct from those in other samples. Separate methods, beyond the scope of this book, handle *dependent* samples.

Using One *F* Test or Several *t* Tests to Compare the Means

Recall

To compare two means while assuming equal population standard deviations, Section 10.2 showed the test statistic is

$$t = \frac{\bar{y}_1 - \bar{y}_2}{s\sqrt{\frac{1}{n_1} + \frac{1}{n_2}}},$$

where the standard deviation s pools information from within both samples. It has $df = n_1 + n_2 - 2 = N - g$ for $N = n_1 + n_2$ and $g = 2$. ◀

With two groups, Section 10.2 showed how a *t* test can compare the means under the assumption of equal population standard deviations. That test also uses between-groups and within-groups variation. The *t* test statistic has the difference *between* the two group means in the numerator and a denominator based on pooling variability *within* the two groups. See the formula in the margin. In fact, if we apply the ANOVA *F* test to data from $g = 2$ groups, it can be shown that the *F* test statistic equals the square of this *t* test statistic. The P-value for the *F* test is exactly the same as the two-sided P-value for the *t* test. We can use either test to conduct the analysis.

When there are several groups, instead of using the *F* test why not use a *t* test to compare each pair of means? One reason for doing the *F* test is that using a *single* test rather than multiple tests enables us to control the probability of a Type I error. With a significance level of 0.05 in the *F* test, for instance, the probability of incorrectly rejecting a true H_0 is fixed at 0.05. When we conduct a separate *t* test for each pair of means, by contrast, a Type I error probability applies for *each* comparison. In that case, we are not controlling the *overall* Type I error rate for all the comparisons.

But the *F* test has its own disadvantages. With a small P-value, we can conclude that the population means are not identical. However, the result of the *F* test does not tell us *which* groups are different or *how* different they are. In Example 3, we have not concluded whether one recording works significantly better than the other two at keeping potential customers on the phone. We can address these issues using confidence intervals, as the next section shows.

14.1   Practicing the Basics

14.1   Hotel satisfaction   The CEO of a company that owns

TRY

five resort hotels wants to evaluate and compare satisfaction with the five hotels. The company's research department randomly sampled 125 people who had stayed at any of the hotels during the past month and

asked them to rate their expectations of the hotel before their stay and to rate the quality of the actual stay at the hotel. Both observations used a rating scale of 0–10, with 0 = very poor and 10 = excellent. The researchers compared the hotels on the gap between prior expectation and actual quality, using the difference score, y = performance gap = (prior expectation score − actual quality score).

a. Identify the response variable, the factor, and the categories that form the groups.

b. State the null and alternative hypotheses for conducting an ANOVA.

c. Explain why the df values for this ANOVA are $df_1 = 4$ and $df_2 = 120$.

d. How large an F test statistic is needed to get a P-value = 0.05 in this ANOVA?

14.2 Satisfaction with banking A bank conducts a survey in which it randomly samples 400 of its customers. The survey asks the customers which way they use the bank the most: (1) interacting with a teller at the bank, (2) using ATMs, or (3) using the bank's online banking service. It also asks their level of satisfaction with the service they most often use (on a scale of 0 to 10 with 0 = very poor and 10 = excellent). Does mean satisfaction differ according to how they most use the bank?

a. Identifying notation, state the null and alternative hypotheses for conducting an ANOVA with data from the survey.

b. Report the df values for this ANOVA. Above what F test statistic values give a P-value below 0.05?

c. For the data, $F = 0.46$ and the P-value equals 0.63. What can you conclude?

d. What were the assumptions on which the ANOVA was based? Which assumption is the most important?

14.3 What's the best way to learn French? The following table shows scores on the first quiz (maximum score 10 points) for eighth-grade students in an introductory level French course. The instructor grouped the students in the course as follows:

Group 1: Never studied foreign language before but have good English skills

Group 2: Never studied foreign language before and have poor English skills

Group 3: Studied at least one other foreign language

French Scores on the Quiz

		Group 1	Group 2	Group 3
		4	1	9
		6	5	10
		8		5
Mean		6.0	3.0	8.0
Std. Dev.		2.000	2.828	2.646

Source	DF	SS	MS	F	P
Group	2	30.00	15.00	2.50	0.177
Error	5	30.00	6.00		
Total	7	60.00			

a. Defining notation and using results obtained with software, also shown in the table, report the five steps of the ANOVA test.

b. The sample means are quite different, but the P-value is not small. Name one important reason for this. (*Hint:* For given sample means, how do the results of the test depend on the sample sizes?)

c. Was this an experimental study, or an observational study? Explain how a lurking variable could be responsible for Group 3 having a larger mean than the others. (Thus, even if the P-value were small, it is inappropriate to assume that having studied at least one foreign language causes one to perform better on this quiz.)

14.4 What affects the F value? Refer to the previous exercise.

a. Suppose that the first observation in the second group was actually 9, not 1. Then the standard deviations are the same as reported in the table, but the sample means are 6, 7, and 8 rather than 6, 3, and 8. Do you think the F test statistic would be larger, the same, or smaller? Explain your reasoning, without doing any calculations.

b. Suppose you had the same means as shown in the table but the sample standard deviations were 1.0, 1.8, and 1.6, instead of 2.0, 2.8, and 2.6. Do you think the F test statistic would be larger, the same, or smaller? Explain your reasoning.

c. Suppose you had the same means and standard deviations as shown in the table but the sample sizes were 30, 20, and 30, instead of 3, 2, and 3. Do you think the F test statistic would be larger, the same, or smaller? Explain your reasoning.

d. In parts a, b, and c, would the P-value be larger, the same, or smaller? Why?

14.5 Outsourcing Example 1 at the beginning of this chapter mentioned a study to compare customer satisfaction at service centers in San Jose, California; Toronto, Canada; and Bangalore, India. Each center randomly sampled 100 people who called during a two-week period. Callers rated their satisfaction on a scale of 0 to 10, with higher scores representing greater satisfaction. The sample means were 7.6 for San Jose, 7.8 for Toronto, and 7.1 for Bangalore. The table shows the results of conducting an ANOVA.

a. Define notation and specify the null hypothesis tested in this table.

b. Explain how to obtain the F test statistic value reported in the table from the MS values shown and report the values of df_1 and df_2 for the F distribution.

c. Interpret the P-value reported for this test. What conclusion would you make using a 0.05 significance level?

Customer Satisfaction with Outsourcing

Source	DF	SS	MS	F	P
Group	2	26.00	13.00	27.6	0.000
Error	297	140.00	0.47		
Total	299	60.00			

14.6   ANOVA and box plots   For two studies, each comparing three groups, the box plots below show results. (Each box plot is based on a random sample of size 40.)

  a. Judging from the box plots, which study will more likely lead to a rejection of the ANOVA null hypothesis of equal population means? Explain.

  b. Which study will have the larger value for the F test statistic? Why?

  c. The P-value for the ANOVA F test for the second study equals 0.001. Does this necessarily imply that all three population means are different from each other?

Group

14.7   How many kids to have?   A recent General Social Survey asked subjects, "What is the ideal number of kids for a family?" Do responses tend to depend on the subjects' religious affiliation? Results of an ANOVA are shown in the printout, for religion categories (Protestant, Catholic, Jewish, or Other).

  a. Define notation and specify the null hypothesis tested in this printout.

  b. Summarize the assumptions made to conduct this test.

  c. Report the F test statistic value and the P-value for this test. Interpret the P-value.

  d. Based on part c, can you conclude that *every* pair of religious affiliations has different population means for ideal family size? Explain.

Ideal Number of Kids in a Family by Religious Affiliation

```
Source     DF     SS      MS      F      P
Religion    3    11.72    3.91    5.40   0.001
Error     1295   922.82   0.71
Total     1298   934.54
```

14.8   Smoking and personality   A study about smoking and personality (by A. Terracciano and P. Costa, *Addiction*, vol. 99, 2004, pp. 472–481) used a sample of 1,638 adults in the Baltimore Longitudinal Study on Aging. The subjects formed three groups according to smoking status (never, former, current). Each subject completed a personality questionnaire that provided scores on various personality scales designed to have overall means of about 50 and standard deviations of about 10. The table shows some

results for three traits, giving the means with standard deviations in parentheses.

	Never Smokers ($n = 828$)	Former Smokers ($n = 694$)	Current Smokers ($n = 116$)	F
Neuroticism	46.7 (9.6)	48.5 (9.2)	51.9 (9.9)	17.77
Extraversion	50.4 (10.3)	50.2 (10.0)	50.9 (9.4)	0.24
Conscientiousness	51.8 (10.1)	48.9 (9.7)	45.6 (10.3)	29.42

  a. For the F test for the extraversion scale, using the 0.05 significance level, what conclusion would you make?

  b. Refer to part a. Does this indicate that the population means are necessarily equal?

14.9   French cuisine   The restaurant guide Zagat compiles customer ratings on the quality of food on a 30-point scale. The data set French Cuisine, available in the *ANOVA (One Way)* app and on the book's website, contains a random sample of ratings of French cuisine restaurants in New York, London, and Paris, compiled in June 2015 from the zagat.com website.

  a. Using software, construct dot plots or side-by-side box plots that show the data and find the mean and standard deviation of the ratings in each city.

  b. Conduct an ANOVA. Report the hypotheses, F test statistic value, P-value, and interpret results. Use a significance level of 0.05.

14.10   French ANOVA   Refer to Exercise 14.3. Using the *ANOVA (One Way)* app or other software,

  a. Enter the data into the *ANOVA (One Way)* app or create the data file and find the sample means and standard deviations.

  b. Find and report the ANOVA table. Interpret the P-value.

  c. Change an observation in Group 2 so that the P-value will be smaller. Specify the value you changed and report the resulting F test statistic and the P-value. Explain why the value you changed would have this effect.

14.11   Comparing therapies for anorexia   The Anorexia data file (available in the *ANOVA (One Way)* app and on the book's website) shows weight change for 72 anorexic teenage girls who were randomly assigned to one of three psychological treatments (cognitive or family therapy and a control treatment). Use the app or other software to analyze these data. (The change scores are in the last three columns of the data set. Alternatively, the website also contains a dataset that shows the data in "long" format, with the treatment in one column and the change score in another column.)

  a. Construct box plots for the three groups. Use these and sample summary means and standard deviations to describe the three samples.

  b. For the one-way ANOVA comparing the three mean weight changes, report the test statistic and P-value. Explain how to interpret.

  c. State and check the assumptions for the test in part b.

14.2 Estimating Differences in Groups for a Single Factor

When an analysis of variance F test has a small P-value, the test does not specify *which* means are different or *how* different they are. In practice, we can estimate differences between population means with confidence intervals.

Confidence Intervals Comparing Pairs of Means

Recall

s^2 is an unbiased estimator of σ^2, regardless of whether H_0 is true in the ANOVA F test. ◄

Remember that one of the assumptions in ANOVA is a common standard deviation σ for the distribution of the response variable in each group. We can estimate this common standard deviation by s, the square root of the within-groups variance s^2 that we used in the denominator of the F test statistic. It is the square root of the mean square error that software reports (the MS in the row for "Error" of any ANOVA table).

> ### SUMMARY: Confidence Interval Comparing Means
>
> For two groups i and j, with sample means $\bar{y}_i$ and $\bar{y}_j$ having sample sizes n_i and n_j, the 95% confidence interval for $\mu_i - \mu_j$ is
>
> $$\bar{y}_i - \bar{y}_j \pm t_{.025}\, s\sqrt{\frac{1}{n_i} + \frac{1}{n_j}}.$$
>
> The t-score from the t table has $df = N - g = $ total sample size $-$ # groups.

The df value of $N - g$ for the t-score is also df_2 for the F test. This is the df for the MS error. For $g = 2$ groups, $N = n_1 + n_2$ and $df = N - g = (n_1 + n_2 - 2)$. This confidence interval is then identical to the one introduced in Section 10.2 for $(\mu_1 - \mu_2)$ based on a pooled standard deviation. In the context of follow-up analyses after the ANOVA F test where we form this confidence interval to compare a pair of means, some software (such as MINITAB) refers to this method of comparing means as the **Fisher method**.

When the confidence interval does not contain 0, we can infer that the population means are different. The interval shows just how different they may be.

Example 5

Fisher Method ◄

Number of Good Friends and Happiness

Picture the Scenario

Chapter 11 investigated the association between happiness and several categorical variables, using data from the General Social Survey (GSS). The respondents indicated whether they were very happy, pretty happy, or not too happy. Is happiness associated with having lots of friends? A recent GSS asked, "About how many good friends do you have?" Here, we could treat either happiness (variable HAPPY in GSS) or number of good friends (NUMFREND in GSS) as the response variable. If we choose number of good friends, then we are in the ANOVA setting, having a quantitative response variable and a categorical explanatory variable (happiness).

For each happiness category, Table 14.3 shows the sample mean, standard deviation, and sample size for the number of good friends. It also shows the ANOVA table for the F test comparing the population means. The small P-value of 0.0025 suggests that at least two of the three population means are different.

Table 14.3 Summary of ANOVA for Comparing Mean Number of Good Friends for Three Happiness Categories

		Very happy	Pretty happy	Not too happy
Mean		7.6	5.7	6.3
Standard deviation		8.7	5.9	8.0
Sample size		267	459	85

Source	DF	SS	MS	F	P
Group	2	617	308.32	6.023	0.0025
Error	808	41362	51.19		
Total	810	41979			

Question to Explore

Use 95% confidence intervals to compare the population mean number of good friends for the three pairs of happiness categories — very happy with pretty happy, very happy with not too happy, and pretty happy with not too happy.

Think It Through

From Table 14.3, the MS error equals 51.19. The estimated standard deviation of the number of friends at each category of happiness is $s = \sqrt{51.19} = 7.15$. For a 95% confidence interval with $df = 808$ (listed in the same row as MS error), the t score is $t_{0.025} = 1.963$. (Because the df are so large, this is essentially the same as the corresponding z-score.) For comparing the very happy and pretty happy categories, the confidence interval for $\mu_1 - \mu_2$ is

$$(\bar{y}_1 - \bar{y}_2) \pm t_{.025}\, s\sqrt{\frac{1}{n_1} + \frac{1}{n_2}} = (7.6 - 5.7) \pm 1.963(7.15)\sqrt{\frac{1}{267} + \frac{1}{459}}$$

which is 1.9 ± 1.1, or $(0.8, 3.0)$.

With 95% confidence, we estimate that the population mean number of good friends is between about 1 and 3 higher for those who are very happy than for those who are pretty happy. Since the confidence interval contains only positive numbers, this suggests that $\mu_1 - \mu_2 > 0$; that is, μ_1 exceeds μ_2. On the average, people who are very happy have more good friends than people who are pretty happy.

For the other comparisons, you can find

> Very happy, not too happy: 95% CI for $\mu_1 - \mu_3$ is
> $(7.6 - 6.3) \pm 1.7$, or $(-0.4, 3.0)$.
>
> Pretty happy, not too happy: 95% CI for $\mu_2 - \mu_3$ is
> $(5.7 - 6.3) \pm 1.7$, or $(-2.3, 1.1)$.

These two confidence intervals contain 0. So there's not enough evidence to conclude that a difference exists between μ_1 and μ_3 or between μ_2 and μ_3.

Insight

The confidence intervals are quite wide, even though the sample sizes are fairly large. This is because the sample standard deviations (and hence s) are large. Table 14.3 shows that the lowest possible value of 0 is less than one standard deviation below the mean, suggesting that the three distributions are skewed to the right. The margin figure shows box plots of the distribution of number of good friends in each group, except for many large outliers (as large as 75). Do non-normal population distributions invalidate this inferential analysis? We'll discuss this next.

▶ *Try Exercise 14.12*

Recall

From Section 10.2, a 95% confidence interval for $\mu_1 - \mu_2$ using separate standard deviations s_1 and s_2 is

$$\bar{y}_1 - \bar{y}_2 \pm t_{.025}\sqrt{\frac{s_1^2}{n_1} + \frac{s_2^2}{n_2}}.$$

Software supplies the *df* value and the confidence interval. ◄

The Effects of Violating Assumptions

The *t* confidence intervals have the same assumptions as the ANOVA *F* test: (1) normal population distributions, (2) identical standard deviations, and (3) data that resulted from randomization. These inferences also are not highly dependent on the normality assumption, especially when the sample sizes are large, such as in Example 5. When the standard deviations are quite different, with the ratio of the largest to smallest exceeding about 2, it is preferable to use the confidence interval formula from Section 10.2 (see the margin Recall) that uses *separate* standard deviations for the groups rather than a single pooled value *s*. That approach does not assume equal standard deviations.

In Example 5, the sample standard deviations are not very different (ranging from 5.9 to 8.7), and the GSS is a multistage random sample with properties similar to a simple random sample. Thus, Assumptions 2 and 3 are reasonably well satisfied. The sample sizes are fairly large, so Assumption 1 of normality is not crucial. It's justifiable to use ANOVA and follow-up confidence intervals with these data.

Controlling Overall Confidence With Many Confidence Intervals

With *g* groups, there are $g(g-1)/2$ pairs of groups to compare. With $g = 3$, for instance, there are $g(g-1)/2 = 3(2)/2 = 3$ comparisons: Group 1 with Group 2, Group 1 with Group 3, and Group 2 with Group 3.

The confidence interval method just discussed is mainly used when *g* is small or when only a few comparisons are of main interest. When there are many groups, the number of comparisons can be large. For example, when $g = 10$, there are $g(g-1)/2 = 45$ pairs of means to compare. If we plan to construct 95% confidence intervals for these comparisons, an error probability of 0.05 applies to *each* comparison. On average, $45(0.05) = 2.25$ of the confidence intervals would *not* contain the true differences of means.

For 95% confidence intervals, the confidence level of 0.95 is the probability that *any particular* confidence interval that we plan to construct will contain the parameter. The probability that *all* the confidence intervals will contain the parameters is considerably smaller than the confidence level for any particular interval. How can we construct the intervals so that the 95% confidence extends to the *entire set* of intervals rather than to *each single* interval? Methods that control the probability that *all* confidence intervals will contain the true differences in means are called **multiple comparison methods.** For these methods, *all* intervals are designed to contain the true parameters *simultaneously* with an overall fixed probability.

Multiple Comparisons for Comparing All Pairs of Means

Multiple comparison methods compare pairs of means with a confidence level that applies simultaneously to the entire set of comparisons rather than to each separate comparison.

To ensure that the overall confidence level is met, we need to make each interval wider. One simple way to achieve this is to construct each confidence interval with a higher confidence level, that is, using a *t*-score that is larger than $t_{0.025}$. To find the exact confidence level at which to construct each interval, the desired overall error probability is split into equal parts for each comparison. Suppose we want a confidence level of 0.95 that *all* confidence intervals will be simultaneously correct. If we plan to construct five confidence intervals comparing means, then the method uses error probability $0.05/5 = 0.01$ for each one; that is, a 99% confidence level for each separate interval. This approach ensures that the overall confidence level is *at least* 0.95. (It may actually be a bit larger.) Called the **Bonferroni** method, it is based on a special case of a probability theorem shown by Italian probabilist, Carlo Bonferroni, in 1936 (Exercise 14.68).

We shall instead use the **Tukey method.** It is designed to give an overall confidence level *very close* to the desired value (such as 0.95) when we compare all possible pairs of means, and it has the advantage that its confidence intervals are slightly narrower than the Bonferroni intervals. The Tukey method is more complex, using a sampling distribution pertaining to the difference between the largest and smallest of the g sample means. We do not present its formula, but it is easy to obtain with the *ANOVA (One Way)* app or other software.

Recall

John Tukey was responsible for many statistical innovations, including box plots and other methods of exploratory data analysis (EDA). See On the Shoulders of... John Tukey in Section 2.7 to read more about Tukey and EDA. ◀

Tukey Method ◀

Example 6

Number of Good Friends

Picture the Scenario

Example 5 compared the population mean numbers of good friends, for three levels of reported happiness. There, we constructed a *separate* 95% confidence interval for the difference between each pair of means. Table 14.4 displays these three intervals. The probability that at least one of them will not contain the true parameter value is larger than 0.05 because these intervals are not constructed using a multiple comparison method. Table 14.4 also displays the confidence intervals that software reports for the Tukey multiple comparison method. The probability that one of these will not contain the true difference is about 0.05.

Table 14.4 Multiple Comparisons of Mean Number of Good Friends for Three Happiness Categories

Groups	Difference of Means	Separate 95% CIs	Tukey 95% Multiple Comparison CIs
(Very Happy, Pretty Happy)	$\mu_1 - \mu_2$	(0.8, 3.0)	(0.6, 3.2)
(Very Happy, Not Too Happy)	$\mu_1 - \mu_3$	(−0.4, 3.0)	(−0.8, 3.4)
(Pretty Happy, Not Too Happy)	$\mu_2 - \mu_3$	(−2.3, 1.1)	(−2.6, 1.4)

Question to Explore

a. Explain how the Tukey multiple comparison confidence intervals differ from the separate confidence intervals in Table 14.4.

b. Summarize results shown for the Tukey multiple comparisons.

Think It Through

a. The Tukey confidence intervals hold with an *overall* confidence level of about 95%. This confidence applies to the entire set of three intervals. The Tukey confidence intervals are wider than the separate 95% confidence intervals because the multiple comparison approach uses a higher confidence level for each separate interval to ensure achieving the overall confidence level of 95% for the entire set of intervals.

b. The Tukey confidence interval for $\mu_1 - \mu_2$ contains only positive values, so we infer that $\mu_1 > \mu_2$. The mean number of good friends is higher, although perhaps barely so, for those who are very happy than for those who are pretty happy. The other two Tukey intervals contain 0, so we cannot infer that those pairs of means differ.

Insight

Figure 14.4 summarizes the three Tukey comparisons from Table 14.4. The intervals have different lengths because the group sample sizes are different.

▲ **Figure 14.4** Summary of Tukey Comparisons of Pairs of Means.

▶ *Try Exercise 14.15*

ANOVA and Regression

ANOVA can be presented as a special case of multiple regression. The factor defining the groups enters the regression model using *indicator variables*. Each indicator variable takes only two values, 0 and 1, and indicates whether an observation falls in a particular group.

With three groups, we need two indicator variables to indicate the group membership. The first indicator variable is

Recall

You can review **indicator variables** in Section 13.5. We used them there to include a categorical explanatory variable in a regression model. ◀

$$x_1 = 1 \text{ for observations from the first group}$$
$$= 0 \text{ otherwise.}$$

The second indicator variable is

$$x_2 = 1 \text{ for observations from the second group}$$
$$= 0 \text{ otherwise.}$$

The indicator variables identify the group to which an observation belongs as follows:

$$\text{Group 1: } x_1 = 1 \text{ and } x_2 = 0$$
$$\text{Group 2: } x_1 = 0 \text{ and } x_2 = 1$$
$$\text{Group 3: } x_1 = 0 \text{ and } x_2 = 0.$$

We don't need a separate indicator variable for the third group. We know an observation is in that group if $x_1 = 0$ and $x_2 = 0$.

With these indicator variables, the multiple regression equation for the mean of y is

$$\mu_y = \alpha + \beta_1 x_1 + \beta_2 x_2.$$

For observations from the third group, $x_1 = x_2 = 0$, and the equation reduces to

$$\mu_y = \alpha + \beta_1(0) + \beta_2(0) = \alpha.$$

So the parameter α represents the population mean of the response variable y for the last group. For observations from the first group, $x_1 = 1$ and $x_2 = 0$, so

$$\mu_y = \alpha + \beta_1(1) + \beta_2(0) = \alpha + \beta_1$$

equals the population mean μ_1 for that group. Similarly, $\alpha + \beta_2$ equals the population mean μ_2 for the second group (for which $x_1 = 0$ and $x_2 = 1$).

Since $\alpha + \beta_1 = \mu_1$ and $\alpha = \mu_3$, the difference between the means

$$\mu_1 - \mu_3 = (\alpha + \beta_1) - \alpha = \beta_1.$$

This shows that the coefficient β_1 of the first indicator variable represents the difference between the first mean and the last mean. Likewise, $\beta_2 = \mu_2 - \mu_3$. In other words, the beta coefficients of the indicator variables represent differences between the mean of each group and the mean of the last group. Table 14.5 summarizes the parameters of the regression model and their correspondence with the three population means.

Table 14.5 Interpretation of Coefficients of Indicator Variables in Regression Model

The indicator variables represent a categorical predictor with three categories specifying three groups.

| Group | Indicator | | Mean of y | Interpretation of β |
	x_1	x_2		
1	1	0	$\mu_1 = \alpha + \beta_1$	$\beta_1 = \mu_1 - \mu_3$
2	0	1	$\mu_2 = \alpha + \beta_2$	$\beta_2 = \mu_2 - \mu_3$
3	0	0	$\mu_3 = \alpha$	

Using Regression for the ANOVA Comparison of Means

Recall

Section 13.3 introduced the **F test** that all the beta parameters in a multiple regression model equal 0. ◄

For three groups, the null hypothesis for the ANOVA F test is H_0: $\mu_1 = \mu_2 = \mu_3$. If H_0 is true, then $\mu_1 - \mu_3 = 0$ and $\mu_2 - \mu_3 = 0$. In the multiple regression model

$$\mu_y = \alpha + \beta_1 x_1 + \beta_2 x_2$$

with indicator variables, recall that $\mu_1 - \mu_3 = \beta_1$ and $\mu_2 - \mu_3 = \beta_2$. Therefore, the ANOVA null hypothesis H_0: $\mu_1 = \mu_2 = \mu_3$ is equivalent to H_0: $\beta_1 = \beta_2 = 0$ in the regression model. If the beta parameters in the regression model all equal 0, then the mean of the response variable equals α for each group. We can perform the ANOVA test comparing means using the F test of H_0: $\beta_1 = \beta_2 = 0$ for this regression model.

Example 7

Regression Analysis ◄

Telephone Holding Times

Picture the Scenario

Let's return to the data we analyzed in Examples 1 to 4 on telephone holding times for callers to an airline for which the recording that they hear is an advertisement, Muzak, or classical music.

Questions to Explore

a. Set up indicator variables to use regression to model the mean holding times with the type of recorded message as the explanatory variable.

b. Table 14.6 shows a portion of a MINITAB printout for fitting this model. Use it to find the estimated mean holding time for the advertisement recording.

c. Use Table 14.6 to conduct the ANOVA F test (note that the table is the same as the one presented in Example 3).

Table 14.6 Printout for Regression Model $\mu_y = \alpha + \beta_1 x_1 + \beta_2 x_2$ for Telephone Holding Times and Type of Recording

The indicator variables are x_1 for the advertisement and x_2 for Muzak.

Term	Coef	SE Coef	T-Value	P-Value
Constant	10.400	1.523	6.83	0.000
x_1	-5.000	2.154	-2.32	0.039
x_2	-7.600	2.154	-3.53	0.004

Analysis of Variance

Source	DF	SS	MS	F-Value	P-Value
Regression	2	149.20	74.60	6.43	0.013
Error	12	139.20	11.60		
Total	14	288.40			

Think It Through

a. The factor (type of recording) has three categories—advertisement, Muzak, and classical music. With three groups, we need to set up two indicator variables x_1 and x_2 with

$$x_1 = 1 \text{ for the advertisement (and 0 otherwise),}$$
$$x_2 = 1 \text{ for Muzak (and 0 otherwise).}$$

When $x_1 = x_2 = 0$, this indicates that the recording played was classical music, and no separate indicator variable for this group is needed.

The regression model for the mean of y = telephone holding time is then

$$\mu_y = \alpha + \beta_1 x_1 + \beta_2 x_2.$$

b. From Table 14.6, the prediction equation is

$$\hat{y} = 10.4 - 5.0x_1 - 7.6x_2.$$

For the advertisement, $x_1 = 1$ and $x_2 = 0$, so the estimated mean is $\hat{y} = 10.4 - 5.0(1) - 7.6(0) = 5.4$. This just equals the sample mean for the five subjects in that group.

c. From Table 14.6, the F test statistic for testing

$$H_0: \beta_1 = \beta_2 = 0$$

is $F = 6.43$, with $df_1 = 2$ and $df_2 = 12$. This null hypothesis is equivalent to

$$H_0: \mu_1 = \mu_2 = \mu_3.$$

Table 14.6 reports a P-value of 0.013. The regression approach provides the same F test statistic and P-value as the ANOVA did in Table 14.2.

Insight

Testing that the beta coefficients equal zero is equivalent to testing that the population means are equal. Because each beta coefficient refers to a particular difference in population means, confidence intervals for those coefficients give us confidence intervals for the difference between two population means. For instance, since $\beta_1 = \mu_1 - \mu_3$, a confidence interval for β_1 is also a confidence interval comparing μ_1 and μ_3. From Table 14.6, the estimate -5.0 of β_1 has $se = 2.154$. Since $df = 12$ ($= 15 - 3$, see margin recall), $t_{.025} = 2.179$, the 95% confidence interval for β_1 (equivalently $\mu_1 - \mu_3$) is

$$-5.0 \pm 2.179(2.154), \text{ or } -5.0 \pm 4.7, \text{ which is } (-9.7, -0.3).$$

Recall

Section 13.3 showed how to find a confidence interval for a multiple regression parameter beta as

estimated slope $\pm\ t_{0.025}(se)$,

where the *df* for the *t*-score is n − number of parameters in the regression equation. ◄

This agrees with the 95% confidence interval you would obtain using the formula presented at the beginning of this section (see summary box on page 750). Note that it is not straightforward to find the confidence interval for $\mu_1 - \mu_2$ using the multiple regression model, so for this interval you use the formula on page 750.

▶ *Try Exercise 14.17*

Notice the similarity between the ANOVA table for comparing means (Table 14.2) and the ANOVA table for regression (Table 14.6), both shown again in the margin. The "between-groups sum of squares" for ordinary ANOVA is the "regression sum of squares" for the regression model. This is the variability explained by the indicator variables for the groups. The "error sum of squares" for ordinary ANOVA is the residual error sum of squares for the regression model. This represents the variability within the groups. This sum of squares divided by its degrees of freedom is the mean square error $= 11.6$ (MS in the error row), which is also the within-groups estimate of the variance of the observations within the groups. The regression mean square is the between-groups estimate $= 74.6$. The ratio of the regression mean square to the mean square error is the F test statistic $(F = 6.4)$.

So far, this chapter has shown how to compare groups for a single factor. This is **one-way ANOVA.** Sometimes the groups to compare are the cells of a cross-classification of two or more factors. For example, the four groups (employed men, employed women, unemployed men, unemployed women) result from cross classifying employment status and gender. The next section presents **two-way ANOVA**, the procedure for comparing the mean of a quantitative response variable across categories of each of two factors.

Table 14.2: ANOVA Table for Comparing Means

Source	DF	SS	MS	F	P
Group	2	149.2	74.6	6.4	0.013
Error	12	139.2	11.6		
Total	14	288.4			

Table 14.6: ANOVA Table for Regression Model

Source	DF	SS	MS	F	P
Regression	2	149.2	74.6	6.4	.013
Error	12	139.2	11.6		
Total	14	288.4			

14.2   Practicing the Basics

14.12 House prices and age   For the House Selling Prices OR data file on the book's website, the output shows the result of conducting an ANOVA comparing mean house selling prices (in $1000) by Age Category (New $= 0$ to 24 years old, Medium $= 25$ to 50 years old, Old $= 51$ to 74 years old, Very Old $= 75 +$ years old). It also shows a summary table of means and standard deviations of the selling prices, by age group.

a. Using information given in the tables, show how to construct a 95% confidence interval comparing the population means of new and medium-aged houses.

b. Interpret the confidence interval.

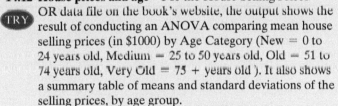

Age	N	Mean	StDev
New	78	305.8	125.9
Medium	72	242.8	79.3
Old	37	217.5	85.4
Very Old	13	316.3	195.4

Source	DF	SS	MS	F	P
Age Condition	3	281852	93951	7.70	0.000
Error	196	2387017	12179		
Total	199	2668870			

14.13 Time on Facebook   Do freshmen spend significantly more time on Facebook than other class ranks? A recent study (R. Junco, *Journal of Applied Developmental Psychology,* 2015, vol. 36, p. 18–29) investigated the amount of time per day freshmen, sophomores, juniors, and seniors spent on Facebook while doing school-work. The students surveyed were U.S. residents from a 4-year, public, primarily residential institution in the Northeastern United States. The data from the survey are available on the book's website, with time measured in minutes. The following computer output shows the mean time each cohort spent on Facebook and an ANOVA table. Construct a 95% confidence interval to compare the population mean time spent per day on Facebook between freshmen and seniors.

Summary Statistics for Time Spent on Facebook by Class Year and ANOVA Table

	FR	SO	JU	SE
n	440	347	403	407
Mean	63.7	56.5	70.4	49.0
Std. Dev.	71.5	67.7	79.0	63.7

Source	DF	SS	MS	F	P
Class	3	102903	34301	6.84	0.000
Error	1593	7988051	5014		
Total	1596	8090954			

14.14 Comparing telephone holding times Examples 2 and 3 analyzed whether telephone callers to an airline would stay on hold different lengths of time, on average, if they heard (a) an advertisement about the airline, (b) Muzak, or (c) classical music. The sample means were 5.4, 2.8, and 10.4, with $n_1 = n_2 = n_3 = 5$. The ANOVA test had $F = 74.6/11.6 = 6.4$ and a P-value of 0.013.

   a. A 95% confidence interval comparing the population mean times that callers are willing to remain on hold for classical music and Muzak is (2.9, 12.3). Interpret this interval.

   b. The margin of error was 4.7 for this comparison. Without doing a calculation, explain why the margin of error is 4.7 for comparing *each* pair of means.

   c. The 95% confidence intervals are (0.3, 9.7) for $\mu_3 - \mu_1$ and $(-7.3, 2.1)$ for $\mu_2 - \mu_1$. Interpret these two confidence intervals. Using these two intervals and the interval from part a, summarize what the airline company learned from this study.

   d. The confidence intervals are wide. In the design of this experiment, what could you change to estimate the differences in means more precisely?

14.15 Tukey holding time comparisons Refer to the previous exercise. We could instead use the Tukey method to construct multiple comparison confidence intervals. The Tukey confidence intervals having *overall* confidence level 95% have margins of error of 5.7, compared to 4.7 for the separate 95% confidence intervals in the previous exercise.

   a. According to this method, which groups are significantly different?

   b. Why are the margins of error larger than with the separate 95% intervals?

14.16 REM sleep A psychologist compares the mean amount of time of rapid-eye movement (REM) sleep for subjects under three conditions. She randomly assigns 12 subjects to the three groups, four per group. The sample means for the three groups were 18, 15, and 12. The table shows the ANOVA table from SPSS.

REM Sleep

Source	DF	SS	MS	F	P
Group	2	72.00	36.00	0.79	0.481
Error	9	408.00	45.33		
Total	11	480.00			

   a. Report and interpret the P-value for the ANOVA F test.

   b. For the Tukey 95% multiple comparison confidence intervals comparing each pair of means, the margin of error for each interval is 13.3. Is it true or false that since all the confidence intervals contain 0, it is plausible that all three population means equal 0?

   c. Would the margin of error for each separate 95% confidence interval be less than 13.3, equal to 13.3, or larger than 13.3? Explain why.

14.17 REM regression Refer to the previous exercise.

   a. Set up indicator variables for a regression model so that an F test for the regression parameters is equivalent to the ANOVA test comparing the three means.

   b. Express the null hypothesis both in terms of population means and in terms of regression parameters for the model in part a.

   c. The prediction equation from fitting the multiple regression model equals $\hat{y} = 12 + 6x_1 + 3x_2$. Use this equation to find the predicted population means for each group.

14.18 Outsourcing satisfaction Exercise 14.5 showed an ANOVA for comparing mean customer satisfaction scores for three service centers. The sample means on a scale of 0 to 10 were 7.60 in San Jose, 7.80 in Toronto, and 7.10 in Bangalore. Each sample size = 100, MS error = 0.47, and the F test statistic = 27.6 has P-value < 0.001.

   a. Explain why the margin of error for separate 95% confidence intervals is the same for comparing the population means for each pair of cities. Show that this margin of error is 0.19.

   b. Find the 95% confidence interval for the difference in population means for each pair of service centers. Interpret.

   c. The margin of error for Tukey 95% multiple comparison confidence intervals for comparing the service centers is 0.23. Construct the intervals. Interpret.

   d. Why are the confidence intervals different in part b and in part c? What is an advantage of using the Tukey intervals?

14.19 Regression for outsourcing Refer to the previous exercise.

   a. Set up indicator variables to represent the three service centers.

   b. The prediction equation is $\hat{y} = 7.1 + 0.5x_1 + 0.7x_2$, where x_1 is an indicator variable for San Jose and x_2 an indicator variable for Toronto. Find the estimate for the difference in population means (i) between San Jose and Bangalore and (ii) between Toronto and Bangalore.

14.20 Advertising effect on sales Each of 100 restaurants in a fast-food chain is randomly assigned one of four media for an advertising campaign: A = radio, B = TV, C = newspaper, D = mailing. For each restaurant, the observation is the change in sales, defined as the difference between the sales for the month during which the advertising campaign took place and the sales in the same month a year ago (in thousands of dollars).

   a. By creating indicator variables, write a regression equation for the analysis to compare mean change in sales for the four media.

b. Explain how you could use the regression model to test the null hypothesis of equal population mean change in sales for the four media.

c. The prediction equation is $\hat{y} = 35 + 5x_1 - 10x_2 + 2x_3$ where x_1, x_2, and x_3 are indicator variables for media A, B, and C, respectively. Estimate the difference in mean change in sales for media (i) A and D, (ii) A and B. (*Hint:* For part (ii), write the prediction equation for the mean for media A, then for media B, and then subtract.)

14.21 French ANOVA   Refer to Exercise 14.3 about studying
 French, with data shown again below. Using the *ANOVA (One Way)* app or other software,

a. Compare the three pairs of means with separate (i.e., not adjusting for multiplicity) 95% confidence intervals. Interpret.

b. Compare the three pairs of means with Tukey 95% multiple comparison confidence intervals. Interpret and explain why the intervals are different than in part a.

Group 1	Group 2	Group 3
4	1	9
6	5	10
8		5

14.22 Multiple comparison for time on Facebook   Refer to Exercise 14.13, which investigated the amount of time freshmen, sophomores, juniors, and seniors spent on Facebook while doing schoolwork. The data from the study are available in the *ANOVA (One Way)* app and on the book's website, where time is measured in minutes.

a. If you want to construct confidence intervals between all possible pairs of means for the four classes, how many intervals do you need to construct?

b. Using software (such as the *ANOVA (One Way)* app), find the confidence intervals for all possible pairs of population means such that the overall error rate of all intervals is 0.05 (use Tukey's method). Visualize the confidence intervals in a figure similar to Figure 14.4. (The app can construct such a plot.)

c. Is it true that seniors spent significantly less time than all other classes? Explain.

14.3 Two-Way ANOVA: Exploring Two Factors and Their Interaction

Recall

A **factor** is a categorical explanatory variable. **One-way ANOVA** has a single factor. ◄

One-way ANOVA is a *bivariate* (two-variable) method. It analyzes the relationship between the mean of a quantitative response variable and the groups that are categories of a factor. ANOVA extends to handle two or more factors. With multiple factors, the analysis is *multivariate*. We'll illustrate for the case of two factors. This extension is a **two-way ANOVA**. It enables us to study the effect of one factor at a fixed level of a second factor.

The great British statistician R. A. Fisher (see *On the Shoulders of R. A. Fisher* at the end of Section 8.2) developed ANOVA methods in the 1920s. Agricultural experiments were the source of many of the early ANOVA applications. For instance, ANOVA has often been used to compare the mean yield of a crop for different fertilizers.

Example 8

Two Factors ◄

Amounts of Fertilizer and Manure

Picture the Scenario

This example presents a typical ANOVA application, based on a study at Iowa State University.[2] A large field was portioned into 20 equal-size plots. Each plot was planted with the same amount of corn seed, using a fixed spacing pattern between the seeds. The goal was to study how the yield of corn later harvested from the plots (in metric tons) depended on the levels of use of nitrogen-based fertilizer and manure. Each factor was measured in a

[2]Thanks to Dan Nettleton, Iowa State University, for data on which this example is based.

binary manner. The fertilizer level was low (45 kg per hectare) or high (135 kg per hectare). The manure level was low (84 kg per hectare) or high (168 kg per hectare).

Did You Know?

A **metric ton** is 1,000 kilograms, which is about 2,200 pounds. A **hectare** is 10,000 square meters (e.g., 100 meters by 100 meters), which is about 2.5 acres. ◄

Questions to Explore

a. What are four treatments you can compare with this experiment?

b. What comparisons are relevant when you control for (keep fixed) manure level?

Think It Through

a. Four treatments result from cross-classifying the two binary factors: fertilizer level and manure level. You can compare corn yield at (i) low levels of both fertilizer and manure, at (ii) low levels of fertilizer and high levels of manure, at (iii) high levels of fertilizer and low levels of manure, and at (iv) high levels for both fertilizer and manure. Table 14.7 shows the four treatments, defined for the $2 \times 2 = 4$ combinations of categories of the two factors (fertilizer level and manure level).

Table 14.7 Four Groups for Comparing Mean Corn Yield

These result from the two-way cross classification of fertilizer level with manure level.

Manure	Fertilizer	
	Low	**High**
Low	(Low, Low)	(Low, High)
High	(High, Low)	(High, High)

b. We can compare the mean corn yield for the two levels of fertilizer, controlling for manure level (that is, at a fixed level of manure use). For fields in which manure level was *low*, we can compare the mean yields for the two levels of fertilizer use. These refer to the first row of Table 14.7. Likewise, for fields in which manure level was *high*, we can compare the mean yields for the two levels of fertilizer use. These refer to the second row of Table 14.7.

Insight

Among the questions we'll learn how to answer in this section are: Does the mean corn yield depend significantly on the fertilizer level? Does it depend on the manure level? Does the effect of fertilizer depend on the manure level, such as the fertilizer having no effect when the manure level is low but having an effect when the manure level is high?

▶ *Try Exercise 14.23*

Inference About Effects in Two-Way ANOVA

In two-way ANOVA, a null hypothesis states that the population means are the same in each category of one factor, at each fixed level of the other factor. For example, we could test

H_0: Mean corn yield is equal for plots at the low and high levels of fertilizer, for each fixed level of manure.

Table 14.8, part (a) displays a set of population means satisfying this null hypothesis of "no effect of fertilizer level."

Table 14.8 Population Mean Corn Yield Satisfying Null Hypotheses: (a) No Effect of Fertilizer Level, (b) No Effect of Manure Level

(a)	Fertilizer		(b)	Fertilizer	
Manure	**Low**	**High**	**Manure**	**Low**	**High**
Low	10	10	Low	10	20
High	20	20	High	10	20

We could also test

H_0: Mean corn yield is equal for plots at the low and high levels of manure, for each fixed level of fertilizer.

Table 14.8b displays a set of population means satisfying this null hypothesis of "no effect of manure level." The effects of individual factors tested with these two null hypotheses are called **main effects**. We'll discuss a third null hypothesis that needs to be tested before these main effects hypotheses later in the section.

As in one-way ANOVA, the F tests of hypotheses in two-way ANOVA assume that

- The population distribution for each group is normal.
- The population standard deviations are identical.
- The data result from random sampling or a randomized experiment.

Here, each group refers to a cell in the two-way classification of the two factors. ANOVA procedures still usually work quite well if the population distributions are not normal with identical standard deviations. As in other ANOVA inferences, the randomization assumption is the most important assumption.

The test statistics have complex formulas so we'll rely on software. As in one-way ANOVA, the test for a factor uses two estimates of the variance for each group. These estimates appear in the mean square (MS) column of the ANOVA table.

SUMMARY: F Test Statistics in Two-Way ANOVA

For testing the main effect for a factor, the test statistic is the ratio of mean squares,

$$F = \frac{\text{MS for the factor}}{\text{MS error}},$$

The MS for the factor is a variance estimate based on between-groups variation for that factor. The MS error is a within-groups variance estimate that is always unbiased.

When the null hypothesis of equal population means for the factor (controlling for the other factor) is true, the F test statistic values tend to fluctuate around 1. When it is false, they tend to be larger. As before, the P-value is the right-tail probability above the observed F value. That is, it is the probability (presuming H_0 is true) of even more extreme results than we observed in the sample.

Testing the Main Effects ◄

Example 9

Corn Yield

Picture the Scenario

Let's analyze the relationship between corn yield and the two factors, fertilizer level and manure level. Table 14.9 shows the data and the sample mean and standard deviation for each group.

Table 14.9 Corn Yield by Fertilizer Level and Manure Level

Fertilizer Level	Manure Level	Plot 1	2	3	4	5	Sample Size	Mean	Std. Dev.
High	High	13.7	15.8	13.9	16.6	15.5	5	15.1	1.3
High	Low	16.4	12.5	14.1	14.4	12.2	5	13.9	1.7
Low	High	15.0	15.1	12.0	15.7	12.2	5	14.0	1.8
Low	Low	12.4	10.6	13.7	8.7	10.9	5	11.3	1.9

Questions to Explore

a. Summarize the factor effects as shown by the sample means.

b. Table 14.10 is typical software output of an ANOVA table for two-way ANOVA. Specify the two hypotheses tested, give the test statistics and P-values, and interpret.

Think It Through

a. Table 14.9 (with means summarized in the margin) shows that for each manure level, the sample mean yield is higher for the plots using more fertilizer. Also, for a given fertilizer level, the sample mean yield is higher for the plots using more manure.

Means from Table 14.9

	Fertilizer	
Manure	Low	High
Low	11.3	13.9
High	14.0	15.1

Table 14.10 Two-Way ANOVA for Corn Yield Data in Table 14.9

> MS values for numerator of F statistics

Source	DF	SS	MS	F	P
Fertilizer	1	17.67	17.67	6.33	0.022
Manure	1	19.21	19.21	6.88	0.018
Error	17	47.44	2.79		
Total	19	84.32			

> MS error is denominator of each F statistic

b. First, consider the hypothesis

H_0: Mean corn yield is equal for plots at the low and high levels of fertilizer, for each fixed level of manure.

For the fertilizer main effect, Table 14.10 reports a mean square (MS) of 17.67. This is the between-groups estimate for the variance of the yield. The within-groups estimate is the MS error, or 2.79. The F test statistic is the ratio,

$$F = 17.67/2.79 = 6.33.$$

From Table 14.10, the df values are 1 and 17 for the two estimates. From the F distribution with $df_1 = 1$ and $df_2 = 17$, the P-value is 0.022, also reported in Table 14.10. If the population means were equal at the two levels of fertilizer (at a given manure level), the probability of an F test statistic value larger than 6.33 would be only 0.022. With such a small P-value, there is strong evidence that the mean corn yield depends on fertilizer level.

Next, consider the hypothesis

H_0: Mean corn yield is equal for plots at the low and high levels of manure, for each fixed level of fertilizer.

For the manure main effect, the F test statistic is $F = 19.21/2.79 = 6.88$. From Table 14.10, we see that $df_1 = 1$ and $df_2 = 17$, and that the P-value is 0.018. There is strong evidence that the mean corn yield also depends on the manure level.

Insight

As with any significance test, the information gain is limited. We do not learn *how large* the fertilizer and manure effects are on the corn yield. We can use confidence intervals to investigate the sizes of the main effects. We'll now learn how to do this by using regression modeling with indicator variables.

▶ **Try Exercise 14.28**

Regression Model With Indicator Variables for Two-Way ANOVA

Let f denote an indicator variable for fertilizer level and let m denote an indicator variable for manure level. (We could have called the indicator variables x_1 and x_2, but f and m reminds us that these indicators stand for fertilizer and manure use, respectively.) Specifically,

$$f = 1 \text{ for plots with high fertilizer level}$$
$$= 0 \text{ for plots with low fertilizer level}$$

$$m = 1 \text{ for plots with high manure level}$$
$$= 0 \text{ for plots with low manure level.}$$

The multiple regression model for the mean corn yield with these two indicator variables is

$$\mu_y = \alpha + \beta_1 f + \beta_2 m.$$

To find the population means for the four groups, we substitute the possible combinations of values for the indicator variables. For example, for plots that have high fertilizer level ($f = 1$) and low manure level ($m = 0$), the mean corn yield is

$$\mu_y = \alpha + \beta_1(1) + \beta_2(0) = \alpha + \beta_1.$$

Table 14.11 shows the four means. The difference between the means at the high and low levels of fertilizer equals β_1 for each manure level. That is, the coefficient β_1 of the indicator variable f for fertilizer level equals the difference

Table 14.11 Population Mean Corn Yield for Fertilizer and Manure Levels

| | | Indicator Variables | | |
| | | f | m | Mean of y |
Fertilizer	Manure			
High	High	1	1	$\alpha + \beta_1 + \beta_2$
High	Low	1	0	$\alpha + \beta_1$
Low	High	0	1	$\alpha + \beta_2$
Low	Low	0	0	α

between the means at its high and low levels, controlling for manure level. The null hypothesis of no fertilizer effect is H_0: $\beta_1 = 0$. Likewise, β_2 is the difference between the means at the high and low levels of manure, for each fertilizer level.

We do not need to use regression modeling to conduct the ANOVA F tests. They're easy to do using software. But the modeling approach helps us to focus on estimating the means and the differences among them. We can compare means using an ordinary confidence interval for the regression parameter that equals the difference between those means. The 95% confidence interval has the usual form of

$$\text{parameter estimate} \pm t_{0.025}(se).$$

The df for the t-score is the df value for the MS error.

Example 10

Estimate and Compare Mean Corn Yields

Picture the Scenario

Table 14.12 shows the result of fitting the regression model for predicting corn yield with indicator variables for fertilizer level and manure level.

Table 14.12 Estimates of Regression Parameters for Two-Way ANOVA of the Mean Corn Yield by Fertilizer Level and Manure Level

Term	Coef	SE Coef	T-Value	P-Value
Constant	11.6500	0.6470	18.01	0.000
fertilizer	1.8800	0.7471	2.52	0.022
manure	1.9600	0.7471	2.62	0.018

Questions to Explore

a. Find and use the prediction equation to estimate the mean corn yield for each group.

b. Use a parameter estimate from the prediction equation to estimate the difference between mean corn yields for the high and low levels of fertilizer, at each manure level.

c. Find a 95% confidence interval comparing the mean corn yield at the high and low levels of fertilizer, controlling for manure level. Interpret it.

Think It Through

a. From Table 14.12, the prediction equation is (rounding to one decimal place)

$$\hat{y} = 11.6 + 1.9f + 2.0m.$$

The y-intercept equals 11.6. This is the estimated mean yield (in metric tons per hectare) when both indicator variables equal 0, that is, with fertilizer and manure at their low level. The estimated means for the other cases result from substituting values for the indicator variables. For instance, at fertilizer level = high and manure level = low, $f = 1$ and $m = 0$, so the estimated mean yield is $\hat{y} = 11.6 + 1.9(1) + 2.0(0) = 13.5$. Doing this for all four groups, we get

| Manure | Fertilizer | |
	Low	High
Low	11.6	11.6 + 1.9 = 13.5
High	11.6 + 2.0 = 13.6	11.6 + 1.9 + 2.0 = 15.5

b. The coefficient of the fertilizer indicator variable f is 1.9. This is the estimate for β_1 and is the estimated difference in mean corn yield between the high and low levels of fertilizer, for each level of manure (for instance, $13.5 - 11.6 = 1.9$ when manure level = low).

c. As shown, β_1 represents the difference in the mean corn yield at the high and low levels of fertilizer. To find a confidence interval for this difference, we simply need to find a confidence interval for β_1. The point estimate of β_1 is 1.9. Its standard error, reported in Table 14.12, is 0.747. From Table 14.10 (see page 762), the df for the MS error is 17. The t-score, $t_{.025} = 2.11$ when $df = 17$. The 95% confidence interval is

$$1.9 \pm 2.11(0.747), \text{ which is } (0.3, 3.5).$$

At each manure level, with 95% confidence, we estimate that the mean corn yield is between 0.3 and 3.5 metric tons per hectare higher at the high fertilizer level than at the low fertilizer level. The confidence interval contains only positive values (does not contain 0), reflecting the conclusion that the mean yield is significantly higher at the higher level of fertilizer. This agrees with the P-value falling below 0.05 in the test for the fertilizer effect.

Insight

The *estimated* means are not the same as the *sample* means in Table 14.9. (Both sets are shown again in the margin.) The model *smooths* the sample means so that the difference between the estimated means for two categories of a factor is *exactly* the same at each category of the other factor. For example, the increase in the mean yield when switching from a low level of the fertilizer to a high level of the fertilizer is the same (namely 1.9 tons) for low manure levels ($13.5 - 11.6 = 1.9$) and high manure levels ($15.5 - 13.6 = 1.9$).

▶ *Try Exercise 14.29*

Estimated Means

| Manure | Fertilizer | |
	Low	High
Low	11.6	13.5
High	13.6	15.5

Table 14.9: Sample Means

| Manure | Fertilizer | |
	Low	High
Low	11.3	13.9
High	14.0	15.1

The regression model assumes that the difference between means for the two categories for one factor is the same in each category of the other factor. The next section shows how to check this assumption. When it is reasonable, we can use a single comparison rather than a separate one at each category of the other variable. In Example 10, we estimated that the difference in mean corn yield between high- and low-level use of fertilizer equals 1.9 tons, regardless of the level of manure use.

Recall

Section 13.5 introduced the concept of **interaction** between two explanatory variables in their effects on a response variable. In a regression context, **no interaction** implied parallel lines (common slopes). ◀

Exploring Interaction Between Factors in Two-Way ANOVA

Investigating whether **interaction** occurs is important whenever we analyze multivariate relationships. *No interaction* between two factors means that the effect of either factor on the response variable is the same at each category of the other factor. The regression model in Example 10 and the ANOVA tests of main effects assume there is no interaction between the factors. What does this mean in this context?

	Fertilizer	
Manure	Low	High
Low	11.6	13.5
High	13.6	15.5

From Example 10, the estimated mean corn yields from the regression model having an indicator variable for fertilizer level and an indicator variable for manure level are shown in the table in the margin.

What pattern do these show? Let's plot the means for the two fertilizer levels, within each level of manure. Figure 14.5 shows a plot in which the y-axis gives estimated mean corn yields, and points are shown for the four fertilizer–manure combinations. The horizontal axis is not a numerical scale but merely lists the two fertilizer levels. The drawn lines connect the means for the two fertilizer levels, for a given manure level. The absence of interaction is indicated by the *parallel lines.*

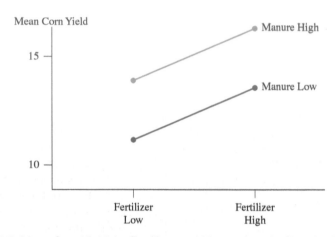

▲ **Figure 14.5** Mean Corn Yield, by Fertilizer and Manure Levels, Showing No Interaction. The parallel lines reflect an absence of interaction. This implies that the difference in estimated means between the two fertilizer levels is the same for each manure level. **Question** Is it also true that the difference in estimated means between the two manure levels is the same for each fertilizer level?

The parallel lines occurs because the difference in the estimated mean corn yield between the high and low levels of fertilizer is the same for each manure level. The difference equals 1.9. Also, the difference between the high and low levels of manure in the estimated mean corn yield is 2.0 for each fertilizer level.

Table 14.13 Means That Show Interaction Between the Factors in Their Effects on the Response

The effect of fertilizer differs according to whether manure level is low or high. See Figure 14.6.

	Fertilizer	
Manure	Low	High
Low	10	14
High	16	12

By contrast, Table 14.13 and Figure 14.6 on the next page show a set of means for which there is interaction. The difference between the high and low levels of fertilizer in the mean corn yield is $14 - 10 = 4$ for low manure and $12 - 16 = -4$ for high manure. Here, the difference in means depends on the manure level: According to these means, it's better to use a high level of fertilizer when the manure level is low, but it's better to use a low level of fertilizer when the manure level is high. Similarly, the manure effect differs at the two fertilizer levels; for the low level, it is $16 - 10 = 6$ whereas at the high level, it is $12 - 14 = -2$. The lines in Figure 14.6 are not parallel.

In Table 14.13, suppose the numbers of observations are the same for each group. Then the overall mean corn yield, ignoring manure level, is 13 for each fertilizer level (the average of 10 and 16, and the average of 14 and 12). The overall difference in means between the two fertilizer levels then equals 0. A one-way analysis of mean corn yield by fertilizer level would wrongly conclude that fertilizer level has no effect. However, a two-way analysis that allows for interaction would detect that fertilizer has an effect, but that effect differs according to the manure level. This demonstrates the advantage of a two-way analysis, which can consider the joint effects of two factors over a one-way analysis that has to ignore the effect of one factor.

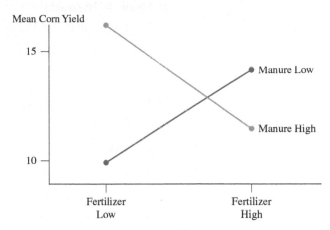

▲ **Figure 14.6** Mean Corn Yield, by Fertilizer and Manure Levels, Displaying Interaction. **Question** What aspect of the plot reflects the interaction?

Testing for Interaction

In conducting a two-way ANOVA, before testing the main effects, it is customary to test a third null hypothesis stating that there is no interaction between the factors in their effects on the response. The test statistic providing the sample evidence of interaction is

$$F = \frac{\text{MS for interaction}}{\text{MS error}}.$$

When H_0 is false, the F statistic tends to be large. Therefore, as usual, the P-value is the right-tail probability.

Testing for Interaction ◀

Example 11

Corn Yield Data

Picture the Scenario

Let's return to our analysis of the corn yield data, summarized in the margin table. In Example 10 we analyzed these data assuming no interaction. Let's see if that analysis is valid. Table 14.14 shows typical output for an ANOVA table for a model that allows interaction in assessing the effects of fertilizer level and manure level on the mean corn yield.

Corn Yields

Fertilizer Level	Manure Level	Mean	Std. Dev.
High	High	15.1	1.3
High	Low	13.9	1.7
Low	High	14.0	1.8
Low	Low	11.3	1.9

Table 14.14 Two-Way ANOVA of Mean Corn Yield by Fertilizer Level and Manure Level, Allowing Interaction

Source	DF	SS	MS	F	P
Fertilizer	1	17.67	17.67	6.37	0.023
Manure	1	19.21	19.21	6.92	0.018
Interaction	1	3.04	3.04	1.10	0.311
Error	16	44.40	2.78		
Total	19	84.32			

F statistic for test of no interaction

Question to Explore

Give the result of the test of H_0: no interaction and interpret.

Think It Through

The test statistic for H_0: no interaction is

$$F = (\text{MS for interaction})/(\text{MS error}) = 3.04/2.78 = 1.10.$$

Based on the F distribution with $df_1 = 1$ and $df_2 = 16$ for these two mean squares, the ANOVA table reports P-value = 0.31. This is not much evidence of interaction. We would not reject H_0 at the usual significance levels, such as 0.05.

Insight

Because there is not much evidence of interaction, we are justified in conducting the simpler two-way ANOVA about main effects. The tests presented previously in Table 14.10 for effects of fertilizer and manure on mean corn yield, as well as the confidence interval we constructed in Example 10, are valid.

▶ **Try Exercise 14.30**

It is not meaningful to test the main effects hypotheses when there is interaction. A small P-value in the test of H_0: no interaction suggests that each factor has an effect, but the size of effect for one factor varies according to the category of the other factor. Then, you should investigate the nature of the interaction by plotting the sample cell means, using a graph such as Figure 14.6. You should compare categories of one factor separately at different levels of the other factor.

In Practice Check Interaction Before Main Effects

In practice, in two-way ANOVA you should *first test the hypothesis of no interaction*. If the evidence of interaction is not strong (that is, if the P-value is not small), then test the main effects hypotheses and/or construct confidence intervals for those effects. But if important evidence of interaction exists, plot and compare the cell means for a factor separately at each category of the other factor.

Recall

From the box at the beginning of Section 14.2, the 95% confidence interval comparing two means is

$$(\bar{y}_i - \bar{y}_j) \pm t_{.025}\, se,$$

$$\text{where } se = s\sqrt{\frac{1}{n_i} + \frac{1}{n_j}},$$

s is the square root of the MS error, and df for the t distribution is df for MS error. ◀

For comparing means in two cells using a confidence interval, use the formula from the box at the beginning of Section 14.2, shown again in the margin. Substitute the cell sample sizes for n_i and n_j and use the MS error for the two-way ANOVA that allows interaction.

Example 12

Interactions and Confidence Intervals ◀

Political Ideology by Gender and Race

Picture the Scenario

In most years, the General Social Survey asks subjects to report their political ideology, measured with seven categories ranging from 1 = extremely liberal, to 4 = moderate, to 7 = extremely conservative. Table 14.15 on the next page shows results from the 2008 General Social Survey on mean political ideology classified by gender and by race.

Caution

When conducting a two-way ANOVA for samples of different sizes, the analysis (using software) will often have to be performed as a General Linear Model. Notice that the Analysis of Variance table here shows both a Seq SS and an Adj SS column. You should use the Adjusted SS and Adjusted MS for the tests. ◄

Table 14.15 Mean Political Ideology by Gender and by Race

	Race	
Gender	**Black**	**White**
Female	4.164 ($n = 165$)	4.268 ($n = 840$)
Male	3.819 ($n = 116$)	4.444 ($n = 719$)

For the test of H_0: no interaction, software reports an F test statistic of 6.19 with $df_1 = 1$ and $df_2 = 1,836$, for a P-value of 0.013. This indicates that when comparing females and males on their mean political ideology, we should do it separately by race. The MS error for the model allowing interaction equals 2.534, so $s = \sqrt{2.534} = 1.592$.

```
Analysis of Variance for POLVIEWS, using Adjusted SS for Tests

Source      DF     Seq SS     Adj SS     Adj MS       F        P

SEX          1      5.138      1.652      1.652      0.65     0.420

RACE         1     24.786     30.780     30.780     12.15     0.001

SEX*RACE     1     15.693     15.693     15.693      6.19     0.013

Error     1836   4651.981   4651.981      2.534

Total     1839   4697.598
```

Questions to Explore

a. Interpret the significant interaction by comparing sample mean political ideology of females and males for each race descriptively and using 95% confidence intervals.

b. Interpret the confidence intervals derived in part a.

Think It Through

a. The sample means show that for Black subjects, females are more conservative (have the higher mean). By contrast, for White subjects, males are more conservative. The margin figure shows the means and the interaction. For a confidence interval comparing mean political ideology for females and males who are Black, the standard error (using the sample sizes reported in the table) is

$$se = s\sqrt{\frac{1}{n \text{ for Black females}} + \frac{1}{n \text{ for Black males}}} =$$

$$1.592\sqrt{\frac{1}{165} + \frac{1}{116}} = 0.193.$$

The 95% confidence interval is

$$(4.164 - 3.819) \pm 1.96(0.193), \text{ which is } 0.345 \pm 0.378, \text{ or}$$

$$(-0.03, 0.72).$$

Likewise, you can find that the 95% confidence interval comparing mean political ideology for females and males who are White is -0.179 ± 0.159, or $(-0.34, -0.02)$.

Gender: ─●─ Female ─●─ Male

b. Since the confidence interval for Black subjects contains zero, we cannot infer that there is a difference in the populations. For White subjects, however, all values in the interval are negative. We infer that White females are *less* conservative than White males in the population.

Insight

The confidence interval for White subjects has an upper endpoint that is close to 0. So, the true gender effect in the population could be very small. In fact, for 2014 GSS data, the interaction is not significant, and the gender main effect is also not significant; see Exercises 14.25 and 14.54.

▶ *Try Exercise 14.34*

Why Not Instead Perform Two One-Way ANOVAs?

When you have two factors, rather than performing a two-way ANOVA, why not instead perform two one-way ANOVAs? For instance, in Example 12 you could compare the mean political ideology for females and males using a one-way ANOVA, ignoring the information about race. Likewise, you could perform a separate one-way ANOVA to compare the means for Blacks and Whites, ignoring the information about gender.

The main reason is that you learn more from a two-way ANOVA. The two-way ANOVA indicates whether there is interaction. When there is, as in Example 12, it is more informative to compare levels of one factor *separately* at each level of the other factor. This enables us to investigate how the effect depends on that other factor. For instance, a one-way ANOVA of mean political ideology by gender might show *no* gender effect, whereas the two-way ANOVA has shown that there *is* a gender effect, but it varies by race.

Similarly, in experimental studies, rather than carrying out one experiment to investigate the effect of one factor and a separate experiment to investigate the effect of a second factor, it is better to carry out a *single* experiment and study both factors at the same time. Besides the advantage of being able to check for interaction, this is more cost effective. If we have funds to experiment with 100 subjects, we can use a sample size of 100 for studying each factor with a two-way ANOVA rather than use 50 subjects in one experiment about one factor and 50 subjects in a separate experiment about the other factor.

Yet another benefit of a two-way ANOVA is that the residual variability (the estimated standard deviation of the response variable in each group), which affects the MS error and the denominators of the F test statistics, tends to decrease. When we use two factors to predict a response variable, we usually tend to get better predictions (that is, less residual variability) than when we use one factor. With less residual (within-groups) variability, we get larger test statistics and, hence, greater power for rejecting false null hypotheses.

Factorial ANOVA

The methods of two-way ANOVA extend to the analysis of several factors. A multifactor ANOVA with observations from all combinations of the factors is called **factorial ANOVA.** For example, with three factors, **three-way ANOVA** considers main effects for those factors as well as possible interactions.

In Practice Use Regression With Categorical and Quantitative Predictors

With several explanatory variables, usually some are categorical and some are quantitative. Then, it is sensible to build a multiple regression model containing both types of predictors. That's what we did in Example 10 in the previous chapter when we modeled house selling prices in terms of house size and condition of the house.

14.3 Practicing the Basics

14.23 Reducing cholesterol An experiment randomly assigns 100 subjects suffering from high cholesterol to one of four groups: low-dose Lipitor, high-dose Lipitor, low-dose Zocor, high-dose Zocor. After three months of treatment, the change in cholesterol level is measured.

a. Identify the response variable and the two factors.

b. What are four treatments that can be compared with this experiment?

c. What comparisons are relevant when we control for dose level?

14.24 Drug main effects For the previous exercise, show a hypothetical set of population means for the four groups that would have

a. A dose effect but no drug effect.

b. A drug effect but no dose effect.

c. A drug effect and a dose effect.

d. No drug effect and no dose effect.

14.25 Political ideology in 2014 The GSS measures political ideology on a seven-point scale, starting with 1 = extremely liberal, to 4 = moderate, to 7 = extremely conservative. The following table shows results from an ANOVA analysis about political ideology, with sex (female, male) and race (Black, White) as two factors, using 2014 GSS data.

a. State the null hypothesis to which the F test statistic in the race row refers.

b. Show how to use mean squares to construct the F test statistic for the race main effect, report its P-value, and interpret.

c. Is there evidence that the mean political ideology in the United States differs between females and males, for either Blacks or Whites? Explain.

Source	DF	SS	MS	F	P
Sex	24	3.0	3.0	1.4	0.229
Race	1	36.5	36.5	17.4	0.000
Error	2203	4524.3	2.1		
Total	2205	4563.8			

14.26 House prices, age, and bedrooms For the House Selling Prices OR data file on the book's website, the output shows the result of conducting a two-way ANOVA of house selling prices (in thousands) by the number of bedrooms in the house and the age (New, Medium, Old, Very Old—see exercise 14.12) of the houses in Corvallis, Oregon.

a. For testing the main effect of age, report the F test statistic value and show how it was formed from other values reported in the ANOVA table.

b. Report the P-value for the main effect test for age and interpret.

Source	DF	SS	MS	F	P
Bedrooms	7	517868	73981	7.325	0.000
Age Condition	3	242042	80681	7.988	0.000
Error	189	1908959	10100		
Total	199	2668870			

14.27 Corn and manure In Example 10, the coefficient of the manure-level indicator variable m is 1.96.

a. Explain why this coefficient is the estimated difference in mean corn yield between the high and low levels of manure, for each level of fertilizer.

b. Explain why the 95% confidence interval for the difference in mean corn yield between the high and low levels of manure is $1.96 \pm 2.11(0.747)$.

14.28 Hang up if recording repeated? Example 2 described an experiment in which telephone callers to an airline were put on hold with an advertisement, Muzak, or classical music in the background. Each caller who was chosen was also randomly assigned to a category of a second factor: whether the recording played was five minutes long or ten minutes long. (In each case, it was repeated at the end.) The table shows the data classified by both factors and the results of a two-way ANOVA

Telephone Holding Times by Type of Recording and Repeat Time		
	Repeat Time	
Recording	**Ten Minutes**	**Five Minutes**
Advertisement	8, 11, 2	5, 1
Muzak	1, 4, 3	0, 6
Classical	13, 8, 15	7, 9

Source	DF	SS	MS	F	P
Recording	2	149.20	74.60	7.09	0.011
Repeat	1	23.51	23.51	2.24	0.163
Error	11	115.60	10.52		
Total	14	288.40			

a. State the null hypothesis to which the F test statistic in the Recording row refers.

b. Show how to use mean squares to construct the F test statistic for the Recording main effect, report its P-value, and interpret.

c. On what assumptions is this analysis based?

14.29 Regression for telephone holding times   Refer to the previous exercise. Let $x_1 = 1$ for the advertisement and 0 otherwise, $x_2 = 1$ for Muzak and 0 otherwise, and $x_1 = x_2 = 0$ for classical music. Likewise, let $x_3 = 1$ for repeating in 10-minute cycles and $x_3 = 0$ for repeating in 5-minute cycles. The display shows results of a regression of the telephone holding times on these indicator variables.

Regression for Telephone Holding Times

Term	Coef	SE Coef	T-Value	P-Value
Constant	8.867	1.776	4.99	0.000
x1	-5.000	2.051	-2.44	0.033
x2	-7.600	2.051	-3.71	0.003
x3	2.556	1.709	1.50	0.163

a. Give the corresponding regression model for the population mean and show the equation for the population mean at each setting of the two factor levels. (Create a table similar to Table 14.11.)

b. State the prediction equation. Interpret the parameter estimates.

c. Find the estimated means for the six groups in the two-way cross-classification of type of recording and repeat time.

d. Find the estimated difference between the mean holding times for 10-minute repeats and 5-minute repeats, for a fixed recording type. How can you get this estimate from a coefficient of an indicator variable in the prediction equation?

e. Find a 95% confidence interval for the difference between the mean holding times for 10-minute repeats and 5-minute repeats.

14.30 Interaction between message and repeat time?   Refer to the previous two exercises. When we allow interaction, two of the rows in the new ANOVA table are

Source	DF	SS	MS	F	P
Group*Repeat	2	15.02	7.51	0.67	0.535
Error	9	100.67	11.19		

where Group*Repeat denotes the interaction effect.

a. Show the hypotheses, test statistic, and P-value for the test of H_0: no interaction.

b. What is the implication of the result of this test? For instance, the analyses in previous exercises assumed a lack of interaction. Was it valid to do so?

14.31 Income by gender and degree   In 2012, the population mean hourly wage for males was $17 for high school graduates, $33 for college graduates, and $43 for males with more advanced degrees. For females, the means were $14 for high school graduates, $24 for college graduates, and $32 for females with more advanced degrees.[3]

a. Identify the response variable and the two factors.

b. Show these means in a two-way classification of the two factors, similar to the table in the margin of Example 9.

c. Compare the differences between males and females for (i) high school graduates and (ii) college graduates. Explain why there is interaction and describe it.

d. Show a set of six population mean wages that would satisfy H_0: no interaction.

14.32 Ideology by gender and race   Refer to Example 12, the sample means from which are shown again below (for 2008 data).

Mean Political Ideology

Gender	Race Black	Race White
Female	4.164	4.2675
Male	3.819	4.4443

a. Explain how to obtain the following interpretation for the interaction from the sample means: "For females there is no race effect on ideology. For males, Whites are more conservative by about half an ideology category, on the average."

b. Suppose that instead of the two-way ANOVA, you performed a one-way ANOVA with gender as the predictor and a separate one-way ANOVA with race as the predictor. Suppose the ANOVA for gender does not show a significant effect. Explain how this could happen, even though the two-way ANOVA showed a gender effect for each race. (*Hint:* Will the overall sample means for females and males be more similar than they are for each race?)

c. Refer to part b. Summarize what you would learn about the gender effect from a two-way ANOVA that you would fail to learn from a one-way ANOVA.

14.33 Attractiveness and getting dates   The results in the table are from a study of physical attractiveness and subjective well-being (E. Diener et al., *Journal of Personality and Social Psychology*, vol. 69, 1995, pp. 120–129). A panel rated a sample of college students on their physical attractiveness. The table presents the number of dates in the past three months for students rated in the top or bottom quartile of attractiveness.

a. Identify the response variable and the factors.

b. Do these data appear to show interaction? Explain.

c. Based on the results in the table, specify one of the ANOVA assumptions that these data violate. Is this the most important assumption?

Dates and Attractiveness

Attractiveness	Number of Dates, Men Mean	Std. Dev	n	Number of Dates, Women Mean	Std. Dev	n
More	9.7	10.0	35	17.8	14.2	33
Less	9.9	12.6	36	10.4	16.6	27

14.34 Diet and weight gain   A randomized experiment[4] measured weight gain (in grams) of male rats under six diets varying by source of protein (beef, cereal, pork) and level of protein

---

[3]*Source:* Data from *The State of Working America*, 12th edition, Economic Policy Institute.

[4]*Source:* Data from G. Snedecor and W. Cochran, *Statistical Methods*, 6th ed. (Iowa State University Press, 1967), p. 347.

(high, low). Ten rats were assigned to each diet. The data are shown in the table that follows and are also available in the Protein and Weight Gain data file on the book's website.

a. Conduct a two-way ANOVA that assumes a lack of interaction. Report the F test statistic and the P-value for testing the effect of the protein level. Interpret.

b. Now conduct a two-way ANOVA that also considers potential interaction. Report the hypotheses, test statistic, and P-value for a test of no interaction. What do you conclude at the 0.05 significance level? Explain.

c. Refer to part b. Allowing interaction, construct a 95% confidence interval to compare the mean weight gain for the two protein levels, for the beef source of protein.

Weight Gain by Source of Protein and by Level of Protein

	High Protein	Low Protein
Beef	73, 102, 118, 104, 81, 107, 100, 87, 117, 111	90, 76, 90, 64, 86, 51, 72, 90, 95, 78
Cereal	98, 74, 56, 111, 95, 88, 82, 77, 86, 92	107, 95, 97, 80, 98, 74, 74, 67, 89, 58
Pork	94, 79, 96, 98, 102, 102, 108, 91, 120, 105	49, 82, 73, 86, 81, 97, 106, 70, 61, 82

14.35 Regression of weight gain on diet Refer to the previous exercise.

a. Set up indicator variables for protein source and for protein level and specify a regression model with the effects both of protein level and protein source on weight gain.

b. Fit the model in part a and explain how to interpret the parameter estimate for the protein level indicator variable.

c. Show how you could test a hypothesis about beta parameters in the model in part a to analyze the effect of protein source on weight gain.

d. Using the fit of the model, find the estimated mean for each of the six diets. Explain what it means when we say that these estimated means do not allow for interaction between protein level and source in their effects on weight loss.

Chapter Review

SUMMARY OF NOTATION

$\mu_1, \mu_2, \ldots, \mu_g$ = population mean in each of g groups
σ = common population standard deviation in each group
$n_1, n_2, \ldots, n_g$ = sample size in each of g groups

$\bar{y}_1, \bar{y}_2, \ldots, \bar{y}_g$ = sample mean in each of g groups
s = estimate of σ = square root of Means Squared Error (MSE)

CHAPTER SUMMARY

Analysis of variance (ANOVA) methods compare several groups according to their means on a quantitative response variable. The groups are categories of categorical explanatory variables. A categorical explanatory variable is also called a **factor**.

■ The **one-way** ANOVA F test compares means for a single factor. The groups are specified by categories of a single categorical explanatory variable. The larger the F test statistic, the smaller the P-value and the more evidence that the population means are different, although the F test doesn't tell which ones are different.

■ **Two-way ANOVA** methods compare means across categories of one factor, at fixed levels of another factor. When there is **interaction** between the two factors, the effect on the mean of one factor differs depending on the particular level of the other factor.

■ **Multiple comparison methods** such as the **Tukey method** compare means for each pair of groups while controlling the overall confidence level.

■ Analysis of variance methods can be conducted by using multiple regression models. The regression model uses **indicator variables** as explanatory variables to represent the factors. Each indicator variable equals 1 for observations from a particular category and 0 otherwise.

■ The ANOVA methods assume randomization and that the population distribution for each group is normal, with the same standard deviation for each group. In practice, *the randomness assumption is the most important*, and ANOVA methods are *robust* to moderate violations of the other assumptions.

LEARNING OBJECTIVES

1. Explain why analysis of variance (ANOVA) is preferred to performing multiple t tests when comparing more than two means.

2. Interpret the results of a one-way ANOVA.

3. Employ a multiple comparison method to compare means for each pair of groups as a follow-up comparison to an ANOVA analysis, controlling for the overall confidence level.

4. Explain the difference between one-way ANOVA and two-way ANOVA.

5. Interpret the results of a two-way ANOVA.

6. Recognize the implication of interaction on interpretation of the factors in a two-way ANOVA.

7. Explain how analysis of variance methods can be conducted using multiple regression methods and indicator variables.

8. Identify the necessary assumptions for ANOVA and which assumption is robust to moderate violations.

ANSWERS TO THE CHAPTER FIGURE QUESTIONS

Figure 14.1 No, even if the population means are equal, we would expect the sample means to vary due to sample-to-sample variability. Differences among the sample means is not sufficient evidence to conclude that the population means differ.

Figure 14.2 The data in Figure 14.2b give stronger evidence against H_0 because Figure 14.2b has less variability within each sample than Figure 14.2a.

Figure 14.3 Evidence suggesting the normal with equal standard deviation assumptions are violated would be (1) graphical methods showing extreme skew for the response variable, or (2) the largest group standard deviation is more than about double the smallest group standard deviation when the sample sizes are unequal.

Figure 14.5 Yes. The parallelism of lines implies that no interaction holds no matter which factor we choose for making comparisons of means.

Figure 14.6 The lines are not parallel.

STATISTICAL SOFTWARE

Art of Stat Web Apps

- **F-Distribution** This app lets you interactively explore the shape of the F distribution and compute tail probabilities and percentiles, which are visualized on the graph.

- **ANOVA (One Way)** This app provides all output associated with a one-way analysis of variance. It comes with several data sets from the book preloaded, but you can provide your own data by entering (or copying and pasting) them into boxes for each group. Standard output includes a table showing the summary statistics for each group, a visualization of the data via side-by-side dot plots, box plots, or histograms, and the ANOVA table. You can ask for all pairwise comparisons of the means, including Tukey multiplicity adjusted confidence intervals, which are visualized in a graph.

R

- **F Distribution:** The `pf` function finds (lower-tail) probabilities under the F distribution, such that `> 1 - pf(6.43, df1=2, df2=12)` returns the upper tail probability 0.013 from the F distribution that is reported as the P-value in Example 3. `qf` returns percentiles, such as `> qf(0.95, df1=2, df2=12)` returning 3.88, as shown in the table and graph in the margin of Example 3.

- **One-way Analysis of Variance:** To obtain the one-way ANOVA table (Table 14.2) for the telephone holding time data (Example 2), we can use R's `aov` function. (Note the way we enter the data.)

```
> y <- c(5, 1, 11, 2, 8, 0, 1, 4, 6, 3, 13,
9, 8, 15, 7) #all observations
> group <- rep(c('A', 'M', 'C'), times=c(5, 5,
5))
> myAnova <- aov(y ~ group) #creates ANOVA
table
> summary(myAnova)
Analysis of Variance Table
          Df Sum Sq Mean Sq F value  Pr(>F)
group      2  149.2    74.6   6.431 0.01264
Residuals 12  139.2    11.6
```

This shows the sum of squares, mean squares, the resulting F statistic and the P-value of 0.013 we obtained in Example 3

(labeled `Pr(>F)`). With the data set up this way, you can get side-by-side box plots (see the one next to Example 4) through `> boxplot(y~group)`. The `times=c(5, 5, 5)` in the definition of `group` tells R to repeat each of the labels 5 times, because we had 5 observations in each group. If we had 3 observations in the first, 7 in the second, and 4 in the third group, we would need to use `times=c(3, 7, 4)`. Alternatively, you can always create a .csv file (with two columns, one for the group labels, the other for the observations), read it into R and provide it to the `aov` function, as we did in the R code for Linear Regression in Chapter 13.

- **Pairwise Comparisons of Means:** To obtain the multiplicity adjusted (Tukey) confidence intervals for all pairwise comparisons of means, such as the ones shown in Table 14.4, use

```
> TukeyHSD(myAnova)
  Tukey multiple comparisons of means
     95% family-wise confidence level
     diff    lwr    upr p adj
C-A   5.0  -0.75  10.75 0.091
M-A  -2.6  -8.35   3.15 0.472
M-C  -7.6 -13.35  -1.85 0.011
```

This shows the estimated difference and lower and upper confidence bounds. You can visualize these intervals by typing:
```
> plot(TukeyHSD(myAnova))
```

■ **Regression and ANOVA:** To obtain the multiple linear regression output from Table 14.6 where R sets up the indicator variables automatically, use

```
> myfit <- lm(y ~ group)
> summary(myfit)
Coefficients:
            Estimate Std. Error t value Pr(>|t|)
(Intercept)   5.400     1.523    3.545  0.00403
groupC        5.000     2.154    2.321  0.03868
groupM       -2.600     2.154   -1.207  0.25068
```

This shows that R uses a different way (compared to MINITAB or other software) to set up indicator variables. It sets the first indicator variable to 1 when the group is Classical (indicated by labeling it groupC) and 0 otherwise, and it sets the second indicator variable to 1 when the group was Muzak (indicated by labeling it groupM) and 0 otherwise. By default, R sorts the group labels alphabetically and with three labels uses the last two to set up indicator variables, making the first the reference category. Results do **not** depend on how indicator variables are set up, and you will find the same fitted means as given in part b of Example 7. You can get the ANOVA table shown in Table 14.6 via > anova(myfit).

■ **Two-way Analysis of Variance:** To replicate Table 14.10 in Example 9 for corn yield, load the data set cornyield.csv from the book's website into R. Using the relationship between regression and ANOVA, we can replicate Table 14.10 through

```
> myfile <- file.choose() #provide path
> corn <- read.csv(myfile) #load file
> head(corn, 3) #show first 3 rows
  fertilizer manure yield
1       high   high  13.7
2       high   high  15.8
3       high   high  13.9
> myfit <- lm(yield ~ fertilizer + manure,
data=corn) #main effects
> anova(myfit)
```

```
Analysis of Variance Table
           Df  Sum Sq  Mean Sq  F value  Pr(>F)
fertilizer  1  17.672  17.6720   6.3324  0.02219
manure      1  19.208  19.2080   6.8828  0.01779
Residuals  17  47.442   2.7907
```

and the regression coefficients for the regression model (Example 10) through

```
> summary(myfit)
Coefficients:
             Estimate Std. Error t value Pr(>|t|)
(Intercept)  15.4900     0.6470   23.941  1.55e-14
fertilizerlow -1.8800     0.7471   -2.516  0.0222
manurelow    -1.9600     0.7471   -2.624  0.0178
```

This shows different values for the parameter estimates from the ones reported in Table 14.12, but it's because R sets up indicator variables differently. (For instance, it set the first indicator to 1 when fertilizer is low instead of high, which you can see by the label fertilizerlow.) Results do **not** depend on the way indicator variables are set up. Plugging in, you get the same results as in Example 10.7. To investigate the interaction (see Example 11), use

```
> myfit2 <- lm(yield ~ fertilizer + manure +
fertilizer:manure, data=corn) #fits interaction
> anova(myfit2)
Analysis of Variance Table
               Df  Sum Sq  Mean Sq  F value  Pr(>F)
fertilizer      1  17.672   17.672   6.3683  0.02258
manure          1  19.208   19.208   6.9218  0.01816
fertilizer:manure 1  3.042    3.042   1.0962  0.31066
Residuals      16  44.400    2.775
```

This replicates Table 14.14.

CHAPTER EXERCISES

Practicing the Basics

14.36 Good friends and marital status Is the number of good friends associated with marital status? For GSS data with marital status measured with the categories (married, widowed, divorced, separated, never married), an ANOVA table reports $F = 0.80$ based on $df_1 = 4, df_2 = 612$.

    a. Introduce notation and specify the null hypothesis and the alternative hypothesis for the ANOVA F test.

    b. Based on what you know about the F distribution, would you guess that the test statistic value of 0.80 provides strong evidence against the null hypothesis? Explain.

    c. Software reports a P value of 0.53. Explain how to interpret it.

14.37 Going to bars and having friends Do people who go to bars and pubs a lot tend to have more friends? A recent GSS asked, "How often do you go to a bar or tavern?" The table shows results of ANOVA for comparing the mean number of good friends at three levels of this variable. The very often group reported going to a bar at least several times a week. The occasional group reported going occasionally, but not as often as several times a week.

Summary of ANOVA for Mean Number of Good Friends and Going to Bars

	Very often	Occasional	Never
Mean	12.1	6.4	6.2
Standard dev.	21.3	10.2	14.0
Sample size	41	166	215

Source	DF	SS	MS	F	P
Group	2	1116.8	558.4	3.03	0.049
Error	419	77171.8	184.2		
Total	421	78288.5			

a. State the (i) hypotheses, (ii) test statistic value, and (iii) P-value for the significance test displayed in this table. Interpret the P-value.

b. Based on the assumptions needed to use the method in part a, is there any aspect of the data summarized here that suggests that the ANOVA test and follow-up confidence intervals may not be appropriate? Explain.

14.38 Singles watch more TV The 2014 General Social Survey asked 1475 subjects how many hours per day they watched TV, on average. Are there differences in population means according to the marital status of the subject (single, married, divorced)? The sample means were 3.27 for singles ($n = 459$), 2.64 for married subjects ($n = 731$), and 2.85 for divorced subjects ($n = 285$). In a one-way ANOVA, the between-groups estimate of the variance is 54.8 and the within-groups estimate is 6.0. (The dataset is available on the book's website as TV Hours 2014.)

a. Conduct the ANOVA test and make a decision using a 0.05 significance level.

b. The 95% confidence interval comparing the population means is (0.3, 0.9) for single and married subjects, (0.06, 0.8) for single and divorced subjects, and (−0.5, 0.1) for married and divorced subjects. Based on the three confidence intervals, indicate which pairs of means are significantly different. Interpret.

c. Based on the information given, show how to construct the confidence interval that compares the population mean TV watching for single and married subjects.

d. Refer to part c. Would the corresponding interval formed with the Tukey method be wider or narrower? Explain why.

14.39 Comparing auto bumpers A consumer organization compares the sturdiness of three types of front bumpers. In the study, a particular brand of car is driven into a concrete wall at 15 miles per hour. The response is the amount of damage, as measured by the repair costs, in hundreds of dollars. Due to the potentially large costs, the study conducts only two tests with each bumper type, using six cars. The table shows the data and some ANOVA results. Show the (a) assumptions, (b) hypotheses, (c) test statistic and *df* values, (d) P-value, and (e) interpretation for testing the hypothesis that the true mean repair costs are the same for the three bumper types.

Bumper A	Bumper B	Bumper C
1	2	11
3	4	15

Source	DF	SS	MS	F	P
Bumper	2	148.00	74.00	18.50	0.021
Error	3	12.00	4.00		
Total	5	160.00			

14.40 Compare bumpers Refer to the previous exercise.

a. Find the margin of error for constructing a 95% confidence interval for the difference between any pair of the true means. Interpret by showing which pairs of bumpers (if any) are significantly different in their true mean repair costs.

b. For Tukey 95% multiple comparison confidence intervals, the margin of error is 8.4. Explain the difference between confidence intervals formed with this method and separate confidence intervals formed with the method in part a.

c. Set up indicator variables for a multiple regression model, including bumper type.

d. The prediction equation for part c is $\hat{y} = 13 - 11x_1 - 10x_2$. Explain how to interpret the three parameter estimates in this model and show how these estimates relate to the sample means for the three bumpers.

14.41 Segregation by region Studies of the degree of residential racial segregation often use the *segregation index*. This is the percentage of non-Whites who would have to change the block on which they live to produce a fully nonsegregated city—one in which the percentage of non-Whites living in each block is the same for all blocks in the city. This index can assume values ranging from 0 to 100, with higher values indicating greater segregation. (The national average for large U.S. metropolitan areas in 2009 was 27, down from 33 in 2000.) The table shows the index for a sample of cities for 2005–2009, classified by region. You can enter this data in the *ANOVA (One Way)* app, or create a data file for other software.

Segregation Index

Northeast	North Central	South	West
Boston: 67	Minneapolis-St. Paul: 56	New Orleans: 64	San Francisco-Oakland: 64
NY, Long Island, Northern NJ: 79	Detroit: 80	Tampa: 58	Dallas-Ft Worth: 57
Philadelphia: 69	Chicago: 78	Miami: 66	Los Angeles: 70
Pittsburgh: 68	Milwaukee: 81	Atlanta: 60	Seattle: 54

Source: Racial and Ethnic Residential Segregation in the United States, 1980–2000, U.S. Bureau of the Census Series CENSR-3, 2002. www.psc.isr.umich.edu/dis/census/segregation.html.

a. Report the mean and standard deviation for each of the four regions.

b. Define notation and state the hypotheses for one-way ANOVA.

c. Report the *F* test statistic and its P-value. What do you conclude about the mean segregation indices for the four regions?

d. Suppose we took these data from the census bureau report by choosing only the cities in which we know people. Is the ANOVA valid? Explain.

14.42 Compare segregation means Refer to the previous exercise.

a. Using the *ANOVA (One Way)* app or other software, find the margin of error that pertains to each comparison, using the Tukey method for 95% multiple comparison confidence intervals.

b. Using part a, determine which pairs of means, if any, are significantly different.

14.43 Georgia political ideology The Georgia Student Survey file on the book's website asked students their political party affiliation (1 = Democrat, 2 = Republican, 3 = Independent) and their political ideology (on a scale from 1 = very liberal to 7 = very conservative). The table shows results of an ANOVA, with political ideology as the response variable.

Georgia Political Ideology and Party Affiliation

		Political Ideology	
Affiliation	*n*	Mean	StDev
Democrat	8	2.6250	1.0607
Republican	36	5.5000	1.0000
Independent	15	3.4667	0.9155

```
Source         DF    SS       MS      F      P
PoliticalAff    2   79.629  39.814  40.83  0.000
Error          56   54.608   0.975
Total          58  134.237
```

a. Does the ANOVA assumption of equal population standard deviations seem plausible, or is it so badly violated that ANOVA is inappropriate?

b. Dot plots reveal skewed distributions for the response variable (and an outlier). Which is more important, the normality assumption or the assumption that the groups are random samples from the population of interest?

c. The next table shows 95% confidence intervals comparing pairs of means. Interpret the confidence interval comparing Republicans and Democrats.

	95% CI		
Affiliations	Lower	Center	Upper
Republican–Democrat	2.10	2.87	3.65
Independent–Democrat	−0.02	0.84	1.71
Republican–Independent	1.43	2.03	2.64

d. Explain how you would summarize the results of the ANOVA *F* test and the confidence intervals to someone who has not studied statistics.

14.44 Comparing therapies for anorexia The Anorexia data file available in the *ANOVA (One Way)* app and on the book's website shows weight change for 72 anorexic teenage girls who were randomly assigned to one of three psychological treatments.

a. Show how to construct 95% confidence intervals to investigate how the population means differ. Interpret them.

b. Report the Tukey 95% multiple comparison confidence intervals. Interpret and explain why they are wider than the confidence intervals in part a.

14.45 Lot size varies by region? A geographer compares residential lot sizes in four quadrants of a city. To do this, she randomly samples 300 records from a city file on home residences and records the lot sizes (in thousands of square feet) by quadrant. The ANOVA table, shown in the table that follows, refers to a comparison of mean lot sizes for the northeast (NE), northwest (NW), southwest (SW), and southeast (SE) quadrants of the city. Fill in all the blanks in the table.

Lot Sizes by Quadrant of City

Source	DF	SS	MS	F	P-value
Quadrant	___	___	___	___	0.000
Error	296	1480	___		
Total	___	4180			

14.46 House with garage Refer to the House Selling Price OR data file on the book's website.

a. The variable "Garage" included in the dataset is an indicator variable for whether a house has a garage (with 1 indicating that it does have one). Using software (such as the *Linear Regression* app), put this as the sole predictor of house selling price (in thousands) in a regression model. Report the prediction equation and interpret the intercept and slope estimates.

b. For the model fitted in part a, conduct the *t* test for the effect of the indicator variable in the regression analysis (that is, test $H_0: \beta = 0$). Interpret.

c. Use software (such as the *ANOVA (One Way)* app) to conduct the *F* test for the analysis of variance comparing the mean selling prices of homes with and without a garage. Interpret.

d. Explain the connection between the value of *t* in part b and the value of *F* in part c.

14.47 Ideal number of kids by gender and race The GSS asks, "What is the ideal number of kids for a family?" When we use a recent GSS to evaluate how the mean response depends on gender and race (Black or White), we get the results shown in the ANOVA table.

a. Identify the response variable and the factors.

b. Explain what it would indicate if there were no interaction between gender and race in their effects. Show a hypothetical set of population means that would show a strong race effect and a weak gender effect and no interaction.

c. Using the table, specify the null and alternative hypotheses, test statistic, and P-value for the test of no interaction. Interpret the result.

ANOVA of Ideal Number of Kids by Gender and Race

Source	DF	SS	MS	F	P
Gender	1	0.25	0.25	0.36	0.546
Race	1	16.98	16.98	24.36	0.000
Interaction	1	0.95	0.95	1.36	0.244
Error	1245	867.72	0.70		
Total	1248	886.12			

14.48 Regress kids on gender and race Refer to the previous exercise. Let $f = 1$ for females and 0 for males and let $r = 1$ for Blacks and 0 for Whites. The regression model for predicting y = ideal number of kids is $\hat{y} = 2.42 + 0.04f + 0.37r$.

a. Interpret the coefficient of f. What is the practical implication of this estimate being so close to 0?

b. Find the estimated mean for each of the four combinations of gender and race.

c. Summarize what you learn about the effects based on the analyses in this and the previous exercise.

14.49 Energy drink In a class experiment at Williams College, students were randomly assigned either to drink or abstain from drinking an energy drink before attempting a straightforward but tedious mathematical task. They were also randomly assigned to start the task at 11 P.M. at night or at 8 A.M. in the morning. (The resulting data set is available on the book's website.) When we regress y = time it took to complete task (in minutes) on e = energy drink (1 = yes, 0 = no) and d = daytime (1 = 11P.M., 0 = 8A.M.) we get the prediction equation $\hat{y} = 9.8 - 0.39e - 2.0d$.

a. Interpret the effect of the energy drink.

b. Interpret the coefficient of d.

c. State a corresponding model for the population and indicate which parameters would need to equal zero for the response variable to be independent of whether one drinks an energy drink, for given time of the day.

d. Fit the regression model with software (such as the *Multiple Linear Regression* app) and comment on whether the mean times differ significantly between consuming and not consuming an energy drink, for a given time of day.

14.50 Income, gender, and education According to the U.S. Census Bureau, as of March 2009, the average earnings of full-time workers was estimated to be $31,666 for females with a high school education, $43,493 for males with a high school education, $60,293 for females with a bachelor's degree, and $94,206 for males with a bachelor's degree.

a. Identify the response variable and the two factors.

b. Show these means in a two-way classification of the factors.

c. Compare the differences between males and females for (i) high school graduates and (ii) college graduates. If these are close estimates of the population means, explain why there is interaction. Describe its nature.

14.51 Birth weight, age of mother, and smoking A study on the effects of prenatal exposure to smoke (by J. Nigg and N. Breslau, *Journal of the American Academy of Child & Adolescent Psychiatry*, vol. 46, 2009, pp. 362–369) indicated that mean birth weight was significantly lower for babies born to mothers who smoked during pregnancy. It also suggested that increasing age of the mother resulted in increased effects. Explain how this suggests interaction between smoking status and age of mother in their effects on birth weight of the child.

14.52 TV watching by gender and race When we use the 2008 GSS to evaluate how the mean number of hours a day watching TV depends on gender and race, we get the results shown in the ANOVA table that follows.

a. Identify the response variable and the factors.

b. From the table, specify the test statistic and P-value for the test of no interaction. Interpret the result.

c. Is there a significant (i) gender effect and (ii) race effect? Explain.

d. The sample means were 2.82 for White females, 2.68 for White males, 4.52 for Black females, and 4.19 for Black males. Explain how these results are compatible with the results of the tests discussed in part c.

Analysis of Variance for TVHOURS, Using Adjusted SS for Tests

Source	DF	Seq SS	Adj SS	Adj MS	F	P
RACE	1	419.60	399.12	399.12	58.32	0.000
SEX	1	8.74	8.74	8.74	1.28	0.259
RACE*SEX	1	1.42	1.42	1.42	0.21	0.649
Error	1198	8199.10	8199.10	6.84		
Total	1201	8628.86				

S = 2.61610 R-Sq = 4.98% R-Sq(adj) = 4.74%

14.53 Salary and gender The American Association of University Professors (AAUP) reports yearly on faculty salaries for all types of higher education institutions across the United States. Regard *Salary* as the response variable, *Gender* as the explanatory variable, and *Academic Rank* as the control variable. A regression analysis using these data could include an indicator variable for *Gender* and an indicator variable for *Rank*. The estimated coefficients are −13 (thousands of dollars) for *Gender* ($x_1 = 1$ for female and $x_1 = 0$ for male) and −40 (thousands of dollars) for a lower assistant *Rank* ($x_2 = 1$ for assistant professor and $x_2 = 0$ for professor).

a. Interpret the coefficient for gender.

b. At particular settings of the other predictors, the estimated mean salary for female professors was 96.2 thousand dollars. Using the estimated coefficients, find the estimated means for (i) male professors and (ii) female assistant professors.

14.54 Political ideology interaction   The first table shown summarizes responses on political ideology (where 1 = extremely liberal and 7 = extremely conservative) from the 2014 GSS by gender and race.

  a. From these sample means, is there evidence of a significant interaction? Explain what this means in the context of this example. (*Hint:* Is the difference between males and females in sample mean ideology about the same for Blacks and Whites?)

  b. From the ANOVA table shown, write a conclusion for testing the null hypothesis of no interaction.

Sample Means for Political Ideology by Sex and Race

	Black	White
Female	3.82	4.13
Male	3.81	4.22

ANOVA for Political Ideology by Sex and Race

Source	DF	SS	MS	F	P
Sex	1	3.0	3.0	1.4	0.229
Race	1	36.5	36.5	17.8	0.000
Interaction	1	0.8	0.8	0.4	0.539
Error	2202	4521.4	2.1		
Total	2205	4563.8			

Concepts and Applications

14.55 Regress TV watching on gender and marital status   When we use the 2014 GSS and regress y = number of hours per day watching TV on g = gender (1 = male, 0 = female) and marital status (m_1 = 1 for singles, 0 otherwise, m_2 = 1 for married subjects, 0 otherwise), we get the following output

Term	Coef	SE Coef	T-Value	P-value
Constant	2.78	0.155	17.95	0.000
g	0.16	0.127	1.29	0.197
m_1	0.41	0.184	2.21	0.027
m_2	-0.21	0.170	-1.26	0.209

  a. Write down the corresponding regression model for the population mean and give the equation for the population mean at each combination of the two factor levels. (Create a table similar to Table 14.11.)

  b. Write down the prediction equation and interpret the estimated gender effect.

  c. From the expression for the population means in part a, find the difference in means between single and divorced subjects, separately for each gender. This difference is equal to what regression coefficient?

  d. Find and interpret a 95% confidence interval for the difference in means between single and divorced subjects, for given gender. (*Note:* The df for the t-score equals 1,471.)

14.56 Number of friends and degree   Using the GSS website (see, e.g., Activity 2 at the end of Section 11.1), analyze whether the number of good friends (the variable NUMFREND) depends on the subject's highest degree (the variable DEGREE). To do so, click the MEANS tab

(next to the default TABLES tab) and enter the variable names. Under Output Options, deselect "Complex std errs" and select "ANOVA stats". Prepare a short report summarizing your analysis and its interpretation.

14.57 Sketch within- and between-groups variability   Sketch a dot plot of data for 10 observations in each of three groups such that

  a. You believe the P-value would be very small for a one-way ANOVA. (You do not need to do the ANOVA; merely show points for which you think this would happen.)

  b. The P-value in one-way ANOVA would not be especially small.

14.58 A = B and B = C, but A ≠ C?   In multiple comparisons following a one-way ANOVA with equal sample sizes, the margin of error with a 95% confidence interval for comparing each pair of means equals 10. Give three sample means illustrating that it is possible that Group A is not significantly different from Group B and Group B is not significantly different from Group C, yet Group A is significantly different from Group C.

14.59 Multiple comparison confidence   For four groups, explain carefully the difference between a confidence level of 0.95 for a single comparison of two means and a confidence level of 0.95 for a multiple comparison of all six pairs of means.

14.60 Another Simpson paradox   The 25 women faculty members in the humanities division of a college have a mean salary of $65,000, whereas the five women faculty in the science division have a mean salary of $72,000. The 20 men in the humanities division have a mean salary of $64,000, and the 30 men in the science division have a mean salary of $71,000.

  a. Construct a 2 × 2 table of sample mean incomes for the table of gender and division of college. Use weighted averages to find the overall means for men and women.

  b. Discuss how the results of a one-way comparison of mean incomes by gender would differ from the results of a two-way comparison of mean incomes by gender, controlling for division of college. (*Note:* This reversal of which gender has the higher mean salary, according to whether one controls division of college, illustrates *Simpson's paradox.*)

Multiple Choice or True/False

14.61 ANOVA/regression similarities   Analysis of variance and multiple regression have many similarities. Which of the following is *not* true?

  a. The response variable is quantitative for each.

  b. They both have F tests for testing that the response variable is statistically independent of the explanatory variable(s).

  c. For inferential purposes, they both assume that the response variable y is normally distributed with the same standard deviation at all combinations of levels of the explanatory variable(s).

d. They are both appropriate when the main focus is on describing straight-line effects of quantitative explanatory variables.

14.62 ANOVA variability One-way ANOVA provides relatively more evidence that $H_0: \mu_1 = \cdots = \mu_g$ is false (choose one):

a. The smaller the between-groups variation and the larger the within-groups variation.

b. The smaller the between-groups variation and the smaller the within-groups variation.

c. The larger the between-groups variation and the smaller the within-groups variation.

d. The larger the between-groups variation and the larger the within-groups variation.

14.63 Multiple comparisons For four means, it is planned to construct Tukey 95% multiple comparison confidence intervals for the differences between the six pairs.

a. For each confidence interval, there is a 0.95 chance that the interval will contain the true difference.

b. The probability that all six confidence intervals will contain the true differences is 0.70.

c. The probability that all six confidence intervals will contain the true differences is about 0.95.

d. The probability that all six confidence intervals will contain the true differences is $0.95 \times 0.95 \times 0.95 \times 0.95 \times 0.95 \times 0.95$.

14.64 Interaction There is interaction in a two-way ANOVA model when:

a. The two factors are associated.

b. Both factors have significant effects in the model without interaction terms.

c. The difference in true means between two categories of one factor varies among the categories of the other factor.

d. The mean square for interaction is about the same size as the mean square error.

14.65 True or false: Interaction For subjects aged under 50, there is little difference in mean annual medical expenses for smokers and nonsmokers. For subjects aged over 50, there is a large difference. Is it true or false that there is interaction between smoking status and age in their effects on annual medical expenses?

Advanced Concepts

14.66 What causes large or small F? An experiment used four groups of five individuals each. The overall sample mean was 60.

a. What did the sample means look like if the one-way ANOVA for comparing the means had test statistic $F = 0$? (*Hint:* What would have to happen for the between-groups variability to be 0?)

b. What did the data look like in each group if $F =$ infinity? (*Hint:* What would have to happen for the within-groups variability to be 0?)

14.67 Between-subjects estimate This exercise motivates the formula for the between-subjects estimate of the variance in one-way ANOVA. Suppose each population mean equals μ (that is, H_0 is true) and each sample size equals n. Then the sampling distribution of each $\bar{y}_l$ has mean μ and variance σ^2/n, and the sample mean of the $\bar{y}_l$ values is the overall sample mean, $\{\bar{y}\}$.

a. Treating the g sample means as g observations having sample mean $\bar{y}$, explain why $\Sigma(\bar{y}_i - \bar{y})^2/(g-1)$ estimates the variance σ^2/n of the distribution of the $\{\bar{y}_i\}$ values.

b. Using part a, explain why the between-groups estimate $\Sigma n(\bar{y}_i - \bar{y})^2/(g-1)$ estimates σ^2. (For the unequal sample size case, the formula replaces n by n_i.)

14.68 Bonferroni multiple comparisons The Bonferroni theorem states that the probability that *at least* one of a set of events occurs can be no greater than the sum of the separate probabilities of the events. For instance, if the probability of an error for each of five separate confidence intervals equals 0.01, then the probability that *at least* one confidence interval will be in error is no greater than $(0.01 + 0.01 + 0.01 + 0.01 + 0.01) = 0.05$.

a. Following Example 10, construct a confidence interval for each factor and guarantee that they both hold with overall confidence level at least 95%. (*Hint:* Each interval should use $t_{.0125} = 2.46$.)

b. Exercise 14.8 referred to a study comparing three groups (smoking status never, former, or current) on various personality scales. The study measured 35 personality scales and reported an F test comparing the three smoking groups for each scale. The researchers mentioned doing a Bonferroni correction for the 35 F tests. If the nominal *overall* probability of Type I error was 0.05 for the 35 tests, how small did the P-value have to be for a particular test to be significant? (*Hint:* What should the Type I error probability be for each of 35 tests for the overall Type I error probability to be no more than 0.05?)

14.69 Independent confidence intervals You plan to construct a 95% confidence interval in five situations with independent data sets.

a. Assuming that the results of the confidence intervals are statistically independent, find the probability that *all* five confidence intervals will contain the parameters they are designed to estimate. (*Hint:* Use the binomial distribution.)

b. Which confidence level should you use for each confidence interval so that the probability that all five intervals contain the parameters equals *exactly* 0.95?

14.70 Regression or ANOVA? You want to analyze $y =$ house selling price and $x =$ number of bathrooms (1, 2, or 3) by testing whether x and y are independent.

a. You could conduct a test of independence using (i) the ANOVA F test for a multiple regression model with two indicator variables or (ii) a regression t test for the coefficient of the number of bathrooms when it is treated as a quantitative predictor in a straight-line regression model. Explain the difference between these two ways of treating the number of bathrooms in the analysis.

b. What do you think are the advantages and disadvantages of the straight-line regression approach to conducting the test?

c. Give an example of three population means for which the straight-line regression model would be less appropriate than the model with indicator variables.

14.71 Three factors An experiment analyzed how the mean corn yield depends on three different fertilizers: Nitrogen (applied at low and high levels), phosphate (applied at low and high levels), and potash (applied at low and high levels). In the experiment, each plot of land received a combination of levels from these three fertilizers.

a. How many groups result from the different combinations of the three factors?

b. Defining indicator variables, state the regression model that corresponds to an ANOVA assuming a lack of interaction.

c. Give possible estimates of the model parameters in part b for which the estimated corn yield would be highest at the high level of nitrogen fertilizer and phosphate fertilizer and the low level of potash.

Student Activities

14.72 **Student survey data** Refer to the student survey data file that your class created in Exercise 1.50 at the end of Chapter 1. For variables chosen by your instructor, use ANOVA methods and related inferential statistical analyses. Interpret and summarize your findings in a short report and prepare to discuss your findings in class.

CHAPTER

15

The various *t* tests introduced in Chapter 10 and the ANOVA *F* test from Chapter 14 compare population means under the assumption of approximately normal population distributions. When such assumptions are questionable, this chapter presents alternative methods to compare two or more groups based on ranking the observations.

15.1 Compare Two Groups by Ranking

15.2 Nonparametric Methods for Several Groups and for Dependent Samples

Nonparametric Statistics

Example 1

How to Get a Better Tan

Picture the Scenario

Statistics students were asked to design an experiment about a topic of choice, conduct the experiment, and then analyze the data. One student, Allison, decided to compare tanning methods without exposure to the sun to avoid skin cancer risk. She investigated two treatments—a bronze tanning lotion applied twice over a two-day period, or a tanning studio where the person is exposed to ultraviolet (UV) light. We'll refer to these treatments as "tanning lotion" and "tanning studio."

The tanning lotion is much less expensive, but Allison predicted that the tanning studio would give a better tan. To investigate this hypothesis, she recruited five untanned female friends to participate in an experiment. Another student in the class used a random number generator to pick three of the friends to use the tanning lotion. The other two friends used the tanning studio. After three days, Allison evaluated the tans produced. She was blinded to

the treatment allocation, not knowing which participants used which tanning method. Allison ranked the friends in terms of the quality of their tans. The ranks went from 1 to 5, with 1 = most natural looking and 5 = least natural-looking

Questions to Explore

■ Once Allison ranked the five tanned participants, how could she summarize the evidence in favor of one treatment over the other?

■ How can Allison find a P-value to determine whether one treatment is significantly better than the other?

Thinking Ahead

You learned in Section 10.2 how to compare means for two treatments using *t* tests. The tests assume a *normal* distribution for a quantitative response variable. The *t* tests are *robust*, usually working well even when population distributions are *not* normal. An exception is when the distribution is skewed, the sample sizes are small, and the alternative hypothesis is one-sided.

To use the *t* test, suppose Allison created a quantitative variable by assigning a score between 0 and 10 for each girl to describe the quality of tan. With such small sample sizes (only 2 and 3 in each group), she would not be able to assess whether quality of tan is approximately normal. Moreover, her prediction that the studio gives a better tan than the lotion was one-sided. In any case, Allison found it easier to rank the participants than to create a quantitative variable. For these reasons, then, it's not appropriate for her to use a *t* test to compare the tanning methods.

We'll now learn about an alternative way to compare treatments (or, more generally, two groups) without having to assume a normal distribution for the response variable. **Nonparametric statistical methods** provide statistical inference without this assumption. They use solely the *ranking* of the subjects on the response variable.

Nonparametric Statistical Methods

Nonparametric statistical methods are inferential methods that do not assume a particular form of distribution, such as the normal distribution, for the population distribution.

Did You Know?

Inferential methods that assume a particular form for the population distribution are called *parametric* methods. They specify the population distribution in terms of parameters, such as the mean and standard deviation for a normal distribution. ◄

In Example 2, we'll use the best known nonparametric method, the Wilcoxon test, to analyze the ranking of the tans from Allison's experiment.

Nonparametric methods are especially useful in two cases:

- When the data are ranks for the subjects (as in Example 1) rather than quantitative measurements.
- When it's inappropriate to assume normality, and when the ordinary statistical method is not robust to violations of the normality assumption. For instance, we might prefer not to assume normality because we think the distribution will be skewed. Or, perhaps we have no idea about the shape of the distribution, and the sample size is too small to give us much information about it.

Statisticians developed the primary nonparametric statistical methods starting in the late 1940s, long after most other methods described in this book. Since then, many nonparametric methods have been devised to handle a wide variety of scenarios. This final chapter is designed to show you the idea behind nonparametric methods. In Section 15.1, we'll learn about the most popular nonparametric test, the Wilcoxon test for comparing two groups. Section 15.2 briefly describes other popular nonparametric methods.

Recall

In Section 10.3, the bootstrap and permutation methods for comparing two groups did not need to assume a normal population distribution in each group, but left the shape of the distribution unspecified. ◄

We have already seen examples of nonparametric methods for comparing two groups in Section 10.3: the bootstrap percentile confidence intervals and the permutation tests for comparing two groups in terms of means or medians. The nonparametric methods introduced in this chapter are special cases of permutation tests when applied to the ranks of the observations instead of using the original values.

15.1 Compare Two Groups by Ranking

Of the five participants in Example 1, three were randomly assigned to use the tanning lotion and two to use a tanning studio. The tans were then ranked from 1 to 5, with 1 representing the most natural-looking tan. Let's consider all the possible outcomes for this experiment. Each possible outcome divides the ranks of 1, 2, 3, 4, 5 into two groups—three ranks for the tanning lotion group and two ranks for the tanning studio group. Table 15.1 shows the possible rankings. For instance, in the first case, the three using the tanning lotion got the three best ranks, (1, 2, 3).

Table 15.1 Possible Rankings of Tanning Quality

Each case shows the three ranks for those using the tanning lotion and the two ranks for those using the tanning studio. It also shows the sample mean ranks and their difference.

Treatment	Possible Ranks				
Lotion	(1, 2, 3)	(1, 2, 4)	(1, 2, 5)	(1, 3, 4)	(1, 3, 5)
Studio	(4, 5)	(3, 5)	(3, 4)	(2, 5)	(2, 4)
Lotion Mean Rank	2	2.3	2.7	2.7	3
Studio Mean Rank	4.5	4	3.5	3.5	3
Difference of Mean Ranks	−2.5	−1.7	−0.8	−0.8	0

Treatment	Possible Ranks				
Lotion	(1, 4, 5)	(2, 3, 4)	(2, 3, 5)	(2, 4, 5)	(3, 4, 5)
Studio	(2, 3)	(1, 5)	(1, 4)	(1, 3)	(1, 2)
Lotion Mean Rank	3.3	3	3.3	3.7	4
Studio Mean Rank	2.5	3	2.5	2	1.5
Difference of Mean Ranks	0.8	0	0.8	1.7	2.5

We summarize the outcome of the experiment by finding the mean rank for each group and taking its difference. Table 15.1 shows the mean ranks and their differences. For example, in the first case the mean is $(1 + 2 + 3)/3 = 2$ for the tanning lotion and $(4 + 5)/2 = 4.5$ for the tanning studio. The difference is $2 − 4.5 = −2.5$. In other words, for the first case the rank for the lotion tanned participants is on average 2.5 less than the rank for the studio tanned participants.

Allison predicted that the tanning studio would tend to give better tans. When this happens in the sample, the ranks for the tanning studio are smaller than those for the tanning lotion. Then the mean rank is larger for the tanning lotion, and the difference between the mean ranks is positive, as in the last case in the table.

Comparing Mean Ranks: The Wilcoxon Test

For this experiment, the samples were independent random samples—the responses for the participants using the tanning lotion were independent of the responses for the participants using the tanning studio. Suppose that the two treatments have identical effects, in the sense that the quality of tan would be the same regardless of which treatment a participant uses. Then, each of the ten possible outcomes shown in Table 15.1 is equally likely. Each has probability 1/10. Using the ten possible outcomes, we can construct a sampling distribution for the difference between the mean ranks. Table 15.2 on the next page shows this sampling distribution. For instance, the difference between the sample mean ranks is 0 for two of the ten samples in Table 15.1, so the probability of this outcome is 2/10.

Figure 15.1 displays this sampling distribution. It is symmetric around 0. This is the expected value for the difference between the sample mean ranks if the two treatments truly have identical effects.

Allison hypothesized that the tanning studio would give a better tan than the tanning lotion. She wanted to test the null hypothesis,

H_0: The treatments are identical in tanning quality,

against the alternative hypothesis

H_a: Better tanning quality results with the tanning studio.

This alternative hypothesis is one-sided. It implies that the mean rank in the population of subjects assigned to the tanning studio is smaller than in the population

Recall

Section 10.2 discussed the null hypothesis of identical population distributions for the *t* test, assuming equal standard deviations, and Section 10.3 discussed the null hypothesis of identical population distributions for the permutation test. ◄

Table 15.2 Sampling Distribution of Difference Between Sample Mean Ranks

These probabilities apply when the treatments have identical effects. For example, only one of the ten possible samples in Table 15.1 has a difference between the mean ranks equal to −2.5, so this value has probability 1/10.

Difference Between Mean Ranks	Probability
−2.5	1/10
−1.7	1/10
−0.8	2/10
0	2/10
0.8	2/10
1.7	1/10
2.5	1/10

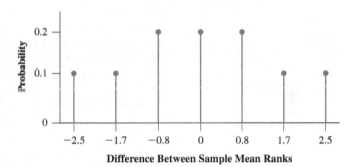

▲ **Figure 15.1** Sampling Distribution of Difference Between Sample Mean Ranks. This sampling distribution, which is symmetric around 0, applies when the treatments have identical effects. It is used for the significance test of the null hypothesis that the treatments are identical in their tanning quality.

of subjects assigned to the tanning lotion. (Remember, a smaller rank indicates a better tanning quality.) If this were true, we would expect that the difference in the sample mean ranks between the tanning lotion and the tanning studio is positive, whereas under the null hypothesis, we would expect this difference to be around 0.

To find the P-value, we presume that H_0 is true. Then, all samples in Table 15.1 are equally likely, and the sampling distribution is the one shown in Table 15.2 and Figure 15.1. The P-value is the probability of observing a difference between the sample mean rankings like the observed difference or one even more extreme, in terms of giving even more evidence in favor of H_a. The test comparing two groups based on the sampling distribution of the difference between the sample mean ranks is called the **Wilcoxon test**. It is named after the chemist-turned-statistician, Frank Wilcoxon, who devised it in 1945.

SUMMARY: Wilcoxon Nonparametric Test for Comparing Two Groups

1. **Assumptions:**   Independent random samples from two groups, either from random sampling or a randomized experiment.

2. **Hypotheses:**
   H_0: Identical population distributions for the two groups (this implies equal population mean ranks)
   H_a: Different population mean ranks (two-sided), or
   H_a: Higher population mean rank for a specified group (one-sided)

3. **Test Statistic:** Difference between sample mean ranks for the two groups (equivalently, can use sum of ranks for one sample, as discussed after Example 2).

4. **P-value:** One-tail or two-tail probability, depending on H_a, that the difference between the sample mean ranks is as extreme or more extreme than observed.

5. **Conclusion:** Report the P-value and interpret in context. If a decision is needed, reject H_0 if the P-value $\leq$ significance level, such as 0.05.

Example 2

P-Value for Wilcoxon Test

Tanning Studio Versus Tanning Lotion

Picture the Scenario

Example 1 describes Allison's experiment to determine whether a tanning lotion or a tanning studio produced a better tan. Table 15.1 showed the possible rankings for five tans. Table 15.2 showed the sampling distribution of the difference between the sample mean ranks, presuming the null hypothesis is true that the tanning treatments have identical effects. For Allison's actual experiment, the ranks were (2, 4, 5) for the three participants using the tanning lotion and (1, 3) for the two participants using the tanning studio.

Questions to Explore

a. Find and interpret the P-value for comparing the treatments, using the one-sided alternative hypothesis that the tanning studio gives a better tan than the tanning lotion.

b. What's the smallest possible P-value you could get for this experiment?

Think It Through

a. For the observed sample, the mean ranks are $(2 + 4 + 5)/3 = 3.7$ for the tanning lotion and $(1 + 3)/2 = 2$ for the tanning studio. The test statistic is the difference between the sample mean ranks, $3.7 - 2 = 1.7$. Differences as or more extreme than this, for which the ranks tended to be better (lower) with the tanning studio, are in the right tail of the sampling distribution in Figure 15.1. For the one-sided H_a, the P-value is the probability,

$$\text{P-value} = P(\text{difference between sample mean ranks at least as large as observed}).$$

Recall

Sampling distribution of the difference between mean ranks:

Difference	Probability
−2.5	1/10
−1.7	1/10
−0.8	2/10
0	2/10
0.8	2/10
1.7	1/10
2.5	1/10

That is, under the presumption that H_0 is true,

$$\text{P-value} = P(\text{difference between sample mean ranks} \geq 1.7).$$

From Table 15.2 (shown again in the margin) or Figure 15.1a on the next page, the probability of a sample mean difference of 1.7 or even larger is $1/10 + 1/10 = 2/10 = 0.20$. This is the P-value. It is not very close to 0. Although there is some evidence that the tanning studio gives a better tan (it *did* have a lower sample mean rank), the evidence is not strong enough. If the treatments had identical effects, the probability would be 0.20 of getting a difference like we observed or one even more extreme.

b. In this experiment, suppose the tanning studio gave the two most natural-looking tans. The ranks would then be (1, 2) for the tanning studio and (3, 4, 5) for the tanning lotion. The difference of sample means then equals $4 - 1.5 = 2.5$. It is the most extreme possible difference, and (from Table 15.2 or Figure 15.1a) its tail probability is 0.10. This is the smallest possible one-sided P-value.

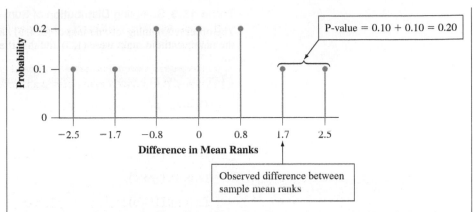

Figure 15.1a P-value for One-Sided Test. The P-value is the probability of observing a difference as large or larger than the observed one, assuming the null hypothesis is true.

Insight

With sample sizes of only 2 for one treatment and 3 for the other treatment, it's not possible to get a very small P-value. If Allison wanted to make a decision using a 0.05 significance level, she would never be able to get strong enough evidence to reject the null hypothesis. To get informative results, she'd need to conduct an experiment with larger sample sizes.

▶ **Try Exercises 15.1 and 15.2**

Suppose Allison instead used a two-sided H_a, namely that there is a treatment difference without specifying which is better. Then the P-value is a two-tail probability. In Example 2, we would get P-value $= 2(0.20) = 0.40$.

The Wilcoxon Rank Sum Statistic   The Wilcoxon test can, equivalently, use as the test statistic the sum of the ranks in just one of the samples. For example, Figure 15.1b and Table 15.3 show the possible sum of ranks for the tanning lotion. They have the same probabilities as the differences between the sample mean ranks because the ranks in one sample determine the ranks in the other sample (since the ranks must be the integers 1 through 5). For example, the ranks were (2, 4, 5) for the participants using the tanning lotion, for which the sum of ranks is 11. This implies that the ranks were (1, 3) for those using the tanning studio, and it implies that the difference between the mean ranks was $(2 + 4 + 5)/3 - (1 + 3)/2 = 3.7 - 2 = 1.7$. The right-tail probability of the observed rank sum of 11 or a more extreme value is again $1/10 + 1/10 = 0.20$, as seen in the following figure. Some software reports the sum of ranks as the *Wilcoxon rank sum statistic*, sometimes denoted by *W*.

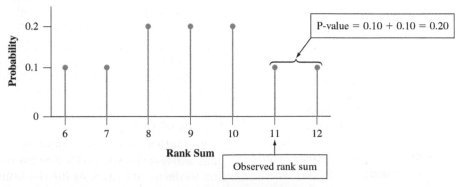

Figure 15.1b Sampling Distribution of the Sum of the Ranks in the Tanning Lotion Group. The sampling distribution of the sum of the ranks is identical to the one for the difference in the mean ranks in Figure 15.1a.

Table 15.3 Sampling Distribution of Sum of Ranks

The observed tanning lotion ranks of (2, 4, 5) have a rank sum of 11. These ranks imply that the tanning studio ranks were (1, 3) and that the difference between the sample mean ranks was 1.7.

Tanning Lotion Ranks	Sum of Tanning Lotion Ranks	Probability
(1, 2, 3)	6	1/10
(1, 2, 4)	7	1/10
(1, 2, 5), (1, 3, 4)	8	2/10
(2, 3, 4), (1, 3, 5)	9	2/10
(2, 3, 5), (1, 4, 5)	10	2/10
(2, 4, 5)	11	1/10
(3, 4, 5)	12	1/10

Large-Sample P-Values Use a Normal Sampling Distribution

With sample sizes of 3 and 2, it was simple to enumerate all the possible outcomes and construct a sampling distribution for the sum of ranks for a sample or for the difference between the mean ranks. With the sample sizes usually used in practice, it is tedious to do this. It's best to use software, such as the *Wilcoxon Test* app, to get the results. Table 15.4 shows the way SPSS reports results for the Wilcoxon test conducted in Example 2. It shows the P-value of 0.20 for the one-sided and the P-value of 0.40 for the two-sided alternative hypothesis.

Table 15.4 SPSS Output for Wilcoxon Test with Example 2

SPSS uses the sum of the two ranks (1, 3) for the tanning studio as the Wilcoxon test statistic W. The P-value for the one-sided test is listed next to "Exact Sig. (1-tailed)," where "Sig." is short for significance. When W is the sum of the ranks for the tanning studio, values of W as *small or smaller* are in favor of the alternative hypothesis. (By contrast, if W is the sum of the ranks for the lotion, values of W as large or larger are in favor of the alternative hypothesis.) The two-sided P-value is listed next to "Exact Sig. [2*(1-tailed Sig.)]." This output was obtained using the Legacy Dialog option under Nonparametrics in the Analyze menu of SPSS 21.

▶ **Activity 1**

The *Wilcoxon Test* app provides the exact P-value whenever possible, i.e., if the sample size is not too large. You can also get the exact P-value for the Wilcoxon test by using the *Permutation Test* app by (i) entering the ranks for the two groups, (ii) selecting Wilcoxon Rank Sum Statistic as the test statistic, (iii) checking the option for all possible permutations, and (iv) pressing Generate Permutation(s). The second tab then shows the same sampling distribution as Figure 15.1b and provides the P-value.

	Ranks			
	Treatment	N	Mean Rank	Sum of Ranks
Tanning	Lotion	3	3.67	11.00
	Studio	2	2.00	4.00
	Total	5		

Test Statistics	
	Tanning
Mann-Whitney U	1.000
Wilcoxon W	4.000
Z	−1.155
Asymp. Sig. (2-tailed)	.248
Exact Sig. [2*(1-tailed Sig.)]	.400
Exact Sig. (1-tailed)	.200

In Example 2, we found the P-value with an exact probability calculation using the actual sampling distribution. With large samples, an alternative approach finds a z test statistic and a P-value based on a normal distribution approximation to the actual sampling distribution. (Some software, such as MINITAB, *only* provides results for the large-sample z test analysis.) For example, in Table 15.4, SPSS reports $z = -1.155$ and Asymp. Sig. (2-tailed) = 0.248. These are the

In Words

"Asymp." is short for **asymptotic**, which in statistics means "large-sample" or "as the sample size grows" (mathematically, as it grows toward infinity).

results of the large-sample approximate analysis. This analysis is not appropriate for Example 2 because the sample sizes are only 2 and 3 for the two groups.

The large-sample test has a z test statistic because the difference between the sample mean ranks (or the sum of ranks for one sample) has an approximate normal sampling distribution. The z test statistic has the form

$$z = (\text{difference between sample mean ranks})/se.$$

The standard error formula is complex but easily calculated by software. The P-value is then the right-tail, left-tail, or two-tail probability, depending on H_a. Using the normal distribution for the large-sample test does not mean we are assuming that the response variable has a normal distribution. We are merely using the fact that the sampling distribution for the test statistic is approximately normal.

Ties Often Occur When We Rank Observations

Often in ranking the observations, some pairs of subjects are tied. They are judged to perform equally well. We then *average the ranks* in assigning them to those subjects. For example, suppose a participant using the tanning studio got the most natural-looking tan (rank 1), two participants using the tanning lotion got the two least natural-looking tans (ranks 4 and 5), but the other participant using the tanning studio and the other participant using the tanning lotion were judged to have equally good tans. Then, those two participants share ranks 2 and 3, and each gets the average rank of 2.5. The ranks are then

Tanning studio: 1, 2.5

Tanning lotion: 2.5, 4, 5

In Practice Software and Implementing the Wilcoxon Test

Software can find tied ranks and then calculate the P-value for the Wilcoxon test. Most software reports only the large-sample approximate P-value when either sample size is larger than some value, typically 20. For example, the *Wilcoxon Test* app or SPSS reports the small-sample exact P-value only when each sample size is about 20 or less.

Using the Wilcoxon Test with a Quantitative Response

In Examples 1 and 2, the response was a rank. When the response variable is quantitative, the Wilcoxon test is applied by first converting the observations to ranks. For the combined sample, the observations are ordered from smallest to largest. The smallest observation gets rank 1, the second smallest gets rank 2, and so forth. The test compares the mean ranks for the two samples. Software can implement the test.

Example 3

Wilcoxon Test: Finding Ranks (Large Sample) ◄

Driving Reaction Times

Picture the Scenario

Example 9 in Chapter 10 discussed an experiment investigating whether cell phone use impairs drivers' reaction times. A sample of 64 college students was randomly assigned to a cell phone group or a control group, 32 to each. On a machine that simulated driving situations, participants were instructed to press a brake button as soon as possible when they detected a red light.

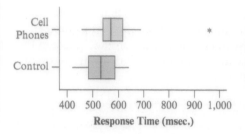

▲ Figure 15.2 Box Plots of Response Times for Cell Phone Study. **Question** Does either box plot show any irregularities that suggest it's safer to use a nonparametric test than a two-sample *t* test?

▶ **Activity 2**

The *Wilcoxon Test* app provides the P-value. To see how the Wilcoxon procedure corresponds to a permutation test, you can also use the *Permutation Test* app, which has these data preloaded, to obtain an accurate approximation of the exact P-value. Select the Reaction Time data set and choose the Wilcoxon Rank Sum Statistic as the test statistic. Generate several thousand permutations. Once this is done (which may take a while), notice how the sampling distribution looks approximately normal, which justifies using the asymptotic P-value. The second tab of the app provides the permutation P-value, which is a very accurate approximation of the exact P-value.

The control group listened to a radio broadcast or to books-on-tape while they performed the simulated driving. The cell phone group carried out a conversation on a cell phone with someone in a separate room.

A subject's reaction time observation is defined as the response time to the red lights (in milliseconds), averaged over all the trials. Figure 15.2 shows box plots of the data for the two groups. Here's some of the data showing the four smallest observations and the four largest observations for each treatment.

| Cell phone: | 456 | 468 | 482 | 501 | .... | 672 | 679 | 688 | 960 |
| Control: | 426 | 436 | 444 | 449 | .... | 626 | 626 | 642 | 648 |

The *t* inferences for comparing the treatment means assume normal population distributions. The box plots do not show any substantial skew, but there is an extreme outlier for the cell phone group. One subject in that group had a very slow mean reaction time, 960 milliseconds.

Questions to Explore

a. Explain how to find the ranks for the Wilcoxon test by showing which of the 64 observations get ranks 1, 2, 63, and 64.

b. Table 15.5 shows the SPSS output for conducting the Wilcoxon test. Report and interpret the mean ranks.

Table 15.5 SPSS Output for Wilcoxon Test with Data from Cell Phone Study

Ranks					Test Statistics	
	group	N	Mean Rank	Sum of Ranks		Reactime
Reactime	Cell Phone	32	38.00	1216.00	Mann-Whitney U	336.000
	Control	32	27.00	864.00	Wilcoxon W	864.000
	Total	64			Z	−2.363
					Asymp. Sig. (2-tailed)	.018

c. Report the test statistic and the P-value for the two-sided Wilcoxon test. Interpret.

Think It Through

a. Let's look at the smallest and largest observations for each group that were shown above:

| Cell phone: | 456 | 468 | 482 | 501 | .... | 672 | 679 | 688 | 960 |
| Control: | 426 | 436 | 444 | 449 | .... | 626 | 626 | 642 | 648 |

We give rank 1 to the *smallest* reaction time, so the value 426 gets rank 1. The second smallest observation is 436, which gets rank 2. The largest of the 64 reaction times, which was 960, gets rank 64. The next largest observation, 688, gets rank 63.

b. Table 15.5 reports mean ranks of 38 for the cell phone group and 27 for the control group. The smaller mean for the control group suggests that that group tends to have smaller ranks and, thus, faster reaction times.

c. The *z* test statistic divides the difference between the sample mean ranks by a standard error. Table 15.5 reports $z = -2.363$. The P-value of 0.018, reported as "Asymp. Sig. (2-tailed)," is the two-tail probability for the two-sided H_a. It shows strong evidence against the null hypothesis that the distribution of reaction time is identical for the two treatments. Specifically, the sample mean ranks suggest that reaction times tend to be slower for those using cell phones.

Insight

The observation of 960 would get rank 64 if it were *any* number larger than 688 (the second largest value). So, *the Wilcoxon test is not affected by an outlier.* No matter how far the largest observation falls from the next largest, it still gets the same rank. Likewise, no matter how far the smallest observation is below the next smallest, it still gets the rank of 1.

▶ *Try Exercise 15.4*

Nonparametric Estimation Comparing Two Groups

Throughout this book, we've seen the importance of *estimating* parameters. We learn more from a confidence interval for a parameter than from a significance test about the value of that parameter. Nonparametric estimation methods, like nonparametric tests, do not require the assumption of normal population distributions.

When the response is quantitative, we can compare a measure of center for the two groups. In Section 10.2, we used the mean as a measure for center and computed a confidence interval for the difference in means. When the distribution of the response variable is skewed rather than normal, comparing the medians is often more informative. In Section 10.3, we introduced the bootstrap approach, which can be used to obtain a confidence interval for the difference in medians.

Under the assumption that *the population distribution for the two groups have the same shape* (e.g., the distribution of the response in group 1 has the same right-skewed shape as the distribution of the response in group 2, as shown in the margin figure), we can also use nonparametric methods based on ranks to find a confidence interval for the difference in medians. The reason for this additional assumption is that under it, one population distribution is shifted relative to the other population distribution, and we can estimate the size of the shift as the difference in the two medians.

Most software for the Wilcoxon test reports point and interval estimates for this shift in the medians. (Some software, such as MINITAB, refers to the equivalent Mann-Whitney test instead. See Exercise 15.35.) Under this extra assumption of the same shape of the two population distributions, here's how software estimates the difference between the population medians. For every possible pair of subjects, one from each group, it takes the difference between the response from the first group and the response from the second group. The point estimate for the difference in medians is the median of all those differences. Software also reports a confidence interval for the difference between the population medians. The mechanics of this are beyond the scope of this book.

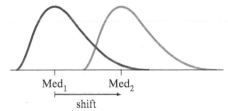

One Population Distribution is Shifted Relative to the Other

Med₁   Med₂

shift

Example 4

Wilcoxon Test
Comparing Medians ◀

Difference Between Median Reaction Times

Picture the Scenario

Example 3 used the Wilcoxon test to compare reaction time distributions in a simulated driving experiment for subjects using cell phones and for a control group. The MINITAB output in Table 15.6 shows results of comparing the distributions using medians. (It uses the Greek letter name *eta*, printed as η, to denote the population median.)

Table 15.6 MINITAB Output for Comparing Medians for Cell Phone Group and Control Group

	N	Median
Cell Phone	32	569.00
Control	32	530.00

Point estimate for $\eta 1 - \eta 2$ is 44.50 ◄——— η (the Greek eta) is MINITAB notation for the median

95.1 Percent CI for $\eta 1 - \eta 2$ is (8.99, 79.01)

W = 1216.0

Test of $\eta 1 = \eta 2$ vs $\eta 1 \neq \eta 2$ is significant at 0.0184 ◄——— P-value

Questions to Explore

a. Report the sample medians and the point estimate of the difference between the population medians.

b. Report and interpret the 95% confidence interval for the difference between the population medians.

Think It Through

a. The median reaction times were 569 milliseconds for the cell phone group and 530 milliseconds for the control group. For the cell phone group, for example, half of the reaction times were smaller than 569 milliseconds and half were larger than 569. Table 15.6 reports a point estimate of the difference between the population medians for the two groups of 44.5 milliseconds. (*Note:* This is not the same as the difference between the two sample medians, which is an alternative estimate and equals 569 − 530 = 39 milliseconds.)

b. Table 15.6 reports that a 95.1% confidence interval for the difference between the population medians is (8.99, 79.01). (For these types of intervals, achieving the exact confidence level is often impossible, so software uses a confidence level that is close to 95%.) Since zero is not contained in the 95.1% interval, this interval supports that the median reaction times are not the same for the cell phone and control groups. We infer from the interval that the population median reaction time for the cell phone group is between 9 milliseconds and 79 milliseconds larger than for the control group. This inference agrees with the conclusion of the Wilcoxon test that the reaction time distributions differ for the two groups (P-value = 0.018).

Insight

Example 9 in Chapter 10 estimated the difference between the population *means* to be 51.5, with a 95% confidence interval of (12, 91). However, those results were influenced by the outlier of 960 for the cell phone group. When estimation focuses on medians rather than means, outliers do not influence the analysis. *The lack of an influence of outliers is an advantage of the analysis reported here for the medians.*

▶ *Try Exercise 15.5*

Recall

From the discussion before the example, the **point estimate** of the difference between the population medians equals the median of the differences between responses from the two groups. ◄

15.1   Practicing the Basics

15.1   Tanning experiment   Suppose the tanning experiment described in Examples 1 and 2 used only four participants, two for each treatment.

a. Show the six possible ways the four ranks could be allocated, two to each treatment, with no ties.

b. For each possible sample, find the mean rank for each treatment and the difference between the mean ranks.

c. Presuming H_0 is true of identical treatment effects, construct the sampling distribution of the difference between the sample mean ranks for the two treatments.

15.2   Test for tanning experiment   Refer to the previous exercise. For the actual experiment, suppose the participants using the tanning studio got ranks 1 and 2 and the participants using the tanning lotion got ranks 3 and 4.

a. Find and interpret the P-value for the alternative hypothesis that the tanning studio tends to give better tans than the tanning lotion.

b. Find and interpret the P-value for the alternative hypothesis that the treatments have different effects.

c. Explain why it is a waste of time to conduct this experiment if you plan to use a 0.05 significance level to make a decision.

15.3   Comparing clinical therapies   A clinical psychologist wants to choose between two therapies for treating severe mental depression. She selects six patients who are similar in their depressive symptoms and overall quality of health. She randomly selects three patients to receive Therapy 1. The other three receive Therapy 2. After one month of treatment, the improvement in each patient is measured by the change in a score for measuring severity of mental depression—the higher the change score, the better. The improvement scores are

Therapy 1: 25, 40, 45

Therapy 2: 10, 20, 30

a. Show all possible ways the ranks from 1 to 6 could be distributed between the two treatments. (*Hint:* There are 20 allocations.)

b. For each possible allocation of ranks, find the mean rank for each treatment and the difference between the mean ranks.

c. Consider the null hypothesis of identical response distributions for the two treatments. Presuming H_0 is true, construct the sampling distribution of the difference between the sample mean ranks for the two treatments.

d. For the actual data shown above, use the *Wilcoxon Test* app to find and interpret the P-value for the alternative hypothesis that the two treatments have different effects. (You can also check your answer by entering the data in the *Permutation Test* app, selecting Wilcoxon Rank Sum Statistic as the test statistic, and selecting the option for generating all possible permutations.)

15.4   Baby weight and smoking   Smoking during pregnancy is a known cause of reduced infant birth weight and other issues that can affect the delivery and mortality. Despite this strong evidence, women who smoke find it difficult to quit even when they are pregnant. Suppose a study is done measuring the birth weight of babies of mothers who smoked during pregnancy and those who did not smoke. The birth weight data in pounds are:

Smokers: 3.1, 4.2, 4.5, 5.0, 6.4, 4.7, 6.0

Nonsmokers: 5.5, 6.5, 7.1, 8.0, 6.8, 7.5, 6.2

a. State the hypotheses for conducting a one-sided (right tailed) Wilcoxon test.

b. Find the ranks for the two groups and their sum and mean of ranks.

c. Software such as the *Wilcoxon Test* app reports a small-sample one-sided P-value of 0.002. Interpret. (You can check your answer by entering the data in the *Permutation Test* app, selecting Wilcoxon Rank Sum Statistic as the test statistic, and selecting the option for generating all possible permutations.)

15.5   Estimating smoking effect   Refer to the previous exercise. For these data, MINITAB reports

```
Point estimate for η1 − η2 is −2.00
95.9 Percent CI for η1 − η2 is (−3.30,−0.70)
W = 31.0
Test of η1 = η2 vs η1 ≠ η2 is significant at 0.006
```

Explain how to interpret the reported (a) point estimate and (b) confidence interval.

15.6   Trading volumes   The following data show the number of shares of General Electric stock traded on Mondays and on Fridays from February through April of 2011. The trading volumes (rounded to the nearest million) are as follows:

Mondays: 45, 43, 43, 66, 91, 53, 35, 45, 29, 64, 56

Fridays: 43, 41, 45, 46, 61, 56, 80, 40, 48, 49, 50, 41

Using the *Wilcoxon Test* app or other software:

a. Plot the data. Summarize what the plot shows.

b. State the hypotheses and give the P-value for the Wilcoxon test for comparing the two groups with a two-sided alternative hypothesis. (You can also find an accurate approximation of the exact P-value by using the *Permutation Test* app.)

c. A 95.5% confidence interval for comparing the population medians equals (−11, 13). Interpret and explain what (if any) effect the day of the week (Monday versus Friday) has on the median number of shares traded.

d. State the assumptions for the methods in parts b and c.

15.7   Teenage anorexia   Previous chapters described a study that used therapy to treat teenage girls who suffered from anorexia. The girls were randomly assigned to the cognitive behavioral treatment (Group 1) or to the control group (Group 2). The study observed the weight change after a period of time. The following output shows results of a nonparametric comparison. (The data set is available from the book's website.)

a. Interpret the reported point estimate of the difference between the population medians for the weight changes for the two groups.

b. Interpret the reported confidence interval and summarize the assumptions on which it is based.

c. Report a P-value for testing the null hypothesis of identical population distributions of weight change. Specify the alternative hypothesis, and interpret the P-value.

MINITAB Output Comparing Weight Changes

```
                             N           Median
Cognitive_change            29            1.400
Control_change              26           -0.350

Point estimate for η1 - η2 is 3.05

95.0 Percent CI for η1 - η2 is (-0.60,8.10)

W = 907.0

Test of η1 = η2 vs η1 ≠ η2 is significant at 0.1111
```

15.2 Nonparametric Methods for Several Groups and for Dependent Samples

This final section describes a few other nonparametric methods. We'll first learn about a method that extends the Wilcoxon test to comparisons of mean ranks for *several* groups. We then study two methods for comparing two *dependent* samples as alternatives to the methods studied in Section 10.4.

Comparing Mean Ranks of Several Groups: The Kruskal-Wallis Test

Chapter 14 showed that comparisons of means for two groups extend to comparisons for many groups, using the **analysis of variance (ANOVA) *F* test**. Likewise, the Wilcoxon test for comparing mean ranks of two groups extends to a comparison of mean ranks for several groups. This rank test is called the **Kruskal-Wallis test**, named after the statisticians who proposed it in 1952.

As in the Wilcoxon test, the Kruskal-Wallis test assumes that the samples are independent random samples, and the null hypothesis states that the groups have identical population distributions for the response variable. The test determines the ranks for the entire sample and then finds the sample mean rank for each group. The test statistic is based on the between-groups variability in the sample mean ranks. To calculate this test statistic, denote the sample mean rank by $\overline{R}_i$ for group i and by $\overline{R}$ for the combined sample of g groups. The Kruskal-Wallis test statistic is

$$\left(\frac{12}{n(n+1)}\right)\Sigma n_i(\overline{R}_i - \overline{R})^2.$$

Recall

Section 11.2 introduced the chi-squared distribution as a right-skewed distribution on the positive real line and with mean equal to the degrees of freedom. ◄

The constant $12/(n(n+1))$ is there so that the test statistic values have approximately a chi-squared sampling distribution. Software, such as the *Kruskal-Wallis* app easily calculates it for us.

The sampling distribution of the test statistic indicates whether the variability among the sample mean ranks is large compared to what's expected under the null hypothesis that the groups have identical population distributions. With g groups, the test statistic has an approximate chi-squared distribution with $g - 1$ degrees of freedom. (Recall that for the chi-squared distribution, the *df* is the mean.) The approximation improves as the sample sizes increase. The larger the differences among the sample mean ranks, the larger the test statistic and the stronger the evidence against H_0. The P-value is the right-tail probability above the observed test statistic value.

When would we use this test? The ANOVA F test assumes normal population distributions. The Kruskal-Wallis test does not have this assumption. It's a safer method to use with small samples when not much information is available about the shape of the distributions. It's also useful when the data are merely ranks and we don't have a quantitative measurement of the response variable. Here's a basic summary of the test:

Summary: Kruskal-Wallis Nonparametric Test for Comparing Several Groups

1. **Assumptions:** Independent random samples from several (g) groups, either from random sampling or a randomized experiment.

2. **Hypotheses:**
   H_0: Identical population distributions for the g groups.
   H_a: Population distributions not all identical.

3. **Test Statistic:** Uses between-groups variability of sample mean ranks.

4. **P-value:** Right-tail probability above observed test statistic value from chi-squared distribution with $df - g - 1$.

5. **Conclusion:** Report the P-value and interpret in context.

Example 5

Kruskal-Wallis Test ◄

Frequent Dating and College GPA

Picture the Scenario

Tim decided to study whether dating was associated with college GPA. He wondered whether students who date a lot tend to have poorer GPAs. He asked the 17 students in the class to anonymously fill out a short questionnaire in which they were asked to give their college GPA (0 to 4 scale) and to indicate whether during their college careers they had dated regularly, occasionally, or rarely.

Figure 15.3 shows the dot plots that Tim constructed of the GPA data for the three dating groups. Since the dot plots showed evidence of severe skew to the left and since the sample size was small in each group, he felt safer analyzing the data with the Kruskal-Wallis test than with the ordinary ANOVA F test.

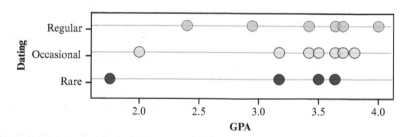

▲ **Figure 15.3** Dot Plots of GPA by Dating Group. **Question** Why might it not be appropriate to use the ordinary ANOVA F test to compare mean GPA for the three dating groups?

Finding ranks for data in Table 15.7

GPA	Rank
1.75	1
2.00	2
2.40	3
2.95	4
3.15	5
3.20	6
3.40	7
3.44	8
3.50	9.5 ← average of 9 and 10
3.50	9.5
3.60	11
3.67	12
3.68	13
3.70	14
3.71	15
3.80	16
4.00	17

Table 15.7 shows the data, with the college GPA values ordered from smallest to largest for each dating group. The table in the margin shows the combined and sorted sample of 17 observations from the three groups and their ranks. Table 15.7 also shows these ranks as well as the mean rank for each group.

Table 15.7 College GPA by Dating Group

Dating Group	GPA Observations	Ranks	Mean Rank
Rare	1.75, 3.15, 3.50, 3.68	1, 5, 9.5, 13	7.1
Occasional	2.00, 3.20, 3.44, 3.50, 3.60, 3.71, 3.80	2, 6, 8, 9.5, 11, 15, 16	9.6
Regular	2.40, 2.95, 3.40, 3.67, 3.70, 4.00	3, 4, 7, 12, 14, 17	9.5

Question to Explore

Table 15.8 shows MINITAB output for the Kruskal-Wallis test. MINITAB denotes the chi-squared test statistic by H. Interpret these results, which you can replicate with the *Kruskal-Wallis* app.

Table 15.8 Results of Kruskal-Wallis Test for Data in Table 15.7

```
Kruskal-Wallis Test on GPA

Date Group        N        Median       Ave Rank         Z

Rare              4         3.325           7.1       -0.85

Occasional        7         3.500           9.6        0.44

Regular           6         3.535           9.5        0.30

H = 0.72      DF = 2    P = 0.696    (adjusted for ties)
```

Think It Through

If H_0: identical population distributions for the three groups were true, the Kruskal-Wallis test statistic would have an approximate chi-squared distribution with $df = 2$. Table 15.8 reports that the test statistic is $H = 0.72$. The P-value is the right-tail probability above 0.72. Table 15.8 reports this as 0.696, about 0.7. It is plausible that GPA is independent of dating group. Table 15.8 shows that the sample median GPAs are not very different, and since the sample sizes are small, these sample medians do not give much evidence against H_0.

Insight

If the P-value had been small, to find out which pairs of groups significantly differ, we could follow up the Kruskal-Wallis test by a Wilcoxon test to compare each pair of dating groups. Or, we could find a confidence interval for the difference between the population medians for each pair.

▶ *Try Exercise 15.8*

Comparing Two Dependent Samples: The Sign Test

Chapter 10 showed that it's possible to compare groups using either *independent* or *dependent* samples. So far in this chapter, the samples have been independent. When the subjects in the two samples are matched, such as when each treatment in an experiment is applied to the same subject, the samples are dependent. Then we must use different methods.

Recall

From Section 9.2, to test H_0: $p = 0.50$ with sample proportion $\hat{p}$ when $n \geq 30$, the test statistic is

$$z = (\hat{p} - 0.50)/se_0,$$

with $se_0 = \sqrt{(0.50)(0.50)/n}$. ◀

For example, the tanning experiment from Examples 1 and 2 could have used a crossover design instead: The participants get a tan using one treatment, and after it wears off they get a tan using the other treatment. The order of using the two treatments is random. For each participant, we observe which treatment gives the better tan. That is, we make comparisons by pairing the two observations for the same participant.

For such a matched pairs experiment, let p denote the population proportion of cases for which a particular treatment does better than the other treatment. Under the null hypothesis of identical treatment effects, $p = 0.50$. That is, each treatment should have the better response outcome about half the time. (We ignore those cases in which each treatment gives the *same* response.) Let n denote the sample number of pairs of observations for which the two responses differ. For large n, we can use the z test statistic to compare the sample proportion $\hat{p}$ to the null hypothesis value of 0.50. (See the margin Recall box.) The P-value is based on the approximate standard normal sampling distribution.

A test that compares two dependent samples in this way is called a **sign test.** The name refers to how the method evaluates for each matched pair whether the difference between the first and second response is *positive* or *negative.*

SUMMARY: Sign Test for Two Dependent Samples

1. **Assumptions:** Random sample of matched pairs for which we can evaluate which observation in a pair has the better response.

2. **Hypotheses:** H_0: Population proportion $p - 0.50$ who have better response for a particular group.
   H_a: $p \neq 0.50$ (two-sided) or H_a: $p > 0.50$ or H_a: $p < 0.50$ (one-sided).

3. **Test Statistic:** $z = (\hat{p} - 0.50)/se_0$, as shown in margin recall box.

4. **P-value:** For large samples ($n \geq 30$), use tail probabilities from standard normal. For smaller n, use binomial distribution (discussed in Example 7).

5. **Conclusion:** Report the P-value and interpret in context.

Sign Test for Dependent Samples ◀ **(Large Samples)**

Example 6

Time Browsing the Internet or Watching TV

Picture the Scenario

Which do most students spend more time doing—browsing the Internet or watching TV? Let's consider the students surveyed at the University of Georgia whose responses are in the Georgia Student Survey data file. The results for the first three students in the data file (in minutes per day) were

Student	Internet	TV
1	60	120
2	20	120
3	60	90

All three spent more time watching TV. For the entire sample, 35 students spent more time watching TV and 19 students spent more time browsing the Internet. (The analysis ignores the 5 students who reported the same time for each.)

Question to Explore

Let p denote the population proportion who spent more time watching TV. Find the test statistic and P-value for the sign test of $H_0: p = 0.50$ against $H_a: p \neq 0.50$. Interpret.

Think It Through

Here, $n = 35 + 19 = 54$. The sample proportion who spent more time watching TV was $35/54 = 0.648$. For testing that $p = 0.50$, the null standard error se_0 of the sample proportion is

$$se_0 = \sqrt{(0.50)(0.50)/n} = \sqrt{(0.50)(0.50)/54} = 0.068.$$

The test statistic is

$$z = (\hat{p} - 0.50)/se_0 = (0.648 - 0.50)/0.068 = 2.18.$$

From the *Normal Distribution* app (or Table A), the two-sided P-value is 0.03. This provides considerable evidence that most students spend more time watching TV than browsing the Internet. The conclusion must be tempered by the fact that the data resulted from a convenience sample (students in a class for a statistics course) rather than a random sample of all college students.

Insight

The sign test uses merely the information about *which* response is higher and *how many* responses are higher, not the quantitative information about *how much* higher. This is a disadvantage compared to the corresponding parametric test, the two dependent sample *t* test of Section 10.4, which analyzes the mean of the differences between the two responses. The sign test is most appropriate when we can order the responses but do not have quantitative information, such as in the next example.

▶ **Try Exercise 15.10**

For small n, we can conduct the sign test by using the *binomial* distribution. The next example illustrates this case as well as a situation in which we can order responses for each pair but do not have quantitative information about how different the responses are.

Example 7

Sign Test for Dependent Samples (Small Sample) ◀

Crossover Experiment Comparing Tanning Methods

Picture the Scenario

When Allison told another student in the class (Megan) about her planned experiment to compare tanning methods, Megan decided to do a separate tanning experiment. She used a crossover design for a different sample of five untanned female friends. The results of her experiment were that the tanning studio gave a better tan than the tanning lotion for four of the five participants.

Question to Explore

Find and interpret the P-value for testing that the population proportion p of participants for whom the tanning studio gives a better tan than the tanning lotion equals 0.50. Use the alternative hypothesis that this population

Recall

Section 6.3 presented the **binomial** distribution. With probability p of success on a trial, out of n independent trials the probability of x successes is

$$P(x) = \frac{n!}{x!(n-x)!} p^x (1-p)^{n-x}. \blacktriangleleft$$

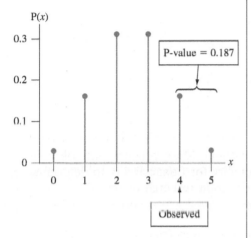

P-value = 0.187

Observed

proportion is larger than 0.50, because Megan predicted that the tanning studio would give better tans.

Think It Through

The null hypothesis is $H_0: p = 0.50$. For $H_a: p > 0.50$, the P-value is the probability of the observed sample outcome or an even larger one. The sample size ($n = 5$) was small, so we use the binomial distribution rather than its normal approximation to find the P-value.

If $p = 0.50$, the binomial probability that $x = 4$ of the $n = 5$ participants would get better tans with the tanning studio is (using the formula for the binomial distribution mentioned in the margin)

$$P(4) = \frac{5!}{4!(5-4)!} (0.50)^4 (0.50)^1 = 0.156.$$

The more extreme result that all five participants would get better tans with the tanning studio has probability $P(5) = (0.50)^5 = 0.031$. The P-value is the right-tail probability of the observed result and the more extreme one, that is, $0.156 + 0.031 = 0.187$. See the margin figure. In summary, the evidence is not strong that more participants get a better tan from the tanning studio than the tanning lotion.

Insight

Megan would instead use the two-sided alternative, $H_a: p \neq 0.50$, if she did not make a prior prediction about which tanning method would be better. The P-value would then be $2(0.19) = 0.38$. With only $n = 5$ observations, the smallest possible two-sided P-value would be $2(0.031) = 0.06$, which occurs when $x = 0$ or when $x = 5$.

▶ *Try Exercise 15.11*

Ranking Paired Observations: The Wilcoxon Signed-Rank Test

The two dependent sample t test in Section 10.4 was based on the differences between the two dependent observations from a pair. The **Wilcoxon signed rank test** is the nonparametric alternative, relying on ranking the differences instead of using them directly. It tests the null hypothesis

$$H_0: \text{population median of differences is 0.}$$

The test uses the quantitative information provided by the n differences (one for each paired observation) by ranking their magnitudes, in absolute value. (Like the sign test, it ignores observation pairs for which the difference equals 0.) The test statistic is the sum of the ranks for those differences that are positive.

SUMMARY: Wilcoxon Signed-Rank Test for Two Dependent Samples

1. **Assumptions:**   Random sample of paired observations for which the differences of observations have a symmetric population distribution and can be ranked.

2. **Hypotheses:**
   H_0: Population median of differences is 0.
   H_a: Population median of differences is not 0 (one-sided also possible).

3. **Test Statistic:** Rank the absolute values of the differences for the paired observations and then find the sum of ranks for those differences that were positive.

4. **P-value:** Software can find a P-value based on all the possible samples with the given absolute differences. (For large samples, it uses an approximate normal sampling distribution, as discussed following.)

5. **Conclusion:** Report the P-value and interpret in context.

Wilcoxon Signed-Rank Test ◄

Example 8

GRE Test Scores

Picture the Scenario

If you want to attend graduate school, taking the Graduate Record Examination (GRE) is usually a requirement. Many graduate schools consider GRE scores for admittance, to qualify for financial aid, to determine fellowships and grants, and for other program research or teaching assignments. The GRE includes three sections designed to test verbal, quantitative, and writing skills.

The verbal and quantitative sections are each scored between 130 and 170. The analytical writing portion of the GRE is given a score between 0 and 6 in half point increments.

In our example, three students volunteered for a study to determine whether taking a two-day workshop on GRE preparation improved their GRE analytical writing score from a previous score. Note: The original data were larger $(n = 12)$, but a small sample is used in this example to make it easier to explain. The results are shown in the following table:

	Student		
	1	**2**	**3**
Before	2.5	4	1.5
After	3	3.5	3

A negative difference (after – before) represents a lower score. A positive difference represents an improved score. Let's test the null hypothesis that the two-day GRE workshop has no effect, in the sense that the population median gained score is 0, against the alternative hypothesis that the population median gained score is positive.

Questions to Explore

a. Find the absolute values of the differences, rank them, and then find the sum of the ranks for those differences that were positive.

b. Consider each of the possible ways that positive and negative signs could be assigned to these three differences. For each case, find the rank sum for the positive differences. Create the sampling distribution of this rank sum that applies if the workshop truly has no effect.

c. Find the P-value for the Wilcoxon signed-rank test, using the sampling distribution of the rank sum created in part b.

Recall

How to handle ties is discussed on page 783. ◄

Think It Through

a. The Wilcoxon test begins by calculating the difference and its absolute value for each paired observation. In most applications of the Wilcoxon procedure, the pairs for which the difference is zero are eliminated from consideration because they provide no useful information; the remaining absolute differences are then ranked from lowest to highest, with tied ranks included where appropriate.

After sorting the GRE data, the differences have absolute values and ranks as follows:

Student	Before	After	Difference	Absolute Value	Rank of Absolute Value
1	2.5	3	0.5	0.5	1.5
2	4	3.5	−0.5	0.5	1.5
3	1.5	3	1.5	1.5	3

The rank sum for the positive differences is $1.5 + 3 = 4.5$.

b. For the difference values of the three subjects, 0.5, −0.5, and 1.5, Table 15.9 shows all the possible ways the differences could have been positive or negative. For each possible sample, this table also shows the sum of ranks for the positive differences. The observed data are Sample 1, which had a rank sum of 4.5.

Table 15.9 Possible Samples with Absolute Difference Values of Sample

Student	1	2	3	4	5	6	7	8	Rank of Absolute Value
1	0.5	0.5	−0.5	0.5	−0.5	0.5	−0.5	−0.5	1.5
2	−0.5	−0.5	−0.5	0.5	−0.5	0.5	0.5	0.5	1.5
3	1.5	−1.5	1.5	1.5	−1.5	−1.5	1.5	−1.5	3
Sum of Ranks for Positive Differences									
	4.5	1.5	3	6	0	3	4.5	1.5	

The columns 1–8 under the header "Possible Sample".

If the workshop has no effect, then the eight possible samples in Table 15.9 are equally likely. The table that follows summarizes the sampling distribution of the rank sum for the positive differences, presuming no effect of the workshop. For example, the rank sum was 4.5 for two of the eight samples, so its probability is 2/8.

Sampling Distribution of Rank Sum for the Positive Differences

Rank Sum	Probability
0	1/8
1.5	2/8
3	2/8
4.5	2/8
6	1/8

c. The larger the sum of ranks for the positive differences, the greater the evidence that the workshop has a positive effect. So, the P-value is the probability that this sum of ranks is at least as large as observed. Since three of the eight possible samples had a rank sum for the positive differences of at least 4.5 (the observed value), the P-value is $3/8 = 0.375$.

Insight

Suppose we instead used the sign test. We then observe that two of the three differences are positive. For the alternative hypothesis that the workshop has a positive effect, the P-value is the probability that at least two of the three differences are positive, when the chance is 0.50 that any particular difference is positive. Using the binomial distribution, you can find that the P-value is 0.50 (Exercise 15.12).

The sign test ignores the fact that the two positive differences are larger than the negative difference. The Wilcoxon signed-rank test uses this information. By taking this extra information into account, its P-value of 0.375 is smaller than the P-value of 0.50 from the sign test. However, the P-value is still not small. With only three observations, the one-sided P-value can be no smaller than one-eighth, which is the P-value for the largest possible value (which is 6) for the rank sum of positive differences.

The MINITAB output for the complete data set with all 12 students is shown below. The Wilcoxon signed-rank test between the two groups results in a P-value of 0.018.

Caution

For **independent** samples, rank all of the data combined and then compare the sum (or mean) of the ranks of the two groups. (See Wilcoxon test in Section 15.1) For **dependent** samples, find the absolute value of the difference for each paired observation and then rank these differences. These methods often are confused—especially if the independent samples have equal sample sizes. ◄

Wilcoxon Signed Rank Test: Difference

```
Test of median = 0.000000 versus median not = 0.000000

                                   Wilcoxon                  Estimated
             N      N for Test     Statistic       P          Median

Diff        12         11            60.0         0.018        1.000
```

One difference was zero, so there are 11 differences to rank

Sum of ranks for positive differences

▶ **Try Exercise 15.12**

Although the Wilcoxon signed-rank test has the advantage compared to the sign test that it can take into account the *sizes* of the differences and not merely their *sign*, it also has a disadvantage. For the possible samples (such as the eight samples shown in Table 15.9) to be equally likely, it must make an additional assumption: The population distribution of the difference scores must be *symmetric*.

The symmetry assumption for the Wilcoxon signed-rank test is a bit weaker than the assumption of a normal population distribution for the differences that the two dependent samples *t* test of Section 10.4 makes. However, with small samples, there's not much evidence to check this symmetry assumption. Also, recall that the *t* test is *robust* for violations of the assumption of normality, especially for two-sided inference. The extra assumption of symmetry for the Wilcoxon signed-ranks test weakens the advantage of using a nonparametric method. Because of this, many statisticians prefer to use the two dependent samples *t* test for such data.

Like the Wilcoxon test for comparing mean ranks for two independent samples, the Wilcoxon signed-rank test can allow for ties, and it has a large-sample z test statistic that has an approximate standard normal sampling distribution. For instance, Example 6 used the sign test to compare times spent on Internet browsing and watching TV for 54 students. If we create the differences

Difference = TV watching time − Internet browsing time

for the students and analyze them with the Wilcoxon signed-rank test, MINITAB reports the results shown in Table 15.10. You can also use the *Wilcoxon Test* app, which has these data preloaded, to obtain these results.

Table 15.10 Results of Wilcoxon Signed-Rank Test for Time Differences Between TV Watching and Internet Browsing (from Example 6)

Wilcoxon Signed Rank Test: Difference

Test of median = 0.000000 versus median not = 0.000000

	N	N for Test	Wilcoxon Statistic	P	Estimated Median
difference	59	54	1012.5	0.020	22.50

The Wilcoxon test statistic is the sum of ranks for the positive differences. The two-sided P-value of 0.020 provides strong evidence that the population median of the differences is not 0. There were 59 subjects, but only 54 were used in the test, because five differences were equal to 0. MINITAB also estimates that the population median difference between the time watching TV and the time browsing the Internet was 22.5 minutes. Separately, it provides a 95% confidence interval for the population median of the differences of 2.5 to 40.0 minutes (not shown).

Advantages and Limitations of Nonparametric Statistics

Nonparametric methods make weaker assumptions than the parametric methods we've studied in the rest of this book. For comparing two groups, for instance, it's not necessary to assume that the response distribution is normal. This is especially appealing for small samples because then meeting the normality assumption is more important than it is for larger samples, for which the Central Limit Theorem applies.

Statisticians have shown that nonparametric tests are often very nearly as good as parametric tests even in the exact case for which the parametric tests are designed. To illustrate, suppose two population distributions are normal in shape and have the same standard deviation but different means. Then, the Wilcoxon test is very nearly as powerful in detecting this difference as the t test, even though it uses only the ranks of the observations.

Nonetheless, nonparametric methods have some disadvantages. For example, confidence interval methods have not been as thoroughly developed as significance tests. Also, methods have not yet been well developed for multivariate procedures, such as multiple regression. Finally, recall that in many cases (especially two-sided tests and confidence intervals), most parametric methods are *robust*, working well even if assumptions are somewhat violated.

15.2 Practicing the Basics

15.8 **How long do you tolerate being put on hold?** Examples 1–4 and 7 in Chapter 14 referred to the following randomized experiment: An airline analyzed whether telephone callers to their reservations office would remain on hold longer, on average, if they heard (a) an advertisement about the airline, (b) Muzak, or (c) classical music. For 15 callers randomly assigned to these three conditions, the table shows the data. It also shows the ranks for the 15 observations as well as the mean rank for each group and some results from using MINITAB to conduct the Kruskal-Wallis test.

   a. State the null and alternative hypotheses for the Kruskal-Wallis test.

   b. Identify the value of the test statistic for the Kruskal-Wallis test and state its approximate sampling distribution, presuming H_0 is true.

   c. Report and interpret the P-value shown for the Kruskal-Wallis test.

   d. To find out which pairs of groups significantly differ, how could you follow up the Kruskal-Wallis test?

Telephone Holding Times by Type of Recorded Message

Recorded Message	Holding Time Observations	Ranks	Mean Rank
Muzak	0, 1, 3, 4, 6	1, 2.5, 5, 6, 8	4.5
Advertisement	1, 2, 5, 8, 11	2.5, 4, 7, 10.5, 13	7.4
Classical	7, 8, 9, 13, 15	9, 10.5, 12, 14, 15	12.1

Kruskal-Wallis Test: Holding Time Versus Group

```
Group        N       Median      Ave Rank
Muzak        5       3.000       4.5
advert       5       5.000       7.4
classical    5       9.000       12.1
H = 7.38 DF = 2 P = 0.025 (adjusted for ties)
```

15.9 **What's the best way to learn French?** Exercise 14.3 gave the data in the table for scores on the first quiz for ninth-grade students in an introductory-level French course. The instructor grouped the students in the course as follows:

Group 1: Never studied foreign language before, but have good English skills

Group 2: Never studied foreign language before; have poor English skills

Group 3: Studied at least one other foreign language The table also shows results of using MINITAB to perform the Kruskal-Wallis test.

   a. Find the rank associated with each observation and show how to find the mean rank for Group 1.

   b. Report and interpret the P-value for the test.

Scores on the Quiz

Group 1	Group 2	Group 3
4	1	9
6	5	10
8		5

```
Kruskal-Wallis Test on response
Group            N         Median       Ave Rank
  1              3         6.000        4.3
  2              2         3.000        2.3
  3              3         9.000        6.2
H = 3.13 DF = 2 P = 0.209 (adjusted for ties)
```

15.10 **Sports versus TV** Which do students spend more time doing—playing sports or watching TV? For the students surveyed at the University of Florida whose responses are in the FL Student Survey data file, 24 students spent more time playing sports and 30 students spent more time watching TV. Let p denote the corresponding population proportion who spend more time watching TV.

   a. Find the test statistic for the sign test of $H_0: p = 0.50$ against $H_a: p \neq 0.50$.

   b. Refer to part a. Find and interpret the P-value using the *Normal Distribution* app or other software.

15.11 **Cell phones and reaction times** Example 13 in Chapter 10 compared reaction times in a simulated driving test for the same students when they were using a cell phone and when they were not. The table shows data for the first four students. For all 32 students, 26 had faster reaction times when not using the cell phone and 6 had faster reaction times when using it.

   a. Are the observations for the two treatments independent samples or dependent samples? Explain.

   b. Let p denote the population proportion who would have a faster reaction time when not using a cell phone. Estimate p based on this experiment.

   c. Using all 32 observations, find the test statistic and the P-value for the sign test of $H_0: p = 1/2$ against $H_a: p > 1/2$ using the *Normal Distribution* app or other software. Interpret.

   d. What is the parametric method for comparing the scores? What is an advantage of it over the sign test? (*Hint:* Does the sign test use the magnitude of the difference between the two scores or just its direction?)

Reaction Times in Cell Phone Study

Student	Using Cell Phone? No	Using Cell Phone? Yes	Difference
1	604	636	32
2	556	623	67
3	540	615	75
4	522	672	150

15.12 Sign test for GRE scores   Consider Example 8, for which the changes in the writing portion GRE scores for the first three people who attended a training workshop were 0.5, −0.5, and 1.5. Show how to use the sign test to test that the probability that the difference is positive equals 0.50 against the alternative hypothesis that it is greater than 0.50.

15.13 Does exercise help blood pressure?   Exercise 10.50 in Chapter 10 discussed a pilot study of people who suffer from abnormally high blood pressure. A medical researcher decides to test her belief that walking briskly for at least half an hour a day has the effect of lowering blood pressure. She randomly samples three of her patients who have high blood pressure. She measures their systolic blood pressure initially and then again a month later after they participate in her exercise program. The table shows the results. Show how to analyze the data with the sign test. State the hypotheses, find the P-value (e.g., using the *Normal Distribution* app), and interpret.

Subject	Before	After
1	150	130
2	165	140
3	135	120

15.14 More on blood pressure   Refer to the previous exercise. The analysis there did not take into account the *size* of the change in blood pressure. Show how to do this with the Wilcoxon signed-ranks test.

a. State the hypotheses for that test, for the relevant one-sided alternative hypothesis.

b. Construct the sampling distribution for the rank sum of the positive differences when you consider the possible samples that have absolute differences in blood pressure of 20, 25, and 15.

c. Using the sampling distribution from part b, find and interpret the P-value. (When every difference is positive, or when every difference is negative, this test and the sign test give the same P-value for a given alternative hypothesis.)

15.15 More on cell phones   Refer to Exercise 15.11. That analysis did not take into account the magnitudes of the differences in reaction times. Show how to do this with the Wilcoxon signed-ranks test, illustrating by using only the four observations shown in the table there.

a. State the hypotheses for the relevant one-sided test.

b. Create the sampling distribution of the sum of ranks for the positive differences.

c. Find the P-value and interpret.

15.16 Use all data on cell phones   Refer to the previous exercise. When we use the data for all 32 subjects, MINITAB reports result in the following for the Wilcoxon signed-ranks test. (You can replicate these results using the second tab for dependent samples in the *Wilcoxon Test* app.)

Wilcoxon Signed-Ranks Test Results

```
Test of median = 0.000000 versus median
not = 0.000000
            N for   Wilcoxon          Estimated
      N     Test    Statistic    P      Median
diff  32    32       490.0     0.000    47.25
```

a. State the null and alternative hypotheses for this test.

b. Explain how MINITAB found the value reported for the Wilcoxon test statistic.

c. Report and interpret the P-value.

d. Report and interpret the estimated median.

Chapter Review

CHAPTER SUMMARY

Nonparametric statistical methods provide statistical inference without an assumption of normality about the probability distribution of the response variable.

- The **Wilcoxon test** is a nonparametric test for the null hypothesis of identical population distributions for two groups. It assumes independent random samples and uses the ranks for the combined sample of observations. The P-value is a one- or two-tail probability for the sampling distribution of the difference between the sample mean ranks.

- Nonparametric methods can also estimate differences between groups, for example to construct a confidence interval for the difference between two population **medians**.

- Other popular nonparametric methods include

- The **Kruskal-Wallis test** for comparing mean ranks of *several* groups with independent random samples.

- The **sign test** for comparing two groups with *matched pairs* data (dependent samples rather than independent samples) in terms of the proportion of times the response is better for a particular group.

- The **Wilcoxon signed-ranks test** for comparing two groups with *matched pairs data* when the differences can be ranked.

LEARNING OBJECTIVES

1. Explain what is meant by a nonparametric procedure.

2. Identify which nonparametric procedure should be used when the conditions for the corresponding parametric procedure are not met.

3. State the hypotheses and check the conditions needed for each nonparametric procedure.

4. Interpret the output for a nonparametric test and state the conclusions in context.

5. Use the Wilcoxon procedure to test that the population distributions are identical for two groups.

6. Recognize under what circumstances nonparametric methods can be used to construct a confidence interval for the difference between two population medians.

7. Use the Kruskal-Wallis test to compare mean ranks of several groups with independent random samples.

8. Use the sign test to compare two dependent samples in terms of the proportion of times the response is better for one of the groups.

9. Use the Wilcoxon signed-ranks test to compare two dependent samples by ranking the differences for matched pairs.

ANSWERS TO THE CHAPTER FIGURE QUESTIONS

Figure 15.2   Yes, there is an extreme outlier for the cell phone group. This may have a large effect on the mean for that group but will not affect the nonparametric test.

Figure 15.3   The dot plots show evidence of severe skew to the left. Because the sample sizes are very small, severe violation of the normality assumption could invalidate the ANOVA F test.

STATISTICAL SOFTWARE

Art of Stat Web Apps

- **Wilcoxon Test**   This app carries out the nonparametric Wilcoxon test, both for two independent and two dependent samples, and shows the standard output for this nonparametric test. The app has several data sets from the book preloaded, but you can enter (or copy and paste) your own data for the groups. The app is similar to the *Compare Two Means* app, but uses nonparametric inference.

- **Kruskal-Wallis Test**   This app carries out the nonparametric Kruskal-Wallis test for comparing several groups. The app has data sets from the book preloaded, but you can enter (or copy and paste) your own data. The app is similar to the *ANOVA (One-Way)* app, but uses nonparametric inference.

R

- **Wilcoxon test:** The `wilcox.test` function in R carries out the Wilcoxon test for comparing two independent or two dependent samples. With the data from the student experiment in Example 1,

```
> lotion <- c(2, 4, 5)
> tan <- c(1, 3)
> wilcox.test(lotion, tan, conf.int=TRUE)
 Wilcoxon rank sum test
W = 5, p-value = 0.4
alternative hypothesis: true location shift
is not equal to 0
80 percent confidence interval:
 −1  4
sample estimates:
difference in location
              1.5
```

R reports a test statistic of `W = 5`. This is the sum of the ranks in the first group *minus* $n_1(n_1 + 1)/2$, where n_1 is the sample size in group 1. (For $n_1 = 3$, this equals 6. Adding 6 to 5 gives $W = 11$, the sum of the ranks in the first sample, as in Example 2. The fact that R uses a slightly different test statistic has no effect on the P-value.) The P-value of `0.4` matches the two-sided P-value given after Example 2 and in Table 15.4. To obtain the one-sided P-value, use `alternative='greater'`. The output also shows an estimate of `1.5` and an 80% confidence interval for the difference in medians of `−1  4`. This output is relevant for a quantitative response and is the one discussed in Example 4.

For two dependent samples, such as the ones in Example 8, type:

```
> before <- c(2.5, 4, 1.5)
> after <- c(3, 3.5, 3)
>wilcox.test(after, before, paired=TRUE,
alternative='greater')
```

The test statistic shown by R is as in Example 8 (`V = 4.5`), but the P-value doesn't quite match the exact one because R uses the asymptotic test.

■ **Kruskal-Wallis** To replicate the output of Table 15.8 in Example 5, we use R's kruskal.test function. We provide the data in "long" format, similar to what we did in the R code for the one-way ANOVA in Chapter 14:

```
> rare <- c(1.75, 3.15, 3.50, 3.68)
> occasional <- c(2.00, 3.20, 3.44, 3.50,
3.60, 3.71, 3.80)
> regular <- c(2.40, 2.95, 3.40, 3.67, 3.70,
  4.00)
> y <- c(rare, occasional, regular)
```

```
> group <- rep(c('rare', 'occasional',
'regular'), times = c(length(rare),
length(occasional), length(regular)))
> kruskal.test(y ~ group)
 Kruskal-Wallis rank sum test
Kruskal-Wallis chi-squared = 0.72463,
df = 2, p-value = 0.6961
```

This shows the same chi-squared test statistic and P-value as Table 15.8.

CHAPTER EXERCISES

Practicing the Basics

15.17 Car bumper damage An automobile company compares two types of front bumper for its new model by driving sample cars into a concrete wall at 15 miles per hour. The response is the amount of damage to the car, as measured by the repair costs, in dollars. Due to the costs, the study uses only six cars, obtaining results for three bumpers of each type. The results are in the table.

a. Find the ranks and the mean rank for each bumper type.

b. Show that there are 20 possible allocations of ranks to the two bumper types.

c. Explain why the observed ranks for the two groups are one of the two most extreme ways the two groups can differ, for the 20 possible allocations of the ranks.

d. Explain why the P-value for the two-sided test equals 0.10.

Bumper A	Bumper B
2,100	1,100
2,500	1,300
2,300	1,400

15.18 Comparing more bumpers Refer to the previous exercise.

a. Would the results of your analysis change if for the second Bumper A the repair cost was $9,000 instead of $2,500? What does this illustrate about the analysis?

b. Suppose the company actually wanted to compare *three* bumper types. Which significance test could it use to do this if it did not want to assume that the repair costs have a normal distribution for each bumper type?

15.19 Telephone holding times In Exercise 15.8, the telephone holding times for Muzak and classical music were
    Muzak: 0, 1, 4, 6, 3
    Classical: 13, 9, 8, 15, 7

a. For comparing these two groups with the Wilcoxon test, report the ranks and the mean rank for each group.

b. Two groups of size 5 each have 252 possible allocations of rankings. For a two-sided test of H_0: identical distributions with these data, explain why the P-value is $2/252 = 0.008$. Interpret the P-value.

15.20 Treating alcoholics The nonparametric statistics textbook by Hollander and Wolfe (1999) discussed a study on a social skills training program for alcoholics. A sample of male alcoholics was randomly split into two groups. The control group received traditional treatment. The treatment group received the traditional treatment plus a class in social skills training. Every two weeks for a year after the treatment, subjects indicated the quantity of alcohol they consumed during that period. The summary response was the total alcohol intake for the year (in centiliters).

a. Suppose the researchers planned to conduct a one-sided test and believed that the response variable could be highly skewed to the right. Why might they prefer to use the Wilcoxon test rather than a two-sample t test to compare the groups?

b. The data were

Controls: 1,042, 1,617, 1,180, 973, 1,552, 1,251, 1,151, 1,511, 728, 1,079, 951, 1,319

Treated: 874, 389, 612, 798, 1,152, 893, 541, 741, 1,064, 862, 213

Show how to find the ranks and the mean ranks for the two groups.

c. MINITAB reports the results shown in the output on the next page, which you can also replicate with the *Wilcoxon Test* app. Report and interpret the P-value.

d. Report and interpret the confidence interval shown in the output.

MINITAB Output

```
             N              Median
control     12             1165.5
treated     11              798.0

Point estimate for η1 − η2 is 435.5

95.5 Percent CI for η1 − η2 is (186.0, 713.0)

Test of η1 = η2 vs η1 ≠ η2 is significant
at 0.0009
```

15.21 Comparing tans Examples 1 and 2 compared two methods of getting a tan. Suppose Allison conducted an expanded experiment in which nine participants were randomly assigned to one of two brands of tanning lotion or to the tanning studio, three participants to each treatment. The nine were ranked on the quality of tan.

a. Which nonparametric test could be used to compare the three treatments?

b. Give an example of ranks for the three treatments that would have the largest possible test statistic value and the smallest possible P-value for this experiment. (*Hint:* What allocation of ranks would have the greatest between-groups variation in the mean ranks?)

15.22 Comparing therapies for anorexia The Anorexia data file on the book's website shows weight change for 72 anorexic teenage girls who were randomly assigned to one of three psychological treatments. Using the *Kruskal-Wallis* app or other software, analyze these data with a nonparametric Kruskal Wallis test to compare the three weight change distributions.

a. State the hypotheses.

b. Report the test statistic and its sampling distribution.

c. Report the P-value and explain how to interpret it.

15.23 Internet versus cell phones For the countries in the Human Development data file on the book's website, in 4 countries a higher percentage of people used the Internet than used cell phones, whereas in 35 countries a higher percentage of people used cell phones than the Internet.

a. Show how you could use a nonparametric test to compare Internet use and cell phone use in the population of all countries. State the (i) hypotheses, (ii) test statistic value, and (iii) find and interpret the P-value.

b. Is the analysis in part a relevant if the 39 countries in the data file are all the countries of interest to you rather than a random sample of countries? Explain.

15.24 Browsing the Internet Refer to the Georgia Student Survey data file on the book's website. Use a method from this chapter to test whether the amount of time spent browsing the Internet is independent of one's political affiliation. State the (a) hypotheses, (b) test statistic, and (c) P-value and interpret the result.

15.25 GPAs The Georgia Student Survey data file has data on college GPA and high school GPA for 59 University of Georgia students.

a. If you wanted to use a nonparametric test to check your friend's prediction that high school GPAs tend to be higher than college GPAs, which would you use?

b. What would be a reason for using the nonparametric method to do this?

c. Use the test in part a to do this analysis and interpret the result.

15.26 Sign test about the GRE workshop In Exercise 15.12 on the effect of a GRE training workshop on the writing, you used the sign test to evaluate the test differences of

0.5, −0.5, and 1.5. Suppose the test differences were 5.5, −0.5, and 1.5 instead of 0.5, −0.5, and 1.5.

a. State the hypotheses and find the P-value for the one-sided sign test for evaluating the effect of the workshop. Interpret.

b. Compare results to those in Exercise 15.12 and indicate what this tells you about the effect that outliers have on this nonparametric statistical method.

15.27 Wilcoxon signed-rank test about the GRE workshop Example 8 on the GRE workshop used the Wilcoxon signed-rank test to evaluate the score differences of 0.5, −0.5, and 1.5. Suppose the test differences were 5.5, −0.5, and 1.5 instead of 0.5 −0.5, and 1.5.

a. State the hypotheses and find the P-value for the one-sided Wilcoxon signed-ranks test for evaluating the effect of the workshop. Interpret.

b. Compare results to those in Example 8 and indicate what this tells you about the effect that outliers have on this nonparametric statistical method.

Concepts and Investigations

15.28 Student survey For the FL Student Survey data file on the book's website, we identify the number of times reading a newspaper as the response variable and gender as the explanatory variable. The observations are as follows:

Females: 5, 3, 6, 3, 7, 1, 1, 3, 0, 4, 7, 2, 2, 7, 3, 0, 5, 0, 4, 4, 5, 14, 3, 1, 2, 1, 7, 2, 5, 3, 7
Males: 0, 3, 7, 4, 3, 2, 1, 12, 1, 6, 2, 2, 7, 7, 5, 3, 14, 3, 7, 6, 5, 5, 2, 3, 5, 5, 2, 3, 3

Using an appropriate app or other software, analyze these data using methods of this chapter. Write a one-page report summarizing your analyses and conclusions.

15.29 Why nonparametrics? Present a situation for which it's preferable to use a nonparametric method instead of a parametric method and explain why.

15.30 Why matched pairs? Refer to Example 7. Describe the advantages of an experiment using a crossover design instead of independent samples to compare the tanning methods.

15.31 Complete the analogy The *t* test for comparing two means is to the one-way ANOVA *F* test as the Wilcoxon test is to the _____ test.

15.32 Complete the analogy The *t* test for comparing two means is to the Wilcoxon test (for independent samples) as the matched pairs *t* test is to the _____ (for dependent samples in matched pairs).

Multiple Choice or True/False

15.33 Nonparametrics Nonparametric statistical methods are used

a. Whenever the response variable is known to have a normal distribution.

b. Whenever the assumptions for a parametric method are not *perfectly* satisfied.

c. When the data are ranks for the subjects rather than quantitative measurements or when it's inappropriate to assume normality and the ordinary statistical method is not robust when the normal assumption is violated.

d. Whenever we want to compare two methods for getting a good tan.

15.34 True or false For a one-sided significance test comparing two means with small samples from highly skewed population distributions, it's safer to use a *t* test than a Wilcoxon test. This is because the Wilcoxon test assumes normal population distributions and is not robust if that assumption is violated.

Advanced Concepts

15.35 Mann-Whitney statistic For the tanning experiment, Table 15.2 showed the sampling distribution of the difference between the sample mean ranks. Suppose you instead use as a test statistic the sample proportion of pairs of participants for which the tanning studio gave a better tan than the tanning lotion. This is the basis of the **Mann-Whitney** test, devised by two statisticians about the same time as Wilcoxon devised his test.

a. The table shows the proportion of pairs for which the tanning studio gave a better tan, for the possible sample results. Explain how to find these proportions.

b. Using this table, construct the sampling distribution that applies under the null hypothesis for this proportion.

c. For the one-sided alternative hypothesis of a better tan with the tanning studio, find the P-value for the observed sample proportion of 5/6. (*Note*: P-values based on this sample proportion are identical to P-values for the Wilcoxon test based on the mean ranks.)

Sample Proportion of Pairs, One from Each Treatment, for Which Tanning Studio Gave Better Tan Than Tanning Lotion

Treatments	Ranks				
Tanning Lotion Ranks	(1, 2, 3)	(1, 2, 4)	(1, 2, 5)	(1, 3, 4)	(1, 3, 5)
Tanning Studio Ranks	(4, 5)	(3, 5)	(3, 4)	(2, 5)	(2, 4)
Proportion	0/6	1/6	2/6	2/6	3/6
Tanning Lotion Ranks	(2, 3, 4)	(1, 4, 5)	(2, 3, 5)	(2, 4, 5)	(3, 4, 5)
Tanning Studio Ranks	(1, 5)	(2, 3)	(1, 4)	(1, 3)	(1, 2)
Proportion	3/6	4/6	4/6	5/6	6/6

15.36 Rank-based correlation For data on two quantitative variables, *x* and *y*, an alternative correlation coefficient uses the *rankings* of the data. Let *n* denote the number of observations on the two variables. You rank the values of the *x*-variable from 1 to *n* according to their magnitudes, and you separately rank the values of the *y*-variable from 1 to *n*. The correlation coefficient computed between the two sets of ranks is called the **Spearman rank correlation coefficient**. Like the ordinary correlation coefficient, it falls between −1 and +1, with values farther from 0 representing stronger association.

a. The ordinary (Pearson) correlation coefficient *r* can be strongly affected by a regression outlier. Is this true also for the Spearman rank correlation coefficient? Why or why not?

b. If you want to test the null hypothesis of no association, what value for the Spearman rank correlation coefficient would go in the null hypothesis?

15.37 Nonparametric regression Nonparametric methods have also been devised for regression. Here's a simple way to estimate the slope: For each pair of subjects, the slope of the line connecting their two points is the difference between their *y* values divided by the difference between their *x* values. (See the figure.) With *n* subjects, we can find this slope for each pair of points. (There are $n(n − 1)/2$ pairs of points.) A nonparametric estimate of the slope is the median of all these slopes for the various pairs of points. The ordinary slope (least squares, minimizing the sum of squared residuals) can be strongly affected by a regression outlier. Is this true also for the nonparametric estimate of the slope? Why or why not?

BIBLIOGRAPHY

Hollander, M., and Wolfe, D. (1999). *Nonparametric Statistical Methods*, 2nd edition. Wiley.

Lehmann, E. L. (1975). *Nonparametrics: Statistical Methods Based on Ranks*. Holden-Day.

Appendix A

Cumulative probability

The cumulative probability for z is the area under the standard normal curve to the left of z

Did You Know?

The *Normal Distribution* app from ArtofStat .com lets you find any cumulative probability or percentile (z-score) from any normal distribution interactively, including a visualization for checking results. ◄

z	.00
−5.0	.000000287
−4.5	.00000340
−4.0	.0000317
−3.5	.000233

Table A Standard Normal Cumulative Probabilities

z	.00	.01	.02	.03	.04	.05	.06	.07	.08	.09
−3.4	.0003	.0003	.0003	.0003	.0003	.0003	.0003	.0003	.0003	.0002
−3.3	.0005	.0005	.0005	.0004	.0004	.0004	.0004	.0004	.0004	.0003
−3.2	.0007	.0007	.0006	.0006	.0006	.0006	.0006	.0005	.0005	.0005
−3.1	.0010	.0009	.0009	.0009	.0008	.0008	.0008	.0008	.0007	.0007
−3.0	.0013	.0013	.0013	.0012	.0012	.0011	.0011	.0011	.0010	.0010
−2.9	.0019	.0018	.0018	.0017	.0016	.0016	.0015	.0015	.0014	.0014
−2.8	.0026	.0025	.0024	.0023	.0023	.0022	.0021	.0021	.0020	.0019
−2.7	.0035	.0034	.0033	.0032	.0031	.0030	.0029	.0028	.0027	.0026
−2.6	.0047	.0045	.0044	.0043	.0041	.0040	.0039	.0038	.0037	.0036
−2.5	.0062	.0060	.0059	.0057	.0055	.0054	.0052	.0051	.0049	.0048
−2.4	.0082	.0080	.0078	.0075	.0073	.0071	.0069	.0068	.0066	.0064
−2.3	.0107	.0104	.0102	.0099	.0096	.0094	.0091	.0089	.0087	.0084
−2.2	.0139	.0136	.0132	.0129	.0125	.0122	.0119	.0116	.0113	.0110
−2.1	.0179	.0174	.0170	.0166	.0162	.0158	.0154	.0150	.0146	.0143
−2.0	.0228	.0222	.0217	.0212	.0207	.0202	.0197	.0192	.0188	.0183
−1.9	.0287	.0281	.0274	.0268	.0262	.0256	.0250	.0244	.0239	.0233
−1.8	.0359	.0351	.0344	.0336	.0329	.0322	.0314	.0307	.0301	.0294
−1.7	.0446	.0436	.0427	.0418	.0409	.0401	.0392	.0384	.0375	.0367
−1.6	.0548	.0537	.0526	.0516	.0505	.0495	.0485	.0475	.0465	.0455
−1.5	.0668	.0655	.0643	.0630	.0618	.0606	.0594	.0582	.0571	.0559
−1.4	.0808	.0793	.0778	.0764	.0749	.0735	.0721	.0708	.0694	.0681
−1.3	.0968	.0951	.0934	.0918	.0901	.0885	.0869	.0853	.0838	.0823
−1.2	.1151	.1131	.1112	.1093	.1075	.1056	.1038	.1020	.1003	.0985
−1.1	.1357	.1335	.1314	.1292	.1271	.1251	.1230	.1210	.1190	.1170
−1.0	.1587	.1562	.1539	.1515	.1492	.1469	.1446	.1423	.1401	.1379
−0.9	.1841	.1814	.1788	.1762	.1736	.1711	.1685	.1660	.1635	.1611
−0.8	.2119	.2090	.2061	.2033	.2005	.1977	.1949	.1922	.1894	.1867
−0.7	.2420	.2389	.2358	.2327	.2296	.2266	.2236	.2206	.2177	.2148
−0.6	.2743	.2709	.2676	.2643	.2611	.2578	.2546	.2514	.2483	.2451
−0.5	.3085	.3050	.3015	.2981	.2946	.2912	.2877	.2843	.2810	.2776
−0.4	.3446	.3409	.3372	.3336	.3300	.3264	.3228	.3192	.3156	.3121
−0.3	.3821	.3783	.3745	.3707	.3669	.3632	.3594	.3557	.3520	.3483
−0.2	.4207	.4168	.4129	.4090	.4052	.4013	.3974	.3936	.3897	.3859
−0.1	.4602	.4562	.4522	.4483	.4443	.4404	.4364	.4325	.4286	.4247
−0.0	.5000	.4960	.4920	.4880	.4840	.4801	.4761	.4721	.4681	.4641

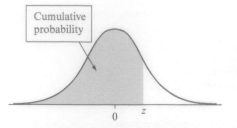

Cumulative probability

The cumulative probability for *z* is the area under the standard normal curve to the left of *z*

Table A Standard Normal Cumulative Probabilities (*continued*)

z	.00	.01	.02	.03	.04	.05	.06	.07	.08	.09
0.0	.5000	.5040	.5080	.5120	.5160	.5199	.5239	.5279	.5319	.5359
0.1	.5398	.5438	.5478	.5517	.5557	.5596	.5636	.5675	.5714	.5753
0.2	.5793	.5832	.5871	.5910	.5948	.5987	.6026	.6064	.6103	.6141
0.3	.6179	.6217	.6255	.6293	.6331	.6368	.6406	.6443	.6480	.6517
0.4	.6554	.6591	.6628	.6664	.6700	.6736	.6772	.6808	.6844	.6879
0.5	.6915	.6950	.6985	.7019	.7054	.7088	.7123	.7157	.7190	.7224
0.6	.7257	.7291	.7324	.7357	.7389	.7422	.7454	.7486	.7517	.7549
0.7	.7580	.7611	.7642	.7673	.7704	.7734	.7764	.7794	.7823	.7852
0.8	.7881	.7910	.7939	.7967	.7995	.8023	.8051	.8078	.8106	.8133
0.9	.8159	.8186	.8212	.8238	.8264	.8289	.8315	.8340	.8365	.8389
1.0	.8413	.8438	.8461	.8485	.8508	.8531	.8554	.8577	.8599	.8621
1.1	.8643	.8665	.8686	.8708	.8729	.8749	.8770	.8790	.8810	.8830
1.2	.8849	.8869	.8888	.8907	.8925	.8944	.8962	.8980	.8997	.9015
1.3	.9032	.9049	.9066	.9082	.9099	.9115	.9131	.9147	.9162	.9177
1.4	.9192	.9207	.9222	.9236	.9251	.9265	.9279	.9292	.9306	.9319
1.5	.9332	.9345	.9357	.9370	.9382	.9394	.9406	.9418	.9429	.9441
1.6	.9452	.9463	.9474	.9484	.9495	.9505	.9515	.9525	.9535	.9545
1.7	.9554	.9564	.9573	.9582	.9591	.9599	.9608	.9616	.9625	.9633
1.8	.9641	.9649	.9656	.9664	.9671	.9678	.9686	.9693	.9699	.9706
1.9	.9713	.9719	.9726	.9732	.9738	.9744	.9750	.9756	.9761	.9767
2.0	.9772	.9778	.9783	.9788	.9793	.9798	.9803	.9808	.9812	.9817
2.1	.9821	.9826	.9830	.9834	.9838	.9842	.9846	.9850	.9854	.9857
2.2	.9861	.9864	.9868	.9871	.9875	.9878	.9881	.9884	.9887	.9890
2.3	.9893	.9896	.9898	.9901	.9904	.9906	.9909	.9911	.9913	.9916
2.4	.9918	.9920	.9922	.9925	.9927	.9929	.9931	.9932	.9934	.9936
2.5	.9938	.9940	.9941	.9943	.9945	.9946	.9948	.9949	.9951	.9952
2.6	.9953	.9955	.9956	.9957	.9959	.9960	.9961	.9962	.9963	.9964
2.7	.9965	.9966	.9967	.9968	.9969	.9970	.9971	.9972	.9973	.9974
2.8	.9974	.9975	.9976	.9977	.9977	.9978	.9979	.9979	.9980	.9981
2.9	.9981	.9982	.9982	.9983	.9984	.9984	.9985	.9985	.9986	.9986
3.0	.9987	.9987	.9987	.9988	.9988	.9989	.9989	.9989	.9990	.9990
3.1	.9990	.9991	.9991	.9991	.9992	.9992	.9992	.9992	.9993	.9993
3.2	.9993	.9993	.9994	.9994	.9994	.9994	.9994	.9995	.9995	.9995
3.3	.9995	.9995	.9995	.9996	.9996	.9996	.9996	.9996	.9996	.9997
3.4	.9997	.9997	.9997	.9997	.9997	.9997	.9997	.9997	.9997	.9998

z	.00
3.5	.999767
4.0	.9999683
4.5	.9999966
5.0	.999999713

Right-tail probability

Table B *t* Distribution Critical Values

	Confidence Level					
	80%	**90%**	**95%**	**98%**	**99%**	**99.8%**
	Right-Tail Probability					
df	$t_{.100}$	$t_{.050}$	$t_{.025}$	$t_{.010}$	$t_{.005}$	$t_{.001}$
1	3.078	6.314	12.706	31.821	63.656	318.289
2	1.886	2.920	4.303	6.965	9.925	22.328
3	1.638	2.353	3.182	4.541	5.841	10.214
4	1.533	2.132	2.776	3.747	4.604	7.173
5	1.476	2.015	2.571	3.365	4.032	5.894
6	1.440	1.943	2.447	3.143	3.707	5.208
7	1.415	1.895	2.365	2.998	3.499	4.785
8	1.397	1.860	2.306	2.896	3.355	4.501
9	1.383	1.833	2.262	2.821	3.250	4.297
10	1.372	1.812	2.228	2.764	3.169	4.144
11	1.363	1.796	2.201	2.718	3.106	4.025
12	1.356	1.782	2.179	2.681	3.055	3.930
13	1.350	1.771	2.160	2.650	3.012	3.852
14	1.345	1.761	2.145	2.624	2.977	3.787
15	1.341	1.753	2.131	2.602	2.947	3.733
16	1.337	1.746	2.120	2.583	2.921	3.686
17	1.333	1.740	2.110	2.567	2.898	3.646
18	1.330	1.734	2.101	2.552	2.878	3.611
19	1.328	1.729	2.093	2.539	2.861	3.579
20	1.325	1.725	2.086	2.528	2.845	3.552
21	1.323	1.721	2.080	2.518	2.831	3.527
22	1.321	1.717	2.074	2.508	2.819	3.505
23	1.319	1.714	2.069	2.500	2.807	3.485
24	1.318	1.711	2.064	2.492	2.797	3.467
25	1.316	1.708	2.060	2.485	2.787	3.450
26	1.315	1.706	2.056	2.479	2.779	3.435
27	1.314	1.703	2.052	2.473	2.771	3.421
28	1.313	1.701	2.048	2.467	2.763	3.408
29	1.311	1.699	2.045	2.462	2.756	3.396
30	1.310	1.697	2.042	2.457	2.750	3.385
40	1.303	1.684	2.021	2.423	2.704	3.307
50	1.299	1.676	2.009	2.403	2.678	3.261
60	1.296	1.671	2.000	2.390	2.660	3.232
80	1.292	1.664	1.990	2.374	2.639	3.195
100	1.290	1.660	1.984	2.364	2.626	3.174
∞	1.282	1.645	1.960	2.326	2.576	3.091

Did You Know?

The *t Distribution* app from ArtofStat .com lets you find any tail probabilities or percentiles (*t*-scores) for Student's *t* distribution interactively, including a visualization for checking results. ◄

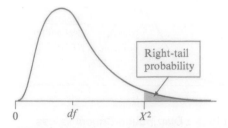

0   df X^2

Right-tail probability

Table C Chi-Squared Distribution for Values of Various Right-Tail Probabilities

df	0.250	0.100	0.050	0.025	0.010	0.005	0.001
			Right-Tail Probability				
1	1.32	2.71	3.84	5.02	6.63	7.88	10.83
2	2.77	4.61	5.99	7.38	9.21	10.60	13.82
3	4.11	6.25	7.81	9.35	11.34	12.84	16.27
4	5.39	7.78	9.49	11.14	13.28	14.86	18.47
5	6.63	9.24	11.07	12.83	15.09	16.75	20.52
6	7.84	10.64	12.59	14.45	16.81	18.55	22.46
7	9.04	12.02	14.07	16.01	18.48	20.28	24.32
8	10.22	13.36	15.51	17.53	20.09	21.96	26.12
9	11.39	14.68	16.92	19.02	21.67	23.59	27.88
10	12.55	15.99	18.31	20.48	23.21	25.19	29.59
11	13.70	17.28	19.68	21.92	24.72	26.76	31.26
12	14.85	18.55	21.03	23.34	26.22	28.30	32.91
13	15.98	19.81	22.36	24.74	27.69	29.82	34.53
14	17.12	21.06	23.68	26.12	29.14	31.32	36.12
15	18.25	22.31	25.00	27.49	30.58	32.80	37.70
16	19.37	23.54	26.30	28.85	32.00	34.27	39.25
17	20.49	24.77	27.59	30.19	33.41	35.72	40.79
18	21.60	25.99	28.87	31.53	34.81	37.16	42.31
19	22.72	27.20	30.14	32.85	36.19	38.58	43.82
20	23.83	28.41	31.41	34.17	37.57	40.00	45.32
25	29.34	34.38	37.65	40.65	44.31	46.93	52.62
30	34.80	40.26	43.77	46.98	50.89	53.67	59.70
40	45.62	51.80	55.76	59.34	63.69	66.77	73.40
50	56.33	63.17	67.50	71.42	76.15	79.49	86.66
60	66.98	74.40	79.08	83.30	88.38	91.95	99.61
70	77.58	85.53	90.53	95.02	100.4	104.2	112.3
80	88.13	96.58	101.8	106.6	112.3	116.3	124.8
90	98.65	107.6	113.1	118.1	124.1	128.3	137.2
100	109.1	118.5	124.3	129.6	135.8	140.2	149.5

Did You Know?

The *Chi-Squared Distribution* app from ArtofStat.com lets you find any tail probability or percentile for the chi-squared distribution interactively, including a visualization for checking results. ◄

Right-tail probability = 0.05

Table D *F* Distribution for Values of Right-Tail Probability = 0.05

df_2	\multicolumn{10}{c}{df_1}
	1	**2**	**3**	**4**	**5**	**6**	**8**	**12**	**24**	**∞**
1	161.45	199.50	215.71	224.58	230.16	233.99	238.88	243.91	249.05	254.31
2	18.51	19.00	19.16	19.25	19.30	19.33	19.37	19.41	19.45	19.50
3	10.13	9.55	9.28	9.12	9.01	8.94	8.85	8.74	8.64	8.53
4	7.71	6.94	6.59	6.39	6.26	6.16	6.04	5.91	5.77	5.63
5	6.61	5.79	5.41	5.19	5.05	4.95	4.82	4.68	4.53	4.37
6	5.99	5.14	4.76	4.53	4.39	4.28	4.15	4.00	3.84	3.67
7	5.59	4.74	4.35	4.12	3.97	3.87	3.73	3.57	3.41	3.23
8	5.32	4.46	4.07	3.84	3.69	3.58	3.44	3.28	3.12	2.93
9	5.12	4.26	3.86	3.63	3.48	3.37	3.23	3.07	2.90	2.71
10	4.96	4.10	3.71	3.48	3.33	3.22	3.07	2.91	2.74	2.54
11	4.84	3.98	3.59	3.36	3.20	3.09	2.95	2.79	2.61	2.40
12	4.75	3.89	3.49	3.26	3.11	3.00	2.85	2.69	2.51	2.30
13	4.67	3.81	3.41	3.18	3.03	2.92	2.77	2.60	2.42	2.21
14	4.60	3.74	3.34	3.11	2.96	2.85	2.70	2.53	2.35	2.13
15	4.54	3.68	3.29	3.06	2.90	2.79	2.64	2.48	2.29	2.07
16	4.49	3.63	3.24	3.01	2.85	2.74	2.59	2.42	2.24	2.01
17	4.45	3.59	3.20	2.96	2.81	2.70	2.55	2.38	2.19	1.96
18	4.41	3.55	3.16	2.93	2.77	2.66	2.51	2.34	2.15	1.92
19	4.38	3.52	3.13	2.90	2.74	2.63	2.48	2.31	2.11	1.88
20	4.35	3.49	3.10	2.87	2.71	2.60	2.45	2.28	2.08	1.84
21	4.32	3.47	3.07	2.84	2.68	2.57	2.42	2.25	2.05	1.81
22	4.30	3.44	3.05	2.82	2.66	2.55	2.40	2.23	2.03	1.78
23	4.28	3.42	3.03	2.80	2.64	2.53	2.37	2.20	2.01	1.76
24	4.26	3.40	3.01	2.78	2.62	2.51	2.36	2.18	1.98	1.73
25	4.24	3.39	2.99	2.76	2.60	2.49	2.34	2.16	1.96	1.71
26	4.23	3.37	2.98	2.74	2.59	2.47	2.32	2.15	1.95	1.69
27	4.21	3.35	2.96	2.73	2.57	2.46	2.31	2.13	1.93	1.67
28	4.20	3.34	2.95	2.71	2.56	2.45	2.29	2.12	1.91	1.65
29	4.18	3.33	2.93	2.70	2.55	2.43	2.28	2.10	1.90	1.64
30	4.17	3.32	2.92	2.69	2.53	2.42	2.27	2.09	1.89	1.62
40	4.08	3.23	2.84	2.61	2.45	2.34	2.18	2.00	1.79	1.51
60	4.00	3.15	2.76	2.53	2.37	2.25	2.10	1.92	1.70	1.39
120	3.92	3.07	2.68	2.45	2.29	2.18	2.02	1.83	1.61	1.25
∞	3.84	3.00	2.60	2.37	2.21	2.10	1.94	1.75	1.52	1.00

Did You Know?

The *F Distribution* app from ArtofStat .com lets you find any tail probabilities or percentiles for the *F* distribution interactively, including a visualization for checking results. ◄

Table E Table of Random Numbers

Line/Col.	(1)	(2)	(3)	(4)	(5)	(6)	(7)	(8)
1	10480	15011	01536	02011	81647	91646	69179	14194
2	22368	46573	25595	85393	30995	89198	27982	53402
3	24130	48360	22527	97265	76393	64809	15179	24830
4	42167	93093	06243	61680	07856	16376	39440	53537
5	37570	39975	81837	16656	06121	91782	60468	81305
6	77921	06907	11008	42751	27756	53498	18602	70659
7	99562	72905	56420	69994	98872	31016	71194	18738
8	96301	91977	05463	07972	18876	20922	94595	56869
9	89579	14342	63661	10281	17453	18103	57740	84378
10	85475	36857	53342	53988	53060	59533	38867	62300
11	28918	69578	88231	33276	70997	79936	56865	05859
12	63553	40961	48235	03427	49626	69445	18663	72695
13	09429	93969	52636	92737	88974	33488	36320	17617
14	10365	61129	87529	85689	48237	52267	67689	93394
15	07119	97336	71048	08178	77233	13916	47564	81056
16	51085	12765	51821	51259	77452	16308	60756	92144
17	02368	21382	52404	60268	89368	19885	55322	44819
18	01011	54092	33362	94904	31273	04146	18594	29852
19	52162	53916	46369	58586	23216	14513	83149	98736
20	07056	97628	33787	09998	42698	06691	76988	13602

Did You Know?

We show Table E for legacy reasons only, but we do not emphasize it in the book. Rather, we generate random numbers using online tools, such as the *Random Numbers* app from ArtofStat.com or websites such as random.org. ◄

Answers

Chapter 1

1.1 (a) The 22,000 physicians, the plan for assigning the physicians to either the aspirin or placebo group, and the plan to obtain percentages of physicians having heart attacks in each group belong to the design phase of the study. Statistical question of interest: Is aspirin or a placebo more effective in preventing heart attacks? Data will come from a study of physicians, where half the participants take aspirin and the other half take a placebo. **(b)** The quoted percentages of suffering a heart attack for those taking aspirin and those taking a placebo. **(c)** The generalization that aspirin reduces the risk of a heart attack, not just for the physicians in the study, but in general. **1.3 (a)** 4,854 (as of 2019) **(b)** 63.8%, 20.6%, 9.1%, 6.6% **(c)** 2018: 61.2%, 2008: 64.3% (about 3 percentage points smaller) **1.5 (a)** 575 **(b)** 40, 36.9% **1.7 (a)** The sample consists of the 3,077 people who responded **(b)** The population is all adults in the U.S. **(c)** The statistic is the proportion of respondents (23%) who said antireligious books should be removed. **(d)** The population parameter is the proportion in the entire U.S. population who think antireligious books should be removed. **1.9 (a)** Each student in the program **(b)** The students identified **(c)** All students in the program **1.11 (a)** Descriptive statistics; they summarize data from a population. **(b)** Parameter, since they refer to a population. **1.13 (a)** Very short bars toward the top indicate very few old men and women in 1750. **(b)** Bars are much longer for both men and women in 2010 than in 1750. **(c)** The bars for women in their 70s and 80s in 2010 are longer than those for men. **(d)** From the graph, the longest bars are associated with the 45–49 age group. **1.15 (a)** Yes, the populations are the same in the two studies. For both, it's all students at your school. **(b)** It is *very* unlikely that you will choose the same 20 students. **(c)** Although it is most likely that the sample proportions will not be the same, they should be close to each other. **1.17 (a)** Predicting that the true proportion of Obama voters is within 3 percentage points of 49%. **(b)** The first four polls are all within the margin of error; however, Rand overestimated and Fox underestimated Obama's proportion. Generally, the polls are fairly accurate. **(c)** In our 10 simulations, the smallest simulated proportion was 0.48 and the largest was 0.54. **1.19 (a)** II **(b)** I **(c)** I **1.21** E.g., Column 1: Friend: 1, 2, 3, 4; Column 2: Age: 21, 20, 20, 21; Column 3: On-Campus Housing: Y, Y, N, N. **1.23** Column 1: Traveler: 1, 2, 3; Column 2: Check in (min): 30, 90, NA; Column 3: Luggage($) 25, 60, NA; Column 4: Airbnb: No, Yes, Yes. **1.25** See solutions for 1.21. **1.27** Training: data set with labels; Test Data: data set without labels. **1.29** For example, on Wikipedia, the number of articles mentioning males is much greater than the number of articles mentioning females. An algorithm trained on Wikipedia data for identifying the target of pronouns may do much better for male-related pronouns than female-related pronouns. **1.31 (a)** All American adults **(b)** The sample data are summarized by a proportion, 0.598. **(c)** The population proportion who would commit suicide. **1.33 (a)** Sample data. **(b)** Percentages reported. **(c)** Reporting margin of error for sample percentage. **1.35 (a)** Sample: the 85 visitors to the site that day. Population: all potential visitors to the site (in March). **(b)** Descriptive aspects: e.g., the average number of minutes the 85 visitors stayed on the site or the proportion of the 85 visitors who use a Chrome browser. Inferential aspects: Predicting the average number of minutes that visitors will stay on the site; Checking if the proportion of all users of the site that use a Chrome browser is larger than 50% **1.37 (a)** 0.3 and 1.0 (answers will vary) **(b)** 0.50 and 0.71 (answers will vary) **(c)** n = 100 **1.39** Will be different for each student. **1.41** This would be extremely surprising. None of the 10,000 simulations results in a proportion this large. So we would not expect to see such a proportion if 50% of the population shares this view. **1.43 (c) 1.45** False **1.47 (a)** 0.491, 0.519, 0.496, 0.497, 0.492, 0.500, 0.518, 0.499, 0.503, 0.497 (answers will vary) **(b)** All 10 intervals contain 0.5 (answers will vary) **(c)** About 95% of all intervals should contain 0.5. **1.49** e.g., "70% of Americans say the U.S. should still play a strong role in world."

Chapter 2

2.1 (a) Categorical: observations belong to one of a set of categories. Quantitative: observations are numerical. **(b)** Examples will differ for each student. **2.3 (a)** Quantitative. **(b)** Categorical. **(c)** Categorical. **(d)** Quantitative. **2.5 (a)** Discrete: possible values are separate numbers, such as 0,1,2,....Continuous: possible values form an interval. **(b)** Examples will differ for each student. **2.7 (a)** Continuous. **(b)** Discrete. **(c)** Discrete. **(d)** Continuous. **2.9 (a)** Nominal. **(b)** Nominal. **(c)** Ordinal. **(d)** Ordinal. **2.11 (a)** The percentages for each of the categories are 3.2, 3.2, 6.3, 23.8, 20.6, 9.5, 6.3, 9.5, and 17.5. **(b)** Australia. **(c)** Regions with most frequent fatal shark attacks are Australia and South Africa. **2.13 (b)** A bar chart. Sketching the precise areas corresponding to the percentages is more challenging in a pie chart. **(c)** It is straightforward to judge the relative sizes when comparing the bars corresponding to the percentages. **(d)** Coal. **2.15 (a)** Categories of a variable. **(b)** Frequency and percentage of weather stations in a given region. **(c)** Bar graph; we can more easily compare the heights of bars. **2.17** With a Pareto chart, it is straightforward to identify the few regions with the largest number of fatal shark attacks. **2.19 (b)** The plot with split stems gives a clearer picture of the shape of the distribution. **(c)** Most hotels charge between $150 and $250 per night, with a few charging more. The distribution of prices is right skewed. **2.21 (a)** With just two stems, the plot is too compact. **(b)** 1|33, 1|4555, 1|666777, 1|88889, 2|, 2|2. **2.23 (a)** −1 to 1, 1 to 3, 3 to 5, 5 to 7, 7 to 9, 9 to 11, 11 to 13, 13 to 15, 15 to 17, and 17 to 19. **(b)** Bimodal; child cereals, on average, have more sugar than adult cereals. **(c)** The dot and stem-and-leaf plots allow us to see all the individual data points. **(d)** The histogram would look exactly the same, and the bimodal shape would not change at all. The relative differences between the bars stays the same. **2.25 (a)** Skewed to the left. **(b)** Skewed to the right. **(c)** Skewed to the left. **(d)** Skewed to the right. **2.27 (a)** Discrete; the value for each person would be a whole number. **(b) (i)** 0; **(ii)** 9; **(iii)** 2; **(iv)** 3. **(c)** Unimodal and somewhat skewed to the right. **(d)** 1/4 or 25%. **2.29 (a)** Somewhat skewed to the left. **(b)** A time plot connects the data points over time to show time trends. **(c)** A histogram shows the number of observations at various temperature intervals more easily than does the time plot. We also can see the shape of the distribution from the histogram but not from the time plot. **2.31** The fertility rate dropped sharply from about 3.6 in 1960 to about 1.8 in 1980, rebounded a bit to 2.1 in 2000, and has been dropping ever since to a current value of 1.8. **2.33 (a)** Median (right skewed). **(b)** Mean (symmetric). **(c)** Median (left skewed). **2.35 (a)** The median for all three data sets is 10. **(b)** Set 1: $x = 10$; Set 2: $x = 27.6$; Set 3: $x = 207.6$. **(c)** The median is unaffected by the outlier, the mean gets higher and higher as the outlier becomes more extreme. **2.37** Management would want to use the mean because the mean would be higher due to the outliers. The workers would prefer the median because it is not affected by the outliers and would be smaller. **2.39 (a)** Middle and right distributions, because they are symmetric. **(b)** Left because it is skewed to the right; the mean would be higher than the median. **2.41 (a)** The median is not affected by the magnitude of the highest score, but the mean is. **(b)** The effect is much weaker. **2.43** Answers will vary. **2.45 (a)** The median is the number in the 183rd position of the sorted data set, 1. **(b)** Mean $= (\Sigma x)/n = (0(102) + 1(233) + 2(18) + 3(9) + 4(2) + 5(1))/365 = 0.85$ **(c)** Since 233 respondents gave an answer of 1, the value in the 183rd place when the data are sorted from smallest to largest (i.e., the median) is still 1. **2.47** Because so many people would report 0 motor accidents, the median is not very useful. **2.49 (a)** Africa, since life expectancies vary much more than for Europe, where all values are very similar. **(b)** Western Europe: $s = 1.05$; Africa: $s = 5.18$ **2.51** $60,000. Not −$15,000 because a standard deviation cannot be negative, $1,000 is too small for a typical deviation and $1,000,000 is too large. **2.53 (a)** 68% of men would be between 68 and 74 inches, 95% of men would be between 65 and 77 inches, all or nearly all men would be between 62 and 80 inches. **(b)** The mean for women is lower than the mean for men. Because each gender's heights would tend to be closer to that gender's mean than to the overall mean, the standard deviation would be smaller when we compared them with the appropriate gender group than when we compared them to the overall group. Would expect bimodal distribution, with the two modes around the female and male means. Empirical rule only applies to unimodal, not bimodal, distributions. **2.55** 68% of women would be able to lift between 66.6 and 93.2 pounds, 95% of women would be able to lift between 53.3 and 106.5 pounds, all or nearly all women would be able to lift between 40.0 and 119.8 pounds. **2.57** Since the lowest possible value is only 1.52 standard deviations below the mean, the distribution likely is skewed to the right. **2.59** Skewed to the right because mean is larger than median. The standard deviation is almost as large as the mean, which indicates right skewness here because the lowest possible value of 0 is only just over one standard deviation below mean. **2.61** Skewed to the left. **2.63 (a)** One possibility: 30, 50, 80. **(b)** One possibility: 10, 50, 90. **(c)** Two 0s and two 100s, with $s = 57.74$. **2.65 (a)** In 2013, half of the European Union nations had an unemployment rate less than 10.15%. **(b)** In 2013, 75% of the European Union nations had an unemployment rate larger than 7.15% (or 25% had rate less than 7.15%). **(c)** In 2013, the unemployment rate was larger than 13.05% for 25% of the European Union nations. **(d)** Around 6% because Q1 = 7.15%. **2.67 (a)** One quarter had weight below 119 and one quarter had weight above 144. **(b)** Mean $\approx$ median and the first and third quartiles are approximately equidistant from the median. Roughly symmetric distribution. **2.69 (a)** (i) 75%; (ii) 25%. **(b)** 36 cents and 100 cents (i.e., one dollar). **(c)** IQR = 64 cents. **(d)** No. Q1 and Q3 are not roughly equidistant from the median and the maximum value is also quite far from Q3. Distribution is skewed to the right. **2.71 (a)** Q1 = 76; Q3 = 101. **(b)** IQR = 25. **2.73 (a)** Skewed to the right because of the distance between the minimum and the median. **(b)** Outliers would be those values more than 1,273.5 kilobytes from the first and third quartiles; 320,000 is a potential outlier. **2.75** The minimum, Q1, median, Q3, and maximum are used in the box plot. **2.77 (a)** Outer box from 7.2 to 13.1. $1.5 \times$ IQR = 8.85. Left (or lower) whisker extends to smallest observation that is not a potential outlier, i.e., to the smallest observation that is above $7.2 - 8.85 = -1.65$, i.e., all the way to minimum, which is 4.9 (Austria). Right (or upper) whisker: extends to largest observation below $13.1 + 8.85 = 21.9$, i.e., whisker extends all the way to 17.2 (Croatia). **(b)** Greece and Spain (values larger than Q3 + 1.5 (IQR)) **(c)** $z = (27.3 - 11.1)/5.6 = 2.9$, Greece has rate 2.9 standard deviations above mean rate. Not an outlier by this criterion. **(d)** Country with a rate equal to the mean rate, 11.1. **2.79 (a)** -3.1. **(b)** The height is below the mean. **(c)** Yes; it is more than three standard deviations from the mean. **2.81** The distribution of room prices is skewed to the right, with a median price of $100. The mean price of rooms is $140. Twenty-five percent of listings charge less than $70, but 25% charge more than $175, resulting in an IQR of $105. The distribution has a very long right tail because there are several listings that charge more than $500 and up to $1,000. **2.83 (a)** The two outliers for Central and South America have a value of roughly 12 metric tons. **(b)** Skewed to the right. The median sits low in the box (pulled toward the first quartile), and the upper whisker stretches out more from the box to the maximum value than the lower whisker stretches to the minimum value. **(c)** The median CO_2 emission is much larger in Europe than the median for Central and South America. The spread of the middle 50% of the distribution of emissions, as measured by the IQR, seems to be about the same for Europe and Central and South America. 75% of the distribution of emissions for Europe is higher than the lower 75% of the distribution of emissions for Central and South America. Overall, emissions are higher for Europe than for Central and South America. **2.85 (a)** $y = 10 + x$, mean = 70, st.dev. = 10. **(b)** $y = 1.1x$, mean = 66, st.dev. = 11. **(c)** $y = 10 + 1.05x$, mean = 73, st.dev. = 10.5. **(d)** Left-skewed. **(e)** Add 20 points to each student's score. **2.87 (a)** 45,000(1.2) = 54,000. **(b)** 40,000(1.2) = 48,000. **(c)** 10,000(1.2) = 12,000. **2.89** The *Imitation Game* has the highest combined z-score: It is 0.12 standard deviation above the mean for critics' scores and 1.2 standard deviations above the mean for users' scores. No other movie achieves such a high combination of z-scores, although

Inside Out is close. (Note: When just averaging the scores, *Inside Out* wins out; but this ignores that the scales for critics' and users' reviews are rather different, as indicated by the different standard deviations.) **2.91 (a)** The percentages do not add up to 100, and the Tesco slice seems too large for 27.2%. Also, contiguous colors are similar. **(b)** Bar graph. We would merely have to identify the highest bar. **2.93 (a)** Because the vertical axis does not start at 0, it appears that six times as many people are in the "no, not" column than in the "yes, safer" column. **(b)** With a pie chart, the area of each slice represents the percentage who fall in that category. Therefore, the relative sizes of the slices will always represent the relative percentages in each category. **2.95** The slices do not seem to have the correct sizes, for instance the slice with 16% seems much larger than the slice with 20% and also larger than the slice with 19%. **2.97** The difference in the tax rates looks more dramatic than it is. As shown, it looks like the tax rate on Jan 1, 2013 will be about 5 times higher than it was, which is exaggerating the impact. The y-axis should start from 0 to more appropriately represent the two rates of 35% and 39.6%. **2.99 (a)** Quantitative. **(b)** Quantitative. **(c)** Categorical. **(d)** Categorical. **2.101 (a)** Categorical. 4.5%, 23%, 5.8%, 64.9%, 1.9%. **(b)** Mode. Most young noncitizens are from Latin America and the Caribbean. **(c)** Latin America and Caribbean, Asia, Europe, Africa, Other. One immediately sees that most young noncitizens are from two regions, Latin America and Caribbean and from Asia. **2.103 (a)** Optical scanning with a two-column ballot. **(b)** One column with either optical scanning or votomatic. **(c)** Bar for each combination (e.g., optical, one column; optical, two columns) with each bar showing the overall percentage of overvotes. **2.105 (c)** The distribution of longevity is right skewed. Most animals live to be between 5 and 15 years old. **2.107 (a)** Symmetric and bimodal. **(b)** Skewed to the right. **(c)** Skewed to the left. **(d)** Symmetric and unimodal. **2.109** Stem-and-leaf plot: 3 | 999, 4 | 00444, 4 | 59999, 5 | 01; The distribution of cost is fairly symmetric, with a mean of $4.46 and a standard deviation of $0.45. There are no apparent outliers. **2.111 (a)** Skewed to the right, mean > median. **(b)** Skewed to the right, mean > median. **(c)** Skewed to the left, mean < median. **(d)** Skewed to the left, mean < median. **2.113** Higher, because the distribution of sale prices is right skewed. **2.115 (a)** Skewed to the right. **(b)** $2,090,012 is the mean and $1,646,853 is the median. **2.117 (a)** 1, 2, 4, 6, 7. **(b)** 2, 2, 3, 5, 6. **2.119 (a)** 12 is best; -10 is negative (not possible); 1 indicates almost no variability; 60 is almost as large as the whole range. **(b)** -20; standard deviations must be nonnegative. **2.121 (a)** Skewed to the right; maximum is much farther from the mean than the minimum is, and the lowest possible value of 0 is only 780/506 = 1.54 standard deviations below the mean. **(b)** Skewed to the right; the standard deviation is almost as large as the mean and the smallest possible value is 0. **2.123 (a)** Because of the extreme right skew. **(b)** Mean and standard deviation would get much smaller, median, IQR, and 10th percentile would not change much. **2.125 (a)** Unimodal distribution, skewed to the right, possible outliers around 200. **(b)** Mean = 72.85, median = 60; skewed to the right. **(c)** $s = 48.00$. **2.127 (b)** Median = 24.5, Q1 = 7.5, Q3 = 46. **(c)** The gaps from 40 to 50 and 60 to 70. **2.129 (a)** Range = $34,048, IQR = $9,980. **(b)** Lower whisker = $35,070, upper whisker = $69,118. **(c)** Skewed to the right because there is a lower limit but no hard upper limit. **(d)** 7,000. The values 100 and 1,000 are too small, and 25,000 is too large given a range of roughly 34,000. 7,000 is most reasonable for the average distance of observations from the mean. **2.133 (a)** Line through box is left of center, indicating skewness to the right. **(b)** Minimum $\approx$ 1,400; Q1 $\approx$ 1,475; Median $\approx$ 1,550; Q3 $\approx$ 1,700; Maximum $\approx$ 1,800. **(c)** We would not see that the distribution is bimodal. **2.135** -2.16; this sodium value falls 2.16 standard deviations below the mean. **2.137 (a)** Bimodal **(b)** Those rating the movie as 0 may strongly deny climate change and/or strongly disagree with Al Gore's agenda; those rating the movie as 10 may strongly believe climate change is real and/or strongly sympathize with Gore's agenda. **(c)** Popular movies are most likely going to show a left-skewed distribution, with many ratings of 8, 9, or 10, and relatively few ratings from 0 to about 5. **2.139 (a)** Both distributions skewed to the left, S more so; smallest observation in S data set is a possible outlier; children on F do better, on average, than those on S. **(b)** If no difference, distribution will be centered around 0. **2.141** Answers will vary. **2.143 (a)** Nominal. **(b)** Because categories are not ordered, they cannot be assigned scores. There is no notion of which category is "better" than another. Categories merely present qualitative, and not quantitative, labels. **(c)** A mean or median requires quantitative data. A nominal variable still has a category (or categories) that occur the most frequently. **2.145** (b). **2.147** (d). **2.149 (a)** False. **(b)** False. **(c)** True. **(d)** True. **2.151** False. **2.153** $\bar{x} \pm 3s$ would encompass all or nearly all scores. A range of $3s + 3s = 6s$ contains all or nearly all scores, so approximates the range. **2.155 (a)** With greater variability, numbers tend to be further from the mean. Thus, the absolute values of their deviations from the mean would be larger. When we take the average of all these values, the overall MAD is larger than for distributions with less variability. **(b)** The MAD is more resistant than the standard deviation because by squaring the deviations using the standard deviation formula, a large deviation has greater effect. **2.157** Answers will vary.

Chapter 3

3.1 (a) Response: Price; Explanatory: Carat. **(b)** Response: Severity of adverse event; Explanatory: Dosage. **(c)** Response: Top speed; Explanatory: Construction type. **(d)** Response: Graduation rate; Explanatory: Type of college. **3.3 (a)** The response variable is happiness and the explanatory variable is income. **(b)** Using 2010 data,

Income	Not Too Happy	Pretty Happy	Very Happy	Total	n
Above average	0.06	0.59	0.35	1.00	360
Average	0.11	0.60	0.29	1.00	850
Below average	0.24	0.57	0.19	1.00	604

The proportion of people who are very happy is larger for those with above-average income (35%) compared to those with below-average income (19%), showing an association between these two variables. Also, the proportion of people who are not too happy is much larger (24%) for people with below-average income compared to people with average (11%) or above-average (6%) income. **(c)** 0.269. **3.5 (a)** Response: binge drinking; explanatory: gender. **(b) (i)** 1,908; **(ii)** 2,854. **(c)** No; these are not proportions of male and female students; these are counts and there are far more females than males in this study. **(d)**

Gender	Binge Drinker	Non-Binge Drinker	Total	n
Male	0.49	0.51	1.00	3,925
Female	0.41	0.59	1.00	6,979

(e) It appears that men are more likely than are women to be binge drinkers. **3.7 (a)** No. We could be interested in the proportion that believes in heaven, studying how it differs between those believing or not believing in hell, or vice versa. **(b)** Using 2008 data,

Do You Believe in Heaven?	Do You Believe in Hell? Yes	No	Total
Yes	955	162	1,117
No	9	188	197
Total	964	350	1,314

(c)

Do You Believe in Hell?	Do You Believe in Heaven? Yes	No	Total	n
Yes	0.991	0.009	1.00	964
No	0.463	0.537	1.00	350

(d)

Do You Believe in Heaven?	Do You Believe in Hell? Yes	No	Total	n
Yes	0.855	0.145	1.00	1,117
No	0.046	0.954	1.00	197

(e) (i) 85.01%; **(ii)** 73.4%. **3.9 (a)** Children and female adult passengers who survived: 69.9%, male adults: 20.3% **(b)** Difference = 69.9 − 20.3 = 49.6. The proportion of children and female adult passengers surviving the sinking of the Titanic is 49.6 percentage points higher than the proportion

for male adult passengers. **(c)** Ratio = 69.9/20.3 = 3.4. The proportion of children and female adult passengers surviving the sinking of the *Titanic* is 3.4 times larger than the proportion for male adult passengers. **3.11 (a)** Contingency Table of Counts:

Gender	Very Happy	Pretty Happy	Not Too Happy
Male	311	583	156
Female	390	724	180

(b) Conditional Percentages:

Gender	Very Happy	Pretty Happy	Not Too Happy
Male	29.6	55.5	14.9
Female	30.1	56.0	13.9

(c) Difference of proportion = 14.9 − 13.9 = 1.00. The proportion of males who are not too happy is 1 percentage point higher than the proportion of females who are not too happy. Ratio of proportions = 14.9/13.9 = 1.07. The proportion of males who are not too happy is 7% higher than the proportion of females who are not too happy. Alternatively: Males are 7% more likely to be not too happy compare to females. **3.13 (a)** GDP (in billions): Min = 204, Q1 = 378, Median = 780, Q3 = 2,015, Max = 16,245; Broadband subscribers: Min = 1,107,200, Q1 = 2,416,737, Median = 6,057,750, Q3 = 15,276,238, Max = 175,624,800. **(b)** For countries with GDP less than $5,000 billion, there is a clear trend in that countries with larger GDP have a larger number of broadband subscribers. Three countries stand out in terms of both their GDP and number of subscribers. Although Japan, the third-largest country in terms of GDP, seems to follow the trend, China (the second-largest country in terms of GDP) has by far the most broadband subscribers, whereas the United States (the country with the largest GDP by far) has fewer broadband subscribers than China. **(c)** China with approximately $x = 8,000$ billion GDP and $y = 160$ million broadband subscribers **(d)** $r = 0.77$; the positive sign indicates a positive relationship between GDP and number of broadband subscribers; as GDP increases, the number of broadband subscribers tends to increase as well. **(e)** The United States has fewer than expected; China has more than expected. **(f)** The correlation coefficient would not change because it does not depend on the units of measurement. **3.15 (a)** Weak. **(b)** Religiosity. **3.17 1.** (c); **2.** (a); **3.** (d); **4.** (b). **3.19** The correlation coefficient is only valid to measure the relationship between two quantitative variables, not between two categorical variables. **3.21** When the relationship is not linear. **3.23 (a)** Positive; Veggie sandwich has the lowest and Chicken & Bacon has the highest protein count, and they deviate somewhat from the overall trend. **(b)** The trend looks approximately linear, although the lower- and uppermost point (Veggie Delite and Chicken & Bacon sandwich, respectively) deviate somewhat from that pattern. **(c) (i)** 0.78 and **(ii)** 0.81. **(d)** The relationship between the protein content and the price of Subway sandwiches is positive, approximately linear, and relatively strong, with a correlation coefficient of $r = 0.78$. Two sandwiches, Veggie Delite and Chicken & Bacon, have relatively low and high cost, respectively, given their protein content. Without these two, the correlation coefficient is even stronger with $r = 0.81$. **3.25 (a)** $a = 7$, $b = 0.5$. **(b)** $a = 7$, $b = 1$. **(c)** $a = 7$, $b = -1$. **(d)** $a = 7$, $b = 0$. **3.27 (a) (i)** $163,200; **(ii)** $240,200. **(b)** For every increase of a thousand square feet, home prices are predicted to increase by $77,000. **(c)** Positive. **(d)** Residual = 300 − 240.2 = 59.8, that is $59,800. The house sold for $59,800 more than we predict with the regression line. **3.29** Service rating; it shows the largest correlation with cost. **3.31 (a)** For every million people increase in the size of the population of a nation, the predicted number of broadband subscriptions increases by 76,100. The relationship is positive. As population size increases, number of broadband subscriptions tends to increase. **(b) (i)** 6,074,668; **(ii)** 108,318,093. **(c)**; residual = 59,100,939. The actual number of broadband subscribers is more than 59 million larger than the one predicted based on the population size. **3.33 (a)** b = −270. **(b) (i)** 28,910; **(ii)** 9,200; **(iii)** 1,910. **3.35 (a)** Small, because not much is gained from using the regression equation with sugar to predict sodium values. **(b)** Almost none (i.e., only 0.03%) of the variability in the sodium content of cereals can be explained by their sugar content. **(c)** $-0.25 = -0.017(77.3/5.322)$ **3.37 (a) (i)** 90; **(ii)** 60. **(b)** $b = r(s_y/s_x) \rightarrow 0.6 = r(10/10) \rightarrow r = 0.6$. **(c)** For every 1-point increase on the midterm score, the final exam score is predicted to increase by 0.6 points. **3.39 (a)** For every 0.01 increase in the batting average, we predict the runs per game to increase by 0.415. **(b)** 81% of the variability in runs per game is accounted for by variability in team batting averages. **3.41 (a)** The scatterplot reveals a positive, approximately linear relationship between GDP and oil consumption. The relationship is relatively strong, with a correlation coefficient of $r = 0.85$. **(b)** $\hat{y} = -0.105 + 0.546x$. For every $1,000 increase in the per capita GDP, the predicted oil consumption per person increases by 0.55 barrels. **(c)** 26 $- 18.47 = 7.53$. Canada's per-person oil consumption is 7.53 barrels higher than what is predicted by its per capita GDP. **3.43 (a)** No. It would be better to calculate separate regression lines for each type of suspension because the relationship differs depending on the type of suspension. **(b)** Front-End: $\hat{y} = 2,136 - 55$(weight); Full: $\hat{y} = 2,432 - 44$(weight). The slope is steeper for front-end suspensions indicating that the predicted price drops faster per each pound increase in weight for bikes with front-end suspension. **(c)** They will be stronger. Front end: $r = -0.888$; full: $r = -0.952$. **(d)** Front end: residual $= 131.5$; full: residual $= -478$; Front end, because residual is smaller. **3.45 (a)** Yes, it is the observation with the largest x value and falls away from the overall trend of the other observations. **(b)** The slope is only about half as much as before. **(c)** -8.25, a negative murder rate. Not sensible because we didn't observe any x-values around 0. **3.47 (a)** $\hat{y} = 27.3 + 0.0127x$. Every year, we predict the annual average U.S. temperature to increase by 0.013 degrees Fahrenheit. **(b)** 52.9; 55.2. **(c)** 2020, because it is hard to predict if the trend will continue until 2200. **(d)** It shows a slightly steeper increase since about 1980 compared to the linear trend, suggesting a slightly larger increase in the predicted average annual temperature. **3.49 (a)** Yes on all three counts. **(b) (1)** the x value (the United States in this case) is relatively low or high compared to the rest of the data; **(2)** the observation (the United States) is a regression outlier, falling quite far from the trend that the rest of the data follow. TV watching in the United States is very high despite the very low birth rate. **(c)** The relationship is **(i)** very weak without the United States because the six countries, although they vary in birth rates, all have very few televisions, and is; **(ii)** very strong with the United States because the United States is so much higher in number of televisions and so much lower on birth rate that it makes the two variables seem related. **(d)** Because that point has a large effect on pulling the line downward. **3.51 (a)** Perhaps Raisin Bran. **(b)** With Raisin Bran removed, r changed from -0.017 to -0.300, which is a substantial change. **3.53 (a)** Not likely. **(b)** Values would be higher on both variables as age increases. **(c)** There is an overall positive correlation between height (in inches) and vocabulary (assessed on a scale of 1–10) if we ignore grade; if we look within each grade, we see roughly a horizontal trend and no particular relationship (scatterplot part of answer). **3.55 (a)** Several possible responses to this exercise (e.g., students who watch TV more may be more likely to see the ads and less likely to spend time with peers who smoke pot). **(b)** Pot smoking (or the lack thereof) might be caused by many variables (e.g., antidrug ads, television watching, regular school attendance, parental influence, neighborhood type). **3.57 (a)** No. While there is a negative, relatively weak relationship between teacher salary and SAT score, decreasing teacher salary does not cause SAT scores to increase. Correlation does not imply causation, especially with the potential for lurking variables. **(b)** There is a clear trend in the color of the dots. Almost all dark-colored dots, indicating low participation rates, are in the upper part of the plot where SAT scores are high. On the other hand, the bright-colored dots, indicating high participation rates, are all close to the x-axis, where the SAT score is low. So, states with high SAT scores have low participation rates, while states with low SAT scores have high participation rates. **(c)** Without taking participation rate into account, we observed a *negative* correlation between average teacher salary and average SAT score in the 50 states. When adjusting for participation, the picture changes completely. For states with low or medium participation, there is only a very

weak, but actually positive, relationship. For states with high participation rates, there is now a *strong positive* relationship between average teacher salary and average SAT score. **3.59 (a)** Response: eighth grade math scores; explanatory: state. **(b)** The third variable is race. Nebraska has the overall higher mean because there is a higher percentage of Whites and a lower percentage of Blacks in Nebraska than in New Jersey, and overall, Whites tended to have higher math scores than Blacks. **3.61 (a)** Response: assessed value; explanatory: square feet. **(b)** Response: political party; explanatory: gender. **(c)** Response: income; explanatory: education. **(d)** Response: pounds lost; explanatory: type of diet. **3.63 (a)** Opinion about life after death and using 2008 data,

Gender	Yes	No	Total
Male	76.9	23.1	808
Female	85.2	14.8	979

(b) 76.9% of males believe in life after death as opposed to 85.2% of females. Difference in proportion between females and males $= 0.852 - 0.769 = 0.083$. The proportion of females believing in life after death is about 8 percentage points higher than the one for males. Ratio of proportions $= 0.852/0.769 = 1.108$. The proportion of females believing in life after death is about 11% higher (or 1.1 times higher) than the one for males. **(c)** Proportions in (b). **3.65 (a)** Income; quantitative. **(b)** Degree; categorical. **(c)** A bar graph could have a separate bar for each degree type. **3.67 (a)** Response: gender; explanatory: year. **(b)** For executive, administrative, and managerial

Year	Female	Male	Total
1972	0.197	0.803	1.00
2002	0.459	0.541	1.00

(c) Yes; women made up a larger proportion of the executive work force in 2002 than in 1972. **(d)** Year and type of occupation. **3.69 (a)** There is a positive, approximately linear relationship between alcohol content and the amount of calories. The relationship is strong, with a correlation coefficient of $r = 0.90$. **(b)** No. **(c)** Predicted calories $= 8.13 + 28.2$ alcohol; For every 1% increase in the alcohol content of a beer, we predict that the amount of calories in a 12-ounce serving increases by 28.2. **(d)** Yes, the slope will be different. **3.71 (a)** Slope: 0.56; as urban goes from 0 to 100, predicted crime rate increases by 56. **(b)** 11.2 crimes. **3.73 (a)** Response: salary; explanatory: height. **(b)** Slope: $789 per inch. **(c)** An increase of seven inches (from 5 foot 5 to 6 feet) is worth $789 per inch, or $5,523. **3.75** y-intercept: 0; slope: 1; this means that your predicted college GPA equals your high school GPA. **3.77 (a)** A 1,000 increase in x would mean a predicted change in y of -5.2 (poorer mileage). **(b)** 14.04; 2.96. The Hummer gets 2.96 more miles/gallon than one would predict. **3.79 (a)** No, for both types of beer, the relationship seems to be equally strong. **(b)** No, the type of beer is not associated with either the alcohol content or the amount of calories. **3.81 (a)** When economic activity is 0%, predicted birth rate is much higher (36.3) than when economic activity is 100% (6.3). **(b)** women's economic activity; the correlation coefficient between birth rate and women's economic activity is larger in magnitude than the correlation coefficient between birth rate and GNP. **3.83 (a)** $-16,000$. **(b)** 3,200; **(c)** same (0.50); correlation coefficient does not depend on the units used **3.85 (a)** D.C. is the outlier to the far, upper right. This would have an effect on the regression analysis because it is a regression outlier. **(b)** When D.C. is included, the y-intercept decreases and the slope increases. **3.87 (a)** The point with a y value of around 1,500 (scatterplot is part of answer). **(b)** Predicted violent crime rate $= 2,545 - 24.6$ high school; for each increase of 1% of people with a high school education, the predicted violent crime rate decreases by 24.6. **(c)** Predicted violent crime rate $= 2,268 - 21.6$ high school; for each increase of 1% of people with a high school education, predicted violent crime rate decreases by 21.6, similar to the slope in part b. **3.89 (a)** Negative relationship (scatterplot is part of answer). **(b)** -0.45; negative relationship. **(c)** Predicted percentage without health ins $= 49.2 - 0.42$ HS Grad Rate; for each increase of one percent in the high school graduation rate, the predicted percentage of individuals without health insurance goes down by 0.42; negative relationship. **3.91 (a)** Men tend to be taller and make more money than women. **(b)** When measured, a lurking variable becomes a confounding variable. **3.93 (a)** As people age, they might both sleep more and be more likely to die. **(b)** Subject's age might actually cause people to sleep more and be more likely to die. **3.95** Responses will vary. **3.97** Predicted number of days $= 15.3 + 0.0063(\text{Year})$. For every century, the predicted number of days that the harvest occurred after Aug 31 increased by an additional 0.6 days. However with an r^2 of only 1.4%, the relationship is very weak and the mean number of days (25.9) that the harvest occurred after August 31 may be an equally good predictor. Largest residual (-37.9) occurs for 2003. **3.99** San Francisco could be higher than other cities on lots of variables, but that does not indicate those variables cause AIDS, as association does not imply correlation. Alternative explanations are that San Francisco has a relatively high gay population or relatively high intravenous drug use, and AIDS is more common among gays and IV drug users. **3.101** Stress level, physical activity, wealth, and social contacts are all possible lurking variables. Any one of these variables may contribute to one's physiological and psychological human health as well as be associated with whether or not a person owns a dog. For example, it may be that people who are more active are more likely to own a dog as well as being physically healthier. **3.103** (b). **3.105** (d). **3.107** (c). **3.109 (a)** False. **(b)** True. **(c)** True. **(d)** True. **3.111** The ratio of standard deviations equals 1, so $b = r(1) = r$. **3.113 (a)** When standard deviations are equal, the slope equals the correlation coefficient. If we use the equation from part b in the previous exercise and substitute 0.70 for b, we get $(\hat{y} - \bar{y}) = 0.70(x - \bar{x})$. **(b)** For example, if the midterm class mean were 80 and your score were 90, you'd be 10 points above the mean. If you multiplied that by 0.70, you'd predict that you'd deviate from the mean on y by seven points. If the mean on y also were 80, your predicted score would be 87. Thus, your predicted score is closer to the mean.

Chapter 4

4.1 (a) Explanatory is whether or not the automated call was placed to the phone on the right ear; response is a specific type of brain activity while the call is being received. **(b)** Experimental; the researchers controlled via randomization to determine whether the call to a given participant would be received during the first PET scan or the second. **4.3 (a)** Response variable – weight loss (weight after 1 year minus weight before experiment). Explanatory variable – low-fat vs. low-carb diet. **(b)** An experimental study. The subjects were randomized by the researchers into one of the two groups. **(c)** No. This is an issue of generalizability. Because patients with heart disease or diabetes were excluded from the study, it is inappropriate to say that this applied to *everyone*. **4.5** For example, it is possible that schools that institute drug testing are those in higher crime areas than are those that did not choose to use drug testing. **4.7 (a)** Explanatory variable – language used (native vs. foreign). Response variable – saving self vs. sacrificing self. **(b)** Observational – no assignment of treatments was made by the researchers; the researchers simply observed the language choice made by the subjects and the response. **(c)** No, the reason someone chooses to speak a foreign language (i.e., his or her global awareness or higher education level) might be the true cause of the choice they made. **4.9 (a)** Observational study; **(b)** Observational study; **(c)** Experiment. **4.11** The seat belt incident might be the exception, rather than what is typical. Death rates are in fact higher for those who do not wear seat belts. **4.13 (a)** An observational study – no assignment of treatments was made by the researchers; the researchers simply observed current habits of the subjects. **(b)** Response variable – weight gain. Explanatory variables – Exercise habits and caloric intake. **(c)** No, it demonstrates a correlation, but an experiment would be needed to show causation. **(d)** Motherhood leads to less exercise, eating more, and a more sedentary lifestyle. **4.15 (a)** PV, PS, PT, PA, VS, VT, VA, ST, SA, TA. **(b)** 1/10. **(c)** 4/10. **4.17** Number the students from 1 to 74. In the *Random Numbers* app, keep the minimum at 1, set the maximum to 74 and the numbers to generate to 5, select Sampling Without Replacement, and press Generate.

The five numbers randomly generated correspond to the five students selected. **4.19** Response bias. **4.21** The first comment is valid; the second comment is not. If the information in the entire collection of ratings is unreliable, no type of sampling will make it reliable. **4.23 (a)** More than 75% of Americans say no when asked, "Would you favor a law giving police the power to decide who may own a firearm?" **(b)** Both statements are leading. **4.25 (a)** All adults in the United States. **(b)** It is almost impossible to ask all adults in the United States their opinions. A random sample gives a reliable estimate of this value with a much smaller set of people. **(c)** Those who chose to respond might feel more strongly than those who did not respond. **4.27 (a)** Those who don't admit to being in an extramarital affair might spend more money to hide the fact. Therefore this estimate may be too low. **(b)** If people lied about how much money they spent on an affair, it seems likely that they would underestimate the amount spent, to assuage their guilt. **4.29 (a)** Not all parts of the population have representation (because they may not be subscribers). **(b)** Instead of random sampling, the newspaper used the 1,000 people who subscribed the longest, who were probably the oldest and most conservative in terms of retirement planning. **(c)** Those who take the time to respond might not be representative. A large percentage of people did not respond. **(d)** The question seems to go out of the way to remind readers of volatility of stocks as of late. **4.31 (a)** Experiment; subjects are randomly assigned to treatments. **(b)** Among the possible answers: unethical, impossible to ensure that subjects do as assigned and smoke or not smoke according to the assignment, too long to wait for answer. **4.33 (a)** Response variable: whether the wart was successfully removed; explanatory variable: type of treatment for removing the wart (duct tape or the placebo). Experimental units: The 103 patients; treatments: duct-tape therapy and the placebo. **(b)** Difference $= 16\% - 6\% = 10\%$. The proportion of patients who had their wart treated successfully was 10 percentage points higher in the duct-tape group compared to the placebo group. **4.35 (a)** Because there was a control group and an experimental group and the researchers assigned the Facebook users to each group. **(b)** The experimental units are Facebook users. **(c)** Explanatory variable – positively manipulated vs. not manipulated. Response variables – percentages of all words that were positive and percentage of all words that were negative. **(d)** If the participants were informed, they would not have acted authentically. They were likely upset that they were not informed because that violates the requirement of informed consent. **4.37** Without a placebo or a control comparison group, there is no way to separate the placebo effect from the actual effect of the medication. **4.39** The researchers being blinded prohibits them from deliberately biasing the results, for example by intentionally or unintentionally providing extra support to one of the treatment groups. **4.41 (a)** Recruit volunteers (the experimental units) with a history of high blood pressure; randomly assign to one of two treatments: the new drug or the current drug; explanatory: treatment type; response: blood pressure after experimental period. **(b)** To make the study double-blind, the two drugs would have to look identical so that neither the subjects nor the experimenters know what drug the subjects are taking. **4.43 (a)** Generate one number from the numbers 1 to 3, and one number from the numbers 4 and 5, using the *Random Numbers* app. **(b)** Because every sample of size 2 does not have an equal chance of being selected (e.g., samples with two males have probability 0 of being selected). **(c)** 1 in 3; 1 in 2. **4.45 (a)** Each school represents a cluster. Keep sampling from the 20 clusters, one at time and without replacement, until the number of students from the sampled clusters reaches roughly 20%. **(b)** In the *Random Numbers* app, set the minimum to 1 and the maximum to 24 and randomly sample 10 (or even 15) numbers without replacement. Go through the sequence of generated numbers and choose the corresponding school as part of the sample until the number of students included reaches 20% (e.g., if 12 is the first random number in the sequence, then school 12 with its 260 students is included first; if 2 is the second random number in the sequence, then include school 2 with its 423 students, etc.). **(c)** See part b. **4.47** It is possible that people with lung cancer had a different diet than did those without. These people might have eaten out at restaurants quite a bit, consuming more fat, and smoking socially. It could have been the fat and not the smoking that caused lung cancer. **4.49 (a)** Yes; if we look at enough data, some coincidental relationships are bound to be encountered. **(b)** Anticipated results stated in advance are usually more convincing than results that have already occurred. **(c)** Prospective. **4.51 (a)** Explanatory variable: Type

of praise; Treatments: praised for effort vs. praised for intelligence; Response variable: whether they chose a challenging task on the subsequent task; Experimental units: study participants. **(b)** A randomized experiment. **4.53 (a)** No; the researchers are not randomly assigning subjects to living situation. **(b)** Yes; those living with smokers and those not living with smokers. **(c)** Yes; randomization of units to treatments occurs within blocks. **4.55** In an observational study, we observe people in the groups they already are in. In an experiment, we actually assign people to the groups of interest. The major weakness of an observational study is that we can't control (such as by balancing through randomization) other possible factors that might influence the outcome variable. **4.57 (a)** Explanatory is status of protein presence; response is memory status. **(b)** Nonexperimental because the researchers are not assigning any treatments. **(c)** No; either the proteins are present or not; its presence is not something the researchers can control for each patient. **4.59 (a)** State results vary so vastly from nationwide results because fans want their favorite teams to win, which often translates into fans thinking their teams will win. **(b)** Sampling bias. The ESPN poll was a sample of volunteers who chose to visit the website and respond. **4.61** Gun ownership. **4.63 (a)** Yes; sampling bias. **(b)** If the sample is biased due to undercoverage and lack of random sampling, it doesn't matter how big the sample. **4.65 (a)** No, it was done by voluntary response. **(b)** They could send out a survey to all sports fans (perhaps using a cluster sampling method by choosing to sample from each sports stadium). **4.67 (a) (i)** Experiment; **(ii)** Prospective. **(b)** Response variable: presence/absence of myocardial infarction; explanatory variable: treatment group. **4.69 (a)** 72.5% of physicians in the aspirin group exercised vigorously, 72.0% of physicians in the placebo group exercised vigorously; yes. **(b)** Yes.
4.71

Aspirin (Factor 1)

Yes   No

Beta-carotene Yes
(Factor 2)   No

4.73 (a) (i) Randomly assign subjects to one of the two treatments, Coke or Pepsi, and have them rate it on a scale such as 0 to 10. Neither the subject nor the experimenter would know which cola the subject was drinking. (For example, an experimenter with no contact with the subjects could put both types of colas into identical cups; a code could be used to later identify the type of cola.) **(ii)** Randomly assign each subject to drink either Coke or Pepsi first, then to drink the other one, and then to indicate which they prefer. Neither the subject nor the experimenter administering the cola would know which type of cola the subject was drinking. **(b)** The completely randomized design eliminates the possibility that drinking one cola would alter one's preference for the second cola. The matched-pairs design decreases the possible effects of lurking variables because the two groups are made up of the same people. **4.75** Every possible *sample* of a given size does not have an equal chance of being selected. **4.77** Region: stratification; 10 schools: clustering; classrooms: clustering. **4.79** Perhaps any relationship is coincidental, not causal. For example, perhaps those genetically susceptible to acquiring schizophrenia are the same group who especially enjoy marijuana. **4.81** Answers will vary, depending on the study. **4.83** No; due to the volunteer nature of the sample. **4.85** Answers will vary. **4.87 (a)** The sample includes only one cluster. **(b)** Sampling just Fridays is an example of sampling bias (values might be higher than usual because days sampled are at start of weekend). **4.89** This is not a random sampling method. People who approach the street corner are interviewed as they arrive (and as they agree to the interview!), and may not be representative. **4.91 (a)** Such a study would measure how well a treatment works if patients believe in it, rather than how much a treatment works independent of subjects' beliefs about its efficacy. **(b)** Patients might be reluctant to be randomly assigned to one of the treatments because they might perceive it as inferior to another treatment. **(c)** The researcher might feel that all patients should get the

new treatment. **4.93** Since the disease is rare, this proposed study might not sample anyone that gets it. With the case-control study, one would find a certain number of people who already have the rare disease (the cases), and compare the proportion of these people who had received the vaccine to the proportion in a group of controls who did not have the disease. **4.95** Number the babies from 1 to 16. In the app, set the minimum to 1, the maximum to 16, and the number to generate to 8. Press Generate. The eight numbers generated correspond to the babies shown the video with the helpful figure first. **4.97** (b). **4.99** (a). **4.101** (d). **4.103** (b). **4.105** Consider the hint. The mean population family size is 6. If you choose families, the possible values are 2 and 10, each equally likely, and the sampling is not biased. If you choose individuals, the value 2 has probability 2/12 and the value 10 has probability 10/12. You are likely to overestimate the mean size. **4.107** If the estimate is not close, one factor that could be responsible is the fairly small sample size.

Chapter 5

5.1 The long-run relative frequency definition of probability refers to the probability of a particular outcome as the proportion of times that the outcome would occur in a long run of observations. **5.3** No. In the short run, the proportion of a given outcome can fluctuate a lot. **5.5 (a)** 35.9% is the subjective probability that Brazil will win the World Cup. It is not based on a proportion in a long run of trials. **(b)** No. Any event with non-zero probability could occur. Even Algeria could have won the World Cup. **5.7** Disagree. A large sample size could still be biased. **5.9** Subjective; it's not based on previous nuclear wars because none have occurred. **5.11 (b)** About 50. **(c)** The results will depend on the answer to part a. **(d)** 42% of the answers were true. We would expect 50%. They are not necessarily identical, because observed percentages of a given outcome fluctuate in the short run. **(e)** There are some groups of answers that appear nonrandom. For example, there are strings of five trues and eight falses, but this can happen by random variation. **5.13 (a)** {A, B, AB, O}. **(b)** P(A) = 0.40, P(B) = 0.10, P(AB) = 0.05, P(O) = 0.45. **(c) (i)** Each probability is between 0 and 1; **(ii)** 0.4 + 0.1 + 0.05 + 0.45 = 1. **5.15 (a)** 1, 2, 3, 4, 5, 6, 7, 8, 9, and 10. **(b)** 0.10. **(c)** 10(0.10) = 1. **5.17 (a)** 2^{10} = 1,024. **(b)** Getting none of the questions wrong. **(c)** 1 − 1/1,024 = 0.999. **5.19 (a)** BBB, BBG, BGB, GBB, BGG, GBG, GGB, GGG. **(b)** 1/8. **(c)** 3/8. **(d)** 6/8 or 3/4. **5.21** 20 heads has probability (1/2) to the 20th power, which is 1/1,048,576 = 0.000001. Risk of a one in a million death: 1/1,000,000 = 0.000001. **5.23 (a)** YS; YD; NS; and ND. **(b) (i)** 0.004; **(ii)** 0.284. **(c)** 0.003. **(d)** Answer would have been P(N and D) = P(N) × P(D) = (0.004)(0.284) = 0.001. This indicates that chance of death depends on seat belt use since 0.001 is not equal to 0.003. **5.25 (b)** If A and B were independent events, P(A and B) = P(A) × P(B). Since P(A and B) > P(A)P(B), A and B are not independent. The probability of responding yes on global warming and less on future fuel use is higher than what is predicted by independence. **5.27 (a)** There are eight possible outcomes. Answer is tree diagram. **(b)** 0.488. **(c)** They assumed independence, but that might not be so (e.g., three customers are friends, or three members of the same family). **5.29 (a)** P(B|S). **(b)** P(B^C|S^C). **(c)** P(S^C|B^C). **(d)** P(S|B). **5.31 (a)** 0.7599. **(b)** 0.3299. **(c)** 0.1579. **5.33 (a)** 0.004. **(b) (i)** 0.001; **(ii)** 0.010. **(c)** Neither P(D|wore seat belt) nor P(D|didn't wear seat belt) equals P(D); specifically, 0.001 and 0.010 are different from 0.004. Thus, the events are not independent.
5.35 (b)

	Identified as Spam by ASG	
Spam	Yes	No
Yes	7,005	835
No	48	

(b) 7,005/(7,005 + 835) = 0.8935. **(c)** 7,005/(7,005 + 48) = 0.9932. **5.37 (a)** 6/4,004 = 0.0015. **(b)** No, P(NEG|D) = 6/54 = 0.111. **5.39 (a)** 147/317 = 46%. **(b) (i)** 69/146 = 47%; **(ii)** 78/171 = 46%. **(c)** The estimated probability for an adult to be very happy is 46%. The estimated probability for an adult to be very happy, given that the adult identifies as

female is also 46%, so we have P(very happy) = P(very happy | female), indicating independence between the events {very happy} and {female}. **5.41 (a)** 0.30. **(b) (i)** 0.40; **(ii)** 0.40. **(c)** No; the probability that he will make the second shot depends on whether he made the first. **5.43** Statements (b) and (c). **5.45 (a)** P(C and A)/P(A) = (1/4)/(1/2) = (1/2). **(b)** No; C implies A. **(c)** P(C and B)/P(B) = (1/4)/(3/4) = (1/3). **(d)** The event "at least one child is female" includes more outcomes than the event "first child is female." **5.47** 0.9329. **5.49** Each student can be matched with 24 other students, for a total of 25(24) pairs. But this considers each pair twice (e.g., student 1 with student 2, and student 2 with student 1), so the answer is 25(24)/2 = 300. **5.51** (13/52)(12/51)(11/50) = 0.0129. **5.53** The explanation should discuss the context of the huge number of possible random occurrences that happen in one's life, and the likelihood that at least some will happen (and appear coincidental) just by chance. **5.55 (a)** False. Sampling without replacement: (26/52) × (25/51) × (24/50) = 0.118. **(b)** No. Outcome of second card drawn depends on outcome of first card drawn. If the first card drawn was red, then P(B) = 25/51. If the first card drawn was not red, then P(B) = 26/51. The probability of B depends on whether event A has happened or not. **(c)** Now, part a is true, and for part b the answer is yes because P(B) = P(B|A) = 26/52. **5.57 (a)** The first answer is a tree diagram. **(b)** P(POS) = P(S and POS) + P(S^c and POS) = 0.0086 + 0.1188 = 0.1274. **(c)** 0.068. **(d)** They are calculated by multiplying the proportion for each branch by the total number. The proportion of positive tests with breast cancer is 1/(1 + 12) = 0.08. **5.59 (a)** Of the 100,000 who suffer abuse, 40 + 5 = 45 are killed; 5 of those 45 are killed by someone other than the partner. **(b)** 99,955 and 40. **(c)** They differ because the number who are abused is much larger than the number killed, whereas of all those killed, most are killed by the partner. **5.61 (a)** P(Innocent|Match) = P(Innocent and Match)/P(Match) = 0.0000005/ 0.4950005 = 0.000001. **(b)** P(Innocent|Match) = P(Innocent and Match)/ P(Match) = 0.00000099/0.00990099 = 0.0001. When the probability of being innocent is higher, there's a larger probability of being innocent given a match. **(c)** P(Innocent|Match) can be much different from P(Match|Innocent). **5.63 (b)** (0.95) × (0.95) × (0.95) ... × (0.95) = a grand total of twenty 0.95s (or 0.95^{20}) = 0.36. **5.65 (a) (i)** Game over after 7 rolls, time = 7×4 = 28 sec.; **(ii)** game over after 9 rolls, time = 9×3 = 27 sec. **(b)** For us, the rapid succession strategy was faster in 16 out of the 20 games simulated, for a probability of 16/20 = 80%. **5.67** The gender of a child is independent of the previous children's genders; the chance is still 1/2. **5.69 (a)** There are 18 possible meals (2 × 3 × 3 × 1) = 18. Tree diagram is part of answer. **(b)** No; some menu options would be more popular than others. **5.71 (a)** 0.8142. **(b)** 0.6629. **(c)** That the responses of the two subjects are independent; married couples share many beliefs. **5.73 (a)** 8; tree diagram is part of answer. **(b)** 0.125. **(c)** 0.343. **(d)** Three friends are likely to be similar on many characteristics that might affect performance. **5.75 (a)** 0.84. **(b)** 0.70. **5.77 (a)** The percentages 31% and 1% are conditional probabilities. The 31% is conditioned on the event that the teen says that parents are never present at the parties. The 1% is conditioned on the event that the teen says that parents are present at the parties. For both percentages, the event to which the probability refers is a teen reporting that marijuana is available at the parties.
(b)

| | Parents Present | |
Marijuana Available	Yes	No
Yes	9	133
No	860	295

(c) 860/(860 + 295) = 0.74. **5.79 (a)** (1,1), (1,2), (1,3), (1,4), (1,5), (1,6), (2,1), (2,2), (2,3), (2,4), (2,5), (2,6), (3,1), (3,2), (3,3), (3,4), (3,5), (3,6), (4,1), (4,2), (4,3), (4,4), (4,5), (4,6), (5,1), (5,2), (5,3), (5,4), (5,5), (5,6), (6,1), (6,2), (6,3), (6,4), (6,5), (6,6). **(b)** (1,1), (2,2), (3,3), (4,4), (5,5), and (6,6); 0.167. **(c)** (1,6), (2,5), (3,4), (4,3), (5,2), and (6,1); 0.167. **(d) (i)** 0; **(ii)** 0.333; **(iii)** 0. **(e)** A and B are disjoint. You cannot roll doubles that add up to seven. **5.81** 0.80. **5.83** 0.67. **5.85 (a)** This strategy is a poor one; the chance of an even slot is the same on each spin of the wheel. **(b)** (18/38) to the 26th

power, which is essentially 0. **(c)** No; events that seem highly coincidental are often not so unusual when viewed in the context of *all* the possible random occurrences at all times. **5.87** False negatives: test indicates that an adult smoker does not have lung cancer when he or she does have lung cancer. False positives: test indicates the presence of lung cancer when there is none. **5.89 (b)** 0.048; because so few people have this cancer, most of the positive tests will be false. **5.91 (c)** 0.999. **(d)** A positive result is more likely to be in error when the prevalence is lower, as relatively more of the positive results are for people who do not have the condition. Tree diagrams or contingency tables are part of the answer. **5.93** Answers will vary. **5.95 (a)** The cumulative proportion of heads approaches 0.50 with larger numbers of flips, illustrating the law of large numbers and the long-run relative frequency definition of probability. **(b)** The outcome will be similar to that in part a, with the cumulative proportion of 3 or 4 approaching one third with larger numbers of rolls. **5.97 (a)** 0.545. **(b)** 0.505. **(c)** 0.500; as *n* increases, the cumulative proportion tends toward 0.50. **5.99 (1)** Specificity: if pregnant, 99% chance of a positive test. **(2)** Sensitivity: if not pregnant, 99% chance of a negative test. **(3)** 99% chance of pregnancy given a positive test. **(4)** 99% chance of not pregnant given a negative test. **5.101 (a)** 2.4%. **(b)** Multiply (1) probability of getting a high school degree by (2) probability of getting a college degree once you had a high school degree by (3) probability of getting a master's once you had the earlier degrees by (4) probability of getting a Ph.D. once you had the earlier degrees. **(c)** 0.06. **5.103** The event of a person bringing a bomb is independent of the event of any other person bringing a bomb. **5.105** Conditioning on an event such as Sept. 11, 2001, the probability of dying while flying seems higher than the probability of dying while driving. However, overall, the probability of dying while driving in a car is higher than the probability of dying while flying in an airplane. **5.107** (c) and (d). **5.109** (e). **5.111** (b). **5.113** False. **5.115** When two events are not independent, P(A and B) = P(A) × P(B|A). If we think about (A and B), as one event, then P[C and (A and B)] = P(A and B) × P(C|A and B). If we replace P(A and B) with its equivalent, P(A) × P(B|A), we see that: P(A and B and C) = P(A) × P(B|A) × P(C|A and B). **5.117 (b)** The simulated probability should be close to 1. **5.119** Answers will vary.

Chapter 6

6.1 (a) Uniform distribution; P(1) = P(2) = P(3) = P(4) = P(5) = P(6) = 1/6. **(b)** There will be a probability for each *x* from 2 through 12; for example, there are three rolls that add up to four {(1,3), (2,2) (3,1)}; thus, the probability of four is 3/36 = 0.083. **(c)** 0 ≤ P(x) ≤ 1; and ΣP(x) = 1. **6.3 (a)** All are between 0 and 1 and they sum to 1. **(b)** 0.4083. **(c)** Over the course of many at-bats, the average number of bases per at-bat is 0.4083. **6.5 (a)** P(4) = 0.20, P(3) = 0.40, P(2) = 0.30, P(1) = 0.10. **(b)** 2.7. **6.7 (a)** 0.001. **(b)** P(0) = 0.999, P(500) = 0.001. **(c)** 0.999(0) + 0.001(500) = 0.50. **(d)** The expected winnings in each game is 0.50, thus in terms of expected values we are indifferent between Pick 3 and Pick 4. **6.9** For each wager, the expected profit is μ = −0.53. Wager on 23: Variance σ² = (350 − (−0.53))²(1/38) + (−10 − (−0.53))²(37/38) = 3,320.8. Standard deviation σ = √3,320.8 = 57.6. Wager on black: Variance σ² = (10 − (−0.53))²(18/38) + (−10 − (−0.53))²(20/38) = 99.7. Standard deviation σ = √99.7 = 10.0. If risk averse, perhaps prefer wager with smaller standard deviation of ($10 on black). If risk tolerant, perhaps prefer wager with larger standard deviation ($10 on 23). **6.11 (a)** P($80,000) = 0.70, P($50,000) = 0.20, P($20,000) = 0.10. **(b)** 0.30. **(c)** $68,000. **(d)** P($77,000) = 0.70, P($47,000) = 0.20, P($37,000) = 0.10; μ = $67,000. **6.13 (a)**

x	P(*x*)
$90	0.50
$120	0.20
$130	0.30

$\mu = 108$. The expected selling price for the sale of a drill is $108. **(b)** $\mu = 110$. **(c)** Original Pricing: Variance $\sigma^2 = (90 - 108)^2(0.5) + (120 - 108)^2(0.2) + (130 - 108)^2(0.3) = 336$, standard deviation $\sigma = \sqrt{336} = 18.3$ dollars. New Pricing: Variance $\sigma^2 = (90 - 110)^2(0.3) + (110 - 110)^2(0.4) + (130 - 110)^2(0.3) = 240$, standard deviation $\sigma = \sqrt{240} = 15.5$ dollars. The new strategy has the smaller standard deviation and results in sale prices closer to the mean in the long run. The new strategy gives higher mean profit, in the long run. **6.15 (a)** The response could fall anywhere within an interval, i.e., exactly 1 hour or 1.835 hours or 2.07 hours. **(b)** Because TV watching was measured to the nearest integer. The histograms then display the frequencies of the rounded (to the nearest integer) values obtained in the sample. **(c)** The two smooth curves would represent the approximate (based on the histograms) shape of the probability distribution for TV watching in the population if we could measure it in a continuous manner. Then, the area under the curve above an interval would represent the probability of an observation falling in that interval. **6.17 (a)** 0.251. **(b)** 0.383. **6.19 (a)** $0.9495 - 0.0505 = 0.899$, which rounds to 0.90. **(b)** $0.9951 - 0.0049 = 0.9902$, which rounds to 0.99. **(c)** $0.7486 - 0.2514 = 0.4972$, which rounds to 0.50. **6.21 (a)** Divide by two for amount in each tail, 0.005. Subtract from 1.0 for cumulative probability, 0.995. Look up this probability on Table A to find the z-score of 2.58. **(b)** (a) 1.96. (b) 1.645; graph is part of answer. **6.23 (a)** 0.67. **(b)** 1.645. **6.25 (a)** 1.19. **(b)** 0.12. **(c)** 0.79. **(d)** 141.5. **6.27 (a)** $z = (1,000 - 673)/556 = 0.59$ has a cumulative probability of 0.72. The probability that household electricity use was greater than 1,000 kilowatt-hours is $1 - 0.72$ or 0.28. **(b)** No, because electricity use $= 0$ gives a minimum possible z-score of $(0 - 673)/556 = -1.21$. **6.29 (a) (i)** 0.106; **(ii)** 0.894. **(b)** 137.3. **(c)** 62.7. **6.31 (a)** $z = 3$, which is unusually high (99.9% of observations fall below that level). **(b)** 71.3 percentile. **(c)** These are similar to the percentages within 1, 2, or 3 standard deviations for the normal distribution. **6.33** $z_{joe} = 1$, $z_{kate} = 0.851$; in terms of math scores, Joe is better. **6.35 (a)** S $=$ successful match, F $=$ no match; Sample space: SSS, SSF, SFS, SFF, FSS, FSF, FFS, FFF, with probabilities $(0.1)^3$, $(0.1)^2(0.9)^1$, $(0.1)^2(0.9)^1$, $(0.1)^1(0.9)^2$, $(0.1)^2(0.9)^1$, $(0.1)^1(0.9)^2$, $(0.1)^1(0.9)^2$, $(0.9)^3$. Probabilities for $x = 0, 1, 2, 3$ are $P(0) = (0.9)^3$, $P(1) = (3)(0.1)^1(0.9)^2$, $P(2) = (3)(0.1)^2(0.9)^1$, $P(3) = (0.1)^3$. **(b)** Same as part a, e.g., $P(1) = (3!/[1!2!])\,(0.1)^1(0.9)^{3-1} = (3)(0.1)^1(0.9)^2$. **6.37 (d)** The graph in part a is symmetric, as is the case anytime $p = 0.50$. **(e)** The graph in part c is most heavily skewed; the graph with $p = 0.01$ would be even more skewed. **6.39 (a)** Each trial ($=$ bid) can result in two outcomes (win/lose), trials are independent, and on each trial there is a constant probability of 25% of winning. The number of winning bids is binomial. **(b)** $P(2) = (4!/[2!2!])\,(0.25)^2(0.75)^{4-2} = 0.211$. **(c)** 0.949. **(d)** 0.051. **6.41 (a)** 0.002. **(b)** 0.027. **6.43 (a)** $\mu = 360$, $\sigma = 6$. **(b)** (342, 378) or within 3 standard deviations of the mean. **(c)** (0.855, 0.945). **6.45 (a)** Binary data (voted for proposition or not), probability of success for each trial $p = 0.50$ is constant from trial to trial, and the trials are independent (one individual's vote unlikely to affect another's vote); $n = 3,000$; $p = 0.50$. **(b)** $\mu = 1,500$, $\sigma = 27.4$. **(c)** (1,418, 1,582). **(d)** p is actually higher than 0.50. **6.47 (a)** 68.04. **(b) (i)** 2.42%; **(ii)** First, find the standard deviation $\sigma = \sqrt{162(0.42)(1 - 0.42)} = 6.2$. With $\mu = 68.04$, $P(81)$ becomes 1.83%. **(c)** Different players, especially the pitchers; different stadiums, weather, etc. **6.49** No; the trials are not independent, and n is greater than 10% of the population size. **6.51 (a)** The independence assumption is not plausible since families tend to make decisions about church attendance together. **(b)** The 100 votes are not randomly selected from the population and do not constitute a random sample. **(c)** The probability of success (selecting a female) doesn't stay the same from trial to trial, because once a female is selected, the probability of selecting another female changes (sampling without replacement). **6.53 (a)** Probability Distribution for Straight: $P(-1) = 999/1,000$, $P(499) = 1/1,000$; Probability Distribution for Boxed: $P(-1) = 994/1,000$, $P(79) = 6/1,000$, since there are 6 three-digit numbers containing 5, 1, and 4. **(b)** Straight: -0.50 or -50 cents; Boxed: -0.52 or -52 cents. **(c)** Straight (but probability of winning anything is higher for boxed). **(d)** Straight, because the average distance from the mean seems much larger. **(e)** Straight: 15.8 dollars; Boxed: 6.2 dollars. **6.55 (a)** Probability distribution: $P(0) = 0.994$, $P(45.50) = 0.006$. **(b)** Probability distribution: $P(0) = 0.999$, $P(45.50) = 0.001$. **(c)** The first, because the expected

winnings are higher. **6.57 (a)** Probability distribution: $P(0) = 0.999999$, $P(100,000) = 0.000001$. **(b)** 0.10. **(c)** Because the flyer's return on each $1 spent averages to only $0.10. **6.59 (a)** 1.01. **(b)** smaller. **6.61 (a)** 1.96. **(b)** 2.58; answer includes graph. **6.63 (a)** 2.33. **(b) (i)** 1.28; **(ii)** 2.33. **6.65** 0.31. **6.67 (a)** 0.0912, 0.092 with table. **(b)** 0.0912, 0.092 with table. **(c)** 0.82. **(d)** 9.96 inches. **6.69 (a)** 39.2%. **(b)** 24.8%. **(c)** $18,187. **6.71 (a)** Yes, changing scale does not change the distribution. **(b)** Mean $= 182.9$, standard deviation $= 10.2$. **(c)** 0.05. **6.73** 0.6561. **6.75 (a)** Head (success) $=$ a correct guess [on any trial]; tail (failure) $=$ an incorrect guess [on any trial]. **(b)** Because with random guessing, she has a constant probability of 0.2 of guessing the right number, for each of the three trials. **(c)** Trials are not affected by the outcomes of previous trials. **6.77 (a)** 0.75 since it rains at least once in 3 out of the 4 equally likely outcomes: RR, RD, DR, DD.

(b) $\quad 1 - P(0) = 1 - \dfrac{2!}{0!(2-0)!}0.5^0(1 - 0.5)^{2-0} = 1 - 0.25 = 0.75$.

6.79 (a) Binary outcome (like or not like), constant probability of success (liking message), responses from users are independent, $n = 15,000,000$, $p = 0.00001$. **(b)** $\mu = 150$, $\sigma = 12.25$. **(c)** Yes, expected number of successes and expected number of failures both larger than 15. **(d)** (113,187). **(e)** Users may not have the same probability of liking the message. Responses may not be independent. (If you see your friend liking the message, you may be more inclined to like it, too, if you received it.) **6.81 (a)** Binomial. **(b)** Mean $= 4.0$, standard deviation $= 2.0$. **(c)** 0.018. **6.83 (d)** $P(3) = 0.25$, $P(4) = 0.375$, $P(5) = 0.375$. **6.85** The median would be the score that falls at 50%; median $= 4$. **6.87 (a)** 0.04. **(b)** 0.75; each day's take must be independent of every other day's take. **6.89** Mean $= 980$, standard deviation $= 22$; since 800 is more than 3 standard deviations below the expected mean, the probability of a female birth in this town is probably less than 0.49. **6.91** (d). **6.93** True. **6.95 (a)** Normal (shape not affected) with mean $23,800(1.06) = 25,228$ and standard deviation $4,380(1.06) = 4,643$. **(b)** Normal (shape not affected) with mean $23,800 + 199 = 23,999$ and standard deviation 4,380. **6.97 (a)** The probability of rolling doubles is 1/6. The outcome on the second die has a 1/6 chance of matching the first. To have doubles occur first on the second roll, you'd have to have no match on the first, a 5/6 chance. You'd then have to have a match on the second roll, a 1/6 chance. The probability of both occurring is $(5/6)(1/6)$. For no doubles until the third roll, the first and the second roll would not match, a 5/6 chance for each, followed by doubles on the third, a 1/6 chance. The probability of all of three events is $(5/6)^2(1/6)$. **(b)** By the logic in part a, $P(4) = (5/6)(5/6)$, $(5/6)(1/6)$, or $(5/6)^3(1/6)$. By extension, we could calculate $P(x)$ for any x by $(5/6)^{x-1}(1/6)$. **6.99 (a)** 5.88. **(b)** Assuming win probability of 50% for every game and independence may not be reasonable. **(c)** $73\,(0.3125) = 22.8$.

Chapter 7

7.1 (a) Although the population proportion is 0.53, by the random nature of the voters included in the exit poll it is unlikely that exactly 53 out of the 100 polled will vote yes. Sample proportions will vary from sample to sample, but it is more likely to get a sample proportion close to 0.53 than far away from 0.53. **(b)** In our simulation, we got a minimum of 0.43 and a maximum of 0.59. **(c)** The sampling distribution is bell shaped, centered at 0.53, and with a standard deviation of 0.05. **(d)** The predicted standard deviation is $\sqrt{0.53(1-0.53)/100} = 0.05$, which is essentially the same as the standard deviation of the 10,000 simulated sample proportions. **(e)** It is still bell shaped, but now centered at 0.70. (The standard deviation also changes slightly, from about 0.050 to 0.046.) **7.3 (a)** Mean $= p = 0.10$, standard deviation $= \sqrt{0.10(1 - 0.10)/500} = 0.0134$. **(b)** Mean $= p = 0.10$, standard deviation $= \sqrt{0.10(1 - 0.10)/2,000} = 0.0067$. **(c)** Mean $= p = 0.10$, standard deviation $= \sqrt{0.10(1 - 0.10)/125} = 0.0268$. As the sample size gets larger (i.e., from 500 to 2,000), the standard deviation decreases (in fact, it is only half as large). As the sample size gets smaller (i.e., from 500 to 125), the standard deviation increases (in fact, it becomes twice as large). **7.5 (a)** $P(1) = 0.409$ and $P(0) = 0.591$. **(b)** Mean $= 0.409$, standard deviation $= 0.008$. **7.7 (a)** Mean $= 0.239$, st.dev. $= 0.043$. **(b)** Approximately normal, because $100(0.239) = 23.9$ and $100(1 -$

0.239) = 76.1 are both larger than 15. **(c)** Yes, very unusual. The z-score for a proportion of 40% equals $z = (0.4 - 0.239)/0.043 = 3.74$. Falling more than 3.7 standard deviations above the mean is highly unusual (chances: 0.01%) under a normal distribution. **(d)** No, because $100(0.02) = 2$, not larger than 15. **7.9 (a)** $P(0 \text{ out of } 3) = 27/64$, $P(1 \text{ out of } 3) = 27/64$, $P(2 \text{ out of } 3) = 9/64$, $P(3 \text{ out of } 3) = 1/64$. **(b)** Mean = 0.25, standard deviation = 0.25. **(c)** For $n = 10$, mean = 0.25, standard deviation = 0.137; for $n = 100$, mean = 0.25, standard deviation = 0.0433; the mean stays the same and the standard deviation gets smaller as n gets larger. **7.11 (a)** The population distribution is based on the x values of the 14,201 students, 95.1% of which are 1 and 4.9% of which are 0, so $P(0) = 0.049$, $P(1) = 0.951$. **(b)** The data distribution is based on the x values in the sample of size 350 of which 330 are 1 and 20 are 0, so the data distribution has $P(0) = 20/350 = 0.0571$ and $P(1) = 330/350 = 0.9429$. **(c)** Mean = 0.951, standard deviation = $\sqrt{0.951(1 - 0.951)/350} = 0.0115$. It represents the probability distribution of the sample proportion of the number of full-time students in a random sample of 350 students. Graph is bell shaped and centered at 0.951. **(d)** Population and sampling distribution graph look the same. Data distribution may look different, since based on a different sample. **7.13 (a)** Population distribution. **(b)** For a population proportion of 0.9 or 0.95, with $n = 30$, the sampling distribution does not look bell shaped but rather skewed to the left. **(c)** Because we expect the bell shape to occur only when $n(p)$ is larger than 15, which is not the case here. **7.15 (a)** Although the mean of the population distribution is 70, by random variability (as expressed by the population standard deviation), the sample mean of a sample of size 12 will sometimes be smaller or larger than 70. **(b)** The simulated sampling distribution is bell shaped and centered at 70. Almost all sample means fall between a score of about 60 to 80. **(c)** It is still bell shaped and centered at 70 but now has smaller variability. Now, almost all sample means fall within about 65 to 75. **7.17 (b) (i)** Mean = 3.50, standard deviation = 1.21; **(ii)** Mean = 3.50, standard deviation = 0.31. As n increases, the sampling distribution becomes more normal in shape and has less variability around the mean. **(c)** For $n = 2$, we expect: mean = 3.5, st.dev. = 1.2; For $n = 30$, we expect: mean = 3.5, st.dev. = 0.31. **7.19 (a)** The population distribution of median college debt of graduates from U.S. colleges is left skewed, with a population mean of $23,710 and a population standard deviation of $5,920. **(b)** The distribution of median college debt in the sample of size 30 (the data distribution) is left skewed, with a mean of $25,250 and a standard deviation of 5,520. (Your simulation results will vary.) **(c)** The sampling distribution is bell shaped (approximately normal), with a mean of $23,700 and a standard deviation of $1,070. (Your simulation results will vary somewhat.) **(d)** Yes. The sampling distribution for the sample mean has mean equal to the population mean ($23,710) and standard deviation equal to $5,920/\sqrt{30} = 1,080$. These theoretical values are close to the ones obtained from the simulation in part c. **(e)** Yes. The CLT predicts an approximate normal distribution of the sampling distribution for large sample sizes, and the simulated sampling distribution looks approximately normal. **7.21 (a)** Since σ is almost as large as μ and 0 is a lower bound only 1.33 standard deviations below the mean, the distribution is right skewed. **(b)** With a random sample, the data distribution picks up the characteristics from the population distribution, so we anticipate it as right skewed. **(c)** With $n = 45$, the sampling distribution of sample mean is approximately normal by the Central Limit Theorem. **7.23 (a)** Mean = 8.20, standard deviation = 0.30. **(b)** 0.994. **7.25 (a)** Mean = 130, standard deviation = 3.46. **(b)** Normal. If the population distribution is normal, then the sampling distribution is normal for any sample size. **(c)** 0.002. **7.27 (a)** Mean is $74,550 and standard deviation is $19,872; likely skewed right because of a few large salaries. **(b)** $75,207 and $18,901; shape similar to population distribution. **(c)** $74,550 and $1,987; approximately normal distribution due to Central Limit Theorem. **(d)** $100,000 is barely one standard deviation above the population mean, but it is more than 12 standard deviations above the mean of the sampling distribution of the sample mean. **7.29** For $n = 2$ and $n = 5$, the sampling distribution of the sample mean is right skewed and far from bell shaped. However, for $n = 30$, the sampling distribution looks approximately normal. As n increases from 2 to 5 to 30, the variability of the

sampling distribution gets smaller and smaller and the shape of the sampling distribution approaches a normal shape. **7.31** Part f. **7.33 (a)** We obtained (results will vary): 13,744, 14,353, 14,258, 14,228, and 12,960. (Results may vary.) **(b)** The bootstrap distribution of the sample mean is bell shaped, with a mean of about 13,600 and a standard deviation of about 780. (Results may vary slightly.) **(c)** No, the Central Limit Theorem predicted the approximately normal shape of the distribution of the sample mean. **(d)** The sample mean payment of $13,620 is likely to fall within 2 or at most 3 standard deviations of the population mean payment, that is, within $2 \times (780) = \$1,560$ or at most $3(780) = \$2,340$ of the population mean. **7.35** Sample, with replacement, from the original sample 100 times to obtain one bootstrap sample. Compute the sample standard deviation s for this bootstrap sample. Repeat these two steps a large number of times to obtain thousands of values for s. The distribution of these thousands of values for s is the bootstrap distribution for the sample standard deviation. **7.37 (a)** The distribution is basically bell shaped, with a very slight skew to the right, with a mean of about 195 BTU and a standard deviation of about 19.7 BTU. (Results may vary slightly.) **(b)** Yes, it is. The sampling distribution, as approximated by the bootstrap, looks approximately normal. **7.39 (a)** The scatterplot reveals an approximate linear relationship that is positive, with a correlation coefficient of $r = 0.73$. However, the relationship is weaker (the scatter is much larger) for students with weekly exercise hours of 15 hours or longer at the beginning. Student 93 may be an outlier, with 18 exercise hours per week at the beginning, but only 4 hours at the end. **(b)** The bootstrap distribution looks fairly bell shaped, with a mean of 0.73 and a standard deviation of about 0.047. **(c)** The correlation changes from 0.73 to 0.75 which is also the new mean of the bootstrap distribution. The standard deviation of the bootstrap distribution changes very slightly to 0.043. The distribution is still bell shaped. **7.41 (a)** Mean = 0.1667, standard deviation = 0.0373. **(b)** Yes; 8.9 standard deviations. **(c)** Set of 0s and 1s describing whether an American has blue eyes (1) or not (0), 17% 1s and 83% 0s; set of 50 0s and 50 1s describing whether the students in your class have blue eyes or not; probability distribution of the sample proportion, having mean = 0.1667 and standard deviation = 0.0373. **7.43 (a)** Mean = 0.45, standard deviation = 0.144. **(b)** 1.39. **(c)** $3/12 = 0.25$ is only 1.39 standard deviations below the mean. **7.45 (a)** 15.9% (sampling distribution is approx. normal with mean 0.04 and standard deviation 0.010). **(b)** 79.8% (sampling distribution is approx. normal with mean 0.06 and standard deviation 0.012). **7.47 (a)** No; many games have zero or one home runs while a few have three or four or more home runs. The random variable is discrete, and the normal distribution is for continuous random variables. **(b)** Approximately normal with mean = 1 and standard deviation = 0.079. **(c)** Essentially 0. **7.49** 0.9545. **7.51 (a)** No, X is discrete where the standard deviation is as big as the mean and the min value of 0 is only 1 standard deviation below mean, indicating skewness. **(b)** Approximately normal with mean = 1.0 and standard deviation = 0.1. Since $n = 100$, we can expect sampling distribution to be approximately normal even if population distribution is skewed. **7.53 (a)** The distribution for the end of month balance of the 300 accounts is extremely right skewed, with a median of $962, a mean of $1,823, an IQR of $1,572, and a standard deviation of $2,484. There are a couple of accounts with very large balances of around $150,000. **(b)** We obtained: $1,493, $1,931, $2,023, $1,821, and $1,642. (Results will vary.) **(c)** The bootstrap distribution of the sample mean is approximately normal (or perhaps very slightly right skewed), with a mean of about $1,820 and a standard deviation of about $140. (Results will vary slightly.) **(d)** Yes, the sample size is relatively large, and despite the population distribution seemingly being right skewed, the distribution of the sample mean is approximately normal, as per the Central Limit Theorem. **7.55 (a)** No, the CLT applies to sample means, not sample standard deviations. **(b)** We obtained: $2,386, $2,496, $2,516, $2,685, $2,645. (Results will vary.) **(c)** The bootstrap distribution of the sample standard deviation is bell shaped, with a mean of about $2,460 and a standard deviation of about $290. (Results may vary slightly.) **(d)** We would expect the population standard deviation of all account balances to fall within two or at most three standard deviations, that is within $2(290) = \$580$ or at most $3(290) = \$870$, of the sample standard deviation of $2,480. **7.57** No, the CLT is a statement about the sample mean, not about the sample correlation coefficient. **7.59** Each time a poll is conducted, a sample proportion of those who think the prime minister is doing a good job is calculated. This sample proportion varies from poll to poll, because different people are asked in each poll. The distribution of all these possible sample proportions is called a sampling distribution. It expresses how much the sample proportions fluctuate around the population proportion (the true proportion of all Canadians approving of the prime minister), with the degree of variability around the population proportion being smaller when the sample size is larger. **7.61** This standard deviation tells us how close a typical sample proportion is to the population proportion. **7.63 (a)** Let X = number of people (out of $n = 3$) preferring pizza A. $P(1) = 3(1/2)^1 (1/2)^2 = 3/8$. **(b)** Sample proportion of 0 occurs with probability $P(0) = (1/2)^3 = 1/8$, sample proportion of 2/3 occurs with probability $P(2) = 3(1/2)^3 = 3/8$, sample proportion of 1 occurs with probability $P(3) = (1/2)^3 = 1/8$. **(c)** Use binomial distribution with $n = 4$, $p = 0.5$, and $x = 0, 1, 2, 3$ and 4 to find probabilities for all the possible sample proportions. Sampling distribution of sample proportion: $P(\text{samp. prop.} = 0) = P(0) = 0.0625$, $P(\text{samp. prop.} = 1/4) = P(1) = 0.25$, $P(\text{samp. prop.} = 2/4) = P(2) = 0.375$, $P(\text{samp. prop.} = 3/4) = P(3) = 0.25$, $P(\text{samp. prop.} = 1) = P(4) = 0.0625$. **7.65 (a)** Mean $= 0(1/8) + (1/3)(3/8) + (2/3)(3/8) + 1(1/8) = 0.5$. **(b)** Yes. When we ran the simulations, we got a mean of 0.496 and a standard deviation of 0.289 for the 10,000 simulated sample proportions, almost identical to the theoretical values. **7.67 (a)** The distribution is close to being approximately normal although the tails of the simulated sampling distribution don't quite match the tails of a normal distribution (i.e., observing sample means of 1, 1.5, 5.5,t or 6 seems to be a bit more frequent than predicted by the normal distribution). The sampling distribution is not expected to be normal because the CLT typically requires a larger sample size than 2 for the sampling distribution of the sample mean to be approximately normal. **(b)** In our simulations, we got a mean of 3.52 and a standard deviation of 1.21 for the simulated sampling distribution. These are very close to the theoretical mean and standard deviation of the sampling distribution, which are 3.5 (the population mean) and $\sigma/\sqrt{n} = 1.71/\sqrt{2} = 1.21$. **(c)** With $n = 30$, the histogram representing the sampling distribution is now approximately normal and shows a much smaller standard deviation compared to the case with $n = 2$. **7.69** (b). **7.71** Part d, because $0.5 \pm \sqrt{0.5(1 - 0.5)/50} = (0.36, 0.64)$. **7.73 (a)** Sample mean would always be the same as the population mean, no variability of the sample means. As such, the standard deviation would equal zero. **(b)** Exactly the same. **7.75 (a)** Target line = mean = 500, control limits are 3 standard deviations from the mean, 494 and 506. **(b)** 0.84, normally distributed population. **7.77 (c)** You expect the mean to be close to the population mean of 196. **(d)** You expect the standard deviation to be close to $57.4/\sqrt{9} = 19.1$, which is the standard deviation of the sampling distribution when $n = 9$. **7.79 (b)** This is a sampling distribution, and with ten coins in each sample, the distribution should be closer to a normal distribution than that in part a. It should also have less variability around the mean than the distribution in part a.

Chapter 8

8.1 (a) Proportion with health insurance in population; mean amount spent on insurance by population. **(b)** Sample proportion and sample mean. **8.3 (a)** 0.548. **(b)** (0.518, 0.578). **(c)** A point estimate gives one specific number, such as a mean. An interval estimate gives a range of numbers. **8.5 (a)** 0.90 or 90%. **(b)** It tells us that the true proportion of Germans who find spying unacceptable is likely to be within 4.5 percentage points of 90%. **8.7 (a)** 62.2. **(b)** (57.3, 67.1). **(c)** An interval estimate gives us a sense of the accuracy of the point estimate whereas a point estimate alone does not. **8.9 (a)** 1.5 days. **(b)** The standard error of 0.06, which is the estimated standard deviation of the sampling distribution of the sample mean, estimates by how much the sample mean in samples of this size varies from sample to sample. **(c)** The margin of error of $\pm$ 0.12 tells us how precise the point estimate of 1.5 days is in estimating the population mean. It is likely that the true mean number of days someone feels lonely in the last 7 days is within $\pm$ 0.12 days of 1.5 days. **8.11** Answers will vary. **8.13 (a)** 0.00615. **(b)** 0.00125. **(c)** 0.00245. **(d)** $0.00615 \pm 0.00245 = (0.00370, 0.00861)$. With 95% confidence, we estimate that the proportion

of people receiving the flu shot but still developing the flu is between 0.37% and 0.86%, with a point estimate of 0.61%. **(e)** Yes. The upper limit of the confidence interval is 0.86%, which is less than 1%. **8.15 (a)** Random sample, number of successes and failures both greater than 15; yes. **(b)** (0.89, 0.92). With 95% confidence, we estimate that the proportion of U.S. adults willing to accept cuts in their standard of living to protect the environment is between 89% and 92%, with a point estimate of 90%. Yes, because the lower bound of the interval is above 50%, there is evidence that a majority is willing. **8.17** Use the confidence interval formula with $\hat{p} = 1 - 0.63 = 0.37$, which will yield the interval (0.35, 0.39). Or, simply subtracting the endpoints of the original interval from 1: $1 - (0.61, 0.65) = (35, 0.39)$. **8.19 (a)** 1.645. **(b)** 2.33. **(c)** 3.29. **8.21** Population = all adults in the U.S. identifying as Republicans. With 95% confidence, we estimate that the proportion of those who identify as Republicans and think stem cell research has merit is between 55% and 61%, with a point estimate of 58%. **8.23 (a)** $0.655 + -2.58\sqrt{(0.655 \times 0.345/316)} = -.655 + -0.069 = (0.586, 0.724)$. At the 99% confidence level, a range of plausible values for the population proportion of chicken breast that contain E. coli is 0.586 to 0.724. Yes, I can conclude the proportion of chicken containing E. coli exceeds 50% because all plausible values are above 0.50. **(b)** The 95% confidence interval would be narrower because the margin of error will decrease. The z-score will be 1.96 compared to 2.58 for the 99% confidence interval. **8.25 (a)** Yes; because 0.50 falls outside of the confidence interval of 0.445 to 0.498. **(b)** No; because 0.50 falls in the confidence interval of 0.437 to 0.506. The more confident we want to be, the wider the confidence interval must be. **8.27** The percentage we'd expect would be 95% and 99%, but the actual values may differ a bit because of sampling variability. **8.29** 379. **8.31 (a)** 97. **(b)** 385. **(c)** 664. **(d)** In both cases we need a larger sample size. **8.33 (a)** 1.0. **(b)** 0; no; the sampling distribution is likely to have *some* variability, because the true probability (which determines the exact standard error) is positive. **(c)** (1.0, 1.0); no, because this method works poorly in this case. **(d)** We don't have at least 15 outcomes of each type. Using the small-sample method based on adding 2 outcomes of each type, we estimate with 95% confidence that the proportion is between 0.51 and 1.0 (note, we used 1.0 instead of the calculated value of 1.05, since p cannot exceed 1). **8.35 (a)** $\hat{p} = 0$, $se = 0$. **(b)** (0, 0). No, the true proportion may be very small, but it is larger than zero. (Google sold some glasses.) **(c)** With this small a sample, we expect $500 \times 0 = 0$ successes, which is well below the 15 required for the large sample method to work. Adding 2 to the number of successes and failures (and 4 to n), we get (0, 0.0095) as the interval. **(d)** Yes, because the entire interval is below 0.01. **8.37 (a)** The sample mean 2.51; $0.87\sqrt{530} = 0.038$. **(b)** In the long run, the interval constructed with this method will contain the true mean ideal number of children for males 95% of the time. **(c)** No. The sample means and standard deviations are very similar, and the two intervals almost overlap completely. The means for females and males are very similar. **8.39 (a)** The distribution of weight changes appears left skewed, but there is an outlier on the higher end, with a weight gain of 22 lbs. The average weight change was +7.3 lbs, with a standard deviation of 7.18 pounds. **(b)** $7.18\sqrt{17} = 1.74$ lbs. **(c)** margin of error = t-score $\times (se) = 2.12(1.74) = 3.69$ lbs. **(d)** $\bar{x} \pm$ margin of error = $7.3 \pm 3.69 = (3.6, 11.0)$ rounded. **(e)** With 95% confidence, we estimate that the mean weight change for girls under the family therapy is between 3.6 lbs and 11.0 lbs, with a point estimate of 7.3 lbs. All values in the confidence interval are positive, indicating that the mean weight change is positive. **8.41 (b)** Take a larger sample size or use a smaller level of confidence such as 90%. **(c)** (54.4, 70.0); the multiplier from the t-table gets larger as the level of confidence gets larger. **(d)** Data collected randomly, population distribution is approximately normal. Random sampling assumption is important, but method is robust to violation of normality assumption. **8.43 (a)** We can estimate the population mean weekly number of hours spent emailing to within 0.6 hours. **(b)** With 95% confidence, we estimate that the mean weekly number of hours spent emailing is between 6.5 hours and 7.7 hours, with a point estimate of 7.1 hours. **(c)** In constructing the interval, we need to assume a normal distribution for the weekly number of hours spent emailing. However, for large samples such as this, the normal assumption is not important, because the Central Limit Theorem applies and the sampling distribution of the sample mean is approximately normal. So it is reasonable to assume the confidence interval is valid. **8.45 (a)** Confidence intervals refer to means, not individual scores. **(b)** This should say: "If random samples of 9 women were repeatedly selected, then 95% of the time, *the confidence interval would contain the population mean.*" **(c)** Replace $\bar{x}$ with μ. **(d)** No need to construct confidence intervals when the entire population is sampled. **8.47 (a)** *se* of mean $= 1.45/\sqrt{1,874} = 0.0336$, margin of error $=$ (*t*-score with $df = 1,873)(se) = (1.96)(0.0336) = 0.0659$. Confidence interval is then $\bar{x}(= 4.0624) \pm$ margin of error. **(b)** No, because values up to 4.13 (the upper bound) are plausible values for the mean. **(c) (i)** wider; **(ii)** wider. **8.49 (i)** 41.3; **(ii)** 19.8. Margin of error decreases as n increases. **8.51 (a)** No, there is a large proportion of observations at the single value of 0. Very little, because with large random samples the sampling distribution of the sample mean is approximately normal. **(b)** (8.0, 12.0); yes, because $15 is not in the confidence interval. **8.53 (a)** 246. **(b)** 375. **8.55** Diverse populations (medical doctors making a wide range of incomes) have a wider range of observed values, and thus larger standard deviations, than homogeneous populations (entry-level McDonald's workers all making close to minimum wage). Larger standard deviations result in larger standard errors and wider confidence intervals. **8.57 (a)** No. This is the *se* of the mean, not the median. There is no general formula for the *se* of the median. **(b)** Using the app and 10,000 bootstrap samples, the 95% bootstrap percentile confidence interval is given by (842, 1,131). (Results may vary slightly.) With 95% confidence, we estimate that the median account balance of customers of this bank is between $842 and $1,131, with a point estimate of $962. **8.59** Based on 10,000 bootstrap samples, the 95% percentile bootstrap confidence interval equals (10,600, 15,200). With 95% confidence, we estimate that the median Social Security payments received by California residents is between $10,600 and $15,200, with a point estimate of $13,000. **8.61 (a)** 95% bootstrap percentile CI: (0.42, 0.62). **(b)** With 95% confidence, we estimate that the population correlation coefficient between self-esteem based on one's appearance and self-esteem based on others' approval is between 0.42 and 0.62 among college freshmen, with a point estimate of 0.53. **(c)** This interval does not include 0 as a plausible value for the population correlation coefficient. Because the lower bound equals 0.42, there is evidence for a positive correlation between the two self-esteem variables. **8.63 (a)** Point estimates. **(b)** No, we would need to know the sample sizes on which these percentages are based. **8.65** $1.96\sqrt{0.86(1 - 0.86)/1,667} = 0.017$ and $1.96\sqrt{0.73(1 - 0.73)/1,667} = 0.021$. **8.67** $0.81 \pm 0.018 = (0.792, 0.828)$; with 95% confidence, we estimate that the proportion of Americans believing in life after death is between 79.2% and 82.8%, with a point estimate of 81%. **8.69 (a)** Data were obtained randomly. **(b)** (0.035, 0.045); mainly because of the very large sample size. **(c)** Yes; 10% falls above the highest plausible value in the confidence interval. **8.71** No; because you have data for the entire population; you don't have to estimate it. **8.73 (a)** With 95% confidence, we estimate that the proportion of U.S. adults regularly watching TV shows via streaming is between 41% and 45%, with a point estimate of 43%. **(b)** Wider. To have more confidence, we need a wider interval. Technically, the z score changes from 1.96 to 2.58, resulting in a wider interval. **(c)** Narrower. With 5,000 adults, we have more information, resulting in a smaller standard error for the sample proportion. A smaller standard error leads to a narrower margin of error and thus narrower interval. **8.75 (a)** FALSE (true percentage may be as large as 52%). **(b)** TRUE, because 76% is no longer a plausible value and is outside the confidence interval. **8.77 (a)** 385. **(b)** 601; if we can make an educated guess, we can use a smaller sample size. **8.79** Fewer than 15 successes, use small sample interval: (0, 0.046). Yes, because upper bound is less than 10%. **8.81 (a)** With 95% confidence, we estimate that the mean price for rooms in NYC listed on Airbnb is estimated to fall between $90 and $122, with a point estimate of $106. **(b)** Based on the dot plot and box plot, the distribution of room prices is right skewed and not normally distributed. However, with a relatively large sample size of 50, the normality assumption for the population becomes less important as the *t*-interval is robust to its violations. **(c)** $se = s/\sqrt{n} = 56.4/\sqrt{50} = 7.98$. **(d)** *t*-score (with $df = 49) = 2.01$, $me = 2.01(7.98) = 16.03$. **8.83 (a)** *t*-score $= 2.262, 2.093,$ 2.045, 1.968, 1.961. **(b)** For large df, the *t*-score approaches the *z*-score. **8.85 (a)** ($37,646, $50,022). **(b)** An approximately normal population distribution. **(c)** Not necessarily; the method is robust in terms of the normal distribution assumption. **8.87 (a)** No; the minimum possible value of 0 is

barely more than one standard deviation below the mean, and the mean is quite a bit larger than the median. **(b)** Yes, because meeting the normal population assumption is not critical with such a large random sample size; (19.4, 21.2); With 95% confidence, we estimate that the mean number of years US adults have lived in their current place is between 19.4 and 21.2 years. **8.89 (a)** Mean Buy It Now selling price of all Samsung phones of this type posted on sale on eBay in July 2014. **(b)** $\bar{x} = 557$. **(c)** $s = 37, se = 10.6$. The average deviation of prices from the sample mean of $557 is $37. The average deviation of the sample mean $\bar{y}$ to the population mean μ is $10.6. **(d)** (554, 600). With 95% confidence, we estimate that the average Buy It Now price for this type of smartphone on eBay is between $554 and $600, with a point estimate of $557. **8.91 (a)** Assumes that strongly agree and agree are the same distance apart as strongly disagree and disagree but there is a larger difference between agree and disagree. **(b)** The sample mean is slightly negative, indicating overall slight disagreement with the statement. A mean score of 0 signals a neutral sentiment in the population. The upper bound of the confidence interval for the population mean equals -0.258, so there is evidence that the population as a whole tends to disagree with the statement. **(c)** Consider the proportion who responded in each way. **8.93 (a)** 385; the solution makes the assumption that the standard deviation will be similar now. **(b)** More than $100 because the standard error will be larger than predicted. **(c)** With a larger margin of error, the 95% confidence interval is wider; thus, the probability that the sample mean is within $100 of the population mean is less than 0.95. **8.95** With 95% confidence, we estimate that the median sugar content in breakfast cereals is between 4.5 grams and 12 grams, with a point estimate of 9.5 grams. **8.97 (a)** With 95% confidence, we estimate that the population correlation coefficient relating scores for cognitive and behavioral eating disorders is between 0.63 and 0.79, with a point estimate of 0.72. **(b)** Yes, the confidence interval does not contain 0 (which would indicate no relationship). The lower bound on the population correlation coefficient is 0.63, indicating a relatively strong correlation. **8.99** Answers will vary but will explain the logic behind random sampling and how the margin of error decreases as the sample size increases. **8.101** Running the house. CI $- (0.134, 0.166)$; because 0.50 does not fall in this range, we can conclude that fewer than half of the population agrees with the statement that women should take care of running their homes and leave running the country up to the men. Man as the achiever: CI $= (0.320, 0.364)$; because 0.50 does not fall in this range, we can conclude that fewer than half of the population agrees with the statement that it is better for everyone involved if the man is the achiever outside the home and the woman takes care of the home and the family. Preschool child: CI $= (0.401, 0.447)$; because 0.50 does not fall in this range and all plausible values are less than 0.50, we can conclude that fewer than half of the population agrees with the statement that a preschool child likely to suffer if her mother works. **8.103** When we have more confidence that our parameter falls within the interval, the interval will be wider; when the sample size is larger, we have greater accuracy in our interval estimate (i.e., the standard error is smaller) so the interval will be narrower. **8.105 (a)** $(0.5)(30) = 15$. **(b)** $(0.3)(50) = 15$. **(c)** $(0.1)($ ... $= 15$. **8.107 (a)** Increasing the confidence level increases z which increases n, **(b)** Decreasing m increases n since m is in the denominator. ... **(a)** The confidence interval refers to the population, ... means, not possible scores. **(c)** x is the sample mean; we know ... **(d)** If we sampled the entire population even once, ... mean exactly. **8.111 (a)** With 95% confi... daily number of hours 18–22-year-... tween 1.0 hours and 2.2 hours ... **(b)** Bootstrap percentile CI $=$ ... the *t*-interval. Although th... TV is right skewed, th... normality assumpti... **8.121 (a)** If we to... that year and ... the inter... penalty... $P(26) =$ ... dence l...

$|1 - p| = 1.96\ \sqrt{p(1 - p)/20}$; If we substitute 0.83887 for p, we get $1 - 0.83887 = 0.16113$ on both sides of the equation. If we substitute 1 for p, we get 0 on the left and on the right. **(b)** This confidence interval seems more believable because it forms an actual interval and contains more than just the value of 1. **8.125** Answers will vary.

Chapter 9

9.1 (a) Null. **(b)** Alternative. **(c)** (a) H_0: $p = 0.50$; H_a: $p \neq 0.50$. (b) H_0: $p = 0.24$; H_a: $p < 0.24$. **9.3 (a)** H_0: The mean toxicity level equals the threshold of 100 ppm ("no effect," H_0 specifies a single value, the threshold of 100 ppm, for the parameter); H_a: The mean toxicity level exceeds the threshold of 100 ppm. **(b)** H_0: The mean toxicity level equals the threshold of 100 ppm; H_a: The mean toxicity level is below the threshold of 100 ppm. **9.5 (a)** Alternative; it has a range of parameter values. **(b)** The relevant parameter is the mean weight change, μ. H_0: $\mu = 0$; this is a null hypothesis. **9.7 (a)** Null and alternative hypothesis are always about population parameters (e.g., p or μ) and never about sample statistics such as $\hat{p}$ or $\bar{x}$. Correct: H_0: $p = 0.5$, H_a: $p > 0.5$. **(b)** The alternative hypothesis needs to specify a range of parameters. Correct: H_0: $\mu = 100$, H_a: $\mu > 100$. **(c)** The range of values in the alternative hypothesis needs to be an "alternative" to the value specified in the null, so it cannot include the null value. ($p > 0.10$ includes the null value 0.30.) Correct: H_0: $p = 0.30$, H_a: $p > 0.30$ or H_0: $p = 0.10$, H_a: $p > 0.10$. **(d)** H_0 needs to specify a particular value, not a range of values such as all values greater than 100. Correct: H_0: $\mu = 100$, H_0: $\mu > 100$. **9.9 (a)** Not strong evidence against null hypothesis. **(b)** Strong evidence against null. **9.11** Parameter of interest: p, the probability of correctly identifying the bladder cancer sample among the 7 urine samples provided. H_0: $p = 1/7$, H_a: $p > 1/7$. **9.13 (a) (i)** 0.006; **(ii)** 0.012; **(iii)** 0.994. **(b)** Yes, those in (i) and (ii) are very small. **9.15 (a)** H_0: $p = 0.5$, H_a: $p \neq 0.5$. **(b)** $z = -0.670$. The test statistic z falls 0.67 standard errors below 0, the value expected if the null hypothesis were true. Equivalently, the sample proportion is 0.67 standard errors below the value of 0.5 specified under the null hypothesis. **(c)** P-value = 0.503. If the null hypothesis were true, the probability of observing a test statistic of −0.67 or even more extreme is equal to 0.503. Because the P-value of 0.503 is large (and greater than the significance level of 0.05), the data provide insufficient evidence for the claim that the population proportion opposing fracking is significantly different from 50%. **(d)** Yes, sample size is sufficient for large sample test since we expect $n(p_0) = 1{,}506(0.5) = 753$ successes and 753 failures. The sample of 1,506 respondents must be a random sample representative of the U.S. population in 2013 (which it was). **9.17 (a)** $p =$ proportion of adults who guess correctly; H_0: $p = 1/3$ and H_a: $p > 1/3$. **(b)** $\hat{p} = 28/83 = 0.337$; $se = \sqrt{p_0(1 - p_0)/n} = \sqrt{0.333(1 - 0.333)/83} = 0.052$; $z = (0.337 - 0.333)/0.052 = 0.08$. **(c)** The P-value is 0.47. If the null hypothesis is true, the probability of getting a test statistic at least as extreme as the value observed is 0.47. We would not conclude that people are more likely to select their correct horoscope than if they are randomly guessing. **9.19 (a)** $\hat{p} = 22/30 = 0.733$; $se = \sqrt{p_0(1 - p_0)/n} = \sqrt{0.5(0.50)/30} = 0.091$; $z = (0.733 - 0.5)/0.091 = 2.56$. **(b)** Area beyond 2.56 is 0.005, doubling to include both tails gives a P-value of 0.01. If the null hypothesis is true, the probability of getting a test statistic at least as extreme as the value observed is 0.01. **(c)** The data must be categorical. Sample size must be large enough for normality assumption. In this case, the data were obtained using randomization, and the sample size must be large enough for normality assumption. In this case, the data were obtained a convenience sample which might not be representative to be selected. **9.21** Plausible values for probability of a female to be selected. The decision reached in. **9.21** Plausible values for probability of a null hypothesis H_0: $p \neq 0.4$ because 0.4 0.16 to 0.44. This is in accordance with variable is whether she previous exercise not to reject the is the proportion among of the alternative hypothesis H_a: H_0: $p = 0.5$ against H_a for that probability. **9.23 (a)** The someone votes for Brown own. The parameter of interest is need to be a random sample s who voted for Brown. **(b)** The variable of whether 9 voters in the exit poll s, which they are. We

expect $3{,}889(0.5) = 1{,}944.5$ successes and failures, which is more than 15, so we can use the normal sampling distribution of the large sample test. **(c)** Test statistic $z = 3.87$. P-value < 0.001. Assuming $p = 0.5$, the probability of observing a sample percentage of 53.1% or higher (or 46.9% or smaller, since two-sided) is highly unlikely, i.e., less than 0.1%. We thus have strong evidence that the proportion voting for Brown in the population is different from 50%. **(d)** Because the P-value is less than 5%, we can reject the null hypothesis. There is very strong evidence that the proportion of voters voting for Brown is different from 50%. Our sample percentage of 53.1% indicates it is higher. We predict that Brown will win the election. **9.25 (1)** Assumptions: The data are categorical, assume the data are obtained randomly, the expected successes and failures are both at least 15 under H_0; $np = (50)(0.5) \geq 15$, and $np \geq (50)(0.5) \geq 15$. **(2)** Hypotheses: H_0: $p = 0.50$; H_a: $p \neq 0.50$. **(3)** Test statistic: $z = 0.85$. **(4)** P-value = 0.40. **(5)** Conclusion: There is weak evidence against H_0. We would not reject H_0. **9.27** False. When the P-value is large, this does not imply that we accept H_0 as the truth, but just as a plausible value for the true population proportion. In fact, the 95% confidence interval (0.16, 0.44) shows all plausible values for the proportion of females tapped for management training. **9.29 (a)** 0.026 or 0.03. **(b)** 0.013. **(c)** 0.987. **9.31 (a)** $se = s/\sqrt{n} = 7.0/\sqrt{109} = 0.67$. **(b)** $t = (\bar{x} - \mu_0)/se = (-5.5 - 0)/0.67 = -8.2$. **(c)** P-value = 0.0000 (less than 0.0001). If the null hypothesis of no weight change is true (i.e., if the mean weight change is 0), observing a test statistic of −8.2 or one even more extreme is highly unlikely (probability less than 0.0001). **(d)** We have strong evidence (P-value < 0.0001) that the mean weight change for subjects on the low-carbohydrate diet differs from 0. **(e)** No. The confidence interval shows that all plausible values for the mean weight change are below zero, indicating a mean weight change different from zero, just as the significance test. The 95% confidence interval shows the actual range of the mean weight change, i.e., that it is estimated to fall between −6.8 kg and −4.2 kg. This tells us about the magnitude of the mean weight change, whereas the significance test only tells us that the mean weight change is different from zero. **9.33 (a)** Variable: Number of friends on Facebook. Parameter: Mean number μ of friends for students at Williams that use Facebook. **(b)** H_0: $\mu = 100$, H_a: $\mu > 100$. **(c)** $t = (122.7 - 100)/(71.8/\sqrt{13}) = 1.14$. The observed sample mean of 122.7 falls 1.14 standard errors above the null hypothesis value of 100. **(d)** P-value = probability in upper tail = 0.138. The probability of observing a test statistic this large or larger (equivalently a sample mean that is this high or even higher) when the null hypothesis is true is not that small (about 14%). This does not provide evidence to reject the null hypothesis. There is insufficient evidence to conclude that the mean number of Facebook friends is larger than 100. **9.35 (1)** Assumptions: Random sample on a quantitative variable having a normal population distribution. Here, the data are not likely produced using randomization. Population distribution may be skewed, but the test is two-sided so is robust to a violation of the normal population assumption. **(2)** Hypotheses: H_0: $\mu = 0$; H_a: $\mu \neq 0$. **(3)** Test statistic: $t = -0.32$. **(4)** P-value: 0.75. **(5)** Conclusion: Since the P-value is large, the data do not provide enough evidence that the change in mean weight in the control group is different from 0. **9.37 (1)** Assumptions: The data are produced using randomization, from a normal population distribution. **(2)** Hypotheses: H_0: $\mu = 5.1$; H_a:

$$\mu \neq 5.1. \text{ (3) Test statistic: } t = \frac{(5.065 - 5.1)}{0.087/\sqrt{4}} = -0.80. \text{ (4) P-value: } 0.48.$$

(5) Conclusion: If the null hypothesis was true, the probability of getting a test statistic at least as extreme as the one observed is 0.48. There is no evidence to support that the population mean is different than 5.1 ounces. **9.39 (a)** The confidence interval does not include 0 and also indicates that coupons led to higher sales than did the outside posters. **(b)** A one-sided test might be problematic because if the population distribution is highly non-normal (such as very skewed) the method is not robust for a one-sided test. **9.41** The test statistic changes from 2.21 to 1.98, and the P-value changes from 0.04 to 0.06. The test statistic is less extreme, and the P-value > 0.05. We can no longer reject the null hypothesis. The conclusion does depend on the single observation of 20.9. **9.43 (a)** Reject H_0, because P-value < 0.05. **(b)** Type I error. Concluding that fewer than 75%

of drivers in Las Vegas stop for a pedestrian waiting in a crosswalk, when in fact 75% or more actually stop. **(c)** P(Type I error) = significance level = 0.05. **9.45 (a)** Concluding that the proportion of adults opposing fracking is different from 50%, when in fact it is equal to 50%. **(b)** Concluding that there is insufficient evidence that the proportion is different from 50%, when in fact it is different from 50%. **(c)** P(Type I error) = significance level = 0.05. **9.47 (a)** Reject H_0 and conclude that there is enough evidence that the mean weight change is positive, i.e., that the therapy had a positive effect of increasing weight. **(b)** Type I. **(c)** Fail to reject H_0 and conclude there is not enough evidence that the mean weight change is positive, i.e., that the therapy has a positive effect of increasing weight. Type II. Incorrectly concluding the therapy does not increase weight, on average, when in fact it does. **9.49 (a)** If H_0 is rejected, we conclude that the new drug is not safe. **(b)** A Type I error would result in finding the drug is not safe when it actually is safe. **(c)** If we fail to reject H_0, we conclude that the drug is safe. **(d)** A Type II error would result in failing to find the drug not safe when it actually is not safe. **9.51 (a)** Diagnose prostate cancer when there is none; results in treatment or further testing for patient who does not need it. **(b)** Fail to diagnose prostate cancer when it is present; results in a patient not receiving needed care. **(c)** Type II error. **(d)** The 2/3 refers to the probability that someone does not have prostate cancer given that he received a positive result. The probability of a Type I error refers to the probability that someone will receive a positive result, given that he does not have prostate cancer. **9.53 (a)** Researcher A: P-value = $2P(z > 2.0) = 0.046$. **(b)** Researcher B: P-value = $2P(z > 1.90) = 0.057$. **(c)** Part a: The proportion is significantly different (P-value = 0.046, a = 0.05) from 0.5. Part b: The proportion is not significantly different (P-value = 0.057, $\alpha = 0.05$) from 0.5. **(d)** If we only know that the proportion is significantly (or not significantly) different from 0.5 (or whether we rejected H_0 or not), we can't assess how strong the evidence is. By not seeing the P-value for those two cases, we wouldn't know that the strength of evidence is actually very similar for the two cases. **(e)** The two intervals overlap. The range of plausible values for p that each researcher is estimating is nearly identical. **9.55 (a)** $t = 0.31$. **(b)** P-value = 0.76. The probability of observing a test statistic this large or larger (in either direction), given the null hypothesis is true, is quite large (about 76%). It is plausible that the population mean score is 4.0. **(c)** $4.09 \pm 2.064(1.43/\sqrt{25}) = (3.5, 4.7)$. **(d) (i)** A decrease in sample size increases the P-value; **(ii)** confidence intervals become wider as sample sizes become smaller. **9.57** If we report only results that are "statistically significant," these are the only ones of which the public becomes aware. There might be many studies on the same topic that did not reject the null and did not get published, which may be misleading to the public because the published result may well be a Type I error. **9.59 (a)** No, it just means that the difference in proportions was not found to be statistically significant. No, not exactly the same, but the difference between the two population proportions is small and not relevant. **(b)** Research that suggests an impact of a therapy or drug tends to get the most media coverage if it's a very large difference. It's possible that studies that found little or no difference did not get media coverage. **9.61 (a)** $se = \sqrt{0.4(1-0.4)/50} = 0.069$; the value 1.645 standard errors below 0.4 is $0.4 - 1.645(0.069) = 0.286$. **(b)** $se = \sqrt{0.2(1-0.2)/50} = 0.0566$, $z = (0.286 - 0.20)/0.0566 = 1.52$, $p(z > 1.52) = 0.06$. Thus, P(Type II error) = 0.06. **9.63 (a)** $z = \frac{0.405 - 0.35}{\sqrt{0.35(1-0.35)/116}} = 1.24$, P(Type II error) = $P(z < 1.24) = 0.89$. **(b)** The chances of failing to reject H_0 when the hypothesized value is close to the true value is higher than when it is far away because we are less likely to detect a difference when that difference is small. **9.65 (a)** If truly $p = 0.2$, then with 60% probability, the proposed trial will lead to a rejection of the null hypothesis H_0: $p = 0.1$ in favor of H_a: $p > 0.1$. **(b)** Not rejecting H_0: $p = 0.1$, when, in fact, $p > 0.1$. **(c)** P(Type II error when $p = 0.2$) = $1 - P$(not committing a Type II error when $p = 0.2$) = $1 - $ (Power when $p = 0.2$) = $1 - 0.60 = 0.4$. **9.67 (a)** Null. **(b)** Alternative. **(c)** Alternative. **(d)** Null. **9.69 (1)** Observed variable is categorical (correct vs. incorrect guess) and obtained through a randomized experiment (coin flips). We expect $np = 30(0.5) = 15$ successes and $n(1-p) = 30(0.5) = 15$ failures, so sample size condition is met. **(2)** H_0: $p = 0.5$, H_a: $p > 0.5$, where $p =$ probability of her guess being

correct. **(3)** $z = 1.1$. **(4)** P-value = 0.137. **(5)** Since the P-value is not small, there is insufficient evidence to support the claim that the probability of a correct guess is larger than 0.5 or 50%. **9.71 (a) (1)** Assumptions: The data are categorical (Brown, Whitman, someone else) and obtained through a random sample; the expected successes and failures are both at least fifteen under H_0; $np = (0.5)(650) \geq 15$, and $n(1-p) = (0.5)(650) \geq 15$. **(2)** $p =$ population proportion of voters who prefer Brown. Hypotheses: H_0: $p = 0.50$; H_a: $p \neq 0.50$. **(3)** Test statistic: $z = \frac{0.554 - 0.50}{\sqrt{0.5(1-0.5)/650}}$ = 2.75. **(4)** P-value: 0.006. **(5)** Conclusion: We can reject the null hypothesis at a significance level of 0.05; we do have strong evidence that the population proportion of voters who chose Brown is different from 0.50. The 95% confidence interval is (0.516, 0.592). This provides a range of plausible values for the proportion voting for Brown, whereas the significance test just indicates that this proportion is different from 0.5. **(b)** If the sample size had been 50, the test statistic would have been $z = \frac{0.56 - 0.50}{\sqrt{0.5(1-0.5)/50}} = 0.849$, and the P-value would have been 0.40. We could not have rejected the null hypothesis under these circumstances. **(c)** With a sample of size 50, the standard error can be too large to reject H_0: p = 0.5. With a sample of size 650, the standard error is small enough to reject H_0, even though the two samples result in roughly the same sample proportion of 0.55. **9.73 (1)** Assumptions: Observed variable is categorical (whether agree or not) and come from a random sample. Expected number of successes and failures both larger than 15 $(1,690(0.5) = 845)$. **(2)** Hypotheses: H_0: $p = 0.5$, H_a: $p \neq 0.5$ where p is proportion of Americans agreeing that homosexuals should be able to marry. **(3)** Test statistic: $se_0 = \sqrt{0.5(1-0.5)/1,690} = 0.0122$; $z = (0.565 - 0.5)/0.0122 = 5.35$. **(4)** P-value < 0.001. **(5)** Conclusion: At the 0.05 significance level, we have strong evidence (P-value < 0.001) that the proportion of Americans agreeing with the statement that homosexuals should have the right to marry is different from 0.5. With a sample proportion of 0.565, a clear majority now supports gay marriage. **9.75 (a)** $p =$ proportion of people who would pick Box A; H_0: $p = 0.50$; H_a: $p \neq 0.50$. **(b)** $z = 5.06$; P-value = 0.000. There is very strong evidence to conclude that the population proportion that chooses Box A is not 0.50. Box A seems to be preferred. **9.77 (a)** With 95% confidence, we estimate that the proportion of bank customers preferring the card with an annual fee is between 0.28 and 0.48. **(b)** Less than 0.05, because the range of plausible values does not include 0.5. So, the test will reject H_0: p = 0.5 at a significance level of 0.05, which corresponds to the confidence level of 95%. **9.79 (a)** Type I error would have occurred if we had rejected the null hypothesis, when really women were not being passed over. A Type II error would occur if we had failed to reject the null, but women really were being picked disproportionate to their representation in the jury pool. **(b)** Type I error. **9.81 (b)** Sufficient evidence to reject null and conclude that the population mean is not 0. **(c)** 0.001; we have strong evidence to conclude that the population mean is positive. **(d)** 0.999; insufficient evidence to conclude that the population mean is negative. **9.83 (a)** H_0: $\mu = 40$, H_a: $\mu \neq 40$. **(b) (i)** The se of 0.50 tells us by how much the sample mean varies from sample to sample when taking samples of such a size. **(ii)** The test statistic of -3.7 indicates that the sample mean falls -3.7 standard errors below the hypothesized population mean of 40 hours. **(iii)** The P-value of 0.0002 tells us that if the population mean is 40 hours, observing a test statistic as or even more extreme than the observed one of -3.7 has an extremely low probability (only 0.02% chance). **(c)** With such a low P-value, there is strong evidence that the mean number of hours women worked in the previous week in all jobs is different from 40 hours. **(d)** No. The hypothesis test indicates that 40 is not a plausible value for the mean, and so the confidence interval would not include the value 40. **9.85 (a) (1)** Data are quantitative and have been produced randomly and have an approximate normal population distribution. **(2)** H_0: $\mu = 130$; H_a: $\mu \neq 130$. **(3)** The sample mean is 150.0 and standard deviation is 8.37; $t = 5.85$. **(4)** P-value = 0.002. **(5)** Strong evidence to conclude that the true mean is different from 130. **(b)** We do not know whether the population distribution is normal, but the two-sided test is robust for violations of this assumption. **9.87 (a)** Software indicates a test statistic of -5.5 and a P-value of 0.001. **(b)** For a significance level of 0.05, we would conclude that the process is not in control. **(c)** If we rejected the null hypothesis when it is in fact true, we have made a Type I error and concluded that the process is not in control when it actually is. **9.89 (1)** Data are quantitative and seem to have been produced randomly; also assume approximately normal population distribution. **(2)** H_0: $\mu = 500$; H_a: $\mu \neq 500$. **(3)** $t = -13.9$. **(4)** P-value $= 0.000$. **(5)** Extremely strong evidence that the population mean is different from 500. **9.91 (a)** We can reject the null hypothesis. **(b)** It would be a Type I error. **(c)** No, because the P-value is less than 0.05; when a value is rejected by a test at the 0.05 significance level, it does not fall in the 95% confidence interval. **9.93 (a)** By choosing a smaller significance level. **(b)** It will be too difficult to reject the null hypothesis, even if the null hypothesis is not true. **9.95 (a)** $\sqrt{0.333(1 - 0.333)/60} = 0.061$. **(b)** When $P(\text{Type I error}) =$ significance level $= 0.05$, $z = 1.645$, the value 1.645 standard errors above 0.333 is 0.433. **(c)** 0.15; Type II error is larger when n is smaller, because a smaller n results in a larger standard error and makes it more difficult to have a sample proportion fall in the rejection region. **9.97 (a)** These data give us a sense of what the probability would look like in the long run. If we look at just a few games, we don't get to see the overall pattern, but when we look at a number of games over time, we start to see the long run probability of the home team winning (in this case 1,359/2,430). **(b)** $z = (0.5592 - 0.5/(\sqrt{0.5(1 - 0.5)}/2,430) = 5.8$. P-value $= 0.000$. We can add and subtract the result of $(1.96)(0.0101)$, namely the z-score associated with a 95% confidence interval multiplied by the standard error, to the sample proportion to obtain a confidence interval of $(0.54, 0.58)$ for the probability of the home team scoring more runs. The test merely indicates whether $p = 0.50$ is plausible whereas the confidence interval displays the range of plausible values. **9.99 (a)** After seeing the data, we know the direction of results; it is cheating to do a one-tailed test now. **(b)** If there really is no effect, but many studies are conducted, eventually someone will achieve significance, and then the journal will publish a Type I error. **9.101** The subgroups have smaller sample size, so for a particular size of effect will have a smaller test statistic and a larger P-value. **9.103** The studies with the most extreme results will give the smallest P-values and be most likely to be statistically significant. If we could look at how results from all studies vary around a true effect, the most extreme results would be out in a tail, suggesting an effect much larger than it actually is. **9.105** Just because the sample statistic was not extreme enough to conclude that the value at H_0 is unlikely doesn't mean that the value in H_0 is the actual value. A confidence interval would show that there is a whole range of plausible values, not just the null value. **9.107** Statistical significance: A small P-value provides evidence that the parameter value falls in the range specified by the alternative hypothesis and differs from the value specified under the null hypothesis. Practical relevance: How far the parameter value falls from the value specified under the null need not be practically relevant. It is practically relevant if it falls a meaningful (practically important) distance away from the value hypothesized under the null. Example: Suppose, for a large random sample, a test indicates, based on a small P-value, that the mean credit score in the population under study is statistically significantly less than 700 points. However, the sample mean turns out to be 696 and the 95% confidence interval turns out to be 693 to 699. Then, the mean credit score in the population, although statistically significantly less than 700, in practical terms, is almost equal to 700. The difference of 4 four points between the hypothesized mean of 700 and the sample mean of 696 is not practically relevant. On the other hand, suppose the sample mean turned out to be 640, and the 95% confidence interval is equal to 635 to 645. Then, this would be a practically relevant difference from the hypothesized mean of 700. **9.109** With the probability of a false-positive diagnosis being about 50% over the course of 10 mammograms, it would not be unusual for a woman to receive a false positive over the course of having had many mammograms. Likewise, if you conduct 10 significance tests at the 0.05 significance level in 10 cases in which the null hypothesis is actually true, it would not be surprising if you sometime reject the null hypothesis just by chance. **9.111** Suppose P-value $= 0.057$. If the significance level were any number above this, we would have enough evidence to reject the null; if it were any number below this, there would not be enough evidence. **9.113** (b). **9.115** (a). **9.117** False. **9.119** False. **9.121** False. **9.123** False. **9.125** This P-value gives strong evidence against the null hypothesis.

It would be very unlikely to have a sample proportion of 1.00 if the actual population proportion were 0.50. **9.127** When the sample proportion is 0, $se = 0$, and we would have to divide by 0 to find the test statistic, which is not defined. Because a significance test assumes H^0: $p = p^0$ is true, it is better and more accurate to use p^0 instead of the sample proportion when computing the standard error (i.e., use se^0). **9.129** Answers will vary.

Chapter 10

10.1 (a) The response variable is unemployment rate and the explanatory variable is race. **(b)** The two groups that are the categories of the explanatory variable are White and Black individuals. **(c)** The samples of White and Black individuals were independent. No individuals could be in both samples. **10.3 (a)** Point estimate $= 0.422 - 0.212 = 0.21$. We estimate that the population proportion of students reporting binge drinking has decreased by 0.21 from the 1999 survey to the 2009 survey. In terms of percentages, the percent of students reporting binge drinking has decreased by 21 percentage points. **(b)** The standard error is the estimated standard deviation of the sampling distribution for the difference between two sample proportions. Using the formula, plugging in the sample proportions, $se = 0.0304$. **(c)** $p_1 =$ proportion of student population in 1999 that binge drinks, $p_2 =$ proportion of student population in 2009 that binge drinks. **(d)** $(0.15, 0.27)$; With 95% confidence, we estimate that the proportion of the student population binge drinking in 1999 is between 0.15 and 0.27 higher than in 2009. Because the interval does not contain 0, i.e., is entirely positive, we can conclude that $p_1 > p_2$, i.e., that the proportion in 1999 was larger. **(e)** The assumptions are that the response variable is categorical (whether students binge drink) and observed in two groups (years 1999 and 2009), that the two samples are independent (the response of students sampled in 1999 is independent from the ones sampled in 2009) and obtained randomly (given), and that the two sample sizes are sufficiently large (both have at least 10 successes and 10 failures). **10.5 (a)** 0.46; 0.63. **(b)** With 95% confidence, we estimate that the population proportion for females is between 0.11 and 0.22 higher than the population proportion for males; 0 is not in this interval, so we conclude that females are more likely to say that they believe in miracles. Assumptions: categorical data, independent and randomly obtained samples, sufficient sample size. **(c)** The confidence interval has a wide range of plausible values, including some (such as 0.11) that indicate a moderate difference and some (such as 0.22) that indicate a relatively large difference. **10.7 (a)** It says that the proportion of patients dying from a heart attack are the same in the population for these two groups. **(b)** If the proportions in the populations were the same, observing a test statistic as or even more extreme than 1.46 has probability 0.144. **(c)** 0.072. **10.9 (a)** Assumptions: Categorical response (whether positive/negative view), two independent and random samples (Whites, Blacks), at least 10 successes and 10 failures in each group (fulfilled here). Hypotheses: H_0: $p_1 = p_2$; H_a: $p_1 \neq p_2$, where p_1 and p_2 are the proportion of Whites and Blacks who have a positive view of the police. Test statistic $z = 17.1$, P-value $= 0.000$. With such a small P-value, there is strong evidence that the population proportion of Whites with a positive view of the police differs from the proportion of Blacks with a positive view. **(b)** $(0.37, 0.47)$; With 95% confidence, we estimate that the proportion of Whites with a positive view is between 37 and 47 percentage points higher than the one for Blacks. This interval tells us about the size of the difference (between 37 and 47 percentage point difference), rather than just telling us that there is strong evidence that the proportions differ significantly. **10.11 (a)** Each sample has at least 10 outcomes of each type; data are categorical; independent random samples; p: probability someone developed cancer; H_0: $p_1 = p_2$; H_a: $p_1 \neq p_2$. **(b)** The test statistic is 1.03, and the P-value is 0.30. The data do not provide strong evidence that the proportions differ. **(c)** We cannot reject the null hypothesis. **10.13** One of the assumptions for the inference in this section is that we have two independent samples. Here, we ask the same subjects two questions, so each subject is measured twice and the responses to the two questions are not independent. Therefore, we cannot use the methods of this section (but see Section 10.4). **10.15 (a)** The response variable is the dollar amount a student is willing to add to the gasoline price; the explanatory variable is whether the student believes that global warming is a serious issue or not. **(b)** Independent samples; the students were randomly sampled, so the responses of students who said yes to the second question are independent of the responses of the students who said no to the second question. **(c)** Let μ_1 be the mean amount of dollars students who think global warming is serious would add to the price of gasoline. Let μ_2 be the mean amount of dollars students who think global warming is not serious would add to the price of gasoline. We are interested in a confidence interval for $\mu_1 - \mu_2$, the difference in the mean amount of dollars students from the two groups would add to the price of gasoline. **10.17 (a)** The margin of error is the t value of 2.58 multiplied by the standard error of 1.20 = 3.1. The bounds are 10.0 and 16.2. With 99% confidence, we estimate that the difference in the population mean housework hours is between 10.0 and 16.2. Because 0 is not in the interval, we can conclude that the population means differ. With 99% confidence, women are estimated to work between 10.0 and 16.2 hours more in the household than men, on average. **(b)** This interval is wider than the 95% confidence interval because we have chosen a larger confidence level, and thus, the t value associated with it is higher. To be more confident, we must include a wider range of plausible values. **10.19 (a)** $se = \sqrt{s_1^2/n_1 + s_2^2/n_2} = \sqrt{0.89^2/921 + 0.85^2/754} = 0.043$. **(b)** $0.04 \pm 1.96(0.043) = (-0.04, 0.12)$. With 95% confidence, we estimate that in the U.S. population, the mean number of children that women think is ideal is between 0.04 smaller and 0.12 larger compared to what men think is ideal. Because 0 is in the confidence interval, with 95% confidence, the population mean number of children that women and men think is ideal does not differ significantly between the sexes. **10.21 (a)** $se = 0.97, me = (2.05)0.97 = 1.99$. **(b)** With 95% confidence, we estimate that the population mean difference is between -4.79 and -0.81. Because 0 does not fall in this interval, we can conclude that, on average, the sexually abused students had a population mean family cohesion score between 4.8 and 0.8 points lower than the nonabused students. **10.23 (a) (i)** Because the mean is very close to 0; **(ii)** Those who reported inhaling had a mean score that was $2.9 - 0.1 = 2.8$ higher. **(b)** Not for the noninhalers. The lowest possible value of 0, which was very common, was only a fraction of a standard deviation below the mean. **(c)** 0.24; it's approximately the standard deviation of the difference between sample means from different studies using these sample sizes. **(d)** Because 0 is not in this interval, we can conclude that there is a difference in population mean HONC scores. **10.25 (a)** 0.36 is the standard deviation of the difference between sample means from different studies using these sample sizes. **(b)** $t = 3.30$; P-value = 0.001; very strong evidence that females have a higher population mean HONC score. **(c)** No, because in each case the lowest possible value of 0 is less than 1 standard deviation below the mean. This does not affect the validity of our inference greatly because of the robustness of the two-sided test for the assumption of a normal population distribution for each group. **10.27 (a)** $H_0: \mu_1 = \mu_2$ versus $H_a: \mu_1 \neq \mu_2$, where μ_1 is the population mean score for clips based on male speakers and μ_2 is the population mean score for clips based on female speakers. **(b)** $t = 1.68 (df = 57.82)$, P-value = 0.098. If there is no difference in the population mean score for clips based on male and female speakers, observing a test statistic of 1.68 or one more extreme has probability 0.098. Compared to a 0.05 significance level, this is not small. There is not enough evidence to conclude that the population mean scores differ. The population mean dominance score for clips based on male speakers may be equal to the one for female speakers. **(c)** Yes, the interval would include 0 because the significance test failed to reject $H_0: \mu_1 = \mu_2$. **(d)** Box plots do not reveal dramatic departures from normality, so assumption is reasonable. **(e)** $t = $ (observed difference $- 0$)$/ se = 11.77/7.00 = 1.68$. **10.29 (a)** Let Group 1 represent the students who planned to go to graduate school and Group 2 represent those who did not. Then, $\bar{x}_1 = 11.67, s_1 = 8.34, \bar{x}_2 = 9.10$, and $s_2 = 3.70$. The sample mean study time per week was higher for the students who planned to go to graduate school, but the times were also much more variable for this group. **(b)** $se = 2.16$. If further random samples of these sizes were obtained from these populations, the differences between the sample means would vary. The standard deviation of these values would equal about 2.2. **(c)** A 95% confidence interval is $(-1.9, 7.0)$. With 95% confidence, we estimate that the difference in the mean study time per week between the two groups is between -1.9

and 7.0 hours. Since 0 is contained within this interval, we cannot conclude that the population mean study times differ for the two groups. **10.31 (a)** Let Group 1 represent males and Group 2 represent females. Then, $\bar{x}_1 = 11.9, s_1 = 3.94, \bar{x}_2 = 15.6$, and $s_2 = 8.00$. The sample mean time spent on social media was higher for females than for males, but notice the apparent outlier for the female group (40). The data were also much more variable for females, but this may also merely reflect the outlier. **(b)** $se = 2.084$. If further random samples of these sizes were obtained from these populations, the differences between the sample means would vary. The standard deviation of these values would equal about 2.1. **(c)** A 90% confidence interval is $(-7.24, -0.17)$. With 90% confidence, we estimate that the difference in the population mean number of hours spent on social media per week is between -7.2 and -0.17 for males and females. Since 0 is not quite contained within this interval, we can conclude that the population mean time spent on social media per week differs for males and females. **10.33 (a)** $se = 0.701$. **(b)** $(4.5, 7.3)$. With 95% confidence, we estimate that the mean body dissatisfaction assessment score is between 4.5 and 7.3 points higher for lean sport athletes compared to non-lean sport athletes. **10.35 (a)** $(-10.6, 6.4)$; With 95% confidence, we estimate that the population mean pain score is between 10.6 points smaller and 6.4 points larger for patients treated with the placebo procedure compared to patients treated with the lavage procedure. Because 0 falls in this interval, it is plausible that the mean pain score is similar if not the same under both procedures. **(b)** Yes, because sample standard deviations s_1 and s_2 are very similar—in fact, identical. **(c) (1)** Assumptions: independent random samples from the two groups (patients are randomly assigned to the two groups), approximately normal population distributions for each group (not crucial because sample size is large) and equal population standard deviations. **(2)** $H_0: \mu_1 = \mu_2$ versus $H_a: \mu_1 \neq \mu_2$. **(3)** t-test statistic value = -0.49. **(4)** P-value = 0.627. **(5)** If there is no difference in the population mean pain score, the probability of observing a test statistic this extreme is 0.63. This is large. There is no evidence of a difference in the population mean pain score between the placebo and lavage arthroscopic surgery procedures. **10.37** We can't use the methods from this section because the samples are not independent. Each checkup provided two measurements on the same person, one before and one after using an inhaler. These two measurements are not independent of each other. One can also argue that the biannual measurements are not independent because they are observed on the same person over time. **10.39 (a)** $(32, 145)$; answers may vary slightly. With 95% confidence, the mean room price on Airbnb is between $32 and $145 higher in Boston than in Seattle. **(b)** $(26, 160)$; answers may vary slightly. With 95% confidence, we estimate that the median room price on Airbnb is between $26 and $160 higher in Boston than in Seattle. **10.41** $(-4.2, -3.1)$; answers may vary slightly. With 95% confidence, we estimate that the median interest rate is between 3.1 and 4.2 percentage points larger for type B loans. **10.43 (a)** The distribution of the improvement scores is the same under Therapy 1 and Therapy 2. **(b)** Under H_0, outcomes for each assignment are equally likely. Because there are a total of six possible assignments, each has probability 1/6. Because two assignments lead to a difference of -20, that difference occurs with probability 2/6. Differences -10 and 10 occur once, so each has probability 1/6. Difference 20 occurs twice, so has probability 2/6 of occurring. **(c)** The P-value is the probability of observing a difference as extreme or even more extreme if H_0 is true. The observed difference was 20, the most extreme possible. Because $P(20) = 2/6 = 1/3$, the P-value is 0.333. If the distribution of improvement scores is the same under Therapy 1 and Therapy 2, we would observe a difference of 20 or more with a probability of 0.33. This would not be considered unusual, indicating that it is plausible the two therapy distributions of improvement scores (and their means) are the same. **10.45 (a)** $\bar{x}_1 = 11.9, \bar{x}_2 = 15.6, \bar{x}_1 - \bar{x}_2 = -3.7$. **(b)** Answers will vary. We got $\bar{x}_1 = 14.6, \bar{x}_2 = 14.1, \bar{x}_1 - \bar{x}_2 = 0.49$. **(c)** Answers will vary. We got less extreme because $-3.7 < 0.49 < +3.7$. **(d)** Answers will vary slightly. We got 1,498 permutations that resulted in a difference smaller than -3.7 or larger than $+3.7$ (two-sided alternative). **(e)** Based on these 10,000 random permutations, permutation P-value = 1,498/10,000 = 0.149. This is not small. If truly the distribution of time spent on social media sites is the same for males and females, then the probability of observing a difference of -3.7 or more extreme (i.e., larger in absolute value) in the sample means is 0.149. The data do not provide sufficient evidence for a difference in the population distributions of time spent on social media. **10.47 (a)** H_0: The population distribution of ratings is the same for clips based on male and female speakers. (This implies the population means are the same.) H_a: The population mean rating is different for clips based on male and female speakers. The observed difference in sample means equals 11.8. Out of 10,000 random permutations, 980 yielded a difference at least as extreme, resulting in a permutation P-value of 0.098. (Your results might differ slightly.) Because $0.098 > 0.05$, there is no evidence of a difference in the population mean dominance rating between clips based on female and male speakers. It is plausible that the distributions are the same. **(b)** $t = 1.69 (df = 57.8)$, P-value $= 0.097$. Results are comparable. The sample size is fairly large (30 in each group), and the histogram of the ratings in each group does not indicate major deviations from normality. **10.49 (a)** The same patients are in both samples. **(b)** 150; 130; 20; "before" mean minus "after" mean equals mean of the differences. **(c)** With 95% confidence, we estimate that the mean blood pressure before exercising is between 7.6 and 32.4 higher compared to after exercising. **10.51 (a)** Dependent; the same students are in both samples. **(b)** The differences should be approximately normal. The dot and box plot do not show that this assumption is grossly violated. There is quite a bit of variability, but there is an outlier in both directions. **(c)** point estimate $\pm me = 4 \pm 11.56 = (-7.6, 15.6)$. (The $me = t$-score$(se) = 2.26(5.11)$.) With 95% confidence, we estimate that the mean number of times students attend a movie per year is between 7.6 smaller and 15.6 larger than the mean number of times students attended sporting events. Because 0 is included in this interval, the mean number of times a student attends might be the same for both types of events. **(d)** t test statistic $= 4/5.112 = 0.782$. There is not enough evidence (P-value $= 0.454$) to conclude that students attend more or fewer movie events than sporting events, on average. **10.53 (a) (1)** Assumptions: the differences are a random sample from a population distribution that is approximately normal. **(2)** H_0: $\mu_1 = \mu_2$. (or population mean of differences is 0); H_a: $\mu_1 \neq \mu_2$. **(3)** $t = -1.62$. **(4)** P-value $= 0.14$. **(5)** Insufficient evidence to conclude that the population means are different for movies and parties. **(b)** $(-21.1, 3.5)$. With 95% confidence, we estimate that the population mean number of times attending movies is between 21.1 less and 3.5 higher than the population mean number of times attending parties. **10.55 (a)** The standard deviation of the change in weight scores could be much smaller because even though there is a lot of variability among the initial and final weights of the women, most women do not see a large change in weight over the course of the study, so the weight changes would not vary much. **(b)** $se = s_d/\sqrt{n} = 2.0/\sqrt{132} = 0.174$. A 95% confidence interval given by $\bar{x}_d \pm t_{.025} (se)$ has lower endpoint $2.1 - (1.98)(0.174) = 1.76$ and upper endpoint $2.1 + (1.98)(0.174) = 2.44$. Thus, the confidence interval is $(1.76, 2.44)$. 15 is not a plausible weight change in the population of freshmen women. The plausible weight change falls in the range from 1.76 to 2.44. **(c)** The data must be quantitative, the sample of differences must be a random sample from a population of such differences, and the differences must have a population distribution that is approximately normal (particularly with samples of size less than 30). **10.57 (1)** Assumptions: the differences in prices are a random sample from a population that is approximately normal. **(2)** H_0: $\mu_d = 0$ vs. H_a: $\mu_d \neq 0$. **(3)** $t = \bar{d}/(s_d/\sqrt{n}) = 4.3/(4.7152/\sqrt{10}) = 2.88$. **(4)** P-value $= 0.02$. **(5)** If the null hypothesis is true, the probability of obtaining a difference in sample means as extreme as that observed is 0.02. We would reject the null hypothesis and conclude that there is a significant difference in the mean price of textbooks used at her college between the two sites for $\alpha = 0.05$. **10.59 (a)** $\hat{p}_1 = 0.9895$, $\hat{p}_2 = 0.9685$. **(b)** With 95% confidence, we estimate that the population proportion of correct results for GDMS is between 0.013 and 0.029 higher than the population proportion of correct results for CDHMM. **10.61 (a) (i)** 0.38; **(ii)** 0.43. Difference $= -0.05$. We estimate the population proportion of people buying Sanka coffee after the advertising campaign was 0.05 larger than before the campaign. In terms of percentages, we estimate that 5% more people in the population bought Sanka coffee after the campaign. **(b)** With 95% confidence, we estimate that the proportion of people buying Sanka coffee after the advertising campaign is between 0.01 and 0.09 larger than before it. This means that we are 95% confident

that between 1% and 9% more people in the population bought Sanka coffee after the advertising campaign. **(c)** H_0: $p_1 = p_2$, where p_1 and p_2 are the (marginal) population proportions of people buying Sanka coffee before and after the advertising campaign, respectively. We have sufficient evidence (P-value of $0.02 < 0.05$ significance level) that the population proportion of people buying Sanka coffee differs before and after the advertising campaign. **10.63 (a)** 0.135. **(b) (i)** Independent, random samples and sums of two counts at least 30; **(ii)** H_0: $p_1 = p_2$; H_a: $p_1 \neq p_2$; **(iii)** $z = 3.00$; **(iv)** P-value: 0.003; **(v)** Strong evidence that there is a difference between the population proportions. **10.65 (a)** This refers to an analysis of three variables, a response variable, an explanatory variable, and a control variable. The response variable is "whether or not at risk for cardiovascular disease," the explanatory variable is "whether drink alcohol moderately," and the control variables would be socioeconomic status and mental and physical health. **(b)** There is a stronger association between drinking alcohol and its effect on risk for cardiovascular disease for subjects who have a higher socioeconomic status. **10.67 (a)** The proportion of shots made is higher for Barry both for 2-point shots and for 3-point shots, but the proportion of shots made is higher for O'Neal overall. **(b)** O'Neal took almost exclusively 2-point shots, where the chance of success is higher. **10.69 (a)** Higher mean for English-speaking families (1.95) than French-speaking families (1.85). **(b)** In each case, higher mean for French-speaking families: Quebec: French (1.80); English (1.64); other provinces: French (2.14); English (1.97). **(c)** There are relatively more English-speaking families in the "other" provinces, and the "other" provinces have a higher mean regardless of language. This illustrates Simpson's paradox. **10.71** There could be no difference in the prevalence of breast cancer now and in 1900 for women of a given age. Overall, the breast cancer rate would be higher now, because more women live to an old age now, and older people are more likely to have breast cancer. **10.73 (a)** Response: opinion on fracking (favor/oppose). Explanatory: type of survey (U.S. adults/scientists). **(b)** Independent samples because each survey uses different subjects. (Highly unlikely that a subject from the scientists' survey was also included in the Pew Research Center survey.) **(c)** Dependent samples (matched pairs) because the same scientists who were asked about fracking were asked about offshore drilling. **10.75 (a)** With 95% confidence, we estimate that the population proportion of females who have used marijuana is between 1 and 9 percentage points lower than the population proportion of males who have used marijuana. Because 0 is not in the confidence interval, we can conclude that the proportion of marijuana use differs between males and females. **(b)** The confidence interval would change only in sign. It would now be $(0.01, 0.09)$ instead of $(-0.09, -0.01)$, rounded. With 95% confidence, we estimate that the population proportion of males who have used marijuana is between 1 and 9 percentage points higher and at most 0.09 higher than the population proportion of females. **10.77 (a)** Pooled $\hat{p} = 0.796$; $se_0 = 0.017$. **(b)** $z = 4.78$; P-value $= 0.000$; we have sufficient evidence (P-value < 0.05) to reject the null hypothesis. The population proportion of females believing in an afterlife is different from the population proportion for males. **(c)** No, the decision was not an error. The proportions differed for females and males, agreeing with our decision. **(d)** Independent random samples of females and males (okay since GSS); at least 5 successes and 5 failures in each sample. **10.79 (a)** Box plots are part of answer. Female crabs have a higher median and more variability if they had a mate (right-skewed distribution) than if they did not have a mate (symmetrical). **(b)** 0.5. **(c)** $se = 0.076$. **(d)** With 95% confidence, we estimate that the mean weight for female crabs with a mate is between 0.375 and 0.625 kg higher than for those without a mate. **10.81 (a)** H_0: $\mu_1 = \mu_2$ vs. H_a: $\mu_1 \neq \mu_2$, where μ_1 and μ_2 are the mean number of hours exercised for college athletes and non-athletes, respectively. **(b)** $t = 7.911/0.7048 = 11.2$; This is a very large test statistic when compared to the t distribution. (Remember, for large df, the t distribution looks like the standard normal distribution.) 11.2 is extremely far out in the right tail, the P-value will be smaller than 0.01. **(c)** There is extremely strong evidence (P-value < 0.01) that the mean number of hours exercised by athletes is different from the mean for nonathletes. **(d)** When we reject the null hypothesis, the confidence interval for the difference in means does not include 0, and vice versa. **(e)** The test only indicates whether there is a significant difference in the mean hours exercised, but the confidence interval tells us by how much the means differ: estimated to be at least 6.5 hours and at most 9.3 hours, with 95% confidence. **10.83 (a)** Response: time on Internet (number of hours per week, quantitative). Explanatory: race (categorical with categories Black and White). **(b)** With 95% confidence, the mean number of hours spent on the Internet per week is estimated to be between 0.3 and 6.1 hours larger for Blacks compared to Whites. **(c) (1)** Assumptions: Quantitative response (hours per week), independent random samples (OK, since GSS employs random sampling), approximate normal distribution in each group (not fulfilled, because 0, the smallest possible value, is less than one standard deviation below the mean, indicating right-skewed distributions. However, sample size is large, so meeting assumption less crucial for valid reference). **(2)** Hypotheses: $H_0: \mu_1 = \mu_2$ vs. $H_a: \mu_1 \neq \mu_2$, where μ_1 and μ_2 are the mean number of hours Blacks and Whites spent on the Internet per week. **(3)** Test statistic: $t = 2.15$. **(4)** P-value $= 0.033$. **(5)** If the null hypothesis of equal population means is true, observing a test statistic of 2.15 or more extreme is unusual (probability $= 0.033$). At a significance level of 0.05, we have sufficient evidence to reject H_0 and conclude that the mean number of hours spent on the Internet differs between Blacks and Whites. **10.85 (a)** μ_1 and μ_2 are the mean number of days men and women, respectively, felt sad in the last 7 days. **(b)** If the population mean number of days feeling sad is the same for men and women, the probability of observing a test statistic as or more extreme than 3.88 is practically 0. There is strong evidence that the population means are not equal. If they were equal, we would expect the difference in the sample means and the t-test statistic to be much smaller (closer to 0). At any reasonable significance level, we have sufficient evidence (P-value < 0.001) to conclude that the mean number of sad days are different for men and women. **(c)** Quantitative response variable (number of days) observed in two groups (females, males) through random and independent samples (okay since GSS). Population distribution of response should be approximately normal in both groups. From the histograms, we see that the distribution of the number of sad days is likely right skewed, violating the approximately normal assumption. However, with such a large sample size, meeting this assumption is not crucial by CLT, and the inference is valid. **10.87 (a)** 95% confidence interval $= (6.2, 14.5)$; $t = 7.11$; P-value $= 0.003$. We can conclude that the population mean is higher for bumper type A since **(i)** the confidence interval lies completely above 0 or since **(ii)** the P-value of 0.003 is very small. **10.89 (a)** Yes, the sampling distribution for the difference in sample means looks approximately normal. This is because of the CLT. **(b)** (6.6, 9.3). With 95% confidence, we estimate that the mean exercise hours per week are between 6.6 and 9.3 hours longer for college athletes compared to nonathletes. **10.91 (a)** The bootstrap distribution of the difference in medians is left skewed, with a mean of 16.7 (median of 18.5) and a standard deviation of 12 (IQR = 16.5). **(b)** (–9.5, 36.5). With 95% confidence, we estimate that the median dominance score is between 9.5 points lower and 36.5 points higher for male politicians compared to female politicians. Because 0 is included in this interval, the median score could be the same. **10.93 (a)** With 95% confidence, we estimate that the true population mean difference is between –0.7 and 7.6. **(b)** If the null hypothesis were true, there would be probability 0.10 of obtaining a test statistic at least this large (in absolute value). **(c)** P-value $= 0.10/2 = 0.05$. If the null hypothesis were true, the probability $= 0.05$ of getting a t statistic of 1.68 or larger. **(d)** Quantitative response variable, independent random samples, and approximately normal population distributions for each group. **10.95 (a)** Dependent samples because the same subject was measured at two occasions, before the crash and in the earlier accident-free period. **(b)** McNemar's test for comparing (marginal) proportions from matched pairs. **10.97 (b)** Increase the sample size and randomizing the side the tire is put on. **10.99 (a)** (–0.1, 5.5). With 95% confidence, we estimate that the mean score for children of alcoholics is between 0.1 lower and 5.5 higher compared to the mean for children of nonalcoholics. **(b)** The confidence interval gives us a range of values for the difference between the population mean scores rather than just telling us whether or not the scores are significantly different. **10.101** 95% confidence interval $= (-5.9, -0.5)$. With 95% confidence, we estimate that the population mean amount of time reading news stories on the Internet is between 5.9 and 0.5 hours less than for communicating on the Internet. Since 0 is not contained in this interval, we conclude that the population means differ. The population consists of the 165 students in the course. **10.103 (a)** With 95% confidence, we estimate that the population mean difference between responses with respect to movies and TV is between –0.43 and 0.76. Because 0 falls in this interval, it is plausible that there is no difference between the population mean responses for TV and movies. **(b)** The P-value $= 0.55$. If the null hypothesis were true, the probability would be 0.55 of getting a test statistic at least as extreme as the value observed. The data do not provide enough evidence to conclude that the population mean scores differ between the influence of movies or TV. **10.105 (a)** No, the same sample is used for both sets of responses, we should use methods for dependent samples. **(b)** No, we would need to know the specific numbers of subjects who said that they believed in ghosts but not in astrology, and who said that they believed in astrology, but not in ghosts. **10.107 (a)** If the United States has a higher proportion of older people (who are more likely to die in both countries than are younger people), and Mexico has a higher proportion of younger people, then the death rate in the United States could be higher. **(b)** Even if older people in South Carolina are more likely to die than are older people in Maine, if Maine has far more older people and far fewer younger people, this could lead to an overall higher death rate in Maine than in South Carolina. **10.109** Use the *Compare Two Proportions* app to obtain bar charts and 95% confidence interval of (0.28, 0.64). With 95% confidence, the proportion of injection drug users adherent to the vaccination series is estimated to be between 28 and 64 percentage points higher for those getting monetary incentives compared to those in an outreach group. Assumptions: Independent random samples (obtained by randomizing users to one group or the other) and at least 10 successes and failures in each group (fulfilled). **10.111** Answers will vary but should include: Men: $\bar{x}_1 - \bar{x}_2 = -0.2$, $t = -0.07$, P-value $= 0.94$, 95% CI $= (-5.6, 5.2)$. Since the confidence interval contains 0 and the P-value > 0.05, we are unable to conclude that there is a difference in the population mean number of dates between more and less attractive men. Women: $\bar{x}_1 - \bar{x}_2 = 7.4$, $t = 1.83$, P-value $= 0.07$, 95% CI $= (-0.7, 15.5)$. Since the confidence interval contains 0 and the P-value ≥ 0.05, we are unable to conclude that there is a difference in the population mean number of dates between more and less attractive women. However, the confidence interval shows there could be a large difference. **10.113** If the population distributions are identical, the sampling distribution of $\bar{x}_1 - \bar{x}_2$ should be centered at around 0. Mean $= \Sigma x P(x) = (-4.67)(1/10) + (-3.83)(2/10) + (0.33)(2/10) + (1.17)(3/10) + (2.00)(1/10) + (6.17)(1/10) = 0$. **10.115 (a)** Whether obese (yes or no) and wage. **(b)** Education level; the women could be paired according to education level and then compared in obesity rates. **10.117** (d). **10.119** False. **10.121** False. **10.123** With 95% confidence, we estimate that the difference between the population mean is between 9.6 and 17.0. **10.125 (a) (i)** $\hat{p}_1 = \hat{p}_2 = 0$ because there are no successes in either group (i.e., $0/10 = 0$); **(ii)** $se = 0$ because there is no variability in either group if all responses are the same (and can also see this from formula for se); **(iii)** The 95% confidence interval would be (0, 0) because we'd be adding 0 to 0 (se multiplied by z would always be 0 with se of 0, regardless of the confidence level). **(b)** The new confidence interval, $(-0.22, 0.22)$, is far more plausible than (0, 0). **10.127 (a)** From Table 10.18, $b = 162$, $c = 9$, and $n = 1,314$, resulting in the null standard error

$$se_0 = \sqrt{(162 + 9)/1{,}314^2} = 0.010.$$ **(b)** $z = \dfrac{(\hat{p}_1 - \hat{p}_2)}{se_0} = \dfrac{0.12}{0.010} = 12$

(or 11.7 if not using rounding). **10.129** Answers will vary.

Chapter 11

11.1 (a) Response: Party identification, explanatory: gender.
(b)

Gender	Political Party Identification			Total	n
	Democrat	Independent	Republican		
Female	35.4%	42.4%	22.2%	100%	1,239
Male	29.2%	45.5%	25.2%	100%	999

Women are more likely than are men to be Democrats, whereas men are more likely than are women to be Republicans or Independents. **(c)** Such a table would have equal conditional percentages for both females and males in the party identification categories, such as 33%, 43% and 24% for identifying as Democrat, Independent and Republican, respectively.

11.3 (a) Y given X.

Gender	Admitted Yes	No	Total	n
Male	18.2%	81.8%	**100%**	3,195
Female	16.9%	83.1%	**100%**	3,658

(b) X and Y are dependent because the probability of a student being admitted differs by gender. **11.5 (a)**

Income	Happiness of Marriage Not Too Happy	Pretty Happy	Very Happy	n
Below	6	62	139	207
Average	7	125	283	415
Above	6	69	115	190

(b)

Income	Happiness of Marriage Not Too Happy	Pretty Happy	Very Happy	n
Above	3%	30%	67%	**100%** (207)
Average	2%	30%	68%	**100%** (415)
Below	3%	36%	61%	**100%** (190)

The conditional distributions of marital happiness for above-average and average income are nearly identical; however, among people of below-average income, the percentage of very happy people is lower, and the percentage of pretty happy people is larger. **(c)** Across all three income categories, the percentage of very happy people is much larger for marital happiness (always over 60%) than for general happiness (always below 40%). **11.7** Answers will vary depending on the column variable selected. **11.9 (a)** H_0: Gender and happiness are independent; H_a: Gender and happiness are dependent (associated). **(b)** If gender and happiness were independent, it would be highly unusual (probability of 0.007) to observe a value for the X^2 statistic of 9.94 or larger. There is strong evidence (P-value $= 0.007$) that happiness depends on gender. **11.11 (a)** H_0: Income and marital happiness are independent; H_a: Income and marital happiness are dependent (associated). **(b)** $df = (3-1)(3-1) = 4$. **(c) (i)** Expected value of chi-squared statistic $= df = 4$; **(ii)** standard deviation $= \sqrt{2(4)} = \sqrt{8} \approx 2.8$. The value 4.58 is 0.2 ($= (4.58-4)/2.8$) standard deviations above the expected value under independence. **(iii)** No, the value is not extreme because it is only 0.2 standard deviations above the value expected under independence. **(d)** If income and marital happiness were independent, observing a value of the X^2 test statistic of 4.58 or larger is quite likely (33%). There is not enough evidence (P-value $= 0.33 > 0.05$) to conclude that marital happiness and income are associated. **(e)** $(207 \times 19)/812 = 4.84$. One of the assumptions of the chi-squared test is that expected cell counts are at least 5. If not, X^2 might not have an approximate chi-squared distribution. **11.13 (a)** (61.1%, 38.9%) and (5.9%, 94.1%); suggests marijuana use much more common for those who have smoked cigarettes than for those who have not. **(b) (1)** Assumptions: two categorical variables (cigarette use and marijuana use), randomization, expected count at least five in all cells. **(2)** H_0: marijuana use independent of cigarette use; H_a: dependence. **(3)** $X^2 = 642.0$. **(4)** P-value: 0.000. **(5)** Extremely strong evidence that marijuana use and cigarette use are associated. **11.15 (a)** H_0: Opinion about helping the environment by cutting standard of living is independent of whether someone is currently in school or retired; H_a: Opinion about helping the

environment depends on whether someone is currently in school or retired. **(b)** $r = 2, c = 5, df = (r-1)(c-1) = 4$. **(c)** about 4, the df value, which is the mean of the chi-squared distribution. **(d) (i)** There is evidence (P < 0.05) for an association between helping the environment and whether someone is in school or retired; **(ii)** There is not enough evidence (P > 0.025) for an association.
11.17 (a)

Treatment	Heart Attack	No Heart Attack
Placebo	28	656
Aspirin	18	658

(b) (1) Assumptions: 2 categorical variables, randomization, expected count at least 5 in all cells. **(2)** H_0: Probability of having a heart attack does not depend on treatment; H_a: Probability of a heart attack depends on treatment. **(3)** $X^2 = 2.1$. **(4)** P-value: 0.14. **(5)** The data do not provide sufficient evidence for an association between treatment and suffering a heart attack. **11.19 (a)** H_0: The distribution of severity of fever is the same in the active and placebo group (homogeneity); H_a: The distributions differ. **(b)** $df = 2$, so we expect the chi-squared statistic to be around 2, with a standard deviation of $\sqrt{4} = 2$. The test statistic 2.49 is less than half a standard deviation away from the mean, which makes it not extreme. **(c)** There is no evidence (P $= 0.287$, which is larger than any reasonable significance level) that the distribution of the severity of fewer differs between the active and placebo group. **11.21 (a)** H_0: $p = 0.75$, where p is the proportion of green seedlings in the population. **(b)** $X^2 = 3.46; df = 1$. **(c)** P-value $= 0.06$. The probability of obtaining a test statistic at least as extreme as that observed, assuming the null hypothesis is true, is 0.06. Some evidence that the proportion of green seedlings differs from 75%, but not too strong. **11.23 (a)** 1/37. **(b)** 100. **(c)** 1. **(d)** $df = 36$. P-value $= 0.54$. Since the P-value is quite large, there is insufficient evidence that the roulette wheel is not balanced. **11.25 (a)** False; larger X^2 might be due to larger sample size rather than stronger association. **(b)** Yes. Confidence interval for race effect includes larger values than confidence interval for gender effect, so race has the stronger association with opinion on death penalty. **11.27** There are several possible answers. The proportion of male victims murdered by females $= 0.77$. The proportion of male victims murdered by males $= 0.70$. Ratio $= 0.77/0.70 = 1.1$. Male victims are 1.1 times more likely (i.e., 10% more likely) to have been murdered by a female than by a male. (That is, relatively more females murder males than males murder males.) **11.29 (a)** The proportion with myocardial infarctions in the naproxen group was 0.003 (or 0.3 percentage points) lower than the proportion in the rofecoxib group. **(b)** The proportion with myocardial infarctions in the naproxen group is 0.2 times (or 80%) lower than the proportion in the rofecoxib group. **(c)** $1/0.2 = 5$ times more likely. **11.31 (a)** The difference of proportions is $0.00135 - 0.00046 = 0.00089$. The proportion of male teenagers who die is 0.089 percentage points higher than the proportion of female teenagers who die. **(b)** The relative risk is $0.00135/0.00046 = 2.9$. Male teenagers are 2.9 times more likely to die than are female teenagers. **(c)** The relative risk seems more useful because it shows there is a substantial gender effect, which the difference does not show when both proportions are close to 0. **11.33 (a)** The proportion of females who identify as Republican is 0.5 percentage points smaller than the proportion for males. **(b)** The proportion of females who identify as Democrat is 6.6 percentage points higher than the proportion for males. **(c)** The proportion of females who identify as Republican is 2% lower than the proportion for males. **(d)** The proportion of females who identify as Democrat is 20% higher than the proportion for males. **(e)** Rather weak association between gender and whether identifying as Republican, as seen from parts a and c. Stronger association between gender and whether identifying as Democrat, as seen in parts b and d. **11.35 (a)** The observed count is -2.49 standard deviations below the expected one for this cell. **(b)** Both show that the observed count is much higher than the expected one (greater than 3 standard deviations). For people with above-average income, many more were very happy than what independence between income and happiness would predict. For people with below-average income, many more were not happy than what independence would imply. **(c)** Both show that the observed count is much lower than the expected one (greater than 3 standard deviations). For people with average income, many fewer were not happy than what independence would predict. For people with below-average income, many fewer were very happy than what independence would imply. **11.37 (a)** Observed count is only 0.9 standard deviations below expected count—not unusual under the null hypothesis of independence. **(b)** These are the cells with positive residuals. Consider category (very happy, very happy). The large positive residual indicates that those very happy in their marriage are more likely also to be very happy in general compared to what would be predicted under independence. **11.39** Females tend to be Democrat more often and males tend to be Democrat less often than one would expect if party ID were independent of gender. **11.41 (a)**

Treatment	S	F	Total
Control	2	6	**8**
Diet & Exercise	12	0	**12**

(b) (1) There are two binary categorical variables, and randomization was used. **(2)** $H_0: p_1 = p_2$; $H_a: p_1 \neq p_2$. **(3)** Test statistic: 2. **(4)** P-value: 0.001. **(5)** Strong evidence that diet and exercise are associated with ability to solve a task. **(c)** Because the expected cell counts are less than 5 for at least some cells. **11.43 (a)** 0.24; no evidence for an association between nervousness and treatment. **(b)** No, two cells have expected count < 5, (2.5 and 3.5, respectively). **11.45 (a)** First row: 5, 0; second row: 6, 6. **(b)** 462 out of 6,188 permutations (= 0.075) have a first cell count as large or larger than 5. **(c)** The (exact or permutation) P-value of 0.075 (> than significance level of 0.05) indicates not sufficient evidence to conclude that the probability to change study habits is larger in the STAT course. **11.47 (a)**

Gender	Y	N	Total
Male	94%	6%	**100%**
Female	94%	6%	**100%**

(b) Yes; percentages of men and women who would vote for a qualified woman may be the same. **11.49 (1)** Assumptions: Two categorical variables, randomization, expected count at least 5 in all cells. **(2)** H_0: Blood test result independent of Down syndrome status; H_a: Blood test result dependent on Down syndrome status. **(3)** $X^2 = 114.4$, $df = 1$. **(4)** P-value = 0.000. **(5)** Very strong evidence of an association between test result and actual status. **11.51 (a)** The chance of any particular happiness category (such as very happy) would be identical for each number of close friends. **(b)** The number of cases we'd expect in a given cell if the two variables were independent. $(169 \times 164)/1,446 = 19.2$. **(c) (i)** Those with highest number of close friends; **(ii)** those with fewest close friends. **11.53 (a)** $df = 9$; chi-squared probability distribution for $df = 9$. **(b)** There is no evidence that income level and job satisfaction are associated. **11.55 (a)** Table with single row of 313, 108, 101, 32 showing the counts for the four combinations RY, RG, WY, and WG. **(b)** (9/16, 3/16, 3/16, 1/16). **(c)** $312.75 (= 556 \times (9/16))$, 104.25, 104.25, 34.75. **(d)** $df = 4 - 1 = 3$. **(e)** Large because the chi-square statistic of 0.47 is well below the expected value of 3, so area above 0.47 under chi-squared curve with $df = 3$ is large. **11.57 (a)** The proportion who were injured is 0.06 higher for those who did not wear a seat belt than for those who wore a seat belt. **(b)** People were 1.95 times as likely to be injured if they were not wearing a seat belt than if they were wearing a seat belt. **11.59 (a)** Relative risk $= (29/127)/(19,485/26,571) = 0.31$. The proportion of organic food samples with pesticide residues present was 69% (or 0.31 times) lower than the proportion of conventional food samples with pesticide residues present. **(b)** The proportion of conventional food samples with pesticide residues present was 3.2 (= 1/0.31) times larger than the proportion for organic food samples with pesticide residues. **(c)** Odd ratio $= (29/98)/(19,485/7,086) = 0.11$. The odds of finding pesticide residues on organic food samples were 89% (or 0.11 times) lower than on conventional food samples. **(d)** The odds of finding pesticide residues on conventional food samples were 9.1 times higher than on organic food samples. **(e)** The *proportion* is only about 3.2 times larger

(= relative risk), but the *odds* are more than 9 times larger. This statement confuses relative risk with the odds ratio. **11.61** Those with no or 2 or more sex partners in the previous year are much less likely to be very happy than would be expected if happiness and number of sex partners were independent. Conversely, those with 1 sex partner are much more likely to be very happy than expected under independence. **11.63 (a)** $H_0: p_1 = p_2$; $H_a: p_1 \neq p_2$; p_1: population proportion of those who are aggressive in the group that watches less than one hour of TV per day; p_2: population proportion of those who are aggressive in the group that watches more than one hour of TV per day. **(b)** 0.0001; very strong evidence that TV watching and aggression are associated. **11.65 (b)** No, many cell counts are very small, leading to expected cell counts that are less than 5. Then, the sampling distribution of X^2 may not be approximately chi-squared. **(c)** Approximate permutation P-value = 9,908/10,000 = 0.9908. This P-value is large and almost 1. There is no evidence that the clarity depends on whether the diamond's cut is good or fair. **11.67** Report could include: Contingency table of summary counts and Pearson chi-squared = 21.4, $df = 6$, P-value = 0.002. **11.69** Answers will vary. **11.71 (a)**

	Has Young Children	
Gray Hair	Yes	No
Yes	0	4
No	5	0

(b) Yes. **(c)** There often are third factors, such as age in this case, that influence an association. **11.73 (a)** Difference of proportion with United States as group 1: 0.000037; Britain as group 1: −0.000037. **(b)** Relative risk with United States as group 1: 4.6; Britain as group 1: 0.22. **(c)** Relative risk; the difference may be very small although one is many times the other. **11.75** Given a large enough sample, even a very weak association may be found significant. It is important to consider whether the association is practical as well. **11.77** True. **11.79** False. **11.81 (a)** The chi-squared value for a right-tail probability of 0.05 and $df = 1$ is 3.84, which is the z value for a two-tail probability of 0.05 squared: $(1.96)(1.96) = 3.84$. **(b)** The chi-squared value for P-value of 0.01 and $df = 1$ is 6.63. This is (apart from rounding) the square of the z value for a two-tail P-value of 0.01, which is 2.58. **11.83** The two observed values in a given row (or column) must add up to the same total as the two expected values in that same row (or column). **11.85** For the top row the last number must be 33 because the numbers must add up to the row total of 100. For the bottom row, the numbers must add to the column totals of 40 for each column. Thus, the bottom row should read 16, 19, 28, 30, and 7. **11.87 (a)**

F1, F2, F3	F1, F2, M1	F1, F2, M2	F1, F2, M3
F1, F3, M1	F1, F3, M2	F1, F3, M3	F1, M1, M2
F1, M1, M3	F1, M2, M3	F2, F3, M1	F2, F3, M2
F2, F3, M3	F2, M1, M2	F2, M1, M3	F2, M2, M3
F3, M1, M2	F3, M1, M3	F3, M2, M3	M1, M2, M3

This contingency table shows that two males were chosen (M1 and M3) and one was not (M2). It also shows that one female was chosen (F2) and two were not (F1 and F3). **(b)** 10 of the 20 tables have a first cell count of 2 or 3. Under a null hypothesis of no gender bias versus an alternative hypothesis of a preference for males, observing tables with 2 or 3 males selected (i.e., a 2 or 3 in the first cell) has a probability of 0.5, which is the P-value from Fisher's exact test. **11.89 (b)** No, there are 6 cells with expected cell count below 5. The chi-squared distribution may not approximate well the actual sampling distribution of X^2. **(c)** (Answers will vary.) We got a value of 3.1, smaller than the observed 14.1. **(d)** (Answers will vary.) For us, none of the 10 permutations gave a value as large or larger than 14.1. **(e)** (Answers will vary slightly.) For us, 233 of the 10,000 permutations resulted in a chi-squared statistic as large or larger than the observed one, giving a P-value of 0.0233. This P-value is interpreted as: if there is no association between grade level and opinion, observing a test statistic as large or larger than the one we have observed is unlikely (probability of 0.02). With such a small P-value, we reject the null hypothesis and conclude that there is an association between the grade level and the opinion about voting with 16.

Chapter 12

12.1 (a) Response: mileage; explanatory: weight. **(b)** $\hat{y} = 45.6 - 0.0052x$; y-intercept is 45.6; slope is -0.0052. **(c)** For each 1,000-pound increase, the predicted mileage will decrease by 5.2 miles per gallon. **(d)** No; the y-intercept is the predicted miles per gallon for a car that weighs 0 pounds. **12.3 (a)** 322.6 kg. **(b)** 117.5 kg. **(c)** The y-intercept indicates that for male athletes who cannot perform any repetitions for a fatigue bench press, the predicted max bench press is 117.5 kg. As repBP increases from 0 to 35, the predicted maxBP increases from 117.5 to 322.6 kg. **12.5** For a given x-value, there will not be merely one y value—not every elementary schoolgirl in your town who is a given height will weigh the same. **12.7 (a)** There appears to be a positive relationship between GPA and study time. **(b)** Predicted GPA = 2.63 + 0.0439 Study time. For every one-hour increase in study time per week, GPA is predicted to increase by about .04 points. **(c)** 3.73. **(d)** -0.13. The observed GPA for Student 2, who studies an average of 25 hours per week, is 3.6, which is 0.13 points below the predicted GPA of 3.73. **12.9 (a)** A clear trend is visible in the scatterplot, showing that phones with larger capacity tend to weigh more. One phone (number 70 with battery capacity of 3,300) has a much larger battery capacity than all the others, yet its weight is about average, not following this trend. This phone is a clear outlier. **(b)** It will pull the regression line toward it. Its residual will be negative and very large in absolute value. **(c)** $\hat{y} = 66.7 + 0.0436x$. Predicted weight at capacity 1,000mAh: 110g; predicted weight at 1,500mAh: 132g. **(d)** For every 100 mAh increase in the capacity of a cell phone's battery, the predicted weight increases by 4.3g. **12.11 (a)** 23. **(b)** -2.07 and 2.07. **(c)** 2.07. **12.13 (a)** On average, the selling price of a house increases between $64 and $90 for every one square foot increase in size. **(b)** On average, the selling price of a house increases between $6,400 and $9,000 for every 100 square feet increase in size. **12.15 (a) (i)** Assume linear relationship between mean maximum leg press and number of 200-pound leg presses, random sample, normal conditional distribution of maximum leg press for given number of 200-pound leg presses with constant standard deviations. These data are not a random sample, so conclusions are highly tentative; **(ii)** $H_0: \beta = 0$; $H_a: \beta \neq 0$; **(iii)** $t = 9.6$; **(iv)** P-value = 0.000; **(v)** Very strong evidence that a linear relationship exists between these variables. **(b)** (4.2, 6.4). On average, maximum leg press increases between 4.2 pounds and 6.4 pounds for every additional 200-pound leg press that the athlete can do. The interval gives us a range of plausible values for the increase. The test only tells us there is strong evidence that the increase (slope) is significantly different from 0. **12.17 (a)** Having more daughters is good. **(b) (i)** Assume that there was roughly a linear relationship between variables, and that the data were gathered using randomization and that the population y-values at each x-value follow a normal distribution, with roughly the same standard deviation at each x-value; **(ii)** $H_0: \beta = 0$; $H_a: \beta \neq 0$; **(iii)** $t = 1.52$; **(iv)** P-value = 0.13; **(v)** There is insufficient evidence for a relationship. **(c)** $(-0.1, 1.0)$. Zero is a plausible value for this slope. **12.19 (a)** Means: advertising is 2, sales is 7. Standard deviations: advertising is 2.16, sales is 2.16. **(b)** $\hat{y} = 5.286 + 0.857x$. **(c)** For $H_0: \beta = 0$; $H_a: \beta \neq 0$, $t = 2.35$, P-value = 0.14; there is insufficient evidence for a relationship between advertising and sales. **12.21** $(-0.11, -0.05)$. On average, GPA decreases by between 0.05 and 0.11 points for every additional class that is skipped. **12.23** 0.0015. **12.25** Answers will vary. **12.27 (a)** There is a strong, positive linear relationship between weight and percent body fat. **(b)** $r^2 = 0.78$. Using the regression equation with weight to predict percent body fat instead of predicting it with the sample mean results in a 78% reduction in the overall prediction error (the sum of the squared errors). **(c)** No. The correlation r does not depend on the units. **12.29 (a)** 650. **(b)** $x = 800$ is 3 standard deviations above the mean, so the predicted y value is 0.5(3) = 1.5 standard deviations above the mean. **12.31 (a)** $r = 0.81$. There is a fairly strong, positive linear relationship between study time and GPA. **(b)** $r^2 = 0.66$. **(i)** The overall prediction error when using the regression equation with study time to predict GPA is 66% smaller compared to using the sample mean GPA; **(ii)** 66% of

the variability observed in college GPA can be explained by the linear relationship with study time. **12.33** Explanatory is midterm score, response is final score. No. These students were very low to start with so the increase could have occurred because of regression to the mean. Subjects who are relatively low at one time will, on the average, be higher at a later time. **12.35** We can expect that the five leaders will, on average, have higher scores in the second round. **12.37** Correlation for the means because there will be less variability. **12.39 (a)** Positive correlation with one outlier. **(b)** The correlation drops so dramatically because it depends in magnitude on the variability in scores. Without the outlier, the range of x values is much smaller. **12.41 (a)** 105.00 = maximum bench press observed for athlete 10; 85.90 = predicted maximum bench press based on BP60 = 15; 19.10 = difference between actually observed and predicted maximum bench press = residual for athlete 10; 2.41 = standardized residual = how many standard errors the residual for athlete 10 falls above 0. **(b)** No; we would expect about 5% of standardized residuals to have an absolute value above 2.0. **12.43 (a)** Distribution of standardized residuals and hence conditional distribution of maximum bench press. **(b)** The conditional distribution seems to be approximately normal. **12.45 (a)** 448 = predicted amount spent on clothes in past year for those in 12th grade of school. **(b)** (427,469): range of plausible values for the population mean of dollars spent on clothes for 12th grade students in the school. **(c)** (101, 795): range of plausible values for the individual observations (dollars spent on clothes) for all the 12th grade students at the school. **12.47 (a)** The square root of 1,303.72 is 36.1. This is the estimated standard deviation of maximum leg presses for female athletes who can do a fixed number of 200-pound leg presses. **(b)** Standard deviation = 36.1; (277.6, 422.0). **12.49 (a)** Total SS = residual SS + regression SS, where residual SS = error in using the regression line to predict y, regression SS = how much less error there is in predicting y using the regression line compared to using $\bar{y}$. **(b)** Sum of squares around mean divided by $n - 1$ is 192,787/56 = 3,442.6, and its square root is 58.7. This estimates the overall standard deviation of y-values whereas the residual s estimates the standard deviation of y-values at a fixed value of x. **(c)** The F test statistic is 92.87; its square root is the t statistic of 9.64. **12.51 (a)** MS values: 200,000, 22,580.6; F: 8.86. **(b)** $H_0: \beta = 0$ against $H_a: \beta \neq 0$.

12.53

Source	Df	SS	MS	F	P
Regression	1	13,682	13,682	29.24	0.000
Error	76	35,560	468		
Total	77	49,242			

(a) Total SS = 49,242 = residual SS + regression SS = 13,682 + 35,560. The total SS is a measure of the overall variability in y (phone weight) but also measures the overall error when using $\bar{y}$ to predict y. The residual SS measures the overall prediction error when using $\hat{y}$ to predict y. Their difference equals the regression SS, which tells us how much the prediction error decreases when using $\hat{y}$ instead of $\bar{y}$ to predict y. **(b)** $s = 21.6$, which is the square root of 468, the mean square error. It estimates the standard deviation of cell phone weight at a given battery capacity value. **(c)** $s_y = 25.3$. This describes the variability in cell phone weight over the entire range of battery capacity values, not just the variability in cell phone weight at a particular capacity value. **12.55 (a)** $(1.072)^{10} = 2.0$. **(b)** $(1.10)^{10} = 2.59$; the effect here is multiplicative, not additive. **12.57 (a)** $\hat{y} = 81.14 \times 1.1339^0 = 81.14$ million; $\hat{y} = 81.14 \times 1.1339^{11} = 323.26$ million. **(b)** 1.1339 is the multiplicative effect on $\hat{y}$ for a one-unit increase in x. **(c)** This suggests a very good fit of data to model. The high correlation coefficient indicates a linear relation between the log of the y values and the x values. **12.59 (a)** 5.53 is the predicted number of cases on March 6th (when $x = 0$). 1.51 is the multiplicative effect on the number of infected people per day (i.e., a 51% increase per day). **(b) (i)** 8.3; **(ii)** 28.7; **(iii)** 1,771.7. **(c)** Every 1.68 days. **12.61 (a)** The exponential model because the log of y values and the x values have a larger (absolute value) correlation coefficient. **(b)** 3.35 weeks. **12.63 (a)** 0.9. **(b)** 68; $\hat{y} = 68 + 0.9x$. **(c)** $\hat{y} = 280 + 0.4x$. **12.65** Response: height of children; explanatory: height of parents. Children tend to be short but not as short as parents. Because of regression toward the mean, the value of y tends (on the average) to be not so far from its mean as the *x* value is from its mean. **12.67 (a)** 210,991. This house sold for $210,991 more than would have been predicted. **(b)** This observation is 4.02 standard errors higher than predicted. **12.69 (a)** Residual standard deviation of *y*: variability of the *y*-values at a particular *x*-value; standard deviation: variability of all of the *y*-values. **(b)** Variability of *y*-values at a given *x* is about the same as variability of all *y* observations; $r^2 = 0.13$. **12.71 (a)** The plausible values range from 338 to 365 for the mean of *y* values for all female high school athletes having $x = 80$. **(b)** For all female high school athletes with a maximum bench press of 80, we predict that 95% of them have maximum leg press between about 248 and 455 pounds. The 95% PI is for a single observation *y*, whereas the confidence interval is for the mean of *y*. **12.73 (a)** $1,000 \times 2^5 = 32,000$. **(b)** $1,000 \times 2^{10} = 1,024,000$. **(c)** $1,000 \times 2^x$. **12.75 (a)** 1,900: $\hat{y} = 1.424 \times 1.014^0 = 1.42$ billion; 2010: $\hat{y} = 1.424 \times 1.014^{110} = 6.57$ billion. **(b)** The fit of the model corresponds to a rate of growth of 1.4% per year because multiplying by 1.014 adds an additional 1.4% each year. **(c) (i)** The predicted population size doubles after 50 years because $1.014^{50} = 2.0$, the number by which we'd multiply the original population size; **(ii)** It quadruples after 100 years: $1.014^{100} = 4.0$. **(d)** The exponential regression model is more appropriate for these data because the log of the population size and the year number are more highly correlated ($r = 0.99$) than are the population size and the year number. **12.77 (a)** The 3 outlying points represent outliers—values more than 1.5 × IQR beyond either Q1 or Q3. **(b)** From software: Diff = $-9.125 + 1.178$ Run; difference is positive when $-9.125 + 1.178(\text{runs}) > 0$, which is equivalent to runs > $9.125/1.178 = 7.7$. **(c)** Runs, hits, and difference are positively related with one another. Errors are negatively related with those three variables.

	Run	Hits	Errors
Hits	0.819		
Errors	−0.259	−0.154	
Difference	0.818	0.657	−0.501

(d) From software, the P-value of 0.000 for testing that the slope equals 0 provides extremely strong evidence that DIFF and RUNS are related. **12.79** Report would interpret results from:

high_sch_GPA = 3.44 − 0.0183 TV

S = 0.446707 R-Sq = 7.2% R-Sq(adj) = 5.6%

Source	DF	SS	MS	F	P
Regression	1	0.8921	0.8921	4.47	0.039
Error	58	11.5737	0.1995		
Total	59	12.4658			

12.81 (a) In this case, the predictions should exactly match the observations, i.e., $y = x$ which translates to the true *y*-intercept equaling 0 and the true slope equaling 1. **(b)** No. The P-value for testing that the true *y*-intercept is 0 is large, so that we are unable to conclude that the *y*-intercept differs from 0. **12.83** Explain how players or teams that had a particularly good or bad year tended to have results in the following year that were not so extreme (i.e., regression toward the mean). **12.85** As the range of values reflected by each sample is restricted, the correlation tends to decrease when we consider just students of a restricted range of ages. **12.87 (a)** The slope would be two times the original slope. **(b)** The correlation coefficient would not change because it is independent of units. **(c)** The *t* statistic would not change because although the slope doubles, so does its standard error. (The result of a test should not depend on the units we use.) **12.89 (a)** There are two parameters α and β, and so $df = n − 2$. **(b)** There is only one parameter, and therefore, $df = n − 1$. **12.91 (a)** The percentage would likely fluctuate over time, and this would not be a linear relationship. **(b)** Annual medical expenses would likely be quite high at low ages, then lower in the middle, then high again, forming a parabolic, rather than linear, relationship. **(c)** The relation between these variables is likely curvilinear. Life expectancy increases for a while as per capita income increases, then gradually levels off. **12.93 (a)** The statement is referring to additive growth, but this is multiplicative growth. There is an exponential

relation between these variables. **(b)** $\hat{y} = \$175,000 \times 0.966^{10} = \$123,825$; the percentage decline for the decade is about 29.2%. **12.95 (b)**. **12.97 (d)**. **12.99** The best response is (b). **12.101 (a)** At 0 impact velocity, there would be 0 putting distance. The line would pass through the point having coordinates $(0, 0)$. **(b)** If *x* doubles, then x^2 (and hence the mean of *y*) quadruples; e.g., if *x* goes from 2 to 4, then x^2 goes from 4 to 16. **12.103** Because $r^2 = (\Sigma(y − \bar{y})^2 − \Sigma(y − \hat{y})^2)/\Sigma(y − \bar{y})^2$, and dividing each term by approximately *n* (actually, $n − 1$ and $n − 2$) gives the variance estimates, it represents the relative difference between the quantity used to summarize the overall variability of the *y* values and the quantity used to summarize the residual variability. **12.105 (a)** Error is calculated by subtracting the mean from the actual score, *y*. If this difference is positive, then the observation must fall above the mean. **(b)** $\epsilon = 0$ when the observation falls exactly at the mean. **(c)** Since the residual $e = y − \hat{y}$, we have $y = \hat{y} + e = a + bx + e$. As $\hat{y}$ is an estimate of the population mean, *e* is an estimate of ϵ. **(d)** It does not make sense to use the simpler model, $y = \alpha + \beta x$ that does not have an error term because it is improbable that every observation will fall exactly on the regression line.

Chapter 13

13.1 (a) $\hat{y} = 134.3$. **(b)** -19.3. The actual total body weight is 19.3 pounds lower than predicted. **13.3 (a) (i)** 3.80; **(ii)** 1.60. **(b)** $\hat{y} = 0.20 + 0.50 x_1 + 0.002(500) = 0.20 + 0.50 x_1 + 1 = 1.20 + 0.50 x_1$. **(c)** $\hat{y} = 0.20 + 0.50 x_1 + 0.002(600) = 0.20 + 0.50 x_1 + 1.2 = 1.40 + 0.50 x_1$. **(d)** The student with college board score 600 has the higher predicted college GPA. **13.5 (a) (i)** 18.3; **(ii)** 12.5. **(b)** When education goes up $10 = 80 − 70$, predicted crime rate changes by 10 multiplied by the slope, $10(−0.58) = −5.8$. **(c) (i)** $\hat{y} = 59.1 − 0.583 x_1 + 0.683(0) = 59.1 − 0.583 x_1$; **(ii)** $\hat{y} = 59.1 − 0.583 x_1 + 0.683(50) = 93.2 − 0.583 x_1$. **(iii)** $\hat{y} = 59.1 − 0.583 x_1 + 0.683(100) = 127.4 − 0.583 x_1$. For each fixed level of urbanization, the predicted crime rate decreases by 5.8 for every 10 percentage-point increase in education. **(d) (i)** Line passing through all data points has positive slope; **(ii)** line when only considering urbanization = 50 has negative slope; when ignoring urbanization, the predicted crime rate increases with increasing education. When controlling (adjusting) for a given level of urbanization, the predicted crime rate decreases with increasing education. **13.7 (a)** $\hat{y} = 26,417,000 + 168,300(\text{GIR}) + 33,859(\text{SS}) − 19,784,000(\text{AvePutt}) − 44,725(\text{Events})$. **(b)** Keeping all other variables constant, the predicted earnings decrease the higher the average number of putts after reaching the green (which results in a higher score and, hence, a lower ranking). **(c)** $\hat{y} = 26,417,000 + 168,300(60) + 33,859(50) − 19,784,000(1.5) − 44,725(20) = 7,637,450$. **13.9** We don't need to control x_2 if it's not associated with x_1. Changes in x_2 will not have an impact on the effect of x_1 on *y*. **13.11 (a)** The relationship between price and age is linear, negative, and strong. The relationship between price and HP is less clear; it may be linear but rather weak. **(b)** Predicted price = $19,348.7 − 1,406.3(\text{Age}) + 25.5(\text{HP})$; **(i)** 10,100; **(ii)** 7,300. **(c)** No, the predicted price difference depends on the age of the two cars because each predicted price depends on it. Only if the age of the two cars is the same does the effect of age cancel out, and the predicted price difference will be $25.5(80 − 60) = 510$. **13.13 (a)** Height because it is more strongly correlated with weight than are age and percent body fat. **(b)** One of the properties of R^2 is that it gets larger, or at worst stays the same, whenever an explanatory variable is added to the multiple regression model. **(c)** No, the reduction in error from using the regression equation to predict weight rather than using the sample mean is only 1% more when adding age. **13.15 (a)** $R^2 = \dfrac{\Sigma(y − \bar{y})^2 − \Sigma(y − \hat{y})^2}{\Sigma(y − \bar{y})^2} = (222,102,253 − 69,534,753)/$ 222,102,253 = 0.69. **(b)** Using both age and horsepower to predict used car price reduces the prediction error by 69%, relative to using the sample mean price $\bar{y}$. **(c)** 69% of the variability in used car prices can be explained by the varying age and horsepower of the cars. **13.17 (a)** The number of hits does not have an effect over and above the effects of runs and errors, because the slope is so small. For every additional hit, keeping everything else constant, the difference is predicted to only increase by 0.026. **(b)** A small increase in R^2 indicates that the predictive power doesn't increase much with the addition of this explanatory variable over and above the other explanatory variables. **13.19** $R^2 = 25.8\%$; $R = 0.51$. Using these variables together to predict college GPA reduces the prediction error by 26%, relative to using $\bar{y}$ alone to predict college GPA. The correlation coefficient between the observed college GPAs and the predicted college GPAs equals 0.51. Only 25.8% of the observed variability in students' college GPA can be explained by their high school GPA and study time. The remaining 74.2% of the variability in college GPA is due to other factors. **13.21 (a)** If the null hypothesis were true, the probability would be 0.63 of getting a test statistic at least as extreme as the value observed. There is sufficient evidence that study time helps predict college GPA, once we control for high school GPA. **(b)** $(-0.02, 0.04)$. Because 0 falls in the confidence interval, it is plausible that the slope is 0 and that study time has no relationship with college GPA once high school GPA is controlled for. **(c)** No. It is likely that study time and high school GPA are highly correlated and therefore it doesn't add much predictive power to the model to include study time once high school GPA is already in the model. This does not mean that study time is not related with college GPA. **13.23 (a) (1)** Assumptions: We assume a random sample and that the model holds. Here, the 57 athletes were a convenience sample, not a random sample, so inferences may not be valid. **(2)** Hypotheses: H_0: $\beta_2 = 0$; H_a: $\beta_2 \neq 0$. **(3)** Test Statistic: $t = 1.39$. **(4)** P-value: 0.17. **(5)** Conclusion: The P-value of 0.17 does not give strong evidence against the null hypothesis that $\beta_2 = 0$. There is insufficient evidence that the number of times an athlete can perform a 200-pound leg press helps predict upper body strength once we control for the number of times the athlete can do a 60-pound bench press. **(b)** $b_2 \pm t_{.025}(se) = 0.211 \pm 2.005(0.152) = 0.211 \pm 0.305$ or $(-0.1, 0.5)$. The small values in the interval suggest a weak impact, if there is one at all. **(c)** When LP200 is included in the model, the P-value of the slope associated with BP60 is 0.000, very strong evidence that the slope of BP60 is not 0. **13.25 (a)** The residual standard deviation estimates the standard deviation of the distribution of maxBP at given values for BP60 and LP200. This standard deviation is assumed to be the same for any combination of BP60 and LP200 values and is estimated as 7.9. The sample standard deviation of maxBP of 13.3 shows how much maxBP values vary overall, over the entire range of BP60 and LP200 values, not over just a particular pair of values. **(b)** Approximately 95% of maxBPs fall within about $2s = 15.8$ of the true regression equation. **(c)** The prediction interval is an inference about where the population maxBP values fall at fixed levels of the two explanatory variables. **(d)** It would be unusual because 100 is not in the prediction interval. **13.27 (a)** $\mu_y = \alpha + \beta_1 x_1 + \beta_2 x_2$; where μ_y is the population mean for monthly revenue, x_1 is a given level of TV advertising and x_2 is a given level of newspaper advertising. **(b)** H_0: $\beta_1 = 0$. **(c)** H_0: $\beta_1 = \beta_2 = 0$. **13.29 (a)** $F = 9.49$, P-value ≈ 0. **(b)** H_a: At least one β parameter differs from 0. **(c)** The result in part a indicates only that at least one of the variables helps with predicting mental health impairment. **13.31 (a)** H_0: $\beta_1 = \beta_2 = 0$; H_a: At least one β parameter differs from 0; $F = 108.60$; P-value $= 0.000$; the P-value of 0.000 gives very strong evidence against the null hypothesis that $\beta_1 = \beta_2 = 0$. It is not surprising to get such a small P-value for this test because size and number of bedrooms are both statistically significant predictors of selling price. **(b)** The t statistic is 2.85 with a P-value of 0.0025. If the null hypothesis were true, the probability would be close to 0 of getting a test statistic at least as extreme as the value observed. The small P-value indicates that there is sufficient evidence that the number of bedrooms helps in predicting the selling price once we control for the house size. **(c)** $b_2 \pm t_{0.025}(se) = 15.170 \pm 1.97(5.330) = 15.170 \pm 10.50 = (4.67, 25.67)$ for given house size, we predict that the selling price increases between 4.7 and 25.7 thousand dollars for every additional bedroom.

```
The regression equation is
HP in thousands = 60.1 + 0.0630 House Size + 15.2
Bedrooms
Predictor      Coef      SE Coef       T       P
Constant      60.10       18.62      3.23    0.001
House Size  0.062983    0.004753    13.25    0.000
Bedrooms      15.170       5.330      2.85    0.005
S = 80.2707 R-Sq = 52.4% R-Sq(adj) = 52.0%
```

```
Analysis of Variance
Source           DF      SS      MS        F       P
Regression        2  1399524  699762  108.60  0.000
Residual Error  197  1269345    6443
Total           199  2668870
```

13.33 (a) The values of BP60 play a role in determining the standardized residuals against which the LP200 values are plotted. **(b)** The residuals are closer to 0 at lower values of LP200. **(c)** Without the three points with standardized residuals around -2, the data do not appear as though there is more variability at higher levels of LP200. We should be cautious in looking at residuals plots because one or two observations might prevent us from seeing the overall pattern. **13.35 (a)** U-shaped scatterplot. **(b)** U-shaped pattern, with residuals above 0 for small age and large age and residuals below 0 for medium-size age values. **13.37** The purpose of performing residual analysis is to determine if assumptions are met for tests. We cannot construct a single plot of the data for all the variables at once because such a plot would require many dimensions. **13.39 (a)** The histogram checks the assumption that the conditional distribution of y is normal, at any fixed values of the explanatory variables. Although the distribution appears mostly normal, there is an outlier with a standardized residual above 6. **(b)** This plot checks the assumption that the regression equation approximates well the true relationship between the predictors and the mean of y. The same large standardized residual (>6) is evident, but there does not appear to be a discernible pattern in the residuals. **13.41 (a)** U.S. cars: predicted price $= 20,493 - 1,185(\text{age}) - 2,379(1) = 18,114 - 1,185(\text{age})$. Foreign cars: predicted price $= 20,493 - 1,185(\text{age}) - 2,379(0) =$ price $= 20,493 - 1,185(\text{age}) - 2,379(0) = 20,493 - 1,185(\text{age})$. **(b)** Both prediction equations in part a have the same slope of $-1,185$. For a one-year increase in the age of a car, we predict that the price drops by $1,185. Since the slope is the same, this applies for both types of cars. **(c) (i)** Predicted price $= 20,493 - 1,185(8) - 2,379(1) = 8,634$; **(ii)** predicted price $= 20,493 - 1,185(8) = 11,013$. Difference in predicted price between U.S. and foreign 8-year-old car $= 8,634 - 11,013 = -2,379$, which is the coefficient for the indicator variable for type. **13.43 (a)** $\hat{y} = 96.3 + 0.0664\,\text{house\_size} + 12.9\,\text{condition}$; Good condition: $\hat{y} = 96.3 + 0.0665\,\text{house\_size} + 12.9(1) = 109.2 + 0.0665\,\text{house\_size}$; Not good condition: $\hat{y} = 96.3 + 0.0665\,\text{house\_size} + 12.9(0) = 96.3 + 0.0665\,\text{house\_size}$. **(c)** The difference between the predicted selling price for the two different conditions of the property, controlling for house size, is the slope for condition, 12.9. **13.45 (a)** $x_1 = 1$ if inner city; 0 if other; $x_2 = 1$ if suburbia; 0 if other. **(b)** Suburbia: $\hat{y} = 5.8 - 0.7(0) + 1.2(1) = 7.0$; interstate exits: $\hat{y} = 5.8 - 0.7(0) + 1.2(0) = 5.8$. Interstate exit restaurants have predicted sales of $1.20 less than suburbia restaurants. **13.47 (a)** The assumption of no interaction means that we are assuming that the slope for house size is the same for houses with or without a garage. **13.49 (a)** We would have two explanatory variables, one for number of people and one for location (campus $= 0$, and mall $= 1$). **(b)** We would have a model with one explanatory variable, number of people, for the campus location, and another model with one explanatory variable, number of people, for the mall location. **13.51 (a)**
$$\hat{p} = \frac{e^{(-6.7+0.0175(359))}}{1 + e^{(-6.7+0.0175(359))}} = 0.397; \hat{p} = \frac{e^{(-6.7+0.0175(369))}}{1 + e^{(-6.7+0.0175(369))}} = 0.440.$$
(b) $\hat{p} = \dfrac{e^{(-6.7+0.0175(465))}}{1 + e^{(-6.7+0.0175(465))}} = 0.808; \hat{p} = \dfrac{e^{(-6.7+0.0175(475))}}{1 + e^{(-6.7+0.0175(475))}} =$ 0.834. **13.53 (a)** $x = -\hat{\alpha}/\hat{\beta} = 2.04$. **(b)** Crabs over 2.04. **(c)** Crabs under 2.04. **13.55 (a)** $x = 50,000$. **(b) (i)** Above $50,000; **(ii)** Below $50,000. **(c)** 0.005. **13.57 (a)** student graduated (yes or no). **(b)**

Race	Gender	Graduated Yes	No	Total
White	Female	10,781	20,468	**31,249**
	Male	10,727	28,856	**39,583**
Black	Female	2,309	10,885	**13,194**
	Male	2,054	15,653	**17,707**

(c) Based on these estimates, White women have the highest estimated probability of graduating. The coefficient for race is positive, indicating that 1 (White) would lead to a higher estimated probability of graduating than would 0 (Black). Similarly, the coefficient for gender is positive, indicating that 1 (female) would lead to a higher estimated probability of graduating than would 0 (male). **13.59 (a)** $\hat{p} = \dfrac{e^{-3.596-0.868(0)+2.404(1)}}{1 + e^{-3.596-0.868(0)+2.404(1)}} = 0.233.$

(b)

	Defendant's Race	
Victim's Race	**White**	**Black**
White	0.113	0.233
Black	0.011	0.027

Defendant's race has the same effect on the predicted probability of receiving the death penalty for both White and Black victims. In both cases, Black defendants are predicted to be more likely to receive the death penalty than are White defendants. **(c)**

Defendant's Race	**Death Penalty**		**Percent**
	Yes	**No**	**Yes**
White	53	430	11.0
Black	15	176	7.9

This is an example of Simpson's paradox because the direction of association changes when we ignore a third variable. When ignoring victim's race, the predicted proportion of Whites receiving the death penalty is now higher than Blacks. This occurs because there are more White defendants with White victims than any other group. **13.61 (a)** $\hat{y} = 78.1$; the residual is $y - \hat{y} = 6.9$. **(b)** $\hat{y} = 64.8 + 1.33$ BP60; the slope of 1.33 indicates that, when controlling for LP200, an increase of one in BP60 relates to an increase of 1.33 in predicted maxBP. **(c)** The additional variable does not add much predictive ability. **13.63 (a)** $\hat{y} = 517.120$; the residual is -41.1; the violent crime rate for Massachusetts is 41.1 lower than predicted from this model. **(b) (i)** $\hat{y} = -270.7 + 28.334\,x_1$; **(ii)** $\hat{y} = 270.9 + 28.334\,x_1$. As percent living in urban areas increases from 0 to 100, the intercept of the regression equation increases from -270.7 to 270.9. When poverty rate is held constant, the increase in percent living in urban areas from 0 to 100 results in an increase in predicted violent crime rate of 541.6. **13.65 (a)** $-0.66.$ **(b)** 0.443. **(c)** 279,160. **(d)** 155,577. **(e)** 44.50. **(f)** 33.455. **(g)** $-5.21.$ **(h)** 0.000. **13.67 (a)** Predicted GDP $= 39{,}892 + 798(\text{CO2}) - 399(\text{NoInternet})$. **(b)** For given percentage of the population not using the Internet, we predict GDP to increase by \$798,000 for every metric ton increase in CO_2 emissions. Controlling for CO_2 emissions, we predict GDP to decrease by \$399,000 for every percentage point increase in the percentage of the population not using the Internet. **13.69 (a)** Estimated probabilities are 0.51 and 0.81, an increase of 0.30. **(b) (i)** $x = 24.9$; **(ii)** above a width of 24.9; **(iii)** below a width of 24.9. **13.71 (a)** This is because the coefficients are positive for all of these explanatory variables. **(b)** Because the estimate divided by the standard error is small (equals -0.93). **13.73** The explanations will be different for each student, but should indicate that multiple regression uses *more than one* characteristic of a subject to predict some outcome. **13.75** Indicator variables for a particular explanatory variable must be binary. Here we need three variables: one for Protestant (1 = Protestant, 0 = other), one for Catholic (1 = Catholic, 0 = other), and one for Jewish (1 = Jewish, 0 = other). Using numerical scores would treat religion as quantitative with equidistant categories, which is not appropriate. **13.77** $R^2 = 1$ only when all residuals are 0 because when all regression predictions are perfect (each $y = \hat{y}$), residual SS $= \Sigma(y - \hat{y})^2 = 0$. When residual SS $= 0$, R^2 is total SS divided by total SS, which must be 1. On the other hand, $R^2 = 0$ when each $\hat{y} = \bar{y}$. In that case, the estimated slopes all equal 0, and the correlation coefficient between y and each explanatory variable equals 0. Under these circumstances, the residual SS would equal the total SS, and R^2 would then be 0. In practical terms, it

means that R^2 is only 1 when the regression model predicts y perfectly, and it is only 0 when it doesn't predict y at all. **13.79 (a)**

Source	DF	SS	MS	F	P
Regression	2	1200.2	600.1	3.74	0.030
Residual Error	54	8674.4	160.6		
Total	56	9874.6			

P-value of 0.030 is less than 0.05. **(b)**

Predictor	Coef	SE Coef	T	P
Constant	54.019	9.677	5.58	0.000
WT (lbs)	0.1251	0.1378	0.91	0.368
BF%	0.3315	0.6950	0.48	0.635

P-values of 0.368 and 0.635 are both larger than 0.35. **13.81** a. **13.83** a. **13.85 (a)** True. **(b)** True. **(c)** False, R^2 cannot exceed 1. **(d)** False; the predicted values $\hat{y}$ cannot correlate negatively with y. Otherwise, the predictions would be worse than merely using $\bar{y}$ to predict y. **13.87** 10: Adjusted $R^2 = 0.357$; 100: Adjusted $R^2 = 0.490$; 1,000: Adjusted $R^2 = 0.499$. As the sample size increases, adjusted R^2 approaches R^2. **13.89** If we wanted to compare two groups on a given variable, we could use regression analysis. The response variable y would be the same. The explanatory variable would be the two levels of the groups; one would be assigned 0 and one would be assigned 1. $\mu_1 = \mu_2$ would correspond to $\beta = 0$. **13.91 (a)** This is a multiple regression model with two variables. If x, for example, is 5, we multiple 5 by β_1 and its square, 25, by β_2. **13.93** $p = e^{\alpha+\beta(-\alpha/\beta)}/(1 + e^{\alpha+\beta(-\alpha/\beta)}) = e^{0}/(1 + e^{0}) = 1/(1 + 1) = 0.50.$

Chapter 14

14.1 (a) Response variable: performance gap; Factor: which hotel the guest stayed in; Categories: five hotels. **(b)** $H_0: \mu_1 = \mu_2 = \mu_3 = \mu_4 = \mu_5$; H_a: at least two of the population means are different. **(c)** $df_1 = g - 1 = 5 - 1 = 4$; $df_2 = N - g = 125 - 5 = 120$. **(d)** From a table or software, $F = 2.45$. **14.3 (a) (i)** Assumptions: Independent random samples, normal population distributions with equal standard deviations; **(ii)** Hypotheses: $H_0: \mu_1 = \mu_2 = \mu_3$; H_a: at least two population means are different; **(iii)** Test statistic: $F = 2.50$ $(df_1 = 2, df_2 = 5)$; **(iv)** P-value $= 0.18$; **(v)** Conclusion: The data do not provide evidence for any difference in the population mean scores for these three groups. **(b)** The sample sizes are very small. **(c)** Observational; a lurking variable might be school GPA. Perhaps higher GPA students are more likely to have previously studied a language and higher GPA students also tend to do better on quizzes than other students. **14.5 (a)** $H_0: \mu_1 = \mu_2 = \mu_3$, where μ_1 represents the population mean satisfaction rating for San Jose, μ_2 for Toronto, and μ_3 for Bangalore. **(b)** $27.6 = 13.00/0.47$; $df_1 = 2$ and $df_2 = 297$. **(c)** Very small P-value of 0.000 gives strong evidence against the null; we would reject the null and conclude at least two population means differ. **14.7 (a)** μ_1 represents the population mean ideal number of kids for Protestant, μ_2 represents the population mean for Catholic, μ_3 for Jewish, μ_4 for those of Another Religion; $H_0: \mu_1 = \mu_2 = \mu_3 = \mu_4$. **(b)** Independent random samples; normal population distributions with equal standard deviations. **(c)** $F = 5.48$; P-value $= 0.001$. Very strong evidence that at least two of the population means differ. **(d)** No; ANOVA tests only whether at least two population means are different. **14.9 (a)** New York: mean $= 21.9$, sd $= 1.9$; London: 20.4, 2.8; Paris: 23.4, 2.8. **(b)** $H_0: \mu_1 = \mu_2 = \mu_3$, H_a: at least two population means are not equal; $F = 2.8$, P-value $= 0.083$. At a significance level of 0.05, we do not have sufficient evidence to reject H_0. There is not enough evidence that the population mean ratings of French restaurants in New York, London, and Paris are different. **14.11 (a)**

Level	N	Mean	StDev
famchange	17	7.265	7.157
cogchange	29	3.007	7.309
conchange	26	−0.450	7.989

The means of these groups are somewhat different. The standard deviations are similar. **(b)** $F = 5.42$; P-value $= 0.006$; strong evidence that at least two population means are different. **(c)** The assumptions are that there are independent random samples and normal population distributions with equal standard deviations. There is evidence of skew, but the test is robust with respect to this assumption. The subjects were randomly assigned to treatments. Note that since this was not a random sample of subjects suffering from anorexia, the scope of inference to the population may be limited. **14.13** $(\bar{y}_1 - \bar{y}_2) \pm t_{0.25}$

$$s\sqrt{\frac{1}{n_1} + \frac{1}{n_2}} = (63.7 - 49.0) \pm 1.961(70.81)\sqrt{\frac{1}{440} + \frac{1}{407}} = 14.7 \pm 9.55;$$

which is $(5.2, 24.2)$. With 95% confidence, we estimate that the mean time spent on Facebook is between 5 and 24 minutes per day higher for freshmen compared to seniors. **14.15 (a)** Classical music and Muzak. **(b)** Because the Tukey method uses an overall confidence level of 95% for the entire set of intervals. **14.17 (a)** $x_1 = 1$ for observations from the first group and $= 0$ otherwise; $x_2 = 1$ for observations from the second group and $= 0$ otherwise. **(b)** H_0: $\mu_1 = \mu_2 = \mu_3$; H_0: $\beta_1 = \beta_2 = 0$. **(c)** For group 1, $x_1 = 1, x_2 = 0$, so predicted mean response $= 12 + 6(1) + 3(0) = 18$. For group 2: $12 + 6(0) + 3(1) = 15$. For group 3: $12 + 6(0) + 3(0) = 12$. **14.19 (a)** $x_1 = 1$ for observations from San Jose and $= 0$ otherwise; $x_2 = 1$ for observations from Toronto and $= 0$ otherwise. **(b) (i)** This is the estimate for β_1, which equals 0.5. The estimated difference between the population means for San Jose and Bangalore is 0.5; **(ii)** This is the estimate for β_2, which equals 0.7. **14.21 (a)** Group 2 – Group 1: $(-8.7, 2.7)$. Group 3 – Group 1: $(-3.1, 7.1)$, Group 3 – Group 2: $(-0.7, 10.7)$. Because 0 falls in all three confidence intervals, we cannot infer that any of the pairs of population means are different. **(b)** Group 2 – Group 1: $(-10.3, 4.3)$, Group 3 – Group 1: $(-4.5, 8.5)$, Group 3 – Group 2: $(-2.3, 12.3)$. Again, we cannot infer that any of the pairs of population means are different. The intervals are wider because we are now using a 95% confidence level for the overall set of intervals. **14.23 (a)** The response variable is change in cholesterol level. The factors are dosage level and type of drug. **(b)** The four treatments are low-dose Lipitor, high-dose Lipitor, low-dose Zocor, and high-dose Zocor. **(c)** When we control for dose level, we can compare change in cholesterol level for the two types of drugs. **14.25 (a)** Mean political ideology in adult U.S. population is identical for blacks and whites, for each of the two sexes. **(b)** $F = 36.5/2.1 = 17.4$; P-value $= 0.000$; if the null hypothesis were true, it is extremely unlikely to observe a value for the F test statistic this large or larger. We have strong evidence that the mean political ideology in the United States depends on race, for each sex. **(c)** There is not enough evidence (P-value $= 0.229$) that mean political ideology in the United States differs by gender, for Blacks and for Whites. **14.27 (a)** The only difference between the equations for the low manure groups and the ones for the high manure groups is the addition of 1.96. **(b)** $2.11 = t_{.025}$ for 17 degrees of freedom. 0.747 is the standard error of the estimate of the manure effect. 1.96 is the estimate of the manure effect. **14.29 (a)** Population regression model: $\mu_y = \alpha + \beta_1 x_1 + \beta_2 x_2 + \beta_3 x_3$.

Recording	Length	x_1	x_2	x_3	Mean of y
Advert	10 min	1	0	1	$\alpha + \beta_1 + \beta_3$
Muzak	10 min	0	1	1	$\alpha + \beta_2 + \beta_3$
Classical	10 min	0	0	1	$\alpha + \beta_3$
Advert	5 min	1	0	0	$\alpha + \beta_1$
Muzak	5 min	0	1	0	$\alpha + \beta_2$
Classical	5 min	0	0	0	α

(b) $\hat{y} = 8.867 - 5.000\,x_1 - 7.600\,x_2 + 2.556\,x_3$; 8.867 is the estimated holding time when a customer listens to classical music repeating every five minutes (all x's $= 0$); -5.0 represents the decrease in estimated mean when an advertisement is played, and -7.6 represents the decrease in estimated mean when Muzak is played—both at each level of repeat time; 2.556 represents the increase in estimated mean

when the repeat time is 10 minutes, for all types of recordings. **(c)** Note: Numbers in parentheses represent values on x_1 and x_2 for type of recording, and on x_3 for repeating time. All numbers are rounded to two decimal places.

	10 minutes (1)	5 minutes (0)
Advertisement (1,0)	6.42	3.87
Muzak (0,1)	3.82	1.27
Classical music (0,0)	11.42	8.87

(d) 2.56. This is the coefficient for x_3, the indicator variable for repeat time. **(e)** Confidence interval for β_3: $2.556 \pm 2.201(1.709) = (-1.2, 6.3)$. **14.31 (a)** Response: hourly wage. Factors: gender and degree. **(b)**

	High School	College	Advanced
Male	17	33	43
Female	14	24	32

(c) (i) For high school graduates, males make on average \$3 more per hour than females; **(ii)** For college graduates, males make on average \$9 more per hour than females. The difference between males and females is not the same for the two types of degrees. In particular, the wage gap is much larger for graduates with a college degree compared to a high school degree. **(d)** One possibility:

	High School	College	Advanced
Male	17	33	43
Female	14	30	40

14.33 (a) Response: number of dates in the last three months; Factors: gender and attractiveness. **(b)** Yes. There appears to be a large effect of attractiveness among women, and little to no effect among men. **(c)** The population standard deviations likely differ, based on the sample standard deviations. ANOVA is typically robust with respect to violations of this assumption. **14.35 (a)** Let $x_1 = 1$ for beef and 0 otherwise, $x_2 = 1$ for cereal and 0 otherwise, and $x_1 = x_2 = 0$ for pork. Likewise, let $x_3 = 1$ for high-protein, $x_3 = 0$ for low protein. $\mu_y = \alpha + \beta_1 x_1 + \beta_2 x_2 + \beta_3 x_3$. **(b)** Weight_gain $= 81.8 + 0.50\,x_1 - 4.20\,x_2 + 14.5\,x_3$; 14.5 is the difference in the estimate of the weight gain between low and high protein diets. **(c)** H_0: $\beta_1 = \beta_2 = 0$. **(d)**

	High	Low
Beef	96.8	82.3
Cereal	92.1	77.6
Pork	96.3	81.8

We assume that the difference between the high and low protein levels is the same for each source of protein. **14.37 (a) (i)** H_0: $\mu_1 = \mu_2 = \mu_3$; H_a: at least two of the population means are different; **(ii)** $F = 3.03$; **(iii)** P-value $= 0.049$; if the null hypothesis were true, the probability would be 0.049 of getting a test statistic at least as extreme as the value observed. We have strong evidence that a difference exists in the population mean number of friends among people going to bars very often, occasionally, or never. **(b)** Yes; the sample standard deviations suggest that the population standard deviations might not be equal and the distributions are probably not normal. This is a concern especially in the "very often" group as the sample size is not that large. **14.39 (a)** The samples are independent and random, the population distributions are normal with equal standard deviations. **(b)** H_0: $\mu_1 = \mu_2 = \mu_3$; H_a: at least two of the population means are different. **(c)** $F = 18.50$; $df_1 = 2$, $df_2 = 3$. **(d)** P-value $= 0.02$. **(e)** If the null hypothesis were true, the probability would be 0.02 of getting a test statistic at least as extreme as the value observed. We have strong evidence that the population mean repair costs differs for at least two of the three types of bumpers.

14.41 (a)

	Mean	Standard Deviation
NE	70.75	5.56
NC	73.75	11.90
S	62.00	3.65
W	61.25	7.18

(b) We can denote the segregation index means for the population that these four samples represent by μ_1 for Northeast, μ_2 for North Central, μ_3 for South, and μ_4 for West. The null hypothesis is H_0: $\mu_1 = \mu_2 = \mu_3 = \mu_4$. The alternative hypothesis is that at least two of the population means are different. **(c)** $F = 2.64$; P-value $= 0.097$; there is some evidence, but not very strong, that a difference exists between at least two of the four regions in terms of the population mean segregation index. **(d)** The ANOVA would not be valid because this would not be a randomly selected sample. **14.43 (a)** Seems plausible given the similar sample standard deviations. **(b)** Meeting the assumption about normality is not as crucial as meeting the assumption that the groups are random samples from the population of interest. However, the influence of the outlier should be investigated. **(c)** With 95% confidence, we estimate that the mean political ideology score for Republicans is between 2.1 and 3.65 points higher compared to Democrats. **(d)** We can conclude that a difference exists among the three political parties in their political ideologies; however, we can only conclude that there is a difference between Republicans and Democrats and between Independents and Republicans. However, the mean political ideology may be similar, if not the same, between Independents and Democrats. **14.45**

Source	DF	SS	MS	F	P-value
Quadrant	3	2700	900	180	0.000
Error	296	1480	5		
Total	299	4180			

14.47 (a) Response: ideal number of kids; Factors: gender and race. **(b)** The difference between population means for the two genders is the same for each race. One possibility

	Female	Male
Black	3.5	3.3
White	1.5	1.3

(c) H_0: no interaction; H_a: there is an interaction. $F = 1.36$; P-value $= 0.24$; if the null hypothesis were true, the probability would be 0.24 of getting a test statistic at least as extreme as the value observed. There is insufficient evidence for an interaction between gender and race on the mean ideal number of kids. **14.49 (a)** For both at 11 P.M. and 8 A.M., the mean time Williams College students need to complete the task is 0.39 minutes shorter when consuming an energy drink. **(b)** The mean time Williams College students need to complete the task is 2 minutes shorter at night (11 P.M.) than in the morning (8 A.M.), whether or not consuming an energy drink. **(c)** $\mu_y = \alpha + \beta_1 e + \beta_2 d$. β_1 needs to equal zero. **(d)** $t = -0.58$, P-value $= 0.57$. No evidence of a difference in means. **14.51** This suggests an interaction since smoking status has a different impact at different levels of age. There is a bigger mean difference between smokers and non-smokers among older women than among younger women. **14.53 (a)** The coefficient for gender, -13 (thousands of dollars), indicates that at fixed levels of race, men have higher estimated mean salaries than women. Women salaries are reduced by 13 (thousands of dollars). **(b) (i)** 109.2 (calculation: 96.2 + 13); **(ii)** 56.2 (calculation: 96.2 − 40). **14.55 (a)** $\mu_y = \alpha + \beta_1 g + \beta_2 m_1 + \beta_3 m_2$.

Gender	Status	g	m_1	m_2	Mean of y
M	Single	1	1	0	$\alpha + \beta_1 + \beta_2$
M	Married	1	0	1	$\alpha + \beta_1 + \beta_3$
M	Divorced	1	0	0	$\alpha + \beta_1$
F	Single	0	1	0	$\alpha + \beta_2$
F	Married	0	0	1	$\alpha + \beta_3$
F	Divorced	0	0	0	α

(b) TV hours $= 2.78 + 0.16g + 0.41m_1 - 0.21m_2$. The mean hours of TV watching are estimated to be 0.16 hours higher for males, for each marital status. **(c)** β_2. **(d)** Find 95% CI for β_2: $0.41 \pm 1.962 \times (0.184) = (0.05, 0.77)$. With 95% confidence, we estimate that the mean number of hours watching TV is between 0.05 hours and 0.77 hours larger for single compared to divorced subjects. **14.57 (a)** Have little variability of points in each group, but large differences between means of different groups. **(b)** Have lots of variability of points in each group and similar means for different groups. **14.59** A confidence level of 0.95 for a single comparison gives 95% confidence for only the one interval. A confidence level of 0.95 for a multiple comparison of all six pairs of means provides a confidence level of 95% for the whole set of intervals. **14.61** (d). **14.63** (c). **14.65** True. **14.67 (a)** $\Sigma(\bar{y}_i - \bar{y})^2/(g - 1)$ estimates the variance σ^2/n of the distribution of the $\{\bar{y}_i\}$ values, because $\Sigma(\bar{y}_i - \bar{y})^2/(g - 1)$ is the formula for the variance for the g "observations" $y_1, y_2, \dots, y_g$. **(b)** If $\Sigma(y_i - \bar{y})^2/(g - 1)$ estimates σ^2/n, then n times $\Sigma(\bar{y}_i - \bar{y})^2/(g - 1)$ estimates σ^2. **14.69 (a)** $(0.95)(0.95)(0.95)(0.95)(0.95) = 0.77$. **(b)** $(0.9898)^5 = 0.95$. **14.71 (a)** Eight groups. **(b)** Let $x_1 = 1$ for the high level of nitrogen and 0 for the low level of nitrogen, $x_2 = 1$ for the high level of phosphate and 0 for the low level of phosphate, and $x_3 = 1$ for the high level of potash and 0 for the low level of potash. Then $\mu_y = \alpha + \beta_1 x_1 + \beta_2 x_2 + \beta_3 x_3$. **(c)** One possibility is $\hat{\alpha} = 6$, $\hat{\beta}_1 = 2$, $\hat{\beta}_2 = 2$, $\hat{\beta}_3 = -2$.

Chapter 15

15.1 (a) and **(b)**

Lotion	(1,2)	(1,3)	(1,4)	(2,3)	(2,4)	(3,4)
Studio	(3,4)	(2,4)	(2,3)	(1,4)	(1,3)	(1,2)
Lotion Mean Rank	1.5	2.0	2.5	2.5	3.0	3.5
Studio Mean Rank	3.5	3.0	2.5	2.5	2.0	1.5
Difference of Mean Ranks	−2.0	−1.0	0.0	0.0	1.0	2.0

(c) $P(-2.0) = 1/6$, $P(-1.0) = 1/6$, $P(0.0) = 2/6$, $P(1.0) = 1/6$, $P(2.0) = 1/6$. **15.3 (a)** and **(b)** Example given for seven combinations only; there would be 20.

Treatment	Ranks						
Therapy 1	(1,2,3)	(1,2,4)	(1,2,5)	(1,2,6)	(1,3,4)	(1,3,5)	(1,3,6)
Therapy 2	(4,5,6)	(3,5,6)	(3,4,6)	(3,4,5)	(2,5,6)	(2,4,6)	(2,4,5)
Therapy 1 Mean Rank	2.0	2.33	2.67	3.0	2.67	3.0	3.33
Therapy 2 Mean Rank	5.0	4.67	4.33	4.0	4.33	4.0	3.67
Difference of Mean Ranks	−3.0	−2.33	−1.67	−1.0	−1.67	−1.0	−0.33

(c) Differences between mean ranks followed by probabilities: $(-3.00, 1/20)$ $(-2.33, 1/20)$ $(-1.67, 2/20)$ $(-1.00, 3/20)$ $(-0.33, 3/20)$ $(0.33, 3/20)$ $(1.00, 3/20)$ $(1.67, 2/20)$ $(2.33, 1/20)$ $(3.00, 1/20)$.

(d) P-value $= 0.20$. If the two therapies had identical effects, the probability of a difference in the mean ranks as observed (or one even more extreme) is 0.20, which is large. There is no evidence of an effect. **15.5 (a)** The point estimate of -2.000 is an estimate of the difference between the population median birth weight for the smokers group and the population median birth weight for the nonsmokers group. **(b)** With 95.9% confidence, we estimate that the population median birth weight for the smokers group is between 3.3 and 0.7 pounds below the population median birth weight for the nonsmoking group. Because 0 does not fall in the confidence interval, there is evidence that there is a difference between the population medians for the two groups. **15.7 (a)** The estimated difference between the population median weight change for the cognitive behavioral treatment group and the population median weight change for the control group is 3.05. **(b)** With 95% confidence, we estimate that the population median weight change for the cognitive-behavioral group is between 0.6 below and 8.1 above the population median weight change for the control group. Because 0 is included in the confidence interval, the medians are similar, if not the same. The assumption needed is that the girls were randomly assigned to the two treatment groups and that the shape of the distribution of weight change is similar in the two groups. **(c)** P-value $= 0.11$ for testing against the alternative hypothesis of different expected median ranks; there is not sufficient evidence that the population distributions differ. **15.9 (a)** Group 1 ranks: 2, 5, 6; Group 2 ranks: 1, 3.5; Group 3 ranks: 3.5, 7, 8. The mean rank for Group $1 = (2 + 5 + 6)/3 = 4.33$. **(b)** P-value $= 0.209$; there is not enough evidence that the population distribution of the quiz scores differ among the three groups. **15.11 (a)** Dependent; all students receive both treatments. **(b)** 0.81. **(c)** $z = 3.54$; P-value $= 0.0002$. Strong evidence that the population proportion of drivers who would have a faster reaction time when not using a cell phone is greater than $1/2$. **(d)** Dependent samples (paired) t test; the sign test uses merely the information about *which* response is higher and how many, not the quantitative information about *how much* higher. **15.13** H$_0$: $p = 0.50$. H$_a$: $p > 0.50$; $P(3) = (0.50)^3 = 0.125$. The evidence is not strong that walking lowers blood pressure. **15.15 (a)** H$_0$: population median of difference scores is 0; H$_a$: population median of difference scores is > 0. **(c)** P-value $= 1/16 = 0.06$; there is some, but not strong, evidence that cell phones tend to impair reaction times. **15.17 (a)** Bumper A: ranks are 4, 6, 5; mean is 5. Bumper B: ranks are 1, 2, 3; mean is 2. **(b)**

Treatment	Ranks
Bumper A	(1,2,3) (1,2,4) (1,2,5) (1,2,6) (1,3,4) (1,3,5) (1,3,6) (1,4,5) (1,4,6) (1,5,6)
Bumper B	(4,5,6) (3,5,6) (3,4,6) (3,4,5) (2,5,6) (2,4,6) (2,4,5) (2,3,6) (2,3,5) (2,3,4)

Treatment	Ranks
Bumper A	(2,3,4) (2,3,5) (2,3,6) (2,4,5) (2,4,6) (2,5,6) (3,4,5) (3,4,6) (3,5,6) (4,5,6)
Bumper B	(1,5,6) (1,4,6) (1,4,5) (1,3,6) (1,3,5) (1,3,4) (1,2,6) (1,2,5) (1,2,4) (1,2,3)

(c) There are only two ways in which the ranks are as extreme as in this sample: Bumper A with 1, 2, 3 and Bumper B with 4, 5, 6, or Bumper A with 4, 5, 6 and Bumper B with 1, 2, 3. **(d)** The P-value is 0.10 because out of 20 possibilities, only two are this extreme. $(2/20 = 0.10)$. **15.19 (a)**

Group	Ranks	Mean Rank
Muzak	1,2,4,5,3	3.0
Classical	9,8,7,10,6	8.0

(b) There are only two cases this extreme (i.e., Muzak has ranks 1–5 or Muzak has ranks 6–10). Thus, the P-value is the probability that one of these two cases would occur out of the 252 possible allocations of rankings. The probability would be 0.008 of getting a difference

like we observed or one even more extreme. There is strong evidence that the distribution of holding times differs between those listening to Muzak or classical music. **15.21 (a)** Kruskal-Wallis test. **(b)** All examples would have one group with ranks 1–3, one with ranks 4–6, and one with ranks 7–9. **15.23 (a) (i)** H$_0$: population proportion $p = 0.50$ who use the cell phone more than Internet; H$_a$: $p \neq 0.50$; **(ii)** $se = \sqrt{(0.50)(0.50)/n} = \sqrt{(0.50)(0.50)/39} = 0.08$, $z = (\hat{p} - 0.50)/se = (0.897 - 0.50)/0.08 = 4.96$; **(iii)** P-value $= 0.000$; if the null hypothesis were true, the probability would be near 0 of getting a test statistic at least as extreme as the value observed. We have extremely strong evidence that a majority of countries have more cell phone usage than Internet usage. **(b)** This would not be relevant if the data file were comprised only of countries of interest to us. We would know the population parameters so inference would not be relevant. **15.25 (a)** We could use the sign test for matched pairs or the Wilcoxon signed-ranks test. **(b)** One reason for using a nonparametric method is if we suspected that the population distribution of the differences was not normal and because we have a one-sided alternative. Then, parametric methods like the paired t-test are not robust. **(c)** For the one-sided test with H$_0$: median difference $= 0$ vs. H$_a$: median difference > 0, software reports a test statistic (sum of ranks of positive differences between high school and college GPA) of 1,271, with a P-value of 0.000. The P-value of 0.000 gives very strong evidence that in the population, the median high school GPA is higher than the median college GPA. **15.27 (a)** H$_0$: population median of difference scores is 0; H$_a$: population median of difference scores > 0.

Possible Samples with Absolute Difference Values of Sample

Subject	1	2	3	4	5	6	7	8	Rank of Absolute Value
1	5.5	5.5	-5.5	5.5	-5.5	5.5	-5.5	-5.5	3
2	-0.5	-0.5	-0.5	0.5	-0.5	0.5	0.5	0.5	1
3	1.5	-1.5	1.5	1.5	-1.5	-1.5	1.5	-1.5	2

Sum of Ranks for Positive Differences

5	3	2	6	0	4	3	1

The rank sum is 5 one-eighth of the time, and is more extreme (i.e., 6) one-eighth of the time (values that were greater than the observed). Thus, the P-value $= 2/8 = 0.25$. If the null hypothesis were true, the probability would be 0.25 of getting a test statistic at least as extreme as the value observed. There is not enough evidence to conclude that the population median of the differences is positive. **(b)** The P-value is smaller than in Example 8. Outliers do not have an effect on this nonparametric statistical method. **15.29** One example is when the population distribution is highly skewed and the researcher wants to use a one-sided test. **15.31** Kruskal-Wallis. **15.33** False. **15.35 (a)** The proportions are calculated by pairing up the subjects in every possible way, and then counting the number of pairs for which the tanning studio gave a better tan. **(b)**

Sample Proportion	Probability
0/6	1/10
1/6	1/10
2/6	2/10
3/6	2/10
4/6	2/10
5/6	1/10
6/6	1/10

(c) The P-value would be 2/10. The probability of an observed sample proportion of 5/6 or more extreme (i.e., 6/6) is $2/10 = 0.20$. **15.37** No; we are taking the median of all slopes, and the median is not susceptible to outliers.

Index

Index of Applications

Credits

Screenshots of Shiny Apps, courtesy of Bernhard Klingenberg.

COVER Peter Kotoff/Shutterstock

PREFACE p. xxii (from top to bottom) Alan Agresti; Courtesy of Anna Fergusson; Bernhard Klingenberg

CHAPTER 1 p. 1 (from left to right) ESB Professional/Shutterstock; Ciprian Stremtan/Shutterstock; Slawomir Kruz/Shutterstock; Triff/Shutterstock **p. 2** ESB Professional/Shutterstock **p. 6** General Social Survey (GSS) Cumulative Datafile 1972-2018 © 2011-2019 NORC **p. 7** Software developed and maintained by CSM program under Institute for scientific analysis with exclusive copyright license agreement from UC Berkeley © 2020 UC Regents **p. 9** Howard Lipin/ZUMApress/Newscom/Newscom **p. 10** Anystock/Shutterstock **p. 12** Forestpath/Shutterstock **p. 21** Screenshot of a spreadsheet to organize data © Microsoft 2020; google.com/analytics © Google LLC **p. 27** Screenshot from Kaggle Inc, http://www.kaggle.com/competition © 2019 Kaggle Inc.

CHAPTER 2 p. 35 Ciprian Stremtan/Shutterstock **p. 39** Dasha Aleksandrova/123RF **p. 42** Jamenpercy/123RF **p. 45** Brian Senic/Shutterstock **p. 55** Sborisov/123RF **p. 63** Wrangler/Shutterstock **p. 70** Andy Dean Photography/Shutterstock **p. 78** Artem Shadrin/Shutterstock **p. 84** Henryk Sadura/Shutterstock **p. 90** N.Z.Photography/Shutterstock **p. 93** Lee Jin-Man/AP/Shutterstock

CHAPTER 3 p. 112 Slawomir Kruz/Shutterstock **p. 114** WB/Shutterstock **p. 125** NetPhotos/Alamy Stock Photo **p. 130** GARY I. ROTHSTEIN/Associated Press **p. 138** Cafaphotos/123RF **p. 141** Bill Florence/Shutterstock **p. 148** Technotr/E+/Getty Images **p. 151** 1x6/E+/Getty Images **p. 163** Jiri Foltyn/Shutterstock **p. 164** Stefanina hill/123RF

CHAPTER 4 p. 182 Triff/Shutterstock **p. 185** Shutterstock **p. 189** Bureau of the Census report 2004, U.S. Department of Commerce **p. 192** Katemedvedeva/Shutterstock **p. 203** BCFC/Shutterstock **p. 210** OZSHOTZ/Alamy Stock Photo **p. 211** Mihai Simonia/Shutterstock **p. 212** Rob Marmion/Shutterstock **p. 214** Diana Eller/123RF

CHAPTER 5 p. 229 (from left to right) Chepko/iStock/Getty Images; Sirtravelalot/Shutterstock; Steve Debenport/E+/Getty Images **p. 230** Chepko/iStock/Getty Images **p. 241** Alexander Raths/123RF **p. 243** Duckycards/E+/Getty Images **p. 245** Michelle Milano/Shutterstock **p. 255** Dizzy/iStock/Getty Images **p. 257** Vlad Mereuta/Shutterstock **p. 263** Images and videos/Shutterstock **p. 265** Zentilia/Shutterstock **p. 267** EThamPhoto/Alamy Stock Photo **p. 271** Terrance Klassen/Alamy Stock Photo **p. 282** Hillary Clinton

CHAPTER 6 p. 285 Sirtravelalot/Shutterstock **p. 287** Jeff Smith - Perspectives/Shutterstock **p. 290** Nikada/E+/Getty Images **p. 292** FOTOG/Tetra Images/Alamy Stock Photo **p. 294** Snapshot of question from 2009 American Community Survey, U.S. Department of Commerce **p. 295** Oliveromg/Shutterstock **p. 299** Prachaya Roekdeethaweesab/Shutterstock **p. 304** Duplass/Shutterstock **p. 307** Tom Wang/Shutterstock **p. 313** Fuse/Corbis/Getty Images **p. 315** JL-Pfeifer/Shutterstock **p. 319** Ilya Andriyanov/Shutterstock **p. 330** Imagenavi/Getty Images

CHAPTER 7 p. 332 Steve Debenport/E+/Getty Images **p. 339** Ellen Isaacs/Alamy Stock Photo

CHAPTER 8 p. 377 (from left to right) Curioso/Shutterstock; GaleanoStock/Shutterstock; Blvdone/Shutterstock **p. 378** Blvdone/Shutterstock **p. 383** ESB Professional/Shutterstock **p. 389** Jose Gil/shutterstock **p. 394** Wallenrock/Shutterstock **p. 397** Karin Hildebrand Lau/Shutterstock **p. 400** Pixellover RM 8/Alamy Stock Photo **p. 413** Hongqi zhang/123RF **p. 414** Matt burgess/123RF

CHAPTER 9 p. 435 Curioso/Shutterstock **p. 438** Zhuda/Shutterstock **p. 442** Green Mountain Montenegro/Shutterstock **p. 452** Andrii Shevchuk/123RF **p. 459** Alexey Stiop/Shutterstock **p. 474** Junial Enterprises/Shutterstock **p. 477** Carsten Reisinger/Shutterstock **p. 481** Antonio Diaz/123RF

CHAPTER 10 p. 500 GaleanoStock/Shutterstock **p. 511** CandyBox Images/Shutterstock **p. 524** Bernard Bodo/123RF **p. 552** IgorZh/Shutterstock **p. 561** Robert J Daveant/Shutterstock

CHAPTER 11 p. 579 (from left to right) Dolgachov/123RF; Tyler Olson/Shutterstock; Andy Dean Photography/Shutterstock; Diego Cervo/Shutterstock; TravnikovStudio/Shutterstock **p. 580** Dolgachov/123RF **p. 588** ESB Basic/Shutterstock **p. 602** Image Source/Getty Images **pp. 610-612** Data from GSS © NORC at the University of Chicago **p. 613** Piyachok Thawornmat/Shutterstock **p. 617** B Christopher/Alamy Stock Photo **p. 625** Data from GSS © NORC at the University of Chicago

CHAPTER 12 p. 630 Tyler Olson/Shutterstock **p. 638** hxdbzxy/Shutterstock **p. 651** XiXinXing/Shutterstock **p. 660** Lisa Young/123RF **p. 671** Blvdone/Shutterstock

CHAPTER 13 p. 685 Andy Dean Photography/Shutterstock **p. 687** StockLite/Shutterstock **p. 699** Muzsy/Shutterstock **p. 718** Brenda Carson/Shutterstock **p. 723** Primagefactory/123RF

CHAPTER 14 p. 738 Diego Cervo/Shutterstock **p. 740** Dirima/Shutterstock **p. 750** De Visu/Shutterstock **p. 759** Maksud/Shutterstock **p. 764** Phovoir/Shutterstock

CHAPTER 15 p. 782 TravnikovStudio/Shutterstock **p. 786** Sandra Cunningham/Shutterstock **p. 792** Susan Montgomery/Shutterstock

A Guide to Choosing a Statistical Method

CATEGORICAL RESPONSE VARIABLE (ANALYZING PROPORTIONS)

1. If there is only one categorical response variable, use
   - Descriptive methods of Chapter 2
   - Inferential methods of Section 8.2 (confidence interval) and Section 9.2 (significance test) for proportions

2. To compare proportions of a categorical response variable for two or more groups of a categorical explanatory variable, use
   - Descriptive methods of Chapter 3 (Sections 3.1 and 3.4)
   - Inferential methods of Sections 10.1 (independent samples) and 10.4 (dependent samples) for comparing proportions between two groups
   - Inferential methods of Chapter 11 for comparing two or more proportions or testing the independence of two categorical variables

3. If working with a binary response variable with quantitative and/or categorical explanatory variables (predictors), use logistic regression methods of Section 13.6

QUANTITATIVE RESPONSE VARIABLE (ANALYZING MEANS)

1. If there is only one quantitative response variable, use
   - Descriptive methods of Chapter 2
   - Inferential methods of Section 8.3 (confidence interval) and Section 9.3 (significance test) for a mean, or bootstrap methods in Section 8.4

2. To compare means of a quantitative response variable for two groups of a categorical explanatory variable, use
   - Descriptive methods of Chapter 2
   - Inferential methods of Sections 10.2 and 10.3 (for bootstrap and permutation approaches) for independent samples
   - Inferential methods of Section 10.4 for dependent samples
   - Nonparametric tests in Section 15.1 for independent samples or Section 15.2 for dependent samples

3. To compare several means of a quantitative response variable for two or more groups of a categorical explanatory variable, use
   - ANOVA methods of Chapter 14 for independent samples, which are equivalent to linear regression methods with indicator variables for categorical predictors
   - Nonparametric methods from Section 15.2

4. To analyze the relationship between a quantitative response variable and a quantitative explanatory variable, use
   - Descriptive methods for correlation and linear regression in Chapters 3 and 12
   - Inferential methods for correlation and linear regression in Chapter 12

5. To analyze the relationship between a quantitative response variable and several explanatory variables (predictors), use
   - Multiple regression methods of Chapter 13 (Sections 13.1–13.4) for several quantitative predictors
   - Multiple regression methods of Section 13.5 with indicator variables for categorical predictors

Data Sets

These data sets are available for download from ArtofStat.com

Chapter 1

Believe in Heaven and Hell
Workhours
FL student survey

Chapter 2

Alligator Food
Animals
Baseball Hitters
Central Park Yearly Temps
Cereal
Cigarette Tax
CO2 Europe & America
College Athletes
Energy Consumption
Europe CO2
Fertility
FL Student Survey
GA Student Survey
Health Coverage
Heights
Hepathlon
HS Female Athletes
HS Graduation
Hurricanes
Iris
Newnan GA Temperatures
NYC Airbnb Room Type
NYY Salaries 2014
Pertussis
SAT 2010
Sharks
Subway Sandwiches
Teacher Salary
Time on Facebook
TV Hours (2012 and 2018)
US Fertility
Wine Harvest Burgundy
Youth Unemployment

Chapter 3

AL Team Statistics
Beers
Buchanan Butterfly Ballot
Car Weight & Mileage
Carbon Footprint
Central Park Yearly Temps
Diamonds
Eyewitness Testimony
FL Crime
Fuel
High Jump
House Prices (FL)
Human Development
Internet Use
Long Jump
Mountain Bikes
NL Team Statistics
Rotten Tomatoes Reviews
SAT 2018
Tour de France Performance
US Statewide Crime
US Temperatures
Zagat Boston

Chapter 7

Arrival Delays (pop.)
Departure Delays (pop.)
College Cost & Dept (pop.)
College Earnings (pop.)
NYC Airbnb (pop.)
Soccer Player Heights (pop.)

Chapter 8

Account Balance
Airbnb Rooms NYC
Departure Delays
Eating Disorders
Email Hours 2018

Self Esteem
Social Security Payments
TV Hours
Weekly Exercise Hours

Chapter 9

Anorexia
Asthma
Bank Loan Amounts
Number of Kids
Political Views
Work Week (2012
   and 2018)

Chapter 10

Anorexia
ATL Flight Arrivals
Boston & Seattle Airbnb
Cell Phone Reaction Time
Exercises (Non-)Athletes
Feeling Sad
Bank Interest Rates
Bank Loan Amounts
Number of Kids
Paired Reaction Times
Social Activities
Stick Figures
Text & Graph
Time on Facebook (FR, SO)
TV Hours by Race

Chapter 11

Benford
Diamonds
Headache

Chapter 12

Car Weight & Mileage
Cell Phone Specs

FL Crime
House Selling Prices FL
HS Female Athletes
Internet Use
Male Athlete Strength
Softball
Stemcells
US Statewide Crime

Chapter 13

College Female Athletes
Credit Card & Income
Fertility & Literacy
High Jump
House Selling Prices OR
HS Female Athletes
Mental Health
Mountain Bike
Quality & Productivity
Softball
Used Cars

Chapter 14

Anorexia
Cornyield
Energy Drink
French Cuisine
Protein & Weight Gain
Time on Facebook (all)
TV Hours (2014)

Chapter 15

Anorexia
Paired Reaction Time

Web Apps

Access these apps at ArtofStat.com

Chapters 2 and 3

Explore Categorical Data
Explore Quantitative Data
Mean vs. Median
Time Series
Association Between Two
   Categorical Variables
Scatterplots & Correlation
Explore Linear Regression
Linear Regression
Guess the Correlation

Chapters 4 to 6

Random Numbers

Normal Distribution
Binomial Distribution

Chapter 7

Sampling Distribution of
   the Sample Proportion
   the Sample Mean
Bootstrap for One Sample
Scatterplots & Correlation

Chapters 8 and 9

Inference for a Proportion
Inference for a Mean
t Distribution
Explore Coverage

Bootstrap for One Sample
Scatterplots & Correlation
Errors and Power

Chapter 10

Compare Two Proportions
Compare Two Means
Bootstrap for Two Samples
Permutation Test

Chapter 11

Chi-Squared Distribution
Chi-Squared Test
Association Between Two
   Categorical Variables

Fisher's Exact Test
Permutation Test for
   Independence

Chapters 12 and 13

Linear Regression
F Distribution
Multiple Linear Regression
Logistic Regression

Chapters 14 and 15

ANOVA (One-Way)
Wilcoxon Test
Kruskal-Wallis Test